RESONANCE
IN ORGANIC
CHEMISTRY

RESONANCE

IN ORGANIC

CHEMISTRY

GEORGE WILLARD WHELAND

Professor of Chemistry, University of Chicago

JOHN WILEY & SONS, INC., NEW YORK

CHAPMAN & HALL, LIMITED, LONDON

Library of Congress Catalog Card Number: 55–9367

This book is dedicated to

LINUS PAULING

without whose leadership and inspiration

it could never have been written

PREFACE

In this preface, I feel that I have the opportunity and the obligation to explain to the reader the ways in which the present book differs from its predecessor, *The Theory of Resonance and Its Application to Organic Chemistry.* Of the several changes that have been made, two are particularly obvious, and therefore require special comment. On the one hand, the original title has been replaced by *Resonance in Organic Chemistry;* and, on the other hand, the number of pages has been considerably increased. The reason for the first of these changes is simply that the title used in the earlier work seems to be somewhat misleading. Indeed, the emphasis on "the theory of resonance" could easily give the erroneous impression that the book is primarily concerned with the development of a purely mathematical theory, and hence that any discussion of organic chemistry is restricted to the bare minimum. The present title, however, should be in better agreement with the fact that, aside from a newly added concluding chapter which is devoted to the development of the mathematical background of the theory, and which is more fully discussed below, the book deals explicitly with organic chemistry, as approached and interpreted from the resonance viewpoint.

The greatly increased length of the book requires a somewhat more detailed explanation. One reason for the additional pages is, of course, that, during the last ten years, there has appeared much important work which must be reported here. The Appendix, which consists of a table of bond lengths and bond angles, for example, has alone expanded from 11 to 105 pages. A second reason is that I have made a more serious attempt to eliminate the unprecise, and often quite misleading, terminology that seems always to have been an unfortunate feature of most discussions of resonance. I have, accordingly, replaced a number of brief and extremely convenient expressions by others which, although longer and sometimes rather awkward, are less likely to leave the meaning in doubt or even to create an impression that is the opposite of the one intended. Similarly, I have also in many instances given detailed explanations of the exact significance to be attached to certain expressions that are frequently used. Having been so completely mistaken in my earlier naïve supposition that, in

The Theory of Resonance, I had avoided all possibilities for misunderstanding, I do not now flatter myself with the belief that I have been entirely successful here; I do feel, however, that the new presentation of the material is significantly clearer and less confusing than the original.

A further change which has also contributed to the increased length of the book was necessitated by the growing interest in, and recognition of, the so-called molecular-orbital method for treating molecular structure. I have, in fact, devoted a considerable amount of space to this parallel and roughly equivalent approach to the problem of valence. I have continued, however, to lay much the greater emphasis upon the resonance concept. My reason for thus relegating the molecular-orbital viewpoint to a secondary role is not that this viewpoint is of relatively little value; actually, it is at least as important as the resonance viewpoint, and, in a number of specific applications, it is more useful. The point is instead that, as an organic chemist, I believe that the resonance approach is clearer and more congenial to the great majority of other organic chemists than is the alternative one. Indeed, when benzene, for example, is described as a resonance hybrid, only a simple extension of the familiar structural theory is required; but, when the same substance is described in terms of molecular orbitals, the structural theory is essentially abandoned from the outset, and an entirely new approach, based upon different principles, must be adopted. Moreover, I am not convinced that, as is frequently asserted, the molecular-orbital treatment is more nearly rigorous, and hence more trustworthy, than the resonance treatment. When the two treatments are carried to their logical extremes, they become mathematically identical; when they are instead applied in their usual, more approximate forms, their relative reliabilities are difficult to judge. The neglect of configuration interaction in the molecular-orbital calculations is as likely to cause serious error as is the neglect of ionic and other unstable structures in the resonance calculations. It is therefore not immediately apparent which procedure should be considered the more generally reliable.

The most important single reason for the increased size of the book is that, in a new and very long concluding chapter, I have presented those elementary aspects of quantum mechanics that are necessary for an understanding of the mathematical basis of both the resonance and the molecular-orbital theories. The reader who has had no previous acquaintance with quantum mechanics will doubtless find this chapter more difficult than any of the eight that precede it. I am, however, convinced that any effort he expends in mastering this material will be more than justified by his improved understanding of the resonance and molecular-orbital concepts. Moreover, although I have attempted to make this discussion as simple and elementary as possible, I am also convinced that an understanding of quantum mechanics cannot be acquired by any process of intellectual osmosis, but can be obtained only at the cost of a certain amount of conscious effort. Consequently, I do not apologize for the fact that this new chapter will require much study and the frequent use of pencil and paper.

It would be undesirable here to omit all mention of the fact that many unusually vitriolic attacks upon the theory of resonance have recently come out of the Soviet Union. So far as I am entitled to express an opinion on the basis of the limited number of papers that I have seen, in translation, I have found that these attacks consist almost entirely of personal and political invective. The small amount of genuine scientific content they contain seems to be directed against a widespread misinterpretation of the theory, which is mistakenly identified as the theory itself. For brief further discussions of this question, the interested reader is referred to a letter of mine in *Chemical and Engineering News*,* and also to Section 9·17 of this book.

In conclusion, I wish to acknowledge my deep appreciation to the many people who have given me invaluable assistance. Special credit is due to all the readers of *The Theory of Resonance* who informed me of the misprints and more serious errors that had escaped notice before publication; to Professors W. G. Brown and M. S. Kharasch for permission to use an unpublished compilation of heats of combustion; to Professors G. S. Hammond, J. R. Platt, J. D. Roberts, W. H. Urry, and F. H. Westheimer for critically reading part or all of the manuscript and for giving me the benefit of their helpful advice; and to Dr. K. D. Kopple for his help in the reading of the proof. Again I should like to express my hope that the readers will call to my attention any mistakes that they may observe.

GEORGE WILLARD WHELAND

Chicago, Illinois
September, 1955

---

* G. W. Wheland, *Chem. Eng. News* **30**, 3160 (1952).

CONTENTS

Chapter 1   THE
THEORY
OF
RESONANCE

1·1 The Structural Theory. Ever since the middle of the nineteenth century, the progress of chemistry, and especially of organic chemistry, has been closely associated with the development of the structural theory. One can, in fact, hardly question that this theory, more than any other single factor, must be given the credit for the remarkable advances that have occurred in the science during the last hundred years. However, in spite of its outstanding success in correlating and systematizing the vast body of facts with which it deals, its history has been marked from the very beginning by a series of attempts to revise and to amplify it in such a way that its field of usefulness might be extended still further.

A number of these attempts have met with complete acceptance, and now form an integral part of the theory. One thinks at once, in this connection, of the stereochemical ideas developed by van't Hoff and by Le Bel, of the concept of coordination developed by Werner, and of the electronic theory of valence developed by Kossel and by Lewis. To these must now apparently be added the theory of resonance, a description of which is the object of the present book.

Many of the features of the theory of resonance had already been anticipated by the organic chemists in their search for a more comprehensive structural theory. Early in the second half of the last century, it was found that for some substances, of which benzene was perhaps the most striking example, *no* completely satisfactory structures of the conventional type could be devised at all. The idea then slowly emerged that perhaps these substances must be described not in terms of one single structure but of two or even more structures simultaneously. At the outset, this idea was probably not essentially different from that now denoted by the word "tautomerism," as, for example, in Kekulé's theory[1] of "oscillation" in benzene. In time, however, a distinction came to be drawn. A vague suggestion of this new point of view is perhaps to be found as early as 1887 in the well-known centric structure of benzene.[2]

[1] A. Kekulé, *Ann.* **162**, 77 (1872).
[2] H. E. Armstrong, *Phil. Mag.* (5) **23**, 73 (1887); *J. Chem. Soc.* **51**, 258 (1887). A. Baeyer, *Ann.* **245**, 103 (1888).

1

Neither Armstrong nor Baeyer was very explicit about the exact significance of the centric bonds in this structure, but the idea was elaborated
further by Claus[3] (on the basis of his own, essentially equivalent, diagonal
structure) so that it became surprisingly similar in some regards to
that accepted now. A rather more definite suggestion appeared a few
years later in Thiele's theory of partial valence,[4] which was applicable
not only to aromatic ring systems but also to open-chain unsaturated
molecules.

1·2 The Theories of Intermediate Stages, Mesomerism, and Resonance.
It was not until after 1920, however, that the ideas to be discussed in this
and the succeeding chapters began to take precise form. The first
important advances were made by two different groups of organic
chemists, who came simultaneously and quite independently to very much
the same final conclusions. On the one hand, Arndt and his co-workers
in Germany brought forward the theory of intermediate stages (Zwischen-
stufen),[5] and, on the other hand, various English chemists, of whom only
Robinson and Ingold need be mentioned explicitly here, brought forward
the theory of mesomerism.[6] With the development of quantum mechanics, however, it soon became apparent that these two parallel theories
were not merely arbitrary hypotheses, as they had appeared to be when
first advanced, but were two equivalent chemical expressions of what is
known as quantum-mechanical resonance. This latter, more precise
concept, which was reached first in 1926 by Heisenberg[7] in quite another
connection, is a simple mathematical consequence of the fundamental
equations of quantum mechanics, and its essential correctness has been
established beyond question. Its application to chemical problems was

---

[3] A. Claus, *J. prakt. Chem.* **37**, 455 (1888).

[4] J. Thiele, *Ann.* **306**, 87 (1899).

[5] F. Arndt, E. Scholz, and P. Nachtwey, *Ber.* **57**, 1903 (1924); F. Arndt, *ibid.*
63, 2963 (1930). Recently the adherents of this school have adopted the terminology
of the English school. For a comprehensive survey of the subject, see B. Eistert,
Tautomerie und Mesomerie, Ferdinand Enke, Stuttgart, 1938; *Chemismus und Konstitu-
tion*, Erster Teil, Ferdinand Enke, Stuttgart, 1948.

[6] Since the theory in its present form is the result of a long and slow development,
it seems desirable here to give references only to a few comprehensive review articles.
Of these may be mentioned especially: R. Robinson, *Two Lectures on an "Outline of
an Electrochemical (Electronic) Theory of the Course of Organic Reactions,"* The Institute
of Chemistry of Great Britain and Ireland, London, 1932; *J. Soc. Dyers Colourists,
Jubilee Issue*, 65 (1934); C. K. Ingold, *J. Chem. Soc.* **1933**, 1120; *Chem. Revs.* **15**, 225
(1934). The use of the word "mesomerism" was proposed by Ingold in the former of
the two papers just mentioned. A particularly detailed and valuable discussion of his
own work and viewpoint is given by C. K. Ingold, *Structure and Mechanism in Organic
Chemistry*, Cornell University Press, Ithaca, New York, 1953.

[7] W. Heisenberg, *Z. Physik.* **38**, 411 (1926).

initiated largely by Pauling and his collaborators.[8] This quantum-mechanical basis of the theory will be described very briefly in Section 1·5, and in much greater detail in Chapter 9. Here, however, we may mention that the newer mathematical approach not only provides a sound theoretical basis for the earlier and less precise ideas mentioned above but also supplements them in several important regards by introducing into them certain refinements or extensions which could have been reached in other ways only with greater difficulty. It leads, for example, to an understanding of the conditions under which a molecule can, or cannot, be expected to exist in an intermediate stage or mesomeric state, and, even more important, it accounts for the observed greater stability of those molecules in which mesomerism or resonance is important. The first of these additional features of the more elaborate theory will be discussed at some length in Section 1·4, and the second will be referred to at frequent intervals throughout the book.

The significant feature which these theories of intermediate stages, of mesomerism, and of resonance have in common is that *in all of them it is considered possible for the true state of a molecule to be not identical with that represented by any single classical valence-bond structure, but to be intermediate between those represented by two or more different valence-bond structures.* Since it is important that this new concept not be confused with tautomerism, let us discuss an example in some detail. We shall consider a molecule which is in an intermediate stage or is mesomeric or is a *resonance hybrid.* For definiteness, we can consider that exactly two structures are involved, and we can think of the substance in question as benzene. If this substance exists as a tautomeric mixture of molecules with the Kekulé structures I and II, then some of the molecules have structure I whereas the others have structure II, or, if the equilibrium is mobile, any one molecule spends part of its time in structure I and the rest in structure II. On the other hand, if the substance is correctly described in terms of the theories of intermediate stages, of mesomerism, or of resonance, the situation is quite different: All the molecules have the same structure; this structure, which does not change

with the time, is not identical with either I or II, but it is intermediate between them.

    [8] See L. Pauling, *The Nature of the Chemical Bond*, Cornell University Press, Ithaca,. N. Y., 1st ed., 1939, 2nd ed., 1940, and numerous further references given there.

Throughout this book, structures will be designated by Roman numerals. The first structure *in each section* will be assigned the number I.

The significance of the above distinction between tautomerism and the newer concepts can be made clearer with the aid of an analogy. A mule is a hybrid between a horse and a donkey. This does not mean that some mules are horses and the rest are donkeys, nor does it mean that a given mule is a horse part of the time and a donkey the rest of the time. Instead, it means that a mule is a new kind of animal, neither horse nor donkey, but intermediate between the two and partaking to some extent of the character of each. Similarly, the theories of intermediate stages, of mesomerism, and of resonance picture the benzene molecule as having a *hybrid* structure, not identical with either of the Kekulé structures, but intermediate between them.

In several respects, the above analogy of the mule is likely to be misleading. Thus, it suggests that, since the horse and the donkey are no less real than the mule, so also the individual structures that are involved in the resonance have as much physical significance as the resulting hybrid. This inference is, however, incorrect. With benzene, for example, the Kekulé structures I and II are merely intellectual constructions which do not correspond to any molecules that actually exist; only their hybrid, the benzene molecule, has physical reality. For this reason, the following rather different analogy[9] offers some advantages over the original one. We may imagine that a medieval traveler, in the course of his wanderings, saw a rhinoceros; and that, after his return to his home, he attempted to describe this strange beast to his friends. A convenient way for him to convey an approximately correct idea of the animal's appearance would be to say that the rhinoceros is intermediate between a dragon and a unicorn; for, as we may assume, the people to whom he was talking would have fairly clear ideas of what these two latter purely mythical creatures were supposed to look like. Similarly, a convenient way to give an approximate description of the true structure of benzene is to say that it is intermediate between the two purely imaginary Kekulé structures; for, just as the fictitious dragon and unicorn formerly called forth clear pictures to medieval men and women, so also the equally fictitious Kekulé structures now call forth clear pictures to modern organic chemists. In each case, therefore, the unfamiliar reality is explained by reference to a familiar fiction.

There exist still additional ways in which the analogy of the mule can be misleading. This analogy suggests that resonance must always involve exactly two structures, and also that the resulting hybrid must always be exactly halfway between the two extremes. Neither of these further

---

[9] The author is indebted to Professor J. D. Roberts for this interesting analogy.

inferences, however, is correct. In general, any desired number of structures can be included in the resonance; and the resulting hybrid can be closer to one or more of the contributing structures than it is to others. Although we might be able to extend the analogy of the rhinoceros to cover such more complex situations, we shall find it more convenient here to introduce still a third analogy which does not suffer from the several defects so far considered. Thus, the best way to describe a man's personality is frequently by means of a comparison with familiar characters of fiction. For example, if we say that a certain actually existing man, John Doe, is a cross between Sherlock Holmes and Don Quixote, we give a fairly clear picture of the real John Doe, even though neither Sherlock Holmes nor Don Quixote ever lived. Moreover, if we now add that John Doe is more like Sherlock Holmes than he is like Don Quixote, and that he has also a slight resemblance to Sir Galahad, we make the picture still more definite. There is no restriction either on the total number of the individual fictional characters or on the relative weights that are assigned to them.

Although the three foregoing analogies may help to make clear the difference between resonance and tautomerism, they shed little if any light on what exactly is meant by the statement that a given molecule has an intermediate, mesomeric, or hybrid structure. Let us therefore return to a consideration of benzene, and let us now center our attention upon some particular bond, say the one between the two carbon atoms on the right sides of the structures I and II above. If benzene consists of a tautomeric mixture of molecules with the Kekulé structures, this bond is a double bond part of the time (structure I) and a single bond the rest of the time (structure II). On the other hand, if the substance is in an intermediate stage, or is mesomeric, between the Kekulé structures, or if it is a resonance hybrid of those structures, the bond does not change with the time. It is neither a double nor a single bond, but it is instead a new type of bond, not envisaged by the classical structural theory. We might call it a "one-and-a-half bond" (however, see Section 4·4) or possibly a "benzene bond." We can obtain a more definite picture by making use of the fact that the average density of electronic charge in the region between two carbon atoms is greater if the atoms are joined by a double bond than it is if they are joined by a single bond. Consequently, we can visualize the bond in benzene as one in which the density of charge is greater than that in the carbon-carbon single bond of ethane, but less than that in the double bond of ethylene. Moreover, the structure of any other resonance hybrid can be interpreted in a completely similar way. In general, in fact, whenever we say that a given substance is a resonance hybrid, we imply that each of its valence bonds has a charge distribution which is intermediate between the extremes represented by the several contributing structures. (However, see page 27.) Even though, as was just pointed out, these latter structures are fictitious, the charge distributions which they represent can usually be inferred from a comparison with the unique structures of certain other molecules (e.g., ethane and ethylene, see above) which are *not* resonance hybrids.

The following difficulty arises in the minds of many people when they first encounter a discussion of the structure of benzene from the present point of view. The structures I and II are completely equivalent since either can be transformed into the other by merely a rotation of 60° in the plane of the paper. What then is the difference between these structures, and what is the meaning of the statement that the true structure of benzene is neither the one nor the other but something intermediate? Moreover, since the carbon atoms are in principle indistinguishable (unless they are of different isotopes), how can we say that a *given pair* of them are joined by a double bond in I and by a single bond in II? A partial answer to these questions has already been implied in the preceding paragraph; the statement that benzene is a hybrid of I and II means that the carbon-carbon bonds are not alternately single and double, as would be true if the molecule had either structure alone, but all are instead of the same, intermediate type. A deeper insight into the problem can be obtained from a more careful examination. Although the various carbon atoms are not distinguishable, the positions in space which they are capable of occupying *are* distinguishable. Consequently, we could define the difference between structures I and II by the statement that the "two easternmost atoms" are joined by a double bond in I and by a single bond in II. This statement has a definite meaning, even though the "two easternmost atoms" cannot be more precisely specified as being identical with, say, atoms 1 and 2, or 3 and 6, or the like. This interpretation is most logical if the molecule is considered to be held in a fixed orientation, as in a crystal, but it is not actually restricted to any such special situation. A further way of evading the present difficulty is by considering a particular case in which two adjacent carbon atoms are distinguished from the remaining four either by being of a different isotope or by carrying different substituents. Then the difference between structures I and II is quite apparent, but the situation has been made too highly specialized to be completely illuminating.

A further question which occasionally arises is the following. If altogether eighteen electrons are employed in benzene to produce the six completely equivalent carbon-carbon bonds, then would it not be satisfactory and highly convenient to describe the bonds as three-electron bonds and to write the structure of the molecule simply as III?

H
·.. C ..·

HC   CH
· · ·   · · ·
HC   CH

·· C ··.
H

III

There are two different reasons why this proposed alternative is inferior to the method of description adopted in the preceding paragraphs. In the first place, the term "three-electron bond" has already been defined to mean something quite different from the type of bond in benzene (see Section 2·5); and, in the second place, no corresponding description can be devised for the apparently similar bonds in naphthalene and other condensed aromatic ring systems. Consequently, the use of the structure III for benzene would be not only confusing but also incapable of generalization to other closely related situations.

1·3 Nomenclature. As we have seen, the theory of intermediate stages, or of mesomerism, or, as we shall say hereafter, of resonance, is an outgrowth of several earlier and less precise theories. Perhaps largely on this account, the language used to describe it is unusually varied, and no single, uniform system of nomenclature has as yet been adopted for it. Although this lack of uniformity in the nomenclature is sometimes inconvenient, it does not often lead to confusion. A much more serious difficulty arises, however, from the fact that only by exercising the utmost care in the choice of words can one avoid the appearance of implying that the molecules of a resonance hybrid are oscillating back and forth among the several structures, and hence that these structures must possess real physical significance. For example, the common statements that the hybrid *resonates* among the structures and that the structures *resonate* with one another almost unavoidably give this quite erroneous impression. When the structures differ in the position of a valence bond (or of an electric charge), the statement that the bond (or the charge) *resonates* around the molecule, or among the various positions, is still more likely to be misleading. Throughout this book, therefore, we shall scrupulously refrain from using the verb "to resonate."

In addition to the foregoing, several of the other expressions that are commonly used in the discussion of resonance are similarly misleading. Thus, the statement that resonance *occurs* among a set of structures is likely to give the impression that resonance refers to some sort of action that the molecule of the resonance hybrid is performing, whereas it instead refers to an approximate description of the state in which the molecule is, and remains. A more precise statement would be that, in the treatment of whatever problem may be under consideration at the time, the substance of interest *is being regarded as a resonance hybrid*. Since, however, this preferred mode of expression is often found in practice to be rather awkward, we shall frequently use the simpler, but still somewhat inexact, statement that resonance *exists*, or that *there is* resonance. In any event, we shall never speak of resonance as a *phenomenon*.

One frequently encounters the statement that a resonance hybrid *receives contributions* from the individual structures of which it is a hybrid; or that these structures *contribute* to the state of the hybrid. This terminology also, however, is somewhat loose for, since the structures exist only in the minds of the persons who are talking about them, they cannot strictly contribute anything to the physically real state of an actual molecule. A better statement would therefore be that the substance *can conveniently be described as a hybrid* of the stated structures. We shall nevertheless continue to make frequent use of the less precise terminology, since otherwise we would often be led into long and awkward circumlocutions; and since, with this much in the way of explanation, the reader should now be able to avoid being misled. In particular, the expression *contributing structure* is almost indispensable and so, since it is not too confusing, it will be used hereafter. Furthermore, in order to indicate that the true state of a resonance hybrid is closer to the extreme represented by some one specified structure than it is to that represented by a certain other structure, we shall occasionally say, in a similarly loose way, that the former structure *makes a larger contribution* than does the latter; here, however, the alternative, and more precise, statement that the former structure *is assigned the greater weight* is often equally convenient. And finally, the structure which makes the larger contribution, i.e., the one which is assigned the greater weight, is frequently said to be *the more important in the resonance*; this terminology, although perhaps not ideal, seems seldom to have caused any confusion, and it will be employed on many occasions throughout the book.

Another common type of loose terminology can be illustrated by the statement that the resonance, or a certain one of the contributing structures (cf. the preceding paragraph), exerts some specified effect upon the properties of a given resonance hybrid. If taken literally, however, a statement of this type is nonsense because resonance is merely a way that has been devised for describing the state of the molecule, and because the contributing structures are merely representations of certain imaginary charge distributions, with which the actual charge distribution in the molecule is to be compared. In order to show how such a statement must be interpreted, let us consider a substance which is a resonance hybrid of some set of structures, A, B, C, · · ·. Now although there are no molecules which have exactly these latter structures, we can nevertheless, by comparison with other molecules to which unique structures can be assigned, state with considerable assurance what properties such molecules ought to have, if only they could exist. In general, these properties that are thus attributed to the structures A, B, C, · · · are different from the observed properties of the actual hybrid. With some justification, therefore, we can say that the resonance does have an effect upon the properties for, if there were no resonance, and if the molecule therefore had some specified one of the limiting structures A, B, C, · · ·, its properties would doubtless be essentially those expected for that structure, and hence different from those observed for the hybrid. For example, from our knowledge of the behavior of aliphatic olefins, we can feel quite confident that, if there were a substance with exactly the cyclohexatriene structure which Kekulé ascribed to benzene, it would rapidly absorb bromine, it would be easily oxidized by a mild oxidizing agent, and so on. The fact that benzene does not have any of these properties can then be considered a result of the resonance between the two Kekulé structures.

With a similar degree of justification, the difference between the observed properties of a resonance hybrid that receives contributions from the structures A, B, C, $\cdot$ $\cdot$ $\cdot$ and the properties which we would expect for a (purely imaginary) hybrid that receives contributions from only the structures B, C, $\cdot$ $\cdot$ $\cdot$ can be considered due to the contribution of the particular structure A. Although, for the reason stated above, neither of the two modes of expression which have been discussed in this paragraph and the preceding one is really correct, each is so extremely convenient that it will often hereafter be used without further apology. Numerous specific examples will, in fact, be given throughout the book. In any event, the statement that the resonance has a stated effect upon the properties of the substance is to be interpreted as meaning that we can devise a more satisfactory explanation for the observed properties if we describe the substance as a resonance hybrid than we can if we instead try to describe it in terms of any single structure; and the statement that a particular structure A exerts a stated effect is to be interpreted as meaning that we can obtain a better picture of the charge distribution in the actual molecule if we assign a finite weight to structure A than we can if we instead assign a weight of zero to that structure.

A further problem of nomenclature is that of the way, or, rather, of the several ways, in which the word "structure" is commonly used. We have already, in fact, implicitly assigned two quite different meanings to this word. On the one hand, when we spoke above of the *structure* of benzene, we were referring to the actual state of the physically real molecule; on the other hand, when we spoke of a Kekulé *structure*, we were instead referring to an imaginary charge distribution which does not correspond to any existing molecule. The ideal way to avoid ambiguities of this sort would doubtless be to use different words for the different concepts. We could, for example, speak of the *state* of benzene, but of a Kekulé *formula*. We have already made frequent use of the word "state" in this sense, and we shall hereafter employ both the words "state" and "formula" from time to time. Most commonly, however, we shall retain the not entirely satisfactory term "structure," since it has desirable connotations which are not shared by "state" or by "formula."

Indeed, "structure" is now so universally accepted that any alternative expression would have little chance of general adoption. Our use of this somewhat ambiguous terminology should cause no confusion if the reader bears in mind that, although the structure of a molecule or of a substance has a real physical significance, the structures which contribute to the state of a resonance hybrid are merely intellectual constructions. Furthermore, on any future occasion when it may not be clear from the context what type of structure is intended, the attempt will be made to explain the meaning more fully. (This question of the significance of the word "structure" will be discussed in greater detail, and from a different point of view, on pages 46f.)

An alternative method for describing the structures that contribute to a resonance hybrid is so widespread that, even though it will not be employed in this book, it requires some mention here. A great many authors speak of resonance between two, or among more than two, *forms*. This terminology seems, however, to have caused much confusion and hence, especially since it is no more convenient than the one just described, its use is unfortunate. The difficulty here is due to the fact that the word "forms" commonly implies the actual existence of distinct substances which could in principle, even if not always in practice, be separated from each other. We speak, for example, of the keto and enol *forms* of acetoacetic ester, the dextro- and levorotatory *forms* of lactic acid, the rhombic and monoclinic *forms* of sulfur, and so on. Consequently, the statement that benzene is a resonance hybrid of the two Kekulé forms or, much worse (see above), the statement that benzene resonates between the two Kekulé forms almost unavoidably gives the erroneous impression that this substance is a tautomeric mixture of molecules which have the specified structures, and that the individual molecules are undergoing transitions back and forth between these structures.

Not infrequently, the word "form" in the sense of "contributing structure" is replaced by "state," which is, if anything, even more likely to be misleading, since no fictitious structure which merely contributes to a resonance hybrid can legitimately be called a *state*. Hence, we shall continue, as heretofore, to restrict the word "state" to the actual condition of a real molecule.

No unique symbols for the graphical representation of resonance hybrids have as yet received unanimous acceptance. The most widely adopted procedure at present is a completely general but rather cumbersome one, which consists in writing down either all the structures involved or else a sufficient number of representative examples. The fact that the substance is considered to be a hybrid of these structures is then indicated either by an explicit statement in the text or by the use of double-headed arrows,[10] as in structure I.   The symbol ↔ must be carefully distinguished

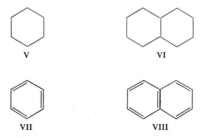

I

from the similar one, ⇄, which is commonly employed to show the existence of a chemical equilibrium.   A further, more compact system of representation, which was devised by the English school of organic chemists,[6] will be described in Section 8·4.   Still another method for depicting the states of resonance hybrids can be illustrated by the diagrams II (or frequently III) for benzene, and IV for a carboxylate ion.

II   III

$$\left[R\!-\!C\!\!\begin{array}{c} {}^{\nearrow O} \\ {}_{\searrow O} \end{array} \right]^{-}$$

IV

Although this method is rather often encountered in the current chemical literature, it will not be employed in this book since it is not entirely general, and since its interpretation is not always completely obvious. For the aromatic hydrocarbons, we shall instead make use of the simple hexagons, like V and VI for benzene and naphthalene, respectively.   In any event, it is to be noted that, since, for example, the structures VII

V   VI

VII   VIII

and VIII must in the following pages be explicitly reserved for the representation of the Kekulé and Erlenmeyer structures, they cannot be used

[10] C. R. Bury, *J. Am. Chem. Soc.* **57**, 2115 (1935); B. Eistert, *Angew. Chem.* **49**, 33 (1936).

for the representation of the corresponding hybrids, benzene, and naphthalene.

1·4   The Conditions for Resonance.   As was mentioned above, the quantum-mechanical approach leads to an understanding of the conditions that must be satisfied if a substance is to be described as a hybrid of any given set of structures.   Although the following rules may perhaps seem arbitrary, since the reasons for them are not self-evident, it must be borne in mind that they, like the concept of resonance itself, are simple corollaries of the basic equations of quantum mechanics.   Their derivation will be briefly discussed on page 25, and more fully described in Section 9·16.   Here, we shall merely state them without proof, and in their simplest and most generally useful forms; in part D of Section 9·18, we shall consider certain refinements in them which are required for complete rigor but which almost never need to be considered explicitly in any practical application of the theory.   (See also pages 62f and 73.)

1.   *There can be resonance only among structures that correspond to the same, or to nearly the same, relative positions of all the atomic nuclei.* Some such restriction as this is obviously necessary, since otherwise isomerism would be impossible.   If resonance between the structures I and II, for example, were possible, these structures could not represent

$$CH_3—CH_2—CH_2—CH_3 \qquad\qquad \begin{array}{c} CH_3—CH—CH_3 \\ | \\ CH_3 \end{array}$$

I   II

two distinct and different substances, as they in fact do, but they would have to represent only a single substance with a structure of intermediate type.   This last possibility, however, is precluded because the two structures correspond to widely different positions of the nuclei, so that resonance is rendered impossible by this condition 1.

The situation encountered generally in those molecules which are described as resonance hybrids can be illustrated by a discussion of benzene.   For this substance, the two Kekulé structures III and IV can

III   IV

be written.   These do not correspond to exactly the same nuclear configuration because the length of a carbon-carbon single bond is normally about 1.54 A, whereas that of a carbon-carbon double bond is normally about 1.34 A.   (The symbol A is an abbreviation for the *angstrom unit*, or *angstrom*, which is equal to 10^{-8} cm.   See Chapter 4.)   However, atoms in molecules do not occupy definitely fixed positions; even at the absolute zero of temperature they are instead constantly executing vibrations about their positions of minimum potential energy with amplitudes of the order of magnitude of 0.1 A.   The above-cited lengths of single and double bonds refer only to the distances between these positions of minimum energy.   Consequently, the Kekulé structures do overlap in a

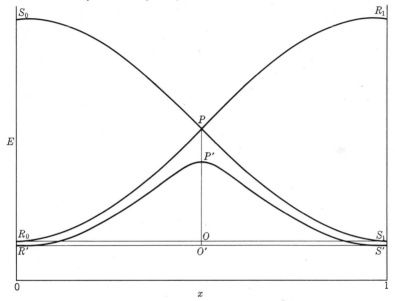

Fig. 1·1.   Energies E of two structures R and S and of their resonance hybrid, when the limiting structures differ greatly in nuclear configuration.   As the abscissa x varies from 0 to 1, the positions of the atoms change continuously from those characteristic of structure R to those characteristic of structure S.

sense, and so we need not be surprised if we find that benzene is indeed a hybrid of the two.

A more detailed analysis of this first rule can be given with the aid of Figures 1·1, 1·2, and 1·3, which show in a schematic manner several possible ways in which the energy E of a given molecule may vary as the atomic positions change in consequence of a transition from some arbitrary structure R to a different structure S.

The energy of a *molecule* is defined as the negative of the amount of energy required to dissociate it, in the gaseous state, into isolated gaseous atoms.   The energy of a stable molecule is therefore always a negative quantity.   In Figures 1·1, 1·2, and 1·3, the zeros from which the energies are measured would lie some distance above any of the curves.   The word "stable," as used here and throughout the remainder of the book, indicates only a low energy and does not necessarily imply a lack of reactivity.

The energy of an *individual structure* that is said to contribute to the state of a reson-ance hybrid cannot be similarly defined in purely experimental terms, since there is then no actual molecule that has this structure. We can still, however, make a fairly reliable estimate of the energy which such a molecule would have if only it could exist,

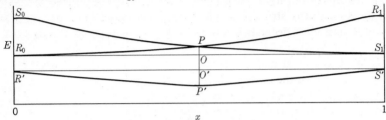

Fig. 1·2. Energies E of two structures R and S and of their resonance hybrid, when the limiting structures differ only slightly in nuclear configuration. The abscissa has the same significance here as in Fig. 1·1.

for we can compare the structure in question with the unique structures of molecules which do exist and which are not regarded as resonance hybrids. With benzene, for example, the energy of each Kekulé structure is the sum of six times the energy of a carbon-hydrogen bond, plus three times that of a carbon-carbon single bond, plus three times that of a carbon-carbon double bond; and these required bond energies

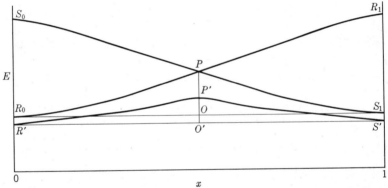

Fig. 1·3. Energies E of two structures R and S and of their resonance hybrid, when the limiting structures differ by an intermediate amount in nuclear configuration. The abscissa has the same significance here as in Fig. 1·1.

can be obtained from the empirical data for methane, ethane, and ethylene. (Cf. Section 3·4.)

In each of Figures 1·1, 1·2, and 1·3, the parameter x is a coordinate (the so-called reaction coordinate) which is described sufficiently well for our purposes by the statement that it assumes the values 0 and 1 when the relative positions of the atomic nuclei are those corresponding to the structures R and S respectively, and that it assumes intermediate values when the atomic positions are intermediate. The energy of a molecule with structure R is obviously a minimum at $x = 0$, since then by definition the molecule is in its most stable configuration, and it must increase along the curve $R_0 P R_1$ as x increases, since in the process the molecule is being distorted from its stable configuration. Conversely, the energy of a molecule with the structure S has a high value (indicating instability) at $x = 0$, and must decrease along the curve $S_0 P S_1$ to a minimum (indicating stability) at $x = 1$. For simplicity in exposition, the energies of structure R at $x = 0$ and of structure S at $x = 1$ have been assumed equal, and likewise the energies of structure R at $x = 1$ and of structure S at $x = 0$ have also been assumed equal; these assumptions are not essential to the following discussion, however, and the extension to the general case should be obvious.

When the possibility of resonance between the structures R and S is taken into account, another factor arises. As has already been mentioned and as will be discussed later in greater detail (see, for example, Section 1·5 and Chapters 2 and 3), an important effect of resonance is to make every molecule of which it is an important feature more stable (that is, of lower energy) than any one of the individual structures involved. This generalization is valid, at any rate, in the most stable state of the system. Although resonance leads also to excited states in which there is an increase in energy, this circumstance has no bearing upon the present problem (see Section 1·5 and Chapter 6); we are discussing a chemical and not a spectroscopic question, and so we are concerned only with the most stable state, since that is the only state in which matter in bulk can be obtained. Thus, it follows that the actual energy of the molecule, when plotted against x, must give a curve $R'P'S'$, always below either $R_0 P R_1$ or $S_0 P S_1$, but becoming nearly coincident with the lower of these at the extremes.

Figure 1·1 represents a case in which the structures R and S differ greatly in the relative positions of the atomic nuclei, so that a large distortion is required to change one configuration into the other. If there were no resonance, the minimum energy necessary for the transition to occur would be represented in the figure by the distance OP; when the resonance is taken into account, this energy is reduced to the smaller value $O'P'$. The distance OP, however, could easily correspond to an energy of 100 kcal per mole or more if the structures R and S differ in atomic configuration as greatly as do those of n-butane and isobutane, for example (structures I and II, respectively). Consequently, even when allowance is made for the resonance effect, the energy $O'P'$ required for the rearrangement may still be large compared with the average thermal energy of the molecules. Under such circumstances, then, the isolation of isomeric or tautomeric forms possessing structures very close to R and

S is possible, and it is not profitable to speak of resonance. (This point is discussed at greater length below in the paragraph in fine print.)

Figure 1·2 represents another extreme case, in which the difference in the atomic configurations of the structures R and S is relatively small. The energy of distortion OP is then also relatively small, being perhaps no greater in order of magnitude than the average thermal energy. If the resonance effect is assumed to be of about the same importance here as in the previous example, the curve $R'P'S'$ has no maximum but a minimum instead at some value of x intermediate between 0 and 1. Under such circumstances, the molecule will take up a configuration corresponding to this minimum. Isolation of isomeric or tautomeric forms possessing structures close to R and S will then be impossible; there will instead exist only a single substance, possessing a structure intermediate between R and S. This is the situation which one ordinarily has in mind when he says that a molecule is a hybrid of two or more structures. In the particular case of benzene, only a single substance is possible whether the resonance is of this particular type or not (in other words, whether the situation is that described by Figure 1·2 or by one of the others) because the two Kekulé structures III and IV are completely equivalent. With o-xylene, on the other hand, the two corresponding structures V and VI are not completely equivalent, and the possibility

III    IV

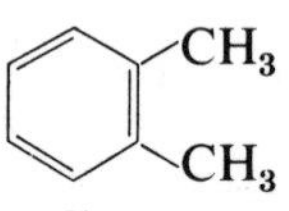

V 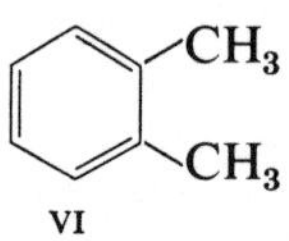   VI

arises that two isomeric substances may exist. However, only one o-xylene is known; it seems probable, therefore, that the relationship between V and VI (and also, from analogy, between III and IV) is that represented by Figure 1·2. Further evidence supporting this conclusion will be advanced in later chapters.

Figure 1·3 represents an intermediate case in which the curve $R'P'S'$ has a low maximum at the point P'. If the energy $O'P'$ is of the same order of magnitude as, or is smaller than, the average thermal energy, no isolation of isomeric forms will be possible. This situation is encountered, for example, in ammonia, NH_3, in which the transition from one structure to the other occurs whenever the nitrogen atom passes through the plane defined by the three hydrogen atoms. In such borderline cases, which fortunately seem to be rather rare, the question whether one should speak of tautomerism or of resonance cannot be answered unambiguously without reference to some specific experimental situation. We shall return to this problem again on pages 611f and 628.

Even in Figure 1·1, the points R' and S' lie slightly below R_0 and S_1, respectively. In a certain sense, therefore, it might be said that the substance is a hybrid of the two structures. This situation, however, is not at all what one ordinarily has in mind when he speaks of resonance. For example, let us suppose that the structures R and S are those given above as I and II respectively. (The small difference in energy between n-butane and isobutane is negligible for our present purposes.) Then, at $x = 0$, the relative positions of the atoms are those characteristic of n-butane, so that structure S should really be written not in the form II but rather in the form II', where the dotted

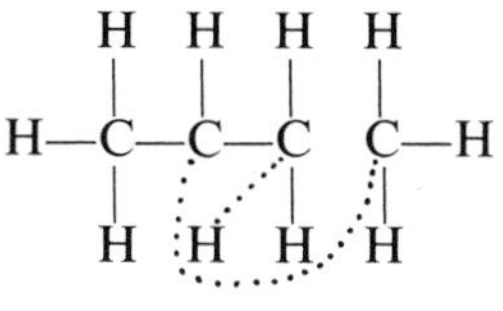

H H H H
| | | |
H—C—C—C C—H
| | | |
H H H H
II'

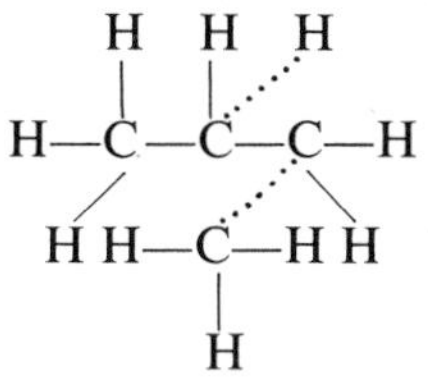

H H H
| | |
H—C—C—C—H
/ | \
H H—C—H H
|
H
I'

lines represent the formal bonds discussed in part 3 of this section. (The structure II' is intended to imply that the electrons are paired as in isobutane, but that the geometrical arrangement of the atoms is as in n-butane.) In the same way, at $x = 1$, the structure R becomes I' instead of I. In other words, the resonance which can be said to exist between the structures of n-butane and isobutane, at either $x = 0$ or $x = 1$, is not between the two normal structures, but between one normal and one highly strained structure. It is true that the actual structures of the butanes are not exactly I and II, but are resonance hybrids of these with extremely small contributions from several others of the kind represented by II' and I', respectively. However, since similar considerations apply to all molecules, it is usually most convenient to think of this type of resonance as already implied by and contained in the simple structures I and II. Consequently, we shall continue to say hereafter that there is no resonance between structures, such as those of n-butane and isobutane, which correspond to distinguishable substances.

2. *There can be resonance only among structures that correspond to similar relative positions of the electrons.* This restriction rarely has to be considered explicitly; it is much less stringent than the one upon the positions of the nuclei, because electrons, having considerably smaller mass and greater mobility than atomic nuclei, cannot be localized so precisely. Some examples in which this present rule is important will be discussed in Chapter 2 in connection with the origin of the valence forces.

3. *There can be resonance only among structures with the same numbers of unpaired electrons.* The significance of the word "unpaired" in this connection requires some comment. For many purposes it is sufficient

to regard an electron as a point particle having a certain definite negative charge and a certain definite mass.   It has been found necessary, however, to assign it one further property, which is called the *spin*.   The statement that an electron has a spin means that it has a magnetic moment, or, in other words, that it behaves like a small bar magnet.   When two electrons interact with each other, they must always orient themselves in such a way that the lines drawn from their north to their south poles are pointing either in approximately the same or in exactly the opposite directions. The former situation is commonly described by the statement that the electrons are *unpaired* or that they have parallel spin; the latter, by the statement that the electrons are *paired* or that they have antiparallel spin. (The word "unpaired" is used also to describe a single electron that has no second electron with which it can interact in this manner.)

When two electrons are engaged in forming the same covalent bond, or when they belong to the same unshared pair, they are necessarily paired with each other.   For example, in the molecule of hydrogen chloride, with the electronic structure VII, each electron is paired with another, so that the total number of unpaired electrons is zero.   An example of a molecule with one unpaired electron is provided by the free methyl radical, VIII; in general, any molecule with an odd number of

$$H : \ddot{C}l :$$

VII.

$$\begin{array}{c} H \\ \cdot \ddot{C} : H \\ H \end{array}$$

VIII

electrons must have at least one of them unpaired.   In the usual structure of ethylene, IX, all electrons are paired, but there is another structure, X, that can be written, and in this each carbon atom has an isolated

$$\begin{array}{c} H-C{=}C-H \\ | \quad | \\ H \quad H \end{array} \qquad \begin{array}{c} H-\overset{\cdot}{C}-\overset{\cdot}{C}-H \\ | \quad | \\ H \quad H \end{array}$$

IX   X

electron.   These two isolated electrons must be either paired or unpaired with each other.   However, the pairing of two electrons on adjacent atoms is equivalent to the forming of a covalent bond and, consequently, if the electrons are paired, this second structure, X, is *identical* with IX. We shall, accordingly, interpret any structure like X as implying that the isolated electrons are unpaired.   Since resonance between the structures IX and X is therefore impossible, the second one of these would be of interest only in connection with the excited states that are observed spectroscopically.   (For a more detailed discussion of electron spin and of the significance of pairing, see Sections 9·7 and 9·10.)

A more complicated example, which brings out a further point of considerable importance, is provided by butadiene.   For this substance, the two structures, XI and XII, analogous to the ones just discussed for

$$
\begin{array}{cc}
\underset{\underset{\text{XI}}{\overset{\displaystyle H\;\;\;H\;\;\;H\;\;\;H}{|\quad|\quad|\quad|}}}{H\!-\!C\!=\!C\!-\!C\!=\!C\!-\!H}
&
\underset{\underset{\text{XII}}{\overset{\displaystyle H\;\;\;H\;\;\;H\;\;\;\overset{\cdot}{H}}{|\quad|\quad|\quad|}}}{H\!-\!\overset{\cdot}{C}\!-\!C\!=\!C\!-\!\overset{\cdot}{C}\!-\!H}
\end{array}
$$

ethylene, can be drawn.   (In each of these, the relative positions of all the atomic nuclei are supposed to be those characteristic of the actual butadiene molecule.)   In structure XII, the question again arises whether the isolated electrons are paired or unpaired with each other.   If they are paired, the result is no longer equivalent to the formation of a bond, because the terminal carbon atoms are so far apart in space that no effective bond between them is possible.   Consequently, if the two electrons in question are paired with each other, there is only what may be called a *formal bond*.   This type of interaction can be represented by the symbol XIII or XIV, in which arrows are used in place of the usual dots in order to indicate the relative orientation of the magnetic moments, or the dotted line represents the formal bond.   Resonance between the conventional structure XI and the one represented by either of the equivalent symbols XIII and XIV is possible because the number of

$$
\begin{array}{cc}
\underset{\underset{\text{XIII}}{\overset{\displaystyle H\;\;\;H\;\;\;H\;\;\;H}{|\quad|\quad|\quad|}}}{H\!-\!\overset{\uparrow}{C}\!-\!C\!=\!C\!-\!\overset{\downarrow}{C}\!-\!H}
&
\underset{\underset{\text{XIV}}{\overset{\displaystyle H\;\;\;H\;\;\;H\;\;\;H}{|\quad|\quad|\quad|}}}{H\!-\!\overset{\cdots}{C}\!-\!C\!=\!C\!-\!\overset{\cdots}{C}\!-\!H}
\end{array}
$$

unpaired electrons is the same, namely zero, in both.   On the other hand, the type of interaction in which the two electrons are unpaired can be represented by the equivalent symbols XII or XV.   Resonance between

$$
\underset{\underset{\text{XV}}{\overset{\displaystyle H\;\;\;H\;\;\;H\;\;\;H}{|\quad|\quad|\quad|}}}{H\!-\!\overset{\uparrow}{C}\!-\!C\!=\!C\!-\!\overset{\uparrow}{C}\!-\!H}
$$

this structure and the conventional one is impossible because the numbers of unpaired electrons are different.   (For further discussion of the significance of the formal bond, see pages 45f and 632.)

The structure XIV must be carefully distinguished from the apparently similar one, XVI, which corresponds to the known substance cyclobutene. The former refers to

$$
\begin{array}{cc}
H_2C & \!\!-\!\!CH \\
| & \| \\
H_2C & \!\!-\!\!CH
\end{array}
$$

XVI

a situation in which the relative positions of the nuclei are those characteristic of butadiene, whereas the latter refers to a situation in which the positions of the nuclei are those characteristic of cyclobutene. Thus, although the electrons are paired in the same way in both structures, the two are actually different, and, in fact, there can be no resonance between them (condition 1). The use of the arrows (as in XIII) would help in avoiding this confusion; it would, however, create the more serious one of making ambiguous any structure with more than two isolated electrons or more than one formal bond. For that reason, we shall hereafter employ the symbolism of the formal bond. A further method of representation, which has been proposed by Hückel,[11] is equivalent to the one given above employing arrows.

4. *Whenever the preceding conditions are satisfied, the substance must in general be regarded as a hybrid, but the resonance can be of importance only if the various structures that are involved are of the same, or nearly the same, stability (that is, energy).* When the resonance is among structures which differ in stability, the actual ground state of the molecule will be most closely approximated by those structures which are most stable (that is, by those which have the lowest energies). This rule is of great practical value because, for any given molecule, one can always write a large number of possible structures. For methane, for example, we could write not only XVII, but also XVIII, and even XIX by going to

$$
\begin{array}{cccc}
H & H^+ & & H:^- \\
| & \cdot\cdot & & \\
H\!-\!C\!-\!H & H\!-\!C^-\!\!-\!H & :H^-\ \ C^{++++}\ \ H:^- \\
| & | & & \\
H & H & & H:^-
\end{array}
$$

XVII   XVIII   XIX

a ridiculous extreme. Most of these "possible" structures, however, correspond to relatively high energies, and so must be assigned relatively small weights. Since they therefore can have only little effect upon the properties of the substance, they can often be entirely neglected. We shall see numerous examples of this situation throughout the remainder of the book.

Before this rule governing the importance of the resonance can be put to practical use, criteria must be established by which the relative stabilities of structures can be estimated. It is doubtful that any completely general and, at the same time, completely rigorous criteria of this sort are possible, but the necessary decisions can usually be made without

[11] E. Hückel, *Z. Elektrochem.* **43**, 752, 827 (1937).

difficulty. In fact, any structure which seems unreasonable from the viewpoint of the classical structural theory is almost certain to be an unstable one (cf. structures XVIII and XIX); and, the more unreasonable a structure seems, the less stable, and hence the less important in the resonance it is likely to be. Moreover, the following more objective principles, which are of a partly empirical and partly theoretical nature, can be laid down, and they are often of considerable help.

(*a*) A structure in which more than two electrons are assigned to any hydrogen or helium atom or in which more than eight valence electrons are assigned to any atom of the first row of the periodic table is so unstable that it can be neglected. For atoms of the second and subsequent rows, no similar rule can be stated with assurance, although there does frequently seem to be a tendency for the maintenance of the octet.

(*b*) The energy of a structure can usually be estimated with fair accuracy by the use of the so-called bond energies. It has been found empirically that a bond of a given type makes an almost constant (negative) contribution to the energy of any molecule in which it occurs. (Cf. Section 3·4.) This rule has exceptions, which are sometimes of appreciable magnitude, but for our present purposes these are negligible. It is often sufficient, in fact, to use the much cruder procedure of merely counting the number of bonds in the various structures; those structures with the largest numbers of bonds are then usually the most stable. Since the magnitude of the energy associated with a bond is large, a difference of even one bond between two structures represents a considerable difference in stability. In butadiene, for example, the normal structure, XI, has eleven bonds (the double bonds being counted twice), whereas the less stable structure, XIII or XIV, has only ten (the formal bond not being counted). Consequently, although resonance is possible and must be considered, the second structure is so unstable relative to the first that its weight is necessarily small. With this substance, then, the concept of resonance does not alter to any marked extent the picture provided by the classical structural theory; the slight alteration that it does introduce, however, proves to be of considerable interest in connection with the properties of the conjugated system, as we shall see in later chapters.

(*c*) Frequently one can distinguish between structures with the same number of bonds on the basis of differences in the distribution of electric charge. For a carboxylic acid, for example, the two most stable structures which can be written are presumably XX and XXI. These have the

$$ R : \overset{\displaystyle :O:}{\underset{\displaystyle\ddots}{C} : \overset{\displaystyle\cdot\cdot}{\underset{\displaystyle\cdot\cdot}{O}} : H} \qquad\qquad R : \overset{\displaystyle :\overset{\cdot\cdot}{O}:^-}{\underset{\displaystyle\cdot\cdot}{C} : : \overset{\cdot\cdot}{O} :^+ H} $$

$$ \text{xx} \qquad\qquad\qquad\qquad \text{xxi} $$

same numbers of the same kinds of bonds, but they differ in that, in XXI, there are formal charges upon the oxygen atoms.

The significance of the *formal charge* is the following: If an atom has a kernel charge Ze (where $-e$ is the charge of an electron), and if it is surrounded by k electrons which are shared, and by p electrons which are not shared with another atom, then its formal charge $F = Z - (k/2) - p$. The kernel charge of an atom is defined as the charge of the ion that would remain after the removal of all the electrons of the valence shell (that is, of all the electrons which are represented by dots in the usual electronic structure). For example, the oxygen atom which is attached to the hydrogen atom in structure XXI has $Z = 6$, $k = 6$, and $p = 2$. Consequently, $F = 6 - (6/2) - 2 = + 1$. Similarly, for the other oxygen atom in that structure, $F = 6 - (2/2) - 6 = - 1$. The formal charge would be equal to the actual charge (expressed in units of e) if the electrons in shared pairs were shared equally between the two atoms involved. Although, as a result of polarization, the sharing is usually not equal, structures with formal charges are always found to be characterized by much larger than average dipole moments (see Chapter 5), so that the indicated separation of charge is, nevertheless, real. The existence of formal charges in any structure will be shown by the placing of plus or minus signs, as required, near the symbols for the atoms concerned. The sum of the formal charges on all the atoms of any molecule must be equal to the total charge of that molecule.

Since energy is required to effect the separation of charge in structure XXI, it seems evident that this structure must be somewhat less stable, and consequently less important, than XX. This conclusion follows because neither of the two atoms with formal charges is strongly electropositive, so that the condition for the existence of a strong ionic bond, as in sodium chloride, is not satisfied. (See Section 2·2.)

An example of a different type is provided by an enolate ion, for which there are again two structures, XXII and XXIII, with the same total

$$: \overset{..}{O}:^-$$
$$R : \overset{..}{C} : : C : R$$
$$R$$
XXII

$$: O :$$
$$R : \overset{..}{C} : \overset{..}{C} :^- R$$
$$R$$
XXIII

number of bonds. The significant difference between these is that now the negative charge is upon the oxygen atom in XXII and upon a carbon atom in XXIII. Since oxygen is a more electronegative element than carbon, there can be little question that, for this ion, structure XXII is the more stable of the two.

(*d*) By the methods just described under the headings (*a*), (*b*), and (*c*), it is usually possible to estimate with some assurance the relative stabilities of the structures which are involved in the resonance. The question still remains, however, how unstable a structure must be before its contribution to the state of the molecule (i.e., its weight) becomes so small that it can be neglected. Unfortunately, no definite, general answer to this question can be given, because the nature of the particular problem under consideration is usually the decisive factor. With butadiene, for example, the normal structure, XI, is quite satisfactory for many purposes, and the resonance can often be ignored. However, an understanding of the characteristic properties of the conjugated system requires that resonance with the less stable structure, XIII or XIV, be recognized; and a discussion of the dipole moments of the carbon-hydrogen bonds requires that resonance with such partially ionic structures as XXIV and XXV also be considered. (See Section 5·2.)

$$H^+ \quad \overset{..}{C}^-\!\!=\!\!C\!-\!C\!=\!C\!-\!H \qquad :H^- \quad C^+\!\!=\!\!C\!-\!C\!=\!C\!-\!H$$

XXIV   XXV

As should be apparent from the above examples, a resonance hybrid may receive a significant contribution from even an extremely unstable structure. Thus, structure XIV for butadiene must be something like 50–100 kcal per mole less stable than the conventional one XI, but still it is considered to exert an appreciable effect upon the properties of the substance. In this further respect, therefore, resonance is sharply distinguished from tautomerism for, if two tautomers differ in energy by 50–100 kcal per mole, the less stable form cannot be expected in any way to influence the behavior of the equilibrium mixture, since essentially all the molecules that are present must have the more stable structure. With a resonance hybrid, on the other hand, the situation is entirely different, inasmuch as there are then no molecules which have either one of the contributing structures. It is, in fact, theoretically possible for the less stable structure to be assigned, say, half as great a weight as the more stable one. (For further details regarding the mathematical principles that are here involved, see pages 606f. Cf. also the following paragraph in fine print.)

The rule that the weight of a contributing structure decreases as its stability decreases must be considered only a useful first approximation, which may have exceptions. For example, detailed but still far from rigorous numerical calculation[12] has led to the conclusion that, with anthracene, the structure XXVI, which has a formal bond, has a greater weight than the doubtless much more stable structure XXVII. (On the other hand, structure XXVIII is, as expected, more important than XXVI.) The reason for

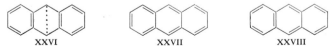

XXVI   XXVII   XXVIII

[12] Cf. M. B. Oakley and G. E. Kimball, *J. Chem. Phys.* **17**, 706 (1949). In this paper, references are given to earlier and still less rigorous calculations.

discrepancies of this type is at present well understood but, since it can be explained only in mathematical terms, we shall postpone further discussion until pages 608 and 639. In the meantime, we shall assume that, in all the problems which we discuss, this type of complication does not occur or, at any rate, is not of sufficient importance to invalidate any of the qualitative conclusions which are reached.

1·5   The Mathematical Basis of Resonance.   In Chapter 9, we shall describe the quantum-mechanical principles upon which the theory of resonance is based.   Here, however, we shall find it profitable to anticipate certain aspects of this later, and more detailed, discussion, and to introduce some of the most elementary and most fundamental concepts that are involved; for, without at least a slight acquaintance with the mathematical background, one can hardly reach an adequate understanding of the theory.

The quantum-mechanical description of any system (i.e., atom, mole-cule, or the like) is contained in the so-called *wave function* or *eigenfunction* of that system.[13]   This is a more or less ordinary mathematical function of the coordinates which define the positions of all the particles of which the system is composed.   (A complete wave function contains also the time, as well as certain additional parameters which describe the states of spin, if any, of the various particles.   These details, however, do not affect the further discussion here and will therefore not be considered.) The wave function, ψ_{100}, for example, which represents the hydrogen atom in its most stable state can, to the present approximation, be written as

$$\psi_{100} = \frac{8\pi^2 \mu e^3}{h^3} \sqrt{\pi \mu}\; e^{-(4\pi\mu e^2 r)/h^2}$$

where μ, the so-called reduced mass, is equal to $mM/(m + M)$, M is the mass of a proton, $-e$ and m are the charge and mass, respectively, of an electron, h is Planck's constant, r is the distance (varying from zero to infinity) between the electron and the proton, e is the logarithmic base $2.718 \cdots$, and π has its usual meaning.   In the general case, the wave functions are much more complicated than this; several pages would be required, in fact, to write out in full the best available approximation to the wave function for even such a simple molecule as that of hydrogen, H_2.

The relationship between a wave function and the state which it describes need not be discussed here in detail.   It will be sufficient to mention merely that, if one knows the wave function of a given system, he can then calculate (by straightforward, but often very laborious mathematical procedures) the numerical value, or at any rate the *average*

[13] For further details, and for references to still more extensive treatments, see Chapter 9.

numerical value, of any property of that system which is capable of experimental measurement. An important step in any quantum-mechanical treatment is thus the setting up of the wave function. In principle, this function is obtained as the solution of a certain partial differential equation, known as the Schrödinger equation or the wave equation. In practice, however, this equation is too complicated to be solved exactly except for the simplest systems; consequently, recourse must be had to approximate methods of solution.

A convenient, although not the only, such approximate method for solving the wave equation is based upon the assumption that the wave function ψ can be expressed as a linear combination of known functions, thus:

$$\psi = k_1\phi_1 + k_2\phi_2 + \cdots + k_n\phi_n \tag{1}$$

where ϕ_1, ϕ_2, $\cdots$ ϕ_n are the known functions and k_1, k_2, $\cdots$ k_n are numerical constants. The values of these latter are then determined (by a method which need not be given here[13]) in such a way that the function ψ defined by them is the best possible approximation to the unknown solution of the Schrödinger equation that can be obtained with the use of the given set of ϕ's. The closeness of the approximation depends naturally upon the cleverness with which the original ϕ's are chosen, and also upon their number. *When this method of approximation is used and when the functions ϕ_1, ϕ_2, $\cdots$ ϕ_n can be correlated in some way with certain definite structures of the molecule in question, then the molecule is said to be a resonance hybrid of those structures, or the structures are said to contribute to the state of the molecule.* (Cf. Section 1·3.) The relative magnitudes of the coefficients k_j are qualitative measures of the relative weights assigned to the respective structures.

The significance of the first three conditions for resonance (cf. Section 1·4) can now be made somewhat clearer than was hitherto possible. Let us, for example, consider two particular functions ϕ_r and ϕ_s, which refer to the respective structures R and S. Now if these structures correspond to sufficiently different positions either of the atomic nuclei or of the electrons, or if they have different numbers of unpaired electrons, it can be shown (see Section 9·16) that, in equation 1, at least one of the constants k_r and k_s must be equal to zero. In other words, unless all three of the conditions are satisfied, there can be no state of the molecule which is a hybrid of both structure R and structure S. If the first three conditions for resonance *are* satisfied, but if structure R is more stable than structure S, then the fourth condition specifies that, in the approximation to the wave function for the ground state, the magnitude of k_r will usually (see the paragraph in fine print at the end of Section 1·4) be greater than that of k_s.

It should be apparent that this method for obtaining an approximate wave function is analogous to the familiar expansion of an arbitrary function in a Fourier series:

$$F(x) = a_1 \sin x + a_2 \sin 2x + \cdots$$
$$+ b_0 + b_1 \cos x + b_2 \cos 2x + \cdots$$

Some functions, $F(x)$, can be expressed with fair accuracy by a single term in this series, whereas others can be expressed with comparable accuracy only with the use of two or more terms; in just the same way, some molecules can be described with fair accuracy by a single structure, whereas others can be described with comparable accuracy only as a hybrid of two or more structures. We should note also that, if the above $F(x)$ describes some certain set of empirical data, say the temperature F at different times x during a single day, then only the complete function $F(x)$ has any physical significance; the individual sine and cosine terms are merely intellectual constructions which need not refer to the dependence of the temperature upon the time during any day whatever. Similarly, with a resonance hybrid, only the hybrid itself has physical significance; the individual contributing structures are merely intellectual constructions which do not refer to any existing molecules whatever. (Cf. Section 1·2.) Finally, just as $F(x)$ does not oscillate back and forth among the contributing sine and cosine functions, so also a resonance hybrid does not oscillate back and forth among the contributing structures. (However, see Sections 9·17 and 9·18.)

The statement that benzene is a hybrid of the two Kekulé structures implies that the quantum-mechanical treatment is to be thought of as proceeding in the following steps. First, wave functions ϕ_I and ϕ_{II} are set up to represent the Kekulé structures, I and II, respectively. Actually,

I   II

no rigorously correct way for setting up such functions is known;[13] this fact would make a numerical calculation by the present method very difficult if not impossible, but it in no way affects the principles involved. Then, the wave function for the molecule is expressed as

$$\psi_{\text{benzene}} = k_I \phi_I + k_{II} \phi_{II}$$

and the values of the coefficients k_I and k_{II} are determined. Since the structures I and II are equivalent, it can be shown that the coefficients k_I and k_{II} are equal in absolute magnitude (at any rate, if the situation in benzene is that described in Figure 1·2, as it undoubtedly is). This means that neither ϕ_I nor ϕ_{II} alone would be a good approximation to the eigenfunction of the molecule, but that a function intermediate between them must be used; or, in other words, that the structure of benzene is neither I nor II but something intermediate. With butadiene,

$$\text{H}_2\text{C}=\text{CH}-\text{CH}=\text{CH}_2 \qquad \text{H}_2\overset{..}{\text{C}}-\text{CH}=\text{CH}-\overset{..}{\text{C}}\text{H}_2$$

III   IV

similarly, resonance between the structures III and IV implies the use of an approximate wave function of the form

$$\psi_{\text{butadiene}} = k_{\text{III}}\phi_{\text{III}} + k_{\text{IV}}\phi_{\text{IV}}$$

In this case, from the inference that structure III is considerably more stable than structure IV, it can be shown that k_{III} must be considerably larger in magnitude than k_{IV}. This means that ϕ_{III} alone would be a fairly good approximation to the correct eigenfunction, with only a slight modification due to the term in ϕ_{IV}; or, in other words, that the structure of butadiene is fairly close to III, with only a small contribution from IV.

The wave function of a resonance hybrid is thus intermediate among the functions that are set up to represent the individual contributing structures. We might therefore anticipate that, since the distribution of electric charge within the molecule of the hybrid can be calculated from the wave function ψ, this distribution should likewise be intermediate among those characteristic of the contributing structures. (Cf. Section 1·2.) The situation is somewhat more complicated, however, than it appears to be, inasmuch as the charge distribution is not specified by simply the wave function ψ, but rather by the product $\psi^*\psi$, where ψ^* is the complex conjugate of ψ.[13]   Hence, from equation 1, we see that the calculated distribution of charge in the hybrid involves not only the terms $k_j^* k_j \phi_j^* \phi_j$ which refer to the distributions in the individual structures j, but also the several *cross terms* $k_j^* k_l \phi_j^* \phi_l$ which may be said to arise from *interactions* among the structures.   Because of the presence of these latter terms, the charge distribution estimated for the hybrid is not just a weighted mean of the distributions that are attributed to the individual structures, and in fact it may even be not intermediate between the extremes represented by those structures.   This complication, however, is seldom so important that it needs to be taken explicitly into account in purely qualitative discussions of the type in which we are now engaged. Consequently, we shall hereafter ignore it, except in those instances in which it does have a significant effect upon the properties of the substance.

Although, within the limitations just described, the distribution of electric charge in a resonance hybrid can be assumed to be intermediate among the distributions expected for the contributing structures, an entirely different situation is encountered with at least one other molecular property, the energy.   It can, in fact, be shown[13] that, as has already been mentioned, the energy of a resonance hybrid in its ground state is always lower than that expected for even the most stable one of the contributing structures. (See, however, the paragraph in fine print, below.)   The so-called *resonance energy*, which is the difference between the energy of the hybrid and that of the most stable structure (cf. page 15), is doubtless the most important effect which resonance has upon the properties of the substance; it will therefore be discussed in considerable detail throughout the remainder of this book, and especially in Chapters 2 and 3. The source of the resonance energy is to be sought in the interaction terms which arise in the calculation of the energy, and which are analogous to, although naturally quite different from, the ones which arose above in the calculation of the charge distribution. With a substance like benzene, with which two (or more) structures make significant contributions to the state of the hybrid, the resonance energy is ordinarily rather large; on the other hand, with a substance like butadiene, with which only a single structure makes an appreciable contribution, the resonance energy is always relatively small. (Cf. Chapter 3.)

When, as in equation 1, we write the approximate wave function ψ for a molecule as a *linear combination* of n simpler functions ϕ_j, these latter functions may always be considered independent of one another, in the sense that their combination ψ can be identically equal to zero only if each one of the n numerical coefficients k_j is itself equal to zero. Consequently, since we have altogether n independent functions ϕ_j to work with, we can set up altogether n independent linear combinations of them, of which in most instances only one refers to the *ground* state of the hybrid. The remaining $n-1$ combinations must then instead refer to $n-1$ different *excited* states, which are of spectroscopic interest. In other words, if we assume resonance among n structures, we obtain approximate descriptions of exactly n states of the system, and each of these states is represented as a resonance hybrid of the structures. As was stated in the preceding paragraph, the most stable of the n states has a lower energy than the most stable contributing structure; on the other hand, the least stable state has a higher energy than the least stable contributing structure.[13] (See, however, the next paragraph.) Except in discussions of spectra, as in Chapter 6, we shall hereafter be primarily interested in the ground states of the systems with which we deal; consequently, we shall ordinarily consider that the resonance hybrid is more stable than any individual structure.

Under special circumstances which are not likely to be encountered in any of the problems that are considered in this book, the most stable state that is a hybrid of the assumed structures may be of exactly the same stability as the most stable structure. Under no circumstances, however, can this most stable state be *less* stable than the most stable structure. Similarly, the least stable state may be of the same stability as, but it can never be of greater stability than, the least stable contributing structure.[13]

From the foregoing discussion we see that resonance is a man-made concept in a more fundamental sense than most other physical theories. It does not correspond to any intrinsic property of the molecule itself, but instead it is only a mathematical device, deliberately invented by the physicist or chemist for his own convenience. Indeed, if the quantum-mechanical problem could be solved rigorously, or even if a different approximate method were employed, the idea of resonance would not arise. Moreover, if a different set of ϕ's were used in equation 1, the molecule whose wave function is approximated by ψ could be described as a hybrid of an entirely different set of structures. As we shall see in the following chapters, these facts in no way detract from the usefulness of the concept from a practical point of view. They do require us, however, always to bear in mind that resonance has meaning only with reference to a *particular* method of *approximating* the actual situation, and constantly to be on guard lest we assign to the various contributing structures a physical significance which they do not in fact possess.

Again, the analogy of the Fourier series (see the above discussion in fine print) may be invoked. Although the functional dependence of the temperature upon the time during a given day can be approximated by such a series, this fact corresponds to no physically significant characteristic of the weather during that day. There is nothing intrinsically "Fourier-like" about the temperature. Consequently, the only reason why one would here use a Fourier series is that it is convenient to do so. If the empirical curve could be satisfactorily described by some single function, a linear combination of a number of terms would then be unnecessary; and, even when such a linear combination is employed, its individual terms do not have to be sine and cosine functions, since they could instead be simple powers of the independent variable, or Legendre polynomials, or the like. As should be quite obvious, however, these considerations in no way detract from the practical usefulness of the Fourier series as an analytical approximation to the empirical function.[14]

1·6 Conclusion. We are now in position to consider the question of the effects which, in the sense defined on pages 8f, resonance exerts upon the physical and chemical properties of hybrid molecules. The succeeding chapters will be devoted to discussions of the various phases of this problem. At the outset, emphasis will be laid upon those properties which are characteristic of the isolated molecules and which do not involve chemical interaction between molecules. It is convenient to start with such comparatively simple applications of the theory and to postpone until later the more complex discussion of reactivity. In order to avoid misconceptions which may arise, however, it is perhaps desirable to state at this time that the *reactions* of a resonance hybrid may be those anticipated for any, for all, or for none of the structures involved. No general rule can be given, but, instead, each problem must be considered on its own merits. (See Chapter 8, and especially Section 8·2.)

[14] For further discussion of the analytical representation of empirical functions, with particular reference to the theory of resonance, see G. W. Wheland, *Advanced Organic Chemistry*, John Wiley & Sons, New York, 2nd ed., 1949, Section 10·6.

Chapter 2 THE
NATURE
OF
VALENCE

2·1 Valence and Energy. The union of two atoms by a valence bond requires that their mutual potential energy be much lower when they are close together than when they are far apart. A theoretical study of the origin and nature of valence resolves itself, therefore, into an investigation of relative energy quantities. Although the problem thus presented was clearly perceived by physicists and chemists more than a hundred years ago, little progress was made toward its final solution until the development of quantum mechanics. In principle, this powerful new tool can provide the complete solution to the problem, but, in practice, as a result of a multitude of purely mathematical difficulties, it has not yet been successfully applied to the accurate numerical calculation of the bond energies in any except the very simplest molecules. Although much thus remains to be worked out, the qualitative features of the theory are sufficiently well understood to be of great value. The present chapter will be devoted to a discussion of some of these simpler aspects.

2·2 The Ionic Bond. One of the earliest theories of valence was the one usually associated with the name of Berzelius.[1] According to this theory, the valence forces were supposed to be due to the electrostatic attractions of oppositely charged particles. After it was discovered,[2] however, that an electronegative atom like chlorine can sometimes replace an electropositive one like hydrogen without a serious alteration in the properties of the substance, the theory was abandoned until comparatively recently. Although it is still recognized as inadequate to account for all the varied phenomena of valence, it is now again accepted as a valid interpretation of the binding in the limited number of cases in which a bond is formed between a strongly electronegative and a strongly electropositive atom. Quantum mechanics then adds relatively little new

[1] For discussions of Berzelius's theory, see H. G. Söderbaum, *Das Buch der grossen Chemiker*, edited by G. Bugge, Verlag Chemie, Berlin, 1929, vol. I, pp. 442ff; T. M. Lowry, *Historical Introduction to Chemistry*, Macmillan & Co., London, 1936, pp. 394–398.

[2] For historical discussions of this discovery, see, for example, J. Dumas, *Ann. chim. phys.* (3) **49**, 487 (1857); C. Schorlemmer, *The Rise and Development of Organic Chemistry*, edited by A. Smithells, Macmillan & Co., London, 1894, pp. 30ff.

to the original simple picture based upon the classical electrostatic theory, which is here quite satisfactory. (Quantum mechanics, of course, is able to go more deeply into the problem than the classical theory and, in particular, it is able to account for the required strongly electronegative and electropositive characters of the atoms involved.)

A typical example of an ionic bond is found in the gaseous sodium chloride molecule, Na^+Cl^-. This bond can be thought of as being formed from sodium and chlorine atoms in the following steps: First, an electron is removed from the sodium atom to leave a sodium ion; then the electron is given to the chlorine atom to form a chloride ion; and finally, the two ions are allowed to approach to their equilibrium distance under the influence of their mutual electrostatic attraction. The first step requires a considerable amount of energy (for the numerical values of the energy quantities, see below), but this is more than counterbalanced in the last two steps. As a result, the molecule, consisting of a positive sodium and a negative chloride ion, is more stable than a system consisting of isolated, neutral sodium and chlorine atoms. In fact, it is even more stable than a hypothetical sodium chloride molecule in which the binding is of the covalent type discussed later. In describing a situation like that in sodium chloride, one speaks of an *ionic bond*.

The actual reaction which is realized experimentally is a much more complicated one in which solid sodium chloride is formed from solid sodium and molecular chlorine. For the complete treatment, the reaction can be broken up into steps 1–6.

Na (solid)	$\rightarrow$ Na (gas)	$-$ 26.0 kcal	(1)
$\frac{1}{2}Cl_2$ (gas)	$\rightarrow$ Cl (gas)	$-$ 29.0 kcal	(2)
Na (gas)	$\rightarrow \varepsilon^- + Na^+$ (gas)	$-$ 120.0 kcal	(3)
Cl (gas) $+ \varepsilon^-$	$\rightarrow Cl^-$ (gas)	$+$ 87.3 kcal	(4)
Na^+ (gas) $+ Cl^-$ (gas)	$\rightarrow$ NaCl (gas)	$+$ 131.2 kcal	(5)
NaCl (gas)	$\rightarrow$ NaCl (solid)	$+$ 54.7 kcal	(6)

The overall reaction

$$Na \text{ (solid)} + \tfrac{1}{2}Cl_2 \text{ (gas)} \rightarrow NaCl \text{ (solid)} \qquad + \ 98.2 \text{ kcal} \qquad (7)$$

is the sum of the reactions 1–6. The discussion in the preceding paragraph was restricted to the reactions 3, 4, and 5, since only these are involved in the actual formation of the ionic bond in the gaseous molecule. All the data of equations 1–7 are taken from the compilation of Rossini et al.,[3] except for the value of 131.2 kcal in equation 5. This figure was chosen arbitrarily so as to make the sum of the first six equations equal the seventh. All the reactions are considered to occur at 25°C, and at 1 atm pressure.

[3] F. D. Rossini, D. D. Wagman, W. H. Evans, S. Levine, and I. Jaffe, *Selected Values of Chemical Thermodynamic Properties*, National Bureau of Standards *Circ.* 500, U.S. Government Printing Office, Washington, D. C., 1952.

The conditions which favor the formation of an ionic bond can now be seen: First, one of the atoms must be strongly electropositive, so that, when an electron is removed from it, a minimum of energy must be supplied; second, the other of the atoms must be strongly electronegative, so that, when the electron is then given to it, a maximum of energy is recovered; and finally, the distance between the two ions must be comparatively small, so that the energy of their mutual electrostatic attraction is large.   Thus, the bond in molecular chlorine, Cl_2, is not ionic because neither atom is strongly electropositive; the bond in molecular sodium, Na_2, is not ionic because neither atom is strongly electronegative; and even the bond in sodium chloride would be no longer ionic if the distance between the nuclei were greater than about 10 A.[4]   (When the interatomic distance is as great as 10 A, it is really meaningless to speak of a bond at all.   The statement that the "bond" is covalent then means merely that the system is more stable when the atoms are electrically neutral, or nearly so, than when an appreciable separation of charge exists.)

Ionic *double* bonds can also be formed in an analogous way by the transference of two electrons from one atom to another.   In the gaseous molecule of magnesium oxide MgO, for example, the bond may possibly be of this type, so that the structure can be written as $Mg^{++}O^=$.   On the other hand, there may here be only an ionic single bond and, in addition, a covalent single bond (cf. Section 2·6), as in the structure Mg^+—O^-; or, finally, the molecule may be a resonance hybrid of these two structures (cf. Section 2·7), with possibly some contribution also from the purely covalent structure Mg=O.   In any event, ionic double bonds are less common than ionic single bonds, because divalent elements are less likely than are univalent elements to have the necessary highly electropositive or electronegative character.   This fact is, of course, to be related to the greater expenditure of energy which is required for the production of doubly charged ions.   Indeed, although the chloride ion Cl^- is stable with respect to a neutral chlorine atom plus an electron (equation 4), the oxide ion $O^=$ cannot exist except when it is stabilized by the proximity of positive ions; for, if the oxide ion were completely isolated, it would spontaneously lose an electron and thereby be transformed into the singly charged ion O^-.[5]   With trivalent elements, the ability to form ionic bonds is still further decreased, so that few, if any, unambiguous examples of ionic triple bonds are known.

2·3   Types of Covalent Bond.   We turn now to a consideration of those cases in which the atoms united by valence bonds are of similar (or

[4] L. Pauling, *J. Am. Chem. Soc.* **54**, 988 (1932).
[5] Cf., for example, G. Briegleb, *Naturwissenschaften* **30**, 532 (1942).

possibly even of identical) electrical character, so that an ionic type of linkage is no longer reasonable. This is the only situation ordinarily encountered in organic compounds, except, of course, in the organic salts. Under such circumstances, the formation of a valence bond is not due to a classical electrostatic attraction between oppositely charged ions, but it is the result of a different type of interaction. For the understanding of such covalent or nonpolar bonds, the concept of resonance is particularly convenient, since it provides a simple and nonmathematical picture of the factors involved. This picture is only roughly qualitative, but it is sufficiently accurate for a large number of purposes.

One often encounters the statement that a covalent bond is the result of an entirely new kind of force, called an *exchange force*, which has no analogy in classical electromagnetic theory. This is not strictly correct, however. The forces involved in a covalent bond are actually almost entirely electrostatic in nature, and Coulomb's law is taken as the basis of the quantum-mechanical calculations. (The very small magnetic interactions are usually negligible.) The significance of the "exchange forces" or, what amounts to the same thing, of the stabilization by resonance (see Sections 2·4, 2·5, and 2·6) is the following. The average distribution of electronic charge in the neighborhood of a covalent bond is not the same as that which would have obtained if the two atoms involved had merely been brought from infinity to the observed distance. This is because each atom is strongly polarized in the powerful field produced by the other atom. When one speaks of exchange forces, or of the stabilization by resonance, as being responsible for a covalent bond, he implies that the energy of the molecule is to be thought of as the sum of two terms: the energy which the molecule would have had without this polarization, and a correction due to the polarization. The exchange, or resonance, effect is equivalent to this latter correction term. The particular function of the theory of exchange forces or of resonance is here only to show the way in which the polarization alters the charge distribution, and hence also the energy, of the system; and it is not to account for any (actually nonexistent) new kind of force. (Cf. also Sections 2·4, 2·6, and 9·5.)

Three different types of covalent bond, called the one-electron, the three-electron, and the two-electron bonds, respectively, are recognized. Of these, only the last type is of sufficient importance to merit a detailed discussion, but the first two are simpler in certain regards, and, for that reason, provide a convenient introduction to the subject. (It is to be noted that double and triple covalent bonds are merely two and three two-electron bonds, respectively, and do not represent distinct types. See Section 2·6.)

2·4 The One-Electron Bond. The simplest of all molecules is the hydrogen molecule-ion, H_2^+, which consists of two protons and one electron. Although this ion is known only spectroscopically, it possesses considerable stability, since the energy required to dissociate it into a proton and a neutral hydrogen atom is about 61 kcal per mole. Calculations have here led to complete numerical agreement with experiment,[6] but, for our purposes, a purely qualitative approach employing the concept of resonance will be more illuminating. First let us consider a situation in which the two nuclei are at some definite, large distance apart. The system can be represented by one or the other of the two equivalent "structures" I and II.

H·   H⁺   H⁺   H·
     I   II

    The quotation marks are used here (and in analogous situations in the following sections) because the "structures" under discussion are not structures in the usual chemical sense; they do not, in fact, when taken individually, contain anything corresponding to a valence bond. The word structure, without the quotation marks, will be applied hereafter only to those conditions of the molecule in which resonance among all necessary "structures" has already been taken into account, and in which valence bonds are present. This rather subtle distinction between structures and "structures" is not ordinarily made by writers on the subject of valence and, if the reader wishes, may be ignored.

    "Structures" I and II differ only in regard to the choice of the proton with which the single electron is associated. They correspond, by definition, to exactly the same relative positions of the atomic nuclei, and they have the same number of unpaired electrons. Thus, they satisfy conditions 1 and 3 of Section 1·4. Moreover, since they are equivalent, they have exactly the same energy (condition 4). Resonance between them, however, cannot be assumed because, with the protons at a great distance apart, they differ too much in the position of the electron (condition 2). Consequently, under these circumstances, the system is correctly described as consisting of a proton plus a hydrogen atom. If now the nuclei are allowed to approach, the energies of the individual "structures" do not at first change greatly since, although one particle is electrically charged, the other is neutral. At sufficiently small distances, however, the single electron is no longer able to shield the nuclei completely from each other; as a result, the energies of the individual "structures" I and II increase. This situation, which is illustrated in curve 1 of Figure 2·1, corresponds to a net repulsion between the two protons, and hence neither "structure" alone can account for the formation of a stable molecule-ion. However, as soon as the two nuclei are so close together that the shielding by the electron begins to be incomplete, resonance between the "structures" can no longer be neglected. As a result of this resonance, there are two states of the system; one has a lower and the other has a higher energy than either of the contributing

    [6] See, for example, L. Pauling and E. B. Wilson, Jr., *Introduction to Quantum Mechanics*, McGraw-Hill Book Co., New York, 1935, pp. 327–340, for a discussion of the calculations and for references to the original literature.

"structures." (Cf. pages 27f.) The energies of these states are represented by curves 2 and 3, respectively, of Figure 2·1. Curve 2 corresponds
to the formation of a stable molecule-ion, with a *binding energy AB* and
an internuclear distance r_e. Curve 3, on the other hand, depicts a state
of the system in which the repulsion between the two protons is even
greater than it would have been in the absence of resonance (curve 1).

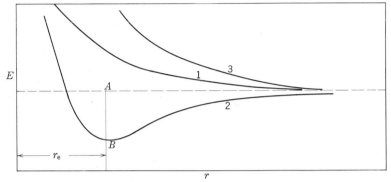

Fig. 2·1. Energy E of a system composed of one hydrogen atom and one
proton as a function of the internuclear distance r. Curve 1 corresponds to
the situation which would exist in the absence of resonance; curve 2 corresponds to the stable hydrogen molecule-ion resulting from the resonance; and
curve 3 corresponds to the second state resulting from the resonance, in which
there is a strong repulsion between the nuclei.

Such a state does not correspond to the formation of a stable molecule-ion,
and hence it is of no interest to us in the present connection.

The *binding energy*, as defined in the preceding paragraph, is not quite the same thing
as the *bond energy*, which is the energy that must be supplied in order to dissociate the
molecule-ion into a proton and a hydrogen atom. This is because the kinetic energies
of the nuclei have still to be allowed for. (It is to be noted that, whereas the energy of
the molecule-ion is negative, the binding energy and the bond energy are both taken as
positive quantities. In a diatomic molecule, the energy of the molecule is thus the
negative of the energy of the one bond that is present.) At the absolute zero of temperature, the two protons would be at rest when at an infinite distance from each other,
but would be executing small vibrations about the position of minimum potential energy
($r = r_e$) when in the molecule-ion. At 0°K, therefore, the bond energy is less than
the binding energy by an amount equal to this zero-point vibrational energy. At
higher temperatures, further small corrections are necessitated by the energies of translation of the molecule-ion and of the isolated proton and hydrogen atom, and by the
energy of rotation of the molecule-ion. The bond energy is thus a function of the
temperature, whereas the binding energy is not. In this chapter hereafter, we shall
discuss the values of the bond energies only at 0°K.

Attention should be called to the fact that the present discussion is
purely qualitative, and that the precise quantitative calculations referred

to above proceed along entirely different lines. Consequently, the curves in Figure 2·1 are only schematic, and the scales along the abscissa and ordinate are not specified.

As was stated in the paragraph in fine print in the preceding section, the fact that curve 2 of Figure 2·1 lies below curve 1 is not the result of any new and mysterious kind of force that is known only to quantum mechanics, but it rather is due to a change in the average distribution of electric charge. If the molecule-ion had either one of the two "structures" I and II (curve 1), the single electron would be distributed about the particular proton with which it is associated in that "structure," just as if the second proton were not present. On the other hand, in the actual stable molecule-ion (curve 2), which is a hybrid of "structures" I and II, the electron is instead distributed in such a way that it is more likely to be found in the region between the two protons than in any other region; and, in the unstable molecule-ion (curve 3), which also is a resonance hybrid of "structures" I and II, the electron is distributed so that it is least likely to be found in the region between the protons. Consequently, curve 1 refers to a situation in which the negative electron is on the average close to one of the positive charges, but moderately distant from the other; on the other hand, curve 2 refers to a different situation in which the negative electron is, again on the average, close to *both* positive charges, whereas curve 3 refers to still a third situation in which the electron is least likely to be in the region of low potential energy between the two nuclei. The relative positions of the three curves are therefore determined by the differences in the coulombic interactions between the oppositely charged particles. The essential contribution of quantum mechanics to this interpretation of the attractive and repulsive forces in the molecule-ion is thus to permit the pertinent charge distributions to be correctly deduced. (For further discussion of these charge distributions, see Section 2·9.)

The hydrogen molecule-ion in its ground state can be described by the statement either that it is a resonance hybrid of the "structures" I and II above or, more conveniently, that it has the structure III. The latter

$$(H \cdot H)^+$$
III

description is in accordance with the usual chemical nomenclature and, in addition, it correctly indicates that the single electron is especially likely to be found in the region between the protons. It will therefore be adopted in any further consideration of the one-electron bond.

The above discussion leads to a qualitative understanding of the nature of the bond that is present in the hydrogen molecule-ion, but it does not provide any quantitative data in regard to the magnitudes of either the binding energy AB or the internuclear distance r_e. Such information can be obtained only from experiment or from actual numerical calculations, a description of which would lie outside the scope of this section (however, see Section 9·23). As has already been mentioned, however, these calculations have been made,[6] and the results obtained from them have been in complete agreement with experiment. The observed (and calculated) value of the binding energy is 64.0 kcal per mole; the bond energy, or energy of dissociation, is less than this by the vibrational energy, which at $0°K$ amounts to 3.2 kcal per mole; and the internuclear distance r_e is 1.06 A.

The one-electron bond is an extremely rare type of interaction between atoms and, in fact, the hydrogen molecule-ion is almost the only unambiguous example of it. Approximate calculations[7] have indicated that a similar situation should occur with the lithium molecule-ion, Li_2^+, which should have a bond energy of about 30 kcal per mole. However, there are here no experimental data for comparison with the calculations.

It was at one time thought possible that one-electron bonds might occur also in the boron hydrides, so that diborane, for example, could be described as a resonance hybrid of several structures like IV and V[8, 9] in which, since the substance is diamagnetic,[10] the two electrons that are represented by the dots would have to be paired with each other. The further suggestion that "no-bonded" structures like VI and VII are involved was also made.[11] It is now generally agreed, however, that neither of these proposals can be correct since the molecule does not have

$$
\begin{array}{cccc}
\text{H H} & \text{H H} & \text{}^+\text{H H} & \text{H H} \\
\text{H—B—B—H} & \text{H—B · B—H} & \text{H—B—B}^-\text{—H} & \text{H—B B—H} \\
\text{H H} & \text{H H} & \text{H H} & \text{H H} \\
\text{IV} & \text{V} & \text{VI} & \text{VII}
\end{array}
$$

the "ethane-like" configuration assumed in structures IV–VII. The present view[12] is instead that diborane has a bridged configuration, and

[7] H. M. James, *J. Chem. Phys.* **3**, 9 (1935).

[8] For example, N. V. Sidgwick, *The Electronic Theory of Valency*, Oxford University Press, Oxford, 1927, p. 103.

[9] L. Pauling, *J. Am. Chem. Soc.* **53**, 3225 (1931).

[10] L. Farkas and H. Sachsee, *Trans. Faraday Soc.* **30**, 331 (1934).

[11] G. N. Lewis, *J. Chem. Phys.* **1**, 17 (1933).

[12] See, for example, H. C. Longuet-Higgins and R. P. Bell, *J. Chem. Soc.* **1943**, 250; K. S. Pitzer, *J. Am. Chem. Soc.* **67**, 1126 (1945); R. S. Mulliken, *Chem. Revs.* **41**, 207 (1947); R. E. Dodd and P. L. Robinson, *Ann. Repts. on Progr. Chem.* (*Chem. Soc. London*), **44**, 52 (1947).

that it is a resonance hybrid of principally the structures VIII, IX, and X. Presumably, therefore, no one-electron bonds are present either in diborane or in any of the other boron hydrides.

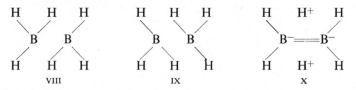

The reason for the rarity of the one-electron bond becomes apparent from a consideration of the resonance involved. The "structures" I and II given above for the hydrogen molecule-ion are equivalent, because the two protons are equivalent. Since they therefore have identical energies, the resonance energy (see pages 27f) must be comparatively great (at any rate, when the nuclei are not too far apart). On the other hand, if the two atoms which are joined by the bond are not equivalent, the "structures" analogous to I and II are also not equivalent and, in general, one is considerably more stable than the other. As a result, the resonance is comparatively unimportant, and the resonance energy must be comparatively small. A strong one-electron bond can, accordingly, be expected to be formed only between two atoms of the same element, although extremely weak ones, which are incapable of surviving molecular collisions, may be relatively common. For example, approximate calculations have suggested[13] that a lithium hydride molecule-ion, LiH^+, may be possible, with a dissociation energy of, at most, only a few kilocalories per mole. Such bonds, however, need concern us no further since they are too unstable to be involved in the ordinary types of molecule in which we are primarily interested.

2·5 The Three-Electron Bond. The three-electron bond is very similar in type to the one-electron bond. The simplest and, at the same time, the clearest example of it occurs in the helium molecule-ion, He_2^+, which is known spectroscopically. The "structures" which may be assumed to be involved in the resonance are now I and II, as shown. Just as with

$$\text{He:} \quad \text{He}^+\cdot \qquad\qquad \text{He}^+\cdot \quad \text{He:}$$
$$\text{I} \qquad\qquad\qquad \text{II}$$

the hydrogen molecule-ion, and for the same reason, the resonance energy is greatest when the nuclei are close together, and it is negligibly small when the nuclei are far apart. The situation can again be described by curves showing the dependence of the total energy upon the internuclear distance. These are qualitatively the same as those of Figure 2·1, in

---

[13] J. K. Knipp, *J. Chem. Phys.* **4**, 300 (1936).

which curve 1 represents the energy of a single contributing "structure" (either I or II), curve 2 shows the formation of a stable molecule-ion, and curve 3 corresponds to a strong repulsion between the nuclei.

The ground state of the molecule-ion is conveniently described by the statement that it has the structure III, with a three-electron bond. The

$$[\text{He} \cdots \text{He}]^+$$
III

"structures" I and II and the resonance between them do not need to be mentioned explicitly any further, now that they have served their purpose.

No accurate numerical calculations for this molecule-ion have been made, but approximate calculations[14] have led to results in satisfactory agreement with experiment. The calculated values of the binding energy and the internuclear distance are 51.2 kcal per mole and 1.097 A, respectively, as compared with the observed values of 57.6 kcal per mole and 1.09 A, respectively. The bond energy, or energy of dissociation, is less than the above figures by the vibrational energy, which here amounts to about 2.3 kcal per mole at $0°K$. The bond is thus very similar to the one-electron bond in the hydrogen molecule-ion, both in regard to its strength and also in regard to the distance between the atoms joined by it.

The rarity of the three-electron bond, like that of the one-electron bond, is due to the requirement that the atoms joined be equivalent or, at any rate, have very nearly the same degree of electronegativity and electropositivity. It seems likely that in the oxygen molecule, O_2, there are two three-electron bonds in addition to one two-electron bond between the atoms, so that the structure should be written as IV and not as V. In any event, the observed spectroscopic state of the molecule

:O ⋮ O: :O::O:
IV   V

requires that there be two unpaired electrons, and so it definitely excludes the double-bonded structure V, in which all electrons are paired. Further substances in which three-electron bonds have been postulated include nitric oxide, nitrogen dioxide,[9] chlorine dioxide,[15] and a few others. In these, the three-electron bonds are between nonequivalent atoms and so are probably rather weak. However, there is little danger that the molecules might be broken at these weak bonds by any ordinary collisions,

---

[14] S. Weinbaum, *J. Chem. Phys.* 3, 547 (1935).   See also L. Pauling and E. B. Wilson, Jr., *Introduction to Quantum Mechanics*, McGraw-Hill Book Co., New York, 1935, pp. 358ff.

[15] L. O. Brockway, *Proc. Natl. Acad. Sci. U. S.* 19, 303, 868 (1933).

because in each molecule the two atoms joined by the three-electron bond are joined by one or more strong two-electron bonds as well.

2·6 The Two-Electron Bond. The two-electron bond is by all odds the most common type, and it is the only one to which we shall have occasion to refer in the future. It can be related to a resonance which is somewhat different from that considered above in connection with the one- and three-electron bonds. The simplest example of the two-electron bond

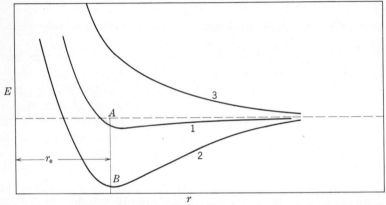

Fig. 2·2.   Energy E of a system composed of two hydrogen atoms, as a function of the internuclear distance r. Curve 1 corresponds to the situation which would exist in the absence of resonance; curve 2 corresponds to the stable hydrogen molecule resulting from the resonance; and curve 3 corresponds to the second state resulting from the resonance, in which there is a strong repulsion between the nuclei.

is provided by the hydrogen molecule, H_2. For this, the two equivalent "structures," I and II, below, can be written. These differ only in an

$$H\cdot \qquad H* \qquad\qquad H* \qquad H\cdot$$
$$_{\text{I}}\qquad\qquad\qquad_{\text{II}}$$

interchange of the two electrons which, for convenience, are represented by a dot and an asterisk, respectively. At large internuclear distances, resonance between these "structures" is impossible because of condition 2, and the system is correctly described as consisting of two hydrogen atoms, each with its own electron. An approximate calculation shows that, as the protons are allowed to approach each other, the energies of "structures" I and II vary in accordance with curve 1 of Figure 2·2.[16] This differs from curve 1 of Figure 2·1 in that it has a shallow minimum

[16] Cf. L. Pauling and E. B. Wilson, Jr., *Introduction to Quantum Mechanics*, McGraw-Hill Book Co., New York, 1935, pp. 340ff, for a discussion of the calculations and for references to the original literature.

corresponding to the formation of a very weak bond with a dissociation energy of only about 10 per cent of that actually observed for the hydrogen molecule. However, when resonance between the two "structures" is taken into account, approximate descriptions of two different states of the molecule are, as usual, obtained. In one of these hybrids, represented by curve 2, the atoms attract each other as long as the distance between them is greater than r_e, but in the other, represented by curve 3, they repel each other at all distances. In the former state, the electrons are paired with each other, and in the latter they are unpaired. (See Section 1·4, condition 3, and also Section 9·10.) Both of these states are known experimentally, the first being that of the normal hydrogen molecule and the second having been observed spectroscopically. (For the same reason as in Figure 2·1, Figure 2·2 is only schematic.)

The reason why the curves 1, 2, and 3 fall in the particular order in which they do is again to be found in the respective distributions of electric charge. In the normal hydrogen molecule (curve 2), the electrons are concentrated in the region between the two nuclei; whereas, in the repulsive state (curve 3) the electrons are to a considerable extent excluded from just that region. (For a more detailed discussion of the respective charge distributions, see Section 2·9.) The superiority of quantum mechanics over the classical electromagnetic theory is therefore once more due to the fact that only the former leads to correct charge distributions, and it is not due to an introduction of some new type of force. It should here be mentioned, however, that the difference between the two extreme charge distributions which give rise to curves 2 and 3 is itself a consequence of a typical quantum-mechanical limitation, the so-called *Pauli exclusion principle* (cf. Section 9·7), which has no classical analog. In the normal hydrogen molecule, the two electrons are paired with each other (see the preceding paragraph) whereas, in the excited (i.e., the repulsive) state, they are unpaired. Now, in order that the exclusion principle be satisfied, as it has to be, the electrons cannot be paired unless the charge distribution is that corresponding to curve 2, and they cannot be unpaired unless the charge distribution is that corresponding to curve 3. Consequently, although the pairing, per se, has a completely negligible effect upon the total energy of the system, it is nevertheless of the utmost importance since, in conjunction with the exclusion principle, it determines the charge distribution.

As with the one- and three-electron bonds, we now need to consider the "structures" responsible for the binding no further, since the single structure, III or IV, provides a sufficient description of the molecule, and,

H—H   H:H

III   IV

in addition, correctly implies that the two electrons are more likely to be found in the region between the nuclei than anywhere else. These electrons which, as we have just seen, are necessarily paired with each other are said to be *shared* by the two atoms, and the bond is frequently called a *shared-electron bond*. The use of the word "shared" in this connection is particularly appropriate since electrons, when so shared, do actually belong to both atoms concerned, in the sense that they serve to fill up their valence shells. With atoms of the first row of the periodic table, in which the number of valence electrons is restricted to eight, this means that no more than eight electrons can be associated with any one atom, whether these are "owned outright," as by the fluoride ion, or are shared, as by the carbon atom in methane, or are partly owned and partly shared, as by the oxygen atom in water. With hydrogen and helium, the valence shell can contain only two electrons, and with atoms of later rows of the periodic table the octet may be expanded, but shared electrons must always be counted in the valence shells of both atoms involved.

Electrons taking part in one- and three-electron bonds are not "shared" in exactly the present sense. In particular, a three-electron bond contributes no more than two electrons to the valence shells of each of the atoms which it joins. Thus, the structures given above for the helium molecule-ion, in which three electrons are associated with each helium atom, and for the oxygen molecule, in which ten electrons are associated with each oxygen atom, do not constitute violations of this rule.

The two-electron bond in the hydrogen molecule is stronger than either the one- or the three-electron bonds in the hydrogen or helium molecule-ions, respectively. The hydrogen molecule has been treated quantum mechanically with considerable accuracy;[16, 17] the calculated values of the binding energy AB (Figure 2·2) and of the internuclear distance r_e are 108.8 kcal per mole and 0.74 A, respectively, in complete agreement with the experimental values. The bond energy, as in the previous examples, is less than the binding energy by the vibrational energy and has the value of 102.7 kcal per mole at $0°K$.

The importance of the two-electron bond is due partly to the fact that it is usually (but perhaps not always)[7] somewhat stronger than the one- and three-electron bonds. A more important reason, however, is that the two-electron bond is not restricted like the other types to situations in which the atoms joined are of the same kind. The reason for this is that the equivalence of the "structures" I and II is ensured by the equivalence of the two electrons and is in no way dependent upon the nature of the atoms joined. It is only reasonable, then, that the two-electron bond, being of so much greater generality than either of the types considered before, should occur more frequently.

[17] H. M. James and A. S. Coolidge, *J. Chem. Phys.* **1**, 825 (1933).

Covalent double and triple bonds are formed in completely similar manners. One can, for example, write the "structures" V, VI, VII, etc., for ethylene, and VIII, IX, X, etc., for acetylene. (The carbon-hydrogen

$$H_2C: \overset{*}{\underset{*}{}}CH_2 \qquad H_2C\overset{*}{\underset{*}{}} \ \overset{*}{}CH_2 \qquad H_2C\overset{*}{\underset{*}{}} \ : CH_2$$

          V   VI   VII

$$HC: \overset{*}{\underset{*}{}}CH \qquad HC\overset{.}{\underset{*}{}} \ \overset{*}{}CH \qquad HC\overset{*}{\underset{*}{}} \ : CH$$

        VIII   IX   X

bonds need not be treated explicitly here.) For these two molecules, the most stable states that can be described as hybrids of the various "structures" are conveniently represented by the usual structures XI or XII, and XIII or XIV, respectively. It is important that the formation of

$$H_2C{=}CH_2 \qquad H_2C::CH_2 \qquad HC{\equiv}CH \qquad HC:::CH$$

        XI   XII   XIII   XIV

these multiple bonds does not require that the maximum permissible number of electrons associated with any one atom ever be exceeded.

No examples of quadruple (or higher) covalent bonds are known. This limitation is probably due to stereochemical factors. It is, in fact, apparent that a tetrahedral atom cannot take part in a quadruple bond without tremendous strain, and that octahedral and other types of atom are subject to similar limitations.

On the basis of the above discussion of the shared electron bond, it may seem strange that a helium molecule, He_2, does not exist, since the relation between the "structures" XV, XVI, XVII, etc., appears to be analogous to that between the corresponding

$$He: \overset{*}{\underset{*}{}}He \qquad He\overset{.}{\underset{*}{}} \ \overset{*}{}He \qquad He\overset{*}{\underset{*}{}} \ : He$$

           XV   XVI   XVII

"structures" in ethylene. The explanation is that, if such a molecule were formed, its structure (without quotation marks) would be XVIII or XIX, with four electrons

$$He{=}He \qquad\qquad He::He$$

        XVIII   XIX

associated with each helium atom. Since there are no one- or three-electron bonds in this structure, all the electrons are shared by the two atoms and so must contribute to the valence shell of each. The structure is therefore impossible because a helium atom can in this way accommodate no more than two electrons. Again, the exclusion principle is the determining factor for, although a state in which the four electrons are concentrated in the region between the nuclei can be imagined, and although such a state would lead to a stable He_2 molecule, it would violate the exclusion principle and so is impossible. The only state that is permitted by the exclusion principle is, in fact, one in which the electrons are most concentrated *outside* the region between the nuclei; the powerful internuclear repulsion is then the predominant force, and so no stable molecule can be formed.

2·7   Resonance between Ionic and Covalent Structures.[4]   The discussions in the preceding sections have been somewhat oversimplified, since no actual bond between two given atoms, A and B, can ever be either purely ionic or purely covalent.   Instead, one can always obtain a better description of the actual bond by postulating resonance among structures of varying types.   With a single bond, for example, there are contributions from I, II, and III;   with a double bond there are contributions from IV, V, VI, VII, etc.;   and with a triple bond there are contributions from VIII, IX, X, etc.

$$A:B \qquad\qquad :A^- \quad B^+ \qquad\qquad A^+ \quad B:^-$$
$$\text{I} \qquad\qquad\qquad \text{II} \qquad\qquad\qquad \text{III}$$

$$A::B \qquad :A^-:B^+ \qquad A^+:B:^- \qquad :A^=\ B^{++}$$
$$\text{IV} \qquad\quad \text{V} \qquad\qquad \text{VI} \qquad\qquad \text{VII}$$

$$A:::B \qquad\qquad :A^-::B^+ \qquad\qquad A^+::B:^-$$
$$\text{VIII} \qquad\qquad \text{IX} \qquad\qquad\qquad \text{X}$$

It frequently happens that one structure is much more stable, and hence much more important, than the others.   The bond is then said to be *essentially ionic* or *essentially covalent*, as the case may be.   There can be little doubt, for example, that the actual structures of sodium chloride and of molecular hydrogen and nitrogen differ only slightly from XI, XII, and XIII, respectively.   Under such circumstances, one is justified

$$Na^+ \quad Cl^- \qquad\qquad H—H \qquad\qquad N{\equiv}N$$
$$\text{XI} \qquad\qquad\qquad \text{XII} \qquad\qquad \text{XIII}$$

in speaking loosely of the most stable structure as *the* structure, as we have done in the preceding sections.   It sometimes happens, however, that two or more structures may make large contributions.   One cannot be entirely sure, for example, whether monomeric hydrogen fluoride is more accurately represented by XIV, with an ionic bond, or by XV,

$$H^+ \quad F^- \qquad\qquad H—F$$
$$\text{XIV} \qquad\qquad\qquad \text{XV}$$

with a covalent bond.   Possibly the two structures are of about equal importance.   Under such circumstances, one is clearly not justified in singling out either as *the* structure of the molecule.

Even when the bonds are essentially ionic or essentially covalent, we frequently find that, in order to understand their observed properties, we must explicitly assign finite weights to the less important structures. The average distribution of electric charge in any given bond is particularly sensitive to small departures from the pure bond type, since this is just the respect in which the ionic and covalent structures differ most strikingly. A rough, qualitative understanding of the origin of dipole moments can, in fact, be reached from this point of view, as will be shown in Section 5·2. In a molecule like H_2, however, which is formed from two atoms of the same kind, the ionic character has no such effect upon the charge distribution. This is because the two ionic structures, XVI and XVII, being

$$H^+ \quad H^- \qquad\qquad H^- \quad H^+$$

XVI   XVII

equivalent, must be assigned the same weight, and so their effects just cancel.

A second effect of the resonance between the ionic and covalent structures is to increase the strength of the bond; for any actual bond must be more stable, on account of the resonance, than it would have been if it were purely ionic or purely covalent. (See Section 3·6.)

It would be exceedingly awkward in writing and speaking if explicit recognition had always to be made of all the ionic and covalent contributions to each bond. For the sake of convenience, therefore, we shall hereafter adopt the convention of writing each bond as either purely ionic or purely covalent (unless a more detailed analysis happens to be necessary for the particular subject under discussion). Thus, we shall speak of sodium chloride, hydrogen, and nitrogen, and even of hydrogen fluoride, *as if* they possessed unique structures of one extreme type or the other. The reader is then to understand that the symbol used should be interpreted as representing the kind of bond which is actually present in the molecule in question, or which (in examples like the Kekulé structure of benzene) we would expect to be present in a molecule with the structure written, if only such a molecule could exist. Similarly, when we are considering a structure with a *formal* bond, we shall continue arbitrarily to represent that bond as purely covalent, and we shall not explicitly mention its partial ionic character. Thus, when we describe 1,3-butadiene, for example, as a hybrid of structures XVIII and XIX, we shall ordinarily mean to imply that the additional structures XX and XXI, which are

$$CH_2{=}CH{-}CH{=}CH_2 \qquad\qquad CH_2{-}CH{=}CH{-}CH_2$$

XVIII   XIX

$$C^+H_2{-}CH{=}CH{-}C^-H_2 \qquad\qquad C^-H_2{-}CH{=}CH{-}C^+H_2$$

XX   XXI

the ionic counterparts of XIX, are also assigned suitable weights. Since, however, these last two structures differ from XIX principally in their wide separations of electric charge, they are presumably even less stable than XIX, and so must have even smaller weights in the ground state of the molecule. For this reason, the procedure which is here adopted seems more logical than a frequently encountered alternative one, which consists in leaving the covalent structure XIX implicit, and in writing only the ionic ones XX and XXI (or else the equivalent single symbol XXII).

$$C^{\pm}H_2-CH{=}CH-C^{\mp}H_2$$
XXII

There is one type of bond in which it is customary to show somewhat more explicitly the ionic and covalent characters. We shall, for example, write the structure of an amine oxide as XXIII or XXIV. The bond

$$
\begin{array}{cc}
R & R \\
| & \ddot{} \\
R-N^+-O^- & R:\overset{\cdot\cdot}{N}:^+\overset{\cdot\cdot}{O}:^- \\
| & \ddot{} \\
R & R \\
\text{XXIII} & \text{XXIV}
\end{array}
$$

between the nitrogen and the oxygen atoms here is, in effect, a double one, consisting of an essentially ionic plus an essentially covalent bond. (The covalent contribution to the former and the ionic contribution to the latter can be left implicit.) Such bonds, which various authors have called semipolar double bonds, dative bonds, and coordinate covalencies, are encountered fairly frequently in both organic and inorganic compounds. Since their occurrence is always apparent from the structure, however, we shall have little occasion in the future to call especial attention to them, other than by representing them in one of the above equivalent manners.

It will be profitable here to consider somewhat more fully the significance of the statement that a given bond in a given molecule is intermediate between the purely covalent and purely ionic extremes. With molecular hydrogen, for example, it may seem unnecessary, if not actually illogical, to introduce the ionic structures XVI and XVII, inasmuch as the single covalent structure XII should by itself be sufficient to provide a perfect description of the molecule. Indeed, one may well ask what the expression "a pure covalent bond" can mean if it is not accepted as an exact description of the relation between the two atoms in the hydrogen molecule. The present difficulty, which is both real and important, can be attributed to the fact that each of the words "bond" and "structure" is commonly used with several closely related, but nevertheless distinct, meanings.

From the usual chemical point of view the *structure* of a molecule is designed primarily to specify the pairs of atoms which are presumed to stay, as a result of restraints upon their relative motions, at fairly definite, short distances from each other. The two members of each such pair are then said to be joined by a *bond* and, in order that the valences of the several elements may remain more or less constant, the concepts of double and triple bonds are introduced. When stereochemical considerations are added to this simple picture, the structures become *configurations*, which summarize the available information regarding the values of the angles between the different bonds that are formed by each multivalent atom; and, when still more refined viewpoints are adopted, the structures may be considered also to imply the actual distances between the pairs of bonded atoms (cf. Section 4·3), the magnitudes and directions of the dipole moments associated with the individual bonds (cf. Section 5·2), and any number of still further properties.

In the application of the resonance theory to chemical problems, however, the concept of structure is approached in a rather different way. By means of a procedure that is outlined in Sections 9·12 and 9·13, one can set up an approximate wave function which is correlated with, and is said to represent, any arbitrary valence-bond structure that may be written for any molecule (cf. also Section 1·5). Thus, for the hydrogen molecule, one can set up certain functions ϕ_{XII}, ϕ_{XVI}, and ϕ_{XVII}, which, in the sense just defined, represent the respective structures XII, XVI, and XVII. Since no one of these functions

$$H\text{---}H \qquad\qquad H^+ \ \ H^- \qquad\qquad H^- \ \ H^+$$
$$\text{XII} \qquad\qquad\quad\ \text{XVI} \qquad\qquad\quad\ \text{XVII}$$

is identical with the correct, but unknown, wave function for the molecule, a better approximation can be obtained in the form of the linear combination

$$\psi = k_{XII}\phi_{XII} + k_{XVI}\phi_{XVI} + k_{XVII}\phi_{XVII}$$

Consequently, the substance is described as a hybrid of the three specified structures even though, if we wished to interpret only those properties that were listed in the preceding paragraph, we would instead find that the single covalent structure XII is the most suitable representation for the molecule. In principle, of course, we could consider that the approximate wave function which represents the structure XII is not ϕ_{XII}, but is instead the best possible combination, ψ, of ϕ_{XII}, ϕ_{XVI}, and ϕ_{XVII}. If we adopted this alternative procedure, there would then no longer be any advantage in considering the substance as a hybrid of structures XII, XVI, and XVII, and hence the resulting description of the molecule would be in rather better agreement with the conventional chemical significance of the word "structure." In practice, however, such a treatment has been found less convenient than the one originally outlined, and it has accordingly been only seldom employed.

In a completely similar way, the statement that the (gaseous) sodium chloride molecule is a hybrid of the ionic and covalent structures implies that the wave function for the molecule is being approximated as a linear combination of the simpler functions that represent the two extreme structures. As with molecular hydrogen, a different approach which makes unnecessary any explicit mention of the resonance is here also quite possible, but it has not proved sufficiently convenient to be generally adopted. And finally, with substances of the type represented by hydrogen fluoride, with which the weights assigned to the covalent and ionic structures are more nearly comparable than in either of the two foregoing examples, the situations are so similar to those already considered that no further discussion should here be required.

2·8 The Hydrogen Bond. A further type of bond which is essentially different from any of the foregoing is the so-called hydrogen bond or hydrogen bridge, in which a hydrogen atom serves to hold two other atoms together. The possibility of such a union seems to have been first clearly suggested by Moore and Winmill,[18] who used it to account for the low base strengths of ammonia and the primary, secondary, and tertiary amines as compared with the quaternary ammonium hydroxides. Their explanation was that fairly stable undissociated molecules of type I or II

$$R_3N^+\!\!-\!\!H\,-\,-\,O^-H \qquad R_3N\,-\,-\,H\!\!-\!\!OH \qquad (R = H \text{ or alkyl})$$
$$\quad\quad\ \text{I} \qquad\qquad\qquad\qquad \text{II}$$

could be formed as long as there was at least one hydrogen atom attached to the nitrogen atom in the ammonium ion. The significance of the apparently divalent hydrogen atom and the distinction between the different symbols used to represent its two "bonds" are discussed later in this section.

This idea of a hydrogen bond has been widely extended in subsequent years,[19] and it has received complete confirmation from studies of association, solubility, spectra, and other physical and chemical properties.[20] It would carry us too far afield here to go into all the experimental evidence bearing upon this point; we shall instead content ourselves with a brief description of the bond itself and with a discussion of the theories which have been proposed to explain its existence. As we shall see, resonance is probably not a major factor in the hydrogen bond; it is often considered to be, however, and for that reason a critical survey of the problem seems desirable here.

It is now generally agreed that the association of hydrogen fluoride and of substances containing hydroxyl or amino groups is due to the formation of hydrogen bonds between the molecules. The structures III, IV, and V can accordingly be written for the dimeric forms of hydrogen

$$\text{H}\!-\!\text{F}\,-\,-\,\text{H}\!-\!\text{F} \qquad \text{H}\!-\!\overset{\overset{\displaystyle H}{|}}{\text{O}}\,-\,-\,\text{H}\!-\!\overset{\overset{\displaystyle H}{|}}{\text{O}} \qquad \text{H}\!-\!\overset{\overset{\displaystyle H}{|}}{\underset{\underset{\displaystyle H}{|}}{\text{N}}}\,-\,-\,\text{H}\!-\!\overset{\overset{\displaystyle H}{|}}{\underset{\underset{\displaystyle H}{|}}{\text{N}}}$$

III   IV   V

[18] T. S. Moore and T. F. Winmill, *J. Chem. Soc.* **101**, 1635 (1912). Cf. also, however, the still earlier paper by G. Oddo and E. Puxeddu, *Gazz. chim. ital.* **36**, II, 1 (1906) (*Chem. Zentr.* **1906**, II, 1191). Soviet authors now claim that the hydrogen bond was discovered in 1887 by the Russian chemist M. A. Il'inskiĭ. See, for example, V. M. Zezyulinskiĭ, *Uspekhi Khim.* **18**, 760 (1949) [*C. A.* **45**, 3666 (1951)].

[19] P. Pfeiffer, *Ann.* **398**, 137 (1913); W. M. Latimer and W. H. Rodebush, *J. Am. Chem. Soc.* **42**, 1419 (1920); M. L. Huggins, *Phys. Rev.* **18**, 333 (1921); **19**, 346 (1922).

[20] For more recent comprehensive discussions of the hydrogen bond, see, for example, L. Pauling, *The Nature of the Chemical Bond*, Cornell University Press, Ithaca, N. Y., 1st ed., 1939, 2nd ed., 1940, Chapter IX; M. Davies, *Ann. Repts. on Progr. Chem.* (*Chem. Soc. London*) **43**, 5 (1946); L. Hunter, *ibid.* **43**, 141 (1946); L. Hunter, *Roy. Inst. Chem.*, *Lectures, Monographs and Repts.* **1950**, No. 1, 3; W. C. Price, *ibid.* 14; A. R. Martin, *ibid.* 21. See also A. E. Lutskiĭ, *Uspekhi Khim.* **23**, 479 (1954) [*C. A.* **48**, 9893 (1954)].

fluoride, water, and ammonia, respectively. With these substances, the association can clearly proceed further, and polymers of any desired complexity can be produced. With a carboxylic acid, on the other hand, the association seems usually to stop with the formation of the dimer,[21] which has the structure VI. The molecules joined by the hydrogen bond

need not be of the same kind; ammonia in aqueous solution, for example, probably exists at least partially in the form of undissociated ammonium hydroxide, as was mentioned above, and similar situations doubtless occur in other mixtures of suitable substances.

Intramolecular hydrogen bonds also are well known. They exist especially in substances like o-nitrophenol, VII, and the enol form of acetylacetone, VIII, in which unsaturated six-membered rings can be

formed, although they do occur under other circumstances as well. The tendencies toward intra- and intermolecular hydrogen bonds sometimes compete with each other, as is shown, for example, by the fact that o-nitrophenol is not associated, whereas its meta and para isomers are.

For reasons which will become apparent later, the strength of a hydrogen bond is in general greatest when the atoms linked by it are most electronegative. Only with fluorine, oxygen, and nitrogen, in fact, do such bonds occur at all frequently, although they are occasionally encountered with other elements. Hydrogen cyanide, for example, is highly associated, and hydrogen bonds of the type IX are doubtless involved. The carbon

$$H\text{---}C\equiv N\text{ - - }H\text{---}C\equiv N \qquad\qquad HC^{+}\!\!\equiv\!N^{-}$$
$$\text{IX}\text{X}$$

atom is here able to enter into a hydrogen bond, presumably because the carbon-nitrogen bond receives relatively large contributions from such partially ionic structures as X and so on. In view of the weights assigned

[21] However, see F. H. MacDougall, *J. Am. Chem. Soc.* **63**, 3420 (1941); H. L. Ritter and J. H. Simons, *ibid.* **67**, 757 (1945); E. W. Johnson and L. K. Nash, *ibid.* **72**, 547 (1950).

to these structures, the carbon atom may be expected here to have a net positive charge and so to be more than usually electronegative. Similar considerations apply also in other substances in which hydrogen bonds are formed with the less electronegative elements.[22]

The apparent paradox that the electro*negativity* of an atom is increased by a *positive* charge is explained by the fact that the word "electronegativity," as used in this book, refers to the ability to attract electrons and not explicitly to the state of charge. No reference is intended to "electronegativity" in the sense in which the term is used by Kharasch and his co-workers.[23]

Even under the most favorable circumstances, hydrogen bonds are always much weaker than the ionic and covalent bonds considered previously. The strongest hydrogen bond that is listed in the tables compiled by Pauling[20] and by Davies[20] is the F—H – – F bond in hydrogen fluoride, with an energy of only about 10 kcal per mole. More recent studies[24] have, to be sure, led to the much larger value of 27 kcal per mole for the energy of the at least superficially analogous bond in the bifluoride ion, HF_2^-; as is discussed below in greater detail, however, this latter bond appears to be highly exceptional, if not actually unique. More typical values[20] for the energies of hydrogen bonds lie in the range 4–9 kcal per mole when two oxygen atoms are linked; or in the lower range 1–3 kcal per mole when atoms of less electronegative elements, such as nitrogen, chlorine, or carbon, are involved. Presumably, the bonds become still weaker as the electronegativities of the heavy atoms are further decreased, so that there is no sharp dividing line between those interactions which can, and those which cannot, be considered due to the formation of hydrogen bonds.

There has in the past been much discussion in regard to the nature of the forces responsible for the hydrogen bond. Originally, the hydrogen atom was simply supposed to be divalent in the usual meaning of the word. According to the electronic theory of valence, this would require that the hydrogen expand its valence shell to include four electrons. The structure of the dimeric form of water, for example, would then have to be written as XI. With the development of quantum mechanics and

$$\text{H} \qquad \text{H}$$
$$\text{H:}\overset{..}{\text{O}}\text{:H:}\overset{..}{\text{O}}\text{:}$$
XI

[22] See, for example, G. F. Zellhoefer, M. J. Copley, and C. S. Marvel, *J. Am. Chem. Soc.* **60**, 1337 (1938).

[23] M. S. Kharasch and A. L. Flenner, *J. Am. Chem. Soc.* **54**, 674 (1932); M. S. Kharasch and O. Reinmuth, *J. Chem. Educ.* **5**, 404 (1928); **8**, 1703 (1931); M. S. Kharasch, O. Reinmuth, and F. R. Mayo, *ibid.* **11**, 82 (1934); **13**, 7 (1936).

[24] See E. F. Westrum, Jr., and K. S. Pitzer, *J. Am. Chem. Soc.* **71**, 1940 (1949).

with a better understanding of the nature of valence, however, it soon became apparent that such a structure was at any rate highly improbable. A large amount of energy would, in fact, have to be supplied if the hydrogen atom were forced to accommodate four electrons, and this would make the system quite unstable.

A reasonable, and probably adequate, explanation of the hydrogen bond is to be found in a consideration of the electrostatic interactions between the atoms or groups that are linked by it.   From this point of view, the above example of the dimeric form of water would be described as follows: It is known that the average distribution of electric charge in the water molecule is unsymmetrical and that, in particular, the hydrogen and oxygen atoms have fairly large net positive and negative charges, respectively.   This distribution can, of course, be related to the partial ionic character of the hydrogen-oxygen bonds.   (See Section 5·2.) The situation can be roughly described by writing the structure of a single water molecule as XII, in which the symbol (+) represents a positive

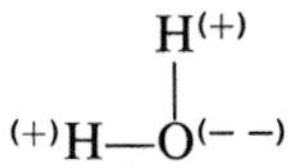

$$H^{(+)}$$
$$|$$
$$^{(+)}H-O^{(--)}$$

XII

charge equal in magnitude to about one-third that of an electron, and (−−) represents a negative charge of twice that magnitude. (These plus and minus signs in parentheses do not represent formal charges.) The dimeric form of water is then XIII.   Although each of the molecules

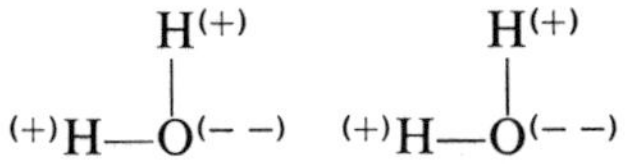

$$H^{(+)} \qquad\qquad H^{(+)}$$
$$| \qquad\qquad\quad |$$
$$^{(+)}H-O^{(--)} \quad\ ^{(+)}H-O^{(--)}$$

XIII

is electrically neutral as a whole, the two are clearly attracted to each other when their relative positions are as illustrated here.   This conclusion follows because the attractions between the oppositely charged regions outweigh, on account of their smaller separations, the repulsions between the like charged regions.

Such an explanation is in accord with the observation that hydrogen bonds exist only between strongly electronegative atoms, since only then are the net charges on the atoms large.   It may seem strange, however, that this type of linkage occurs only when *hydrogen* is present.   In acetone, for example, the net charges on the carbon and oxygen atoms are apparently larger than those present in water and, consequently, a dimeric molecule, XIV, with "carbon bonds" or "oxygen bonds" might be anticipated. (The symbols (+) and (−) represent charges of greater

$$
\begin{array}{c}
CH_3 \\
\diagdown \\
C^{(+)}\!\!=\!\!O^{(-)} \quad CH_3 \\
\diagup \qquad \diagup \\
CH_3 \quad O^{(-)}\!\!=\!\!C^{(+)} \\
\diagdown \\
CH_3
\end{array}
$$

XIV

magnitude here than in the corresponding structure for water.) Actually, the substance is not measurably associated, although the fact that its boiling point is higher than that of a hydrocarbon of comparable molecular weight does show that this electrostatic interaction produces some attraction between the molecules. The explanation is perhaps steric; the oppositely charged portions of the two acetone molecules may not be able to get close enough together for the attraction between them to be very great. It is doubtless significant that the hydrogen atom, which *can* come in close enough to a negative center, is not only extremely small but also is univalent, so that any steric interference is at a minimum.

An alternative interpretation of the hydrogen bond involves the idea of resonance. Returning to the example of the dimeric form of water, we see that we can write for this the two structures, XV and XVI, in

$$
\begin{array}{cccc}
H & H & H & H \\
| & | & | & | \\
H\!\!-\!\!O & H\!\!-\!\!O & H\!\!-\!\!O^+\!\!-\!\!H & O^- \\
\end{array}
$$

XV   XVI

each of which the usual valence rules are obeyed. If these structures correspond to the same relative positions of all the nuclei, there must be resonance between them. Since the resulting stabilization of the system would then be greatest when the oxygen atoms are close together, the necessary condition for the existence of a valence bond is satisfied. An effect of this type may be involved, but there are reasons to suspect that it is of considerably less importance than the electrostatic interactions considered above.

The problem is complicated by the fact that the magnitude of the resonance energy may be expected to depend upon the position of the proton which is responsible for the bond. One possibility is that this proton is equidistant from the two atoms joined by it. Then the two structures in question would correspond to the same nuclear configuration, and resonance should be important. Under these conditions, however, a difficulty arises which can be most easily illustrated by a comparison of the relative stabilities of the dimeric forms of water and of formic acid. For the first of these, the structures XV and XVI, which are presumed to be involved in the resonance, are not equivalent, and the former is much more stable than the latter; for the second, on the other hand, the corresponding structures, XVII and XVIII, are equivalent and so equally

$$
\begin{array}{cc}
\ce{H-C}\!\!\begin{array}{c}\nearrow O \quad H-O\searrow\\ \searrow O-H \quad O\nearrow\end{array}\!\!\ce{C-H} & \ce{H-C}\!\!\begin{array}{c}\nearrow O-H \quad O\searrow\\ \searrow O \quad H-O\nearrow\end{array}\!\!\ce{C-H}\\
\text{XVII} & \text{XVIII}
\end{array}
$$

stable. Experience has shown that the resonance energy is always tremendously greater when the structures involved are of the same stability than when they differ considerably in that regard. Dimeric formic acid ought, therefore, to have a much greater energy of dissociation than dimeric water. Actually, however, the energy of dissociation per hydrogen bond is only about 50 per cent higher for formic acid than for water (7 and 4.5 kcal per mole, respectively).[20]

The other possibility for the position of the hydrogen atom which forms the link is that it is closer to one of the two atoms joined by it than it is to the other. If there are two possible positions for the proton, there are then altogether four structures which have to be considered for each substance. For dimeric water these are XIX–XXII, and for dimeric

$$
\begin{array}{cc}
\begin{array}{cc}\overset{H}{\underset{|}{H-O}} & \overset{H}{\underset{|}{H-O}}\end{array} & \begin{array}{cc}\overset{H}{\underset{|}{H-O^{+}}}\cdots\cdots H & \overset{H}{\underset{|}{O^{-}}}\end{array}\\
\text{XIX} & \text{XX}\\[2ex]
\begin{array}{cc}\overset{H}{\underset{|}{H-O}} \quad H\cdots\cdots & \overset{H}{\underset{|}{O}}\end{array} & \begin{array}{cc}\overset{H}{\underset{|}{H-O^{+}-H}} & \overset{H}{\underset{|}{O^{-}}}\end{array}\\
\text{XXI} & \text{XXII}
\end{array}
$$

formic acid they are XXIII–XXVI. An attempt has been made here to indicate the actual geometrical arrangements as closely as possible, and

$$
\begin{array}{cc}
\ce{HC}\!\!\begin{array}{c}\nearrow O \quad H-O\searrow\\ \searrow O-H \quad O\nearrow\end{array}\!\!\ce{CH} & \ce{HC}\!\!\begin{array}{c}\nearrow O \cdots\cdots H \quad O\searrow\\ \searrow O \quad H\cdots\cdots O\nearrow\end{array}\!\!\ce{CH}\\
\text{XXIII} & \text{XXIV}\\[2ex]
\ce{HC}\!\!\begin{array}{c}\nearrow O \quad H\cdots\cdots O\searrow\\ \searrow O \cdots\cdots H \quad O\nearrow\end{array}\!\!\ce{CH} & \ce{HC}\!\!\begin{array}{c}\nearrow O-H \quad O\searrow\\ \searrow O \quad H-O\nearrow\end{array}\!\!\ce{CH}\\
\text{XXV} & \text{XXVI}
\end{array}
$$

the dotted lines, as usual, represent formal bonds. In those structures in which the hydrogen atom is linked by a formal bond to the more distant oxygen atom, it is not bonded in any way to the closer one. If we apply the rule that there can be resonance only between structures with the same relative positions of the atomic nuclei, we see that, for either water or formic acid, resonance is possible only between the first and second or between the third and fourth structures; the two resonance hybrids which result for each substance are then in something like tautomeric equilibrium with each other. The resonance which *can* be postulated is always between nonequivalent structures, so that the stabilization attributable to it should be small for both water and formic acid—probably smaller than that resulting from the electrostatic interaction.

The question at issue here can be described with the aid of Figures 1·2 and 1·3 of Section 1·4. If the proton is equidistant from the two atoms joined by it, the energy has a minimum, as in Figure 1·2; if the proton is nearer one atom than the other, the energy has a low maximum, as in Figure 1·3. Only in the former case can the resonance produce any large stabilization. The problem can be looked at also from the point of view elaborated in part D of Section 9·18; in this way, too, the same conclusion is reached that the resonance can produce appreciable stabilization only if the proton is centered in the bond.

The considerations of the preceding paragraphs suggest that probably the hydrogen atom is not in the center of the bond. This conclusion receives further support from the observed distances between the atoms linked by the bond. An O—H – – O bond, for example, is usually found to be about 2.5–2.8 A in length,[20] which is considerably more than twice the ordinary oxygen-hydrogen distance of 0.96 A. (See Section 4·3.) If the hydrogen atom is in the center, then the oxygen-hydrogen bond in each structure must have been greatly stretched. A different method of attacking the problem has been given by Pauling,[25] who has shown that the observed entropy of ice requires that each proton be closer to one oxygen atom than to any other. Spectroscopic data also have been interpreted[20, 26] as leading to the same conclusion in regard to the hydrogen bonds between the oxygen atoms both here and in several other substances. Moreover, electron-diffraction studies[27] of several carboxylic acids have shown that, in the respective dimers, the two

[25] L. Pauling, *J. Am. Chem. Soc.* **57**, 2680 (1935).

[26] See, for example, P. C. Cross, J. Burnham, and P. A. Leighton, *J. Am. Chem. Soc.* **59**, 1134 (1937); R. C. Herman and R. Hofstadter, *Phys. Rev.* **53**, 940 (1938); *J. Chem. Phys.* **6**, 534 (1938); E. Bauer and M. Magat, *J. phys. radium*, **9**, 319 (1938).

[27] J. Karle and L. O. Brockway, *J. Am. Chem. Soc.* **66**, 574 (1944). For a discussion of the comparable crystal-structure data for several dibasic acids, see D. C. Hodgkin and G. J. Pitt, *Ann. Repts. on Progr. Chem.* (*Chem. Soc. London*) **47**, 443 (1950).

carbon-oxygen bonds formed by an individual carbon atom have appreciably different lengths. (Cf. Table 4·3, Section 4·3.) This observation would be difficult to explain if the dimers were resonance hybrids of equivalent structures like XVII and XVIII, since then the two carbon-oxygen bonds should be equivalent; it is, however, an immediate consequence of resonance between nonequivalent structures like XXIII and XXIV. Finally, in ice, the protons have been conclusively shown by means of neutron diffraction to be not equidistant from the adjacent oxygen atoms.[28]

An x-ray examination of the crystal structure of nickel dimethylglyoxime has led[29] to the conclusion that the relative positions of the atoms in the molecule of this substance are those shown in structure XXVII; and that each of the two equivalent O—H - - O

$$
\begin{array}{c}
CH_3 \qquad O\!-\!H\,-\,-\,O^- \qquad CH_3 \\
\diagdown \qquad\qquad\qquad\qquad\qquad \diagup \\
C\!=\!N^+ \qquad\qquad N^+\!\!=\!C \\
\mid \qquad\quad >Ni^{--}< \qquad\quad \mid \\
C\!=\!N^+ \qquad\qquad N^+\!\!=\!C \\
\diagup \qquad\qquad\qquad\qquad\qquad \diagdown \\
CH_3 \qquad O^-\,-\,-\,H\!-\!O \qquad CH_3 \\
\text{XXVII}
\end{array}
$$

bonds has the exceptionally short length of only 2.42 A. Moreover, the substance shows no absorption in the regions of the infrared that are characteristic of either free or hydrogen-bonded hydroxyl groups; and, since only a single NO stretching frequency is observed, all four nitrogen-oxygen bonds appear to be equivalent. It can therefore be presumed that here the protons are centered.[29] Similar situations have been encountered also in a number of other analogous nickel and palladium complexes.[29] The reason why the hydrogen bonds in these substances should thus be different from those found elsewhere is not at present completely understood; the especially short oxygen-oxygen distances may perhaps, however, be forced upon the molecules by the steric requirements of the complex ring systems. In any event, there seems to be no reason to doubt that *ordinarily* the hydrogen nucleus in an O—H - - O bond is appreciably nearer to one oxygen atom than to the other.

Since, as has just been shown, the protons are (usually) not centered in the relatively strong hydrogen bonds between oxygen atoms, we can be fairly certain, on theoretical grounds,[24] that they are also not centered in the weaker bonds between atoms of the less electronegative elements. Centered protons are, in fact, most likely to be found in the particularly strong bonds between atoms of the most electronegative element, fluorine. Although there is no evidence that the hydrogen bonds in polymeric hydrogen fluoride (HF)$_n$ are of this exceptional type, there is completely

---

[28] E. O. Wollan, W. L. Davidson, and C. G. Shull, *Phys. Rev.* **75**, 1348 (1949).

[29] L. E. Godycki, R. E. Rundle, R. C. Voter, and C. V. Banks, *J. Chem. Phys.* **19**, 1205 (1951); R. C. Voter, C. V. Banks, V. A. Fassel, and P. W. Kehres, *Anal. Chem.* **23**, 1730 (1951); R. E. Rundle and M. Parasol, *J. Chem. Phys.* **20**, 1487 (1952); L. E. Godycki and R. E. Rundle, *Acta Cryst.* **6**, 487 (1953).

convincing evidence that such a bond does exist in the bifluoride ion HF_2^-. The observation[24] that the entropy of the salt KHF_2, unlike that of ice,[25] approaches zero at the temperature of $0°K$ appears to preclude the possibility that, in the bifluoride ion, there is more than a single stable position for the proton. This conclusion has been supported[24] also by spectroscopic evidence, by consideration of the temperature dependence of the dielectric constant of the salt, and by a study of the magnetic resonance spectrum;[30] and it has received complete confirmation from a study of neutron diffraction.[31]

The difference between the hydrogen bonds in polymeric hydrogen fluoride and in the bifluoride ion is in the expected direction; for, in the former system, the structures which would have to be assumed to be involved in the resonance must still differ considerably in energy even if the protons are centred (cf. the analogous structures XV and XVI), whereas the corresponding structures XXVIII and XXIX are equivalent if the proton is equidistant from the two fluorine atoms. At least part

F—H F⁻   F⁻ H—F

XXVIII   XXIX

of the exceptional strength of the bond in the ion must therefore be attributable to resonance; there is, however, no way in which we can estimate how much stronger the bond is in the actual hybrid than it would have been if the charge distribution had instead been that represented by either of the structures XXVIII and XXIX alone.

No complete uniformity exists as yet in regard to the graphical representation of the hydrogen bond. Throughout this book, we shall continue to use the method which has been employed in the preceding pages, and which consists in writing one full and one broken line between the hydrogen atom and the two atoms linked by it. Whenever a reasonable guess can be made as to the approximate position of the proton (on the assumption that it is not centrally located), the full line will be drawn to the nearer neighbor; in any event, the full line can be considered to represent an essentially covalent bond, and the broken line to represent an electrostatic interaction. The broken line must be carefully distinguished from the dotted line that is used to represent a formal bond. Similarly, there is as yet no complete uniformity in regard to the name by which the type of linkage that is discussed in this section should be described. Many authors employ the same terminology that has here been adopted, and hence refer to the linkage as a *hydrogen bond*. Other authors, however, prefer the expression *hydrogen bridge*; still others prefer

[30] J. S. Waugh, F. B. Humphrey, and D. M. Yost, *J. Phys. Chem.* **57**, 486 (1953).
[31] S. W. Peterson and H. A. Levy, *J. Chem. Phys.* **20**, 704 (1952).

the expression *proton bond* or *proton bridge*; and so on. Throughout this book, we shall continue to use the expression *hydrogen bond.*

2·9 The Molecular-Orbital Treatment of Valence.[32] In the preceding sections, we have seen how several types of bond can be interpreted with the aid of the theory of resonance. Let us now, however, consider the problem of valence from a superficially quite different viewpoint which, in its simplest applications, does not explicitly use the resonance concept, but which turns out to be mathematically equivalent to the previously described viewpoint that does explicitly use this concept.

As before, it will again be convenient to begin by considering the hydrogen molecule-ion H_2^+. If the two protons are at a great distance from each other, the system is correctly described as consisting of an isolated hydrogen atom plus an isolated proton. The corresponding

(a)   (b)

Fig. 2·3.   Nonbonding orbitals for a system consisting of two
equivalent nuclei at an infinite separation.

average distribution of electric charge can then be schematically represented by the appropriate one of the Figures 2·3a and 2·3b, in each of which the two plus signs represent the two protons, and the closed curve or, more precisely, the closed surface of which it is the trace, surrounds the region of space in which the single electron is most likely to be found. (Cf. also the following paragraph in fine print.)   The fact that this curve is a circle or, more precisely, that the closed surface to which it corresponds is a sphere implies that the electron is exactly as likely to be found in any one direction from the nucleus as in any other.

In Figure 2·3, as has just been stated, each circle is a schematic representation of the average distribution of electric charge within a single isolated hydrogen atom in its ground state.   This distribution can, however, be more precisely defined in either one of the two equivalent ways shown in Figure 2·4.   In part *a* of this figure, the probability P that the distance between the electron and the proton is less than r is plotted against r.   Since the charge distribution is spherically symmetric (see above), no additional independent variables besides r need here be considered.   In part *b*, on the other hand, the same information is given in a different way which, although less familiar, is more closely related to the method of representation employed in Figure 2·3.   In this further figure, the seven concentric circles are the traces of seven concentric spheres; the values listed along the horizontal axis are equal to the distances (in angstroms) from the

[32] For further details, see Sections 9·22–9·27. Cf. also C. R. Noller, *J. Chem. Educ.* **27**, 504 (1950).

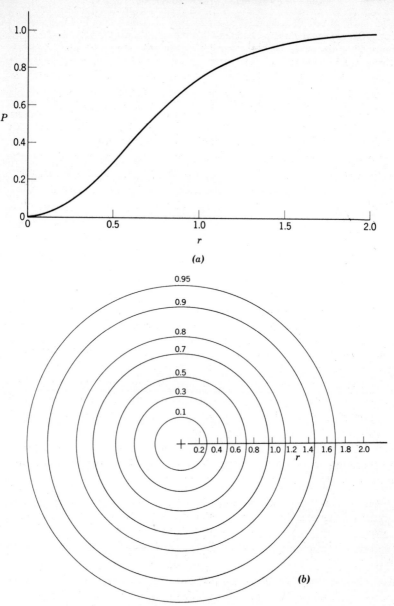

Fig. 2·4. The charge distribution in the normal hydrogen atom. (a) The probability P that the electron will be found at a distance less than r from the nucleus, plotted against r (in angstroms). (b) The traces of seven spheres, with different radii (r), about the proton ($+$) as center, and the probabilities that the electron lies within them.

proton which, as before, is depicted by a plus sign; and the values listed on the individual circles are equal to the probabilities that the electron would be found somewhere within the corresponding spheres. Since the sphere associated with unit probability would have an infinite radius, it is, of course, not explicitly represented in the figure (cf. equation 6, Section 9·6). The single circle that appears in Figure 2·3a (or 2·3b) can then be identified with any desired one of the circles in Figure 2·4b; if, for example, the outermost circle is chosen, the electron is nineteen times as likely to be inside the corresponding sphere, with a radius of about 1.7 A, as it is to be outside that sphere. Since, except for a few especially simple systems containing only one or two electrons, the exact charge distributions are not known, we shall not hereafter attempt to employ the detailed representations of the kinds illustrated in Figure 2·4. We shall instead return to the simpler, and purely qualitative, descriptions that were originally introduced. For the same reason, we shall not specify either the exact dimensions of the closed surfaces which are depicted or the exact values of the probabilities that the electrons will be found within those surfaces; frequently, in fact, we may even be somewhat vague in regard to the shapes of the regions enclosed by the surfaces. The more quantitative features of the treatment, which we thus ignore, are not essential to an understanding of the basic principles involved.

If, in a system consisting of two protons and one electron, the interprotonic distance is very great, then, as we have seen, the electron belongs essentially to just one of the protons, and the average distribution of charge is that represented symbolically in the appropriate one of Figures 2·3a and 2·3b.

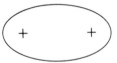

If, however, the interprotonic distance has the much smaller value r_e which obtains in the normal hydrogen molecule-ion (cf. Figure 2·1, Section 2·4), the electron

Fig. 2·5. A bonding orbital for a system containing two equivalent nuclei.

can no longer belong uniquely to either one of the protons, but it must instead belong equally to both protons. The resulting charge distribution is then of the type schematically represented by Figure 2·5. The closed surface that surrounds the region where the electron is most likely to be is now obviously not a sphere, but it is still a surface of revolution, obtainable by rotation of the oval in the figure about an axis passing through the two protons. Since the electron is therefore concentrated in the region between the nuclei, the electrostatic interactions between the charged particles lead to an attraction, and hence to the formation of a valence bond. (Cf. page 36.)

The charge distributions that are depicted in Figures 2·3, 2·4, and 2·5 are commonly described by the statement that, in Figures 2·3 and 2·4, the electron is in an *atomic orbital*, centered about one or the other of the individual nuclei; whereas, in Figure 2·5, it is instead in a *molecular orbital*, encompassing both nuclei. Since, even at small internuclear distances, the presence of an electron in either of the equivalent atomic orbitals of Figure 2·3 would lead to no attraction between the nuclei, and hence to the formation of no bond, these orbitals are said to be *non-bonding*; on the other hand, the molecular orbital of Figure 2·5 is clearly *bonding*. Furthermore, the spherical symmetry of the nonbonding (atomic) orbitals is commonly expressed, in spectroscopic terminology, by the statement that these are *s* orbitals; and the cylindrical symmetry of the bonding (molecular) orbital about the nuclear axis is similarly expressed by the statement that this orbital is a σ, or sigma, orbital.

In Section 2·4, we described the hydrogen molecule-ion as a resonance hybrid of the two "structures" H· H$^+$ and H$^+$ H·; here, we describe it by saying that it contains a single electron in a molecular orbital of the form depicted in Figure 2·5. It can be shown, however, that these two alternative descriptions are not conflicting, but identical; for, although they are expressed in quite different language, and although they call forth quite different mental images, they both specify exactly the same average distribution of electric charge, and hence they are indistinguishable in every respect that is physically significant.

The neutral hydrogen molecule differs from the hydrogen molecule-ion in that it contains an additional electron. Since the most stable molecular orbital is still one of the form shown in Figure 2·5, the ground state of the hydrogen molecule must result when both its electrons are put into that orbital. The Pauli exclusion principle (cf. page 41 and also Section 9·7), however, now requires that the electrons have exactly antiparallel spins or, in other words, that they be paired with each other. Consequently, just as in our earlier discussion (cf. page 41), we again find that the normal hydrogen molecule has no unpaired electrons. Since both electrons are in a bonding orbital, each is again found to be concentrated in the region between the two nuclei, so that the electrostatic interactions must lead to the production of a bond. Indeed, since two bonding electrons ought to be approximately twice as good as one, we can anticipate that the two-electron bond in the hydrogen molecule ought to be approximately twice as strong as the one-electron bond in the molecule-ion; this expectation is in agreement with the data quoted in Sections 2·4 and 2·6.

The distribution of electric charge which results when the bonding molecular orbital is doubly occupied is, as we have just seen, qualitatively similar to that found by the method of Section 2·6. The two distributions, however, are not identical, as were the corresponding ones for the hydrogen molecule-ion. In fact, in order to express, in terms of resonance, exactly the same charge distribution that is obtained in the molecular-orbital treatment, we must describe the neutral hydrogen molecule as a resonance hybrid receiving contributions not only from the purely covalent structure I, but also from the two ionic structures II and III; and, more precisely, we must consider that the covalent structure makes exactly the same contribution to the hybrid as do the ionic ones. Since, however, the covalent structure must be much more stable than the ionic ones, and since the bond in the actual molecule must therefore be considerably

$$\text{H—H} \qquad \text{H}^+ \quad \text{H:}^- \qquad \text{:H}^- \quad \text{H}^+$$
$$\text{I} \qquad\qquad \text{II} \qquad\qquad\qquad \text{III}$$

nearer to the covalent than to the ionic extreme, the charge distribution calculated by the molecular-orbital method is slightly less accurate than even the one calculated for a purely covalent bond with no ionic character at all.

From a consideration of resonance, we found in Section 2·6 that the interaction of two hydrogen atoms gives rise to two different states of the resulting system. Only one of these states, however, has so far appeared in our discussion of the molecular-orbital method. In order to obtain the missing state, i.e., the one in which the electrons are unpaired, and in which there is a repulsion between the two atoms, we must now take into account a new type of molecular orbital which we have not hitherto encountered, and which is schematically represented in Figure 2·6. An electron occupying this orbital is most likely to be found in one or the other of the two equivalent, but unconnected, volumes that

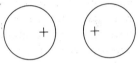

Fig. 2·6. An antibonding molecular orbital for a system containing two equivalent nuclei.

result when the two closed curves are rotated about an axis passing through the two nuclei; it can never be found at any point equidistant from the nuclei. Since such an electron is therefore largely excluded from the region between the nuclei, the orbital, which is again of the sigma type (see above), is *antibonding*. If we now assign one of the two electrons to the bonding orbital, and the other to the antibonding orbital, the spins can then be either parallel or antiparallel. If they are parallel, the resulting state of the system is identical with the repulsive one found in Section 2·6; if they are antiparallel, the resulting state can be described as arising from resonance between just the two ionic structures II and III. The reason why the first of these two states is repulsive (as is also the second) is that the antibonding orbital is somewhat more antibonding than the bonding orbital is bonding.

The necessity that there be an antibonding molecular orbital in addition to the bonding one can be seen in the following way. On page 28, it was pointed out that resonance among n independent structures must give rise to exactly n different states of the system. Now, the two atomic orbitals of Figure 2·3 correspond to the two "structures" H· H$^+$ and H$^+$ H·, and so the two molecular orbitals of Figures 2·5 and 2·6 are simply the two different resonance hybrids of these "structures." The bonding orbital is more stable, and the antibonding orbital is less stable, than either of the nonbonding orbitals. Incidentally, a comparison of Figures 2·3, 2·5, and 2·6 may help to make it clear how each of two entirely dissimilar charge distributions (Figures 2·5 and 2·6) can be half-way between the same pair of extremes (Figures 2·3a and 2·3b).

We have so far considered two different assignments of the electrons to the molecular orbitals: one in which both electrons are put into the bonding orbital, and one in which a single electron is put into each orbital. To these assignments, which are conventionally referred to as *electronic configurations*, can now be added a third, in which both electrons are put into the antibonding orbital. In this way, there is obtained a very strongly repulsive state, which like the ground state, is describable as a resonance hybrid receiving equal contributions from the covalent and ionic structures I, II, and III. It is here of interest that, from the resonance among these three structures with no unpaired electrons, we have thus derived approximate descriptions for altogether three states, one from each of the three electronic configurations.

As we have seen above, the description which the molecular-orbital method, in its simplest form, gives for the normal hydrogen molecule is made relatively inaccurate by an overemphasis of the purely ionic structures II and III. This defect can, however, be removed by a refinement of the treatment. From the most stable configuration, in which both electrons are in the bonding orbital, and from the least stable configuration, in which both electrons are in the antibonding orbital, we obtained two different charge distributions, each of which we described as a hybrid of structures I, II, and III. Since neither of these two calculated distributions is exactly correct, however, there is a possibility that, by assuming an additional resonance between them, we might be able to obtain a better calculated distribution. Indeed, one can easily show that, by this more elaborate procedure, which is described as the molecular-orbital method with *configuration interaction*, the ionic character of the bond can be decreased to any desired extent (see pages 659f). The treatment then becomes completely equivalent to the most general one of Section 2·7.

The electronic configuration in which one electron is assigned to each molecular orbital also gives rise to a charge distribution that can be described in terms of resonance between the ionic structures II and III. (See page 61.) The reader may therefore have wondered why this configuration was ignored in the above discussion of configuration interaction. The reason is that, although all the conditions stated in Section 1·4 are here satisfied, resonance is nevertheless rendered impossible by still another condition which need not be described in this book since it arises comparatively seldom, and since it can be precisely stated only in mathematical terms (viz., resonance is impossible unless the corresponding wave functions belong to the same row of the same irreducible representation of the symmetry group;[33] see also the paragraph in fine print on page 73).

The molecular-orbital treatment of the three-electron bond in the helium molecule-ion He_2^+ is closely analogous to the above treatments of the hydrogen molecule-ion and molecule. The significant differences are that the plus signs in Figures 2·3, 2·5, and 2·6 must now be considered to represent helium nuclei rather than protons, and that there are now altogether three electrons. Two of these electrons, with antiparallel spins, are assigned to the most stable molecular orbital, i.e., the bonding one; and the third electron is assigned to the next most stable orbital, i.e., the antibonding one. With two bonding and one antibonding electron, the bond is a comparatively weak one, and its energy is roughly half that of a two-electron bond. The approximate charge distribution obtained in this way is identical with that obtained by the resonance method in Section 2·5.

If two neutral helium atoms are forced to come close to each other, the resulting system then has two bonding and two antibonding electrons. Hence, there is a strong repulsion between the atoms, and no stable molecule is formed. Again, the charge distributions obtained by this procedure and by the earlier one (page 43) are identical.

The relation between the resonance and the molecular-orbital viewpoints has been brought out by J. W. Baker[34] in an amusing extension of the original analogy described in Section 1·2. If the resonance treatment of a molecule is compared with the description of a mule as a hybrid between a horse and a donkey, the molecular-orbital treatment of the same molecule can be compared with an alternative description that starts with a picture of the bare skeleton of a mule and then considers the way in which the flesh in the complete animal is distributed with respect to the bones. A farmer would doubtless prefer the first of these two descriptions, but an anatomist might find the second more valuable. Similarly, each of the two ways for looking at the structure of a molecule has its own special fields of usefulness and so is most appealing to the workers in those fields. In general, the resonance viewpoint has proved to be particularly well adapted to qualitative discussions of organic chemistry, whereas the molecular-orbital viewpoint has proved to be particularly well adapted to more quantitative discussions of spectroscopy and of theoretical physics.

2·10   The Molecular-Orbital Treatments of Unsaturated and Aromatic Hydrocarbons.[32] When ethylene is treated by the molecular-orbital method, the various atomic and molecular orbitals are found automatically to divide themselves into two principal sets. On the one hand, the orbitals which are involved in the four carbon-hydrogen single bonds

[33] Cf., for example, E. Wigner, *Gruppentheorie und ihre Anwendung auf die Quantenmechanik der Atomspektren*, Friedr. Vieweg & Sohn, Braunschweig, 1931, Chapter XII.
[34] J. W. Baker, *Hyperconjugation*, Oxford University Press, Oxford, 1952, p. 3.

and in one of the two components of the carbon-carbon double bond
correspond to charge distributions that are cylindrically symmetric about
the respective bond axes; hence these are sigma orbitals, and the bonds
which they produce are sigma bonds.   On the other hand, the orbitals
which are involved in the second component of the double bond do not
correspond to such cylindrically symmetric charge distributions; hence

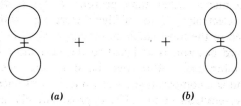

(a)   (b)

Fig. 2·7.   The *p* orbitals on the two carbon atoms in a
molecule of ethylene.

they are not sigma orbitals, and the bond in question is not a sigma bond.
(Cf. Section 9·24.)   These last orbitals are schematically represented in
Figures 2·7, 2·8, and 2·9 which show, respectively, the two original atomic
(nonbonding) orbitals and the corresponding bonding and antibonding
molecular orbitals.   In each figure, as heretofore, the plus signs represent
the atomic kernels, and the closed curves are the traces of surfaces that
surround the regions in which the electrons are concentrated (cf. the

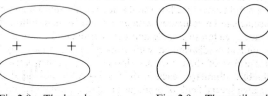

Fig. 2·8.   The bond-   Fig. 2·9.   The antibonding pi orbital in   ing pi orbital in ethylene.
ethylene.

paragraph in fine print on pages 57ff).   The plane of the molecule is to
be thought of as perpendicular to that of the paper.   In Figure 2·7, the
individual unconnected regions are more or less spherical; although each
atomic orbital is therefore cylindrically symmetric about a vertical axis
that lies in the plane of the paper and passes through the nucleus, it is
not of the sigma type since its axis of symmetry is not identical with the
internuclear axis.   In Figure 2·8, the molecular orbital consists of two
parts, one above and one below the plane of the molecule; each part
somewhat resembles an ellipsoid of revolution.   An electron occupying

this orbital is equally likely to be found in either one of the two parts, but it can never be found in the plane of the molecule. In Figure 2·9, the four individual regions of electron concentration are again more or less spherical; two are above and two are below the plane of the molecule. An electron occupying this orbital can never be found either in the plane of the molecule or in the plane which is the perpendicular bisector of the carbon-carbon bond.

The two equivalent atomic orbitals which are shown in Figure 2·7 are said to be p or, more precisely, $p\pi$ orbitals; the two dissimilar molecular orbitals which are shown in Figures 2·8 and 2·9, and which are resonance hybrids of the two atomic ones, are said to be π, or pi, orbitals. The second component of the double bond is therefore a pi bond.

It is both possible and convenient to treat the sigma and the pi bonds independently of each other. Consequently, since most of the characteristic properties of the unsaturated system can be satisfactorily understood without reference to the sigma bonds, we shall hereafter take for granted the framework that is formed by these latter bonds; and we shall deal explicitly with only the pi bond. In other words, we shall consider only those respects in which the actual molecule of ethylene differs from the divalent cation I, which could be obtained by removing from a molecule

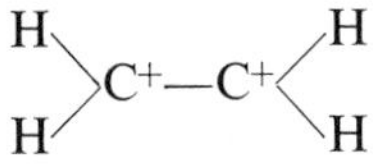

$$\begin{array}{c} \mathrm{H} \diagdown \qquad \diagup \mathrm{H} \\ \qquad \mathrm{C^+ - C^+} \\ \mathrm{H} \diagup \qquad \diagdown \mathrm{H} \\ \mathrm{I} \end{array}$$

of ethylene its two pi electrons. Moreover, in our subsequent discussions of more complex systems, we shall adopt exactly analogous procedures.

In the most approximate description of the normal ethylene molecule, two electrons with opposite spins are assigned to the bonding molecular orbital of Figure 2·8. Since this is a pi, rather than a sigma, orbital, and since it is therefore not cylindrically symmetric, the corresponding charge distribution would be greatly distorted if one of the two methylene groups were rotated, with respect to the other, about the bond axis. An important result of such a distortion would then be to decrease the concentration of the electrons in the region between the nuclei, and hence to decrease the strength of the bond. A force, therefore, acts to hold the molecule in a single plane; hence, the rotation about the double bond is not free.

As with the hydrogen molecule, which was considered in the preceding section, so also with the normal ethylene molecule the present approximate description is mathematically equivalent to one involving resonance among covalent and ionic structures. In fact, exactly the same calculated average distribution of electric charge is obtained if ethylene is considered to be a hybrid of structures II, III, and IV, with the ionic structures again making contributions which seem unreasonably large.

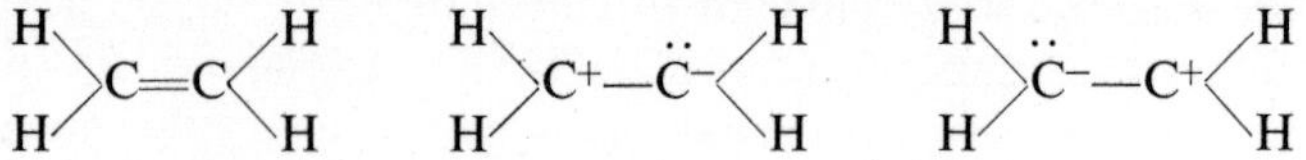

II   III   IV

A further resemblance between the molecular-orbital treatments of the hydrogen and ethylene molecules is that, with both, several less stable states arise from the excited electronic configurations, in which one or both of the electrons are assigned to the antibonding orbital of Figure 2·9. These additional spectroscopically interesting states, like the ground

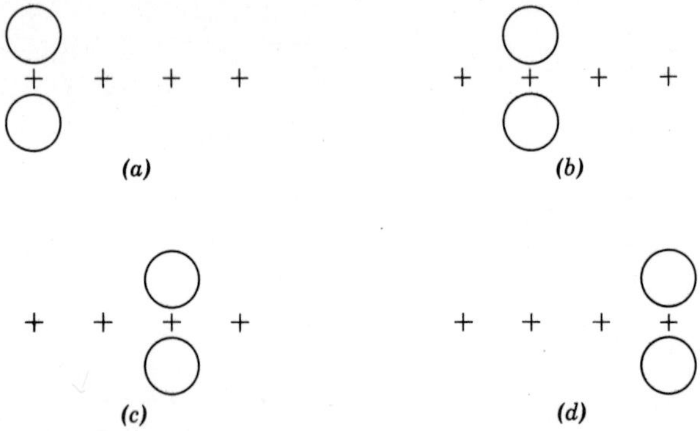

(a)   (b)

(c)   (d)

Fig. 2·10.   The four atomic $p\pi$ orbitals in butadiene.

state, can be described as resonance hybrids of the covalent structure II and the two ionic structures III and IV.   Consequently, the excessive ionic character which the simplest molecular-orbital treatment ascribes to the carbon-carbon bond can, as before, be decreased if proper allowance is made for configuration interaction.   (Cf. page 62.)

A more complicated system, which can similarly be treated by the method either of resonance or of molecular orbitals, is provided by butadiene.   In Section 1·4, we considered this substance to be a hybrid of (principally) the two structures V and VI; here we shall instead discuss

$H_2C{=}CH{-}CH{=}CH_2$ $H_2C{-}CH{=}CH{-}CH_2$

V   VI

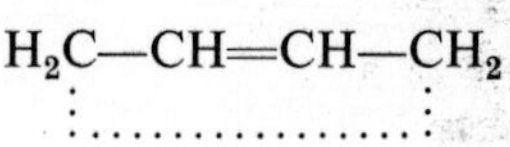

it from the alternative viewpoint.   Since there are now altogether four carbon atoms in the molecule, there are altogether the four atomic $p\pi$ orbitals that are schematically represented in Figure 2·10.   As in the corresponding diagrams for ethylene (see above), the unsaturated molecule is here again assumed to lie in a single plane, perpendicular to that of the paper, and the sigma bonds are not represented; moreover, merely for the sake of simplicity and ease of visualization, no attempt is here made to indicate the true zigzag form of the chain of carbon atoms. Interaction among these four atomic orbitals gives rise to four different molecular orbitals. each of which is still of the pi type. The most stable of these,

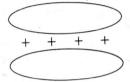

Fig. 2·11. The most stable pi molecular orbital in butadiene.

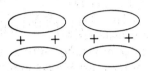

Fig. 2·12. The second most stable pi molecular orbital in butadiene.

schematically represented in Figure 2·11, corresponds to a concentration of electronic charge in each of the three regions between adjacent nuclei; this orbital is therefore bonding with respect to each pair of adjacent atoms. On the other hand, the next most stable molecular orbital, represented in Figure 2·12, is bonding only with respect to the two terminal pairs of atoms, and it is antibonding with respect to the central pair. In the ground state of the molecule, two electrons with opposite spins are assigned to each of these two most stable orbitals. Since there

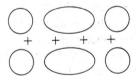

Fig. 2·13. The third most stable pi molecular orbital in butadiene.

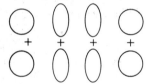

Fig. 2·14. The least stable pi molecular orbital in butadiene.

are only four electrons, one from each atom, which must go into pi orbitals, we need not now consider the two remaining, and still less stable, molecular orbitals, shown schematically in Figures 2·13 and 2·14. (However, see below.)

As can be shown by the more quantitative calculations that are briefly described in Sections 9·24 and 9·25, the net result of the bonding and antibonding characters of the occupied orbitals in the normal butadiene molecule is to produce a strong attraction between the terminal pairs of atoms, and a rather weaker one between the central pair. When account is taken of the sigma orbitals, which are, of course, also occupied by electrons, each of the terminal bonds is found to be slightly weaker than a pure double bond of the type in ethylene, and the central bond is found to be somewhat stronger than a pure single bond of the type in ethane. This conclusion is essentially the same as that reached from a consideration of the resonance between the two structures V and VI; for, from either point of view, the average distribution of electric charge in the butadiene molecule is described as intermediate between the distributions represented by structures V and VI, but materially closer to the former than to the latter extreme. The most important difference between these two approximate descriptions is that the one derived from a consideration of molecular orbitals seems again to overemphasize the importance of the several ionic structures like VII, VIII, and IX. As before, however,

$$H_2C^+ \!\!-\!\! \overset{..}{C}{}^-\!H\!-\!CH\!=\!CH_2 \qquad\qquad H_2C^+\!\!-\!\!CH\!=\!CH\!-\!\overset{..}{C}{}^-H_2$$

VII   VIII

$$H_2C^+\!\!-\!\!\overset{..}{C}{}^-\!H\!-\!C^+H\!-\!\overset{..}{C}{}^-H_2$$

IX

we can eliminate this defect by taking into account the interactions with the excited configurations that arise when one or more electrons are assigned to the still less stable molecular orbitals of Figures 2·13 and 2·14.

When the molecular-orbital treatment of butadiene is carried out in the more quantitative way described in Sections 9·24 and 9·25, the total strength of the three carbon-carbon bonds is found to be slightly greater than would be expected for a hypothetical molecule with the conventional structure V. Since the substance is therefore slightly more stable than it would be if it had exactly this structure, the concept of resonance energy arises here just as it does when the molecule is considered to be a resonance hybrid. (Cf. also the last paragraph of this section.)

With benzene, each carbon atom again has one $p\pi$ orbital. Interaction among the six atomic orbitals then leads in the usual way to six molecular pi orbitals; since altogether six electrons must be assigned to these orbitals, only the three most stable ones are, as a first approximation, occupied in the ground state. If schematic diagrams, analogous to those in Figures 2·3, 2·5–2·14, were set up to represent the occupied orbitals, each would look more or less like a pair of doughnuts, so oriented that one doughnut lies on each side of, and is parallel to, the plane ring which is formed by the carbon nuclei. The cross section of either doughnut at any point is to be taken as a measure of the probability that an electron occupying the orbital would be found at that point. The doughnuts that represent the most stable orbital would then have fairly constant cross sections; on the other hand, the ones that represent the two less stable occupied orbitals would be relatively thinner at the midpoints of the carbon-carbon bonds, and correspondingly thicker at the carbon nuclei. (However, see the paragraph below in fine print.)   Although each occupied orbital is bonding with respect to each pair of adjacent carbon atoms, the most stable one is therefore more strongly bonding than are the less stable ones.   When two electrons with opposite spins are assigned to each of these three pi orbitals, and when the effects of the occupied sigma orbitals are also taken into account, the resulting average distribution of electric charge is such that each carbon-carbon bond is stronger than a pure single bond, but weaker than a pure double bond.   Hence, the picture of the benzene molecule which is obtained by the present method is essentially the same as the earlier one which was based on the idea of resonance between the Kekulé structures X and XI.   The most important

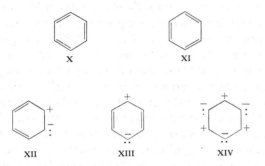

difference is again that the molecular-orbital treatment appears to over-emphasize the importance of the numerous ionic structures like XII, XIII, and XIV in the resonance; as before, however, this defect could be eliminated by a consideration of configuration interaction.

Of the three molecular orbitals which are occupied in the ground state of benzene, the two less stable ones have exactly the same stability, i.e., energy.   Consequently, as is generally true in all such cases of *degeneracy*, these orbitals are not uniquely defined, since they can be set up in an infinite number of apparently different, but actually equivalent, ways.   The above description of these orbitals in terms of rather irregular doughnuts was based upon one particular representation, which was here chosen for reasons of convenience.   Different representations are, however, not only possible but perhaps even more frequently encountered in the literature than is the present one.   (See also pages 666ff.)

Although, as was stated above, each of the equivalent carbon-carbon bonds in the benzene molecule is intermediate in strength between a pure single and a pure double bond, it is not exactly halfway between these two extremes.   By means of a more quantitative treatment,[32] one can show that the strength of the actual bond is somewhat greater than the arithmetic mean of the strengths of a single and of a double bond; and hence that it is somewhat greater than the average strength of the six nonequivalent carbon-carbon bonds in a Kekulé structure. The actual benzene molecule is therefore calculated to be somewhat more stable than an imaginary one with the Kekulé structure would be, if only such a molecule could exist. The concept of resonance energy thus again arises in the molecular-orbital treatment of benzene, just as in that of butadiene. (See above.) Moreover, in agreement both with experiment (see Sections 3·2 and 3·3) and with the qualitative conclusions that can be derived from the resonance theory (see page 28), the calculated resonance energy of benzene is much greater than that of butadiene.

2·11 The Binding Forces in Addition Compounds.[35] Addition compounds belong to so many different types that we cannot expect any single explanation to be applicable throughout the entire field. Frequently, the classical structural theory is quite adequate, as, for example, with ethylene bromide, which can be thought of as an addition compound between ethylene and bromine. In numerous other instances, however, some simple and well-recognized extension of the structural theory is required, as, for example, with the various classes of "onium" compound, and with those substances in which the molecules are linked by hydrogen bonds. In still other instances, the molecules of one component of an addition compound are merely trapped in cavities that are left by the molecules of the other component; typical examples of such (mostly solid) *inclusion*[36] compounds are apparently provided by the complexes formed between urea and a number of paraffin hydrocarbons,[37] and by those formed between hydroquinone and hydrogen chloride, sulfur dioxide, the rare gases, or any of several other substances which have small molecules.[36, 38]

In the addition compounds of the types mentioned above, the molecules of the component substances are held together either by valence bonds that act between individual and identifiable atoms, or else by forces which can be regarded as more mechanical than chemical. With the addition compounds of many other important types, however, the binding forces seem to be essentially chemical, but seem to act between whole groups of

[35] For a more comprehensive discussion which, although recent, is already out of date, see G. W. Wheland, *Advanced Organic Chemistry*, John Wiley & Sons, New York, 1949, Chapter 2.

[36] H. M. Powell, *J. Chem. Soc.* **1948**, 61; *Endeavour* **9**, 154 (1950); *J. Chem. Soc.* **1954**, 2658; F. Cramer, *Einschlussverbindungen*, J. Springer, Berlin, 1954.

[37] F. Bengen, German Patent Application O. Z. 12438 (March 18, 1940); W. J. Zimmerschied, R. A. Dinerstein, A. W. Weitkamp, and R. F. Marschner, *J. Am. Chem. Soc.* **71**, 2947 (1949); A. E. Smith, *J. Chem. Phys.* **18**, 150 (1950).

[38] D. E. Palin and H. M. Powell, *J. Chem. Soc.* **1947**, 208; H. M. Powell and M. Guter, *Nature* **164**, 240 (1949); H. M. Powell, *J. Chem. Soc.* **1950**, 468.

atoms, or even between entire molecules. It is with such substances, for which Dewar[39] has proposed the name "pi complexes," that we shall be concerned in this section.

The addition compound $C_6H_6 \cdot I_2$ between benzene and iodine has been especially carefully studied from both the experimental[40] and the theoretical[41] viewpoints. The best present interpretation of its constitution can most easily be explained in terms of molecular orbitals. Diagram I can be considered to represent the situation which would arise if the benzene and iodine molecules were merely brought to the relative positions which they occupy in the actual complex (see below), and if neither molecule in any way altered the distribution of electric charge within the other. Diagram II, on the other hand, represents the different situation

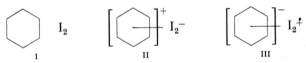

which would arise if all the atomic nuclei were in the same relative positions as in I, but if one electron were transferred from the least stable occupied molecular orbital of the benzene to the most stable unoccupied molecular orbital of the iodine. This operation leaves a singly occupied orbital in the benzene part of the complex, and it provides a second singly occupied orbital in the iodine part. The horizontal straight line which, in diagram II, is drawn between the components then signifies that these two orbitals are "bonded" to each other or, in other words, that the two electrons which they contain are paired with each other.

In addition to diagrams I and II, there can be written still a third one, III, the significance of which should now be clear. The known values of the pertinent ionization potentials and electron affinities (cf. equations 3 and 4, Section 2·2) show, however, that this additional diagram corresponds to an extremely unstable distribution of electric charge and so can here be ignored.

From the valence-bond (or resonance) point of view, diagram I can be thought of as merely a convenient symbol to represent a hybrid of a great

[39] M. J. S. Dewar, *Nature* **156**, 784 (1945); *J. Chem. Soc.* **1946**, 406, 777; *The Electronic Theory of Organic Chemistry*, Oxford University Press, Oxford, 1949, pp. 17f.

[40] H. A. Benesi and J. H. Hildebrand, *J. Am. Chem. Soc.* **70**, 2832 (1948), **71**, 2703 (1949); T. M. Cromwell and R. L. Scott, *ibid.* **72**, 3825 (1950).

[41] R. S. Mulliken, *J. Am. Chem. Soc.* **72**, 600 (1950), **74**, 811 (1952); *J. Chem. Phys.* **19**, 514 (1951); *J. Phys. Chem.* **56**, 801 (1952). For earlier and less complete formulations of the theory, see S. Winstein and H. J. Lucas, *J. Am. Chem. Soc.* **60**, 836 (1938); J. Weiss, *J. Chem. Soc.* **1942**, 245; M. J. S. Dewar (reference 39); W. Brackman, *Rec. trav. chim.* **68**, 147 (1949); J. Collin and L. D'Or, *J. Chem. Phys.* **23**, 397 (1955); R. S. Mulliken, *ibid.* **23**, 397 (1955).

many such structures as IV, V, and VI.   Similarly, the alternative diagram II can be considered to represent a hybrid of a great many such additional, highly polar structures as VII, VIII, and IX.   It should therefore be

evident that the first of these diagrams corresponds to a much more favorable charge distribution, and hence to a much lower internal energy, than the second.

Since the benzene and iodine molecules could hardly come close together without in some way perturbing each other, diagram I cannot, by itself, provide a completely accurate description of the system.   Hence we may assume that a more nearly accurate description can be expressed in terms of resonance between the charge distributions I and II, with presumably only a small weight assigned to the latter, less stable one (see the preceding paragraph).   As a result of this resonance, the system is, as always, made more stable.   Since the stabilization is greatest when the two molecules are close together, there must therefore be an attraction between the benzene and iodine molecules; but, since the stabilization can never be very large, the attraction must be weak.   This conclusion is in quite satisfactory agreement with the observation[42] that, in solution in carbon tetrachloride, the benzene-iodine complex has a heat of dissociation that is equal to only some 1.3–1.5 kcal per mole.

The foregoing rather general considerations have been made much more precise by Mulliken[41] in a careful study of the conditions which must be satisfied in order that the assumed resonance may be possible.   Although his detailed arguments are too technical and too highly specialized to be given here, one of his important conclusions may nevertheless be stated without proof (cf., however, the following paragraph in fine print). Diagrams I and II correspond, by definition, to the same relative positions of all the atomic nuclei;   they do not differ too much in their average distributions of the electrons;   and they have the same number (namely,

[42] T. M. Cromwell and R. L. Scott, *J. Am. Chem. Soc.* **72**, 3825 (1950).

zero) of unpaired electrons; consequently, all the requirements which were listed in Section 1·4 are satisfied. Even so, however, there can still be no resonance unless the iodine molecule has one or another of a small number of narrowly defined orientations with respect to the benzene molecule. Of the several orientations which are thus permitted, the one which seems most likely to be correct is that in which the iodine-iodine axis lies in a plane parallel to the benzene ring, with its center on the sixfold axis of the ring. A less symmetrical orientation is, however, required by the infrared data of Collin and D'Or[41].

Although, for the reasons mentioned above, Mulliken's treatment[41] cannot be reproduced here, a few remarks in regard to its underlying principles may help to make the conclusion seem less arbitrary. The conditions for resonance, which were given in Section 1·4, are not the only ones which must be satisfied; they are instead merely the ones which are most easily stated and which are most commonly used. A further condition is that there can be resonance only if the wave functions which are combined with each other (cf. Section 1·5) have compatible symmetries. Although the precise meaning of this condition can best be explained in the language of group theory, a simple analogy may help to clarify the issue involved. The function x^2 is even in x since it is unchanged when x is replaced by $-x$; on the other hand, the function x^3 is odd in x since it is multiplied by -1 when x is replaced by $-x$. Now, let us consider whether we can set up a linear combination $ax^2 + bx^3$, with constant coefficients a and b, which is either an even or an odd function of x. The answer is clearly that we cannot do so unless we let either b or a, respectively, be equal to zero. In this event, however, we have only a single term instead of the desired linear combination. In other words, as far as this simple problem is concerned, the symmetries of the functions x^2 and x^3 are incompatible. Similarly, the wave functions that correspond to diagrams I and II have definite symmetries, which are much more complex than are the simple evenness and oddness just considered. These mathematical symmetries naturally depend upon the geometrical symmetry of the system, i.e., upon the relative orientations of the iodine and benzene molecules; and only for certain special orientations are they compatible. For any other orientation, the linear combination of the two wave functions reduces to a single term, so that there can then be no resonance.

A study of the dipole moment (cf. Chapter 5) of the benzene-iodine complex has led to some fairly satisfactory experimental evidence in support of the above interpretation.[43] Thus it has been found that, in the complex, there is a small, but appreciable, separation of electric charge. Hence the true state of the system appears to be intermediate between the two imaginary ones that are represented by diagrams I and II, but to be much closer to the former extreme than to the latter. Additional evidence has also been obtained from a spectroscopic study, which will be briefly described in Section 6·7.

The same theoretical principles which have been applied in the discussion of the benzene-iodine complex can be extended to other analogous addition compounds. A number of relatively simple examples of such

[43] F. Fairbrother, *Nature* **160**, 87 (1947); *J. Chem. Soc.* **1948**, 1051.

complexes are provided by the compounds formed between unsaturated hydrocarbons and metal ions.　Thus, we can describe the complex that results from the interaction of isobutylene and silver ion in either of two more or less equivalent ways.　On the one hand, we can speak of resonance between the charge distributions that are represented by the rather formalized diagrams X and XI (cf. I and II);　or, on the other hand, we can instead speak of resonance among the conventional valence-bond structures XII, XIII, and XIV.[44]　(In the latter event, we might wish to include also the additional structure XV, which is ordinarily ignored in

$$[i\text{-}C_4H_8]\ Ag^+ \qquad\qquad [i\text{-}C_4H_8]\!\!\not\!\!\pm Ag$$
$$\text{X} \qquad\qquad\qquad\qquad \text{XI}$$

$$(CH_3)_2C\!\!=\!\!CH_2 \quad (CH_3)_2C\!\!-\!\!C^+H_2 \quad (CH_3)_2C^+\!\!-\!\!CH_2 \quad (CH_3)_2C\!\!-\!\!CH_2$$
$$\begin{array}{cccc} Ag^+ & Ag & Ag & Ag^+ \\ \text{XII} & \text{XIII} & \text{XIV} & \text{XV} \end{array}$$

the first formulation.)　With an addition compound of this class, one of the conclusions that have been derived from the theoretical treatment has been experimentally confirmed.　According to Mulliken,[41] the silver ion in the complex $C_6H_6 \cdot Ag^+$ ought not to lie on the sixfold axis of the benzene ring, as might possibly have been supposed, but ought instead to be situated near the middle of one of the carbon-carbon bonds (cf. the paragraph above in fine print);　a crystal-structure study[45] of the addition compound $C_6H_6 \cdot AgClO_4$ has shown that the silver ion does here indeed occupy just such a position.

Quinhydrone, anthracene picrate, and their many respective analogs are examples of addition compounds which are rather more complicated than the ones discussed above, but which appear to be explainable on a quite similar basis.　Since these further systems therefore add nothing new to the present discussion, we shall here say nothing more about them.

[44] Cf. S. Winstein and H. J. Lucas, *J. Am. Chem. Soc.* **60**, 836 (1938).
[45] R. E. Rundle and J. H. Goring, *J. Am. Chem. Soc.* **72**, 5337 (1950).

Chapter 3   RESONANCE
ENERGY

3·1 Introductory Remarks. Resonance always has the effect of in-creasing the stability, or, in other words, of decreasing the energy, of any molecule in which it is an important feature.   (In regard to the significance of the statement that resonance has a specified effect upon an observable property of a substance, see pages 8f.)   The *resonance energy*, which is defined as the quantity obtained by subtracting the actual energy of the molecule from that of the most stable contributing structure, is therefore always positive.   This new principle is probably the most important addition to chemical theory that has been made since about 1930.   We have already seen in Chapter 2 how it accounts, in a qualitative way, for the existence of covalent bonds and so, in a certain sense, for the existence of chemistry itself.   We shall now consider its application to the less fundamental but more familiar problem of resonance among ordinary valence-bond structures.   We shall be concerned, for example, with the resonance between the two Kekulé structures of benzene, but we shall have little further occasion for explicitly mentioning the kinds of resonance which, in Sections 2·6 and 2·7, we invoked in order to explain both the existence and the partial ionic characters of the bonds themselves.   (It is, however, worthy of note that the word "mesomerism" is commonly applied only to resonance of the present restricted type and is not used to describe the relation between the "structures" discussed in Chapter 2.)

The initial statement of the preceding paragraph is somewhat too broad, inasmuch as the resonance leads also to states of higher energy, as was pointed out in Section 1·5. However, these latter *excited* states are of only spectroscopic interest and so do not ordinarily need to be considered explicitly in the discussion of any chemical problem. For that reason, we shall ignore them in this and in most of the succeeding chapters. (However, see Chapter 6.)

The expression *resonance energy* is sometimes replaced by the completely equivalent one, *delocalization energy*.   The significance of this alternative expression is that the motions of the electrons in the (actually existing) resonance hybrid are presumably rather less restricted than we would expect them to be in an (imaginary) molecule with any specified one of the structures to which we assign finite weights.   Such a "delocal-ization" of the electrons is always an essential feature of the treatment, even when the molecular-orbital viewpoint is adopted, and even when the word "resonance" is not used.   In this book, however, since we are dealing explicitly with the theory of resonance we shall retain the earlier terminology.

There are two distinct points of view that can be adopted in the dis-cussion of resonance energy, and also of the other molecular properties to be taken up in the following chapters.   In the first place, the empirical data can be interpreted as showing that the substances of interest are, or are not, profitably described as resonance hybrids, as the case may be; and, in this way, information regarding the structures of the substances can be obtained.   In the second place, the importance of the resonance can be deduced from general considerations and, in this way, the empirical data can be "explained."   We shall adopt both of these points of view, as the particular occasions demand, and we shall make no effort to develop a single consistent approach.

It is desirable to have information regarding the magnitudes of the resonance energies in as large a number of substances as possible.   The ways in which such information can be derived from thermochemical data will be described in the following sections.

The relations among the various energy quantities are shown schematically in Figure 3·1, in which the heights of the horizontal lines represent the energies of the appropriate structures or systems.   For definiteness, we shall consider that we are dealing with a substance which can be satisfactorily described as a hybrid of only two structures, R and S, of which the latter is the more stable.   The highest line of the figure corresponds to the isolated gaseous atoms, and so, in accordance with the convention introduced in Section 1·4, it defines the zero of energy from which all the other (necessarily negative) energies are measured.   The resonance energy is given by the distance BC (or $AC - AB$) between the lines corresponding to the more stable structure S and the resonance hybrid. The energy which is needed for the dissociation of the substance into atoms is therefore increased by the resonance, since AC is greater than AB.   As is shown in this example, the energy of any molecule, being negative in sign, is *increased* in absolute magnitude by being *decreased* in value.

The lines labeled X and Y are drawn to represent two extreme possible values of the energies of the elements in their *standard states* (i.e., diamond or graphite, molecular hydrogen, molecular oxygen, and so on).   Clearly, the energy required to dissociate the compound into the elements in these standard states could be either positive or negative, and its magnitude could be either increased or decreased by the resonance, since either line X or line Y, respectively, might apply to the particular substance under consideration.   (Clearly also, still a further situation would arise if the energy of the elements in their standard states were intermediate between the energies of the more stable structure S and the resonance hybrid.)

Since it is ordinarily impracticable to measure directly either the energy that is liberated when a complicated organic molecule is formed from its isolated atoms, or the energy that is consumed when such a molecule is dissociated into its atoms, the resonance energy BC of Figure 3·1 is most easily obtained indirectly from other kinds of thermochemical data.   Thus, let us suppose that the substance of interest can be either hydrogenated or burned, and that the energy which is liberated in the reaction can be directly measured.   Moreover, let us further suppose that the horizontal line at the bottom of the figure represents the total energy of all the products which are formed in the hydrogenation, or combustion.   (More precisely, this bottom line represents the energy of the stated products, minus that of the hydrogen, or oxygen, molecules which take part in the reaction; the reason why the energy of these latter molecules must here be subtracted is that suitable allowance must be made for the hydrogen, or oxygen, atoms which are contained in the products, but which are not present in the structures or systems represented by the upper lines of the figure.)   The distance *EF* now corresponds to the energy of hydrogenation, or of combustion, of the actual hybrid molecule; as was noted above, this energy can be directly measured.   On the other hand, the distance *DF* corresponds to the energy of hydrogenation, or of combustion, of an imaginary

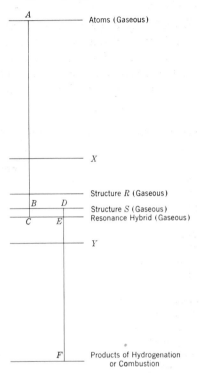

Fig. 3·1. Diagram illustrating the relation between the resonance energy *BC = DE*, and the experimentally accessible thermal data. The heights of the various horizontal lines above some arbitrary base line correspond to the energies of the appropriate structures or systems.

molecule with the more stable structure *S*.   Since no molecule with exactly this structure exists, the required energy cannot be directly measured but must instead be estimated by comparison with the experimental data for other molecules which do exist, and which have closely analogous structures.   The resonance energy *BC* is then equal to *DE*, or to *DF − EF*, which is in turn equal to the amount by which the observed energy of hydrogenation, or of combustion, is less than we would expect it to be if there were no resonance, and if the substance had structure *S*.   In the following sections, we shall see a number of examples of the ways in which this procedure is applied.   Here, however, it may be noted that, although we have in the foregoing discussions dealt with the *energies* of the several reactions, we shall hereafter deal instead with the *heats*, or *enthalpies*, of the reactions. Our justification for thus replacing the energies by the heats is that the small differences between these quantities affect equally the heights of the horizontal lines passing through the points *B*, *C*, *D*, and *E*, and hence they always cancel in any calculation of resonance energy.

3·2 Resonance Energies from Heats of Hydrogenation. The most accurate thermochemical data available for the determination of resonance energies are the heats of hydrogenation of certain unsaturated compounds. In Table 3·1 are listed the results of measurements made by Kistiakowsky and his co-workers[1] upon a number of monoölefins. The quantities

TABLE 3·1

HEATS OF HYDROGENATION OF MONOOLEFINS

Substance	Heat of Hydrogenation[a] (kilocalories per mole)
1. Ethylene	32.8
2. Propylene	30.1
3. 1-Butene	30.3
4. 1-Heptene	30.1
5. Isopropylethylene	30.3
6. Neopentylethylene	29.5
7. *tert*-Butylethylene	30.3
8. 2-Butene (*cis*)	28.6
9. 2-Butene (*trans*)	27.6
10. 2-Pentene (*cis* and *trans* mixture)	28.0
11. Cyclopentene	26.9
12. Cyclohexene	28.6
13. Cycloheptene	26.5
14. Cycloöctene	23.5
15. Isobutylene	28.4
16. *unsym*-Methylethylethylene	28.5
17. *unsym*-Methylisopropylethylene	28.0
18. 2,4,4-Trimethyl-1-pentene	27.2
19. Trimethylethylene	26.9
20. 2,4,4-Trimethyl-2-pentene	28.4
21. Tetramethylethylene	26.6

[a] The quantities listed are the amounts of heat liberated when the hydrogenations are carried out at 1 atm pressure and 82°C. The data listed here are taken from the work of Kistiakowsky and co-workers. See reference 1.

[1] See R. B. Williams, *J. Am. Chem. Soc.* **64**, 1395 (1942), and other papers which are listed there.

listed are the amounts of heat liberated at a constant pressure of 1 atmosphere and at a temperature of 82°C in the reactions

$$X \text{ (gas)} + H_2 \text{ (gas)} \rightarrow XH_2 \text{ (gas)}$$

where X is the unsaturated, and XH_2 is the saturated compound. It is to be noted that the data apply to reactions in which all the substances are gaseous; this fact is important since it makes unnecessary any corrections for the large interactions that operate between the molecules in the solid and liquid phases. It is seen that the values given in the table are dependent upon the number of substituents on the unsaturated atoms, but that they are fairly constant for all the molecules of any given degree of substitution. (An explanation of this variation is given in Section 3·10. For the present, however, we shall regard it merely as an empirical fact.) Some irregularities are observed, mostly in cases of *cis-trans* isomerism or of ring formation, but these are generally smaller than the differences accompanying changes in the number of substituents. This uniformity makes it possible for one to predict the heat of hydrogenation of any olefin to usually within about 1 kcal per mole.

In Table 3·2 similar data are given for hydrocarbons containing two or more double bonds per molecule. We might anticipate that, as a first approximation, the total heats of hydrogenation would be the sums of the heats characteristic of the individual bonds. As long as these latter are not conjugated with each other, this is actually what is observed. For example, the heat of hydrogenation of 1,5-hexadiene is 60.5 kcal per mole, which is almost exactly twice the value found generally for substances with the structure $RCH=CH_2$. With limonene, the agreement is not quite so good, but is still fair; the observed value of 54.1 kcal per mole is only 0.8 kcal per mole less than the sum of the values for the monoölefins with the most closely analogous double bonds, *unsym*-methylisopropylethylene and trimethylethylene.

When the double bonds are conjugated with each other, the situation is different, and the observed heats of hydrogenation are lower than the predicted. With 1,3-butadiene, for example, the observed value of 57.1 kcal per mole is less by 3.5 kcal per mole than twice the value for 1-butene. Since the same product, *n*-butane, is obtained in both reactions, the only possible explanation of the data is that 1,3-butadiene is more stable by 3.5 kcal per mole than would have been anticipated by comparison with 1-butene. The other conjugated dienes also show anomalous stabilities of about the same magnitude, so that the phenomenon appears to be quite general. Moreover, with cycloheptatriene, the only non-aromatic, fully conjugated triene for which data are available, the effect is greater, the extra stability here amounting to 6.7 kcal per mole.

TABLE 3·2

HEATS OF HYDROGENATION OF HYDROCARBONS WITH MORE THAN ONE DOUBLE BOND

Substance	Heat of Hydrogenation[a] (kilocalories)		Reference Substances[b]	Resonance Energy (kilocalories)
	Calculated	Observed		
1,4-Pentadiene	60.6	60.8	3	—
1,5-Hexadiene	60.6	60.5	3	—
1,4-Dihydronaphthalene[c]	28.6	27.6	12	—
Limonene	54.9	54.1	17, 19	—
1,3-Butadiene	60.6	57.1	3	3.5
1,3-Cyclopentadiene	53.8	50.9	11	2.9
1,3-Pentadiene	58.3	54.1	3, 10	4.2
1,3-Cyclohexadiene	57.2	55.4	12	1.8
2,3-Dimethyl-1,3-butadiene	56.8	53.9	15	2.9
1,3,5-Cycloheptatriene	79.5	72.8	13	6.7
1,3-Cycloheptadiene	53.0	51.3	13	1.7
α-Phellandrene	55.5	53.4	12, 19	2.1
α-Terpinene	53.8	50.7	19	3.1
Benzene	85.8	49.8	12	36.0
Ethylbenzene	84.1	48.9	12, 19	35.2
o-Xylene	82.4	47.3	12, 19	35.1
Hydrindene	82.4	45.8	12, 19	36.6
Mesitylene	80.7	47.6	19	33.1
Styrene	114.4	77.5	3, 12, 19	36.9
Indene	109.3	69.9	11, 12, 19	39.4
1,2-Dihydronaphthalene[c]	28.6	24.6	12	4.0
1,2-Diphenylethylene (cis)[c]	28.6	26.3	8	2.3
1,2-Diphenylethylene (trans)[c]	27.6	20.6	9	7.0
1,4-Diphenyl-1,3-butadiene[c]	55.2	44.5	9	10.7

[a] See note a, Table 3·1.

[b] The entries in this column refer to the numbers assigned to the various hydrocarbons in Table 3·1.

[c] This substance was investigated in solution, but its heat of hydrogenation was corrected to the gas phase in order to make it directly comparable with the others in this table and in Table 3·1. The calculated and observed heats are for the hydrogenation of only the bond, or bonds, not in intact benzene rings. The resonance energy given in the last column is therefore only the excess over that in these benzene rings.

The fact that conjugated systems exhibit a special stability in comparison with unconjugated systems of analogous structure has long been recognized and indeed formed one of the chief supports of Thiele's theory of partial valence.[2]   However, it was not until the development of the theory of resonance that a completely logical and convincing explanation was found.   Thus, for butadiene, we can write not only the usual structure I but also the less stable one II, with a formal bond between the terminal

$$CH_2{=}CH{-}CH{=}CH_2 \qquad\qquad CH_2{-}CH{=}CH{-}CH_2$$

I   II

carbon atoms (cf. Section 1·4).   Since the substance is a hybrid of these structures, it is more stable than it would have been if it had instead possessed the most stable unique structure I.   Clearly, therefore, the resonance energy is here equal to about 3.5 kcal per mole, the observed extra stability.   With cycloheptatriene, the conclusion that the resonance energy is still greater can be accounted for in the following manner. There are altogether five structures, III–VII, which need to be considered. The relation between III and IV, or between III and V, is essentially the same as that between I and II for butadiene.   If the resonance were restricted to III and IV, or to III and V, the resonance energy of the triene

III   IV   V

VI   VII

should therefore be about the same as that of a diene.   The resonance cannot be thus restricted, however, and so the effect of the remaining structures must be to increase the resonance energy.

Two further points require some elaboration in connection with the above discussion of the resonance energy of cycloheptatriene.   In the first place, there are still many further structures which can be written for this substance in addition to III–VII.   Some of these are of the type of structure VIII with crossing bonds (either formal or effective).

² J. Thiele, *Ann.* **306**, 87 (1899).

Such structures add nothing new, however, since they can be shown[3] to be themselves resonance hybrids of the structures without crossing bonds. In particular, structure VIII is a resonance hybrid in which III and VII have equal weights. (For further details, see pages 599f.) Structures which, like VIII, have crossing bonds can therefore be ignored. Other structures of the type of IX are also possible. These will be

$$
\begin{array}{cc}
\text{HC=CH} & \text{H C=C—H} \\
\text{HC} \quad \text{CH} & \text{H C} \quad \text{C—H} \\
\text{HC} \quad \text{CH} & \text{H—C} \quad \text{C—H} \\
\text{CH}_2 & \text{CH}_2 \\
\text{VIII} & \text{IX}
\end{array}
$$

neglected since their contributions are particularly unimportant. Resonance with them would be an example of second-order hyperconjugation. (Cf. Section 3·10.) In the second place, the statement that the resonance energy of the triene must be greater than that of a diene because of the additional structures for the former substance must not be taken as expressing the common, but fallacious, view that, of two molecules, the one which is described as a hybrid of the larger number of structures must have the greater resonance energy. The point at issue here is that the triene has structures analogous to *all those of the diene, and some other ones in addition.* On the other hand, octatetraene, CH_2=CH—CH=CH—CH=CH—CH=CH_2, doubtless has a smaller resonance energy than benzene, although the former has altogether fourteen structures of the above type without crossing bonds and the latter has only five; this is because octatetraene has only one, whereas benzene has two, particularly stable structures without formal bonds.

It may seem that resonance could be important also in an unconjugated diene like 1,4-pentadiene, for which the two structures X and XI can be written. For such a substance, however, the less stable structure, XI, has *two* formal bonds, so that it has

$$
\begin{array}{cc}
\text{CH}_2\text{=CH—CH}_2\text{—CH=CH}_2 & \text{CH}_2\text{—CH—CH}_2\text{—CH—CH}_2 \\
\text{X} & \text{XI}
\end{array}
$$

two fewer effective bonds than X. It is therefore particularly unstable, and the resulting resonance energy is negligibly small. It can be shown also that in this molecule, and in other ones of similar type, the "coupling" between the structures is of such nature as to lead to especially small resonance energies. (For the significance of "coupling," see page 608.) It is not possible here to go further into this rather technical point.

For each of the simple conjugated systems considered up to the present, there has been a single structure of greater stability than any of the others. As a result, the resonance has been of only minor importance—that is, the actual structures of the molecules have differed only slightly from the most stable structures, and the resonance energies have been small. In fact, the resonance energies have been so small that one might

[3] G. Rumer, *Nachr. Ges. Wiss. Göttingen, Math. physik. Klasse* **1932**, 337.

feel justified in questioning their reality. This is especially true since, in determining their values, we have had to make estimates of what the heats of hydrogenation of the substances under consideration would have been if there were no resonance. Any errors in these estimates are then contained in the values found for the resonance energies. It is fortunate, therefore, that data are available also for a number of aromatic hydrocarbons; these substances have such large resonance energies that small uncertainties in regard to the exact magnitudes are inconsequential. The observed heats of hydrogenation of these substances are also given in Table 3·2. It will be noted that benzene and its simple alkyl derivatives all have resonance energies in the neighborhood of 35 kcal per mole. This is about ten to fifteen times as great as the resonance energies of the simple conjugated dienes and about five times as great as that of cycloheptatriene.

The reason for these tremendously greater resonance energies in the aromatic hydrocarbons can be seen from a consideration of benzene. This substance is a hybrid of the two equivalent Kekulé structures XII and XIII; since these structures correspond to the same energy, the resonance between them must be very important—that is, the actual structure of the molecules cannot be close to either of the Kekulé structures, and the resonance energy must be large. The three Dewar structures XIV, XV, and XVI must also be given small weights but, since they are

| XII | XIII | XIV | XV | XVI |

relatively unstable, they are much less important than the Kekulé structures. They can, therefore, be ignored in a qualitative discussion like the present one, and we shall refer to them very little hereafter. Approximate calculations of the sort discussed in Section 3·8 have shown that they are responsible for only about 20 per cent of the total resonance energy.[4] (Cf. also Section 9·19.)

With some of the other aromatic hydrocarbons, such as o-xylene, for example, the Kekulé structures which are assumed to be involved in the resonance are not quite equivalent, on account of the presence of substituents. Even under such circumstances, however, the structures differ so little in stability that, for all practical purposes, they may be considered equivalent. This conclusion is borne out by the above-mentioned approximate constancy of the resonance energy in benzene and its alkyl derivatives.

In those molecules in which the benzene rings are conjugated with olefinic double bonds, the resonance energies are still greater. This is

    [4] L. Pauling and G. W. Wheland, *J. Chem. Phys.* **1**, 362 (1933).

to be expected since we can consider resonance not only among the Kekulé and Dewar structures but also with such additional ones as XVII.

XVII

All these have at least one formal bond and so make only small contributions either to the states of the molecules or to the resonance energies. It is interesting that the additional stabilization resulting from the conjugation of a double bond with a benzene ring is of the same order of magnitude as that resulting from the conjugation of two double bonds with each other. This is not unreasonable in view of the similarity between the types of resonance involved. It is interesting also that when the conjugated system becomes fairly long, as in diphenylbutadiene, the resulting resonance energy becomes of appreciable magnitude. This again is not unreasonable because, as was explained above in connection with cycloheptatriene, the possibilities for resonance increase with the length of the conjugated system. Finally, attention may be called to the striking difference in resonance energies of *cis* and *trans* stilbene; the lowered stability of the *cis* compound is probably due to its considerable amount of steric strain and to its nonplanar configuration. (Cf. Section 4·2.)

Data similar to the foregoing are given in Table 3·3 for a number of olefins containing oxygen. Since the heat of hydrogenation of allyl alcohol is close to that of propylene, it appears that the mere presence of an oxygen atom in the neighborhood of the olefinic double bond produces no significant effect. Comparison is apparently permissible, therefore, with the hydrocarbons discussed above. The fact that the heat of hydrogenation of crotonaldehyde is less than that of *trans* 2-butene, for example, can be taken as evidence that a carbon-carbon double bond can be conjugated with an aldehydic carbonyl group as well as with a second ethylenic linkage. The situation is different, however, with methyl methacrylate, which has practically the same heat of hydrogenation as isobutylene; this approximate equality shows that only a negligibly small resonance energy results from conjugation involving the carbonyl part of a carbomethoxy group. In *cis* methyl cinnamate and in ethyl fumarate and maleate, the significance of the data is obscured by the steric strains and by the large electrostatic interactions. In *trans* methyl cinnamate, on the other hand, the strains and the electrostatic interactions are smaller, and the conjugation of the ethylenic double bond with the benzene ring apparently leads to a resonance energy of the usual magnitude.

TABLE 3·3

HEATS OF HYDROGENATION OF SUBSTANCES CONTAINING OXYGEN

Substance	Heat of Hydrogenation[a] (kilocalories)		Reference Substances[b]	Resonance Energy (kilocalories)
	Calculated	Observed		
Allyl alcohol	30.1	31.5	2	—
Crotonaldehyde	27.6	25.2	9	2.4
Methyl methacrylate	28.4	28.6	15	—
Ethyl maleate	28.6	34.0	8	—
Ethyl fumarate	27.6	29.8	9	—
Methyl cinnamate (cis)[c]	28.6	28.7	8	—
Methyl cinnamate (trans)[c]	27.6	24.7	9	2.9
Vinyl ether	60.6	57.2	3	3.4
Ethyl vinyl ether	30.3	26.7	3	3.6
2-Ethoxypropene	28.4	25.1	15	3.3
2-Methoxy-2-butene	26.9	24.8	19	2.1
Vinyl acetate	30.3	31.1	3	—
Furan	53.8	36.6	11	17.2

[a] See note a, Table 3·1.
[b] See note b, Table 3·2.
[c] See note c, Table 3·2.

A somewhat different type of resonance is illustrated by vinyl ether. The observed heat of hydrogenation here is 57.2 kcal per mole, which is less than twice the value for the analogous 1-butene. The difference of 3.4 kcal per mole may be due to the resonance among the structures XVIII, XIX, and XX. The effect is so small, however, that it cannot be

$$H_2C=CH-O-CH=CH_2 \qquad H_2\overset{..}{C^-}-CH=O^+-CH=CH_2$$
$$\text{XVIII} \qquad\qquad\qquad \text{XIX}$$

$$H_2C=CH-O^+=CH-\overset{..}{C^-}H_2$$
$$\text{XX}$$

accepted without some reserve, since there is no assurance that, even if vinyl ether could be exactly described by the single structure XVIII, its heat of hydrogenation would be exactly twice that of 1-butene. It is also surprising that the resonance energy of ethyl vinyl ether seems to be slightly greater than that of vinyl ether; it would have been expected to be smaller since only a single structure analogous to XIX and XX can be written for this substance. (For a possible explanation of this discrepancy, however, see page 160.) In vinyl acetate, on the other hand, an apparently similar type of structure seems to result in no resonance energy at all, the observed heat of hydrogenation being, in fact, higher than that calculated. The possibility cannot be excluded that in all these substances the actual resonance energies are negligibly small, and that the observed effects are due to some other factors which are not at present understood.

In view of the above uncertainties, it is fortunate that in furan a rather similar type of resonance produces a stabilization that is large enough to be beyond question. For this substance, the heat of hydrogenation is only 36.6 kcal per mole, as compared with 53.8 kcal for two moles of cyclopentene. The difference of 17.2 kcal apparently requires that resonance among the structures XXI–XXVI be involved. The first two of these structures, XXI and XXII, are of the type characteristic of any conjugated diene; resonance between them alone should therefore produce only a small resonance energy, as in cyclopentadiene. The structures XXIII and XXIV are analogous to XIX and XX; their contribution to the resonance energy is also presumably rather small, as in vinyl ether. The structures XXV and XXVI, however, have no close

$$
\begin{array}{ccc}
\overset{\displaystyle HC\text{—}CH}{\underset{\displaystyle \underset{O}{HC\quad CH}}{}} & \overset{\displaystyle HC\text{=}CH}{\underset{\displaystyle \underset{O}{HC\cdots CH}}{}} & \overset{\displaystyle HC\text{—}\overset{..}{C}\text{-}H}{\underset{\displaystyle \underset{O^{+}}{HC\quad CH}}{}} \\
\text{XXI} & \text{XXII} & \text{XXIII}
\end{array}
$$

$$
\begin{array}{ccc}
\overset{\displaystyle \overset{..}{HC}^{-}\text{—}CH}{\underset{\displaystyle \underset{O^{+}}{HC\quad CH}}{}} & \overset{\displaystyle HC\text{=}CH}{\underset{\displaystyle \underset{O^{+}}{H\text{-}C: \quad CH}}{}} & \overset{\displaystyle HC\text{=}CH}{\underset{\displaystyle \underset{O^{+}}{HC\quad :C\text{-}H}}{}} \\
\text{XXIV} & \text{XXV} & \text{XXVI}
\end{array}
$$

analogs in either cyclopentadiene or vinyl ether, and, moreover, are relatively stable since the formal charges have not been widely separated; they are therefore probably responsible for a large part of the comparatively great resonance energy of furan.

3·3 Resonance Energies from Heats of Combustion. Although the heats of hydrogenation provide the most accurate available data for the determination of resonance energies, they are not so extensive as might be desired. Recourse must therefore be had to other types of thermochemical data if the treatment is to be extended further. For this purpose, the heats of combustion are particularly useful since they have been measured for a large number of substances. They suffer, however, from the disadvantage of being subject to relatively large experimental errors. The reason for this limitation can be seen from the following example.

The heat of combustion of benzene is 789 kcal per mole, so that an error of 0.1 per cent would amount to 0.79 kcal per mole.   The heat of hydrogenation, on the other hand, is only 49.8 kcal per mole, so that a similar error of 0.1 per cent would amount to only 0.05 kcal per mole.   The same percentage error thus leads to about sixteen times as great an absolute error in the heat of combustion as in the heat of hydrogenation. This difficulty, which is encountered quite generally, is especially serious since relatively few thermochemical measurements can be relied upon to 0.1 per cent, and since many of the values in the literature may be in error by as much as 1 per cent or more.   It is evident then that the heats of combustion will be most useful in connection with the aromatic compounds, for which the resonance energies are large, and relatively unreliable for the simple conjugated systems like 1,3-butadiene, for which the resonance energies are smaller than the uncertainties in the data.

A second, and more serious disadvantage in the use of the heats of combustion for the determination of resonance energies arises from the fact that we do not now have any sufficiently accurate method for estimating what these heats would be if there were no resonance.   *Approximate* values, to be sure, can be obtained with the aid of the well-known empirical rule that, for substances to which unique structures can be assigned, the heats of combustion, Λ, can be expressed as the sums of certain contributions, $\lambda(A—B)$, which are characteristic of the various bonds, $A—B$, in the molecules, and which are at least roughly constant from substance to substance.   Moreover, these approximate values can often be materially improved by the introduction of a number of additional correction terms which are related to the structural features of the molecules of interest, and which are added to the sums of the $\lambda(A—B)$'s (for examples, see below).   Different authors have assigned different values to the various $\lambda(A—B)$'s and to the various corrections.[5]   Although

[5] See, for example, J. Thomsen, *Thermochemistry*, Longmans, Green & Co., London, 1908 (translated by K. A. Burke); W. Swietoslawski, *J. Am. Chem. Soc.* **42**, 1312 (1920); M. S. Kharasch, *Bur. Standards J. Research* **2**, 359 (1929); F. Klages, *Chem. Ber.* **82**, 358 (1949); R. S. Mulliken and R. G. Parr, *J. Chem. Phys.* **19**, 1271 (1951); V. M. Tatevskiĭ, V. V. Korobov, and E. A. Mendzheritskiĭ, *Doklady Akad. Nauk. S. S. S. R.* **74**, 743 (1950); **78**, 67 (1951) [*C. A.* **45**, 3232, 8869 (1951)]; V. M. Tatevskiĭ, *Zhur. Fiz. Khim.* **25**, 241 (1951) [*C. A.* **45**, 5988 (1951)]; *Doklady Akad. Nauk S. S. S. R.* **75**, 819 (1950) [*C. A.* **45**, 3233 (1951)]. Attention should be called also to L. Pauling, *The Nature of the Chemical Bond*, Cornell University Press, Ithaca, N. Y., 1st ed., 1939, pp. 53, 123; 2nd ed., 1940, pp. 53, 131; O. K. Rice, *Electronic Structure and Chemical Binding*, McGraw-Hill Book Co., New York, 1940, p. 190. In these last two references are given tables of bond energies, from which heats of combustion can be calculated. Cf. Section 3·4. Quite different sets of bond energies are given by G. Glockler, *J. Chem. Phys.* **21**, 1242, 1249 (1953); M. L. Huggins, *J. Am. Chem. Soc.* **75**, 4123 (1953).

these values are sometimes not in very good detailed agreement with each other, any one set, if used consistently, is usually found to be reasonably satisfactory. However, the error in the heat of combustion that is thus calculated for an individual valence-bond structure may amount to as much as 1–2 per cent, or more, of the total. Hence, this error may be of the same order of magnitude as the resonance energy itself; indeed, with a substance like a simple conjugated diene, it may be several times as great as the resonance energy.

In spite of the foregoing limitations, the heats of combustion have in practice provided a valuable, and often the only, source of data for the calculation of resonance energies. Consequently, we must here consider the ways which have been found most satisfactory for the estimation of heats of combustion. Of the several procedures which are now available, one of the most generally applicable is based upon a set of $\lambda(A—B)$'s and of corrections which have been derived by Klages.[5] The most important values from this set are listed, with a few minor changes, in Table 3·4. It is especially to be noted that these $\lambda(A—B)$'s and corrections can be applied only to molecules in which each atom exhibits its normal

TABLE 3·4

BOND CONTRIBUTIONS AND CORRECTIONS USED IN KLAGES'S METHOD FOR CALCULATING HEATS OF COMBUSTION[a]

Bond	Contribution (kilocalories)	Types of Compound in Which Used
C—H	54.0	All types
C—C	49.3	All types
C=C	121.2[b]	Ethylene
	119.1	Monosubstituted ethylenes
	117.4	*cis* 1,2-Disubstituted ethylenes, including 6-membered rings
	115.7	*cis* 1,2-Disubstituted ethylenes in 5-membered rings
	116.4	*trans* 1,2-Disubstituted ethylenes
	115.5[c]	1,1-Disubstituted ethylenes
	114.0[c]	Trisubstituted ethylenes
	112.0[c]	Tetrasubstituted ethylenes
C≡C	202.6[d]	Acetylene
	197.7	Monosubstituted acetylenes
	193.6	Disubstituted acetylenes
N—H	30.5	All types
C—N	33.0	All types
C=N	60.3	All types
C≡N	97.6	All types
O—H	7.5	Alcohols[e]
C—O	10.0	All types

TABLE 3·4 (contd.)

Bond	Contribution (kilocalories)	Types of Compound in Which Used
C=O	26.5[f]	Formaldehyde
	19.8	Other aldehydes
	13.5	Ketones
S—H	67.0	All types
C—S	69.0	All types
C—Cl	2.9	All types
C—Br	26.6[g]	All types
C—I	38.7[h]	All types

Correction for:		
tertiary carbon atom[i]	— 1.7 kcal
quaternary carbon atom	— 4.2
secondary alcohol	— 3.6
tertiary alcohol[j]	— 8.8
acetal[k]	— 3.0
methoxyl group	+ 3.0
5-membered ring	+ 6.0
6-membered ring	+ 1.0

[a] Except as noted, these figures are taken from F. Klages, *Chem. Ber.* **82**, 358 (1949).

[b] Klages's value is 121.6 kcal.

[c] Klages's value is slightly greater than the one given here since he made a correction of — 1.7 kcal for each carbon atom joined to three other carbon atoms. Cf. note *i*, below.

[d] Klages's value is 204.5 kcal.

[e] For water, the value is 5.25 kcal, or half the heat of vaporization. Cf. equations 1 and 2.

[f] Klages's value is 26.1 kcal.

[g] Klages's value is 21.7 kcal.

[h] Klages's value is 32.7 kcal.

[i] Klages uses this correction with every compound, including olefins, in which a carbon atom is linked to three other carbon atoms. We here restrict it, however, to *saturated* atoms and, with the unsaturated ones, we absorb it in the bond contribution. Cf. note *c*, above.

[j] Klages gives no correction for tertiary alcohols. The value listed here was chosen so as to obtain agreement with *tert*-butyl alcohol. See Table 3·5.

[k] Klages's value is — 11.8 kcal.

valence—that is to say, four for carbon, three for nitrogen, two for oxygen and sulfur, and one for hydrogen and the halogens—and to structures which contain no formal bonds. The heats of combustion to which these figures refer are the values of Λ which appear in the equations

$$C_a H_b O_c N_d S_e Cl_f Br_g I_h \text{ (gas)} + [a + (b - f)/4 + e - c/2]O_2 \text{ (gas)} \rightarrow$$
$$a CO_2 \text{ (gas)} + (b - f)/2 H_2 O \text{ (liq)} + d/2 N_2 \text{ (gas)} + e SO_2 \text{ (gas)}$$
$$+ f \text{ HCl (gas)} + g/2 Br_2 \text{ (vapor)} + h/2 I_2 \text{ (sol)} + \Lambda \text{ kcal} \qquad (1)$$

The substance of interest, $C_aH_bO_cN_dS_eCl_fBr_gI_h$, is always to be taken as gaseous. Data referring to other states can be used with the aid of the relation

$$\Lambda = \Lambda_x + \mu_x \tag{2}$$

where Λ_x and μ_x are the heats of combustion and vaporization, respectively, of the substance in the state x (solid or liquid). As with the heats of hydrogenation, this emphasis upon the gaseous state is for the purpose of avoiding the complications that arise from the large intermolecular interactions which are always present in solids and liquids. The remaining substances (oxygen, carbon dioxide, water, etc.) are arbitrarily taken in whatever states may be experimentally convenient. The fact that some of these (for example, water) may not be gaseous is of no moment, since the making of the necessary corrections would change both the "observed" heats of combustion and the values of the $\lambda(A—B)$'s in such a way that the agreement would not be affected. The combustions are assumed to occur at a constant pressure of 1 atm and at a temperature of 25°C.

Since the heats of combustion, Λ, that appear in equation 2 refer to a temperature of 25°C, the heats of vaporization, μ_x, that also appear in this equation should likewise refer to 25°C. For the estimation of these required values of μ_x, Klages[5] has suggested the following convenient method. The heat of vaporization, $\Delta H_v(t)$, of any unassociated liquid at its normal boiling point, t°C, is given, with an accuracy that is sufficient for our purposes, by Trouton's rule

$$\Delta H_v(t) = 0.021(273 + t) \text{ kcal per mole} \tag{3}$$

Moreover, the heat of vaporization, $\Delta H_v(25)$, of the *liquid* substance at 25°C must be equal to

$$\Delta H_v(25) = \Delta H_v(t) - \Delta C_p(t - 25) \tag{4}$$

where ΔC_p is the average value of the difference C_p (vapor) $-$ C_p (liquid) over the temperature range from 25°C to t°C; and C_p (vapor) and C_p (liquid) are, respectively, the molar heat capacities of the vapor and of the liquid at constant pressure. Combination of equations 3 and 4 now leads to the relation

$$\Delta H_v(25) = 5.733 + 25\Delta C_p + (0.021 - \Delta C_p)t \tag{5}$$

in which all energies are expressed in kilocalories per mole. Since a satisfactory value of ΔC_p seems to be about -0.015 kcal per mole degree, we obtain the final approximate equation

$$\Delta H_v(25) = (5.4 + 0.036t) \text{ kcal per mole} \tag{6}$$

The errors in the value of $\Delta H_v(25)$ which are thus obtained for unassociated liquids are usually of the order of a few tenths of a kilocalorie per mole, and they are seldom greater than 1 kcal per mole.   With associated liquids, however, equation 6 cannot be used without modification.   For both monohydric and polyhydric alcohols, Klages[5] gives the somewhat different equation

$$\Delta H_v(25) = (6.8 + 0.045t) \text{ kcal per mole} \qquad (7)$$

which corresponds to a Trouton constant of about 0.0266 kcal per mole degree, and to a value of ΔC_p equal to about -0.0184 kcal per mole degree; on the other hand, for phenols and for carboxylic acids, no analogous expressions are now available.   Evidently, therefore, any values of $\Delta H_v(25)$ that are estimated for substances of these latter types must be relatively unreliable.

If the substance of interest is a solid at 25°C, the heat of vaporization μ_x of equation 2, is the sum of the above $\Delta H_v(25)$ and the heat of fusion. In principle, the heat of fusion, like the heat of vaporization of the liquid, should be corrected to 25°C.   In practice, however, since this correction seems usually to be rather small, and since the necessary data are seldom available, the uncorrected heat of fusion at the melting point will hereafter be used.

Data are frequently given in the literature for reactions in which the products of combustion are different from those listed in equation 1, for example, H_2SO_4 (dil aq) in place of SO_2 (gas) for compounds containing sulfur.   Under such circumstances, the λ's of Table 3·4 cannot be used unless either they or the "observed" heats of combustion are corrected in a suitable manner.

The magnitudes of the errors that are introduced by the use of the $\lambda(A—B)$'s and corrections listed in Table 3·4 can be seen from a comparison of the second and third columns of Table 3·5.   The substances here considered are ones which are not ordinarily regarded as resonance hybrids, and which should therefore have essentially zero resonance energies.   They have been chosen more or less at random, but in such a way as to cover a fairly large number of different types of compound. (The effort has been made, however, to avoid substances, like carbon tetrachloride, in which the electrostatic interactions between nearby, highly polar groups might be important.)   It will be seen that the agreement is usually to within less than 1–2 per cent, and is sometimes quite good, but that the discrepancies are considerably larger than with the heats of hydrogenation.   Comparable small, but significant, errors must of course be presumed to be present also in the heats of combustion which are similarly estimated for the individual structures that are considered to contribute to the state of a resonance hybrid.   Clearly, therefore, the

TABLE 3·5

Substance	Heat of Combustion^a (kilocalories)		
	Observed^b	Calculated	
		K^c	F^d
Methane	212.798	216.0	—
Ethane	372.820	373.3	372.8
Propane	530.605	530.6	530.3
n-Butane	687.982	687.9	687.7
Isobutane	686.342	686.2	686.4
n-Pentane	845.16	845.2	845.1
Isopentane	843.24	843.5	843.8
Neopentane	840.49	841.0	840.5
2,2,3-Trimethylbutane	1155.94	1153.9	1156.5
n-Octane	1317.45	1317.1	1317.5
2,2,3,3-Tetramethylbutane	1313.27	1308.7	1313.6
2,3,4-Trimethylpentane	1315.29	1312.0	1315.7
2-Methyl-3-ethylpentane	1316.79	1313.7	1315.6
Cyclopentane	793.39	792.5	792.9
Cyclohexane	944.79	944.8	944.2
Ethylcyclohexane	1257.90	1256.7	1258.5
Ethylene	337.234	337.2	—
Propylene	491.987	492.4	492.0
1-Butene	649.757	649.7	649.4
cis 2-Butene	648.115	648.0	648.1
trans 2-Butene	647.072	647.0	647.1
Isobutylene	646.134	646.1	646.1
2-Methyl-2-pentene	959.26	959.2	959.1
Tetramethylethylene	958.31	957.2	958.3
2-Ethyl-3-methyl-1-butene	1117.06	1116.3	1117.1
Acetylene	310.615	310.6	310.6
1-Propyne	463.109	463.0	463.1
1-Butyne	620.86	620.3	620.6
2-Butyne	616.533	616.2	615.6
1-Octyne	1250.34	1249.5	1250.3
Methyl alcohol	182.6	179.5	178.7
Ethyl alcohol	336.8	336.8	336.2
Isopropyl alcohol	489.4$^{e, f}$	490.5	489.2
Isobutyl alcohol	649.2$^{e, f}$	649.7	649.7
tert-Butyl alcohol	642.6$^{e, f}$	642.6^g	639.1
Methyl ether	348.8	347.0	345.6
Ethyl ether	660.3^e	658.6	660.5
Allyl ether	906.6^e	896.8	898.8

TABLE 3·5 (contd.)

Substance	Heat of combustion[a] (kilocalories)		
	Observed[b]	Calculated	
		K[c]	F[d]
Formaldehyde	134.7	134.7	—
Acetaldehyde	285.0	285.1	285.0
Isobutyraldehyde	596.8[e, h]	598.0	598.5
Acetone	434.6[e]	436.1	435.3
Methyl isopropyl ketone	744.8[e, f]	749.0	748.9
Formaldehyde dimethylacetal	469.9[e, f]	469.0	467.9
Formaldehyde diethylacetal	783[e, f]	783.6	782.8
Acetaldehyde dimethylacetal	627.7[e, f]	626.3	628.0
Methyl chloride	164.8	164.9	164.8
Ethyl chloride	321.2	322.2	322.2
Methyl bromide	188.0	188.6	188.0
Ethyl bromide	345.9	345.9	345.4
Methyl iodide	201.4	200.7	201.1
Ethyl iodide	359.5[f]	358.0	358.5
Methylamine	258.1	256.0	257.5
Ethylamine	415.6	413.3	414.9
Dimethylamine	420.6	420.5	419.0
Diethylamine	730.6[e]	735.1	733.9
Trimethylamine	579·5[e]	585.0	578.4
Triethylamine	1044[e, f]	1056.9	1050.7
Methyl mercaptan	298.7	298.0	297.2
Ethyl mercaptan	455[f]	455.3	454.7
Methyl sulfide	457.1	462.0	455.4
Acetonitrile	311.3	308.9	310.0
Propionitrile	464.9[e, f]	466.2	467.5

[a] Of the gaseous substance.

[b] Except as noted, the data for the hydrocarbons are taken from F. D. Rossini, K. S. Pitzer, W. J. Taylor, J. P. Ebert, J. E. Kilpatrick, C. W. Beckett, M. G. Williams, and H. G. Werner, *Selected Values of Properties of Hydrocarbons*, U. S. Government Printing Office, Washington, D. C., 1947; those for the remaining substances are taken from F. D. Rossini, D. D. Wagman, W. H. Evans, S. Levine, and I. Jaffe, *Selected Values of Chemical Thermodynamic Properties*, U. S. Government Printing Office, Washington, D. C., 1952.

[c] Calculated by the method of Klages (see Table 3·4).

[d] Calculated by the method of Franklin (see Table 3·6).

[e] Taken from an unpublished table of heats of combustion, compiled by M. S. Kharasch and W. G. Brown.

[f] Heat of vaporization estimated with the aid of equation 6 or 7.

[g] See note *j* of Table 3·4.

[h] For this substance, Landolt-Börnstein gives the values 599.9 kcal.

TABLE 3·6

GROUP CONTRIBUTIONS AND CORRECTIONS USED IN FRANKLIN'S
METHOD FOR CALCULATING HEATS OF COMBUSTION[a]

Group[b]	Contribution (kilocalories)	Group[b]	Contribution (kilocalories)
—CH$_3$	186.41	$\overset{\mid}{-}$C=O	62.5
—CH$_2$—	157.443	—O— (ether)	− 27.2
$-\overset{\mid}{\underset{\mid}{C}}H-$	127.12	—NH$_2$	71.1
$-\overset{\mid}{\underset{\mid}{C}}-$	94.85	—NH—	46.2
—CH=CH$_2$	305.58	$-\overset{\mid}{N}-$	19.2[c]
—CH=CH— (trans)	274.25	—CN	123.6
—CH=CH— (cis)	275.30	—NC	138.5
$-\overset{\mid}{C}$=CH$_2$	273.31	—SH	110.8
$-\overset{\mid}{C}$=CH—	242.45	—S—	82.6
$-\overset{\mid}{C}=\overset{\mid}{C}-$	212.67	≡CH	155.31
—OH (primary)	− 7.7	≡C—	121.39
—OH (secondary)	− 10.7	—Cl[g]	− 21.6[d]
—OH (tertiary)	− 15.0	—Br[g]	1.6[d]
—CHO	98.6[h]	—I[g]	14.7[d]

Correction for: 3-membered ring　　　　　　　24.22 kcal
　　　　　　　　　4-membered ring　　　　　　　18.4
　　　　　　　　　5-membered ring　　　　　　　 5.68
　　　　　　　　　6-membered ring　　　　　　　− 0.45
　　　　　　　　　C$_2$H$_5$ side chain[e]　　　　　 0.8

3 adjacent —$\overset{\mid}{C}$H— groups　　　　　2.3

adjacent —$\overset{\mid}{C}$H— and —$\overset{\mid}{\underset{\mid}{C}}$—　　　2.5

adjacent —$\overset{\mid}{\underset{\mid}{C}}$— and —$\overset{\mid}{\underset{\mid}{C}}$—　　　5.4

—$\overset{\mid}{\underset{\mid}{C}}$— not adjacent to terminal —CH$_3$　1.7

TABLE 3·6 (*contd.*)

1,2-dimethyl or 1,3-methylethyl[f]	0.6 kcal
1,2-methylethyl or 1,2,3-trimethyl[f]	1.4
acetal of formaldehyde	$- 8^d$
acetal of any other aldehyde	$- 4^d$

[a] Except as noted, the values listed in this table are derived from, and are equivalent to, the frequently rather different ones given by J. L. Franklin, *Ind. Eng. Chem.* **41**, 1070 (1949) for the calculation of heats of *formation*. They refer to reactions at a constant pressure of 1 atm and at a temperature of 25°C.

[b] The valence bonds which, in this column, are represented by dashes, and which serve to join the groups to the remainders of the respective molecules, are to ·be considered linked to other groups that are listed in the table.

[c] The value of $- 19.2$ kcal given by Franklin (reference [a]) seems to be a misprint.

[d] This value is not given by Franklin in his table.

[e] A "side chain" is here defined as a chain of atoms which is linked to, but does not form a part of, the longest chain of carbon atoms in the molecule. For example, although *n*-butane has two ethyl groups, neither is a side chain; on the other hand, 3-ethylpentane has one ethyl side chain.

[f] As substituents joined to an aromatic ring.

[g] Joined to a *carbon* atom.

[h] For this group, the data of Franklin lead to a value of 94.3 kcal, which seems definitely too low. The value of 98.6 kcal, given here, is chosen so as to obtain agreement with acetaldehyde. See Table 3·5.

resonance energies that are calculated from such figures may often be quite unreliable.

The foregoing errors in the estimated heats of combustion can be made smaller if the calculations are further elaborated by the inclusion of additional corrections. There is, however, a practical limit to the accuracy that can thus be achieved for, as the number of empirical parameters is increased, the procedure becomes more complicated and less useful. Most authors have therefore been willing to accept rather large errors, or else they have restricted their attention to relatively small groups of similar compounds. The first of these alternatives was adopted, for example, by Pauling[5] and by Rice,[5] whose schemes are simpler, but less accurate, than the one of Klages; the second was adopted by Mulliken and Parr,[5] and by Tatevskiĭ, Korobov, and Mendzheritskiĭ,[5] who considered only the unstrained hydrocarbons.

A fairly satisfactory compromise between the irreconcilable demands of simplicity, accuracy, and generality has been reached by Franklin[6] in a slightly different approach to the problem. (However, see the paragraph below, in fine print.) When this further method of calculation is

[6] J. L. Franklin, *Ind. Eng. Chem.* **41**, 1070 (1949).

employed, the major part of the total heat of combustion, Λ, of any given substance is expressed as the sum of contributions, λ, which ordinarily are not related, as heretofore, to individual valence bonds, but which instead usually arise from somewhat larger groupings within the molecule; the remainder of the calculated heat of combustion is then provided by certain small corrections which are determined by the structural features of the molecule. In Table 3·6 are listed the most important of these group contributions and corrections, together with a few additional values which were not included in Franklin's compilation, but which are here supplied for the sake of greater completeness. The extent to which this more elaborate procedure improves the accuracy with which the heats of combustion can be estimated is shown by a comparison of the last three columns of Table 3·5. It will be seen that, for the hydrocarbons, the agreement between the observed and calculated values is now in general excellent; but that, for the compounds of the remaining types, it is little if any better than that obtained by the simpler method of Klages. Franklin's method is exceptionally successful in making proper allowances for the crowding of bulky groups in the molecules of such substances as 2,2,3,3-tetramethylbutane but, in most other respects, it apparently needs to be still further elaborated by the introduction of many additional corrections. We shall not here attempt, however, to develop any such more accurate, but also more complicated, procedure.

Inasmuch as Franklin[6] discussed only the heats and free energies of *formation*, and did not explicitly consider the heats of *combustion*, it is not strictly correct to speak of the above procedure as "Franklin's method." However, since the heats of formation and of combustion are so closely related that either can easily be obtained from the other (in the way described more fully in Sections 3·4 and 3·5), the calculations of the latter quantities are implicit in Franklin's paper. We shall, therefore, continue to describe such calculations as being in accordance with Franklin's method.

The use of the heats of combustion for the determination of the resonance energies can be illustrated with the example of benzene. Each of the Kekulé structures of this substance contains six carbon-hydrogen bonds, three carbon-carbon single bonds, and three *cis* carbon-carbon double bonds in a six-membered ring. Consequently, when the method of Klages is used, the calculated heat of combustion is

$$\Lambda_{calcd} = (6 \times 54.0) + (3 \times 49.3) + (3 \times 117.4) + 1.0 = 825.1 \text{ kcal}$$

Since the observed heat of combustion, however, is only 789.1 kcal (see Table 3·7), the resonance energy is seen to be 825.1 − 789.1, or 36.0 kcal. On the other hand, when Franklin's method of calculation is used, the

Kekulé structure is characterized by the presence of three *cis* —CH═CH— groups and of one six-membered ring.   The calculated heat of combustion is therefore

$$\Lambda_{calcd} = (3 \times 275.30) - 0.45 = 825.45 \text{ kcal}$$

so that the resonance energy now becomes 825.45 − 789.1, or 36.4 kcal.[7] These two values are in satisfactory agreement with each other, and also with the value of 36.0 kcal, found in Section 3·2, from the heats of hydrogenation.

The *empirical* resonance energies which are thus calculated for a number of further substances are listed in Table 3·7.   The observed heats of combustion from which they are derived have been corrected to the gaseous state when the published data refer to the solid or liquid states. Since experimental values for these corrections are seldom available, the approximate method for estimating heats of vaporization, which was described on pages 90f, has again been used whenever applicable.   The values that have thus been obtained are probably fairly accurate and may, in fact, be more reliable than many of the measured heats of combustion. In other instances, in which neither of the equations 6 and 7 can be used, the estimated heats of vaporization are little better than guesses; with no compound, however, should the error be greater than perhaps 5 kcal per mole.   The opportunities for individual judgment, both in making the corrections to the gaseous state and in selecting the original experimental data, are responsible for the fact that the heats of combustion given in Table 3·7 are often different from those given by other authors for the same substances.

Several of the individual values of the resonance energy deserve special comment.   With the simple conjugated dienes, these values are uniformly small and are, in fact, of the same order of magnitude as those which, in Section 3·2, were found for the same compounds.   Appreciable deviations do occur, however, presumably because the methods for predicting heats of combustion are less satisfactory than are the ones for predicting heats of hydrogenation.   It is therefore probable that, for these substances, the resonance energies in Table 3·2 are more trustworthy than those in Table 3·7.

With the aromatic hydrocarbons, the resonance energies are relatively large; this result is to be expected since, for any such compound, it is always possible to write two or more stable structures, which are at least approximately equivalent to each other.   The values found for benzene and for its alkyl derivatives are practically identical with those obtained from the heats of hydrogenation (see Table 3·2).   It is also gratifying

---

[7] J. L. Franklin, *J. Am. Chem. Soc.* **72**, 4278 (1950).

TABLE 3·7

HEATS OF COMBUSTION OF RESONANCE HYBRIDS

Substance	Heat of Combustion (kilocalories)			Resonance Energy (kilocalories)	
	Observed[a]	Calculated		K^b	F^c
	K^b	K^b	F^c		
1,3-Butadiene	608.5[d]	611.5	611.2	3.0	2.7
1,3-Cyclopentadiene	707.7[d]	709.3	713.7	1.6	6.0
2,3-Dimethyl-1,3-butadiene	917.3[d]	918.9	919.4	1.6	2.1
Benzene	789.1[e]	825.1	825.5	36.0	36.4
Toluene	943.6[e]	979.0	979.0	35.4	35.4
Ethylbenzene	1101.1[e]	1136.3	1136.4	35.2	35.3
n-Propylbenzene	1258.2[e]	1293.6	1293.9	35.4	35.7
Isopropylbenzene	1257.3[e]	1291.9	1292.5	34.6	35.2
o-Xylene	1098.5[e]	1133.6	1134.7	35.1	36.2
m-Xylene	1098.1[e]	1132.9	1132.6	34.8	34.5
p-Xylene	1098.3[e]	1132.9	1132.6	34.6	34.3
o-Ethyltoluene	1256.7[e]	1290.9	1292.9	34.2	36.2
1,2,3-Trimethylbenzene	1254.1[e]	1288.2	1290.6	34.1	36.5
Mesitylene	1252.5[e]	1286.8	1286.1	34.3	33.6
Hexamethylbenzene	1726.3[f]	1752.7	1759.6[g]	26.4	33.3
Diphenylmethane	1675.0[f]	1742.0	1743.1	67.0	68.1
9,10-Dihydroanthracene	1764.0[h]	1836.2	1837.0	72.2	73.0
Bibenzyl	1829.3[f]	1899.3	1900.5	70.0	71.2
Styrene	1060.0[f]	1098.1	1098.2	38.1	38.2
Stilbene (trans)	1781.5[f]	1858.4	1859.5	76.9	78.0
Biphenyl	1513.7[f]	1584.7	1585.2	71.0	71.5
Fluorene	1608.0[f]	1683.9	1685.7	75.9	77.7
1,3,5-Triphenylbenzene	2955.0[f]	3103.9	3104.7	148.9	149.7
Phenylacetylene	1034[i]	1068.7	1069.3	35	35
Diphenylacetylene	1756[i]	1827.6	1828.0	72	72
Naphthalene	1249.7[f]	1310.7	1310.9	61.0	61.2
Anthracene	1712.1[h]	1795.6	1795.8	83.5	83.7
Phenanthrene	1705.0[h]	1796.3	1797.4	91.3	92.4
Naphthacene	2170.6[h]	2280.6	2280.6	110.0	110.0
Benz[a]anthracene	2169.8[h]	2281.4	2282.3	111.6	112.5
Benzo[c]phenanthrene	2172.5[h]	2282.1	2283.8	109.6	111.3
Chrysene	2165.8[h]	2282.3	2284.2	116.5	118.4
Triphenylene	2164.4[h]	2282.1	2283.9	117.7	119.5
5,12-Dihydronaphthacene	2225.5[h]	2321.3	2322.0	95.8	96.5
9,10-Diphenylanthracene	3166.0[h]	3317.6	3321.5	151.6	155.5
9,9'-Bianthryl	3361.9[h]	3528.5	3532.2	166.6	170.3

TABLE 3·7 *(contd.)*

Substance	Heat of Combustion (kilocalories)			Resonance Energy (kilocalories)	
	Observed[a]	Calculated		K[b]	F[c]
		K[b]	F[c]		
Furan	506.9[f]	522.7	529.1	15.8	22.2
Thiophene	612.0[f]	640.7	639.7	28.7	27.7
Pyrrole	578.0[f]	599.2	602.5	21.2	24.5
Indole	1040[i]	1086.5	1088.5	47	49
Carbazole	1500[i]	1573.8	1574.5	74	75
Pyridine	674.7[s]	697.7	—	23.0	—
Quinoline	1136.9[f]	1184.2	—	47.3	—
Phenol	749[i]	785[j]	785[j]	36	36
Anisole	914[i]	950	950	36	36
Aniline	823.8[f]	862	864	38	40
Methylaniline	986.8[f]	1026	1025	39	38
Dimethylaniline	1155.8[f]	1191	1185	35	29
α-Naphthylamine	1283.6[f]	1348	1349	64	65
β-Naphthylamine	1283.9[f]	1348	1349	64	65
Diphenylamine	1553.8[f]	1632	1631	78	77
Benzaldehyde	856.1[f]	891	891	35	35
Acetophenone	1005.2[f]	1042	1042	37	37
Benzophenone	1576.4[f]	1648	1648	72	72
Benzoquinone	671.5[f]	676	675	4	3
Formic acid	75.7[e]	88[k]	90[k]	12	14
Acetic acid	220[e]	233[k, l]	234[k, l]	13	14
Propionic acid	378[i]	391[k, l]	391[k, l]	13	13
Isobutyric acid	531[i]	547[k, l]	547[k, l]	16	16
Phenylacetic acid	950[i]	996[k, l]	998[k, l]	46	48
Benzoic acid	791[i]	838[k, l]	840[k, l]	47	49
Methyl formate	241.1[e]	256	260	15	19
Methyl acetate	389[i]	407[l]	408[l]	18	19
Ethyl formate	398[i]	413	417	15	19
Ethyl acetate	548[i]	564[l]	566[l]	16	18
sec-Butyl butyrate	1169.6[f]	1192[l]	1194[l]	22	24
Methyl benzoate	956[i]	1013[l]	1014[l]	57	58
Ethyl benzoate	1112[i]	1170[l]	1172[l]	58	60
Formamide	150[e]	172	171	22	21
Acetamide	303[e]	319[l]	320[l]	16	17
Benzamide	870[i]	925[l]	926[l]	55	56
Formanilide	879[i]	938	939	59	60
Acetanilide	1033[i]	1089[l]	1088[l]	56	55

TABLE 3·7 (*contd.*)

Substance	Heat of Combustion (kilocalories)			Resonance Energy (kilocalories)	
	Observed[a]	Calculated		K[b]	F[c]
	K[b]	K[b]	F[c]		
Acetic anhydride	441[m]	470[l]	471[l]	29	30
Propionic anhydride	758[i]	784[l]	785[l]	26	27
Succinic anhydride	389[i]	417[l]	418[l]	28	29
Methyl carbonate	350[i]	379[l]	381[l]	29	31
Ethyl carbonate	656[i]	693[l]	696[l]	37	40
Urethan	412[i]	447[l]	450[l]	35	38
Urea	172[e]	202[l]	205[l]	30	33
Cyanogen	261.7[e]	245	247	—[n]	—[n]
o-Tolunitrile	1043[i]	1069	1071	26	28
Phenylpropiolic nitrile	1131[i]	1158	1159	27	28
Carbon dioxide	0.0	27[l]	—	27	—
Methyl isocyanate	276[i]	269	—	—[n]	—
Ethyl isocyanate	433[i]	426	—	—[n]	—
Cycloöctatetraene	1095[r]	1099	1101	4	6
Azulene	1279[o]	1312	1316	33	37
Tropolone	826[p]	847[q]	848[q]	21	22

[a] When necessary, these values have been corrected to the gas phase with the use of equations 6 and 7, above, and with the aid of any pertinent data given either in *Landolt-Börnstein* or in *International Critical Tables*.

[b] Calculated from the values listed in Table 3·4.

[c] Calculated from the values listed in Table 3·6.

[d] Calculated by combining the heat of hydrogenation of the diene with the heat of combustion of the corresponding paraffin. Cf. Tables 3·2 and 3·5.

[e] F. D. Rossini, K. S. Pitzer, W. J. Taylor, J. P. Ebert, J. E. Kilpatrick, C. W. Beckett, M. G. Williams, and H. G. Werner, *Selected Values of Properties of Hydrocarbons*, U. S. Government Printing Office, Washington, D. C., 1947; F. D. Rossini, D. D. Wagman, W. H. Evans, S. Levine, and I. Jaffe, *Selected Values of Chemical Thermodynamic Properties*, U. S. Government Printing Office, Washington, D. C., 1952.

[f] F. Klages, *Chem. Ber.* **82**, 358 (1949).

[g] The correction for six pairs of ortho methyl groups was here assumed to be equal to 3.6 kcal (cf. Table 3·6).

[h] A. Magnus, H. Hartmann, and F. Becker, *Z. physik .Chem.* **197**, 75 (1951).

[i] Taken from an unpublished table of heats of combustion compiled by M. S. Kharasch and W. G. Brown.

[j] The hydroxyl group is here treated as if in a *primary* alcohol. The reason for this choice is explained in the text (see pages 106f).

[k] The hydroxyl group is here treated as if in a *tertiary* alcohol or, with formic acid, in a *secondary* alcohol.

[l] The carbonyl group is here treated as if in a *ketone*.

[m] This value was obtained by combining that for acetic acid with the heat of hydrolysis of acetic anhydride. See J. B. Conn, G. B. Kistiakowsky, R. M. Roberts, and E. A. Smith, *J. Am. Chem. Soc.* **64**, 1747 (1942).

[n] The significance of this apparently *negative* value for the resonance energy is discussed in the text. (See pages 110f.)

[o] This value is calculated from the figures quoted by E. Heilbronner and K. Wieland, *Helv. Chim. Acta* **30**, 947 (1947). These authors used a different method for estimating the heat of combustion for a single contributing structure, and they derived the value of 46 kcal per mole for the resonance energy.

[p] G. R. Nicholson quoted by J. W. Cook, A. R. Gibb, R. A. Raphael, and A. R. Somerville, *J. Chem. Soc.* **1951**, 503. These authors derived a resonance energy of 28.6 kcal per mole. See also W. N. Hubbard, C. Katz, G. B. Guthrie, Jr., and G. Waddington, *J. Am. Chem. Soc.* **74**, 4456 (1952).

[q] No correction was made for the hydrogen bond (cf. page 139). The derived resonance energies are therefore perhaps a little too high.

[r] Cf. E. J. Prosen, W. H. Johnson, and F. D. Rossini, *J. Am. Chem. Soc.* **69**, 2068 (1947). For this substance, H. D. Springall, T. R. White, and R. C. Cass, *Trans. Faraday Soc.* **50**, 815 (1954) have derived a resonance energy of 4.8 kcal per mole.

[s] J. D. Cox, A. R. Challoner, and A. R. Meetham, *J. Chem. Soc.* **1954**, 265. For this substance, Klages (reference *f*) gives a heat of combustion of 697.7 kcal per mole, from which is obtained an empirical resonance energy of 27.9 kcal per mole.

that, with these latter substances, the resonance energies vary only slightly from compound to compound. This approximate constancy could have been anticipated since, in each instance, only the two Kekulé structures can have large weights; hence the nature of the resonance and the value of the resonance energy ought not to be significantly affected by the alkyl substituents. The largest deviation occurs with hexamethylbenzene, for which Klages's method of calculation gives a value that is about 10 kcal per mole lower than is found either for benzene itself or for its other homologs. This deviation, however, appears to be merely the result of the failure of Klages's method to make proper allowance for the crowding of the bulky methyl groups; at any rate, Franklin's method, which in this respect is somewhat better than Klages's, leads even here to a normal resonance energy. A further gratifying feature of the figures cited in Table 3·7 is that, within the limits of accuracy of the present treatment, the resonance energies found for compounds, such as diphenylmethane, with two *isolated* benzene rings per molecule, are just twice that of benzene.

In the earlier version of this book,[8] it was noted that, when the resonance energies of benzene and of its homologs were calculated from the heats of combustion, they

[8] G. W. Wheland, *The Theory of Resonance and Its Application to Organic Chemistry*, John Wiley & Sons, New York, 1944, Table 3·6 and p. 68.

were found to be too large, and to increase with the complexity of the molecule.   Thus, the reported values ranged from 41 kcal per mole for benzene to 50 kcal per mole for mesitylene.   As was there pointed out, however,[8] both the individual errors and the pronounced trend were due merely to the inadequacy of the method used for calculating the heats of combustion.   Consequently, when the more satisfactory methods that have subsequently been devised by Klages and by Franklin are used instead, the discrepancies are, as we have seen above, largely removed.

In styrene, the aromatic ring is conjugated with an ethylenic double bond; hence, the resonance can here include not only the two Kekulé structures I and II but also such further ones as III, IV, and V, which have

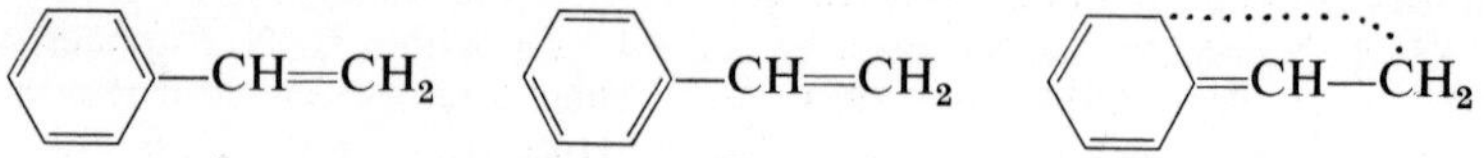

no close analogs either in benzene or in any of its alkyl derivatives. Since, however, these several additional structures contain formal bonds, they must be relatively unstable, and so they can have only small weights. Consequently, the resonance energy of styrene should not be much greater than that of benzene or of any of its homologs.   This expectation is indeed correct since the increase in resonance energy amounts to only some 2–4 kcal per mole.   The effect of the conjugation is therefore of the same order of magnitude here as in the simple conjugated dienes like 1,3-butadiene.   (Cf. also Table 3·2.)   There is, of course, a possibility that the resonance energy is actually the same for styrene as for benzene, and that the observed difference is merely an apparent one resulting from inaccuracies either in the experimental data or in the method of calculation (or in both).   However, since the corresponding increase of resonance energy is *trans* stilbene, in which the double bond is conjugated with *two* benzene rings, is approximately twice as great as that in styrene, the alternative view that these increases are in fact due to resonance with the quinoid structures III–V, and their analogs, seems quite logical.

In order to minimize the possibility of a more or less serious misunderstanding and confusion, let us here briefly recall a point that was brought out in our earlier discussion of terminology.   As was mentioned on pages 8f, we cannot take literally the statement that certain specified structures exert specified effects upon the hybrid to which they contribute.   Instead, we must interpret any such statement as meaning that the observed properties of the real molecule differ, in the particular way described, from those which analogy would lead us to expect for an (imaginary) molecule, to which the structures in question do not contribute.   Thus, when we say that the quinoid structures like III–V increase the resonance energy of styrene, we mean that styrene actually is more stable than we would have predicted it to be if we had assumed that it is a hybrid of only the two Kekulé structures I and II.

A further matter which also should be recalled here concerns the reason why, for example, we expect the resonance energy of styrene to be greater than that of benzene. The point is not that we can write a larger total number of structures for the former substance than for the latter, but rather that the structures which we can write for styrene include one which is completely analogous to each of those which we can write for benzene, and *in addition* still further ones (i.e., III–V) which have no analogs with benzene. (Cf. also page 82.)

In the molecule of biphenyl, the two benzene rings are conjugated with each other. Consequently, since resonance with such quinoid structures as VI and VII is therefore possible, we might here expect to find a

resonance energy that is slightly greater than twice that of benzene. No such effect, however, is observed. With the apparently analogous fluorene, on the other hand, there is an appreciable increase in resonance energy. As will be more fully explained in Section 4·2, the difference between these two hydrocarbons may perhaps be due to the restriction of rotation about the bond that joins the aromatic rings in the latter substance.

Conjugation of a phenyl group with an acetylenic triple bond, as in phenylacetylene and diphenylacetylene, apparently leads to a negligibly small, or even zero, additional stabilization. The reason for this difference between a triple bond and a double one is not immediately apparent. We may, however, note that each of the quinoid structures like VIII contains

an allenic system of cumulative double bonds and hence should be relatively less stable than is the otherwise analogous one V. (Cf. also page 111.)

It may be suggested that the stability of each quinoid structure like VIII is further decreased by strain, since the normal value for a C=C—H bond angle is about 120° whereas, in the actual molecule of phenylacetylene, the terminal hydrogen atom is doubtless collinear with the two acetylenic carbon atoms. There is, however, no reason to suppose that the usual bond angles are here significant. The value of 120° just cited applies when the carbon atom to which the hydrogen atom is bonded takes part in four *effective* bonds; in structure VIII, on the other hand, this atom takes part in only three effective bonds in addition to the one formal bond. Since the formal bond is of essentially zero strength, the strain in structure VIII may well be quite negligible.

The resonance energy of naphthalene is appreciably greater than that of benzene, but it is definitely less than twice as great. This conclusion is entirely consistent with the view that the substance is a hybrid receiving large contributions from the Erlenmeyer and Erdmann structures IX–XI, and (presumably) smaller ones from a considerable number of less stable structures, like XII and XIII, with formal bonds. Indeed, if the resonance

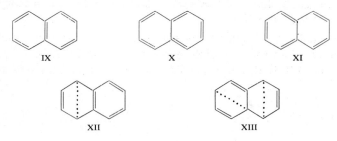

could be restricted to only those structures in which, as in IX, XI, and XII, carbon atoms 1 and 2 (at the top right of the figures) and likewise carbon atoms 3 and 4 (at the bottom right) are linked to each other by double bonds, the situation would then be just like that in benzene, or in one of its homologs, and the resonance energy should be the same as that of benzene, or of a homolog. There is, however, no way in which the resonance can be thus restricted. Since naphthalene is therefore a hybrid, not only of all these specified structures but also of many additional ones (including the relatively stable structure X), the resonance energy must be, as is observed, greater than that of benzene. (Cf. the discussion of styrene on pages 102f.) On the other hand, since the two rings in the naphthalene molecule have two atoms in common and so are not independent of each other, the possibilities for resonance are less than in, say, diphenylmethane. Consequently, the resonance energy should be, as again is observed, less than twice that of benzene.

With the higher condensed aromatic hydrocarbons, such as anthracene, phenanthrene, etc., the resonance energies are still greater and, in general, they increase by some 20–30 kcal per mole for each additional aromatic ring. As should now require no further comment, this increase in resonance energy can be related to the increased possibilities for resonance. A comparison of isomeric hydrocarbons containing the same total number of aromatic rings shows that the resonance energy is highly dependent also upon the arrangement of the rings. Thus, phenanthrene is more stable than anthracene by about 8–9 kcal per mole, and triphenylene is more stable than naphthacene by about the same amount. As in these examples, the resonance energy seems always to increase with what may be called the *angularity* of the hydrocarbon.

Since the number of the particularly stable structures without formal bonds can be shown[9] also to increase with the angularity, one is naturally tempted to assume that the magnitude of the resonance energy is primarily determined by the number of these structures. Although such an assumption seems rather logical, it is probably not justified for, with the more complex hydrocarbons, the structures with formal bonds become extremely numerous, and their total contribution to the state of the hybrid can be shown greatly to outweigh that of the individually more stable structures without formal bonds. Moreover, there are even instances in which a less stable structure makes a larger contribution than does a more stable one. (Cf. pages 23f.)

The molecule of 5,12-dihydronaphthacene contains a benzene ring and, "insulated" from it by two saturated methylene groups, a naphthalene grouping. Since these two aromatic systems are therefore independent of each other, the resonance energy of the substance should be equal to the sum of the resonance energies of benzene and of naphthalene. This expectation is supported by the figures listed in Table 3·7. On the other hand, the molecules of 9,10-diphenylanthracene and of 9,9'-bianthryl contain aromatic systems that are conjugated with each other. With each of these substances, there appears to be no corresponding increase in stability if Klages's method of calculation is used, but a small increase if Franklin's method is used. In any event, the effects are so small in comparison with the total heats of combustion that no great significance can be assigned to them.

The resonance energy of furan agrees reasonably well with the value found from the heat of hydrogenation. The discrepancy is, however, rather larger when Franklin's method of calculation is used than when Klages's is used. As might have been expected from a comparison of the relative stabilities of the compounds, as reflected in their observed chemical properties, the resonance energy of thiophene is appreciably greater than is that of furan, even though the possibilities for resonance appear to be essentially the same in the two substances (see page 86). It has, however, been suggested[10] that, since the octet rule does not rigorously apply to sulfur, thiophene may receive significant contributions from structures like XIV, in which the sulfur atom has ten electrons in

$$
\begin{array}{c}
HC = CH \\
| \qquad | \\
HC \diagdown \;\; \ddot{}\;\; \diagup CH \\
S
\end{array}
$$

XIV

[9] See, for example, G. W. Wheland, *J. Chem. Phys.* **3**, 356 (1935); A. Pullman, Thèses présentées à la Faculté des Sciences de l'Université de Paris, Masson et Cie., Paris, 1946, pp. 11ff.

[10] V. Schomaker and L. Pauling, *J. Am. Chem. Soc.* **61**, 1769 (1939); H. C. Longuet-Higgins, *Trans. Faraday Soc.* **45**, 173 (1949).

its valence shell. Inasmuch as the oxygen atom of furan could not similarly expand its octet, the difference between this substance and thiophene may thus be explained. It should, however, be noted that no similar interpretation can be proposed for the observation that the resonance energy of pyrrole is also rather larger than that of furan, although smaller than that of thiophene. Indole and carbazole, with their condensed ring systems, need not be specially discussed here since they are related to the corresponding monocyclic substances, benzene and pyrrole, in very much the same way as that in which naphthalene and anthracene are related to benzene. Pyridine and quinoline do not differ in any respect that is important here from their respective carbocyclic analogs, benzene, and naphthalene.

On the basis of the figures given in Table 3·7, the resonance energy of phenol is seen to be slightly greater than the average for benzene and its homologs. The increase in stability which thus appears to result from the attachment of the hydroxyl group to an unsaturated carbon atom is of the order of magnitude that might have been expected from a comparison with the structurally analogous vinyl ethers that were discussed in Section 3·2. Moreover, as we shall see in later chapters, a number of the characteristic chemical properties of phenol can be most easily interpreted if this substance is assumed to be a hybrid of not only the Kekulé (and Dewar) structures, but also of the quinoid structures XV, XVI, and XVII. Unfortunately, however, we cannot have much confidence in the accuracy of the value 36 kcal per mole, which is here assigned

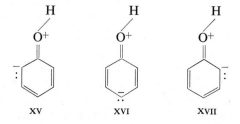

to the resonance energy. The difficulty arises because, both in the treatment of Klages and in that of Franklin, the contribution of a hydroxyl group to the total heat of combustion depends upon the nature of the carbon atom to which that group is bonded (cf. Tables 3·4 and 3·6). As a result of this dependence, the calculated resonance energy of phenol is found, by the method of Klages, to be 36 kcal per mole if the substance is regarded as a *primary* alcohol, 33 kcal per mole if it is regarded as a *secondary* alcohol, or 27 kcal per mole if it is regarded as a *tertiary* alcohol; similarly, the resonance energies obtained by the method of

Franklin are, respectively, 36, 33, and 29 kcal per mole.   None of these values, however, is strictly applicable since phenol is not an alcohol belonging to any one of the three types.   It might seem most logical to think of this substance as a tertiary alcohol, inasmuch as the carbon atom that carries the hydroxyl group is not directly bonded to even a single hydrogen atom.   Then, however, the resonance energy is less than that of benzene and so, on theoretical grounds, is quite unacceptable.   On the other hand, we might have some justification for thinking of phenol as a secondary alcohol, inasmuch as the carbon atom that carries the hydroxyl group is directly bonded to exactly two other carbon atoms.   The resonance energy is then essentially identical with that of a benzene homolog.   Although this value is not theoretically impossible, it nevertheless seems somewhat unlikely since, for the reasons mentioned above, the effects of the quinoid structures XV, XVI, and XVII are expected to be detectable, though small.   For this reason, we have arbitrarily treated phenol as if it were a primary alcohol.   Such a procedure can be justified only because it leads to the particular conclusion which, at the outset, we expected finally to reach.   Since the argument is therefore largely, if not entirely, circular, we can have little confidence that the resonance energy of phenol is indeed slightly greater than that of benzene.

With anisole, aniline, and all the other substances in which atoms with unshared pairs of electrons are directly joined to benzene rings, the situations are similar to the one just discussed.   These substances, like phenol, appear to have resonance energies that are slightly greater than can be accounted for by merely the resonance in the isolated aromatic rings which they contain.   Consequently, it is possible that quinoid structures analogous to XV, XVI, and XVII here also make appreciable contributions to the states of the respective molecules.   Once more, however, the interpretation of the data is far from clear, since the observed effects are small, and since the uncertainties in the calculated heats of combustion are large.   Klages and Franklin, to be sure, give no corrections which are to be used when secondary or tertiary carbon atoms are joined to oxygen atoms in ethers or to nitrogen atoms in amines.   This fact, however, does not imply that such corrections are unnecessary, but rather than their values cannot at present be reliably determined.   Only after the heats of combustion have been measured with high accuracy for a large number of different compounds can this situation be materially improved.   The maximum conclusion which can at present be drawn is therefore that the data presented in Table 3·7 are consistent with the view, but do not prove, that the resonance energies of anisole, aniline, etc., like that of phenol, are slightly increased by resonance with quinoid structures. (See also pages 372f.)

The conjugation of a carbonyl group with a benzene ring, as in benz-aldehyde and acetophenone, or with an ethylenic double bond, as in *p*-benzoquinone, would be expected to result in some stabilization. The results obtained in the study of heats of hydrogenation (see Section 3·2) have shown, however, that the effect is here rather small and often is no larger than the uncertainties in either the measured or the calculated heats of combustion. We should therefore not be surprised that, from an examination of Table 3·7, we cannot be completely sure whether the expected stabilization does or does not exist.

With the carboxylic acids, the only conventional structures that can be written are the ones of the type XVIII. The further structures XIX may also be involved in the resonance, but the weights of these in the ground states of the respective hybrids ought not be very great; for, although XVIII and XIX contain the same numbers of the same kinds of bonds,

             XVIII   XIX

the structures XIX must be made relatively unstable by their wide separ-ations of charge (cf. pages 21f). Consequently, we might expect that, with the purely aliphatic compounds like formic and acetic acids, the resonance energies should be small; and that, with the aromatic com-pounds like benzoic and phenylacetic acids, the resonance energies should be only slightly greater than can be accounted for by the presence of the benzene rings. The rather large values that in Table 3·7 are listed for these compounds are therefore somewhat surprising. A possible explan-ation for this unexpected result (however, see below) is that the heats of combustion which are calculated for the structures XVIII may be too high. Thus, if the *correct* calculated value for propionic acid were, say, 380 instead of 391 kcal per mole, then the derived resonance energy would be reduced to only 2 kcal per mole. There are, in fact, valid reasons for questioning the accuracy of these calculated heats of com-bustion. Thus, with formic acid, the structure XVIII (R = H) does not exactly correspond to either an aldehyde or a secondary alcohol; con-sequently, the calculations for this substance (cf. footnote *k* of Table 3·7) are not rigorously valid. Similarly, with the higher acids, the structures XVIII (R ≠ H) do not exactly correspond to either ketones or tertiary alcohols; consequently, the calculations for these substances (cf. footnotes *k* and *l* of Table 3·7) are also not rigorously valid. The reason why formic acid was thus treated as both an aldehyde and a secondary alcohol was that, since its homologs were treated as both ketones and tertiary alcohols (see below), this procedure seemed to be the one most consistent with the structural relationships among the several substances. The reason why the higher acids were treated as both ketones and tertiary alcohols was that this procedure leads to the lowest possible values for the calculated heats of combustion, and hence also for the resonance energies. There is, however, no assurance that a still more accurate treatment would not lead to still smaller values. Since the group contributions and corrections which are listed in Tables 3·4 and 3·6 vary rather widely with the environments of the carbonyl and hydroxyl groups, it would not be at all surprising if the calculated values given in Table 3·7 for the carboxylic acids are too high. In particular, one might with some justification argue that the corrections for the acetal groupings (cf. Tables 3·4 and 3·6) should here be made since, like an acetal, a carboxylic acid contains a carbon atom bonded to two different oxygen atoms.

As we have just seen, we can advance fairly convincing arguments to show that the resonance energies of the carboxylic acids may not really be as great as is indicated in Table 3·7. There is still, however, a possibility that the methods of calculation are not seriously in error after all, and that the resonance energies are indeed rather large. Although, for the reasons that have already been stated, such an eventuality would be somewhat surprising, a certain amount of independent experimental evidence can nevertheless be brought forward to support it. This evidence cannot here be described but, in subsequent chapters, it will be discussed in greater detail. (See pages 160 and 235ff.) For the present, therefore, we can conclude only that the treatment of the carboxylic acids is rather uncertain.

The resonance energies of the alkyl esters of carboxylic acids ought to be approximately equal to those of the parent acids, since the possibilities for resonance in the two types of compound are essentially the same. In Table 3·7, to be sure, the esters are assigned appreciably larger resonance energies than are the acids from which they are derived. These differences, however, are probably not real; for, although negative corrections for the secondary and tertiary carbon atoms that are bonded to oxygen atoms were made with the acids, no corresponding corrections were made with the esters. Consequently, the treatments of the acids and of their esters were not equally refined, and so their results are not strictly comparable.

For an acid amide, one can write not only the conventional structure XX, but also the doubtless much less stable one XXI. Since the relation

$$R-C\overset{\displaystyle O}{\underset{\displaystyle NH_2}{<}} \qquad\qquad R-C\overset{\displaystyle O^-}{\underset{\displaystyle N^+H_2}{<}}$$

XX   XXI

between these two structures is similar to that between XVIII and XIX, we may anticipate that the resonance energy of the amide will not be very different from that of an analogous acid or ester. This expectation is indeed consistent with the values cited in Table 3·7; we must realize, however, that these values are subject to the same sorts of uncertainty which were considered in the preceding paragraphs. Consequently, although we can be fairly sure that the resonance energies of the amides are greater than zero, we can have little confidence in their exact magnitudes.

The resonance in an acid anhydride can include, in addition to the conventional structure XXII, also the *two* less stable ones XXIII and XXIV. Since each of these last structures is analogous to XIX, we can

$$
\underset{\text{XXII}}{R-\overset{\overset{\textstyle O}{\|}}{C}-O-\overset{\overset{\textstyle O}{\|}}{C}-R}
\qquad
\underset{\text{XXIII}}{R-\overset{\overset{\textstyle O^{-}}{|}}{C}=O^{+}-\overset{\overset{\textstyle O}{\|}}{C}-R}
\qquad
\underset{\text{XXIV}}{R-\overset{\overset{\textstyle O}{\|}}{C}-O^{+}=\overset{\overset{\textstyle O^{-}}{|}}{C}-R}
$$

readily understand why the resonance energies of these substances appear to be greater than those of the related acids. Again, however, the exact values are somewhat uncertain.

Alkyl carbonates, like acid anhydrides, have increased possibilities for resonance, since they can be assumed to be hybrids of the three structures XXV, XXVI, and XXVII. The resonance energies are again therefore

$$
\underset{\text{XXV}}{R-O-\overset{\overset{\textstyle O}{\|}}{C}-O-R}
\qquad
\underset{\text{XXVI}}{R-O^{+}=\overset{\overset{\textstyle O^{-}}{|}}{C}-O-R}
\qquad
\underset{\text{XXVII}}{R-O-\overset{\overset{\textstyle O^{-}}{|}}{C}=O^{+}-R}
$$

larger than with the esters of the monobasic acids. For the same reason, the resonance energies of urethan and of urea are also relatively large. As with the above analogs of these substances, however, the significance of the treatment is decreased by the unavoidable uncertainties in the method of calculation.

Cyanogen, like 1,3-butadiene, should have a small but appreciable resonance energy. The value of about -15 kcal per mole, which can be derived from the data in Table 3·7, is therefore unexpected. This value, however, is certainly incorrect since a negative resonance energy is theoretically impossible. The explanation for the present discrepancy is undoubtedly that both of the methods for calculating the heat of combustion are here rather seriously inaccurate. It is not surprising that these methods should fail with cyanogen, since the structure of this substance is significantly different from that of any of the other cyanides with which it is being compared. In particular, since the cyano group is associated with a very large dipole moment (cf. Chapter 5), and since the two dipoles have their positive ends adjacent, the stability of the molecule must be considerably decreased by the unfavorable distribution of electric charge.

The resonance energies found for o-tolunitrile and for phenylpropiolic nitrile are likewise unexpected, and doubtless incorrect, since each is smaller than that of benzene. The difficulty here may lie either in the methods of calculation or in the experimental heats of combustion. No definite conclusion seems at present to be possible.

Carbon dioxide appears to have a surprisingly large resonance energy even though, in order to obtain the smallest possible value, we have here treated the two carbonyl groups as if they were ketonic. It is, of course, quite possible that, since carbon dioxide is not in fact a diketone, the calculated heat of combustion which is thus obtained for the structure XXVIII is still considerably too large. There seems little possibility,

$$O=C=O$$
XXVIII

however, that the error in the calculation can be as great as 27 kcal per mole. Moreover, the error that does exist may well be in such a direction as to increase, rather than to decrease, the derived resonance energy. The carbon atom of carbon dioxide forms two double bonds and so, in this respect, resembles the central carbon atom of allene. Now, since the heat of hydrogenation of allene is 71.3 kcal per mole[11] whereas that of 1,4-pentadiene is only 60.8 kcal per mole (cf. Table 3·2), we can conclude that the presence of such a system of *cumulative* double bonds leads to a loss of stability. If we "correct" the calculated heat of combustion of carbon dioxide in order to take this effect into account, we obtain a still larger resonance energy of about 38 kcal per mole. Apparently, therefore, we must accept the conclusion that carbon dioxide really is appreciably more stable than we would have expected a substance with the structure XXVIII to be. The problem of explaining this high stability remains to be considered. In the first place, it may be noted that the symbol XXVIII does not represent just one structure, as has hitherto been assumed, but that instead it represents two different though equivalent structures, which must be assigned equal weights in the resonance (see the following paragraphs in fine print). Quite possibly, therefore, the major part of the resonance energy is due to the resonance which is thus

[11] G. B. Kistiakowsky, J. R. Ruhoff, H. A. Smith, and W. E. Vaughan, *J. Am. Chem. Soc.* **58**, 146 (1936).

already implied in the symbol XXVIII. A second type of resonance, which involves the further, much less stable structures XXIX and XXX is

$$^-O—C{\equiv}O^+ \qquad\qquad\qquad ^+O{\equiv}C—O^-$$

XXIX   XXX

probably less important than the foregoing (cf. the discussion of the isocyanates, below).

The familiar symbolism of structural organic chemistry is inadequate for the description of the difference between the two structures that are represented by the single diagram XXVIII. This distinction can, in fact, be precisely stated only in quantum-mechanical terms.[12] The following discussion may serve, however, to demonstrate the existence of the two structures even though it may not make their exact natures entirely clear. As was mentioned in Section 2·10, the carbon-carbon double bond in ethylene may be considered to consist of one sigma and one pi component. Similarly, each of the two carbon-oxygen double bonds in structure XXVIII for carbon dioxide may also be considered to consist of one sigma and one pi component. Now, in order to describe the charge distributions in these latter bonds, let us use dots to designate electrons that are assigned to sigma orbitals, but either asterisks or small open circles to designate electrons that are assigned to pi orbitals. As is implied by this method of representation, there are two different types of pi orbital which must here be distinguished from each other. (There are also different kinds of sigma orbital, but, for our present purposes, these do not have to be similarly distinguished.) For definiteness, we may specify that the carbon dioxide molecule lies on the z axis of a Cartesian coordinate system; that an electron depicted by an asterisk can be found, with equal probabilities, on either side of the xz plane but can never be found in that plane; and that an electron depicted by an open circle can be found, with equal probabilities, on either side of the yz plane but can never be found in that plane. These conventions can be made more concrete by reference to Figure 2·7, Section 2·10. If the two nuclei are here considered to lie on the z axis, and if the plane of the paper is taken as the xz plane, then an electron occupying either of the two atomic pi orbitals that are shown would be represented by an open circle. The further atomic pi orbitals, which were not considered in our earlier discussion of ethylene, but which become important with the *linear* molecule of carbon dioxide, are obtained from those of Figure 2·7 by a rotation of 90° about the internuclear axis, so that one of the closed surfaces lies on each side of the plane of the paper; an electron occupying such an orbital would be represented by an asterisk. With the aid of the definitions that have just been stated, the two structures that are implied by the single symbol XXVIII become XXXI and XXXII. These are clearly

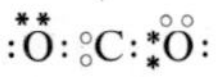

$$ \overset{**}{:}\!\overset{}{O}:{}_{\circ}^{\circ}C:{}^{*}_{*}\!\overset{}{O}: \qquad\qquad :\overset{\circ}{O}:{}^{*}_{*}C:{}_{\circ}^{\circ}\overset{**}{O}: $$

XXXI 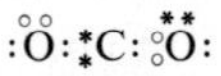   XXXII

equivalent to each other since either is transformed into the other by a rotation of 90° about the molecular axis. Since the Pauli exclusion principle (cf. Section 9·7) makes it impossible for any atom to be associated with more than two electrons that are represented either by asterisks or by open circles, there are no additional structures corresponding to the symbol XXVIII.

[12] See, for example, C. A. Coulson, *Valence*, Oxford University Press, Oxford, 1952, pp. 211f. A discussion from the molecular-orbital viewpoint has also been given by R. S. Mulliken, *J. Chem. Phys.* **3**, 720 (1935).

Although the conventional diagram XXVIII thus implies two distinguishable structures, each of the further diagrams XXIX and XXX is unique since the respective, more detailed representations XXXIII and XXXIV can be shown to correspond to charge

$$-: \overset{\bullet\bullet}{\underset{\circ\circ}{O}} : C : \overset{\circ}{\underset{\bullet}{O}} : ^+ \qquad\qquad +: O : \overset{\circ}{\underset{\bullet}{C}} : \overset{\bullet\bullet}{\underset{\circ\circ}{O}} : ^-$$

XXXIII   XXXIV

distributions which are cylindrically symmetric about the molecular axis, and which accordingly are unaffected by any rotation about that axis.

The alkyl isocyanates are structurally somewhat analogous to carbon dioxide; consequently, the former substances might be expected, like the latter one, to have fairly large resonance energies. As is readily seen, however, this expectation is not in agreement with the values reported in Table 3·7. In fact, since the heats of combustion which are calculated for the isocyanates are actually lower than are the ones observed, the resonance energies appear here to be less than zero. Such negative values are, however, unacceptable. A partial explanation of this discrepancy is doubtless that the isocyanates contain cumulative double bonds, and hence that the above calculated heats of combustion may be as much as 11 kcal per mole too low (see above). In this way, the derived resonance energies can indeed be made positive, as they must be, but they can hardly be increased enough so that they become comparable with that of carbon dioxide. The data therefore strongly suggest that, in spite of their apparent resemblance, the structures of the isocyanates and of carbon dioxide must differ in some fundamental respect. It can in fact be shown (see the following paragraph) that, although the familiar diagram XXVIII for carbon dioxide corresponds to two different, but equivalent, stable structures, the superficially analogous diagram XXXV for an isocyanate

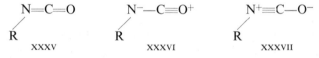

XXXV   XXXVI   XXXVII

corresponds to one stable and one extremely unstable structure. Consequently, as far as these two structures are concerned, only a small resonance energy can be expected. Furthermore, this conclusion need not be changed if the resonance is considered to include also the additional, relatively unstable structures XXXVI and XXXVII. In fact, these latter structures should have an even smaller effect upon the properties of an isocyanate than their analogs, XXIX and XXX, have upon those of carbon dioxide; for, although XXXVI is presumably comparable to XXIX and XXX in stability, XXXVII must be made especially unstable by the strain that results from the nonlinearity of the molecule. Once more, therefore, we see that the resonance energy of an alkyl isocyanate should be small.

It was stated above that the symbol XXXV for an isocyanate corresponds to one stable and one extremely unstable structure. These two structures, which can be written in greater detail as XXXVIII and XXXIX, respectively, are readily seen to be not

$$\text{R}\diagup\overset{\circ\circ}{\text{N}}:\overset{**}{\text{C}}:\overset{**}{\text{O}}:\qquad\qquad\text{R}\diagup\overset{**}{\text{N}}:\overset{\circ}{\text{C}}:\overset{\circ\circ}{\text{O}}:$$

$$\text{XXXVIII}\qquad\qquad\qquad\text{XXXIX}$$

equivalent to each other. The nitrogen, carbon, and oxygen atoms are here presumed to lie on the z axis; the group R is presumed to lie in the xz plane; and the dots, asterisks, and open circles have the same meanings as before. Consequently, the electrons of the unshared pair on the nitrogen atom are concentrated in the plane of the paper in structure XXXVIII, but in a plane perpendicular to that of the paper in structure XXXIX. Although structure XXXVIII therefore involves only as much strain as is inherent in its system of cumulative double bonds (see above), structure XXXIX must involve a large additional strain since its charge distribution is such that the group R would normally lie in the yz plane, rather than in the xz plane as is here assumed. Inasmuch as we can accordingly assign only a small weight to structure XXXIX, the situation is here quite different from that in carbon dioxide, where the two structures XXXI and XXXII are equivalent and so must be assigned equal, large weights. One may object that, if only the R—N—C bond angle were 180°, the structures XXXVIII and XXXIX would then be equivalent, just like the corresponding ones for carbon dioxide; in such an event, however, *both* structures would be rather highly strained, and so again no great stability would be expected. (See also page 180.)

It would be interesting to have a value for the resonance energy of carbon monoxide since, for this substance, there can be written altogether three structures that look fairly reasonable. Two of these structures are completely equivalent to each other, and can be represented by the single symbol XL (cf. the paragraphs in fine print above); the third structure,

$$:\text{C}\overset{**}{=\!=}\text{O}:\qquad\qquad\qquad:\text{C}^-\!\!\equiv\!\!\text{O}:^+$$

$$\text{XL}\qquad\qquad\qquad\qquad\text{XLI}$$

XLI, requires a separation of electric charge, but it should still be comparatively stable since it contains an additional covalent bond. Unfortunately, however, no reliable value for the resonance energy can be obtained. Since the carbon atom is here in an exceptional valence state in each of the three contributing structures, there is no way in which the heat of combustion can be calculated. Consequently, the present method cannot be used. From a consideration of bond energies (see Section 3·4), Pauling has concluded that the resonance energy is 58 kcal per mole.[13] Although this value is perhaps not unreasonable, we can have little confidence that it is even approximately correct; for, even though its derivation does not explicitly require that the heat of combustion be calculated, it nevertheless implicitly involves the certainly incorrect

[13] L. Pauling, *The Nature of the Chemical Bond*, Cornell University Press, Ithaca, N. Y., 1st ed., 1939, p. 128; 2nd ed., 1940, p. 136.

assumption that the carbonyl group in either of the two structures represented by the symbol XL is just like one in a ketone. (See also pages 118f.)

The last three compounds listed in Table 3·7 are cycloöctatetraene,
azulene, and tropolone. Since these substances present certain special
problems with which we are not yet in position to deal, we shall postpone
until Section 3·9 the discussion of the types of resonance which are here
involved.

3·4 Resonance Energies from Bond Energies. For the determination
of resonance energies from heats of combustion, the method of Klages
can be replaced by an alternative, less direct one. (The corresponding
modification of Franklin's method is described in Section 3·5.) This
further procedure, which involves the use of the so-called *bond energies*,
is essentially equivalent to Klages's, and so it seldom leads to any information which could not have been obtained equally well by the original,
simpler method. (Cf., however, the next-to-last paragraph of the preceding section, and also Section 3·6.) We shall here, accordingly, merely
outline the relation between the two procedures and briefly discuss the
experimental significance of the bond energies.

Let us first consider the treatment of a hydrocarbon with the general
molecular formula C_aH_b. The total energy E of such a substance is
defined by the equation

$$C_aH_b \text{ (gas)} \rightarrow a\text{C (gas)} + b\text{H (gas)} + E \text{ kcal} \qquad (1)$$

A reaction of this sort is not suitable for direct investigation, but the
value of E can be obtained from a study of the series of simpler reactions:[14]

$$C_aH_b \text{ (gas)} + (a + b/4)O_2 \text{ (gas)} \rightarrow a\text{CO}_2 \text{ (gas)}$$
$$+ b/2\text{H}_2\text{O (liq)} + \Lambda \text{ kcal} \qquad (2)$$

$$a\text{CO}_2 \text{ (gas)} \rightarrow a\text{C (graphite)} + a\text{O}_2 \text{ (gas)} - 94.1a \text{ kcal} \qquad (3)$$

$$a\text{C (graphite)} \rightarrow a\text{C (gas)} - 171.7a \text{ kcal} \qquad (4)$$

$$b/2\text{H}_2\text{O (liq)} \rightarrow b/2\text{H}_2 + b/4\text{O}_2 \text{ (gas)} - 34.2b \text{ kcal} \qquad (5)$$

$$b/2\text{H}_2 \text{ (gas)} \rightarrow b\text{H (gas)} - 52.1b \text{ kcal} \qquad (6)$$

Equation 1 is the sum of equations 2–6, so that E is given by the relation

$$E = \Lambda - (265.8a + 86.3b) \text{ kcal} \qquad (7)$$

According to equation 2, the heat of combustion Λ to be used here is
that of the gaseous substance; if data are available only for the substance

---

[14] The thermochemical data given here are taken from F. D. Rossini, D. D. Wagman,
W. H. Evans, S. Levine, and I. Jaffe, *Selected Values of Chemical Thermodynamic
Properties*, U. S. Government Printing Office, Washington, D. C., 1952. They refer
to a constant pressure of 1 atm and to a temperature of 25°C.

in some other state, then these must be corrected to the gaseous state. As in Section 3·3, the effect of such correction is to replace Λ in equation 7 by $\Lambda_x + \mu_x$, where Λ_x and μ_x are the heats of combustion and of vaporization, respectively, of the substance in the state x (solid or liquid).

The reactions 1–6 are considered to occur at a constant pressure of 1 atm and at a temperature of 25°C. Since the *pressure* is held constant, the quantity E as so defined does not strictly represent the *internal energy*, which is the negative of the energy necessary to dissociate the isolated gaseous molecule into isolated gaseous atoms; it represents, rather, the heat content or enthalpy (more customarily designated by the letter H) of the molecule. Similarly, the quantities $D(A—B)$ defined later are not strictly bond *energies*. This incorrect terminology has become firmly established in the literature, however, and for that reason will be adopted here without further apology. In any event, the calculated resonance energies would not be changed significantly if the calculations were based upon the true molecular and bond energies. (However, the quantities referred to in Chapter 2 as bond energies were the true bond energies.)

It can be shown (see the following paragraph) that the total energies E of molecules are additive properties of their bonds to exactly the same extent as are the heats of combustion Λ (or $\Lambda_x + \mu_x$). This means that, whenever the total heats of combustion Λ can be expressed as the sums of the contributions $\lambda(A—B)$ from the individual bonds $A—B$, then the energies E can be similarly expressed as *minus* the sums of certain analogous contributions, the so-called bond energies, $D(A—B)$. (The minus sign is here introduced because, although the energies E are necessarily negative for stable molecules, the bond energies are customarily taken as positive quantities.) With many substances, however, satisfactory estimates of the heats of combustion are possible only if a number of correction terms, of the sorts shown in Table 3·4, are added to the sum of the $\lambda(A—B)$'s. Under such circumstances, the calculated molecular energies are also subject to exactly these same corrections (see below).

The relation between the bond energies $D(A—B)$ and the contributions $\lambda(A—B)$ to the heats of combustion can be found in the following way. Let us first consider the substance methane. In the molecule of this compound, there are just four carbon-hydrogen bonds. Consequently, since no correction terms are here required, the heat of combustion is expressed as

$$\Lambda_{\text{methane}} = 4\lambda(C—H)$$

and the energy is expressed as

$$E_{\text{methane}} = -4D(C—H)$$

Equation 7 then gives

$$-4D(C—H) = 4\lambda(C—H) - (265.8 + 4 \times 86.3) \text{ kcal}$$

or $D(C—H) = 152.75 \text{ kcal} - \lambda(C—H) = 98.75 \text{ kcal}$

The value of $\lambda(C\!-\!H)$ used in the last of the above equations is taken from Table 3·4. Similarly, for ethane

$$E_{\text{ethane}} = -D(C\!-\!C) - 6D(C\!-\!H)$$
$$= \Lambda_{\text{ethane}} - (2 \times 265.8 + 6 \times 86.3) \text{ kcal}$$
$$= \lambda(C\!-\!C) + 6\lambda(C\!-\!H) - 1049.4 \text{ kcal}$$

or $D(C\!-\!C) = 83.6$ kcal

The extension to carbon-carbon double and triple bonds should now require no further comment.

When.elements other than carbon and hydrogen are present, the treatment proceeds along similar lines but becomes rather more complicated. For example, if a substance has the formula $C_aH_bO_cN_dS_eCl_fBr_gI_h$, its energy E is defined by equation 1':

$$C_aH_bO_cN_dS_eCl_fBr_gI_h \text{ (gas)} \rightarrow aC \text{ (gas)} + bH \text{ (gas)} + cO \text{ (gas)} + dN \text{ (gas)}$$
$$+ eS \text{ (gas)} + f\text{Cl (gas)} + g\text{Br (gas)} + h\text{I (gas)} + E \text{ kcal} \tag{1'}$$

and its heat of combustion by equation 2':

$$C_aH_bO_cN_dS_eCl_fBr_gI_h \text{ (gas)} + [a + (b - f)/4 + e - c/2]O_2 \text{ (gas)} \rightarrow aCO_2 \text{ (gas)}$$
$$+ (b - f)/2H_2O \text{ (liq)} + d/2N_2 \text{ (gas)} + eSO_2 \text{ (gas)} + f\text{HCl (gas)}$$
$$+ g/2Br_2 \text{ (vapor)} + h/2I_2 \text{ (solid)} + \Lambda \text{ kcal} \tag{2'}$$

(See Section 3·3.) The relation between E and Λ can be derived in the same way as before. For this purpose, equation 5 must be multiplied by $(b - f)/b$, so that it becomes 5' and the further equations[14] 8–15 must be used. Equation 1' is now the sum of equations 2', 3, 4, 5', 6, 8–15:

$$(b - f)/2H_2O \text{ (liq)} \rightarrow (b - f)/2H_2 \text{ (gas)} + (b - f)/4O_2 \text{ (gas)}$$
$$- 34.2\,(b - f) \text{ kcal} \tag{5'}$$

$$c/2O_2 \text{ (gas)} \rightarrow cO \text{ (gas)} - 59.2c \text{ kcal} \tag{8}$$

$$d/2N_2 \text{ (gas)} \rightarrow dN \text{ (gas)} - 85.6d \text{ kcal} \tag{9}$$

$$eSO_2 \rightarrow eS \text{ (rhombic)} + eO_2 \text{ (gas)} - 71.0e \text{ kcal} \tag{10}$$

$$eS \text{ (rhombic)} \rightarrow eS \text{ (gas)} - 53.3e \text{ kcal} \tag{11}$$

$$f\text{HCl (gas)} \rightarrow f/2H_2 \text{ (gas)} + f/2Cl_2 \text{ (gas)} - 22.1f \text{ kcal} \tag{12}$$

$$f/2Cl_2 \text{ (gas)} \rightarrow f\text{Cl (gas)} - 29.0f \text{ kcal} \tag{13}$$

$$g/2Br_2 \text{ (gas)} \rightarrow g\text{Br (gas)} - 26.7g \text{ kcal} \tag{14}$$

$$h/2I_2 \text{ (sol)} \rightarrow h\text{I (gas)} - 25.5h \text{ kcal} \tag{15}$$

so that

$$E = \Lambda - (265.8a + 86.3b + 59.2c + 85.6d + 124.3e + 16.9f$$
$$+ 26.7g + 25.5h) \text{ kcal} \tag{7'}$$

The derivation of the bond energies $D(A\!-\!B)$ from the contributions $\lambda(A\!-\!B)$ to the heat of combustion then proceeds in the manner illustrated above for the carbon-hydrogen and carbon-carbon bonds.

Since any desired energies can always be readily obtained in the way that has just been described, and since we shall have little further occasion to refer to these quantities, we need not here give a list of the numerical values (however, see below in this paragraph, and also Section 3·6). We shall, nevertheless, find it worth-while to illustrate, with the single example of benzene, the use of the bond energies for the calculation of resonance energies. As we noted above, the energies of a carbon-hydrogen bond and of a carbon-carbon single bond are, respectively, 98.75 and 83.6 kcal per mole. Moreover, that of a *cis* 1,2-disubstituted carbon-carbon double bond in a six-membered ring (cf. Table 3·4) can similarly be shown to be equal to 148.4 kcal per mole. The calculated energy of a Kekulé structure is therefore

$$E_{\text{calcd}} = -[(6 \times 98.75) + (3 \times 83.6) + (3 \times 148.4) - 1.0]$$
$$= -1287.5 \text{ kcal per mole}$$

where the term $-[-1.0]$ is the correction for the six-membered ring (cf. Table 3·4). On the other hand, since the heat of combustion of benzene is 789.1 kcal per mole (cf. Table 3·7), the observed energy is found from equation 7 to be

$$E_{\text{obs}} = 789.1 - [(6 \times 265.8) + (6 \times 86.3)] = -1323.5 \text{ kcal per mole}$$

The resonance energy is therefore $-1287.5 - (-1323.5) = 36.0$ kcal per mole. This value is identical with the one found directly from the heat of combustion, as it must be in view of the equivalence of the two treatments.

As was mentioned above, no new information is obtainable with the aid of the bond energies, except for a substance like carbon monoxide, in which at least one of the elements represented displays an anomalous valence. With such substances, however, the treatment is far from satisfactory, and the conclusions to which it leads are not at all reliable. (See the next-to-last paragraph of Section 3·3.) As a matter of fact, the direct use of the heats of combustion is not only more convenient, since it does not require the unnecessary step of calculating the molecular energies, but also avoids a certain more fundamental difficulty as well in connection with the thermochemical data included in equations 3–6, 8–15. Some of the values given there are of questionable accuracy; the heat of sublimation of graphite (equation 4) in particular may be as much as about 35 kcal per gram atom too high,[15] and the heat of dissociation

---

[15] See, for example, H. Branson and C. Smith, *J. Chem. Phys.* **20**, 1047 (1952); A. Langer, J. A. Hipple, and D. P. Stevenson, *J. Chem. Phys.* **22**, 1836 (1954); T. L. Cottrell, *The Strengths of Chemical Bonds*, Academic Press, New York, 1954, pp. 156ff; however, cf. R. E. Honig, *J. Chem. Phys.* **22**, 126 (1954).

of nitrogen (equation 9) may be about 25 kcal per gram atom too low.[16] The actual values of the bond energies are sometimes therefore quite unreliable. However, as long as one is dealing only with substances in which each element is displaying its normal valence, the usefulness of this present treatment for the determination of resonance energies is not affected in any way, because the values found for the resonance energies are independent of the data put into the equations mentioned.

The bond energies that can thus be calculated from Klages's values of the $\lambda(A-B)$'s differ somewhat from the ones given by Pauling[5] and by Rice.[5] For example, although we found above that $D(C-C)$ is equal to 83.6 kcal per mole, Pauling gives 58.6 kcal per mole and Rice gives 69.2 kcal per mole for this same quantity. The reason for these variations is that the three sets of bond energies are based upon different numerical data and, in particular, that they involve different assumptions regarding the heat of sublimation of graphite (equation 4).

Since the term "bond energy" is commonly used with several quite different meanings, we should now briefly consider the significance of the particular kind of bond energies with which we have just been dealing. From equation 1 (or 1'), it is evident that the sum of these bond energies for all the bonds within any given molecule is equal to the total energy that must be supplied in order to break all the bonds. It does not follow, however, that the bond energy of any individual bond must be equal to the energy required for the rupture of just that bond in the original molecule. For example, in order to decompose a molecule of ethane into its isolated gaseous atoms, we must break altogether six carbon-hydrogen bonds, and one carbon-carbon single bond. Within the limits of accuracy of the present treatment, therefore, the total energy required will be $6D(C-H) + D(C-C)$, but we cannot be sure how this energy will be divided among the seven steps of the complete decomposition. There is, in fact, no reason why the same energy must be required to remove a hydrogen atom from the intact ethane molecule as from, say, the fragment CH_3-CH; nor is there any reason why the same energy must always be required to break the carbon-carbon bond, regardless of how many hydrogen atoms have previously been removed. In other words, the bond energies are merely empirical parameters which we can use in estimating the total energies (or the heats of combustion) of normal molecules; they give us no reliable information, however, regarding either the energies required to break any individual bonds or even the total energies (or heats of combustion) of molecules in which, as in carbon monoxide, there are atoms in exceptional valence states. Moreover, attention should here again be called to the fact that, as was mentioned

[16] See, for example, A. E. Douglas and G. Herzberg, *Can. J. Phys.* **29**, 294 (1951).

in the paragraph in fine print on page 116, the various energy quantities considered in this section ought really to be referred to as enthalpies.

3·5 Resonance Energies from Group Energies. Unlike Klages's method for estimating the heats of combustion, Franklin's method cannot readily be re-expressed in terms of bond energies. The reason for this difference is that, although Klages relates the total heats of combustion to contributions from the individual bonds, Franklin relates them instead to contributions from (usually) larger groupings within the molecules. The two methods of calculation differ also in the further significant respect that, in Klages's treatment, the different bonds share atoms with each other whereas, in Franklin's, the different groupings are completely independent. Thus, in the ethane molecule, one carbon-carbon bond and three carbon-hydrogen bonds are formed by each carbon atom, but the two methyl groups do not similarly overlap.

Franklin's method can nevertheless be re-expressed in terms of *group energies*; in fact, it was so formulated in the author's original paper.[6] Two examples will be sufficient to illustrate the relation between these different, but equivalent treatments. Since the ethane molecule consists of two methyl groups, the calculated heat of combustion is seen from Table 3·6 to be

$$\Lambda_{calcd} = 2 \times 186.41 = 372.8 \text{ kcal per mole}$$

(cf. also Table 3·5). From equation 7 (or 7′) of Section 3·4, the calculated energy is therefore

$$E_{calcd} = 372.8 - [(2 \times 265.8) + (6 \times 86.3)]$$
$$= -676.6 \text{ kcal per mole}$$

Hence the group energy of the methyl group is $^1/_2 \times (-676.6)$, or -338.3 kcal per mole. This derivation is, however, somewhat more complicated than it needs to be for, in order to deal with a complete molecule, we have here started with 2 methyl groups, and then divided the final answer by 2. Because of the independence of these groups, however, we would have obtained the same group energy if we had started with only one methyl group. Similarly, the group energy of the *cis* —CH=CH— group can be derived without reference to any specific molecule. Since this group makes a contribution of 275.30 kcal per mole to the heat of combustion (Table 3·6), its group energy is $275.30 - [(2 \times 265.8) + (2 \times 86.3)]$, or -428.9 kcal per mole.

The values just derived for the energies of the —CH$_3$ and *cis* —CH=CH— groups appear to be quite different from those listed by Franklin.[6] The explanation of these discrepancies is, however, very simple. Both in this section and in Section 3·4, we have been concerned with the energies (or, rather, with the heats) of formation from isolated gaseous atoms; on the other hand, Franklin has instead considered only the energies (or heats) of formation from the elements in their standard states. The respective values that are obtained for the group energies must therefore be different because they are measured from different zeros (cf. Figure 3·1, Section 3·1).

The use of the group energies for the calculation of resonance energies can be illustrated with the example of benzene. Since a Kekulé structure consists of three *cis* —CH=CH— groups in a six-membered ring, the calculated energy is

$$E_{calcd} = 3 \times (-428.9) - 0.45 = -1287.15 \text{ kcal per mole}$$

where the term -0.45 is the correction for the ring (cf. Table 3·6). Since the observed energy of benzene is -1323.5 kcal per mole (cf. page 118), the resonance energy is therefore $-1287.15 - (-1323.5)$, or 36.4 kcal per mole. This value is, of course, identical with the one given in Table 3·7.

Like the similar calculations described in Section 3·4, so also these present ones are in practice slightly less convenient than are the ones more directly based on the heats of combustion. Moreover, they again offer no compensating advantages since they do not lead to any reliable additional information. One might perhaps suppose that the group energy of, for example, the methyl group would represent the energy of formation of a free methyl radical. This view is, however, not correct for, like the bond energies, the group energies are applicable only to normal molecules in which each atom has its standard valence.[17] Indeed, if some such limitation were not imposed, the treatment would then lead to the obviously fallacious conclusion that no energy is ever required to break up a molecule into the groups of which it is composed (e.g., to dissociate an ethane molecule into two methyl radicals).

3·6 The Effect of Resonance between Ionic and Covalent Structures upon Bond Energies.[18]   In Section 2·7 it was pointed out that the strength of an essentially covalent bond should be increased by resonance with ionic structures. This conclusion cannot be verified directly from the experimental data without some arbitrariness, but the facts are sufficiently suggestive to warrant a brief discussion of them here. The difficulty arises because no purely ionic or purely covalent bonds are available for comparison. We can overcome this difficulty to some extent, however,

[17] For an extension of the treatment to a restricted group of free radicals, see J. L. Franklin and F. H. Field, *J. Am. Chem. Soc.* **75**, 2819 (1953); J. L. Franklin, *J. Chem. Phys.* **21**, 2029 (1953).

[18] For recent critical discussions, see M. G. Evans, *Proc. Roy. Soc. (London) A* **207** 1 (1951); E. Warhurst, *ibid.* **207**, 32 (1951); T. L. Cottrell and L. E. Sutton, *ibid.* **207**, 49 (1951); C. A. Coulson, *ibid.* **207**, 63 (1951).

by adopting the following procedure, which is due to Pauling.[19]   As has already been pointed out, bonds formed between two atoms of the same kind (such as hydrogen-hydrogen or carbon-carbon bonds) are largely covalent.   For the hydrogen molecule, for example, approximate numerical calculations[20] have shown that the ionic structures each contribute very little to the actual state of the molecule, and that the resulting resonance energy amounts to only about 5.5 kcal per mole.   Such essentially covalent bonds, therefore, provide convenient standards of reference with which the other bonds can be compared.   This is because a bond between two dissimilar atoms, A and B, must presumably have a somewhat greater ionic character, since one of the ionic structures, $A:^-\ B^+$ or $A^+\ :B^-$, must be relatively more stable than either $A:^-\ A^+$ or $B:^-\ B^+$.   We shall now make the not unreasonable assumption that, except for this variation in ionic character, the energy of a single bond between A and B would be the arithmetic mean of the energies of the single bonds between two atoms A and between two atoms B. (However, see below.)   Since in general the ionic character of the bond A—B is greater than that of either A—A or B—B, the actual bond should then be made stronger than the arithmetic mean by this increase in resonance.   In other words, if $D(A$—$B)$, $D(A$—$A)$, and $D(B$—$B)$ are the energies of the three bonds, the quantity $\Delta_{AB} = D(A$—$B) - \frac{1}{2}[D(A$—$A) + D(B$—$B)]$ should always be positive.

The extent to which this expectation is borne out by the experimental data can be seen from an examination of Table 3·8, in which are listed the observed values of $D(A$—$A)$, $D(B$—$B)$, and $D(A$—$B)$, together with the derived value of Δ_{AB} for several different choices of the elements A and B. (As is true throughout the present chapter, the quantities here designated as bond energies are not strictly energies, but are instead heats, or enthalpies.)   It will be seen that, in most instances, Δ_{AB} is indeed positive, but that, with the hydrides of the alkali metals, it is instead negative.   Such discrepancies are doubtless due to errors in the assumption that, if the bond A—B were purely covalent, its energy would be the arithmetic mean of $D(A$—$A)$ and $D(B$—$B)$.   We cannot, of course, be surprised that this assumption thus proves to be somewhat inadequate, since there is no sound theoretical reason why it should be universally valid.   Coulson, to be sure, has stated[21] that a rough molecular-orbital calculation suggests that the use of the arithmetic mean ought to give a

---

[19] L. Pauling, *J. Am. Chem. Soc.* **54**, 3570 (1932); *The Nature of the Chemical Bond*, Cornell University Press, Ithaca, N. Y., 1st ed., 1939, 2nd ed., 1940, pp. 58ff.   For a vigorous criticism of this procedure, see A. Burawoy, *Trans. Faraday Soc.* **39**, 79 (1943).

[20] S. Weinbaum, *J. Chem. Phys.* **1**, 593 (1933).

[21] C. A. Coulson, *Valence*, Oxford University Press, Oxford, 1952, p. 127.

reasonable approximation to the desired energy.   Pauling and Sherman, on the other hand, have concluded from a considerably more complicated

TABLE 3·8

IONIC CONTRIBUTIONS TO THE ENERGIES OF SINGLE BONDS[a]

	H	F	Cl	Br	I	Li	Na	K
H	104.2	134.6	103.2	87.5	71.4	58.5	48.2	43.6
		70.4	81.1	75.2	70.2	65.4	61.1	58.2
		64.2	22.1	12.3	1.2	− 6.9	− 12.9	− 14.6
F		36.6	60.6				116	
			47.3				27	
			13.3				89	
Cl			58.0	52.2	50.3	119.1	98.5	102.1
				52.1	47.1	42.3	38.0	35.1
				0.1	3.2	76.8	60.5	67.0
Br				46.1	42.4	105	89.0	
					41.1	36	32.1	
					1.3	69	56.9	
I					36.1	79	72.4	
						31	27.1	
						48	45.3	
Li						26.5		
Na							18.0	
K								12.2

[a] For each type of bond, the observed bond energy in kilocalories per mole is given in the first row; the bond energy calculated by the rule of the arithmetic mean is given in the second row; and the value of Δ_{AB} is given in the third row.   The observed bond energies are obtained from F. D. Rossini, D. D. Wagman, W. H. Evans, S. Levine, and I. Jaffe, *Selected Values of Chemical Thermodynamic Properties*, U. S. Government Printing Office, Washington, D. C., 1952.

series of numerical calculations[22] that the *geometric* mean ought to give a more reliable estimate; and, in fact, with this indicated change in the treatment, the hydrides of the alkali metals are no longer anomalous.

[22] L. Pauling and J. Sherman, *J. Am. Chem. Soc.* **59**, 1450 (1937).

Thus, for lithium, sodium, and potassium hydrides, the calculated energies of the imaginary, purely covalent bonds then become, respectively, 52.5, 43.3, and 35.7 kcal per mole, so that the corresponding values of the Δ_{AB}'s become, respectively, $+6.0$, $+4.9$, and $+7.9$ kcal per mole. In all other instances as well, the effect of replacing the arithmetic by the geometric mean is similarly to make the values of the Δ_{AB}'s more positive (or less negative).

Although the arithmetic mean therefore appears to lead to a less generally satisfactory treatment than the geometric mean, we shall nevertheless continue to use the former approximation. A partial justification for this procedure is that, with but a few exceptions, the differences between the two means are rather small. In fact, these differences are large only when, as with the hydrides of the alkali metals, the differences between the energies $D(A—A)$ and $D(B—B)$ of the two corresponding symmetrical bonds are themselves very large. Moreover, even fairly large errors in the calculated energies of the purely covalent bonds $A—B$ can cause no serious trouble except when the magnitudes of the Δ_{AB}'s are small.

The most important reason, however, for our here retaining the original assumption of the arithmetic mean is quite different from the foregoing. Although the values listed in Table 3·8 seem to be relatively reliable, most of the analogous data that can at present be given for the remaining bonds of other types are much more questionable. In particular, the uncertainties in the heat of sublimation of graphite and in the heat of dissociation of molecular nitrogen (cf. pages 118f) lead to corresponding uncertainties in the energies of all the bonds in which carbon or nitrogen atoms take part. Any errors that may arise from this cause can be shown to enter the treatment in such a way that, in the calculation of the Δ_{AB}'s, they always exactly cancel if the arithmetic mean is used, but do not do so if instead the geometric mean is used. Consequently, although the procedure which is here adopted is perhaps not the best one possible, it nevertheless does have the advantage of being generally applicable.

The attempt to extend Table 3·8 by the inclusion of data for still further types of bond encounters not only the difficulties just referred to, but also the following equally serious one. If a molecule contains more than two atoms, so that it is held together by more than one valence bond, the division of its total energy among its several bonds is unambiguous only in those special instances in which, as in water, ammonia, or methane, all the bonds are completely equivalent (cf. page 119). Consequently, the energy of any bond in which a multivalent atom takes part can usually not be uniquely determined. In order to avoid this difficulty, Pauling assumed[19] that the *average* bond energies, which were introduced in

Section 3·4 for the calculation of total molecular energies, could here be used.   For the reasons stated on page 119, this procedure is not strictly correct, but, since no better one has as yet been proposed, it will here be adopted.

Even with the aid of the foregoing approximations and simplifying assumptions, the treatment is still rather severely limited by a lack of experimental data.   In fact, if all the contributions $\lambda(A-B)$ to the heats of combustion, which were given by Klages and which are listed in Table 3·4, Section 3·3, are re-expressed in terms of bond energies, the only additional values of Δ_{AB} which can then be derived are the ones for the C—H, C—Cl, C—Br, and C—I bonds.   In the way that has already been described, these four values are found to be, respectively, 4.9, 9.7, 1.7, and −6.6 kcal per mole.   As before, therefore, the Δ_{AB}'s are again predominantly, but not invariably, positive.   The discrepancy which is here observed with the carbon-iodine bond is presumably again due to the inadequacy of the assumption that the energy of the hypothetical, purely covalent bond would be the arithmetic mean of the values observed for the carbon-carbon and iodine-iodine bonds.   Indeed, if we could here legitimately use the geometric mean, we would then find that Δ_{CI} has the better, but still negative, value of −1.7 kcal per mole; as was explained on page 124, however, this alternative method of calculation is especially unreliable with any bond in which a carbon atom takes part.

The somewhat more complete table of Δ_{AB}'s that is given by Pauling[19] is derived from older, and presumably less accurate, bond energies.   Since we shall have no need to refer to any of the individual values from this table, we shall here mention merely that the present discussion would not have had to be altered in any significant respect if it had been based on Pauling's original table.

If the Δ_{AB}'s are considered to measure the extents to which the respective bonds $A-B$ are strengthened by resonance with ionic structures, then the values of these energy differences should increase with the polarities of the bonds.   In other words, Δ_{AB} should be small if the atoms A and B have about the same electronegativity, and it should be large if A and B differ greatly in electronegativity.   On the whole, this expectation seems to be in reasonably good qualitative agreement with the observations.   With the hydrogen halides, for example, Δ_{AB} increases uniformly from 1.2 kcal per mole with hydrogen iodide to 64.2 kcal per mole with hydrogen fluoride, and similar trends can be found in other groups of analogous bonds.   (Cf. Table 3·8.)   The exceptions to the rule that the Δ_{AB}'s must be positive occur only when the atoms that are linked to each other are of comparable electronegativity, and hence only when the Δ_{AB}'s would be expected to be small.   These several regularities doubtless provide the most satisfactory evidence for the belief that, in spite of its extreme crudity, the present treatment does nevertheless have some theoretical significance.

The foregoing, largely qualitative discussion can be put on a slightly more quantitative basis. For this purpose, the atoms A of the various elements are assigned certain numerical parameters, x_A, which are customarily called their *electronegativities*. If the values of these parameters

TABLE 3·9

THE ELECTRONEGATIVITIES OF SOME OF THE MORE IMPORTANT ELEMENTS[a]

H				
2.1				
2.52				
2.13				
0.00				
Li	C	N	O	F
1.0	2.5	3.0	3.5	4.0
0.95	—	—	—	4.06
0.95	2.55	2.98	3.45	3.95
—	0.47	1.02	1.46	1.97
Na		P	S	Cl
0.9		2.1	2.5	3.0
0.91		—	—	3.01
0.90		2.1	2.53	2.97
—		− 0.12	0.30	1.09
K				Br
0.8				2.8
0.77				2.76
0.80				2.75
—				0.88
				I
				2.4
				2.46
				2.45
				0.47

[a] Of the entries under the symbol for each element, the first gives the value of the electronegativity in Pauling, *The Nature of the Chemical Bond*, Cornell University Press, Ithaca, N. Y., 1st ed., 1939, 2nd ed., 1940, p. 64; the second gives the one listed by L. Pauling, *loc. cit.* p. 66, as calculated by the method of R. S. Mulliken, *J. Chem. Phys.* **2**, 782 (1934), **3**, 573 (1935); the third is that of W. Gordy, *J. Chem. Phys.* **14**, 305 (1946); and the last is that of O. K. Rice, *Electronic Structure and Chemical Binding*, McGraw-Hill Book Co., New York, 1940, p. 196. For still a further set of electronegativities, and for a summary of the older ones, see M. L. Huggins, *J. Am. Chem. Soc.* **75**, 4123, 4126 (1953).

are chosen in any one of the four ways shown in Table 3·9, then the values of the Δ_{AB}'s are found empirically to be given very roughly by the equation

$$\Delta_{AB} = 23(x_A - x_B)^2 \text{ kcal per mole}$$

Although the sets of electronegativities that are due to Pauling,[19] to Mulliken,[23] and to Gordy[24] are very similar to each other, the one that is due to Rice[25] appears to be quite different from the other three.   Indeed, for each atom A, Rice's value of x_A is about 2 units lower than the corresponding value from any of the other sets.   However, since the difference is therefore approximately constant, and since, from the above equation, Δ_{AB} depends only on the quantity $(x_A - x_B)^2$, the Δ_{AB}'s that are calculated from Rice's electronegativities are always in satisfactory agreement with those obtained from the values given by the other authors.

From the above discussion, it may appear that the electronegativities have no absolute significance, since only their relative values, $x_A - x_B$, have so far been defined in experimental terms.   For this reason, the reader has possibly wondered how the particular absolute values given in Table 3·9 were obtained.   A logical procedure would be arbitrarily to assign some specified value, say zero, to some specified element, say hydrogen, and then to express all the remaining electronegativities with reference to that chosen element.   This procedure was, in fact, the one followed by Rice[25] (and also by Pauling in his original paper[19]).   More recently, however, Mulliken[23] and Gordy[24] have described two entirely independent, but mutually consistent, methods for deriving absolute electronegativities (and Pauling has modified his earlier relative values so that they are now essentially identical with the absolute ones given by these latter authors).   On theoretical grounds, which need not here be described, Mulliken has concluded that the electronegativity x_A of an atom A ought to be proportional to the sum of its ionization energy I_A and its electron affinity E_A; and, from a comparison of the empirical data, he found that, if I_A and E_A are both expressed in kilocalories per mole, the proportionality constant is equal to about $1/130$, so that[23]

$$x_A \cong \frac{I_A + E_A}{130}$$

The values of the electronegativities that are attributed to Mulliken in Table 3·9 are obtained from this approximate equation.   Gordy,[24] on the other hand, has established the empirical relation

$$k_{AB} \cong [1.67(x_A x_B/r_{AB}^2)^{\frac{3}{4}} + 0.30] \times 10^5 \text{ dynes per centimeter,}$$

[23] R. S. Mulliken, *J. Chem. Phys.* **2**, 782 (1934); **3**, 573 (1935).   The numerical values upon which the present discussion is based are taken from L. Pauling, *The Nature of the Chemical Bond*, Cornell University Press, Ithaca, N. Y., 1st ed., 1939, 2nd ed., 1940, p. 66.

[24] W. Gordy, *J. Chem. Phys.* **14**, 305 (1946).

[25] O. K. Rice, *Electronic Structure and Chemical Binding*, McGraw-Hill Book Co., New York, 1940, p. 196.

where k_{AB} is the stretching force constant (cf. Section 6·11) for a single bond between atoms A and B, and r_{AB} is the internuclear distance expressed in angstrom units (cf. Section 4·3).   This equation must be somewhat modified (in a way that is explicitly stated[24]) if the molecule of interest is not a stable one, or if each of the atoms A and B is not exhibiting its normal valence, or if, in the molecule, the valence shell of each atom contains only the two electrons that are responsible for the bond; it is, however, sufficiently general for our purpose.   The values of the electronegativities that are attributed to Gordy in Table 3·9 are the ones which this author has found to give the best agreement with his above equation.

As should be evident from their respective definitions, the electronegativities derived by the methods of Mulliken and of Gordy are indeed absolute, rather than relative.   The fact that they agree so well with each other, and with the corresponding quantities obtained by Pauling and by Rice from thermochemical data, is therefore most gratifying; and it provides some additional support for the view that the electronegativities are actually significant properties of the respective atoms.

Attention should here be called to certain important limitations upon the use of the electronegativities discussed above.   As has already been explicitly mentioned in connection with Gordy's treatment, the values of the x_A's that are given in Table 3·9 are strictly applicable only if the atoms A are in their standard valence states.   Furthermore, these atoms must not be taking part in any double or triple bonds.   Consequently, we cannot expect a nitrogen atom to have the same electronegativity in an ammonium ion as in an ammonia molecule; nor can we expect a carbon atom to have the same electronegativity in a molecule of ethylene, or of acetylene, as in one of ethane.   In general, the electronegativity of an atom of any specified element increases with the (algebraic) value of its net charge and with its degree of unsaturation.   Since the electronegativity of an atom is presumed to be a measure of its attraction for electrons, the reason for the first of these variations should be immediately apparent.   The reason why the electronegativity depends also upon the unsaturation is, however, less obvious.   From a detailed study of the charge distributions in the respective molecules, it can be shown[26] that the electrons which are responsible for the formation of single bonds spend larger fractions of their times near the nuclei of unsaturated atoms than near those of comparable saturated atoms.   Thus, the electrons are more concentrated in the region near the carbon nucleus in a $C—H$ bond of ethylene than in one of ethane.   Moreover, this concentration is still greater in a C—H bond of acetylene.   Since the region near a positively

---

[26] See, for example, R. S. Mulliken, *J. Phys. Chem.* **41**, 318 (1937); W. E. Moffitt, *Proc. Roy. Soc. (London)* **202**, 534, 548 (1950).

charged nucleus is one in which a negatively charged electron is particu-larly stable, it therefore follows that the electronegativity of an atom must increase with its degree of unsaturation. Gordy, for example, has estimated[24] that, with respect to the C—H bond, the acetylenic carbon atom at the right of the grouping —C≡C—H has an electronegativity of 2.83, as compared with the value of 2.55 given in Table 3·9 for a saturated carbon atom. Presumably, the corresponding electronegativity of an ethylenic carbon atom would be intermediate between the two extremes.

3·7 Empirical and Vertical Resonance Energies.[27] The so-called *empirical* resonance energies, to which our discussion has so far been restricted, are of great practical importance since they are closely and simply connected with both the observed heats of combustion and the molecular energies of the respective resonance hybrids. From the theoretical viewpoint, however, they are rather more complicated than are certain other, related quantities, which we must now consider.

For the sake of both definiteness and simplicity, let us begin by discussing the molecule of benzene, which we shall here suppose to be a hybrid of only the two equivalent Kekulé structures. Figure 1·2, Section 1·4, is a schematic representation of the way in which, for such a molecule, the energies of the imaginary contributing structures and of the actually existing hybrid vary with the relative positions of the atomic nuclei. The points R_0 and S_1 correspond to the energies of the respective undistorted Kekulé structures R and S, and hence to the molecular energies that are calculated for these structures by the methods briefly described in Sections 3·4 and 3·5. Similarly, the point P' corresponds to the observed energy of the undistorted benzene molecule, and hence to the molecular energy that is derived from the observed heat of combustion. The empirical resonance energy is therefore, given by the height of the point R_0 (or S_1) above P' or, in other words, by the distance OP'. This resonance energy, however, is not necessarily equal to the stabilization resulting from the resonance at any particular value of the parameter x—i.e., at any particular nuclear configuration. It is instead a more complex quantity which can be described as the difference between two independent terms. The first, and larger, of these terms is the so-called *vertical* resonance energy PP' of the benzene molecule in its normal configuration ($x = \frac{1}{2}$); the second is the *compressional* energy PO required to distort a Kekulé

[27] Cf. J. E. Lennard-Jones, *Proc. Roy. Soc.* (*London*) *A* **158**, 280 (1937); J. E. Lennard-Jones and J. Turkevich, *ibid. A* **158**, 297 (1937); R. S. Mulliken, C. A. Rieke, and W. G. Brown, *J. Am. Chem. Soc.* **63**, 41 (1941); D. F. Hornig, *ibid.* **72**, 5772 (1950); R. S. Mulliken and R. G. Parr, *J. Chem. Phys.* **19**, 1271 (1951); C. A. Coulson and S. L. Altmann, *Trans. Faraday Soc.* **48**, 293 (1952); G. G. Hall, *Proc. Roy. Soc.* (*London*) *A* **213**, 102, 113 (1952).

structure from its normal configuration ($x = 0$ or 1) to the configuration that actually obtains in benzene. Alternatively, the empirical resonance energy OP' can be described as the sum of the different vertical resonance energy R_0R' (or S_1S', or OO') of a distorted benzene molecule that has the nuclear configuration characteristic of a Kekulé structure, plus the different compressional energy $O'P'$ required to produce such a distorted molecule. As is clear from the figure, the two vertical resonance energies PP' and OO' are, respectively, greater than and less than the empirical resonance energy OP'. The conclusion that PP' must therefore be greater than OO' is completely in agreement with the general rule (cf. Section 1·4) that the maximum resonance energy results when the individual contributing structures have the same energy.

The compressional energy PO can be calculated from the known values of the stretching force constants (cf. Section 6·11) that apply to carbon-carbon single and double bonds; similarly, the different compressional energy $O'P'$ can be calculated from the values of the analogous force constants that apply to the carbon-carbon bonds of benzene. In a recent critical study of this problem, Coulson and Altmann[27] have thus estimated that the energy PO is equal to about 27 kcal per mole, whereas the energy $O'P'$ is equal to about 26.4 kcal per mole. If the empirical resonance energy is taken as 36.0 kcal per mole (cf. Table 3·2, Section 3·2), the two vertical resonance energies are therefore about 63 and 9.6 kcal per mole. From the large difference between these values, it is evident that the magnitude of the vertical resonance energy is very dependent on the configuration of the molecule. In order to avoid confusion, therefore, we shall hereafter adopt the convention that, whenever we speak of a vertical resonance energy, without further qualification, we shall refer to the value of that quantity for the most stable configuration of the actual hybrid.

Although the foregoing treatment is in principle quite general, it has in practice[27] been applied to only a few substances besides benzene, and then usually with the aid of additional simplifying assumptions and approximations. For this reason, we shall ordinarily hereafter restrict our attention to the much more readily available, but theoretically less significant, empirical resonance energies, which we shall, as heretofore, designate simply as resonance energies.

3·8 Theoretical Calculations of Resonance Energies of Hydrocarbons. Several methods are at present available for the theoretical calculation of the resonance energies of hydrocarbons. These are all extremely crude —so crude, in fact, that they might better be regarded as empirical methods which are not based upon theory at all, but which nevertheless are suggested by, and can be correlated with, theory. In spite of their lack of rigor, however, they lead to results which are in general remarkably consistent with each other and with experiment.   This fact forms their only real justification.

The simplest and most widely used of these methods are relative rather than absolute ones, since the quantities to which they directly lead are not the resonance energies themselves, but rather the ratios of these quantities.   More precisely, the calculated resonance energies are obtained as multiples of a certain parameter, which in the different kinds of treatment is known either as an *exchange integral* or as a *resonance integral* (cf. Sections 9·19, 9·20, and 9·25), and which in any such treatment is evaluated empirically by comparison with the experimental data.   This limitation, however, does not introduce any serious difficulty because, if the resonance energy of any one hydrocarbon is known from its heat of hydrogenation or of combustion, then that of any other can be calculated.

The *valence-bond* (or *resonance*) and *molecular-orbital* methods for calculating resonance energies are described in some detail in Sections 9·19, 9·20, and 9·25.   Here, however, we shall outline only a single extremely crude method, which is almost entirely empirical in nature, but which seems to provide about as satisfactory answers as the other more elaborate ones.   This method is based on the very simple equation

$$\text{Resonance energy} = (10M + 3.5N) \text{ kcal per mole} \qquad (1)$$

where M is the number of bonds in the molecule which are represented as single in any one of the contributing structures without formal bonds, but as double in at least one of those structures; and N is the number of bonds that are represented as single in *all* the structures without formal bonds, but as double in at least one of the structures with just one formal bond.   For example, in benzene and in mesitylene, $M = 3$ and $N = 0$, and in styrene $M = 3$ and $N = 1$.   The calculated resonance energies are therefore 30 kcal per mole for benzene and for mesitylene, and 33.5 kcal per mole for styrene.   Comparison of these values with the experimental ones listed in Tables 3·2, Section 3·2, and 3·7, Section 3·3, shows that the agreement is moderately satisfactory.   Additional examples are given in Table 3·10.   The relative, as distinguished from absolute, character of the calculations which are based on equation 1 enters in the fact that the numerical coefficients 10 and 3.5 (which are here *not* exchange or resonance integrals; see above) have been chosen empirically in such a way that the calculated and observed resonance energies agree as closely as possible for a considerable number of substances.

Aside from the above procedure, which is based on equation 1, and which has no clear theoretical significance, most of the remaining relative methods of calculation involve a certain theoretical inconsistency, which

TABLE 3·10

CALCULATED RESONANCE ENERGIES FOR SOME HYDROCARBONS

Resonance Energy

Substance	Observed[a]	Calculated			
		I[b]	II[c]	III[d]	IV[e]
1,3-Butadiene	3	3.5	3.2	3.5	5.4
1,3,5-Cycloheptatriene	6.7	7.0	7.0	7.7	11.4
1,4-Diphenyl-1,3-butadiene[g]	10.7	10.5	9.3[f]	10.6	—
Benzene	35	30	33	35	30.2
Naphthalene	61	60	61	61	52.6
Anthracene	84	90	89	86	—
Phenanthrene	92	90	90	90	—
Naphthacene	110	120	115[f]	110	—
Chrysene	117	120	118[f]	118	—
Triphenylene	119	120	119[f]	121	—
Styrene	38	33.5	39	40	—
Stilbene	77	67	78	81	—
Biphenyl	71	63.5	71	74	65.4
1,3,5-Triphenylbenzene	149	130.5	143	152	—
Azulene	35	53.5	34	53	—

[a] The experimental values in this column are taken whenever possible from Table 3·2, and otherwise from Table 3·7. The data for all the compounds with the conjugated system of interest are here averaged, so that the figures do not always apply to the particular substances specified.

[b] Calculated from equation 1.

[c] Calculated by the valence-bond method (cf. Sections 9·19 and 9·20), with the exchange integral J set equal to -14 kcal per mole for all the substances above the dotted line, and to -30 kcal per mole for all those below that line. See G. W. Wheland, *J. Am. Chem. Soc.* **63**, 2025 (1941); B. Pullman and A. Pullman, *Les Théories électroniques de la chimie organique*, Masson et Cie., Paris, 1952, pp. 226f.

[d] Calculated by the molecular-orbital method, corrected for nonorthogonality (cf. Section 9·25), with the parameter β set equal to -20 kcal per mole for all the substances above the dotted line, and to -33 kcal per mole for all those below that line. See also the references given in footnote c.

[e] Calculated by the molecular-orbital method with correction for the compressional energy. See J. E. Lennard-Jones, *Proc. Roy. Soc. (London)* A **158**, 280 (1937); J. E. Lennard-Jones and J. Turkevich, *ibid.* A **158**, 297 (1937).

[f] The valence-bond method was here approximated by the procedure of C. Vroelant and R. Daudel, *Bull. soc. chim. France* **1949**, 37. (Cf. pages 640f.)

[g] The values listed for this compound refer to the amount by which the total resonance energy exceeds that of the two benzene rings.

somewhat limits their usefulness. Thus, the calculated resonance energies are ordinarily the vertical ones defined in Section 3·7, but the observed resonance energies, with which the calculated values are compared, are instead ordinarily the empirical ones. As we have seen, these two different kinds of resonance energy may be far from identical, even when determined for the same substance. The justification that is usually offered for this failure to distinguish between the vertical and empirical resonance energies is that, as long as the treatment is restricted to closely similar substances like benzene, naphthalene, anthracene, etc., the compressional and vertical resonance energies should both be more or less proportional to the size of the molecule. Hence, to the extent that this assumed proportionality is valid, the ratios of the vertical resonance energies must be at least approximately equal to the respective ratios of the empirical resonance energies. Consequently, since the former ratios are all that can be directly obtained from the calculations, the treatments may still be fairly satisfactory in spite of their underlying lack of self-consistency. In other words, there is some reason to expect that the errors which are introduced by the incorrect identification of the vertical and empirical resonance energies can be largely eliminated by a suitable choice of the values that are assigned to the exchange and resonance integrals. In any event, whether this proposed explanation is correct or not, the figures cited in Table 3·10 show that the several treatments do in fact lead to rather satisfactory calculated resonance energies for a number of hydrocarbons. As is not at all surprising, however, the best values of the exchange and resonance integrals for the aromatic hydrocarbons, with which both the resonance and compressional energies are large, are rather different from the best values for the simple conjugated polyenes, with which the resonance and compressional energies are much smaller.

The inconsistency referred to in the preceding paragraph can be eliminated in still a different, and theoretically more attractive, way. As was pointed out in Section 3·7, the compressional energies are in principle always calculable; hence, the vertical resonance energies are in principle always obtainable from the empirical ones, and vice versa. However, as was also pointed out in the earlier section, the more refined treatments[27] are in practice so tedious that they have as yet been carried through for only a small number of hydrocarbons. A few results that have thus been obtained are shown in Table 3·10. Perhaps unexpectedly, the "improvement" of the calculations seems usually to lead to a slight worsening of the agreement between the calculated and observed resonance energies; the reason for this trend is presumably that any increase in the precision of the treatment necessarily implies a decrease in the possibilities for obtaining agreement by arbitrarily adjusting the values of the empirical parameters.

In addition to the foregoing relative calculations, there have been also a very few absolute ones, in which the only empirical data that were employed were such quantities as the charge and mass of an electron, Planck's constant, and the observed internuclear distances. The most detailed such treatments seem to be those of Craig[28] who, however, has dealt mostly with the total molecular energies and has not ordinarily estimated resonance energies. In somewhat less elaborate treatments, however, Mulliken and Parr[27] have calculated that, aside from some terms which they could not estimate but presumed to be small, the (empirical) resonance energies of 1,3-butadiene and of benzene are, respectively, 3.7 and 36.5 kcal per mole. These purely theoretical values are remarkably close to the experimental ones listed in Tables 3·2 and 3·7. The agreement is, in fact, so good that, in view of the many drastic simplifications and approximations which are involved in the calculations, it must to an appreciable extent be due to fortuitous cancellations of errors. The fact, however, that the calculations lead to answers which are of the right orders of magnitude is gratifying and, undoubtedly, significant.

The agreement between the calculated and observed resonance energies, which Mulliken and Parr claim in their paper,[27] is not quite so good as is that indicated above. By using a somewhat different method for estimating the heats of formation that are associated with the individual contributing structures, these authors have derived the respective values of 6.5 and 41.8 kcal per mole for the observed empirical resonance energies of 1,3-butadiene and benzene. As a result, however, of the extremely approximate character of the calculations, no particular significance can be attached to the small differences between these latter figures and the corresponding ones derived in the preceding sections.

3·9   The General Theory of Aromatic Systems.   In organic chemistry, the term "aromatic" is used rather loosely for the designation of a certain group of characteristic, but not very precisely defined, physical and chemical properties, and also for the description of the particular (always cyclic) compounds which exhibit these properties. Thus, benzene is said to be aromatic because it combines a high degree of apparent unsaturation with both a high thermochemical stability (i.e., a low internal energy) and a relatively small tendency to enter into addition reactions. Other substances which have similar properties, and which are likewise said to be aromatic, include a large number of more complex hydrocarbons, such as diphenylmethane, biphenyl, and naphthalene, with two (or more) isolated, conjugated, or condensed benzene rings. Still other aromatic

[28] See, for example, D. P. Craig, *Proc. Roy. Soc. (London) A* **200**, 474 (1950); *ibid. A* **202**, 498 (1950); *J. Chem. Soc.* **1951**, 3175. Cf. also M. Goeppert-Mayer and A. L. Sklar, *J. Chem. Phys.* **6**, 645 (1938).

substances contain *hetero*cyclic rings, in which the hetero atoms are most commonly nitrogen, sulfur, or oxygen. In many instances, as, for example, with pyridine, pyrimidine, and quinoline, the heterocyclic rings are six-membered, and quite analogous to the carbocyclic ones in the above-mentioned hydrocarbons. In many other instances, however, as in pyrrole, thiophene, and furan, the rings are five-membered, and hence superficially rather different from the foregoing. Finally, as we shall see below, a few compounds with seven-membered rings seem also to have a recognizable aromatic character.

In the preceding sections, we discussed several specific examples of the ways in which the resonance concept leads to an explanation for the special stabilities of aromatic compounds. Here, we may further mention that this same concept leads also to at least a partial explanation for the relatively saturated behaviors of these compounds. Thus, in any addition reaction, the aromatic character must to a greater or less extent be destroyed, and so the resonance energy must be materially decreased; consequently, we can expect that such a reaction will be more difficult with an aromatic compound than with a nonaromatic but otherwise analogous one.

Long before the theory of resonance had been formulated, the organic chemists had sought for a satisfactory explanation of the properties that characterize aromatic systems. One suggestion that was brought forward in this search, namely, Thiele's theory of partial valence, has already been briefly mentioned (cf. Section 1·1). Let us now, however, discuss an even earlier and rather different idea that was due originally to Bamberger.[29] When re-expressed in modern terminology (cf. also the paragraph, below in fine print), Bamberger's proposal takes the following form. The principal difficulty in writing a satisfactory structure for benzene consists in accounting for the six electrons which, in a Kekulé structure I, are responsible for one component of each of the three double bonds; or which, in the Armstrong-Baeyer centric structure II, are responsible for the six "affinities" that are directed toward the middle of the ring. The

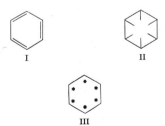

[29] E. Bamberger, *Ann.* **257**, 1 (1890); *Ber.* **24**, 1758 (1891); *Ann.* **273**, 373 (1893). Cf. also J. W. Armit and R. Robinson, *J. Chem. Soc.* **1925**, 1604.

situation can be readily visualized with the aid of structure III, in which, for the sake of clarity, the six electrons of the so-called *aromatic sextet* are indicated by asterisks, and the finer details of the binding have been ignored. Moreover, with a rather small number of exceptions, which are discussed below, and which may be only apparent, an analogous sextet, consisting of six *aromatic electrons*, can be found in every other recognized aromatic ring system, but is absent in every nonaromatic one. Thus, in the same sense in which the structure of benzene is represented as III, the structures of pyridine, pyrrole, and thiophene can be similarly represented as IV, V, and VI. (For discussion of the electrons which are here indicated by *dots*, see the paragraph, below in fine print.) The nonaromatic *p*-benzoquinone VII has only four aromatic electrons, and so no aromatic sextet can be formed. When, however, two additional electrons are added, as in the divalent hydroquinone anion VIII, the aromatic sextet becomes possible, and the aromatic character is restored. Conversely, when the pyrrole molecule is transformed into the cation IX by the addition of a proton, the aromatic sextet is destroyed, and so the cation should be relatively unstable. In this way, an explanation is provided for the extreme weakness of pyrrole as a base. Similarly, the acidity of cyclopentadiene is explained as resulting from the presence of six aromatic electrons in the anion X; on the other hand, the corresponding anion XI, derived from cycloheptatriene, has *eight* aromatic electrons, and so the hydrocarbon is not appreciably acidic. For the same reason, cycloöctatetraene XII would not be expected to exhibit aromatic character,

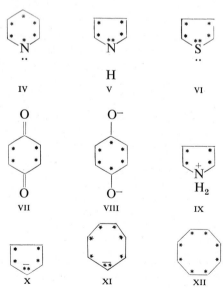

even though, from the viewpoint of Thiele's theory of partial valence, there is no obvious reason why this substance should be significantly different from benzene (cf., however, pages 144ff).

With a condensed ring system like that in naphthalene or pyrene, there are not enough aromatic electrons per molecule to permit each ring to have its own independent sextet.   Such substances are, however, definitely aromatic.   We shall therefore assume that, if an aromatic electron is contributed by an atom that is simultaneously a part of two, or three, different rings, then it can take part in the sextet in *each* of these rings. In this way, a sufficient number of (partially overlapping) sextets can be provided.

There is often some ambiguity regarding the numbers of electrons that are available for the formation of the aromatic sextets.   If the various electrons that are represented by dots rather than by asterisks are considered to be available in the present sense, then the molecules of pyridine, IV, and of thiophene, VI, have octets, and not merely sextets, of such electrons.   Bamberger[29] did not run into exactly this same difficulty in his original formulation of the theory since, in 1890, he obviously knew nothing about the role that electrons are now considered to play in chemical binding.   Instead, he spoke of the *affinities* of the several atoms, and he accordingly wrote the structures III, IV, V, and VI as III′, IV′, V′, and VI′, respectively.   The total number of lines ending at

III′   IV′   V′   VI′

any atom in one of these latter diagrams is equal to the total valence of that atom, so that carbon is here considered to be quadrivalent in all the compounds, nitrogen is considered to be trivalent in pyridine but quinquivalent in pyrrole, and sulfur is considered to be quadrivalent in thiophene.   These interpretations of the structures do not, however, remove the ambiguity, inasmuch as there is no obvious reason why nitrogen should not be quinquivalent in pyridine, as well as in pyrrole, or why sulfur should not be sexivalent in thiophene, as Bamberger doubtless considered it to be in sulfur trioxide. At the present time, the situation is much clearer than it was in 1890, for it is now recognized, on quantum-mechanical grounds, that the electrons belong to two principal classes, the sigma electrons and the pi electrons (cf. pages 63ff); that only the pi electrons can contribute to the aromatic sextet; and that no atom can have more than two of these "aromatic" pi electrons.   Thus, in structures IV and VI, the electrons that are represented by dots are sigma electrons, as are also the ones that are responsible for the valence bonds indicated by lines, and for the carbon-hydrogen bonds which, in these structures, are not explicitly mentioned.   Hence, of all the electrons associated with the atoms that form the rings, only the ones represented by asterisks are pi electrons. The more recent approach also removes a further difficulty that was inherent in the original theory.   In order to have a complete sextet of affinities for each of the rings in a hydrocarbon like naphthalene, Bamberger wrote such structures as XIII, in which

the two central carbon atoms are not directly bonded to each other in any way. Structures of this type, however, seem quite unreasonable, especially when used with a still
more complex hydrocarbon like pyrene XIV; and they have never been generally

XIII   XIV

accepted. From the modern viewpoint, however, each carbon atom makes use of its
sigma electrons for the formation of a bond to each of its immediate neighbours, and
then it still has its (aromatic) pi electron, or electrons, which can contribute to as many
different sextets as may be necessary.

As was mentioned above, there are a few substances which have more
or less aromatic character, but which do not seem to have an aromatic
sextet. One example of such a substance is given by azulene, which can
be described as a hybrid of the two equivalent structures XV and XVI,

XV   XVI

with smaller contributions from numerous other, less stable structures.
The resonance energy of azulene can be seen from Table 3·7 to be fairly
large, but only about half as great as that of the isomeric naphthalene.
In its chemical properties as well, azulene again shows an appreciable,
though reduced, aromatic behavior. Nevertheless, there is no obvious
aromatic sextet in either ring. Two ways out of this dilemma may be
suggested. In the first place, as will be more fully explained on pages
145f, the presence of altogether *ten* aromatic electrons might be expected
to lead to some special stability. In the second place, it has been found[30]
that, in the molecule of azulene, the aromatic electrons are not uniformly
distributed among the different carbon atoms; and it has been concluded
that they are instead concentrated to a greater extent in the five-membered
ring than in the seven-membered one (cf. also page 231). As a result,
since the former ring has, on the average, more than five aromatic electrons,
whereas the latter has fewer than seven such electrons, each ring is
approaching a condition such that the desired sextet is possible.

[30] G. W. Wheland and D. E. Mann, *J. Chem. Phys.* **17**, 264 (1949).

A second example of a substance which has considerable aromatic character, but no obvious sextet of electrons, is provided by tropolone XVII.[31] This substance has a resonance energy of about 20 kcal per

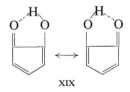

XVII   XVIII

mole (cf. Table 3·7) and, although it is relatively resistant to both oxidation and reduction, it enters into a number of substitution reactions, such as coupling with a diazonium salt, which are characteristic of phenols. Moreover, it further resembles phenols in that it appears to be completely enolic, and also in that it is an acid with an ionization constant of about 10^{-7}. (The corresponding value for the roughly analogous o-nitrophenol is 5.6×10^{-8}.)

Nevertheless, we cannot draw for tropolone any second structure that has approximately the same energy as XVII, unless we assume that the hydrogen atom of the hydroxyl group is equidistant from the two oxygen atoms, and hence that the structures XVII and XVIII correspond to the same relative positions of all the atomic nuclei and, in addition, are equivalent to each other. This assumption has been made by some authors, but it is now generally regarded as untenable. To be sure, there is presumably a hydrogen bond between the oxygen atoms but, since the added ring contains neither the six atoms nor the two double bonds that are ordinarily required (cf. Section 2·8), this bond is doubtless relatively weak. Consequently, there is here no reason to expect an exception to the general rule that the hydrogen atom in a bond of the type O—H – – – O is always considerably closer to one oxygen atom than it is to the other. If the special stability of tropolone were due to resonance between the structures XVII and XVIII, then the analogous compound XIX, with a

XIX

[31] For a comprehensive review of the chemistry of tropolone, and for additional references to the original literature, see J. W. Cook and J. D. Loudon, *Quart. Revs.* **5**, 99 (1951).

five-membered carboxyclic ring, ought to be similarly stabilized. Although this latter substance is not known, one of its monomethyl derivatives has been prepared[32] and has been found not to resemble tropolone in any significant respect; instead, it seems to exist in a typical tautomeric equilibrium among the expected structures XX, XXI, and XXII. Still

further evidence against the belief that resonance between the structures XVII and XVIII is an important factor contributing to the stability of tropolone has been derived from a study of the bond between the two carbon atoms that are linked to the oxygen atoms. This bond is single in each of the structures XVII and XVIII, and so, in the actual hybrid, it should be essentially different from the other carbon-carbon bonds of the ring. A crystal-structure investigation[33] of the copper salt has shown, however, that the seven carbon atoms lie very nearly at the corners of a regular plane heptagon, and that the carbon-carbon distances are about the same as in benzene. A completely similar result has also been obtained[34] in an electron-diffraction study of tropolone itself in the gaseous state; and in a crystal-structure study of tropolone hydrochloride.[35] Hence it can be concluded that the seven carbon-carbon bonds are at least approximately equivalent to one another, and that each is about halfway between a single and a double bond.

Thus it appears that the aromatic character of tropolone is anomalous, since it can be attributed neither to the presence of an aromatic sextet nor to resonance among stable structures with the same, or nearly the same, energies. The most likely explanation that has so far been offered is based on the assumption that the double bond of the carbonyl group is exceptionally ionic so that, as a first approximation, the molecule can be considered a hybrid of such structures as XXIII, XXIV, and XXV. This interpretation can be supported by several different kinds of argument. In the first place, we may note that, since tropolone does not undergo most of the usual reactions of an unsaturated ketone, there is some justification for the belief that its carbonyl group is exceptional. In

[32] E. Dane, J. Schmitt, and C. W. Rautenstrauch, *Ann.* **532**, 29 (1937).

[33] J. M. Robertson, *J. Chem. Soc.* **1951**, 1222.

[34] E. Heilbronner and K. Hedberg, *J. Am. Chem. Soc.* **73**, 1386 (1951); M. Kimura and M. Kubo, *Bull. Chem. Soc. Japan* **26**, 250 (1953).

[35] Y. Sasada, K. Osaki, and I. Nitta, *Acta Cryst.* **7**, 113 (1954).

the second place, we may further note that, in each of the structures XXIII, XXIV, XXV, and so on, there are just six aromatic electrons, and

XXIII	XXIV	XXV

hence that an aromatic sextet is now possible (cf. also the above discussion of azulene). Furthermore, since the structures under consideration are at least approximately equivalent, the carbon-carbon bonds should also be at least approximately equivalent. One may raise the objection that the individual structures like XXIII, XXIV, and XXV must be relatively unstable in consequence of their wide separation of electric charge. These structures are, however, rather numerous and, since the presence of an aromatic sextet should ensure that the resonance among them is particularly effective, they might well make larger contributions to the state of the hybrid than would ordinarily be expected. (See pages 144 and 146 for discussion of a possibly similar situation that arises with anthracene.) Some evidence bearing on this point is provided by a study[36] of the dipole moments of tropolone and of several of its simple alkyl derivatives; in this way it has been shown that the separation of charge is indeed considerable, but much smaller than would be observed if the molecule were a hybrid of *only* the ionic structures XXIII, XXIV, XXV, and their analogs (cf. Chapter 5). Although the situation is therefore still not entirely clear, the explanation which has just been offered seems nevertheless to contain enough truth so that it can be accepted as a useful working hypothesis.

The most conclusive evidence supporting the belief that a seven-membered ring with 6 pi electrons can have significant aromatic character has been obtained by Doering and Knox.[37] These authors have found that cycloheptatrienyl bromide, C_7H_7Br, is not a typical nonpolar substance, but is instead a salt, which is largely, if not entirely, dissociated into the cycloheptatrienyl cation $C_7H_7^+$ and the bromide anion Br^-. Since the former ion doubtless has the shape of a regular plane heptagon, it can be described as a hybrid of 7 completely equivalent structures in each of which there are just 6 aromatic electrons. Consequently, its

[36] M. Kubo, T. Nozoe, and Y. Kurita, *Nature* **167**, 688 (1951).

[37] W. v. E. Doering and L. H. Knox, *J. Am. Chem. Soc.* **76**, 3203 (1954).

observed exceptional stability lends more than a little support to the above interpretation of the properties of azulene and of tropolone.

Bamberger's concept of the aromatic sextet has so far been treated from only an empirical point of view, and no attempt has been made to derive it from any more fundamental principles. Let us now, however, consider what theoretical basis, if any, can be found for it. In the first place, we must admit that neither the theory of resonance nor the closely related valence-bond method for the quantum-mechanical treatment of molecular structure (cf. Sections 3·8, 9·19, and 9·20) lends much support to the idea that there must be exactly six aromatic electrons in every aromatic ring. Some very rough valence-bond calculations[38] have, to be sure, led to the conclusion that the cyclopentadienyl anion X should be appreciably more stable than the superficially analogous cycloheptatrienyl anion XI. There seems to be no way, however, in which the necessity for this particular conclusion can be explained nonmathematically in terms of resonance among the several valence-bond structures. Moreover, a quite different conclusion is reached when analogous calculations are made for cyclobutadiene, benzene, and cyclooctatetraene. Although only the second one of these hydrocarbons has the required six aromatic electrons, the possibilities for resonance are very similar in all three. In cyclobutadiene, there can be resonance between the structures XXVI and XXVII, which appear to be completely analogous to the Kekulé structures

XXVI   XXVII

for benzene; and, in cyclooctatetraene, there can be resonance among the two corresponding "Kekulé-like" structures XXVIII and XXIX and a number of such additional "Dewar-like" structures as XXX and XXXI.

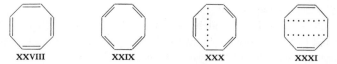

XXVIII   XXIX   XXX   XXXI

We might therefore feel justified in making the qualitative prediction that these two latter hydrocarbons, like benzene, ought to have large resonance energies, and hence ought to be aromatic. Indeed, from the more quantitative, but still only crudely approximate, calculations of the valence-bond type, the *predicted* resonance energies of cyclobutadiene and of cyclooctatetraene are found to be, respectively, about 30 and about 39 kcal per mole. (Cf. also Table 3·10, Section 3·8.)

[38] G. W. Wheland, *J. Chem. Phys.* **2**, 474 (1934).

Although, as we have just seen, no generally applicable justification for the concept of the aromatic sextet can be derived from the theory of resonance, there still remains the fact that aromatic character is encountered only when the sextet is indeed present (however, see the above discussions of azulene and of tropolone). In some instances, to be sure, the observations can be explained in an alternative way, which appears to be satisfactory, and which assigns no unique significance to the number six. With cycloöctatetraene, for example, the two structures XXVIII and XXIX are equivalent if the molecule has the symmetry of a regular plane octagon and if, therefore, each C—C—C bond angle is equal to 135°. Since, however, the normal value for this angle is more nearly 120°, the molecule would then be highly strained, and hence unstable. There is, in fact, reason to suppose that the most stable configuration would be one in which the ring is puckered into, say, the "tub" form XXXII. Under such circumstances, structures XXVIII and XXIX are

XXXII

not at all equivalent, since one of them is strain free whereas the other is highly strained by rotations about its double bonds. Consequently, the substance would have essentially the former, much more stable structure, with only a small contribution from the latter, less stable one; and the resonance energy should be small. This interpretation is in complete agreement with the available experimental evidence. From crystal-structure, electron-diffraction, and spectroscopic studies, the ring has been shown to be definitely puckered and probably in the tub form,[39] and the internuclear distances (cf. Section 4·3) have been found to be more nearly those expected for an individual one of the structures XXVIII and XXIX, than for a hybrid of the two. And, as is noted in Table 3·7 (Section 3·3), the resonance energy is indeed small.

In spite of its inherent reasonableness, however, this stereochemical explanation for the negligible effect of resonance in cyclooctatetraene is

[39] For a discussion of the evidence, see W. B. Person, G. C. Pimentel, and K. S. Pitzer, *J. Am. Chem. Soc.* **74**, 3437 (1952).

probably insufficient to provide a satisfactory and consistent interpretation of all the pertinent data. . In cyclobutadiene, both the maximum resonance energy and the minimum strain should result when the molecule is planar, and square. Consequently, there is here no geometrical factor of the kind in cycloöctatetraene, and so the compound should be almost as aromatic as is benzene itself. Since cyclobutadiene is not known, this prediction can be neither confirmed nor disproved by direct comparison with the experimental data, but it is almost certainly incorrect. The very fact that every one of the numerous attempts to prepare cyclobutadiene, or any simple derivative of it, has so far failed can be accepted as good evidence for the belief that, although the substance may not be incapable of existence, it can hardly have the high stability of a typical aromatic compound. Moreover, crystal-structure[40] and electron-diffraction[41] studies (cf. Section 4·3) have found that, in biphenylene, XXXIII, the two carbon-carbon bonds that link the benzene rings to each other have the lengths that are characteristic of ordinary single bonds. Hence, since it therefore appears that, in biphenylene, only a small weight can be assigned

XXXIII   XXXIV

to structure XXXIV, this substance cannot be considered a dibenzocyclo-butadiene in the same sense in which anthracene can be considered a dibenzobenzene. Once more, therefore, we come to the conclusion that cyclobutadiene can possess little, if any, aromatic character.

It has been suggested that the instability of cyclobutadiene is not due to any lack of resonance energy, but is instead the result of an exceptionally great strain in the molecule. This explanation, however, seems inadequate in view of the fact that extraordinary difficulties have not been encountered in the preparation of such other highly strained compounds as cyclobutene, or even cyclopropene. Furthermore, it fails also to account for the fact that, although the central ring in anthracene has approximately the shape of a regular hexagon, as is expected for an aromatic system, the corresponding ring in biphenylene is far from square (see above).

It should now be evident that some new principle not contained in the simple resonance theory must be found before the characteristic properties of aromatic ring systems can be completely understood. Some insight into the nature of this additional principle can be gained from the application of one of the alternative quantum-mechanical approaches to the problem of chemical binding. As we saw in Section 2·9, and as we shall

[40] J. Waser and C.-S. Lu, *J. Am. Chem. Soc.* **66**, 2035 (1944).
[41] J. Waser and V. Schomaker, *J. Am. Chem. Soc.* **65**, 1451 (1943).

explain later in much greater detail (see Sections 9·22–9·26), the individual electrons in any molecule can be considered to occupy certain molecular orbitals or, in other words, to move about the molecule in certain poorly defined, but more or less independent, paths.   Let us now apply this picture to a monocyclic molecule and, more precisely, to just its aromatic electrons, i.e., to just those electrons which are of the pi type represented by asterisks in structures III–XII on pages 135f.   Now, of the possible paths which the electrons can follow, there must be one which is more stable than any of the others.   This particular path can be shown to correspond to zero angular momentum about the center of the ring; hence an electron which follows this path, i.e., which occupies this orbital, does not move round the ring in either the clockwise or the counter-clockwise direction.   On the other hand, the remaining, less stable paths can be expected in general to correspond to nonzero angular momenta, so that the electrons that follow these paths do move round the ring in one or the other of the two directions.   Since the total energy of an electron cannot depend upon whether its motion is clockwise or counter-clockwise, these latter paths must occur in pairs, the two members of which are equivalent and have the same energy.

In the preceding paragraph, the discussion has been based not so much on the molecular-orbital treatment as on the closely related, but more general, *free-electron model*.   This model, which is described in greater detail in Section 9·28, involves the assumption that, in an aromatic molecule, the pi electrons can move freely round the perimeter of the ring, more or less as if this were constructed of a perfectly conducting wire.

We can now consider the assignment of the electrons to the several different paths, or orbitals.   Since we wish to obtain the most stable possible molecule, we must make use of the most stable possible paths. The *Pauli exclusion principle* (cf. Section 9·7), however, states that no more than two electrons can ever follow the same path, i.e., occupy the same orbital.   Hence we must adopt the following procedure.   First, we assign two electrons to the unique, most stable orbital; then we assign four more electrons to the two equivalent next-most-stable orbitals; and so on until we have taken care of all the aromatic electrons.   This pro-cedure is obviously analogous to the more familiar one in which a complex atom is considered to be built up by the successive addition of electrons to the initially bare nucleus.   Just as the especially stable and unreactive atoms of the rare gases are obtained when each electronic shell that is occupied at all is completely full, so also the most stable and least reactive molecules may be expected to result when there are no partially occupied groups of orbitals with the same energy, or, in other words, when the total number of aromatic electrons is equal to $2 + 4n$, where $n = 0, 1, 2,$

· · ·. The simplest case which satisfies this condition is that in which $n = 0$, and in which there are accordingly just two aromatic electrons; an example is provided by the molecule of ethylene, which may here be considered to contain a two-membered ring. The next simplest case is that in which $n = 1$, and in which there are accordingly six aromatic electrons; examples are provided by benzene, pyridine, pyrrole, thiophene, the cyclopentadienyl anion, and many other substances with more or less pronounced aromatic character (cf. pages 135f). When $n = 2, 3, · · ·$, there are ten, fourteen, · · · aromatic electrons. Single rings which are big enough to accommodate such large numbers of electrons could hardly be planar, however, and so, for the stereochemical reasons discussed above in connection with cyclooctatetraene, they would not be expected to be especially stable. In any event, no monocyclic aromatic compounds with such rings are now known (however, see below).

An important conclusion which can be derived from the foregoing argument is that, in spite of the qualitative and semiquantitative results of the resonance treatments, neither cyclobutadiene nor cyclooctatetraene should be aromatic (even if the molecule of the latter substance were planar). Indeed, the present treatment is in essential agreement with Bamberger's theory of the aromatic sextet, for which it provides a considerable amount of support.

With more complicated substances like naphthalene and anthracene, in which there are systems of condensed aromatic rings, the situation is rather less clear than it is with the monocyclic analogs. In naphthalene, for example, the bond that links the two central carbon atoms provides an alternative path for the electrons in their motions around the molecule; and, in anthracene, there are two such bonds. Some success has, however, been achieved with the aid of the assumption that these "cross linkages" introduce only small perturbations, so that, as a very rough first approximation, they can be ignored.[42] Naphthalene is therefore treated as if it were a slightly modified cyclodecapentaene; anthracene and phenanthrene are treated as if they were slightly modified cyclotetradecaheptaenes; and so on. Even though this procedure may seem unrealistic and arbitrary, it is at any rate in agreement with the fact that, with a few exceptions such as pyrene, the number of aromatic electrons in a condensed aromatic ring system is usually of the form $2 + 4n$. For example, naphthalene, anthracene, and phenanthrene have, respectively, 10, 14, and 14 such electrons. Moreover, azulene is like its isomer naphthalene in having 10 aromatic electrons, and it also exhibits a recognizable, though less extreme, aromatic character (cf. Table 3·7 and page 138). On the other hand, the superficially analogous pentalene

[42] For example, see J. R. Platt, *J. Chem. Phys.* **17**, 484 (1949).

XXXV, with only eight aromatic electrons, has as yet successfully resisted all the attempts that have been made to prepare it, and so it may be presumed to be either relatively unstable or very reactive (or both).

XXXV

In the preceding discussion of aromatic character, the emphasis has been placed upon the resonance energies of the substances of interest. There is, however, still another property which is also of considerable importance, and which here requires further comment. This property can be described in general terms as the identity of the ground state of the molecule. With noncyclic substances, and with such typical aromatic substances as benzene, naphthalene, pyrrole, azulene, and so on, the valence-bond (or resonance) and the molecular-orbital treatments seem always to be in complete agreement as to which of the innumerable electronic states is the one with the lowest energy. With some other substances, however, the two treatments are in complete *dis*agreement. A particularly flagrant example is provided by cyclobutadiene. According to the valence-bond treatment, the molecule of this substance in its ground state should have no unpaired electrons, and it should be diamagnetic. According to the molecular-orbital treatment, however, the molecule in its ground state should have two unpaired electrons, and it should be paramagnetic. Thus, the state which is found by the first treatment to be the ground one is found by the second treatment to be an excited one, and vice versa. The conclusion reached by each method is unambiguous, and is dependent upon no additional assumptions or approximations that are not inherent in the (very approximate) method itself.[43] A more complete disagreement could hardly be imagined. A second, and less extreme, example is provided by pentalene XXXV. Here, the two treatments agree that the molecule in its ground state should have no unpaired electrons and that it should be diamagnetic; they disagree, however, as to which of the diamagnetic states is the one with lowest energy. Again the discrepancy is complete and irreconcilable. Further examples are also known, but the two which have already been given are sufficient to show the kinds of difficulty that are encountered.

Since both the valence-bond and the molecular-orbital treatments are only approximate, it is not surprising that they should thus occasionally lead to different answers. When such disagreements are encountered,

[43] For example, see G. W. Wheland, *Proc. Roy. Soc.* (*London*) *A* **164**, 397 (1938).

however, one would naturally like to know whether either answer is trustworthy and, if so, which one. Unfortunately, this problem cannot at the present time be solved with any assurance. Appeal to experiment is quite impossible since the major discrepancies under consideration do not arise except with substances like cyclobutadiene and pentalene, which are unknown and which resist preparation. The only remaining way in which the problem can be attacked therefore consists in a more refined theoretical calculation. Although a rigorous treatment of any polyatomic molecule is out of the question in view of its extreme mathematical complexity, the crude and only semiquantitative treatments to which the discussion in this section has so far been restricted can nevertheless be materially improved. Craig[28] has, in fact, carried through an absolute, and hence completely quantitative, calculation for cyclobutadiene by an approximate procedure which is based on the "molecular-orbital method with configuration interaction" (cf. Section 2·9), but which is mathematically equivalent to the valence-bond method with consideration of resonance with not only the covalent structures XXVI and XXVII but also all the ionic ones like XXXVI, XXXVII, and so on. The conclusion

XXXVI   XXXVII

to which Craig was led by his somewhat improved calculations was that, as applied to cyclobutadiene, each of the earlier treatments is partly right and partly wrong. Thus, he found that, in agreement with the result of the simple valence-bond treatment, the molecule in its ground state probably has no unpaired electrons and is diamagnetic; but he found also that, in agreement with the result of the simple molecular-orbital treatment, the resonance energy is probably very small. If these conclusions are accepted as essentially correct, we see that cyclobutadiene can indeed be regarded as a resonance hybrid of the two structures XXVI and XXVII, in which all electrons are paired, but that its resonance energy is much smaller than analogy with the corresponding values for other apparently similar compounds would lead us to expect. If the *vertical* resonance energy (cf. Section 3·7) is so small that the molecule is not forced into a square configuration, then the four carbon-carbon bonds would have lengths very close to those characteristic of one or the other of the two contributing structures XXVI and XXVII, and the state of the molecule would be fairly accurately described by just that one structure. Under such circumstances, the *empirical* resonance energy would, of course, be extremely small.

No other compound besides cyclobutadiene has as yet been treated with comparable care.   Consequently, we have no basis for judging to what extent the results obtained for this substance can be generalized to other, more complicated ones.   Our best present procedure is therefore doubtless to place no confidence in the conclusions that are drawn by either of the simple methods for any compound with which the methods are in serious disagreement.   Craig[28] has stated a general rule by which, without any quantum-mechanical manipulations at all, such *pseudo-aromatic* compounds can be immediately recognized from their structures. For our purposes, however, it will here be sufficient to mention that no pseudo-aromatic compound has ever been prepared (except for cyclo-öctatetraene, which is not really pseudo-aromatic since its molecule is not planar).   Consequently, where we are dealing with known substances, we can have considerable confidence that the simple valence-bond and molecular-orbital treatments are in reasonably good agreement with each other, and hence that each is reasonably reliable.

3.10   Resonance Energy due to Hyperconjugation.   In Section 3·2, attention was called to the fact that the heat of hydrogenation of an olefin is appreciably decreased by the presence of alkyl substituents upon the unsaturated carbon atoms.   This effect has been explained by Mulliken and his co-workers[44] on the basis of a new type of conjugation, for which they have proposed the name "hyperconjugation."   Although some features of the ideas advanced by these authors are difficult to translate exactly into the language of the classical valence theory, the following discussion will explain the essential principles involved.   Later in this section, a further discussion along more conventional lines is given, and, in Section 9·27, the problem is reviewed from the same molecular-orbital viewpoint that was used by Mulliken, Rieke, and Brown.[44]

In propylene, I, the three hydrogen atoms of the methyl group have three valence electrons in all.   In acrylonitrile, II, the nitrogen atom

$$H_3C—CH{=}CH_2 \qquad\qquad N{\equiv}C—CH{=}CH_2$$
$$\text{I} \qquad\qquad\qquad\qquad\qquad \text{II}$$

similarly has three valence electrons.   (The two further electrons of the valence shell that form an unshared pair do not take part in the binding and so can be ignored here.)   This formal resemblance suggests that the

[44] R. S. Mulliken, C. A. Rieke, and W. G. Brown, *J. Am. Chem. Soc.* **63**, 41 (1941). Similar treatments had been applied earlier to other problems by G. W. Wheland, *J. Chem. Phys.* **2**, 474 (1934), and by J. W. Baker and W. S. Nathan, *J. Chem. Soc.* **1935**, 1844.   For comprehensive discussions, see C. L. Deasy, *Chem. Revs.* **36**, 145 (1945); J. W. Baker, *Hyperconjugation*, Oxford University Press, London, 1952; F. Becker, *Angew. Chem.* **65**, 97 (1953).

structure of propylene might profitably be written as III, so that it appears analogous to that of acrylonitrile.   The next logical step is to suppose that propylene is a resonance hybrid of the normal structure III and a less stable one IV, just as acrylonitrile is presumably a hybrid of the normal structure II and the less stable one V.   The resonance which results

$$H_3 \equiv C-CH=CH_2 \qquad H_3 \bar{=}C=CH-\overset{..}{\overset{..}{C}}H_2 \qquad \overset{..}{N}=C=CH-\overset{..}{\overset{..}{C}}H_2$$

III   IV   V

from the *hyperconjugation* of the methyl group with the double bond then stabilizes the molecule in the usual way and so reduces its heat of hydrogenation.   Similarly, in isobutylene, the hyperconjugation produces still greater stabilization as a result of resonance between the normal structure VI and the two less stable ones VII and VIII.   In general, the

$$H_3 \equiv C-\underset{\underset{\displaystyle H_3}{\overset{\displaystyle \|}{C}}}{C}=CH_2 \qquad H_3 \bar{=}C=\underset{\underset{\displaystyle H_3}{\overset{\displaystyle \|}{C}}}{C}-\overset{..}{\overset{..}{C}}H_2 \qquad H_3 \equiv C-\underset{\underset{\displaystyle \overset{..}{H_3}}{\overset{\displaystyle \|}{\overset{..}{C}}}}{C}-\overset{..}{\overset{..}{C}}H_2$$

VI   VII   VIII

stabilization is increased, and the heat of hydrogenation is decreased, as the number of alkyl substituents upon the unsaturated carbon atoms is increased.   These alkyl groups need not be methyl, as in propylene and isobutylene, since similar hyperconjugation is possible under other conditions as well.   The structures IX and X for 1-butene, for example, are

$$\begin{pmatrix} H_3C \\ H_2 \end{pmatrix} \!\! \equiv C-CH=CH_2 \qquad \begin{pmatrix} H_3\overset{..}{C} \\ H_2 \end{pmatrix} \!\! =C=CH-\overset{..}{\overset{..}{C}}H_2$$

IX   X

$$(CH_3)_3 \equiv C-CH=CH_2 \qquad (\overset{..}{C}H_3)_3 =C=CH-\overset{..}{\overset{..}{C}}H_2$$

XI   XII

analogous to III and IV, respectively, for propylene, as are also XI and XII for *tert*-butylethylene.

A further type of hyperconjugation, which may be called second-order hyperconjugation, can be supposed to result from the interaction of an alkyl group with a second alkyl group instead of with a double bond.

For ethane, for example, the structures XIII and XIV are analogous to XV and XVI, respectively, for cyanogen.

$$H_3\!\!\equiv\!\!C\!\!-\!\!C\!\!\equiv\!\!H_3$$

XIII

$$H_3\!\!=\!\!C\!\!=\!\!C\!\!=\!\!H_3$$

XIV

$$N\!\!\equiv\!\!C\!\!-\!\!C\!\!\equiv\!\!N$$

XV

$$N\!\!=\!\!C\!\!=\!\!C\!\!=\!\!N$$

XVI

The structures III, IV, and so on, are of such a radically different type from those with which chemists are familiar that one has difficulty in grasping their significance. For that reason, it is convenient to approach the problem of hyperconjugation from another, more or less equivalent, point of view. In propylene, for example, there can be resonance between the usual structure I and such less stable ones as XVII. Similarly, the second-order hyperconjugation in ethane can be related to the possibility

$$H_2C\!\!=\!\!CH\!\!-\!\!CH_2$$

$$H\cdots\cdots\cdots$$

XVII

$$\underset{\displaystyle H\;\;\; H}{H_2C\!\!-\!\!CH_2}$$

XVIII

$$H_2C\!\!=\!\!CH_2$$

$$H\cdots H$$

XIX

of resonance between the usual structure XVIII and such less stable ones as XIX.

In each of the structures XVII and XIX, and also in every further structure that is analogous to these two, there is always at least one atom which is represented as being not linked in any way to the particular other atom to which, in the real molecule, it is in fact bonded. For this reason, hyperconjugation is frequently known as *no-bond resonance*. One must not imagine, however, that the molecule is in any especially great danger of spontaneously breaking in two at the site of such a "no-bond." Since the relatively unstable structures XVII and XIX can have only small weights in the propylene and ethane molecules, the true structures of these substances cannot greatly differ from I and XVIII, respectively. Consequently, the hydrogen atoms which, in the *structures* XVII and XIX, appear to be essentially free are actually, in the *molecules* themselves, linked by strong bonds to the appropriate carbon atoms. The only effect of the resonance is therefore slightly to weaken the carbon-hydrogen bonds, and slightly to strengthen the carbon-carbon bonds that are written as double in structures XVII and XIX. In this respect, hyperconjugation is closely analogous to the ordinary conjugation in, for example, 1,3-butadiene where the resonance between the structures XX and XXI slightly weakens the terminal carbon-carbon bonds, and slightly

$$CH_2{=}CH{-}CH{=}CH_2 \qquad CH_2{-}CH{=}CH{-}CH_2$$

XX   XXI

strengthens the central one.   With both types of conjugation, the increases in the bond strengths always outweigh the decreases, so that the net effects of the resonance are always to make the molecules a little more stable than they would have been if their true structures had been identical with their conventional, most stable ones.

Hyperconjugation in propylene, for example, is often explained in terms of resonance between the classical structure I and the *ionic* "no-bonded" one XXII.   This alternative interpretation, however, does not necessarily add anything new to the one given above, since both the particular ionic structure XXII and the second one XXIII are already

$$H_2C{=}CH{-}\overset{..}{C}{-}H_2 \qquad\qquad H_2C{=}CH{-}C^+H_2$$

$$H^+ \qquad\qquad\qquad\qquad H{:}^-$$

XXII   XXIII

implied in the symbol XVII.   (See pages 45f.)   The situation is completely analogous with all other molecules in which hyperconjugation is considered to be involved.

Ordinary, or first-order, hyperconjugation, such as is present in propylene, appears to produce a resonance energy of about the same order of magnitude as does the conjugation between two double bonds, as in butadiene.   This is shown, for example, by the fact that the difference between the heats of hydrogenation of ethylene and propylene, on the one hand, is about the same as that between the heats of hydrogenation of 1,4-pentadiene and 1,3-butadiene, on the other.   However, the hyperconjugation never achieves an importance comparable with that of the resonance in benzene.   Consequently for most purposes it can be safely neglected, and only occasionally need it be taken explicitly into account. The second-order hyperconjugation, as in ethane, is probably even less important.   It is difficult to evaluate, however, because it can be assumed present in practically all imaginable substances (except for the very simplest ones like methane), and because, therefore, its effect may be expected to cancel whenever different substances are compared with each other.[45]   All the discussions in this book are, in the last analysis, based upon such comparisons and, consequently, we shall be justified in hereafter ignoring this second-order hyperconjugation.

[45] Cf. G. W. Wheland and J. T. Pinkston, Jr., *J. Chem. Phys.* **12**, 69 (1944).

Chapter 4   STERIC EFFECTS OF RESONANCE

4·1 Molecular Symmetry. One of the first ways in which the Kekulé structure of benzene was found to be inadequate was that it led to incorrect predictions of the numbers of isomeric substitution products $C_6H_nX_{6-n}$. The two structures I and II, for example, are definitely

different, and yet they correspond to only a single known substance, *o*-xylene. In order to explain this discrepancy, Kekulé himself postulated[1] that there was an "oscillation" (i.e., a rapid tautomerism) between the two structures, and other authors advanced various other explanations. The final solution of the problem was not found, however, until after the development of the theory of resonance, when it became apparent that *o*-xylene can possess neither of the structures I and II, but must be a resonance hybrid with a structure intermediate between them.

This question of isomer number is only a special case of a much more general problem, that of molecular symmetry. From studies of x-ray[2] and electron[3] diffraction, of dipole moments,[4] and of spectra,[5] it is now fairly definitely known that the six carbon atoms in a molecule of benzene are located at the corners of a regular plane hexagon, and that all six carbon-carbon bonds are equivalent to each other. The reason why the Kekulé structure does not give the correct number of isomers is essentially that it does not reproduce the true symmetry of the molecule.

The theory of resonance leads to a logical interpretation of the observed symmetry of benzene and also, as a corollary, of the observed isomer

---

[1] A. Kekulé, *Ann.* **162**, 77 (1872).

[2] L. O. Brockway and J. M. Robertson, *J. Chem. Soc.* **1939**, 1324.

[3] L. Pauling and L. O. Brockway, *J. Chem. Phys.* **2**, 867 (1934).

[4] J. W. Williams, *Fortschr. Chem., Physik. u. physik. Chem.* **20**, 257 (1930). C. P. Smyth, *Dielectric Constant and Molecular Structure*, Chemical Catalog Co., New York, 1931, Chapter VI.

[5] C. K. Ingold, *Proc. Roy. Soc. (London) A* **169**, 149 (1938); *Structure and Mechanism in Organic Chemistry*, Cornell University Press, Ithaca, N. Y., 1953, pp. 177f.

numbers as well. That this is true can be shown in the following way. Let us first consider resonance between only the two Kekulé structures III and IV. These are equivalent to each other and, consequently, must make identical contributions to the state of the molecule. No one of the carbon-carbon bonds can then be different in any way from any of the others. From this conclusion, we might not be justified in saying that the ring necessarily lies in a single plane, but most of the other features of the symmetry follow at once. (See the further discussion of the planarity of the molecule in Section 4·2.) The situation is not altered by a consideration of the three Dewar structures V, VI, and VII. These

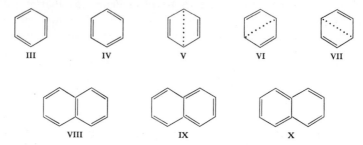

are equivalent to each other and so make identical small contributions. Taken together, therefore, they lead to the same molecular symmetry as do the two Kekulé structures.

With naphthalene, the Erlenmeyer structure VIII has the observed symmetry of the molecule and, as far as the present considerations are concerned, might be the actual structure of the substance. As was pointed out earlier, however, the large resonance energy shows that resonance with the two Erdmann structures IX and X must also be taken into account. Although these latter structures are not equivalent to the former one, they must be assigned approximately the same weight as VIII, since they have the same numbers of the same kinds of bond and so are of about the same stability. (However, see pages 608 and 639.) It is therefore necessary to make sure that they do not disturb the symmetry of the Erlemeyer structure. That they do not do so is almost obvious since, being equivalent to each other, they must be equally important in the resonance. As in benzene, there are a number of further, less stable structures with one or more formal bonds. One of these, XI, has the required symmetry itself, and the others can be grouped in sets of two or

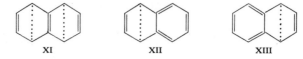

of four, such as XII and XIII, or XIV, XV, XVI, and XVII, respectively, in such a way that the original symmetry is not disturbed.

XIV   XV   XVI   XVII

Considerations similar to the foregoing apply to the other condensed aromatic ring systems. For some of these (for example, anthracene), no single structure without formal bonds reproduces the actual symmetry of the molecule, whereas for other (for example, phenanthrene) such structures can be written. However, the correct symmetry is always automatically accounted for when we realize that equivalent structures must be given identical weights.

The problem of molecular symmetry is not limited to the aromatic hydrocarbons. For example, the existence of only a single α-methyl-pyridine (or, in other words, the equivalence of the two carbon-nitrogen bonds in pyridine) follows from the equal contributions of the two Kekulé-like structures, XVIII and XIX, in the unsubstituted molecule.

XVIII   XIX

An example of a different type, in which the question of isomer number is not directly involved, is provided by the carbonate ion. From investigations of crystal structure,[6] this ion is known to lie entirely in one plane, with the oxygen atoms at the corners, and the carbon atom at the center, of an equilateral triangle. Each of the three carbon-oxygen bonds is therefore of the same length as the other two, and so is presumably equivalent to them in all other respects as well; and each of the angles between any two of these bonds is equal to 120°. Such a geometrical arrangement is inconsistent with any one of the three equivalent structures XX, XXI, and XXII alone, but is an immediate consequence of resonance among them all. In the same sense in which we speak of one-and-a-half

XX   XXI   XXII

[6] N. Elliott, *J. Am. Chem. Soc.* **59**, 1380 (1937).

bonds in benzene, we can describe the situation here in terms of one-and-a-third bonds.   In the nitrate ion also, resonance among the three corresponding structures, XXIII, XXIV, and XXV, leads to the same

trigonal symmetry, so that again the three bonds are equivalent and the three angles are each 120°.   Similarly, the equivalence of the two oxygen atoms in a carboxylate ion,[7] or in a nitro group,[8] is ensured by the resonance between the structures XXVI and XXVII, or XXVIII and XXIX,

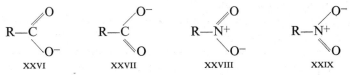

respectively.   In each of these latter examples, the resonance is between only two equivalent structures, and so the resulting equivalent bonds can be described as one-and-a-half bonds.   (In regard to the suitability of the terms "one-and-a-half bonds" and "one-and-a-third bonds" see Section 4·4.)

As was pointed out on pages 111f, the conventional structure XXX of carbon dioxide describes the two different but equivalent charge distributions that can be depicted as XXXI and XXXII; and the great stability

$$O{=}C{=}O \qquad\qquad \overset{**}{:}\overset{\;\;oo}{O}\!:\!\overset{o}_{o}C\!:\!\overset{*}_{*}\overset{}{O}: \qquad\qquad :\overset{oo}{O}\!:\!\overset{*}_{*}C\!:\!\overset{o}_{o}\overset{**}{O}:$$

          XXX   XXXI   XXXII

of the substance must be largely due to the resonance between these distributions.   We are now, however, in position to consider a still further important effect of the resonance.   Neither of the structures XXXI and XXXII is cylindrically symmetrical about the molecular axis, and neither has a center of symmetry.   Furthermore, although each of the less stable structures XXXIII and XXXIV is cylindrically symmetrical, neither has

$$:O^{+}{\equiv}C{-}\overset{..}{O}\!:^{-} \qquad\qquad :\overset{..}{O}^{-}{-}C{\equiv}O\!:^{+}$$

          XXXIII   XXXIV

[7] L. Pauling and L. O. Brockway, *Proc. Natl. Acad. Sci. U. S.* **20**, 336 (1934); L. Pauling and J. Sherman, *ibid.* 340 (1934); W. H. Zachariasen, *Z. Krist.* **89**, 442 (1934); *Phys. Rev.* **53**, 917 (1938); J. M. Robertson and I. Woodward, *J. Chem. Soc.* **1936**, 1817.   See also the Appendix.

[8] L. O. Brockway, J. Y. Beach, and L. Pauling, *J. Am. Chem. Soc.* **57**, 2693 (1935); A. J. Stosick, *ibid.* **61**, 1127 (1939).   See also the Appendix.

a center of symmetry. However, since the structures XXXI and XXXII make equal contributions to the state of the hybrid, as do also the less important ones XXXIII and XXXIV, the actual molecule must be cylindrically symmetrical, and it must have a center of symmetry.[9] This conclusion has been completely confirmed by spectroscopic evidence.[10]

Numerous further examples, similar to the foregoing, could be mentioned, but no attempt will here be made to give an exhaustive survey of the field. The reader should now be able to apply the above principles to any other ions or molecules that may be of interest, such as the guanidinium ion or the nitrogen dioxide molecule.

4·2 Coplanarity. In biphenyl, the most important resonance is that involving the two Kekulé structures of each ring separately. Less stable structures can be written, however, and a completely satisfactory description of the molecule may require that these also be given appreciable, though small, weights. A number of these additional structures are of the type of I, in which a formal bond is drawn from one ring to the other, and in which a double bond connects the two rings. Now, if structure I

I

(or any of the other ones of the same type) were the actual structure of biphenyl, elementary stereochemical considerations would require that all six atoms marked with asterisks lie in the same plane. In reality, such structures are rather unimportant in the resonance, but the possibility remains that their effect upon the properties of the substance may be sufficient to make this particular arrangement of the atoms more stable than any other. If so, then the entire molecule would tend to be planar, inasmuch as the two benzene rings are themselves planar.

An idea of the magnitude of the forces acting to produce coplanarity of the two rings can be obtained by treating the problem from a slightly different point of view. The reason why resonance with such structures as I might be expected to favor the planar configuration is that these structures are most stable, and hence should lead to the largest possible resonance energy, when the molecule is planar. Consequently, if the resonance were the only factor restricting the freedom of rotation about the central carbon-carbon bond, the maximum energy barrier to such rotation ought not to be greater than the amount by which the resonance

[9] Cf. R. S. Mulliken, *J. Chem. Phys.* 3, 720 (1935).

[10] Cf. G. Herzberg, *Infrared and Raman Spectra of Polyatomic Molecules*, D. Van Nostrand Co., New York, 1945, pp. 21, 272.

energy of biphenyl exceeds twice that of benzene. Now in Section 3·3, we saw that biphenyl receives no appreciable additional stabilization from the conjugation of the two rings with each other (cf. Table 3·7, Section 3·3). Apparently, therefore, we must conclude that the contributions of structure I and of its numerous analogs are insufficient to produce a significant preference for the planar configuration. On the other hand, if the two rings are *forced* to be coplanar, as in fluorene, the resonance energy is increased by about 5 kcal per mole. Although this difference is so small that we can perhaps not be entirely certain of its reality, both its existence and its order of magnitude are nevertheless rather reasonable. In biphenyl, the steric repulsions of the hydrogen atoms in the four ortho positions may well be large enough to overcome the tendency of the rings to be coplanar. Under such circumstances, the molecule would then have a nonplanar configuration, and it would gain little or no stabilization from the resonance with the highly strained structures like I. In fluorene, on the other hand, the steric repulsions should be only half as great as they are in biphenyl, and the five-membered ring should hold the molecule more or less rigidly in the planar configuration. Consequently, although we might not have expected the additional resonance energy to be so great as is apparently observed, we cannot be surprised that fluorene is relatively somewhat more stable than biphenyl.

The problem of coplanarity in biphenyl can be studied by other experimental methods which do not explicitly involve the resonance energy. In an investigation of the crystal structure of the solid substance,[11] the molecule has been found to lie entirely in a single plane. This result is somewhat in conflict with the conclusions reached in the preceding paragraph, but its significance is not entirely clear. In a crystal, there must be large intermolecular forces, and these could easily distort the molecules from their preferred configurations; one might also anticipate that planar molecules could be more compactly and more efficiently packed in the solid than nonplanar ones. The investigations of biphenyl in the gas phase and in solution have been somewhat inconclusive. From a study of electron diffraction, Bastiansen[12] has concluded that, in the molecules of biphenyl and of its simple derivatives, the planes of the two aromatic rings form an angle of about 50° with each other. This value, however, is far from precise, and it may be rather seriously in error. Moreover, the fact that the ultraviolet spectrum of biphenyl is diffuse, whereas the corresponding spectra of its planar analogs (such as fluorene,

[11] J. Dhar, *Indian J. Phys.* **7**, 43 (1932); *Proc. Natl. Inst. Sci. India* **15**, 11 (1949) [*C. A.* **43**, 4655 (1949)].

[12] O. Bastiansen, *Acta Chem. Scand.* **3**, 408 (1949). See also I. L. Karle and L. O. Brockway, *J. Am. Chem. Soc.* **66**, 1974 (1944).

biphenylene oxide, etc.) are much sharper, has been cited[13] as evidence that, in the gaseous state and in solution, the molecule of biphenyl is not planar. (However, see the paragraph below in fine print.) On the other hand, certain other characteristics of the ultraviolet spectra, which will be more fully described in Section 6·8, can apparently be explained only on the assumption that this molecule is planar or, at any rate, approximately so.

The preferred configuration of the biphenyl molecule is therefore still not certainly established. Probably the best present view is that this molecule is not completely planar, but that its departure from planarity is only moderate. In any event, there is good evidence[12] that the substance is not restricted to the extreme configuration in which the two rings are mutually perpendicular. Presumably, the rotation about the central carbon-carbon bond is more or less free, but the molecule spends a large fraction of its time in the configurations that are near the planar one. Hence, although the experimental evidence is far from conclusive, we can nevertheless feel fairly safe in believing that the configuration of biphenyl is largely determined by the two factors which have already been mentioned, i.e., by the steric repulsions and by the resonance effect; and that these factors are fairly evenly matched. There does, however, seem to be a small, but recognizable, tendency toward coplanarity.

If, as has just been suggested, there is an appreciable freedom of rotation about the central carbon-carbon bond in biphenyl, this circumstance alone would doubtless be sufficient to explain the diffuseness of the ultraviolet spectrum[13] (see above); for, since the energy of the molecule must be somewhat dependent upon its configuration, and since different molecules may at any given time have different configurations, the energy change that is involved in the electronic transition (cf. Chapter 6) must be rather indefinite. On the other hand, with such other compounds as fluorene, biphenylene oxide, etc., the planar molecules are held rigidly in unique configurations, and so their energies are much more precisely determined. In other words, the diffuseness of the biphenyl spectrum may be due primarily to the nonrigidity, rather than to the nonplanarity, of the molecule.

The principle of coplanarity is, as we have seen, a rather unprecise one. It refers only to the tendency of a molecule to approach a planar configuration, and it does not imply that that molecule must always be exactly planar. The principle is, however, a very general one since it applies to any molecule with conjugated double bonds. 1,3-Butadiene, nitrobenzene, and benzaldehyde, for example, should also tend to lie entirely in one plane. We have, in fact, already made use of this principle in our discussion of cyclooctatetraene (cf. pages 143f). A different type of structure which should similarly lead to coplanarity is illustrated by the

---

[13] E. Merkel and C. Wiegand, *Z. Naturforsch.* **3b**, 93 (1948).

carboxyl and carboalkoxyl groups. In methyl formate, for example, there is apparently resonance between the structures II and III; the effect

$$\underset{\text{II}}{H-C\underset{O-CH_3}{\overset{O}{\big<}}} \qquad\qquad \underset{\text{III}}{H-C\underset{O^+-CH_3}{\overset{O^-}{\big<}}}$$

of the second of these should be to make the carbon atom of the methyl group lie in the plane formed by the four atoms of the formate radical. Since the resonance energy of a carboalkoxyl group is apparently rather large (Table 3·7, Section 3·3) the resistance to deformation out of the plane should be relatively great in esters of this sort. In Section 5·6, we shall see some experimental evidence that supports this expectation.

A closely related structure, in which coplanarity can again be anticipated, is that of a vinyl or aryl ether. Ethyl vinyl ether, for example, presumably receives a small contribution from the relatively unstable structure IV (cf. pages 85f); and anisole presumably receives similar small contributions from the corresponding structures V, VI, and VII (cf. pages 106f and

$$\underset{\text{IV}}{CH_3-CH_2-O^+=CH-\overset{\cdot\cdot}{C}^-H_2}$$

$$\underset{\text{VIII}}{CH_2=CH-O^+=CH-\overset{\cdot\cdot}{C}^-H_2} \qquad \underset{\text{IX}}{\overset{\cdot\cdot}{C}^-H_2-CH=O^+-CH=CH_2}$$

also Section 5·6). With vinyl ether, on the other hand, the construction of a scale model shows that no planar configuration in which each of the structures VIII and IX is strain free can be achieved unless atoms which are not directly bonded to each other are forced to come unreasonably close together. Since it is therefore unlikely that the molecule is completely planar, the conclusion that the resonance energy of vinyl ether is no greater than that of ethyl vinyl ether (cf. Section 3·2) is now seen to be not unreasonable.

Still another type of structure with which resonance similarly favors the planar configuration can be illustrated by pyrrole. Although both the conventional structure X and the less stable one XI, with a formal bond, should here be most stable when the nitrogen atom is pyramidal,

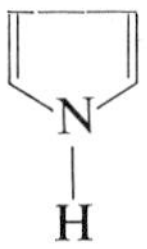

X 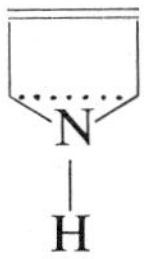 XI 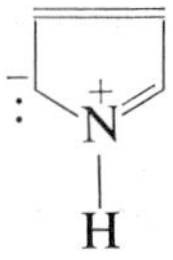 XII

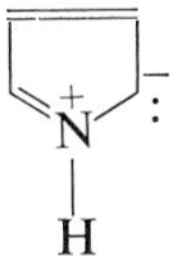

XIII 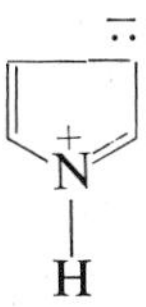 XIV 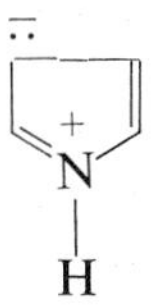 XV

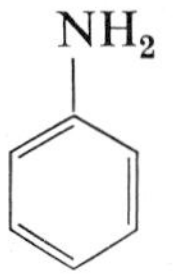

XVI 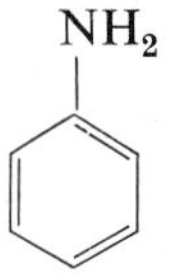 XVII 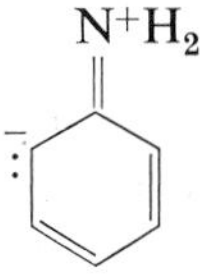 XVIII 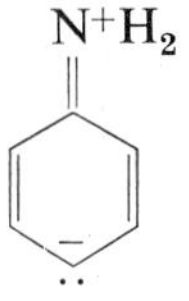 XIX 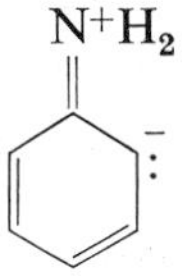 XX

the further structures XII–XV (cf. Section 3·2 for a discussion of the analogous resonance in furan) are doubtless most stable when the molecule is completely planar. Since the effects due to the two groups of structures are therefore in opposition, no definite prediction can be made. From studies of dipole moment,[14] however, it has been concluded that the angle between the N—H bond and the plane of the ring must be less than 7°; and from an analysis of the microwave absorption spectrum,[15] it has been concluded that this angle is actually 0°. Apparently, therefore, the molecule is planar. With aniline, on the other hand, the somewhat analogous resonance among the structures XVI–XX has no corresponding effect, and the nitrogen atom is definitely pyramidal.[16] The difference between these

[14] H. Kofod, L. E. Sutton, and J. Jackson, *J. Chem. Soc.* **1952**, 1467.

[15] W. S. Wilcox and J. H. Goldstein, *J. Chem. Phys.* **20**, 1656 (1952).

[16] This conclusion is based principally upon dipole-moment studies with aromatic amines. See, for example, L. Tiganik, *Z. physik. Chem.* B **14**, 135 (1931); L. E. Sutton, *Trans. Faraday Soc.* **30**, 789 (1934); R. J. B. Marsden and L. E. Sutton, *J. Chem. Soc.* **1936**, 599; K. B. Everard and L. E. Sutton, *ibid.* **1951**, 2818.

two compounds is quite reasonable since, although the structures XVIII–XX lead to only a small stabilization of the aniline molecule (cf. pages 107 and 372f), the corresponding structures XII–XV are apparently responsible for a much greater stabilization of pyrrole (cf. page 99).

Some fairly satisfactory, but not entirely conclusive, evidence that the molecule of biphenyl tends to be planar in the gaseous and liquid states has already been given. Additional, and perhaps less inconclusive, evidence will be given later in Sections 6·3–6·8 both for biphenyl and for a number of other substances belonging to the several foregoing types. Coplanarity in the *solid* phase, on the other hand, has been demonstrated in a number of substances besides biphenyl (see above) by the determination of their crystal structures. In this way, the molecules of the following substances have been found to lie in a single plane: terphenyl, quaterphenyl, *trans* stilbene, *trans* azobenzene, diphenylacetylene, diphenylbiacetylene, cyanuric triazide, the tricyanmelamine ion, 1,3,5-trinitrobenzene, oxalic acid, and numerous others. (See the Appendix for additional planar molecules, and for the references to the original papers.) Coplanarity is not universal, however, as a certain number of exceptions do exist. The ring in cyclooctatetraene, for example, is puckered, presumably because of the strain in the eight-membered ring (cf. pages 143f). The two benzene rings in any of the optically active biphenyls[17] are necessarily noncoplanar, since the achievement of coplanarity would result in racemization. These substances do not form significant exceptions to the general rule, however, because the steric interactions between the bulky substituents in the 2, 6, 2′, and 6′ positions are certainly very large. For the same reason, the observed lack of coplanarity in solid *o*-diphenylbenzene[18] and *cis* azobenzene is only to have been expected. On the other hand, there are a few examples in which the molecules have been found to be not entirely planar even in the absence of an important steric effect. This is true, for example, of 1,3,5-triphenylbenzene,[19] *trans* stilbene, *trans* azobenzene, and the oxalate ion in ammonium oxalate monohydrate. Exceptions of this type are not very common but, since we know little about the intermolecular forces in solids, we are probably not justified in drawing definite conclusions from any of these results of crystal-structure determinations. (The reason why

---

[17] See R. L. Shriner, R. Adams, and C. S. Marvel in H. Gilman, *Organic Chemistry*, John Wiley & Sons, New York, 1st ed., 1938, vol. I., pp. 259ff; 2nd ed., 1943, vol. I., pp. 343ff.

[18] C. J. B. Clews and K. Lonsdale, *Proc. Roy. Soc. (London) A* **161**, 493 (1937).

[19] K. Lonsdale, *Z. Krist.* **97**, 91 (1937); M. S. Farag, *Acta Cryst.* **7**, 117 (1954). See also O. Bastiansen, *Acta Chem. Scand.* **6**, 205 (1952) for electron-diffraction evidence that the molecule of 1,3,5-triphenylbenzene is nonplanar in the gas phase.

trans stilbene and *trans* azobenzene appear in the lists of both the planar and nonplanar molecules is that the crystals of these substances contain two sterically different kinds of molecule.   For each compound, half the molecules are planar and half are not.)

4·3 Interatomic Distances.   There are several experimental methods for the measurement of bond lengths or, in other words, of the distances between atoms joined by valence bonds.   It will not be possible here to describe any of these in detail, but a few words regarding the fields of usefulness, and the limitations, of each may be of interest.

The spectroscopic method[20, 21] is the most precise of all, when it can be rigorously applied to a substance in the gaseous state.   Under favorable circumstances, it can give a bond length to within a few thousandths of an angstrom unit.   Unfortunately, however, it is restricted to simple molecules, and the reliability of the results to which it leads is usually open to some question if the molecule contains more than a very few atoms.   For that reason, it is of limited use in the study of organic compounds.   Two comparatively recent developments, however, have made possible the extension of this method to molecules which, although still simple from the viewpoint of organic chemistry, are nevertheless considerably more complex than any that could have been treated even a few years ago.   In the first place, by comparing the spectra of substances which have the same chemical structure but differ in isotopic composition, one can now obtain a great deal of additional information regarding the sizes and shapes of the individual molecules.   In the second place, by studying the pure-rotation spectra in the microwave region (i.e., at a wave length of approximately 1–5 cm), one can now avoid the complications that are introduced by vibrational or electronic transitions, and that are unavoidable in the Raman, infrared, visible, and ultraviolet spectra (cf. Section 6·1).

The methods based upon the diffraction of x-rays by crystals[22] or of

---

[20] D. M. Dennison, *Revs. Mod. Phys.* **12**, 175 (1940).

[21] G. Herzberg, *Molecular Spectra and Molecular Structure*, I, *Spectra of Diatomic Molecules*, D. Van Nostrand Co., New York, 2nd ed., 1950; *Infrared and Raman Spectra of Polyatomic Molecules*, D. Van Nostrand Co., New York, 1945.

[22] For further discussions of the x-ray method, see R. W. G. Wyckoff, *The Structure of Crystals*, Chemical Catalog Co., New York, 1931; M. J. Buerger, *X-Ray Crystallography*, John Wiley & Sons, New York, 1942; I. Fankuchen in A. Weissberger, *Physical Methods of Organic Chemistry*, Interscience Publishers, New York, 1st ed., 1945, vol. I, Chapter XIV, 2nd ed., 1949, vol. I, part II, Chapter XVIII; K. Lonsdale, *Crystals and X-Rays*, D. Van Nostrand Co., New York, 1949; J. M. Bijvoet, N. H. Kolkmeyer, and C. H. Macgillavry, *X-Ray Analysis of Crystals* (based on a translation by H. L. Furth), Interscience Publishers, New York, 1951; J. M. Robertson, *Organic Crystals and Molecules*, Cornell University Press, Ithaca, N. Y., 1953.

electrons by gases[23] are rather less precise than the spectroscopic one. By either of these methods, a bond length can ordinarily be measured to within, at best, a few hundredths of an angstrom unit.   The restriction to simple molecules is not so serious here as with the spectroscopic method, so that relatively complex organic molecules can often be treated satisfactorily.   However, each of the diffraction methods is subject to an awkward difficulty which is not shared by the spectroscopic one, namely, that, except under certain rare circumstances,[24] the complete structure of the crystal or molecule cannot be calculated *directly* from the positions and intensities of the lines, spots, or rings appearing on the x-ray or electron-diffraction photographs.   Instead, an indirect procedure must be adopted; this consists in finding (usually by trial and error, at any rate in the concluding steps) a structure which leads to a calculated diffraction photograph identical with the observed.   Since the structure of the crystal or molecule is often defined by a large number of parameters which can be varied independently of each other, the search for the best set of values may be, and usually is, extremely tedious.   As a result, the precision that is permitted by the method itself is not always achieved in practice.   (It should, however, be mentioned that, as soon as a fairly accurate structure has been derived by trial and error, a Fourier analysis of the x-ray, but not of the electron-diffraction, photographs can sometimes lead directly to a final solution.[25]   Such a procedure is extremely laborious, but it seems now to be becoming almost standard practice.) Since neither x-rays nor electrons are very effectively scattered by extremely light atoms, the positions of hydrogen atoms cannot be precisely determined by either of the two methods just mentioned.   Recently, however, the protons in a few simple molecules have been located by *neutron* diffraction (cf. pages 55f).

In a strict sense, the length of a covalent bond does not have a unique value, because the two atoms that are linked by it are constantly in motion with respect to each other. Consequently, when we speak of a "bond length" or of an "interatomic distance," we have reference not to the actual distance between the atoms themselves, but instead either to the *average* distance of the nuclei, or else to the distance r_e (see Figure 2·2, Section 2·6) at which the mutual potential energy is a minimum.   These latter two distances are not necessarily exactly equal to each other, but the difference between them is so small that it may here be ignored.

[23] For further discussions of the electron-diffraction method, see L. O. Brockway, *Revs. Mod. Phys.* **8**, 231 (1936); in A. Weissberger, *Physical Methods of Organic Chemistry*, Interscience Publishers, New York, 1st ed., 1945, vol. I, Chapter XV, 2nd ed., 1949, vol. I, part II, Chapter XIX.

[24] For an example (phthalocyanine), see J. M. Robertson, *J. Chem. Soc.* **1936**, 1195.

[25] For an example (naphthalene), see S. C. Abrahams, J. M. Robertson, and J. G. White, *Acta Cryst.* **2**, 233, 238 (1949).

Before the rather extensive data regarding bond lengths can be interpreted in terms of resonance among various structures, a method must be established by which the bond lengths in molecules that are not resonance hybrids can be predicted. For this purpose, use can be made of the important empirical rule that the length of a pure single, double or triple covalent bond between a given pair of atoms usually varies only slightly

TABLE 4·1

LENGTHS OF PURE SINGLE, DOUBLE, AND TRIPLE BONDS

Type of Bond	Length Calculated[a]	Observed[b]	Substance
C—H	1.07 (1.10)	1.07	Chloroform
		1.07	Hydrogen cyanide
		1.10	Methyl chloride
		1.09	Methane
		1.06	Acetylene
		1.08	Ethylene oxide
N—H	1.00 (1.03) ·	0.99	Isocyanic acid
		1.01	Isothiocyanic acid
		1.01	Ammonia
O—H	0.96 (0.98)	0.96	Water
S—H	1.34 (1.37)	1.33	Hydrogen sulfide
C—C	1.54 (1.54)	1.54	Diamond
		1.50	Acetyl fluoride
		1.46	Methyl cyanide
		1.54	Ethane
		1.54	Cyclopropane
		1.55	Acetone
		1.47	Dimethylacetylene
		1.47	Diketopiperazine
		1.51	Succinic acid[c]
		1.50	Succinic acid[d]
		1.54	2-Butene (cis)
		1.54	Isobutylene
		1.44	Pimelic acid[c]
		1.49	Pimelic acid[e]
		1.50	Pimelic acid[f]
		1.54	Hexamethylethane[g]
		1.58	Hexamethylethane[d]
		1.53	Hexamethylbenzene[h]
		1.46	Bibenzyl[d]

TABLE 4·1 (*contd.*)

Type of Bond	Length Calculated[a]	Observed[b]	Substance
C—N	1.47 (1.46)	1.46	Nitromethane
		1.47	Methyl azide
		1.47	Methylamine hydrochloride
		1.43	Methyl isocyanide
		1.39	Glycine
		1.46	Dimethylnitroamine
		1.47	1,2-Dimethylhydrazine
		1.50	Alanine (racemic)
		1.49	Trimethylamine oxide
		1.41	Diketopiperazine[i]
		1.45	N-Acetylglycine[i]
		1.49	Threonine
C—O	1.43 (1.42)	1.43	Methyl alcohol
		1.44	Ethylene oxide
		1.40	Trioxane
		1.44	Dioxane
		1.37	Pentaerythritol tetranitrate
		1.42	Cyclohexene oxide
		1.41	Bi-1,3-dioxacyclopentyl[j]
C—S	1.81 (1.81)	1.82	Ethylene sulfide
		1.78	Dimethyl trisulfide
		1.81	Thioacetaldehyde trimer
C—F	1.41 (1.36)	1.36	Methylene fluoride
		1.39	Methyl fluoride
C—Cl	1.76 (1.71)	1.76	Fluorotrichloromethane
		1.76	Carbon tetrachloride
		1.77	Chloroform
		1.78	Methyl chloride
		1.78	Ethylene chloride
		1.74	Neopentyl chloride
C—Br	1.91 (1.88)	1.94	Carbon tetrabromide
		1.94	Methyl bromide
		1.94	Ethylene bromide
C—I	2.10 (2.09)	2.12	Methylene iodide
		2.14	Methyl iodide
C=C	1.34 (1.35)	1.35	Ethylene
		1.34	1-Methylcyclobutene
		1.34	Methylenecyclobutane

TABLE 4·1 (*contd.*)

Type of Bond	Length Calculated[a]	Observed[b]	Substance
C=N	1.28	1.29	Acetoxime
	(1.27)	1.31	*p*-Chlorobenzaldoxime (syn)
C=O	1.24	1.21	Formaldehyde
	(1.225)	1.22	Acetone
C≡C	1.20	1.21	Chloroacetylene
		1.20	Acetylene
		1.21	Methylacetylene
C≡N	1.15	1.16	Cyanogen chloride
		1.15	Hydrogen cyanide
		1.16	Methyl cyanide
		1.16	Cyanocamphor

[a] In angstrom units. The values which are not in parentheses are obtained from L. Pauling, *The Nature of the Chemical Bond*, Cornell University Press, Ithaca, N. Y., 1st ed., 1939, p. 154; 2nd ed., 1940, p. 164. The values which are in parentheses are obtained, for single bonds, from V. Schomaker and D. P. Stevenson, *J. Am. Chem. Soc.* **63**, 37 (1941); and for double bonds, from W. Gordy, *J. Chem. Phys.* **15**, 81 (1947).

[b] In angstrom units. For probable errors, statements of experimental methods, and references to the original literature, see the Appendix.

[c] This value applies to the bond adjacent to the carboxyl group.

[d] This value applies to the distance between the two central carbon atoms.

[e] This value applies to the distance between the α and β carbon atoms.

[f] This value applies to the distance between the β and γ carbon atoms.

[g] This value applies to the distance between one of the methyl carbon atoms and the central carbon atom to which it is joined.

[h] This value applies to the distance between one of the methyl carbon atoms and the atom of the benzene ring to which it is joined.

[i] This value applies to the distance between the nitrogen atom and the carbon atom of the methylene group.

[j] This value is the average of four different ones, ranging from 1.40 to 1.42 A, which were found for the eight essentially equivalent C—O bonds.

from molecule to molecule. The extent to which this generalization is valid, and the limitations to which it is subject, are illustrated by the data in the third column of Table 4·1. (A much more complete table of bond lengths in molecules of various types is given in the Appendix. The reader will find it advantageous to examine this larger list in order to obtain a better idea of the extent and self-consistency of the data.) It is seen that, on the whole, the observed interatomic distances are indeed very nearly constant. The length of the carbon-hydrogen bond, for example, varies only within the range 1.06–1.10 A, in a series of different molecules; that of the carbon-chlorine bond varies similarly within the range 1.74–1.78 A; and so on. However, there are a number of exceptions in which the variations are larger than the foregoing. For example, the length of a carbon-carbon single bond, which has a nearly constant value of 1.54 A in diamond and in most of the other substances investigated, is decreased to 1.46 A in methyl cyanide, and to 1.47 A in dimethylacetylene and diketopiperazine; in general it seems to be true that a carbon-carbon single bond is appreciably shortened when it is adjacent to a triple bond or (with the exception of acetone, which differs here from its analogs) to a carbon-oxygen double bond. Strangely enough, however, a carbon-carbon single bond that is adjacent to a carbon-carbon double bond, as in isobutylene, or to an aromatic ring, as in hexamethylbenzene, seems usually to be little if any shorter than normal. In a few molecules, carbon-carbon single bonds that are adjacent only to other single bonds appear also to be anomalously short; examples are given by succinic and pimelic acids, and by bibenzyl. Some of the remaining kinds of bond show similar variations. The carbon-nitrogen single bond, for example, has a length that is close to the expected value of 1.47 A (or 1.46 A) in most of the substances studied. In glycine, diketopiperazine, and methyl isocyanide, however, it is appreciably shorter than usual, and in trimethylamine oxide it is slightly longer.

Some of the above inconsistencies are doubtless due to errors in the experimental determinations. In the original study[26] of racemic alanine, for example, the length of the carbon-nitrogen bond was found to be 1.42 A; but, in a subsequent and more careful investigation,[27] this distance was increased to 1.50 A. Very probably, therefore, the especially low value of 1.39 A for glycine is similarly incorrect.[28] In many other instances, however, the variations are presumably due instead to differences in the valence states of the bonded atoms. It is, for example, not surprising that the lengths of the *single* bonds which are formed by saturated, acetylenic, and carbonyl carbon atoms should be somewhat different. Neither is it surprising that the carbon-nitrogen bond should be shorter in N-acetylglycine, where the nitrogen atom is trivalent and formally neutral, than it is in alanine, where the nitrogen atom takes part in four covalent bonds and has a formal positive charge. In still other instances, certain bonds may be shortened by hyperconjugation, as will be more fully discussed on page 183. And finally, the lengthening of the central

[26] H. A. Levy and R. B. Corey, *J. Am. Chem. Soc.* **63**, 2095 (1941).
[27] J. Donohue, *J. Am. Chem. Soc.* **72**, 949 (1950).
[28] Cf. the third paragraph on page 2343 of D. P. Shoemaker, J. Donohue, V. Schomaker, and R. B. Corey, *J. Am. Chem. Soc.* **72**, 2328 (1950).

carbon-carbon bond in hexamethylethane to 1.58 A could have been anticipated in view of the steric repulsions of the bulky methyl groups.

In the several ways just described, most of the observed variations in bond length can be satisfactorily explained. There remain, however, a few exceptions that seem to be definitely anomalous. In bibenzyl, for example, the central carbon-carbon bond is almost unbelievably short, even though each of the atoms which it links is saturated, and even though the experimental work[29] was carried through with more than usual care. Moreover, there is here no reason for supposing that hyperconjugation is a sufficiently important factor to produce the observed effect. The existence of such apparently unexplainable discrepancies introduces some uncertainty into any prediction of bond lengths, but it does not invalidate the general rule that bonds of the same type *usually* have approximately the same length. With the aid of the several regularities which have been established (e.g., the shortening of a single bond adjacent to a triple one), we can ordinarily, in fact, expect that the error in the length predicted for any pure single, double, or triple bond should not exceed a few hundredths of an angstrom.

A further useful generalization in regard to interatomic distances is that the length r_{AB} of a bond between any two atoms A and B can be expressed as

$$r_{AB} = r_A + r_B \qquad (1)$$

where r_A and r_B are the so-called *radii* of A and B, respectively. It is found empirically that the atomic radii are usually constant from molecule to molecule to about the same extent that the bond lengths themselves are, provided that the values of the radii of the various atoms are allowed to depend not only upon the natures of the atoms involved but also upon the types of bond formed (i.e., single, double, or triple, and ionic or covalent). In ethylene, for example, each carbon atom must be considered to have two different radii—a covalent single-bond radius for each of its links with hydrogen atoms and a covalent double-bond radius for its link with the other carbon atom. These two carbon radii are different from each other and also from the hydrogen radius.

Of the several sets of covalent radii that have been proposed by various authors on the basis of the simple equation 1, the most extensive is that of Pauling.[30] A number of these radii are listed as the values which are *not* in parentheses in Table 4·2. The significance of the double-bond radii of fluorine, chlorine, etc., and of the triple-bond radii of oxygen,

[29] G. A. Jeffrey, *Proc. Roy. Soc. (London) A* **188**, 222 (1947).

[30] For the complete list in its most recent form, see L. Pauling, *The Nature of the Chemical Bond*, Cornell University Press, Ithaca, N. Y., 1st ed., 1939, p. 154; 2nd ed., 1940, p. 164.

sulfur, etc., will become clearer in the following section. (Ionic radii will
not be considered in this book, because they are of relatively little interest
in connection with organic molecules.) The method of using these
atomic radii for the prediction of bond lengths can be illustrated with a
few examples.   The calculated lengths of the carbon-carbon single, double,

TABLE 4·2

COVALENT RADII[a]

	H			
Single-bond radius	0.30			
	(0.37)			

	C	N	O	F
Single-bond radius	0.77	0.70	0.66	0.64
	(0.77)	(0.74)	(0.74)	(0.72)
Double-bond radius	0.67	0.61	0.57	0.55
	(0.665)	(0.60)	(0.55)	(0.54)
Triple-bond radius	0.60	0.55	0.51	—

	P	S	Cl
Single-bond radius	1.10	1.04	0.99
	(1.10)	(1.04)	(0.99)
Double-bond radius	1.00	0.95	0.90
		(0.94)	
Triple-bond radius	0.93	0.88	—

	Br
Single-bond radius	1.14
	(1.14)
Double-bond radius	1.05

	I
Single-bond radius	1.33
	(1.33)
Double-bond radius	1.24

[a] In angstrom units.   The figures not in parentheses are those of L. Pauling,
The Nature of the Chemical Bond, Cornell University Press, Ithaca, N. Y., 1st ed.,
1939, p. 154, 2nd ed., 1940, p. 164.   The single-bond radii which are in parentheses are taken from V. Schomaker and D. P. Stevenson, *J. Am. Chem. Soc.* **63**,
37 (1941).   The double-bond radii which are in parentheses are taken from
W. Gordy, *J. Chem. Phys.* **15**, 81 (1947).

and triple bonds are just twice the carbon single-, double-, and triple-bond
radii, or $2 \times 0.77 = 1.54$, $2 \times 0.67 = 1.34$, and $2 \times 0.60 = 1.20$ A,
respectively; that of a carbon-chlorine single bond is the sum of the
carbon and chlorine single-bond radii, or $0.77 + 0.99 = 1.76$ A; that of
a carbon-oxygen double bond is the sum of the carbon and oxygen

double-bond radii, or $0.67 + 0.57 = 1.24$ A; and so on. The agreement between the observed bond lengths and the calculated ones is shown by a comparison of the second and third columns of Table 4·1. It will be seen that the agreement is usually to within 0.02–0.03 A, which is about the order of magnitude of the uncertainty in the experimental values.

It has been found that small, but significant, discrepancies often occur if a single set of atomic radii is used to calculate the lengths of bonds between atoms of the same or similar electronegativity and also between atoms of widely different electronegativity. Consequently, a slight modification in Pauling's scheme has been proposed by Schomaker and Stevenson,[31] who replace equation 1 by the slightly more complicated expression

$$r_{AB} = r_A + r_B - \beta \, |x_A - x_B| \text{ A} \qquad (2)$$

in which β is equal to 0.09 if the bond between the atoms A and B is single,[31] but equal to 0.06 if that bond is double;[32] and the quantity $|x_A - x_B|$ is the absolute magnitude of the difference between the electronegativities of the atoms A and B (see Table 3·9, Section 3·6). The atomic radii r_A and r_B to be used in conjunction with equation 2 are frequently different from those employed by Pauling; they are given by the values in parentheses in Table 4·2. The interatomic distances calculated with their aid, which are listed in the second column of Table 4·1, in parentheses, are often in somewhat better agreement with the experimental values than are those derived from Pauling's radii, but the difference is seldom great.

We have seen above that we can, with some assurance, predict the distance between any two given atoms in a molecule, provided that they are joined by a bond that is definitely single, double, or triple. We turn now to a consideration of those cases in which the bond of interest is of a hybrid type. In benzene, for example, each carbon-carbon bond is a hybrid of a single and a double bond. Its length, therefore, might be expected to be intermediate between the single-bond value of 1.54 A and the double-bond value of 1.34 A. Indeed, since the two Kekulé structures are equivalent to each other and so are equally important in the resonance, we might, as a first approximation, anticipate a bond length of 1.44 A, just halfway between the extremes. Spectroscopic data show, however, that a double bond is always stiffer than a comparable single bond[33] or, in other words, that more energy is required to stretch a double bond by a given amount than to contract a single bond by that same amount.

[31] V. Schomaker and D. P. Stevenson, *J. Am. Chem. Soc.* **63**, 37 (1941).

[32] W. Gordy, *J. Chem. Phys.* **15**, 81 (1947).

[33] See, for example, J. W. Linnett, *Quart. Revs. (London)* **1**, 73 (1947). Cf. also Section 6.11.

TABLE 4·3

LENGTHS[a] OF HYBRID BONDS

Atoms Bonded	Lengths of Pure Bonds[b]		Lengths Observed[c]	Substance[d]
CC	1.54	(1.54)	1.42	Graphite
	1.34	(1.35)	1.33	Ketene
	1.20		1.47	Glyoxal
			1.37	Cyanogen
			1.46	Acrolein[e]
			1.28	Carbon suboxide
			1.37	Biacetylene[e]
			1.39	Pyrazine
			1.46	Furan[e]
			1.44	Thiophene[e]
			1.47	Butadiene[e]
			1.41	p-Dibromobenzene
			1.39	Benzene
			1.39	Resorcinol
			1.38	Dimethyltriacetylene[e]
			1.35	Cycloöctatetraene[f]
			1.50	Cycloöctatetraene[f]
			1.40	Naphthalene[g]
			1.41	Biphenylene[h]
			1.46	Biphenylene[e]
			1.39	Hexamethylbenzene[h]
			1.40	Diphenylacetylene[e]
CN	1.47	(1.46)	1.21	Isocyanic acid
	1.28	(1.27)	1.22	Isothiocyanic acid
	1.15		1.34	Diazomethane
			1.34	Urea
			1.17	Methyl isocyanide[i]
			1.19	Methyl isocyanate[i]
			1.35	Pyrazine
			1.35	Picryl iodide[j]
			1.45	Picryl iodide[k]
			1.35	Isatin[l]
			1.38	Isatin[m]
			1.31	Tetramethylpyrazine
			1.33	Phenazine
CO	1.43	(1.42)	1.31	Calcium carbonate
	1.24	(1.225)	1.17	Isocyanic acid
	1.11		1.27	Sodium formate
			1.26	Urea
			1.13	Carbon monoxide
			1.16	Carbon oxysulfide
			1.16	Carbon dioxide

TABLE 4·3 (*contd.*)

Atoms Bonded	Lengths of Pure Bonds[b]		Lengths Observed[c]	Substance[d]
CO	1.43	(1.42)	1.24	Calcium formate
	1.24	(1.225)	1.15	Ketene
	1.11		1.17	Acetyl bromide
			1.17	Acetyl chloride
			1.18	Methyl isocyanate
			1.22	Methyl formate[n]
			1.37	Methyl formate[o]
			1.25	Formic acid (dimeric)[n]
			1.36	Formic acid (dimeric)[o]
			1.21, 1.27	Alanine
			1.19	Carbon suboxide
			1.40	Furan
			1.40	Vinyl ether
			1.36	Resorcinol
			1.28	Bis- (*p*-bromophenyl) ether
CCl	1.76	(1.71)	1.63	Cyanogen chloride
	1.57		1.64	Dichloroacetylene
			1.72	Tetrachloroethylene
			1.63	Chloroacetylene
			1.69	Vinyl chloride
			1.82	Acetyl chloride
			1.75	Methyl chloroformate
			1.69	Chlorobenzene
			1.76	1,5-Dichloronaphthalene
CBr	1.91	(1.88)	1.79	Cyanogen bromide
	1.72		1.80	Dibromoacetylene
			1.86	Vinyl bromide
			2.00	Acetyl bromide
			1.79	Methylbromoacetylene
			1.84	1,3,5-Tribromobenzene
			1.84	*p*-Dibromobenzene
CI	2.10	(2.09)	2.00	Cyanogen iodide
	1.91		2.03	Vinyl iodide
			2.21	Acetyl iodide
			1.99	Methyliodoacetylene
			2.02	*p*-Diiodobenzene
CS	1.81	(1.81)	1.56	Isothiocyanic acid
	1.62	(1.61)	1.56	Carbon oxysulfide
	1.48		1.55	Carbon disulfide
			1.78	Thioacetic acid

TABLE 4·3 (*contd.*)

Atoms Bonded	Lengths of Pure Bonds[b]		Lengths Observed[c]	Substance[d]
NN	1.40	(1.48)	1.13	Diazomethane
	1.22	(1.24)	1.10	Methyl azide[p]
	1.10		1.24	Methyl azide[q]
			1.13	Nitrous oxide
NO	1.36	(1.44)	1.21	Nitromethane
	1.18	(1.20)	1.26	Methyl nitrate[p]
	1.06		1.36	Methyl nitrate[q]
			1.21	Sodium nitrate
			1.15	Nitric oxide
			1.19	Nitrous oxide

[a] In angstrom units.

[b] The values which are not in parentheses are derived from the atomic radii of Pauling (cf. Table 4·2 and equation 1); the values which are in parentheses are derived from the atomic radii of Schomaker and Stevenson and of Gordy (cf. Table 4·2 and equation 2). In each column, the first, second, and third entries for each pair of atoms refer, respectively, to single, double, and triple bonds.

[c] For probable errors, statements of experimental methods, and references to the original literature, see the Appendix.

[d] Data for a great many additional compounds are given in the Appendix.

[e] The distance given here applies to the bond which, in the conventional structure, is represented as single and as lying between two multiple bonds, or between one multiple bond and an aromatic ring, or between two aromatic rings.

[f] In cycloöctatetraene, the bond lengths are alternately long and short round the ring. See page 143.

[g] The value given here is the average for the eleven different carbon-carbon bonds. The individual values range from 1.365 to 1.425 A. See Table 4.5, Section 4.4, and also page 194.

[h] The value given here is for the distance between adjacent atoms *within* a benzene ring.

[i] This value applies to the bond linking the nitrogen atom to the carbon atom that is not part of the methyl group.

[j] This value applies to the bond that is para to the iodine atom.

[k] This value applies to the bonds that are ortho to the iodine atom.

[l] This value applies to the bond that is adjacent to the carbonyl group.

[m] This value applies to the bond that is adjacent to the benzene ring.

[n] This value applies to the bond which, in the conventional structure, is represented as double.

[o] This value applies to the bond which is formed by the carbon atom of the carbonyl group and which, in the conventional structure, is represented as single.

[p] This value applies to the bond that is farther from the methyl group.

[q] This value applies to the bond that is nearer to the methyl group.

Consequently, as a second approximation, we could anticipate that the actual bond length should be somewhat less than the simple mean. This prediction is in complete agreement with the observed distance of 1.39 A.

The frequently encountered statement that resonance "shortens" bond distances is not quite strictly correct. In benzene, for example, the observed length of 1.39 A is indeed less than the normal single-bond length of 1.54 A, but it is also greater than the normal double-bond length of 1.34 A. There is no more logical reason for comparing the observed length with one of the extremes than with the other. The observed *average* bond length is less, however, than would correspond to a Kekulé structure.

The situation is similar in other molecules in which a bond is a hybrid between single and double, between double and triple, or among all three types of bond. The observed distance is almost always intermediate between the extremes, but closer to the lower extreme than would correspond to a simple weighted mean. This regularity makes it possible to obtain considerable information in regard to the detailed structure of a molecule from a study of its interatomic distances. Such information is subject to some uncertainty since, as we have already seen, the various bond lengths are not always constant even in the absence of resonance. However, if due attention is paid to the known deviations from constancy, and if the present method of investigation is used in conjunction with other independent data, an accumulation of evidence, which appears to be quite incontrovertible, can often be obtained.

In table 4·3, the observed bond lengths in a number of resonance hybrids are compared with the values calculated for pure single, double, or triple bonds. (Additional data for a considerable number of further substances can be found in the Appendix.) In most of the substances listed, the measured interatomic distances are in agreement with the conclusions reached above. With butadiene, for example, the structure I can be assigned only a small weight in the ground state of the molecule,

$$H_2C-CH=CH-CH_2$$
I

and yet its effect is apparently sufficient to decrease the length of the central carbon-carbon bond from 1.54 A to only 1.47 A. (It is important here that a single bond adjacent to only one double bond, as in isobutylene, or to only one aromatic ring, as in hexamethylbenzene, is not appreciably shortened.) We should, however, note that in cycloöctatetraene the observed bond lengths are essentially the ones expected for a single Kekulé-like structure, II or III; and hence that they are inconsistent with the view that these two structures make equal large contributions to the state of the molecule. As was pointed out in Section 3·9, this apparent anomaly is probably due to at least two different factors. In the first place, since the molecule is not planar, the structures II and III are not

at all equivalent to each other; in the second place, since there are altogether eight potentially aromatic (i.e., pi) electrons, instead of the preferred six, the resonance in even a hypothetical planar molecule should here be relatively ineffective. A second and somewhat similar anomaly is presented by biphenylene, in which the bonds that link the two benzene rings with each other are considerably longer than are those within these rings. Apparently, therefore, structure IV makes a much smaller contribution to the state of the molecule than any of the four other ones, such as V, in which each six-membered ring has a Kekulé structure. This

conclusion is, of course, entirely consistent with the belief that fully aromatic character is possible only in rings with exactly six aromatic electrons (cf. pages 144ff).

In vinyl chloride, the relatively unimportant structure VI is apparently responsible for the reduction of the carbon-chlorine distance from 1.76 A

$$H_2\overset{..}{C}{}^- —CH{=}Cl^+$$
VI

to 1.69 A. The evidence here, to be sure, is not entirely conclusive since, with the carbon-chlorine bond, we have no independent support for the assumption that the observed shortening is not due merely to the change in the valence state of the carbon atom; in Section 5·4, however, we shall see an additional reason for believing that structure VI does indeed make a small contribution to the state of the molecule. In most of the remaining substances listed in Table 4·3, entirely similar situations are encountered; thus, one usually finds that, just as in vinyl chloride, a bond represented as single in the most stable structure is shorter than would be expected on the basis of the single-bond radii if, in that structure, it lies between a multiple bond and an atom with an unshared pair of electrons. A number of exceptions, however, do exist. The length of the carbon-chlorine bond in acetyl chloride, for example, is appreciably *greater* than that expected for a pure single bond, even though resonance of the same type as in vinyl chloride would appear here to be possible. Similar, but even larger, discrepancies occur also with acetyl bromide and acetyl iodide. On the other hand, in methyl formate, the corresponding carbon-*oxygen* bond is appreciably shorter than would be expected for a pure single bond. Allen and Sutton,[34] in discussing the anomalous distances in the acetyl halides, cite evidence that the carbon-halogen bonds in these compounds are also exceptionally weak, and they suggest that there is a direct connection between the increased lengths and the decreased strengths. They were unable, however, to advance any entirely satisfactory explanation for the occurrence of the observed anomalies. (See also the following paragraph in fine print.) Apparently, therefore, the unexpected lengthening of the carbon-halogen bonds in the acetyl halides, like the unexpected shortening of the central carbon-carbon bond in bibenzyl (cf. page 169), must be related to certain additional factors which are not at present understood, but which fortunately seem only rather rarely to be important.

A possible explanation[35] for the anomalous bond lengths in the acetyl halides is that, with these substances, unexpectedly large weights must be assigned to the structures VII, in which X represents a chlorine, bromine, or iodine atom. If such structures

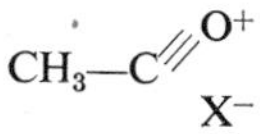

$$CH_3-C{\underset{X^-}{\overset{O^+}{\diagup\!\!\diagup}}}$$

VII

are indeed important in the resonance, the observation that the carbon-halogen bonds are longer than pure single bonds would then seem entirely reasonable; moreover, the further observation that the carbon-*oxygen* bonds in these compounds are shorter than pure double bonds (cf. Table 4·3) would also seem entirely reasonable. Apparently, however, no completely satisfactory interpretation of all the pertinent data can be obtained in this way. For example, if the structures VII have large weights in the ground states of the respective acetyl halides, there is no obvious reason why the analogous structure VIII should not have a similar weight in the ground state of methyl

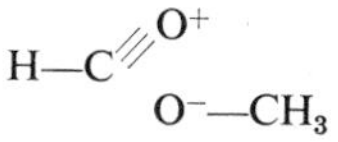

$$H-C{\underset{O^--CH_3}{\overset{O^+}{\diagup\!\!\diagup}}}$$

VIII

formate. In fact, since oxygen is a more electronegative element than chlorine, bromine, or iodine, structure VIII ought to be even more important in the resonance than is any one of the structures VII. Nevertheless, the anomalies which these several structures were designed to explain are less evident in methyl formate than they are in the acetyl halides; and, with the acetyl halides themselves, they decrease with increasing electronegativity of the halogen atom. (Cf. also pages 188f.)

[34] P. W. Allen and L. E. Sutton, *Trans. Faraday Soc.* **47**, 236 (1951).

[35] For the application of essentially this same explanation to nitrosyl chloride, NOCl, with which a similar discrepancy exists, see J. A. A. Ketelaar and K. J. Palmer, *J. Am. Chem. Soc.* **59**, 2629 (1937); J. A. A. Ketelaar, *Rec. trav. chim.* **62**, 289 (1943).

Although the carboxyl group, or, more generally, the carboalkoxyl group, appears to offer essentially the same possibilities for resonance as the vinyl group (however, see the preceding paragraph in fine print), the carboxylate anion differs in the important respect that here the contributing structures IX and X are completely equivalent to each other. Consequently, the two carbon-oxygen bonds, since they must likewise be

R—C<O:⁻ / O: IX   R—C<O: / O:⁻ X

equivalent to each other, have the same length (cf. Section 4·1). Since each bond is, in a sense, just halfway between single and double, its length is intermediate between that of a pure single bond and that of a pure double one; and, as is true also with the carbon-carbon bond in benzene (cf. page 175), the observed distance is considerably closer to the shorter than to the longer extreme. Similarly, in the nitro group, with which the two corresponding structures are XI and XII, the two nitrogen-oxygen

R—N⁺<O:⁻ / O: XI   R—N⁺<O: / O:⁻ XII

bonds are equivalent, and their lengths are little, if any, greater than that of a pure double bond.

The carbonate ion is a hybrid of the *three* equivalent structures XIII, XIV, and XV. Each of the equivalent carbon-oxygen bonds is therefore

somewhat nearer to a pure single bond than is either of the ones in a carboxylate ion; accordingly, the observation that the internuclear distance is slightly greater in the carbonate ion than in a carboxylate ion is only to be expected. On the other hand, although the nitrate ion is similarly a hybrid of structures XVI, XVII, and XVIII, the nitrogen-oxygen bond has practically the same length here as in the nitro group.

This difference between the carbon-oxygen and the nitrogen-oxygen bonds cannot at present be explained. It may be related to the presence of a formal positive charge upon the nitrogen atom of the nitrate ion, and to

the absence of such a charge on the carbon atom of the carbonate ion;[6] and, in any event, the discrepancy is possibly no greater than the uncertainty in the experimental data.

As we saw on pages 111f, carbon dioxide is a hybrid receiving equal large contributions from the two structures that are represented by the single symbol XIX, and presumably smaller ones from the additional structures XX and XXI.   As a consequence of this resonance, the bonds

are stronger than they would have been if they had been ordinary double bonds, and the carbon-oxygen distances are accordingly decreased. Although we could hardly have predicted, in advance of the facts, what the resulting bond lengths should be, the observed values of 1.16 A are far from unreasonable. Similarly, with carbon suboxide, the conventional structure XXII represents two distinct structures which must be assigned equal, large weights in the resonance; and the two additional structures XXIII and XXIV must also presumably be assigned small weights.

Although we could again have made no quantitative predictions, we could have anticipated the observation that both the carbon-carbon and the carbon-oxygen bonds are significantly shorter than ordinary double bonds.

Nitrous oxide is somewhat analogous to carbon dioxide.   The diagram XXV, like its analog XIX, corresponds to two different, but equivalent, structures which doubtless have large, equal weights. Of the remaining structures, XXVI and XXVII, however, the first is presumably about as stable, and hence about as important, as either of the ones XXV; whereas the second must be made extremely unstable, and hence negligible, by its especially unfavorable distribution of electric charge. As might therefore have been anticipated, the lengths of the nitrogen-nitrogen and nitrogen-oxygen bonds differ only slightly from those predicted for pure triple and pure double bonds, respectively.

With isocyanic acid and methyl isocyanate, each of the respective symbols XXVIII and XXIX corresponds to two distinct structures, just

$$\text{H} \diagdown \ddot{\text{N}}\!=\!\text{C}\!=\!\ddot{\text{O}}\!: \qquad\qquad \text{H}_3\text{C} \diagdown \ddot{\text{N}}\!=\!\text{C}\!=\!\ddot{\text{O}}\!:$$

XXVIII   XXIX

like the analogous symbols XIX, XXII, and XXV for carbon dioxide, carbon suboxide, and nitrous oxide. With each of the two former substances, however, the indicated structures differ so greatly in energy that we shall here and hereafter ignore the less stable one, and we shall consider that the symbol XXVIII, or XXIX, represents only the single more stable structure. Of the two further structures, XXX and XXXI

$$\text{R} \diagdown \ddot{\text{N}}^-\!\!-\!\text{C}\!\equiv\!\text{O}\!:^+ \qquad\qquad \text{R} \diagdown \text{N}^+\!\!\equiv\!\text{C}\!-\!\ddot{\text{O}}\!:^-$$

XXX   XXXI

(with R equal to either H or CH_3), the second one should be made especially unstable by strain, since it calls for an H—N—C, or C—N—C, bond angle of 180°, whereas the observed[36] values are, respectively, 128° and 125°. (See the Appendix.) Consequently, we have also this additional reason for expecting the nitrogen-carbon and carbon-oxygen bonds in the isocyanate group to be nearer to ordinary double bonds than are the bonds in carbon dioxide, carbon suboxide, and nitrous oxide. This expectation is perhaps not inconsistent with the experimental data of Table 4·3, but no certain conclusion can be drawn.

Methyl azide can be described as a hybrid of the three structures XXXII, XXXIII, and XXXIV, where, as with the isocyanates, we ignore

$$\text{H}_3\text{C} \diagdown \ddot{\text{N}}\!=\!\text{N}^+\!=\!\ddot{\text{N}}\!:^- \qquad \text{H}_3\text{C} \diagdown \ddot{\text{N}}^-\!\!-\!\text{N}^+\!\equiv\!\text{N}\!: \qquad \text{H}_3\text{C} \diagdown \text{N}^+\!\equiv\!\text{N}^+\!-\!\ddot{\text{N}}\!:^=$$

XXXII   XXXIII   XXXIV

---

[36] L. H. Jones, J. N. Shoolery, R. G. Shulman, and D. M. Yost, *J. Chem. Phys.* **18**, 990 (1950); E. H. Eyster, R. H. Gillette, and L. O. Brockway, *J. Am. Chem. Soc.* **62**, 3236 (1940).

the second, highly strained structure that is represented by the symbol XXXII. Now, the final structure XXXIV, like structure XXVII for nitrous oxide, must be extremely unstable because of its especially unfavorable charge distribution; consequently, this structure can be expected to make only a negligible contribution to the state of the molecule. The observed bond lengths bear out this expectation since the nitrogen-nitrogen bond that is intermediate between single and double is 0.14 A longer than is the one that is intermediate between double and triple. With diazomethane, the data are consistent with the supposition that there is resonance between the structures XXXV and XXXVI, which are

$$CH_2\!\!=\!\!N^+\!\!=\!\!\overset{..}{N}:^- \qquad\qquad \overset{..}{C}{}^-H_2\!\!-\!\!N^+\!\!\equiv\!\!N:$$

$$\text{XXXV} \qquad\qquad\qquad \text{XXXVI}$$

analogous to XXXII and XXXIII, respectively. (No structure analogous to XXXIV can be drawn for this substance.)

Carbon monoxide can be described as a resonance hybrid of the two structures represented by the symbol XXXVII, with presumably an additional contribution from a third structure XXXVIII (cf. page 114).

$$:C\!\!=\!\!\overset{..}{O}: \qquad\qquad :C^-\!\!\equiv\!\!O:^+$$

$$\text{XXXVII} \qquad\qquad \text{XXXVIII}$$

Since the oxygen atom is in an exceptional valence state in the last one of these structures, and since the carbon atom is in such a state in all three of them, we cannot make any definite prediction of bond length. Pauling has estimated[37] that either one of the two equivalent structures XXXVII should correspond to a carbon-oxygen distance of about 1.15 A. The small further shortening to 1.13 A may then be due to the strengthening of the bond by resonance among the three stated structures. The observed effect, however, is so small, and its significance is so uncertain, that we can have little confidence in the foregoing interpretation.

Methyl isocyanide is closely analogous to carbon monoxide since it can be considered a hybrid of the two structures represented by the symbol XXXIX, and also of the third structure, XL. It should here be especially noted that, since the C—N—C bond angle is 180°[38] (see also

$$CH_3\!\!-\!\!\overset{..}{N}\!\!=\!\!C: \qquad\qquad CH_3\!\!-\!\!N^+\!\!\equiv\!\!C:^-$$

$$\text{XXXIX} \qquad\qquad\qquad \text{XL}$$

[37] L. Pauling, *The Nature of the Chemical Bond*, Cornell University Press, Ithaca, N. Y., 1st ed., 1939, p. 180; 2nd ed., 1940, p. 195.

[38] For a recent study of methyl isocyanide, see M. Kessler, H. Ring, R. Trambarulo, and W. Gordy, *Phys. Rev.* **79**, 54 (1950).

below), the two structures XXXIX are equivalent to each other; in this important respect, the isocyan*ide* differs from the corresponding isocyan*ate* (see above).   In view of the exceptional valence states of the nitrogen and carbon atoms in the structures XXXIX and XL, however, we are again unable to draw rigorous conclusions from the observed length, 1.17 A, of the carbon-nitrogen bond in the isocyanide group.   If the same correction that was given by Pauling[37] for the carbon atom in the structure XXXVII of carbon monoxide is applicable here also, then the bond length expected for either one of the structures XXXIX would be 1.19 A.   The small further shortening may then be attributed to the stabilization by the resonance but, as before, this conclusion can be accepted only with considerable caution.   Although no definite conclusion can therefore be drawn from the bond *length*, the fact that the C—N—C bond *angle* is 180° [38] provides valuable additional information.   Such a linear arrangement of the heavy atoms is clearly in agreement with the structure XL, but it could hardly have been anticipated on the basis of resonance between only the two structures XXXIX.   Indeed, the striking difference between the bond angles in methyl isocyanide and in methyl isocyanate (see above) provides good evidence for the belief that the triply bonded structure XL has an appreciably greater weight in the isocyanide than the corresponding structure XXXI has in the isocyanate.

Nitric oxide may appear to be somewhat analogous to carbon monoxide but, from a consideration of the respective possibilities for resonance, this resemblance is seen to be purely superficial.   With nitric oxide, *each* of the *two* diagrams XLI and XLII corresponds to a pair of distinct, but

$$: \ddot{N} = \ddot{O}: \qquad\qquad : \ddot{N}^- = \dot{O}:^+$$

$$\text{XLI} \qquad\qquad\qquad \text{XLII}$$

equivalent, structures; and no additional structure with a triple bond can be drawn.   Moreover, instead of invoking resonance among the four structures that are represented by the diagrams XLI and XLII, we may instead describe nitric oxide, in a completely equivalent way, but somewhat more simply, as a hybrid of just two equivalent structures, each of which can be written as XLIII, and in each of which the nitrogen and

$$: N \equiv O :$$

$$\text{XLIII}$$

oxygen atoms are linked by one double bond and also by one three-electron bond (cf. Section 2·5).   Consequently, the fact that the nitrogen-oxygen distance is a little shorter than would be expected for a pure double bond is entirely reasonable.

Data of a different kind can be used as additional evidence for the belief that nitric oxide is a hybrid of not only the structures XLI in which the unpaired electron is on the nitrogen atom, but also of the further structures XLII, in which that electron is on the oxygen atom.[39] From a study of the fine structure of the microwave absorption by this substance, the magnitude of the magnetic interaction between the spins of the odd electron and of the nitrogen nucleus (the oxygen nucleus has no spin) can be measured; and from this information, it has been concluded that the odd electron has approximately the same probability of being near the nitrogen nucleus that it has of being near the oxygen nucleus. Apparently, therefore, the structures XLI and the structures XLII must have approximately equal importance in the resonance. (For further discussion of this method, see pages 392f.)

If hyperconjugation is taken into account, a number of the variations in bond length, which were referred to above as occurring apparently in the absence of resonance, may perhaps find an explanation in terms of resonance. It has been suggested,[40] for example, that in methylacetylene the relatively unstable structure XLIV has an appreciable weight, so that

$$H \cdots \cdots$$

$$H_2C{=}C{=}CH$$

XLIV

the carbon-carbon bond that is represented as single in the conventional structure is more accurately described as intermediate between single and double. Similarly, the fact that carbon-carbon and carbon-nitrogen single bonds are shortened when adjacent to carbonyl groups is readily understandable. From what has already been said, however, it should be evident that hyperconjugation cannot be the *only* factor responsible for the observed variations in bond length. The shortness of the carbon-hydrogen bond in acetylene, for example, appears to require that the valence states of the multivalent atoms be also taken into account (see page 168); and the shortness of the central carbon-carbon bond in bibenzyl has so far defied explanation (see page 169). Clearly, therefore, our understanding of bond lengths is still far from complete, and probably nothing is to be gained by trying to extend the present interpretation too far.

4·4   Per Cent Double-Bond Characters and Fractional Bond Orders. In Section 4·3 we saw in a qualitative way that, when a bond is a hybrid between single and double, its length is usually intermediate between the extremes. It would be useful if a more quantitative correlation could be made between the observed lengths of the various bonds and the relative

---

[39] See R. Beringer and J. G. Castle, Jr., *Phys. Rev.* **78**, 581 (1950); C. H. Townes and J. Turkevich, *ibid.* **77**, 148 (1950).

[40] L. Pauling, H. D. Springall, and K. J. Palmer, *J. Am. Chem. Soc.* **61**, 927 (1939); R. S. Mulliken, C. A. Rieke, and W. G. Brown, *ibid.* **63**, 41 (1941).

weights of the singly and doubly bonded structures. Two essentially different schemes for effecting such a correlation have been proposed. The first of these, which is due to Pauling and his co-workers,[41] defines the *per cent double-bond character*, p, of a bond by means of the equation

$$r = r_s - (r_s - r_d)\frac{3p}{2p + 100} \tag{1}$$

or

$$p = \frac{100(r_s - r)}{2r + r_s - 3r_d} \tag{2}$$

where r is the observed length of the actual bond, and r_s and r_d are the lengths of pure single and pure double bonds, respectively, between the two atoms in question. It is seen that p assumes the values of 0 for $r = r_s$, and of 100 for $r = r_d$. The significance of the interpolation for intermediate values of r and of p becomes apparent from a consideration of the carbon-carbon bond, for which Pauling's atomic radii (see Table 4·2, Section 4·3, lead to the values $r_s = 1.54$ A and $r_d = 1.34$ A. In benzene, with $r = 1.39$ A, and in graphite, with $r = 1.42$ A, the bonds are found to have 50 and $33\frac{1}{3}$ per cent double-bond character, respectively. These values seem quite reasonable if all structures which have formal bonds are ignored. In benzene, for example, the two Kekulé structures, being equivalent, must make equal contributions to the state of the molecule, so that each bond can be considered just halfway between a single and double bond. Similarly, in graphite, each bond is represented as single in two-thirds of the structures, and as double in one-third of the structures, without formal bonds. (This statement follows from the fact that the carbon atoms in graphite are arranged in parallel planes, each of which is essentially a single giant molecule that can be regarded as a hybrid of a tremendously large number of structures of the type indicated

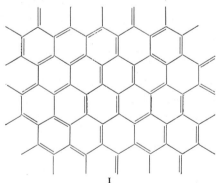

I

[41] L. Pauling, L. O. Brockway, and J. Y. Beach, *J. Am. Chem. Soc.* **57**, 2705 (1935); L. Pauling and L. O. Brockway, *ibid.* **59**, 1223 (1937).

by I.   The individual planes are separated from each other by such great distances—3.41 A between adjacent planes—that the only effective interactions between them can be the van der Waals forces.   See the Appendix.) The precise forms of equations 1 and 2 were indeed chosen in order to bring out these suggestive relationships.

The per cent double-bond characters of several representative bonds of varying types are listed in Table 4·4.   The values found for the carbon-

TABLE 4·4

PER CENT DOUBLE-BOND CHARACTERS

Atoms Bonded	Substance[a]	Observed Bond Length[b]	Per Cent Double-Bond Character[c]
CC	Graphite	1.42	$33\frac{1}{3}$
	Glyoxal	1.47	15
	Cyanogen	1.37	65
	Acrolein	1.46[d]	18[d]
	Biacetylene	1.37[d]	65[d]
	Pyrazine	1.39	50
	Furan	1.46[d]	18[d]
	Thiophene	1.41[d]	38[d]
	Dimethylacetylene	1.47[d]	15[d]
	Benzene	1.39	50
	Cycloöctatetraene	1.35[e]	87
	Cycloöctatetraene	1.50[e]	8
	Naphthalene	1.40[f]	44[f]
	Diphenylacetylene	1.40[d]	44[d]
CN	Diazomethane	1.34	42
	Urea	1.34	42
	Pyrazine	1.35	36
	Picryl iodide	1.35[g]	36[g]
	Picryl iodide	1.45[h]	4[h]
CO	Calcium carbonate	1.31	36
	Sodium formate	1.27	64
	Urea	1.26	74
	Methyl formate	1.22[i]	140[i]
	Methyl formate	1.37[d]	13[d]
	Acetyl chloride	1.17	520
	Furan	1.40	5
CCl	Cyanogen chloride	1.63	42
	Chloroacetylene	1.63	42
	Vinyl chloride	1.69	16
	Acetyl chloride	1.82	−9
	Chlorobenzene	1.69	16

TABLE 4·4 (*contd.*)

Atoms Bonded	Substance[a]	Observed Bond Length[b]	Per Cent Double-Bond Character[c]
CBr	Cyanogen bromide	1.79	36
	Dibromoacetylene	1.80	31
	Vinyl bromide	1.86	11
	Acetyl bromide	2.00	−12
	1,3,5-Tribromobenzene	1.84	16
NO	Nitromethane	1.21	$62\frac{1}{2}$
	Sodium nitrate	1.21	$62\frac{1}{2}$

[a] Additional bond lengths, from which additional per cent double-bond characters can be computed, are given in the Appendix.

[b] In angstrom units. The values are taken from Tables 4·1 and 4·3.

[c] Calculated from equation 2 (or 1).

[d] This value applies only to the bond which, in the conventional structure, is represented as single and lying adjacent to or between multiple bonds.

[e] In the molecule of cycloöctatetraene, the carbon-carbon bonds are alternately long and short. See page 143.

[f] This is the average value for all carbon-carbon bonds. See also page 194.

[g] This value applies to the carbon-nitrogen bond para to the iodine atom. See also page 196.

[h] This value applies to the carbon-nitrogen bonds ortho to the iodine atom. See also page 196.

[i] This value applies to the carbon-oxygen bond which, in the conventional structure, is represented as double.

oxygen bonds in the carbonate and carboxylate ions are fairly close to the values of $33\frac{1}{3}$ and 50 per cent, respectively, which might have been anticipated in view of the natures of the structures involved in the resonance. The agreement, although not perfect, is probably as good as could be hoped for. The value of $62\frac{1}{2}$ per cent, which is found for the nitrogen-oxygen bonds both in the nitro group and in the nitrate ion, respectively, is considerably less satisfactory, however. The suggestion has been made[6] that the difficulty here may be due to the presence of formal positive charges upon the nitrogen atoms. Further possible explanations are that the assumed length of the pure double bond may be slightly too great, and that the observed lengths of the actual bonds may be slightly in error. Most of the remaining values given in Table 4·4 are of quite reasonable magnitude, but it should be evident that no great quantitative significance can be assigned to them. Considerable uncertainty is always introduced into the treatment by the fact that variations in bond length are often encountered even when there are no obvious and reasonable possibilities for resonance. Extreme examples of the difficulties which may arise from such a cause are presented by acetyl chloride, acetyl bromide, and methyl formate.   In the first two of these substances, the carbon-halogen bonds appear to have *negative* double-bond characters or, in other words, to have some "no-bond" character; in all three substances, the carbon-oxygen bonds that are conventionally represented as double appear to have much more than 100 per cent double-bond character or, in other words, to have some triple-bond character.   Although these calculated values may possibly have a close relation to the *strengths* of the respective bonds (see page 177), they cannot readily be interpreted in terms of resonance among any valence-bond structures of the usual type (however, see the paragraph in fine print on page 177).

Less striking, but perhaps equally important, difficulties are encountered also with compounds like dimethylacetylene, in which each of the carbon-carbon bonds that are represented as single in the conventional structure II is 0.07 A shorter than an ordinary single bond between saturated atoms (see Table 4·1, Section 4·3).   As was suggested on page 183, this observed shortening may be due to the hyperconjugation that results from resonance with the less stable structures III and IV; the 15 per cent

$$H_3C-C\equiv C-CH_3 \qquad H_2C=C=C-CH_3 \qquad H_3C-C=C=CH_2$$

$$H\cdots\cdots \qquad\qquad\qquad \cdots\cdots H$$

$$\text{II} \qquad\qquad\qquad \text{III} \qquad\qquad\qquad \text{IV}$$

double-bond character that in Table 4·4 is ascribed to these "single" bonds would then presumably be significant.   On the other hand, the shortening could instead be due to the difference between the valence states of saturated and acetylenic carbon atoms or, what amounts to the same thing, to the presence of an adjacent triple bond.   Hence, there is a possibility that the dimethylacetylene molecule is quite accurately represented by the unique structure II, and that the carbon-carbon single bonds (now without the quotation marks) have 0 per cent double-bond character. And finally, the true situation may be intermediate between these two extremes.

Biacetylene, V, cannot exhibit hyperconjugation of the type that is possible with dimethylacetylene; the shortness of the central carbon-carbon bond in this compound may, however, be due to the conjugation of the triple bonds with each other (i.e., to resonance with the two additional, less stable structures that are represented by the symbol VI.

$$H-C\equiv C-C\equiv C-H \qquad\qquad H-C=C=C=C-H$$

$$\cdots\cdots\cdots$$

$$\text{V} \qquad\qquad\qquad\qquad \text{VI}$$

See pages 111f for a discussion of the somewhat analogous situation that arises with carbon dioxide). If only this one factor is important, then the central carbon-carbon bond may be presumed actually to have the 65 per cent double-bond character that is assigned to it in Table 4·4. On the other hand, the observed variations in bond lengths may instead be due solely to the differences in the valence states of the carbon atoms (cf. the preceding paragraph). If only this second factor is important, then the structures VI do not make significant contributions to the resonance, and the central carbon-carbon bond has essentially 0 per cent double-bond character. The truth probably lies somewhere between these two extremes. In order to obtain a slightly more definite picture of the situation, let us for the moment assume that *dimethylacetylene* has exactly the conventional structure II, and hence that in this substance hyper-conjugation plays no role. Each of the terminal carbon-carbon bonds is then a pure single bond which, however, is made 0.07 A shorter than usual by the presence of an adjacent triple bond. Now, if biacetylene had the unique structure V, the central carbon-carbon bond would be a pure single bond that is adjacent to *two* triple bonds. The shortening which results from the altered valence states of the acetylenic carbon atoms might therefore be expected to be approximately twice as great here as in dimethylacetylene or, in other words, to be approximately 2×0.07 A, or 0.14 A. Consequently, in making the calculation for the actual molecule, we should set r_s of equation 1, or 2, equal to about $(1.54 - 0.14)$ A $= 1.40$ A, and not, as heretofore, to 1.54 A. In this way, the central bond is found to have about 25 per cent double bond character. Since, however, we are probably not justified in assuming that the hyper-conjugation in dimethylacetylene is completely negligible, the most that we can conclude from this treatment is doubtless that the central carbon-carbon bond in biacetylene may possibly have between 25 and 65 per cent double-bond character.

With many of the other substances that are listed in Table 4·4, similar difficulties are encountered. Cyanogen, for example, is closely analogous to biacetylene; hence, for the former substance, as for the latter, the 65 per cent double-bond character that is found is of doubtful significance. With other compounds, a somewhat different type of problem arises. Since, as was pointed out on page 168, the lengths of single bonds that are adjacent to carbonyl groups are frequently anomalous, the fact that, for example, the carbon-nitrogen bond in urea is 0.13 A shorter than would be expected for a pure single bond does not conclusively prove that this bond has exactly the stated 42 per cent double-bond character.

Still another factor which decreases the quantitative significance of the present treatment is that relatively enormous differences in the calculated bond characters can be caused by small changes in either the observed interatomic distances or the assumed lengths of pure single and double bonds.   Thus, with methyl formate, the carbon-oxygen bond of the carbonyl group is found to have 140 per cent double-bond character (Table 4·4).   However, if the observed length of this bond had been only 0.02 A greater, or if the assumed length of a pure double bond had been only 0.02 A less, the calculated value would have been reduced to 100 per cent.   These small changes of 0.02 A are doubtless no greater than the uncertainties in the experimental value for the length of the actual bond and in the assumed value for that of a hypothetical pure double bond. Consequently, in this and numerous other instances, we cannot be entirely sure that the discrepancies of the kinds discussed above really exist. Clearly, therefore, any quantitative conclusions that may be drawn from the values listed in Table 4·4 can be accepted only with the greatest reserve.

What is probably the most significant limitation of the foregoing method for the interpretation of bond lengths still remains to be mentioned.   There is no *independent* experimental or theoretical way in which the double-bond characters that are derived from equations 1 and 2 can be determined, or even defined.   Indeed, one might reasonably argue that the several kinds of uncertainty which we discussed in the preceding paragraphs are really irrelevant inasmuch as the per cent double-bond character of any bond has no meaning aside from that given it by equations 1 and 2.   Since the double-bond character is therefore merely an alternative statement of the bond length, and since the relation between these two equivalent quantities is uniquely fixed by the equations 1 and 2, no discrepancy is ever possible (in the absence of purely arithmetical errors).   Although such a view is perhaps entirely logical, it is nevertheless too extreme to be useful.   A more satisfactory approach consists in admitting from the outset that the treatment is little more than qualitative, and that the numerical values which are obtained for the per cent double-bond characters are, at best, only very roughly approximate.   Within this limitation, however, the treatment is useful in that it provides a convenient way for picturing the variations in bond type from molecule to molecule.

The second method of correlating interatomic distances and bond character is due to Penney.[42]   In this treatment, which rests upon a rather better theoretical basis than Pauling's, the *order* of a bond is defined in such a way that it assumes the values 1, 2, and 3 for pure single, double, and triple bonds, respectively, and is a linear function of the bond energy for bonds of intermediate type.   In benzene, for example, each carbon-carbon bond would be of order 1.5 if the resonance energy were zero,

[42] W. G. Penney, *Proc. Roy. Soc.* (*London*) *A* **158**, 306 (1937).

since then the energy of each bond would be just the average between the energies of a pure single and a pure double bond.   The resonance energy, however, stabilizes the molecule by some 36 kcal per mole, so that each carbon-carbon bond is strengthened to the extent of about 6 kcal per mole. The bond order is therefore somewhat greater than 1.5. Similarly, the bond order in graphite is somewhat greater than $1\frac{1}{3}$.   The exact numerical values of the bond orders in these and in other substances can be found only by elaborate, but still crudely approximate, quantum-mechanical calculations which cannot be described here in complete detail.   In outline, however, the procedure is as follows: When the approximate quantum-mechanical treatment of any substance is carried through by the so-called *valence-bond method* (cf. Sections 9·12–9·20), the total energy of the molecule can be expressed as a sum of terms.   For example, if the six carbon atoms of the benzene ring are designated by the letters a, b,

VII

$\cdots f$, as in structure VII, the energy of the molecule is, to this approximation, found (cf. page 636) to be

$$W = Q + (2.61/6)(J_{ab} + J_{bc} + J_{cd} + J_{de} + J_{ef} + J_{fa}) = Q + 2.61J \quad (3)$$

Here, Q is a constant with which we need not be further concerned; J_{ab} is an additional constant that is known as the *single-exchange integral* between the adjacent atoms a and b; J_{bc} is the similar integral between the atoms b and c; and so on.   Since the six pairs of adjacent atoms are equivalent to one another, the six corresponding integrals $J_{ab}, J_{bc}, \cdots J_{fa}$ must be equal.   Hence

$$J_{ab} = J_{bc} = J_{cd} = J_{de} = J_{ef} = J_{fa} = J$$

Now it can be shown that, if in the actual molecule any given pair of adjacent atoms, say c and d, were linked by a single bond, then the coefficient of J_{cd} in equation 3 would be $-\frac{1}{2}$; but that, if these atoms were instead linked by a double bond, the coefficient of the integral would instead be $+1$.   Consequently, since the correct value of the coefficient is neither $-\frac{1}{2}$ nor $+1$, but 2.61/6, the order of the bond can be found by a linear interpolation (see below) to be 1.623.   In a similar way, the order of each carbon-carbon bond in graphite is found to be about 1.45. With other substances, in which all the bonds are not equivalent, and in which therefore the coefficients of all the integrals J_{ab}, etc., need not be equal, the calculation becomes somewhat more difficult; since, however, the underlying principle remains the same, we need not here consider these added complications.

In order to make the linear interpolation that was referred to in the preceding paragraph, we adopt the definition that the order p_{jk} of the bond between any pair of adjacent atoms j and k is related to the coefficient r_{jk} of the integral J_{jk} (cf. equation 3) by the equation

$$p_{jk} = A + Br_{jk}$$

where A and B are numerical constants which we must now determine. Since p_{jk} is equal to 1 when r_{jk} is equal to $-\frac{1}{2}$, but to 2 when r_{jk} is equal to $+1$ (see above), we obtain the pair of simultaneous equations

$$1 = A - \tfrac{1}{2}B$$

and

$$2 = A + B$$

Solution of these equations shows that A and B are respectively equal to $\frac{4}{3}$ and $\frac{2}{3}$ so that finally

$$p_{jk} = \tfrac{4}{3} + \tfrac{2}{3}r_{jk}$$

With benzene, for which $r_{jk} = 2.61/6$, therefore, the bond order becomes

$$p_{jk} = \tfrac{4}{3} + \tfrac{2}{3}(2.61/6) = 1.623$$

We are now in position to consider the way in which the bond length varies with the bond order. As we have already seen, the orders of the carbon-carbon bonds in ethane, graphite, benzene, ethylene, and acetylene are (by definition or by calculation) 1.000, 1.45, 1.623, 2.000, and 3.000, respectively, whereas the corresponding distances are 1.54, 1.42, 1.39, 1.35, and 1.20 A, respectively. A smooth curve showing the relation between bond order and bond length is drawn. Then, for any further molecule, such as butadiene, the orders of the various bonds are calculated theoretically, by the method briefly described above, and the predicted lengths are read off from the empirical curve. The results obtained in this way for a number of hydrocarbons are listed in Table 4·5. Also listed in this table are the results of similar treatments that have been carried through by Coulson[43] for the same substances. These additional values of both the bond orders and the bond lengths have been derived by a method which is essentially the same as Penney's, but which differs in the quantum-mechanical approximations introduced into the theoretical calculations of the bond orders. More specifically, although Penney carried through his calculations by the valence-bond method, Coulson employed instead the molecular-orbital approach (see Sections 9·22–9·25). The agreement of the two procedures with each other and with the

[43] C. A. Coulson, *Proc. Roy. Soc. (London) A* **169**, 413 (1939); *Proc. Roy. Soc. (Edinburgh) A* **61**, 115 (1941); J. E. Lennard-Jones and C. A. Coulson, *Trans. Faraday Soc.* **35**, 811 (1939).

TABLE 4·5

CALCULATED ORDERS AND LENGTHS[a] OF BONDS IN HYDROCARBONS

Substance	Bond Order		Bond Length[a]			
	P^b	C^c	P^b	C^c	LJ^e	Observed[f]
Graphite	1.45	1.53	(1.42)	(1.42)	—	1.42
Butadiene[g] A	1.33	1.45	1.43	1.43	1.41	1.47
B	1.91	1.89	1.34	1.35	1.34	1.37
Benzene	1.623	1.667	(1.39)	(1.39)	1.37	1.39
Hexatriene[g] A	1.81	1.79	1.36	1.37	1.35	—
B	1.37	1.48	1.42	1.42	1.40	—
C	1.88	1.87	1.35	1.35	1.35	—
Styrene[h] A	1.92	1.943	1.34	1.34	1.34	—
B	1.31	1.328	1.45	1.44	1.44	—
C	1.58	1.630	1.40	1.37	1.37	—
D	1.63	1.674	1.39	1.38	1.38	—
E	1.62	1.662	1.39	1.37	1.37	—
Octatetraene[g] A	1.46	1.53	1.41	1.42	1.40	—
B	1.76	1.76	1.37	1.37	1.35	—
C	1.37	1.50	1.42	1.42	1.40	—
D	1.88	1.86	1.35	1.35	1.35	—
Naphthalene[i] A	1.433	1.518	1.42	1.42	—	1.393
B	1.516	1.555	1.40	1.40	—	1.425
C	1.690	1.725	1.38	1.37	—	1.365
D	1.530	1.603	1.40	1.40	—	1.404
Biphenylene[j] A	—	1.263	—	1.47	—	1.46
B	—	1.565	—	1.41	—	1.41
C	—	1.683	—	1.38	—	1.41
D	—	1.621	—	1.40	—	1.41
E	—	1.691	—	1.38	—	1.41
Biphenyl[k] A	—	1.370	—	1.46	1.44	1.48
B	—	1.619	—	1.40	1.40	1.42
C	—	1.677	—	1.39	1.40	1.42
D	—	1.660	—	1.38	1.40	1.42
Pyrene[l] A	1.280	1.536	1.46	1.41	—	1.45
B	1.516	1.524	1.41	1.41_5	—	1.39
C	1.587	1.594	1.38	1.40	—	1.42
D	1.587	1.669	1.38	1.39	—	1.39
E	1.141	1.503	1.49_5	1.42	—	1.45
F	1.931	1.777	1.35	1.37	—	1.39

TABLE 4·5 (contd.)

Substance	Bond Order		Bond Length[d]			
	P^b	C^c	P^b	C^c	LJ^e	Observed[f]
Anthracene[m] A	—	1.606	—	1.40	—	1.396
B	—	1.485	—	1.42	—	1.436
C	—	1.535	—	1.41	—	1.423
D	—	1.738	—	1.37	—	1.370
E	—	1.586	—	1.40	—	1.408
Coronene[n] A	1.816	1.757	1.36	1.37	—	1.385
B	1.316	1.538	1.45	1.41	—	1.415
C	1.629	1.538	1.39	1.41	—	1.430
D	1.328	1.522	1.45	1.41_5	—	1.430

[a] These calculations are based on the assumption that the C=C distance in ethylene is 1.33 A.   If the value of 1.35 A, given in Table 4·1, were used instead, many of the calculated bond lengths listed here would be slightly increased.

[b] Calculated by the method of W. G. Penney, *Proc. Roy. Soc.* (*London*) *A* **158**, 306 (1937).

[c] Calculated by the method of C. A. Coulson, *Proc. Roy. Soc.* (*London*) *A* **169**, 413 (1939); *Proc. Roy. Soc.* (*Edinburgh*) *A* **61**, 115 (1941).   See also J. E. Lennard-Jones and C. A. Coulson, *Trans. Faraday Soc.* **35**, 811 (1939).

[d] In angstrom units.

[e] Calculated by the method of J. E. Lennard-Jones, *Proc. Roy. Soc.* (*London*) *A* **158**, 280 (1937).   See also J. E. Lennard-Jones and J. Turkevich, *ibid. A* **158**, 297 (1937).

[f] These values are taken from Table 4·3, Section 4·3, and from the Appendix.

[g] The bond A is the one in the center of the molecule; the bond B is the one adjacent to A; and so on to the terminal bond.

[h] The bond A is the terminal one, represented as double in the conventional structure; the bond B is the one adjacent to A and connecting it to the ring; and the bonds C, D, and E are the bonds in the benzene ring, taken in sequence. The calculation by Penney's method was made by W. G. Penney and G. J. Kynch, *Proc. Roy. Soc.* (*London*) *A* **164**, 409 (1938); that by Coulson's method was made by G. Berthier and B. Pullman, *Compt. rend.* **228**, 397 (1949).

[i] The bond A is the one in the center of the molecule; the bond B is the one adjacent to A; the bond C is the one between an alpha carbon atom and its beta neighbor; and the bond D is the one between two adjacent beta carbon atoms.   The calculation by Coulson's method was made by C. A. Coulson and H. C. Longuet-Higgins, *Rev. sci.* **85**, 929 (1947).

[j] The several bonds are here designated as in the diagram

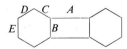

The calculation was made by J. Waser and V. Schomaker, *J. Am. Chem. Soc.* **65**, 1451 (1943).

[k] The bond A is the one in the center of the molecule, joining the two rings;

the bond B is the one of the benzene ring, adjacent to A; and C and D are the successive bonds of the ring. The calculation was made by Buu-Hoï, C. A. Coulson, P. Daudel, R. Daudel, M. Martin, A. Pullman, and B. Pullman, *Rev. sci.* **85**, 1041 (1947); A. Pullman and B. Pullman, *J. chim. phys.* **46**, 212 (1949).

[l] The several bonds are here designated as in the diagram

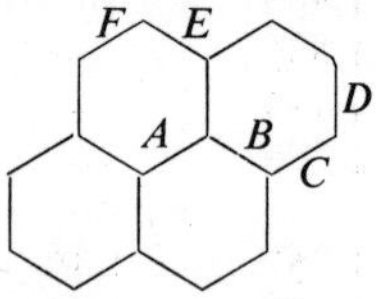

F E
A B D
C

The calculations were made by W. E. Moffitt and C. A. Coulson, *Proc. Phys. Soc.* (*London*) **60**, 309 (1948).

[m] The several bonds are designated as in the diagram

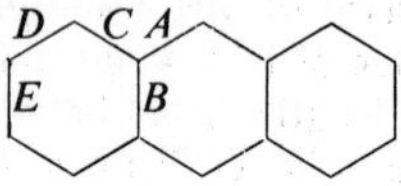

D C A
E B

The calculations were made by C. A. Coulson and H. C. Longuet-Higgins (note *i*).

[n] The several bonds are designated as in the diagram

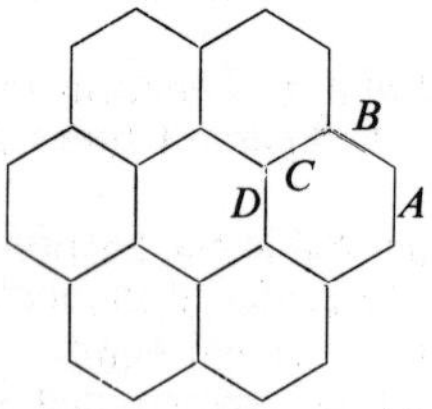

B
D C A

The calculations were made by W. E. Moffitt and C. A. Coulson (note *l*).

experimental data is far from perfect, but it is probably about as satisfactory as could have been anticipated.

The calculations for naphthalene are of interest in that they predict an appreciable difference among the various carbon-carbon bonds. Pauling's method of treatment also leads to a similar conclusion,[41] for, if all structures containing formal bonds are neglected, the bonds between the α and their adjacent β carbon atoms have $66\frac{2}{3}$ per cent double-bond character and a predicted length of 1.37 A, whereas all the other carbon-carbon bonds have $33\frac{1}{3}$ per cent double-bond character and predicted lengths of 1.42 A. (Cf. equations 1 and 2.) This extremely simple and approximate calculation is, in fact, about as reliable as is either of the more detailed and better-grounded ones of Penney and of Coulson. In any event, it is gratifying that all three methods of treatment are consistent with the observation that the bonds which are designated as C in Table 4·5 are considerably shorter than any of the others. Similarly, in anthracene, if all structures with formal bonds are again ignored, the bonds A, B, C, D, and E (cf. Table 4·5) have 50, 25, 25, 75, and 25 per cent double-bond character, respectively; and their predicted lengths are 1.39, 1.44, 1.44, 1.36, and 1.44 A, respectively. Once more, therefore, the simpler treatment is seen to be little, if any, inferior to Coulson's. With substances like butadiene, however, no treatment in which the structures with formal bonds are ignored can be satisfactory; hence, with such substances, only the more elaborate procedures can be used.

The methods of Penney and of Coulson, although superior to that of Pauling on theoretical grounds, suffer from certain handicaps which somewhat limit their usefulness. In the first place, they are restricted to the treatment of hydrocarbons, and, in the second place, they can be applied to new problems only by persons who are familiar with the quantum-mechanical methods employed in the calculations. Moreover, they merely accept the empirically established relations between the bond lengths and the two respective, independently defined, bond orders; and they make no attempt to derive these relations from any more fundamental principles. The first two of these limitations apply also to a fourth method, due to Lennard-Jones,[44] by which bond lengths can be directly calculated without explicit reference to bond orders and without use of the observed lengths of the bonds in benzene and graphite. Although the details of this additional method are too technical to be profitably given here, we can nevertheless briefly outline the underlying principles. From spectroscopic data (cf. Section 6·11), one can estimate the energy which, in the absence of resonance, would be required in order to distort a molecule into any desired size and shape from any one of the different sizes and shapes which are characteristic of the individual contributing structures. Moreover, with the aid of these same data, one can further estimate the variation in the resonance energy which must accompany such a distortion of the molecule. The predicted lengths of the several bonds are then, of course, the ones which lead to the lowest possible value for the calculated *total* energy. The results obtained by this method are also listed in Table 4·5; they are seen to be in satisfactory agreement with those mentioned before.[45]

[44] J. E. Lennard-Jones, *Proc. Roy. Soc.* (*London*) A **158**, 280 (1937). J. E. Lennard-Jones and J. Turkevich, *ibid.* A **158**, 297 (1937).

[45] For recent critical discussions, which put Lennard-Jones's method upon a somewhat more satisfactory theoretical basis, see D. F. Hornig, *J. Am. Chem. Soc.* **72**, 5772 (1950); C. A. Coulson and S. L. Altmann, *Trans. Faraday Soc.* **48**, 293 (1952). For still further calculations of bond lengths, which are even more complex than that of Lennard-Jones, and which are also less dependent on the use of empirical data, see H. O. Pritchard and F. H. Sumner, *Proc. Roy. Soc.* (*London*) A **226**, 128 (1954).

In such compounds as carbon dioxide, carbon suboxide, methyl azide, etc., certain bonds may have more or less *triple*-bond character or, in other words, may have orders that are greater than 2. Although these substances can profitably be discussed from the purely qualitative viewpoint that was adopted on pages 184ff, no entirely satisfactory extensions of the more quantitative treatments have as yet been given. We shall here, therefore, make no attempt to amplify our earlier discussions.

4·5 Miscellaneous Applications. (a) It was pointed out in Section 4·2 that a molecule like that of biphenyl should preferentially exist in a completely planar configuration as a result of the partial double-bond character of the central carbon-carbon bond. Conversely, the length of that bond should be less if the molecule were actually planar than it would be if the molecule were in some way held in a nonplanar configuration. Similar considerations apply generally to all molecules having conjugated double bonds. The experimental evidence bearing upon this point is meager and not completely conclusive. In solid picryl iodide, for example, the nitro group para to the iodine atom is coplanar with the benzene ring, but the two nitro groups ortho to the iodine are forced by steric repulsions to lie in planes nearly perpendicular to that of the ring. The corresponding carbon-nitrogen distances are 1.35 and 1.45 A, respectively, in agreement with expectation. (See Table 4·3, Section 4·3, and the Appendix.) In solid *cis* azobenzene, the molecule departs considerably from planarity, and the length of the carbon-nitrogen bond is 1.46 A, or very nearly that of a pure single bond. A smaller effect is observed in solid *trans* azobenzene, in which the molecules are not all crystallographically equivalent but belong to two types. In one of these, the molecule is completely planar and the carbon-nitrogen bond length is 1.40 A; in the other, the molecule is not completely planar, and the carbon-nitrogen distance is 1.43 A. The situation is similar in *trans* stilbene, the corresponding carbon-carbon bond lengths being 1.44 and 1.45 A, respectively. The reported variations in distance in these last substances are in the correct direction, but are too small to be trustworthy. Especially with stilbene, the uncertainties in the experimental values are greater than the observed effects. Further data of high accuracy would be necessary before any conclusions could be drawn.

(b) If the partial double-bond character of the central bond in butadiene holds the molecule in a single plane, then two stereoisomeric forms, represented by I and II, should be possible. The energy required for a

$$CH_2{=}CH \qquad\qquad CH_2{=}CH$$
$$| \qquad\qquad\qquad\quad |$$
$$CH_2{=}CH \qquad\qquad HC{=}CH_2$$
$$\text{I} \qquad\qquad\qquad\quad \text{II}$$

molecule to pass from one form to the other should be small, however, and so we could not expect an isolation of stable isomers to be possible. Actually no examples are known in which isomers of this type have been separated from each other (unless the existence of such substances as *cis* cinnamic acid in several crystalline modifications should prove to be due to such an effect). Conversely, the partial single-bond character of the central double bond in stilbene should facilitate rotation about that bond. This prediction is supported by the observation that, although the energy required for rotation about the double bond in 1,2-dideuteroethylene is about 61.3 kcal per mole,[46] that required for the corresponding rotation in stilbene is instead only about 43 kcal per mole.[47] Calvin and his co-workers[48] have shown that in *p*-nitro-*p'*-aminostilbene, III, with which the quinoid structure IV might be expected to have a particularly large

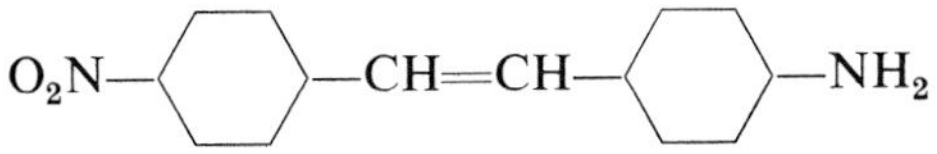

III

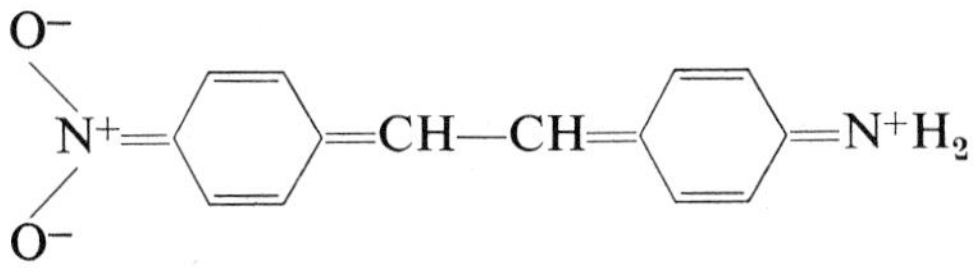

IV

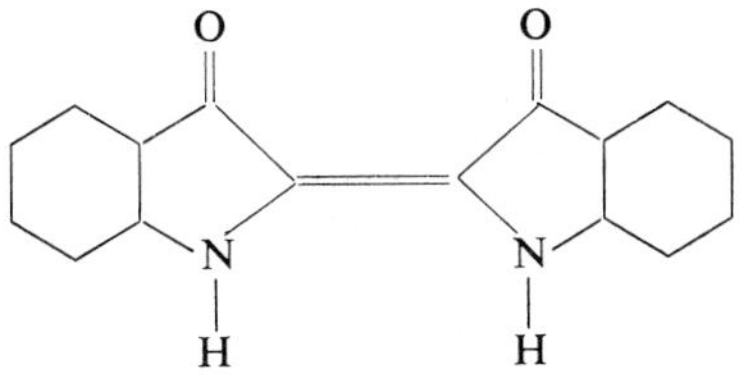

V

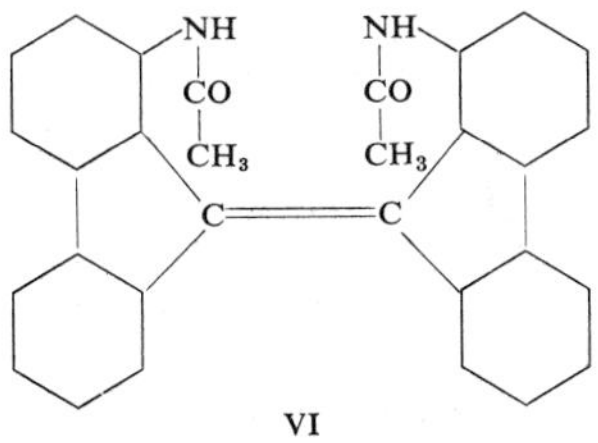

VI

[46] B. S. Rabinovitch, J. E. Douglas, and F. S. Looney, *J. Chem. Phys.* **20**, 1807 (1952).

[47] G. B. Kistiakowsky and W. R. Smith, *J. Am. Chem. Soc.* **56**, 638 (1934).

[48] M. Calvin and R. E. Buckles, *J. Am. Chem. Soc.* **62**, 3324 (1940); M. Calvin and H. W. Alter, *J. Chem. Phys.* **19**, 768 (1951).

weight (cf. pages 223ff and 320), the *cis-trans* interconversion is exceptionally easy. In indigo, one form (doubtless the *cis* form, V) reverts spontaneously to its isomer in a few hours even in the solid state,[49] and, with such compounds as 2,2'-diacetylaminodibiphenyleneëthylene, VI and VII,[50] and 2-nitro-9-(*p*-nitrobenzylidene)fluorene, VIII and IX,[51] the *cis-*

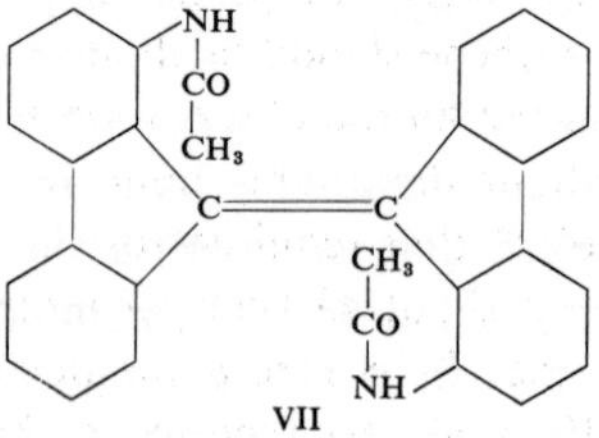

VII

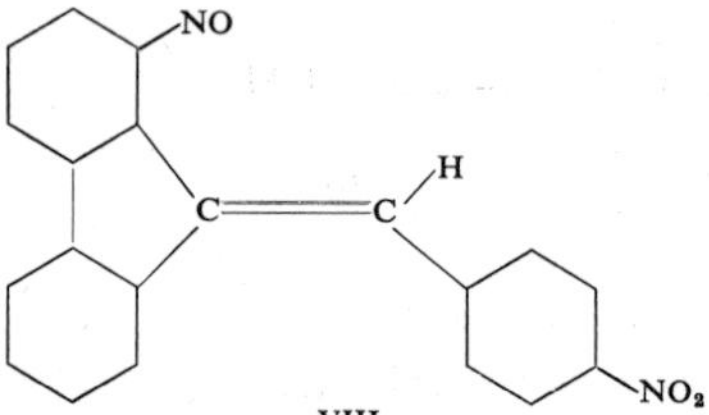

VIII

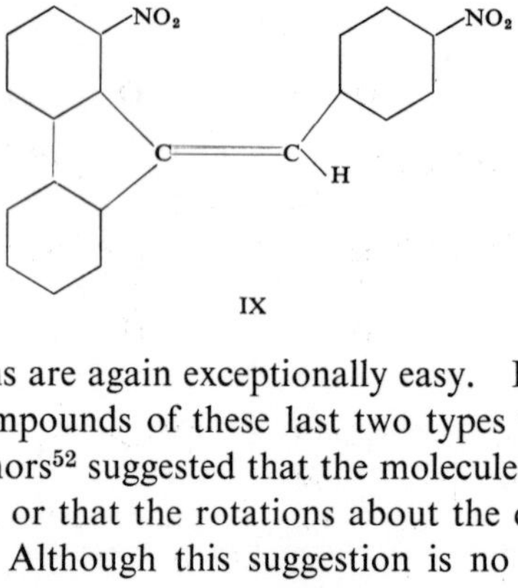

IX

trans interconversions are again exceptionally easy. Indeed, since stereoisomerism in the compounds of these last two types was for many years unknown, some authors[52] suggested that the molecules of such substances might be nonplanar, or that the rotations about the double bonds might be essentially free. Although this suggestion is no longer tenable, the

[49] G. Heller, *Ber.* **72**, 1858 (1939). However, see also W. R. Brode, E. G. Pearson, and G. M. Wyman, *J. Am. Chem. Soc.* **76**, 1036 (1954) for more recent evidence suggesting that, as a result of the stabilization of the *trans* isomer by its intramolecular hydrogen bonds, *cis* indigo does not exist at all.

[50] E. K. Weisburger, J. H. Weisburger, and F. E. Ray, *J. Org. Chem.* **14**, 488 (1949).

[51] E. D. Bergmann and E. Fischer, *Bull. soc. chim. France*, **1950**, 1084; E. D. Bergmann, E. Fischer, and Y. Hirshberg, *ibid.* **1950**, 1103.

[52] See, for example, E. D. Bergmann, *Isomerism and Isomerization of Organic Compounds*, Interscience Publishers, New York, 1948, p. 49.

ready transformations of the substances into their isomers does show that the molecules are considerably less rigid than are those of, say, *cis* and *trans* 2-butene, or of *cis* and *trans* stilbene. A reasonable explanation for this difference in properties is that, when a double bond is conjugated with three or four other double bonds, it must have a rather appreciable single-bond character, and so it can offer only a relatively small resistance to rotation. Thus, the calculated orders of the relevant bonds in 2-butene (with neglect of hyperconjugation), stilbene, triphenylethylene, tetraphenylethylene, and dibiphenyleneëthylene are found[53] by Coulson's method (see pages 191ff) to be, respectively, 2.00, 1.82, 1.75, 1.69, and 1.67. In drawing conclusions from these figures, however, we must bear in mind that, in the several calculations, all the carbon atoms of each molecule are assumed to be coplanar. Although this assumption is probably correct for 2-butene and for *trans* stilbene, it can hardly be valid with either triphenylethylene or tetraphenylethylene, and it is perhaps questionable with dibiphenyleneëthylene. In triphenyl- and tetraphenylethylene, coplanarity of two benzene rings that are attached to the same carbon atom would require that two hydrogen atoms in the ortho positions be forced to come impossibly close together; furthermore, just as in *cis* stilbene (see page 196 for a discussion of the analogous *cis* azobenzene), the interference of phenyl groups which are *cis* to each other may here also cause departures from the completely planar configurations. With dibiphenyleneëthylene, the first of these two factors does not enter, but the second could have a small effect of about the same magnitude as in *cis* stilbene. In any event, the orders of the bonds in these compounds ought to be somewhat greater than the above calculated values, and so the respective molecules ought to be somewhat more rigid than might have been anticipated. Since the steric forces which prevent coplanarity, and which hence diminish the effect of the resonance, are smallest with dibiphenyleneëthylene, it is not surprising that the difficulty of obtaining *cis* and *trans* isomers seems to be greatest with the derivatives of this parent substance (and with those of the related 9-benzylidenefluorene).

[53] Cf. B. Pullman and A. Pullman, *Les Théories électronique de la chimie organique*, Masson et Cie., Paris, 1952, pp. 598, 599, 570.

Chapter 5   RESONANCE
AND
DIPOLE
MOMENTS

5·1 General Discussion.[1] In the same way in which we define the center of mass (or center of gravity) of a material object, we can define also the centers of the positive, and of the negative, charges of a molecule. If, in a given molecule, these centers of the positive and negative charges do not coincide with each other, the substance is said to be polar; if they do coincide, the substance is said to be nonpolar. Evidently, the molecules of a polar substance are distinguished from those of a nonpolar one in that the former, but not the latter, have positive and negative ends. For example, in the typically polar substance, hydrogen chloride, the centers of the positive and negative charge undoubtedly lie in the direction of the hydrogen and chlorine nuclei, respectively, so that the hydrogen and chlorine atoms can be considered to carry net positive and negative charges, respectively; on the other hand, in the typically nonpolar substance, molecular hydrogen, each atom must be electrically neutral.

The quantitative measure of the polarity of a substance is its electric dipole moment, μ, which is defined by the equation

$$\mu = Er \tag{1}$$

The letter E here represents the magnitude of the total positive, or negative, charge, and r is the distance between the two centers of charge. The dipole moment of a nonpolar substance is equal to zero because the distance r is equal to zero, whereas that of a polar substance cannot be zero because neither E nor r can be zero; this difference suggests an

[1] For further details, the reader is referred to the many excellent general discussions that have been published in the past. For example, see P. Debye, *Polar Molecules*, Chemical Catalog Co., New York, 1929; P. Debye (editor), *The Dipole Moment and Chemical Structure* (translated by W. M. Deans), Blackie & Son, London and Glasgow, 1931; C. P. Smyth, *Dielectric Constant and Molecular Structure*, Chemical Catalog Co., New York, 1931; J. H. Van Vleck, *The Theory of Electric and Magnetic Susceptibilities*, Oxford University Press, Oxford, 1932; C. P. Smyth in A. Weissberger, *Physical Methods of Organic Chemistry*, Interscience Publishers, New York, 1st ed., 1946, vol. II, Chapter XX, 2nd ed., 1949, vol. I, Part II, Chapter XXIV; R. J. W. Le Fèvre, *Dipole Moments*, Methuen & Co., London, 1948; C. J. F. Böttcher, *Theory of Electric Polarization*, Elsevier Publishing Co., Amsterdam, 1952.

alternative way for stating the distinction between polar and nonpolar substances.

The above definition of the electric dipole moment is unique only for neutral molecules, since only then are the magnitudes of the total positive and negative charges equal. Consequently, we shall restrict ourselves in the future to the discussion of neutral molecules, and we shall not consider the dipole moments of ions. Moreover, since we shall have no occasion in this chapter to refer to *magnetic* dipole moments, we shall adopt the common procedure of describing the electric dipole moments simply as "dipole moments" or, more simply still, as "moments."

An idea of the magnitude of the dipole moment of a polar substance can be obtained in the following way. The charges of the particles contained in the molecule, that is, the charges of the nuclei and the electrons, are of the order of 10^{-10} electrostatic unit; and the intramolecular distances are of the order of 10^{-8} cm. Consequently, the dipole moments should be of the order of $10^{-10} \times 10^{-8} = 10^{-18}$ electrostatic unit. This quantity, 10^{-18} esu, is a convenient unit in terms of which dipole moments may be expressed; it is called the debye unit, or simply the debye, and it is represented by the symbol D. Thus, a nonpolar substance can be described as one with a moment equal to 0.00 D.

From its definition in equation 1, a dipole moment is seen to have a direction as well as a magnitude, because the distance r between the two centers of charge has a definite direction. A dipole moment is therefore a vector quantity and can be represented by an arrow. The convention has been adopted of drawing this arrow so that it is parallel to the line joining the centers of charge, and so that its head and tail are pointed in the directions of the negative and positive centers, respectively. The tail is commonly crossed, as in $+\!\!\rightarrow$, in order to emphasize that it represents the positive end of the dipole. The length of the arrow is proportional to the magnitude of the moment, that is, to the magnitude of the product, Er, which is, of course, always a positive quantity.

It is frequently convenient to think of the total dipole moment of a molecule as the sum of partial moments, which may be either localized in different parts of the molecule, or due to different causes. Since a dipole moment is a vector, the sum must be a vector sum, or a resultant. The method of forming such a vector sum is illustrated in the diagram

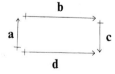

which represents the vector equation

$$\mathbf{a} + \mathbf{b} + \mathbf{c} = \mathbf{d}$$

The procedure is simply to arrange the arrows that represent the individual vectors to be summed (**a**, **b**, and **c** in the present example) so that the head of the first is coincident with the tail of the second, the head of the second is coincident with the tail of the third, and so on. For this purpose, the arrows can be moved to any necessary positions, but their directions, as well as their lengths, must be left unchanged; this requirement ensures that the arrows will be kept always parallel to their original directions or, what amounts to the same thing, to the dipole moments which they represent. The sum of the vectors, or their resultant, is then represented in magnitude and direction by the arrow **d**, which is drawn with its head, and tail, coincident with the head of the last, and tail of the first, of the component vectors, respectively. It can be shown that the order of addition is immaterial, so that, for example,

$$\mathbf{a} + \mathbf{b} + \mathbf{c} = \mathbf{a} + \mathbf{c} + \mathbf{b} = \mathbf{c} + \mathbf{b} + \mathbf{a}, \text{ and so on}$$

Several important corollaries can be drawn from the above graphical scheme for the representation of vector addition. In the first place, the two arrows which represent a vector, **a**, and its negative, $-\mathbf{a}$, are of the same length and are parallel to each other, but they point in opposite directions, as

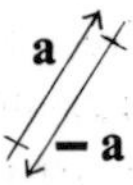

a $-\mathbf{a}$

The sum of a set of vectors is equal to zero if, in the diagram from which the sum is computed, the head of the last arrow coincides with the tail of the first. And finally, the magnitude of the sum of two vectors is equal to the sum of the magnitudes if the vectors are parallel and pointed in the same direction; it is equal to the magnitude of the difference between the magnitudes if the vectors are parallel and pointed in opposite directions; and it has an intermediate value if the vectors make an angle with each other. In general, the magnitude of a sum of vectors is greater the more nearly the vectors point in the same direction. The method of vector addition and its above-mentioned corollaries will be illustrated further in the following sections.

It will not be possible here to describe the ways in which the values of dipole moments can be experimentally measured. Brief mention may be made, however, of the basic principles involved.[1] As has already been noted, a polar molecule has a positive and a negative end; in an electrostatic field, therefore, it tends to be oriented so that its dipole moment lies parallel to the field. This tendency toward a definite orientation is opposed, however, by the thermal motion, which favors a completely random orientation. Some sort of compromise between the competing effects must therefore be reached. At low temperatures, at which the thermal energy is small, the orientation along the direction of the field should be more nearly complete than at high temperatures, at which the thermal energy is large. Since the degree of orientation is reflected in the dielectric constant, ε, of the substance, it follows that the dielectric constant of a polar substance should vary with temperature. Indeed, calculation has led to equation 2:

$$\frac{\varepsilon - 1}{\varepsilon + 2} \cdot \frac{M}{d} = P_E + P_A + \frac{4\pi N\mu^2}{9kT} \tag{2}$$

where M is the molecular weight and d is the density of the substance, N is Avogadro's number, k is Boltzmann's constant, T is the absolute temperature, and P_E and P_A are the so-called electron and atom polarizations, respectively. (Actually, P_E and P_A are *polarizabilities* rather than *polarizations*, but the latter term seems to be generally adopted for them in dipole-moment work.) It is important that the dipole moment, μ, appears in equation 2 only in the form of the square of its magnitude, which is no longer a vector. Consequently, the direction of the moment cannot be measured.

Some discussion of the fundamental equation 2 is desirable here, in order that its significance and its methods of application may be made clear. In the first place, it should be remarked that the equation applies strictly only to a substance in the form of a highly attenuated gas. The experimental study of such a gas is difficult, because its dielectric constant is always only slightly greater than unity, so that the term $\varepsilon - 1$ in the numerator on the left side of equation 2 is a small difference between larger quantities and cannot be measured very precisely. Moreover, many substances of interest cannot be vaporized without decomposition. For these reasons, most of the measurements of dipole moments have been carried out in dilute solution in some nonpolar solvent like benzene or carbon tetrachloride. Equation 2 then has to be replaced by the more general one, 2′:

$$\frac{\varepsilon - 1}{\varepsilon + 2} \cdot \frac{f_1 M_1 + f_2 M_2}{d} = f_1(P_{E1} + P_{A1}) + f_2(P_{E2} + P_{A2}) + \frac{4\pi f_2 N\mu_2^2}{9kT} \tag{2'}$$

in which the subscripts 1 and 2 refer to the nonpolar solvent and to the solute, respectively; f_1 and f_2 are the mole fractions of the appropriate components; and the other symbols have the same meanings as in equation 2. The value of the term $P_{E1} + P_{A1}$ is determined by measuring the dielectric constant of the pure solvent, for which $f_1 = 1$ and $f_2 = 0$. Equation 2′, which cannot be derived as rigorously as equation 2, seems to be fairly, but not absolutely, satisfactory. As a result, dipole moments measured in solution may be in error by several tenths of a debye unit. In the future, therefore, we shall use the values obtained in the gas phase whenever possible; when such values are not available, we shall try to limit ourselves to comparisons of the moments obtained for substances of similar structure under comparable conditions.

Since P_E and P_A are found experimentally to be practically independent of temperature, it follows from equation 2 that, when the quantity $\frac{\varepsilon - 1}{\varepsilon + 2} \cdot \frac{M}{d}$ is plotted against the reciprocal of the absolute temperature, a straight line with a slope of $4\pi N\mu^2/9k$ should be obtained, provided that the dipole moment, μ, does not itself vary with temperature. (For the sake of simplicity, we shall in the following assume that we are dealing with a gaseous substance, so that we can employ equation 2.) In principle, this relation provides the most precise method for the evaluation of μ. In practice, however, the accurate determination of the slope of the line often requires that the dielectric constant be measured over an impracticably great temperature range; moreover, the method cannot be used at all if μ is a function of temperature. For these reasons, a different procedure (the *optical*, as distinguished from the *temperature-variation*, method) has been commonly adopted.   The electron polarization, P_E, can be calculated directly from the index of refraction, n, of the substance, with the aid of the Lorenz-Lorentz equation

$$\frac{n^2 - 1}{n^2 + 2} \cdot \frac{M}{d} = R_M = P_E \tag{3}$$

for the molecular refraction, R_M.   Since the index of refraction depends upon the wave length of the light used, the value of P_E measured for visible light should be extrapolated to infinite wave length.   The atom polarization, P_A, is usually small and is ordinarily either ignored or else arbitrarily assigned a value equal to some definite factor, say one-tenth, times that of P_E.   In this manner, the dipole moment can be obtained from a measurement of the dielectric constant at a single temperature.   An error of uncertain magnitude and sign, however, is introduced by the approximations and assumptions in the calculation.   This error can sometimes be large,[2] but it is usually assumed to be at most only a few tenths of a debye.

A considerably more precise method for the measurement of dipole moments has recently been developed.[3]   This method, which unfortunately has not as yet been extended to any but the simplest of organic compounds, is based upon a study of the Stark effect in the microwave spectra.   The underlying principle is that, when a molecule with a nonvanishing dipole moment is placed in an external electrostatic field, the energies of its various rotational levels are changed in characteristic ways.   By a method which need not here be described, one can then calculate the value of the dipole moment from the observed changes in the pure-rotation spectrum of the substance.

5·2   The Origin of Dipole Moments.   Although we shall later find that the underlying assumptions are not always entirely justified, let us for the moment consider that the measured moment of each substance is the vector sum of contributions which are known as *bond moments*, and which are made by all the bonds that are present in the molecule.   By adopting this procedure, we can first deal with each bond separately, and then consider the combination of the various bond moments into the resultant moment of the molecule as a whole.

The existence of a dipole moment can frequently be correlated with the presence of formal charges in the molecule.   Trimethylamine oxide, I, for example, has a moment which, in solution in either benzene or dioxane, is equal to about 5 D,[4] and which undoubtedly resides largely

[2] I. E. Coop and L. E. Sutton, *J. Chem. Soc.* **1938**, 1269.   For a general discussion of atom polarization, see L. E. Sutton, *Ann. Repts. on Progr. Chem.* (*Chem. Soc. London*) **37**, 57 (1940).

[3] For a recent discussion, and for references to the original literature, see C. A. McDowell, *Ann. Repts. on Progr. Chem.* (*Chem. Soc. London*) **48**, 32 (1951).

[4] For a recent extensive table of dipole moments, see L. G. Wesson, *Tables of Electric Dipole Moments*, Technology Press, Massachusetts Institute of Technology, Cambridge, Massachusetts, 1948.   An older compilation appears as an appendix in *Trans. Faraday Soc.* **30**, (1934).   Throughout this chapter, dipole moments which are listed without further reference have been taken from these sources.

in the nitrogen-oxygen bond.   The nitrogen and oxygen atoms lie at the positive and negative ends, respectively, of this bond moment.   Similarly, nitromethane, which is a hybrid of structures II and III, probably owes

$$
\begin{array}{ccc}
\text{CH}_3 & \text{O} & \text{O}^- \\
| & \diagup\!\!\!\!= & \diagup \\
\text{CH}_3\!-\!^+\!\text{N}\!-\!\text{O}^- & \text{CH}_3\!-\!^+\!\text{N} & \text{CH}_3\!-\!^+\!\text{N} \\
| & \diagdown & \diagdown\!\!\!\!= \\
\text{CH}_3 & \text{O}^- & \text{O} \\
\text{I} & \text{II} & \text{III}
\end{array}
$$

its moment of 3.50 D in the gas phase (Table 5·2, Section 5·3) largely to the formal charges; again, the nitrogen and oxygen atoms are undoubtedly positive and negative, respectively.   Frequently, however, appreciable dipole moments exist in molecules in which no formal charges are present; under such circumstances, the resonance theory gives considerable insight into the factors involved.

In Section 2·7, it was pointed out that any actual bond must be intermediate between the purely ionic and purely covalent extremes, and it was mentioned that this conclusion provides a qualitative picture of the origin of dipole moments.   It seems reasonable to suppose, for example, that in hydrogen chloride, in which there is resonance among the structures IV, V, and VI, the hydrogen atom must be positive relative to the chlorine,

$$
\begin{array}{ccc}
\text{H}\!-\!\text{Cl} & \text{H}^+ \quad \text{Cl}^- & \text{H}^- \quad \text{Cl}^+ \\
\text{IV} & \text{V} & \text{VI}
\end{array}
$$

because structure V is certainly more stable, and so must be assigned a greater weight, than structure VI.   In the hydrogen molecule, on the other hand, the resonance among the three corresponding structures, VII, VIII, and IX, leads to zero moment.   The two ionic structures,

$$
\begin{array}{ccc}
\text{H}\!-\!\text{H} & \text{H}^+ \quad \text{H}^- & \text{H}^- \quad \text{H}^+ \\
\text{VII} & \text{VIII} & \text{IX}
\end{array}
$$

VIII and IX, being equivalent, must have the same weight, and therefore their effects upon the moment exactly cancel each other.

It has not yet been possible to develop a satisfactory quantitative theory of bond moments on the above basis, since, in the attempt to do so, several difficulties arise which have so far not been resolved.   In the first place, it is possible that even a purely covalent structure may correspond to a nonvanishing dipole moment, and, in fact, approximate calculations have suggested that this may be the rule rather than the exception when the bond is between dissimilar atoms.[5]   Such a covalent moment should lie with its positive end at the larger of the two atoms,

[5] R. S. Mulliken, *J. Chem. Phys.* **3**, 573 (1935).

and therefore it might tend either to increase or to diminish that due to the ionic structures. In any event, its exact effect upon the observed bond moment could not be determined without detailed and laborious numerical computation. A second difficulty arises because the moment of a given bond is not simply a weighted mean of the moments expected for the structures which are involved in the resonance. Instead, account must be taken of further terms, which are due to the interaction between the structures, and which are of uncertain magnitude and direction. These bear some analogy to the resonance energy, which likewise can be considered to be a term due to the interaction between the structures. They differ, however, in the significant respect that they may either increase or decrease the moment (or they may possibly even leave it unchanged), whereas the resonance energy can never increase the energy. (See also pages 27f.)

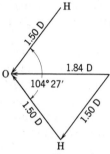

Fig. 5·1. Vector diagram showing the dipole moment of a water molecule as the sum of the moments of the two O—H bonds.

Still a further factor which makes a quantitative treatment difficult is that experiment gives only the total dipole moment of the molecule as a whole, and not the moments of the individual bonds. In some especially simple molecules, to be sure, the bond moments can be inferred from the measured moments of the substances. A trivial example of this situation is encountered in any diatomic molecule, such as that of hydrogen chloride, because then only one bond is present, and consequently the bond moment and the measured moment are identical. A more interesting example is provided by water. Since the two oxygen-hydrogen bonds are equivalent, they must have the same moment. This relation, when combined with the measured moment[4] of 1.84 D for the substance, and with the measured value of 104° 27' for the H—O—H bond angle,[6] shows that the oxygen-hydrogen bond moment must be 1.50 D. In the calculation, the principle of which should be apparent from Figure 5·1, the further reasonable assumption must be made that the bond moments lie along their respective bond axes. Similarly, from the observations that the total moment of ammonia is 1.46 D, and that each of the H—N—H bond angles is 107°,[6] the moment of the nitrogen-hydrogen bond is found to be 1.31 D. In each of these examples, the hydrogen is presumably positive with respect to the central atom. On the other hand, the measured moment of methane is 0.00 D. This value is a direct consequence merely of the tetrahedral symmetry of the molecule and sheds

[6] D. M. Dennison, *Revs. Mod. Phys.* **12**, 175 (1940); G. Herzberg, *Infrared and Raman Spectra*, D. Van Nostrand Co., New York, 1945.

no light whatever upon the moment of the carbon-hydrogen bond. In the following discussion, we shall assume that the carbon-hydrogen bond moment is equal to 0.4 D, and that the carbon and hydrogen atoms are, respectively, positive and negative.

The assumption which is here made regarding the C—H bond moment is only partially consistent with the views which seem now to be most commonly held. Although a majority of chemists would probably agree that the *magnitude* of this moment must be fairly near to 0.4 D, there is a widespread feeling that the *direction* ought to be the opposite of the one stated. Since carbon is a more electronegative element than hydrogen (see Table 3·9, Section 3·6), the carbon atom would ordinarily be expected to mark the negative end of the dipole. The difference in electronegativities is, however, so small that its effect could easily be reversed by other factors. In any event, there have recently been advanced several independent arguments which strongly suggest (but perhaps do not conclusively prove) that, in the C—H bond, the carbon atom is positive with respect to the hydrogen.[7] These arguments are based partly upon experimental evidence and partly upon theoretical calculations; since they are rather complex and since they are also largely irrelevant to the following discussion, we shall here limit ourselves to a brief description of one of the theoretical approaches to the problem.

Of the several factors that appear to be responsible for the reversal of the direction of the C—H bond moment, one has already been mentioned. Since a carbon atom is larger than a hydrogen atom, a purely covalent bond between the two should have a dipole moment with the carbon atom at its positive end; hence, in the actual bond, the contribution that is made by the covalent structure must increase the positive charge, or decrease the negative charge, on the carbon atom. This one factor, however, is probably insufficient, by itself, to overcome the effect of the difference in electronegativity. According to approximate calculations by Coulson,[7] the direction of the bond moment is instead largely determined by a so-called *atomic dipole*, which arises in the following way. In Sections 2·9 and 2·10, the average distributions of electric charge in a few simple atoms and molecules were described with the aid of schematic drawings, in which the closed surfaces surrounding the regions of greatest electronic concentration were represented by closed curves. From Figure 2·3, Section 2·9, and from Figure 2·7, Section 2·10, in particular, it is readily seen that, when an electron occupies either a spherically symmetric *s* orbital or a dumbbell shaped *p* orbital, the associated center of negative charge is coincident with the positively charged nucleus. Consequently,

[7] For a survey of the evidence, see W. L. G. Gent, *Quart. Revs. (London)* **2**, 383 (1948). See also C. A. Coulson, *Trans. Faraday Soc.* **38**, 433 (1942).

an electron in such an orbital does not give rise to any dipole moment. In the methane molecule, however, the carbon orbitals which take part in the carbon-hydrogen bonds almost certainly do not belong to either of these two types. Instead, they are "*sp* hybrids," which are formed by superposition of (i.e., by resonance between) *s* and *p* orbitals (see the following paragraph); and, with the same conventions that were employed in Figures 2·3 and 2·7, they can be schematically depicted as in Figure 5·2. The hydrogen orbital, which also takes part in the bond, but which need not now be explicitly shown, is to be thought of as situated somewhat to the right of the figure. The feature of such an *sp* hybrid orbital which is significant here is that it corresponds to an average charge distribution such that the electron is much more likely to be found in the region on the right side of the nucleus than in the one on the left side of it. In other words, even without reference to any changes in

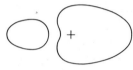

Fig. 5·2. A carbon *sp* hybrid orbital of the type in methane.

charge distribution that may be caused by the formation of the bond, we find that the carbon atom, by itself, contains a dipole moment, and that the negative end of this moment points toward the hydrogen atom. Since such an atomic dipole is associated with each of the bonds in methane, and since the vector sum of these four dipoles can be shown to be zero, the carbon atom as a whole, like the methane molecule, is nonpolar. With respect to the individual bonds, however, the electrons are appreciably displaced away from the center of the molecule. Principally for this reason, according to Coulson,[7] the hydrogen atoms are negative with respect to the carbon atom. (For further discussion of atomic dipoles, see also below.)

The belief that the carbon orbitals in methane are *sp* hybrids can be supported by two kinds of argument. In the first place, although the four orbitals in the valence shell of the carbon atom are of the two quite dissimilar types that are known as *s* and *p* (cf. page 560), the four carbon-hydrogen bonds are completely equivalent to one another and hence must be formed by completely equivalent orbitals.[8] Only by means of hybridization can such a set of four different, but equivalent orbitals be provided. In the second place, there are theoretical reasons[8, 9] for believing that the hybrid orbitals form stronger bonds, and therefore lead to a more stable molecule, than would the pure *s* and *p* orbitals.

With molecules that are more complex than the ones considered above, further difficulties arise. For example, in methyl ether, the total moment is the resultant of two carbon-oxygen, and six carbon-hydrogen bond

[8] See, for example, L. Pauling, *J. Am. Chem. Soc.* **53**, 1367 (1931).
[9] See, for example, R. S. Mulliken, *J. Am. Chem. Soc.* **72**, 4493 (1950).

moments. If the moments of the carbon-hydrogen bonds are the same as in methane, and if the H—C—C and C—O—C bond angles are tetrahedral, then the observed moment of 1.3 D for the molecule requires that the moment of each carbon-oxygen bond be 1.5 D. In a similar way, the moments of other types of bond can be obtained. The values of several representative bond moments, calculated in this way, are given in Table 5·1. It should be apparent that the exact values of these are

TABLE 5·1

BOND MOMENTS AND PARTIAL IONIC CHARACTERS OF BONDS

Bond[a]	Moment[b] (D)	r^c (A)	er^d (D)	Per Cent Ionic Character[e]	Difference in Electronegativities[f]
C—H	(0.4)	1.07	5.1	8	0.4
H—N	1.31	1.00	4.8	27	0.9
H—O	1.50	0.96	4.6	33	1.4
H—S	0.68	1.34	6.4	11	0.4
H—Cl	1.03	1.27[g]	6.1	17	0.9
H—Br	0.78	1.41[g]	6.8	11	0.7
H—I	0.38	1.60[g]	7.7	5	0.3
C—N	1.15[h, i]	1.47	7.1	18	0.5
C—O	1.5[h, j]	1.43	6.8	22	1.0
C—Cl	2.3[h]	1.76	8.4	27	0.5
C—Br	2.2[h]	1.91	9.2	24	0.3
C—I	2.0[h]	2.10	10.2	20	0.1
K—Cl	10.1[k]	2.79[g]	13.4	75	2.2[l]

[a] The atom which is stated first is presumed to be positive.

[b] Except as noted, these values are taken from L. Pauling, *The Nature of the Chemical Bond*, Cornell University Press, 1st ed., 1939, p. 68; 2nd ed., 1940, p. 68.

[c] Except as noted, the values of the internuclear distances, r, given here are the sums of Pauling's covalent radii. See Table 4·2, Section 4·3.

[d] The quantities listed in this column are the products of the magnitude of the electronic charge e ($= 4.80 \times 10^{-10}$ esu) by the distance r.

[e] The quantities listed in this column are the values of $100\mu/er$, where the μ's are the bond moments listed in the second column.

[f] Pauling's values are used. See Table 3·9, Section 3·6.

[g] See G. Herzberg, *Molecular Spectra and Molecular Structure*, I, *Spectra of Diatomic Molecules*, D. Van Nostrand Co., New York, 2nd ed., 1950.

[h] This value has been "corrected" for the change in the convention regarding the direction of the C—H bond moment. See pages 207f, 212f.

[i] C. P. Smyth, *J. Am. Chem. Soc.* **60**, 183 (1938).

[j] See above on this page.

[k] P. A. Tate and M. W. P. Strandberg, *J. Chem. Phys.* **22**, 1380 (1954).

[l] L. Pauling (reference *b*, 1st ed., p. 64; 2nd ed., p. 64) gives the electronegativity of potassium as 0.8.

subject to some uncertainty if they have had to be derived in the rather indirect manner illustrated above in connection with the carbon-oxygen bond moment. Moreover, the value derived for the moment of a given type of bond is often found to vary slightly from substance to substance.

The bond moments which are listed in Table 5·1 are based upon the assumption that the total dipole moment of each molecule is the vector sum of contributions which arise solely from the individual valence bonds. The existence of atomic dipoles, however, shows that this assumption is not necessarily valid. In a molecule like that of methane, in which there are no unshared pairs of electrons, no serious difficulty is encountered, inasmuch as the atomic dipole associated with each valence bond can be considered a part of the resultant bond moment. On the other hand, in a molecule like that of water, in which there are two unshared pairs of electrons on the oxygen atom, the atomic dipoles that are associated with these unshared pairs cannot be considered similarly to contribute to the moments of any specified bonds. Consequently, the total moment of the water molecule is not simply the resultant of the two oxygen-hydrogen bond moments, as was assumed above, but it is instead the resultant of these two bond moments *and* of the two atomic dipoles on the oxygen atom. Only if these latter moments are zero is the simple treatment strictly valid. The significance of the value, 1.50 D, which was derived for the oxygen-hydrogen bond moment is therefore far from clear. Similar uncertainties are encountered also with the moments of all other bonds linking atoms that have unshared pairs of electrons.

As was shown on pages 207f, an atomic dipole can exist only if the atomic orbital that is involved is a hybrid. Before we can answer the question whether the total moment of a molecule like that of water can be satisfactorily expressed as the resultant of merely its bond moments, we must therefore first have information regarding the extent to which the pertinent atomic orbitals are hybridized. Now, although the orbitals of a carbon atom that forms four bonds are necessarily hybridized, as was noted above with reference to methane, there is no analogous generalization that can, with any assurance, be made for the orbitals of trivalent nitrogen or phosphorus atoms, of divalent oxygen or sulfur atoms, or of univalent halogen atoms. Consequently, with molecules which contain one or more of these latter atoms, or of other similar atoms, there is no a priori way for estimating the importance of the atomic dipoles; usually also, there is no different way in which the desired information can be obtained (however, see the two following paragraphs).

Information regarding the hybridization of orbitals that are occupied by unshared pairs of electrons can in principle be obtained by quantum-mechanical calculations. Such calculations are in practice, however, so difficult that they have only seldom been attempted.   Among the few substances that have been treated in this way are included water, ammonia, and nitrogen fluoride.[10]   In each instance, the detailed but still only approximate calculation has supported the belief that the atomic dipoles are fairly large.

An independent method for studying the problem has recently been devised.   The nuclei of some atoms have *quadrupole moments*; in other words, the average distributions of electric charge within these nuclei are not spherically symmetric.   Although the exact charge distributions are in general not known, the magnitudes of the quadrupole moments can nevertheless be measured by experimental methods which need not here be described.   Now, the total energy of any atom or molecule must depend upon the electrostatic interaction between the nuclear quadrupole moment, or moments, and the charges of the extranuclear electrons.   Consequently, if the values of the quadrupole moments are known, information regarding the average distribution of the electronic charges can be obtained from precise knowledge of the energy levels.   Such knowledge can itself be obtained from a study of the fine structure of the microwave spectrum of the substance.   Although the details of the procedure are much too technical to be given here, attention may nevertheless be drawn to the fact that there has in this way been derived rather convincing evidence that, in methyl chloride for example,[11] the several orbitals in the valence shell of the chlorine atom are extensively hybridized.   Apparently, therefore, an appreciable part of the dipole moment which, in Table 5·1 is ascribed to the carbon-chlorine bond must instead arise from the atomic dipoles associated with the three unshared pairs of electrons.   Although similar evidence is at present available for only a few other substances, there is no reason to doubt that the situation which is here encountered is quite general.

From the foregoing discussion, it is evident that no great reliance can be placed in the validity of the bond moments which are listed in Table 5·1.   We shall nevertheless find it interesting now to consider whether any significant conclusions can be reached by the crudely approximate procedure which, until a few years ago, was almost universally followed, and which consists in simply ignoring all the difficulties mentioned above. For the remainder of this section, therefore, let us assume (in most instances, incorrectly) that the magnitude of the moment of any purely covalent bond is zero, that that of any purely ionic bond is equal to the product of the electronic charge (4.80×10^{-10} esu) by the internuclear distance, that the actual moment of the bond is the weighted mean of the two, that the atomic dipoles are always negligibly small, and that the "observed" bond moments of Table 5·1 are correct.   For hydrogen chloride, for example, the covalent, ionic, and actual moments are 0.00 D, 6.14 D, and 1.03 D, respectively, so that the bond must be 83 per cent covalent and 17 per cent ionic.   This conclusion is not unreasonable, but obviously, in view of the considerations of the preceding paragraphs, it must be regarded only as the roughest sort of approximation.

[10] J. Lennard-Jones and J. A. Pople, *Proc. Roy. Soc. (London)* A **202**, 166 (1950); J. A. Pople, *ibid.* A **202**, 323 (1950); C. A. Coulson, *Valence*, Oxford University Press, Oxford, 1952, p. 210.

[11] C. H. Townes and B. P. Dailey, *J. Chem. Phys.* **17**, 782 (1949).   For a serious criticism of the validity of this method, however, see P. N. Schatz, *ibid.* **22**, 755 (1954).

The results of similar calculations for several further kinds of single bond are given in Table 5·1. These also seem quite reasonable in the majority of cases, although some exceptions do occur. The comparatively large value of the carbon-iodine bond moment, for example, seems surprising since the electronegativities listed in Table 3·9, Section 3·6, indicate that the ionic structures X and XI should make only small, and

$$R_3C^+ \quad I^- \qquad\qquad R_3C^- \quad I^+$$
$$\text{x} \qquad\qquad\qquad\qquad \text{xi}$$

approximately equal, contributions. Moreover, it can hardly be explained as due to an especially large moment of the covalent structure, inasmuch as the iodine atom should then be at the positive end of the dipole instead of at the negative end, where it must certainly be. Undoubtedly, therefore, we have here an example in which the neglect of the atomic dipoles has led to a rather serious error. With the remaining carbon-halogen bonds, the situation appears to be entirely similar. In the gaseous potassium chloride molecule, on the other hand, the observed moment is unexpectedly small since here, if anywhere, an almost completely ionic bond should be found. The explanation for this discrepancy presumably lies in the polarization of the chloride ion by the potassium ion (see Section 5·3); in any event, there is good independent experimental evidence[11] that, in the closely analogous sodium chloride, the bond contains less than about 3 per cent covalent character. These examples illustrate the difficulties encountered in the application of the present treatment and the uncertainties inherent in the interpretation of the results obtained with its aid.

A different sort of quantitative approach, which suffers from similar difficulties, consists in correlating the observed bond moments with the differences in electronegativities of the two atoms concerned.[12] It is found empirically that, in many instances, the magnitude of a bond moment, when expressed in debyes, is approximately equal to the difference between the values of the electronegativities listed in Table 3·9, Section 3·6. The observed moment of hydrogen chloride, for example, is 1.03 D, whereas the difference in electronegativities, $x_{Cl} - x_H$, is 0.9. Similar data for several other bonds are also given in Table 5·1. Since there is, however, no theoretical reason why such a simple relation should be always valid, we cannot be surprised that more or less serious discrepancies often occur. Even with the carbon-hydrogen bond, where the agreement seems at first sight to be satisfactory, the most probable *direction* of the moment is the opposite of that expected from the difference in electronegativities (see pages 207f). We can remove this particular

[12] J. G. Malone, *J. Chem. Phys.* **1**, 197 (1933).

discrepancy by assuming that the hydrogen atom is, after all, at the positive end of the dipole. By making this assumption, we automatically improve also the agreement with all the other bonds that involve carbon atoms, since we must then decrease uniformly by 0.8 D all the corresponding "observed" bond moments; indeed, the correlation which is the subject of the present paragraph was somewhat better when it was first stated than it is now, since it was originally based on the older view that the carbon and hydrogen atoms are, respectively, negative and positive. Even with this suggested improvement, however, the discrepancies are still large with the carbon-halogen and potassium-chlorine bonds. Consequently, there seems to be no point in thus trying to find a simple relation between bond moments and relative electronegativities. Apparently, the covalent moments and the atomic dipoles are of sufficient importance to make any such attempt fruitless.

5·3 Polarization. All the alkyl chlorides, $C_nH_{2n+1}Cl$, might be expected to have exactly the same dipole moment; experimentally, however, small

TABLE 5·2

EFFECT OF POLARIZATION ON DIPOLE MOMENTS[a]

Substituent

Alkyl Group	F	Cl	Br	I	NO$_2$	CN[b]
Methyl	1.81	1.87	1.78	1.59	3.50	3.94[c]
Ethyl	1.92	2.05	2.02	1.90	3.70[d]	4.04[c]
n-Propyl	—	2.10	2.15	2.01	3.72	4.05[c]
n-Butyl	—	2.09	2.15	2.08	3.55[e]	4.09[c]
n-Amyl	—	2.12	—	—	—	—
n-Heptyl	—	—	2.15	—	—	—
Isopropyl	—	2.15	2.19	—	3.73	—
Isobutyl	—	2.04	—	—	—	—
sec-Butyl	—	2.12	2.20	—	—	—
tert-Butyl	—	2.13	—	—	3.71	—

[a] The quantities listed in the body of this table are the dipole moments (expressed in debye units) of the gaseous molecules RX, where the alkyl group R is given at the left of the row, and the substituent X is given at the top of the column. Except where noted, the data are taken from R. H. Wiswall, Jr., and C. P. Smyth, *J. Chem. Phys.* **9**, 356 (1941). A number of the individual values quoted by Wiswall and Smyth in this paper are due to L. G. Groves and S. Sugden, *J. Chem. Soc.* **1937**, 158.

[b] These substances are cyanides and not isocyanides.

[c] L. G. Groves and S. Sugden, note a.

[d] E. C. Hurdis and C. P. Smyth, *J. Am. Chem. Soc.* **64**, 2829 (1942).

[e] This value obtained by L. G. Groves and S. Sugden (note a) is probably too low, because these authors reported low values for several other aliphatic nitro compounds as well.

variations are found to occur. It will be seen, in fact, from the data of Table 5·2 that the observed moments increase in magnitude as the alkyl groups become either larger or more highly branched. The moments are affected appreciably, however, only by structural changes in the fairly immediate neighborhood of the chlorine atom.

The proof of the initial statement of the preceding paragraph can be obtained by application of the rule of vector addition, provided that all carbon-hydrogen bonds are assumed to have the same moment, all carbon-carbon bonds are assumed to have zero moment, and all bond angles are assumed to have the same values from molecule to molecule. A simpler proof, which is based upon the same assumptions, is as follows: The dipole moment of methane is zero. Therefore, the resultant of the moments of any three of its carbon-hydrogen bonds must be equal in magnitude and opposite in direction to the moment of the fourth. Therefore, the dipole moment of a substance should not be changed if a hydrogen atom *joined to carbon* is replaced by a methyl group, or vice versa. Since any alkyl chloride can be made (in thought) from any other by a succession of such replacements, it at once follows that all alkyl chlorides should have the same dipole moment.

The above deviations from the strict constancy of bond moments find a simple explanation in the polarization of the hydrocarbon radicals by the carbon-chlorine dipoles. In methyl chloride, for example, the existence of the large carbon-chlorine bond moment (now including the atomic dipoles on the chlorine atom) requires that the carbon atom be relatively positive. This atom therefore exerts a larger than usual attraction for the electrons which it shares with the hydrogen atoms, and so pulls them in closer than normal. In other words, a small dipole is induced in the methyl group by the large moment of the carbon-chlorine bond, and the observed moment is the sum of the two. Since the primary and the induced dipoles are at any rate roughly in the same direction, the effect of the polarization must be to increase the magnitude of the moment of the molecule. In ethyl chloride the situation is similar. On account of its greater size, however, the ethyl group is more polarizable than the methyl group, and so both the induced and the total moments must be larger for ethyl chloride than for methyl chloride.

In *n*-propyl chloride, a further increase in the observed moment occurs, but it is smaller than that noted in passing from methyl to ethyl chloride. The reason for this leveling off is that the additional methylene group in *n*-propyl chloride is at a considerable distance from the carbon-chlorine bond (and from the atomic dipoles of the chlorine atom); it is therefore in a region of relatively low electrostatic potential and is only slightly polarized. For a similar reason, the observed moment of *n*-butyl chloride is not appreciably greater than that of *n*-propyl chloride.

The moment of isopropyl chloride is slightly larger than that of *n*-propyl chloride. The difference is probably due not to any intrinsically greater polarizability of the isopropyl group, but rather to the circumstance that this group is more closely bunched about the carbon-chlorine bond and so has a more favorable steric arrangement for polarization. The difference is small, however, and may be no greater than the uncertainties in the experimental data. Similarly, no reliance can be put in the reported small difference between the moments of *sec-* and *tert-*butyl chlorides.

The phenomenon of polarization is not restricted to the alkyl chlorides but occurs generally whenever a strongly polar group is present in the neighborhood of another, polarizable group. A number of further examples, also taken from the aliphatic series, are included in Table 5·2. It will be seen that the general situation is always closely parallel to that encountered above with the alkyl chlorides, so that a single explanation accounts satisfactorily for a considerable body of data. It seems strange, however, that the large nitro *group moment* apparently produces less polarization than the smaller carbon-chlorine bond moment. The explanation is perhaps that the nitro group moment lies largely in the nitrogen-oxygen bonds, as is indeed suggested by the formal charges. If this supposition is correct, then the large primary dipoles are farther away from the polarizable groups, upon which they act, in the nitro compounds than in the alkyl halides, and so they have relatively smaller effects.

The significance of a group moment is the following: In nitromethane, for example, the total moment that can be referred to the nitro group is the sum of the moments of the carbon-nitrogen and nitrogen-oxygen bonds. Since there is no way for determining the values of the individual bond moments separately, and no advantage in doing so anyhow, we shall lump them together and call their sum the nitro group moment. The group moments of other polyatomic substituents can be defined in completely analogous manners. Group moments can be handled in just the same way as the bond moments characteristic of monatomic substituents, *provided that* they lie along the bond joining the substituent to the rest of the molecule. If this condition is satisfied, as with the nitro, cyano, methyl, and numerous other groups (including all monatomic groups), the moment or the corresponding group is said to be axial; if the condition is not satisfied, as with the hydroxy, amino, and many other groups, the moment or the group is said to be nonaxial. The treatment of nonaxial group moments is comparatively difficult, because the angles between the different component vectors in the complete molecule not only may be unknown but also may vary as the group rotates about the bond which links it to the rest of the molecule. For example, although the dipole moment of *p*-dinitrobenzene must be zero because the nitro group moment is axial,[2] that of the dimethyl ether of hydroquinone cannot be predicted because the methoxy group moment is nonaxial. (Actually the moment of the substance in solution is 1.73 D, as compared with 1.28 D for anisole. Cf. page 238.) For these reasons, we shall restrict ourselves, throughout the remainder of this chapter, to axial groups to as great an extent as possible.

Polarization, which has been treated hitherto as a purely classical effect, can also be discussed from the viewpoint of resonance. The example of methyl chloride will again serve to illustrate the principles involved. In this substance, the partially ionic structures I and II

$$
\begin{array}{cc}
\overset{\displaystyle H}{\underset{\displaystyle H}{^{+}H\;\;\overset{|}{\underset{|}{C^{-}}}\!\!-\!\!Cl}} & \overset{\displaystyle H}{\underset{\displaystyle H}{^{-}H\;\;\overset{|}{\underset{|}{C^{+}}}\!\!-\!\!Cl}} \\
\mathrm{I} & \mathrm{II}
\end{array}
$$

(among many others) must make small contributions to the state of the molecule. Now the carbon atom is relatively positive on account of the large carbon-chlorine bond moment. The effect of such a positive charge on the carbon must be to increase the stability of structure I and to decrease that of structure II. Consequently, these must make larger and smaller contributions, respectively, than do the corresponding structures in methane. In other words, the carbon-hydrogen bond that is here under discussion is polarized by the carbon-chlorine moment. Similar considerations apply, naturally, also to the remaining carbon-hydrogen bonds, as well as to any further bonds that may be present in more complex molecules. By an extension of the argument, it can be shown that the present method of treatment accounts for the rapid decrease in polarizing power with distance, and consequently for the qualitative features discussed above and summarized in Table 5·2.

5·4 Dipole Moments and Resonance. In Section 5·2 we found that, in many of their qualitative aspects, the bond moments of essentially covalent bonds can be explained in terms of resonance between purely covalent and purely ionic structures. We turn now to a consideration of the effect of resonance among structures of more conventional type, in which each valence bond is considered already to possess its own characteristic bond moment (and in which each atomic dipole, if any, is considered already to be present). A simple example is provided by carbon dioxide, which may be considered a hybrid of the two equivalent structures that are represented by the symbol I, and also of the two less stable structures II and III (see pages 111ff). Of these, the two structures I correspond

$$
\begin{array}{ccc}
\mathrm{O}\!\!=\!\!\mathrm{C}\!\!=\!\!\mathrm{O} & \mathrm{O}^{+}\!\!\equiv\!\!\mathrm{C}\!\!-\!\!\mathrm{O}^{-} & \mathrm{O}^{-}\!\!-\!\!\mathrm{C}\!\!\equiv\!\!\mathrm{O}^{+} \\
\mathrm{I} & \mathrm{II} & \mathrm{III}
\end{array}
$$

to zero dipole moment, since the two carbon-oxygen bond moments exactly cancel each other. The remaining structures, II and III, correspond to moments which are individually very large. Consequently, even though these latter structures are presumably rather unimportant in the resonance, they might nevertheless have an appreciable effect upon the observed moment of the substance. However, since they are equivalent to each other, and since they must therefore make identical contributions to the state of the hybrid, they cannot alter the original conclusion that the molecule must be completely nonpolar.

It will be interesting and instructive to consider at this point the changes in the above discussion which would be required if carbon dioxide were a tautomeric substance, consisting of molecules with the structures I, II, and III. Two extreme situations can be taken up separately. In the first place, the molecules might undergo transitions from one structure to another so readily that the average time which they spend between transitions is small compared with the time required for them to be oriented in an electrostatic field, say about 10^{-10} sec. Under such circumstances, the molecules could not be oriented in the field; they would therefore behave like nonpolar molecules, and the measured dipole moment would be zero, as it actually is. However, this could hardly be the real state of affairs, because it would not correspond to a true tautomerism, but rather to resonance of a rather special type which will be more fully described in Sections 9·17 and 9·18. If the frequency of the interconversion were thus greater than about 10^{10} sec^{-1}, the energy of each molecule could then be shown to be indefinite by an amount which, when multiplied by Avogadro's number, corresponds to more than about 1 cal per mole (see Section 9·17). Since such a large uncertainty in the energy is quite inconsistent with the observed spectra of the substance, this first possibility can evidently be excluded. The second extreme situation would arise if the average time which the molecules spend between transitions is large compared with the time required for them to be oriented. Under such circumstances, carbon dioxide would behave like an ordinary mixture of substances with the structures I, II, and III. The measured dipole moment would therefore have a *magnitude* intermediate among those of the structures involved. Consequently, since the structures II and III have moments of large magnitude, the measured moment could not be zero if these were involved to any appreciable extent. It follows, then, that this second possibility also is excluded, unless we should choose to ignore the structures II and III, and to assume that carbon dioxide is a tautomeric mixture of molecules with only the two distinct, but equivalent, structures I.[13]

A rather more interesting example of the effect of resonance upon dipole moments is provided by nitrous oxide, N_2O. The most stable structures for this substance are presumably the two equivalent ones which are represented by the diagram IV (cf. the above discussion of carbon dioxide) and, in addition, the structure V. The still further

$$N^-\!\!=\!\!N^+\!\!=\!\!O \qquad N\!\!\equiv\!\!N^+\!\!-\!\!O^- \qquad {}^=\!\!N\!\!-\!\!N^+\!\!\equiv\!\!O^+$$

$$\text{IV} \qquad\qquad\qquad \text{V} \qquad\qquad\qquad \text{VI}$$

structure VI is probably too unstable, on account of its especially unfavorable charge distribution, to require consideration. As a result of their formal charges, the structures IV and V must correspond separately to large moments in opposite directions. However, the observed moment is zero within the experimental uncertainty. This value can be explained

[13] Cf. L. E. Sutton, *Trans. Faraday Soc.* **30**, 789 (1934).

on the assumption that the negative charge which the two structures IV impart to the terminal nitrogen atom is almost exactly counterbalanced by that which structure V imparts to the oxygen. Such a qualitative discussion as the present would not have enabled us to predict the actual magnitude of the moment, but it does permit an interpretation of the experimental data, which would otherwise have appeared entirely anomalous. It is of particular interest that the zero dipole moment of this substance, unlike that of carbon dioxide, cannot be accounted for on the basis of any single structure but requires the consideration of resonance among altogether three structures. The facts are completely inconsistent also with the assumption of any sort of tautomerism among the structures.

In the azide group, the resonance is similar to that in nitrous oxide, except that here the structures which are the analogs of the two represented by diagram IV are no longer equivalent to each other. Indeed, as was pointed out on pages 180f (see also pages 113f for a discussion of the similar situation that arises with the isocyanates), one of these structures is so much less stable than the other that we are doubtless justified in ignoring it. We can therefore describe phenyl azide, for example, as a hybrid with which the two *unique* structures VII and VIII must be given the largest weights. (Again, an additional structure, IX, can be written,

$$C_6H_5{-}N{=}N^+{=}N^- \qquad C_6H_5{-}N^-{-}N^+{\equiv}N \qquad C_6H_5{-}N^+{\equiv}N^+{-}N^=$$
$$\text{VII} \qquad\qquad\qquad \text{VIII} \qquad\qquad\qquad \text{IX}$$

but is probably too unstable to require consideration.) Although the observed moment of 1.55 D (in benzene solution) is rather larger than that of nitrous oxide, it is still so small that it can be explained only on the basis of resonance between the structures VII and VIII.

It is known that in this substance the phenyl group is at the positive end of the dipole, so that apparently structure VII is more important than VIII. The method by which the direction of the moment is determined is as follows. The moments of nitrobenzene, X, and of *p*-nitrophenyl azide, XI, are 3.95 D and 2.96 D, respectively (in benzene

$$\text{X} \qquad\qquad\qquad\qquad\qquad \text{XI}$$

solution). Since the moment of nitrobenzene must be due largely to the formal charges on the nitrogen and oxygen atoms, it is certain that the nitro and phenyl groups lie in the negative and positive directions, respectively. Since the moment of nitrobenzene is *decreased* by the introduction of the azide group, it follows that the moments due to the two substituents in *p*-nitrophenyl azide must be in approximately (although probably not exactly) opposite directions. From analogy, then, the conclusion is drawn that in phenyl azide itself the direction of the moment is as stated above.

Carbon monoxide presents a difficult problem on account of the anomalous valence state of the carbon atom.   In Sections 3·3 and 4·3 we brought forward some not entirely conclusive evidence to show that this substance is a hybrid of the two equivalent structures that are represented as XII, and also of a third structure XIII.   Each of the structures

$$C{=}O \qquad\qquad C^-{\equiv}O^+$$
$$\text{XII} \qquad\qquad\qquad \text{XIII}$$

XII probably corresponds to a dipole moment of considerable magnitude, which lies in such direction that the carbon atom is positive and the oxygen is negative.   This conclusion follows from the fact that oxygen is a more electronegative element than carbon.   Although the substances are hardly comparable, it is interesting and probably significant in this connection that aldehydes and ketones have moments of the order of 2.5–3.0 D, with the oxygen negative.   Structure XIII, on the other hand, must have a large moment in the opposite direction, on account of the formal charges.   The actual moment of the substance is 0.1 D (of unknown direction).   This value, although it could not have been predicted in advance, is entirely reasonable as a result of resonance among the structures XII and XIII, and it provides perhaps the most satisfactory evidence for the existence of the resonance.   It seems probable that here, as with nitrous oxide, no single structure could account for the observed moment.

In the isocyanides, the situation is similar to that in carbon monoxide. The moment of phenyl isocyanide (in solution) is 3.5 D, and its direction is such that the phenyl group is at its positive end.   (For the method of establishing the direction of the moment, see the above discussion of phenyl azide.)   This result is consistent with the supposition that the substance receives equal, rather small contributions from the two equivalent structures XIV, and a considerably larger contribution from the

$$C_6H_5{-}N{=}C \qquad\qquad C_6H_5{-}N^+{\equiv}C^-$$
$$\text{XIV} \qquad\qquad\qquad \text{XV}$$

third structure, XV.   The fact that the moment of the isocyanide group is axial also supports a large contribution from structure XV.

In Section 5·3, attention was called to those variations in the dipole moments of the alkyl halides and similar compounds which are due to differing polarizabilities of the alkyl groups.   On the basis of the considerations discussed there, the moment of vinyl chloride, XVI, would be

$$\begin{array}{cc} H_2C{=}CH & \qquad H_2C^-{-}CH \\ \quad\mid & \qquad\qquad\parallel \\ \quad Cl & \qquad\qquad Cl^+ \\ \text{XVI} & \qquad\qquad \text{XVII} \end{array}$$

expected to be particularly large, possibly about 2.2 D or 2.3 D, since the vinyl radical is known to have a larger polarizability than any comparable saturated radical. The observed moment, however, is only 1.44 D, which is smaller than even that of methyl chloride. (See Tables 5·2 and 5·3.) The explanation of this apparent discrepancy is presumably that there is resonance between the structures XVI and XVII. The second of these structures can have only a small weight, but, on account of the presence of the formal charges, it must have a very large moment in a direction approximately opposite to that of structure XVI. The effect of the resonance must therefore be to decrease the value of the actual moment of the substance, in agreement with the observation. The present considerations are, of course, completely consistent with those of Section 4·3, in which the shortness of the carbon-chlorine bond in vinyl chloride was attributed to a partial double-bond character of the bond.

In chloroacetylene, XVIII and XIX, the resonance effect appears to be still greater, since the dipole moment is further reduced to 0.44 D, even though the ethynyl group is known to be highly polarizable. (See Table 5·3.) Bromoacetylene has zero dipole moment, so that apparently the ionic structure analogous to XIX makes an even greater contribution

$$HC\equiv C-Cl \qquad\qquad HC^-\!=\!C\!=\!Cl^+$$
$$\text{XVIII} \qquad\qquad\qquad \text{XIX}$$

when the electronegativity of the halogen is decreased. We might therefore anticipate that iodoacetylene would have a nonvanishing moment with the iodine at the positive end. Although this substance seems not to have been investigated, the expectation is confirmed by the fact that in phenyliodoacetylene, $C_6H_5C\equiv CI$, the iodine atom has been found to be positive.[14] (For the method of establishing the direction of the moment, see the above discussion of phenyl azide.)

In chlorobenzene also, the observed moment of 1.73 D seems lower than that expected from analogy with the aliphatic chlorides, since the phenyl group, like the vinyl and ethynyl groups, is highly polarizable. The explanation again presumably involves the idea of resonance. In this case, the two Kekulé structures XX and XXI are doubtless the most important, but the less stable quinoid structures XXII, XXIII, and

XX   XXI   XXII   XXIII   XXIV

[14] C. J. Wilson and H. H. Wenzke, *J. Am. Chem. Soc.* **56**, 2025 (1934).

XXIV have such large moments that, even though their weights must be small, they are apparently able to decrease the resultant moment of the substance to an appreciable extent.

It is probable that resonance is not the only factor causing the above variations in the moments of the unsaturated halogen compounds. There are reasons for believing that, on account of differences in the respective valence states (cf. pages 128f and 168), an ethylenic, or especially an acetylenic, carbon atom is more electronegative than a saturated one. The carbon orbital which takes part in the carbon-halogen single bond is in all instances a hybrid between the pure s and the pure p orbitals (cf. pages 207f). The relative amount of s character, however, increases with the degree of unsaturation. Since the average distance of an electron from the nucleus is less when that electron is in an s orbital than when it is in the corresponding p orbital, the stability of the resulting hybrid should increase with its s character. These two relations then lead directly to the stated effect of unsaturation upon electronegativity. Consequently, even the conventional structures XVI, XVIII, etc., may correspond to less negative halogen atoms than do any other structures in which the halogen atoms are bonded to saturated carbon atoms. It is impossible at the present time, however, to compare the importance of this further effect with that of the resonance.

It is of interest that the above conclusions regarding the contributions of the zwitterionic structures XVII, XIX, etc., are at least qualitatively consistent with the ones reached earlier from a study of interatomic distances (see page 176). Thus, both the dipole moments and the carbon-halogen bond lengths decrease progressively in the order: alkyl halide, vinyl or aromatic halide, acetylenic halide. Whether these two trends are primarily due to resonance, to differences in electronegativity, or to both factors at the same time, their parallelism strongly suggests that they are the results of similar causes.

Further evidence that resonance cannot be the only important reason for the observed variations in the lengths and dipole moments of carbon-halogen bonds has recently been obtained from a study of the interactions, in a few simple molecules, between the nuclear quadrupole moments and the charges of the extranuclear electrons[15] (cf. page 211). Although the details of this evidence cannot here be described, we may nevertheless mention that the hybridization of the orbitals appears not to change in exactly the way expected. Whether this discrepancy can be referred to the differences in electronegativity or whether still additional factors must be assumed to play important roles is not at present known.

In nitrobenzene, the effect of the resonance would be expected to increase the moment, because the large moments of the relatively unstable

[15] A. A. Westenberg, J. H. Goldstein, and E. B. Wilson, Jr., *J. Chem. Phys.* **17**, 1319 (1949).

structures XXIX, XXX, and XXXI are in the same (or nearly the same) direction as those of the Kekulé structures XXV–XXVIII. As

XXV   XXVI   XXVII   XXVIII

XXIX   XXX   XXXI

a result, although the dipole moment of even 2-nitro-2-methylpropane, $(CH_3)_3C$—NO_2, is only 3.71 D, that of nitrobenzene (in the gas phase) is 4.24 D. The facts here could be accounted for on the assumption of an unexpectedly large polarizability of the phenyl group; such an explanation, however, would be inconsistent with the observed moment of chlorobenzene and with certain further data discussed later in Section 5·5. Any correction which might be made for the supposedly increased electronegativity of the aromatic carbon atom to which the nitro group is attached would decrease, rather than increase, the expected moment of the substance. Consequently, the explanation that is provided by the theory of resonance appears to be the only completely satisfactory one.

There have been found several such instances in which bond or group moments appear to have different values in saturated and in unsaturated molecules. A number of these are listed in Table 5·3. The observed changes in moment are always in the directions to be expected on the basis of resonance, and are of reasonable order of magnitude. (However, see the discussion of the moments of the unsaturated cyanides near the end of this section.) Similar tables, which are not directly comparable with this one, because they refer to dipole moments measured in solution rather than in the gas phase, have been given by various authors.[13, 16, 17]

[16] C. P. Smyth, *J. Org. Chem.* **1**, 17 (1936); M. T. Rogers, *J. Am. Chem. Soc.* **69**, 1243 (1947). For some further data which, although they apply to moments in the vapor phase, are for other reasons not directly comparable with the above, see N. B. Hannay and C. P. Smyth, *ibid.* **68**, 1005 (1946).

[17] K. B. Everard, L. Kumar, and L. E. Sutton, *J. Chem. Soc.* **1951**, 2807; K. B. Everard and L. E. Sutton, *ibid.* **1951**, 2818, 2826.

TABLE 5·3

EFFECT OF RESONANCE ON BOND AND GROUP MOMENTS[a]

Substance

X	RX^b	$H_2C{=}CHX^c$	$HC{\equiv}CX^c$	$C_6H_5X^c$
Cl	2.15	1.44	0.44	1.73
Br	2.20	1.41	0.0	1.71
I	2.08	1.26	—	1.50
NO_2	3.73	—	—	4.24^d

[a] The quantities listed in the body of the table are the values (in D) of the dipole moments of the specified substances in the vapor phase.

[b] Some arbitrariness necessarily exists in the choice of the alkyl compound used in this column for comparison. The values given for each substituent, X, are the largest reported for any of the alkyl groups, R. This choice is made in order that the polarizabilities may be as nearly comparable as possible. The data for these alkyl compounds are taken from Table 5·2.

[c] J. A. C. Hugill, I. E. Coop, and L. E. Sutton, *Trans. Faraday Soc.* **34**, 1518 (1938).

[d] L. G. Groves and S. Sugden, *J. Chem. Soc.* **1935**, 971.

Additional interesting information regarding resonance in aromatic molecules can be obtained from the dipole moment of *p*-nitroaniline, XXXII. The effect of resonance in aniline itself, as in chlorobenzene, is to shift electrons from the substituent to the ring, whereas the effect of the resonance in nitrobenzene is to shift electrons from the ring to the substituent. In *p*-nitroaniline, these two effects can be considered to reinforce each other, since the structure XXXIII may be expected to have

XXXII   XXXIII

a fairly large weight. That the situation actually is as suggested can be shown in the following way. In this substance, the amino and nitro group moments cannot lie in the same direction, because the former is nonaxial, and so the magnitude of their vector sum must be less than the sum of their magnitudes. Since the moments of aniline and of nitrobenzene (in benzene solution) are 1.53 D and 3.95 D, respectively, we should therefore expect that the moment of *p*-nitroaniline would be less than $1.53 + 3.95 = 5.48$ D. (The values of the moments in solution must be used for these substances, because no data are available for *p*-nitroaniline in the vapor phase. Since solvent effects of several tenths of a debye unit are often observed, significant comparisons can be made only between moments measured under the same conditions.) The observed value, however, is 6.35 D, so that interaction of the sort represented by structure XXXIII is apparently an important feature of the molecule.[17] (See also Section 5·5.) A similar effect might be expected to occur also in *p*-nitrochlorobenzene, since a structure quite analogous to XXXIII can be written for this substance. However, the rule of vector addition is obeyed here, so that the interaction must be small. In Section 8·11 we shall find independent evidence to support the view that the electrons of an amino group are much freer to be shifted into an attached benzene ring than are those of a chlorine atom.

The conclusion that resonance with still more extended quinoid structures can also have appreciable effects upon charge distributions is suggested by the fact that, in benzene solution, the dipole moment of 4-nitrobiphenyl is about 4.41 D,[17] whereas that of nitrobenzene is only 3.95 D. Although the difference between these two values is perhaps not much greater than could have resulted from solvent effects or from experimental errors, its direction is the one to be expected if the former

XXXIV   XXXV   XXXVI   XXXVII   XXXVIII   XXXIX   XL   XLI substance receives small contributions not only from the structures XXXIV, XXXV, and XXXVI (cf. structures XXIX, XXX, and XXXI), but also from the further structures XXXVII, XXXVIII, and XXXIX. Similarly, with *trans* 4-nitrostilbene, XL, and *trans trans* 1-(4-nitrophenyl)-4-phenyl-1,3-butadiene, XLI, the observed moments[17] have the still larger values of 4.56 D and 4.75 D, respectively. Consequently, with these substances also, small weights must apparently be assigned to the extreme structures in which both benzene rings are quinoid. Furthermore, the dipole moments (in benzene solution) of dimethylaniline, 4-dimethylaminobiphenyl, *trans* 4-dimethylaminostilbene, and *trans trans* 1-(4-dimethylaminophenyl)-4-phenyl-1,3-butadiene are, respectively, 1.58 D, 2.04 D, 2.41 D, and 2.58 D.[17]   (See the following paragraph.)   Here again, therefore, the resonance apparently includes structures with extended quinoid systems.   And finally, the moments of *p*-nitroaniline and 4-nitro-4'-aminobiphenyl are, respectively, 6.35 D and 6.49 D;[17] those of *p*-nitrodimethylaniline and *trans* 4-nitro-4'-dimethylaminostilbene are, respectively, 6.87 D and 7.42 D.[17, 18]

Since, in amines, the nitrogen atoms doubtless lie at the negative ends of the carbon-nitrogen bonds, the net charges on such atoms must be decreased by the contributions of the quinoid structures like, say, XLII and XLIII (cf. structures XXII, XXIII, and

XXIV).   Consequently, one might perhaps have expected that the total moments of the molecules would be decreased by the resonance.   This expectation is, however, incorrect for, in general, the aromatic amines are more polar than are their aliphatic analogs.   The moments of most aliphatic primary amines are in the range 1.3–1.4 D, whereas that of aniline is 1.53 D; the moments of most aliphatic tertiary amines are in the range of 0.7–0.9 D, whereas that of dimethylaniline is 1.58 D.   With the aromatic amines that were mentioned in the preceding paragraph, the moments increase with the presumed effectiveness of the resonance.   These several observations require some explanation.   The point is here that the direction of the total molecular moment for each amine is largely determined by all three of the bonds that are formed by the nitrogen atom, and not merely by the one bond that links this atom to some particular aromatic (or aliphatic) group.   Consequently, although the nitrogen atom of any aromatic amine is negative with respect to the ring, the negative end of the dipole that is due to the entire amino group must point more nearly toward the ring than away from it.   The transfer of electrons from the nitrogen atom to the ring should therefore increase the observed moment, as it in fact does.

[18] For additional data which have been obtained for a group of azo compounds, see T. W. Campbell, D. A. Young, and M. T. Rogers, *J. Am. Chem. Soc.* **73**, 5789 (1951); T. W. Campbell, W. A. McAllister, and M. T. Rogers, *ibid.* **75**, 864 (1953).

The moment of toluene may be due in part to a resonance effect. If all the carbon-carbon bonds had strictly zero moments, and if all the carbon-hydrogen bonds had exactly the same moment, then this substance would necessarily be nonpolar. Actually, however, it is found to have a dipole moment of 0.4 D, with the methyl group positive with respect to the phenyl.[19] It is possible, of course, that the moment of a $C_{aromatic}$—$C_{aliphatic}$ bond may not be zero, and that the moment of a $C_{aromatic}$—H bond may not be equal to that of a $C_{aliphatic}$—H bond. Such an effect would actually be anticipated, since, as was mentioned above, an unsaturated carbon atom is probably more electronegative than a saturated one. This difference presumably provides at least a part, and it may provide all, of the complete explanation for the moment of toluene, but a further factor also requires consideration. Hyperconjugation of the methyl group with the ring may be a significant feature. That is to say, structures of the sort represented by XLIV and XLV, which are merely the ionic analogs of XLVI, may have small weights in the resonance. If

this interpretation is correct, and if the structures like XLIV are more important than those like XLV, then a small moment in the observed direction could be anticipated. It is difficult, however, to estimate the relative importance of these two effects (i.e., variations in the values of bond moments and hyperconjugation) or, indeed, to show conclusively that either one is involved at all. This is a point that will require further clarification before it can be considered settled.

A further type of structure in which resonance affects the dipole moment is contained in the α,β-unsaturated aldehydes and ketones.[13, 20, 21] The dipole moments of propionaldehyde and of acrolein, for example, are equal to 2.73 D and 3.04 D, respectively, in the vapor phase, and to 2.54 D and 2.88 D, respectively, in benzene solution. Similarly, the moments of n-butyraldehyde and of crotonaldehyde are equal to 2.72 D and 3.67 D, respectively, in the vapor phase, and to 2.57 D and 3.54 D,[21] respectively, in solution. The fact that, in each instance, the unsaturated

[19] For example, see J. W. Williams, *Fortschr. Chem. Physik u. physik. Chem.* **20**, 257 (1930), Table 11.

[20] E. C. Hurdis and C. P. Smyth, *J. Am. Chem. Soc.* **65**, 89 (1943).

[21] J. B. Bentley, K. B. Everard, R. J. B. Marsden, and L. E. Sutton, *J. Chem. Soc.* **1949**, 2957.

compound has an appreciably higher moment than does its saturated analog is doubtless a result of resonance between the conventional structures XLVII (with R = H or CH_3) and the zwitterionic ones XLVIII.

$$R—CH=CH—CH=O \qquad\qquad R—C^+H—CH=CH—O^-$$

XLVII   XLVIII

Even though these latter, much less stable structures can be assigned only small weights, they correspond to extremely large moments in approximately the same directions as those of the more important structures XLVII; consequently, the resonance should somewhat increase the total moment. The further fact that the moment of crotonaldehyde is greater than that of acrolein may be due to hyperconjugation or, in other words, to a significant contribution from structure XLIX.

$$H^+CH_2=CH—CH=CH—O^-$$

XLIX

The correctness of the above explanation for the moments of the unsaturated aldehydes is strongly supported by the observed moments of 3,5-dimethyl-2-cyclohexen-1-one, L, and of pulegone, LI. In these substances, the conjugated systems are held by the six-membered rings more

L   LI

or less rigidly in the *s-trans* and *s-cis* configurations, respectively (see the following paragraph). The shapes of the molecules are therefore such that the moment of the normal structure and that of the less stable structure analogous to XLVIII are more nearly in the same direction in the former compound than in the latter. The observed moments are respectively, 4.00 D and 3.02 D[21] (in benzene solution), in agreement with expectation.

The words *trans* and *cis* are ordinarily used for the designation of stereochemical configurations that differ by rotation about *double* bonds. Consequently, they are not strictly applicable when, as with 3,5-dimethyl-2-cyclohexen-1-one, L, and pulegone, LI, the rotations of interest are instead about *single* bonds. Under such circumstances, the more precise terms[22] *s-trans* and *s-cis* are now rather commonly employed.

[22] R. S. Mulliken, *Revs. Mod. Phys.* **14**, 265 (1942).

A somewhat similar situation is encountered with dimethyl-γ-pyrone.[23] The resonance here involves not only the normal structure LII and the less stable one LIII, which are analogous to XLVII and XLVIII, respectively, but also a second structure that is completely equivalent to LIII and, in

addition, two further ones of the type represented by LIV.   The resonance between these last Kekulé-like structures must counterbalance their un-favorable distribution of charge to a considerable extent and so must increase their contribution to the state of the molecule.   As a result, the dipole moment is increased from a calculated value of about 1.75 D for the structure LII to the observed value of 4.05 D (in solution).

In benzene solution, the dipole moment of cycloheptatrienone (tropone), LV, is equal to 4.3 D,[24] and hence is a little greater than that of dimethyl-γ-pyrone, LII.   Apparently, therefore, not only the usual ionic structure LVI but also the six additional ones of the type LVII and LVIII must

[23] E. C. E. Hunter and J. R. Partington, *J. Chem. Soc.* **1933**, 87.   Additional data are given by M. Rolla, M. Sanesi, and G. Traverso, *Ann. chim. (Rome)* **42**, 673 (1952) [*C. A.* **47**, 11934 (1953)].

[24] A. Di Giacomo and C. P. Smyth, *J. Am. Chem. Soc.* **74**, 4411 (1952).

have relatively large (but still only small) effects upon the charge distribution. The conclusion that the total weights of the seven structures LVI, LVII, LVIII, etc., are thus exceptionally great might have been anticipated[25] since, in each of these structures, there are exactly six pi electrons that are available for the formation of an aromatic sextet (cf. Section 3·9). On the other hand, with cyclopentadienone, LIX, a considerably smaller dipole moment would be expected since, in the five structures analogous to LVI, LVII, LVIII, etc., there are only four potentially "aromatic" electrons. Although, unfortunately, no data are available for this substance, which is in fact unknown,[26] the moment of its tetraphenyl derivative, tetracyclone, LX, is only 3.43 D.[24] Since, with this latter substance, the resonance can include not only the five structures in which the formal positive charge is on one of the atoms of the five-membered ring but also the numerous quinoid structures like LXI, the

LIX   LX   LXI

moment of the parent compound LIX should probably be rather smaller than 3.43 D.

The dipole moment of ketene, LXII, in the gas phase is 1.52 D,[27] whereas that of formaldehyde, LXIII, under the same conditions is

LXII   LXIII

2.27 D. The difference between these two values may be due merely to the difference between the valence states of the carbon atoms in the carbonyl groups of the two compounds.[28] Indeed, since the carbonyl carbon atom in ketene is bonded to just two other atoms and is characterized by 180° bond angles, the hybridization of its orbitals should be more like that in, say, acetylene than like that in formaldehyde (cf. pages 128f).

    [25] Cf. H. J. Dauben, Jr., and H. J. Ringold, *J. Am. Chem. Soc.* **73**, 876 (1951); W. von E. Doering and F. L. Detert, *ibid.* **73**, 876 (1951).

    [26] C. F. H. Allen and J. A. Van Allan, *J. Am. Chem. Soc.* **72**, 5165 (1950).

    [27] N. B. Hannay and C. P. Smyth, *J. Am. Chem. Soc.* **68**, 1357 (1946); C. L. Angyal, G. A. Barclay, C. A. Hukins, and R. J. W. Le Fèvre, *J. Chem. Soc.* **1951**, 2583.

    [28] A. D. Walsh, *J. Am. Chem. Soc.* **68**, 2408 (1946).

Consequently, the electronegativity of this atom should be relatively great, and the moment of the carbon-oxygen bond should be relatively small. On the other hand, the difference in dipole moments may instead be due to the circumstance that, although ketene may receive a significant contribution from structure LXIV, formaldehyde offers no comparable

$$\begin{array}{c} H \diagdown \\ \quad\ddot{C}^{-}\!\!-\!\!C\!\!\equiv\!\!O\!:^{+} \\ H \diagup \end{array}$$

LXIV

possibility for resonance.[27]   And finally, it would be quite reasonable for us to suppose that each of these factors is partly responsible for the observed effect.   No definite decision among the several alternative explanations can at present be made.

With some unsaturated nitriles, the observed dipole moments appear somewhat anomalous. Although the observed moments of propionaldehyde, LXV, and of acrolein, LXVI, are, respectively, 2.73 D and 3.04 D (see page 226), those of ethyl cyanide, LXVII, and of acrylonitrile, LXVIII, are, respectively, 4.04 D and 3.88 D.

$CH_3\!\!-\!\!CH_2\!\!-\!\!CH\!\!=\!\!O$ $CH_2\!\!=\!\!CH\!\!-\!\!CH\!\!=\!\!O$ $CH_3\!\!-\!\!CH_2\!\!-\!\!C\!\!\equiv\!\!N$ $CH_2\!\!=\!\!CH\!\!-\!\!C\!\!\equiv\!\!N$
LXV   LXVI   LXVII   LXVIII

The unsaturation, which has the expected effect of increasing the moment with the aldehydes, therefore has just the opposite effect of decreasing the moment with the nitriles.   A possible explanation is that, for some reason, the structure LXIX must be assigned a greater weight with acrylonitrile than must the corresponding structure LXX

$C^-H_2\!\!-\!\!CH\!\!=\!\!C\!\!=\!\!N^+$ $C^-H_2\!\!-\!\!CH\!\!=\!\!CH\!\!-\!\!O^+$
LXIX   LXX

with acrolein.   If this interpretation is correct, acrylonitrile would be more analogous to vinyl chloride than to acrolein.   An alternative explanation is that the relatively great electronegativity of the unsaturated carbon atom to which the formyl or cyano group is attached has a greater effect with the nitrile than with the aldehyde.   In neither event, however, is there any obvious reason why there should be such a great difference between the two apparently analogous types of compound.

With both acrolein and acrylonitrile, there is a marked increase in the magnitude of the dipole moment when a hydrogen atom in the β position is replaced by a methyl group.   Thus, the moment of *trans* crotonaldehyde, LXXI, is 3.67 D, as was noted on

$CH_3\!\!-\!\!CH\!\!=\!\!CH\!\!-\!\!CH\!\!=\!\!O$ $CH_3\!\!-\!\!CH\!\!=\!\!CH\!\!-\!\!C\!\!\equiv\!\!N$
LXXI   LXXII

page 226, and that of *trans* crotononitrile, LXXII, is 4.50 D.   It has been suggested that hyperconjugation, resulting from unexpectedly large weights for such structures as LXXIII and LXXIV, must here be involved.   Evidently, however, the variations

$H^+CH_2\!\!=\!\!CH\!\!-\!\!CH\!\!=\!\!CH\!\!-\!\!O^-$ $H^+CH_2\!\!=\!\!CH\!\!-\!\!CH\!\!=\!\!CH\!\!=\!\!N^-$
LXXIII   LXXIV

discussed both in this paragraph and in the preceding one are not at present clearly understood.

With fulvene, LXXV (R = H), the situation is somewhat analogous to that encountered above with cycloheptatrienone, LV. Here, however, the special stability of an aromatic sextet of electrons (cf. Section 3·9) should favor a charge distribution in which electrons have been drawn into, rather than away from, the ring. Consequently, the substance should have a dipole moment which is significantly greater than the ones found generally for unsaturated hydrocarbons, and the direction of the moment should be such that the ring is negative with respect to the side chain. Both these predictions have been experimentally confirmed.[29] In benzene solution, the moments of 6,6-dimethylfulvene, LXXV (R = CH_3), and of 6,6-diethylfulvene, LXXV (R = C_2H_5), are, respectively, 1.48 D and 1.44 D, whereas that of a typical unsaturated hydrocarbon is never more than a few tenths of a debye; and, from the observations that the moments of the corresponding diphenyl- and di-*p*-chlorophenylfulvenes are, respectively, 1.34 D and 0.68 D, it is readily seen that the dipole is indeed in the direction stated (cf. the discussion of phenyl azide on page 218). Similarly, in azulene, LXXVI, a rather large moment may be

LXXV

LXXVI

expected (cf. page 138) to result from a migration of the electrons out of the seven-membered ring into the five-membered one. This expectation is in satisfactory agreement with the observation that, in benzene solution, the moment of the substance is 1.0 D;[29] the direction of the dipole has not yet, however, been experimentally determined. The foregoing qualitative considerations, which were based on the concept of the aromatic sextet, have been put on a better theoretical foundation by some approximate quantum-mechanical calculations,[29, 30] which have led to at

[29] G. W. Wheland and D. E. Mann, *J. Chem. Phys.* **17**, 264 (1949); E. D. Bergmann and E. Fischer, *Bull. soc. chim. France*, **1950**, 1084.

[30] See, for example, C. A. Coulson and G. S. Rushbrooke, *Proc. Cambridge Phil. Soc.* **36**, 193 (1940); C. A. Coulson and H. C. Longuet-Higgins, *Rev. Sci.* **85**, 929 (1947); C. A. Coulson, D. P. Craig, and A. Maccoll, *Proc. Phys. Soc.* (*London*) **61**, 22 (1948); G. Berthier, *J. Chem. Phys.* **21**, 953 (1953); *J. chim. phys.* **50**, 344 (1953). The last of these papers contains further references to a number of earlier calculations.

least semiquantitative agreement with the observed moments of the simpler fulvenes and of azulene.

5·5 Steric Inhibition of Resonance.   The steric inhibition of resonance provides evidence which supports both the rule of coplanarity discussed in Section 4·2 and also the interpretation of the dipole moments of nitrobenzene and of *p*-nitroaniline given in Section 5·4.   In nitrobenzene, for example, the effect of the quinoid structures XXIX, XXX, and XXXI of Section 5·4 should be both to make the molecule lie wholly in a single plane and also to increase its dipole moment.   The expected increase in moment can be observed experimentally, as has already been pointed out, and this fact provides some evidence that the molecule does indeed tend to be planar.   As a corollary of this argument, it follows that the moment should be decreased to approximately the aliphatic value if the nitro group were rotated about the carbon-nitrogen bond in such a way that its plane was no longer the same as that of the benzene ring.   This is because the above quinoid structures would then be made even less stable by the departure of the nitro group from coplanarity with the ring, so that their importance would be greatly reduced.

In nitrodurene, I, the methyl group moments cancel in pairs; consequently, a strict application of the rule of additivity would lead to the

I

prediction that the dipole moment of the molecule should be the same as that of nitrobenzene, that is, about 3.95 D, because in this latter substance the four corresponding carbon-hydrogen bond moments also cancel in pairs.   (In order to have a common basis of comparison, we shall in this section refer only to dipole moments measured in solution in benzene.) There is reason to believe, however, that in nitrodurene the nitro group cannot lie in the plane of the ring because of the presence of the bulky substituents in the two positions *ortho* to it.   If the molecule were planar, each oxygen atom would be at a distance of about 2.5 A from a methyl carbon atom, whereas the usual distance of closest approach of an oxygen atom and a methyl carbon atom to which it is not bonded is about 3.4 A.[31]   It is therefore evident that there must be in operation large

[31] L. Pauling, *The Nature of the Chemical Bond*, Cornell University Press, Ithaca, N. Y., 1st ed., 1939, p. 176; 2nd ed., 1940, p. 189.

repulsive forces which twist the nitro group about the carbon-nitrogen bond, so that one oxygen atom lies above, and the other lies below, the plane of the ring.   The dipole moment of nitrodurene, if these arguments are correct, should then be less than that of nitrobenzene, and approximately equal to that of an aliphatic nitro compound.   The observed value[32] is only 3.62 D, in fair agreement with expectation.   (The moments of the aliphatic nitro compounds are less in solution than in the vapor phase and are usually in the neighborhood of 3.3 D.)   This fact provides strong support for the interpretation of the data in this section and in Section 5·4.

Further evidence can be brought forward which also supports the views expressed above.   In bromodurene, II, for example, no inhibition of resonance by steric factors is possible, because no reasonable deformation of the molecule by the methyl groups can decrease the stability of the quinoid structures analogous to XXII, XXIII, and XXIV of Section 5·4. Consequently, the dipole moment of bromodurene should be approximately the same as that of bromobenzene.   This expectation is, in fact, found to be correct, the observed values being 1.55 D and 1.52 D, respectively.   It is apparent, therefore, that the methyl groups do not *directly* alter the moment of the molecule to any significant extent.   With aniline and aminodurene, similarly, the observed moments are nearly the same (1.53 D and 1.39 D, respectively), so that apparently there is no important inhibition of resonance in the latter substance.   This conclusion also might have been anticipated in view of the small size of the amino group. In nitrodimethylaminodurene, III, on the other hand, the contribution of

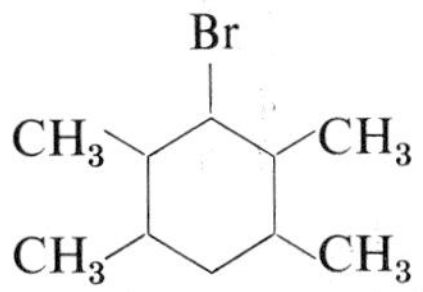

II

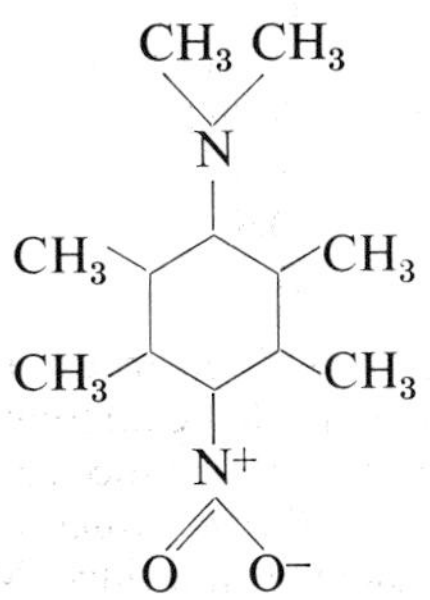

III

the quinoid structure must be greatly decreased by the steric interference of both the nitro and the dimethylamino groups with their neighbors. As a result, the moment is reduced to only 4.11 D as compared with

[32] R. H. Birtles and G. C. Hampson, *J. Chem. Soc.* **1937**, 10; H. Kofod, L. E. Sutton, W. A. de Jong, P. E. Verkade, and B. M. Wepster, *Rec. trav. chim.* **71**, 521 (1952).

6.87 D for *p*-nitrodimethylaniline. Also in nitromesitylene, IV, the moments of the methyl groups cancel each other, as they do in nitrodurene. Consequently, if it were not for the inhibition of resonance, this substance too should have the same moment as nitrobenzene. Actually, its

IV

TABLE 5·4

EFFECT OF STERIC INHIBITION OF RESONANCE ON DIPOLE MOMENTS[a]

X	Y	Benzene Derivative p-C_6H_4XY	Durene Derivative $C_6(CH_3)_4XY$	Mesitylene Derivative $C_6H_2(CH_3)_3X$
NO_2	H	3.95	3.62[b]	3.67
$N(CH_3)_2$	H	1.58	—	1.03
NH_2	H[c]	1.53	1.39	1.40
OH	H[c]	1.57	1.68	1.36
F	H[c]	1.47	—	1.36[d]
Cl	H[c]	1.56	—	1.55[d]
Br	H[c]	1.52	1.55	1.52[d]
I	H[c]	1.38[e]	—	1.42[d]
NO_2	$N(CH_3)_2$	6.87	4.11	—
NO_2	OC_2H_5	4.74[e, f]	3.69	—
NO_2	NH_2	6.35[g]	4.98	—
NO_2	OH	5.02	4.08	—
NO_2	Br	2.65[e]	2.36	—

[a] The quantities listed in the body of the table are the dipole moments (in debyes) of the indicated compounds in benzene solution. Except as noted, the temperature is in each instance 25°C, and the data are taken from L. G. Wesson, *Tables of Electric Dipole Moments*, The Technology Press, Massachusetts Institute of Technology, Cambridge, Mass., 1948. See also R. H. Birtles and G. C. Hampson, *J. Chem. Soc.* **1937**, 10; C. E. Ingham and G. C. Hampson, *ibid.* **1939**, 981.

[b] H. Kofod, L. E. Sutton, W. A. de Jong, P. E. Verkade, and B. M. Wepster, *Rec. trav. chim.* **71**, 521 (1952).

[c] No inhibition of resonance is to be expected with this substance.

[d] At 30°C.

[e] At 20°C.

[f] This value applies to *p*-nitroanisole.

[g] K. B. Everard and L. E. Sutton, *J. Chem. Soc.* **1951**, 2826.

moment has been found to be 3.67 D, so that the steric effect of the methyl groups is essentially the same here as in nitrodurene.   The data for all the above, and for a number of additional, substances are summarized in Table 5·4.[33]

5·6   Dipole Moments and Free Rotation.   Although the complex problem of free rotation lies outside the scope of the present book, there is one aspect of the subject which is of sufficient importance from the viewpoint of resonance to merit a brief description here.   The following discussion will be concerned with the restriction of rotation about bonds which, in the conventional structures, are represented as single, but which, as a result of resonance, may be expected to have more or less double-bond character (cf. also pages 196ff).

The first example to be considered is that of the esters of carboxylic acids, with which there appears to be little, if any, freedom of rotation about the bond that links the carbon atom of the carbonyl group to the oxygen atom of the alkoxyl group.[34]   The dipole moment of any ester formed between a saturated monohydric alcohol, ROH, on the one hand, and a saturated monocarboxylic acid, $R'CO_2H$, on the other, is found to be approximately equal to 1.7–1.9 D.   This independence of the natures of the radicals R and R' is to be expected on the basis of the rule of vector addition of bond moments, just as in the alkyl halides and the like.   More important from our present point of view, however, is the fact that these moments do not vary appreciably with the temperature over temperature ranges of as much as 190°.   Now, if rotation could occur about all bonds that are represented as single bonds in the conventional structure, an ester molecule could assume the two extreme geometrical configurations (or conformations) represented by I and II, as well as an infinite number of intermediate ones.   Since a carbon-oxygen bond is associated with a moment of about 1.5 D (see Table 5·1,

          I   II

[33] For several additional, but less striking, examples in which dipole moments are affected by steric inhibition of resonance, see R. G. Kadesch and S. W. Weller, *J. Am. Chem. Soc.* **63**, 1310 (1941); J. B. Bentley, K. B. Everard, R. J. B. Marsden, and L. E. Sutton, *J. Chem. Soc.* **1949**, 2957; K. B. Everard and L. E. Sutton, *ibid.* **1951**, 2817.

[34] The following discussion is taken from R. J. B. Marsden and L. E. Sutton, *J. Chem. Soc.* **1936**, 1383.

Section 5·2), it is evident that the moments of the molecule in the two extreme configurations must be widely different. In fact, a calculation based upon the usual bond angles and upon the values of the bond moments found in other aliphatic compounds leads to predicted moments of 1.53 D and 3.53 D for I and II, respectively.

The fact that the observed moment is independent of temperature can be explained in only two ways. The first possibility is that rotation about the carbon-oxygen bond is completely free, so that there are no forces which favor one (or more) of the possible configurations over the others. Under these circumstances, the molecule would spend the same fraction of the time in any one configuration as in any other, regardless of temperature, and the observed moment would be an average, with equal weights (actually, the root mean square, as is shown in the paragraphs in fine print on pages 239ff), of the moments corresponding to all the various configurations. The second possible explanation is that the molecule is rigidly held in some definite configuration by forces that are too strong to be overcome by the thermal motion at the temperatures investigated. Under these circumstances, the observed moment would be just that of the favored configuration. That the second alternative is the correct one is strongly suggested by the fact that the observed moment is in satisfactory agreement with the value calculated for configuration I, but seems much too small to be any sort of average of the values for I and II. This conclusion is further supported by the fact that the moment of γ-butyrolactone, III, in which the configuration is

$$CH_2\!\!-\!\!CH_2$$
$$H_2C \qquad\qquad C\!=\!O$$
$$O$$

III

uniquely determined by the five-membered ring, is 4.12 D, in fair agreement with the value calculated for the configuration II.

From the foregoing discussion, it follows that an acyclic ester of a carboxylic acid is held rigidly in the planar configuration I. There still remains the problem of deciding the nature of the forces responsible for this rigidity. One explanation, which has already been discussed in Section 4·2, is that resonance with the structure IV gives considerable

$$O^-$$
$$R'\!\!-\!\!C$$
$$O^+\!\!-\!\!R$$

IV

double-bond character to the carbon-oxygen bond under discussion and so prevents rotation about it. The question which of the two possible configurations, I or II, is the more stable is then presumably determined by specific dipole or van der Waals interactions between the alkyl radical R and the carbonyl group (or, in the γ-lactone, by the formation of the ring). An alternative explanation is that a particularly powerful attraction may exist between the alkyl group and the carbonyl oxygen atom, and that this is strong enough, except in the lactone, to hold the molecule rigidly in the configuration I. It would be difficult, however, to account satisfactorily for an attraction powerful enough to produce such a large effect. More direct evidence against this second explanation has been obtained from an investigation of the ε-lactone, V. The seven-membered

$$\begin{array}{c} CH_2-CH_2 \\ \diagup \qquad\qquad \diagdown \\ H_3C-CH \qquad\qquad CH-CH(CH_3)_2 \\ | \qquad\qquad\qquad | \\ CH_2-C-O \\ \| \\ O \end{array}$$

V

ring in this substance is of sufficient size so that it does not necessarily hold the ester grouping in the configuration II, or even very close to it, but it is not large enough to permit the molecule to achieve the configuration I. Consequently, if an exceedingly powerful attraction does exist between the alkyl radical and the carbonyl oxygen atom, the actual configuration, and hence the dipole moment, should be intermediate between those characteristic of a γ-lactone and of an ordinary, acyclic ester. In fact, calculation has led to an estimated value of 2.7 D or less for such a situation. The observed moment, 4.33 D, is instead practically the same as that of γ-butyrolactone, and so only the first explanation, based on resonance, remains. This conclusion supports the belief, reached originally in Section 3·3, that the resonance energy of a carboalkoxy group must be large.

Not all esters show this rigidity. The dipole moments of methyl carbonate, methyl chloroformate, and ethyl chloroformate, for example, have been reported[35] to vary with temperature, so that apparently some not entirely free rotation can occur. The explanation is possibly that in these substances the double bonds must be distributed among *three* positions, as in the structures VI, VII, and VIII. They cannot, therefore, impart as much rigidity to the carbon-oxygen bonds as in the simple esters, where they are distributed between only *two* positions. In this

[35] S. Mizushima and M. Kubo, *Bull. Chem. Soc. Japan* **13**, 174 (1938).

connection, it is significant that the carbon-oxygen bond is somewhat longer, and so has less double-bond character, in the carbonate ion than in a carboxylate ion. (See Table 4·3, Section 4·3.)

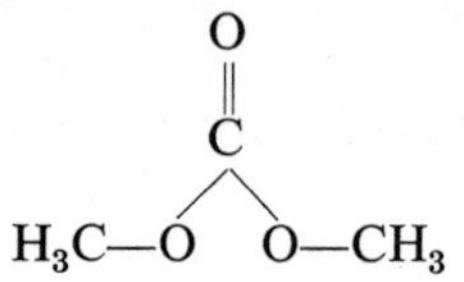

$$
\begin{array}{ccc}
& O & \\
& \| & \\
& C & \\
& \bigwedge & \\
H_3C\!-\!O & & O\!-\!CH_3 \\
& \mathrm{VI} &
\end{array}
\qquad
\begin{array}{ccc}
& O^- & \\
& | & \\
& C & \\
& \bigwedge & \\
H_3C\!-\!^+O & & O\!-\!CH_3 \\
& \mathrm{VII} &
\end{array}
$$

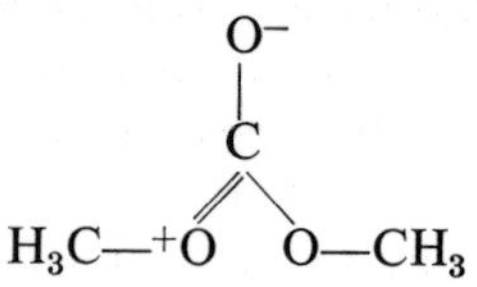

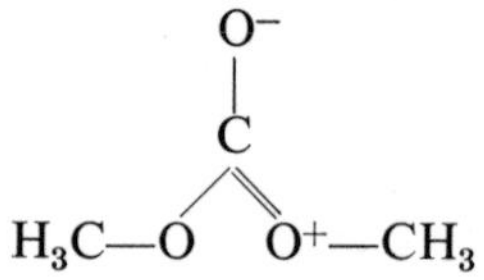

$$
\begin{array}{ccc}
& O^- & \\
& | & \\
& C & \\
& \bigwedge & \\
H_3C\!-\!O & & O^+\!-\!CH_3 \\
& \mathrm{VIII} &
\end{array}
$$

A second example of restricted rotation about a bond which is conventionally regarded as single, but which has some double-bond character, is apparently provided by certain phenolic ethers.[36] In anisole, for example, resonance with the quinoid structures IX, X, and XI might be expected to favor the configurations in which the carbon atom of the

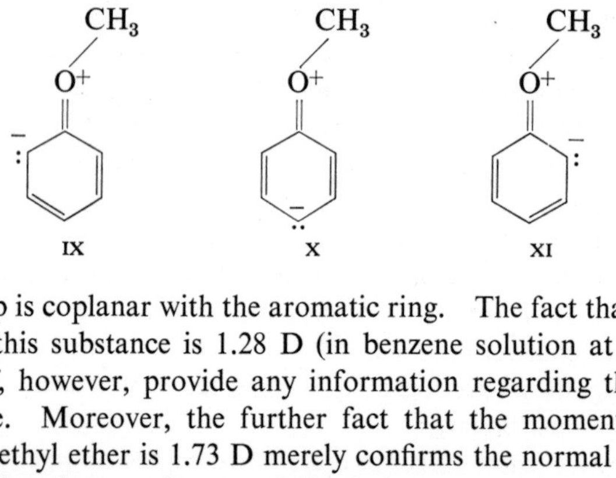

$$
\begin{array}{ccc}
\mathrm{CH_3} & \mathrm{CH_3} & \mathrm{CH_3} \\
\mathrm{O^+} & \mathrm{O^+} & \mathrm{O^+} \\
\mathrm{IX} & \mathrm{X} & \mathrm{XI}
\end{array}
$$

methyl group is coplanar with the aromatic ring. The fact that the dipole moment of this substance is 1.28 D (in benzene solution at 25°C) does not by itself, however, provide any information regarding the shape of the molecule. Moreover, the further fact that the moment of hydroquinone dimethyl ether is 1.73 D merely confirms the normal expectation that the methoxyl group is not axial (cf. the paragraph in fine print on page 215), and hence that the C—O—C bond angle is less than 180°. From these data alone, we cannot determine whether the carbon atoms of the methyl groups are firmly held in the planes of the respective benzene rings, or whether there is freedom of rotation about the bonds by which the methoxyl groups are linked to the rings. In fact, the data are equally

[36] The discussion in the remainder of this section is based on the work of K. B. Everard and L. E. Sutton, *J. Chem. Soc.* **1949**, 2312; **1951**, 16.

consistent with all three possible views: (1) the rotation is completely restricted, so that the molecules of anisole are rigidly held in the planar configuration XII, whereas those of hydroquinone dimethyl ether are similarly held in the two nonequivalent configurations XIII and XIV;

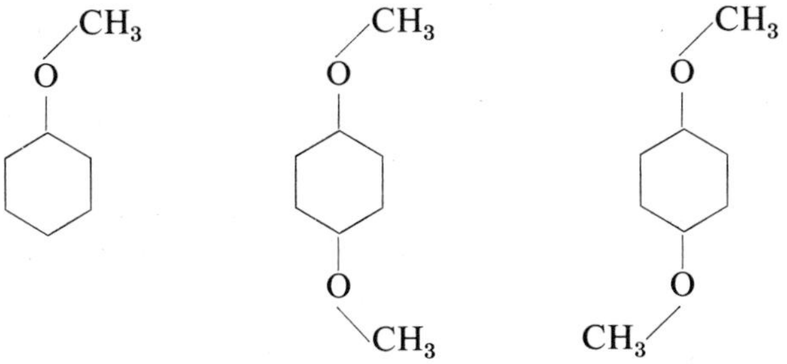

(2) the rotation is completely free, so that all relative orientations of the methoxyl groups are equally probable; and (3) the rotation is neither completely restricted nor completely free, so that, although all relative orientations are possible, some are more probable than others. (See the following paragraphs in fine print.)

It will be instructive here to consider in somewhat greater detail the justification for the statements just made. The reader will be assumed to have at least some familiarity with vector analysis and, in particular, to be acquainted with the representation of vectors in terms of their components along mutually perpendicular directions (cf. also Section 5·1). Let us imagine that the benzene ring of an anisole molecule lies in the xy plane of a Cartesian coordinate system, that the center of the ring is at the origin, and that the oxygen atom lies on the y axis, as in Figure 5·3. If all carbon-carbon bond moments are equal to zero, and if the moments of the four carbon-hydrogen bonds that are ortho and meta to the methoxyl group cancel in pairs, then the total moment of the entire molecule is the resultant of the group moment due to the methoxyl group and the bond moment of the para carbon-hydrogen bond. The components of these two partial moments along the three coordinate axes can be designated, in an obvious manner, as $\mu_{OCH_3,x}$, $\mu_{OCH_3,y}$, $\mu_{OCH_3,z}$, $\mu_{CH,x}$, $\mu_{CH,y}$, and $\mu_{CH,z}$. Since the hydrogen atom of the CH group lies on the y axis, $\mu_{CH,x} = \mu_{CH,z} = 0$.

The value of $\mu_{OCH_3,y}$ may be thought of as a constant which does not depend on the orientation of the methoxyl group. (In a more careful treatment, we would have to allow $\mu_{OCH_3,y}$ to vary somewhat with the rotation about the phenyl-oxygen bond, since the weights of the structures IX, X, and XI would certainly vary. The error which we here introduce is doubtless small, however, and in any event can be shown not to alter in any significant way the conclusions which we shall reach below.) The values of $\mu_{OCH_3,x}$ and of $\mu_{OCH_3,z}$, on the other hand, must be dependent on the position of the methyl group; more precisely, they must be at least approximately equal to $M \cos \theta$ and $M \sin \theta$, where M is a constant, and θ is the angle between the plane of the benzene ring and the plane defined by the two carbon-oxygen bonds. For the sake of definiteness, the value of θ is to be taken as 0°, or as 180°, when the carbon atom of the methyl group is in the plane of the ring and on the *right* side, or on the *left* side,

respectively, of the oxygen atom.   The total moment of the anisole molecule then has
the components

$$\mu_{C_6H_5OCH_3,x} = M \cos \theta$$

$$\mu_{C_6H_5OCH_3,y} = \mu_{CH,y} + \mu_{OCH_3,y}$$

and
$$\mu_{C_6H_5OCH_3,z} = M \sin \theta$$

Hence, the square of the magnitude of the moment, which is the quantity that is directly
measured experimentally (cf. equation 2, Section 5·1) is

$$\left|\mu_{C_6H_5OCH_3}\right|^2 = M^2 \cos^2 \theta + (\mu_{CH,y} + \mu_{OCH_3,y})^2 + M^2 \sin^2 \theta$$
$$= M^2 + (\mu_{CH,y} + \mu_{OCH_3,y})^2 \qquad (1)$$

It is important to observe that, although the methoxyl group is not axial, the dipole
moment of anisole is independent of the angle θ;   this simple situation is encountered,

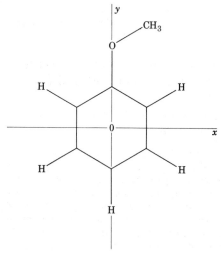

Fig. 5·3.   A molecule of anisole lying in the xy plane.   The z axis is to
be considered perpendicular to the plane of the paper.

however, only when, as with anisole, there is just one nonaxial group (see below), and
when certain other conditions with which we need not here be concerned are also
satisfied.

Hydroquinone dimethyl ether can be treated in a way which is an obvious extension
of the one just described for the simpler compound, anisole.   Thus, we shall imagine
that, as before, the benzene ring lies in the xy plane with the origin at its center, and
that now *both* oxygen atoms are on the y axis.   Since there is here no carbon-hydrogen
bond which is not para to a second one equivalent to it, we now have no term corresponding to the $\mu_{CH,y}$ of the preceding example.   Moreover, the further terms
$\mu_{OCH_3,y}$ for the two methoxyl groups must cancel each other and so can be ignored.
The total moment of the molecule then has the components

$$\mu_{p-C_6H_4(OCH_3)_2,x} = M \cos \theta_1 + M \cos \theta_2$$

$$\mu_{p-C_6H_4(OCH_3)_2,y} = 0$$

and
$$\mu_{p-C_6H_4(OCH_3)_2,z} = M \sin \theta_1 + M \sin \theta_2$$

where θ_1 and θ_2 are the angles between the plane of the ring and the two different planes defined by the two pairs of carbon-oxygen bonds. The square of the magnitude of the moment is then

$$|\mu_{p-C_6H_4(OCH_3)_2}|^2 = (M\cos\theta_1 + M\cos\theta_2)^2 + (M\sin\theta_1 + M\sin\theta_2)^2$$
$$= 2M^2 + 2M^2\cos(\theta_1 - \theta_2) \tag{2}$$

We are now in position to deal with several matters of interest. In the first place, we should note that the foregoing equations 1 and 2 contain so many unknown quantities that, even though the values of $|\mu_{C_6H_5OCH_3}|$ and $|\mu_{p-C_6H_4(OCH_3)_2}|$ are known to be 1.28 D and 1.73 D, respectively (see above) we cannot derive the desired values of the angles θ, θ_1, and θ_2. In the second place, if $\theta_1 = \theta_2 = 0°$, as in configuration XIII, then the resultant moment of hydroquinone dimethyl ether is equal to $2M$; if $\theta_1 = 0°$, but $\theta_2 = 180°$, as in configuration XIV, then the resultant moment is zero. If half the molecules have configuration XIII while the rest have configuration XIV, then the measured value of $|\mu_{p-C_6H_4(OCH_3)_2}|^2$ must be just halfway between the two corresponding values of $(2M)^2$ and 0, respectively, and so must be equal to $2M^2$. The observed moment would then be $M\sqrt{2}$. And finally if there is completely free rotation, the measured value of $|\mu_{p-C_6H_4(OCH_3)_2}|^2$ must be the average value of $2M^2 + 2M^2\cos(\theta_1 - \theta_2)$, where θ_1 and θ_2 are allowed to vary independently and at random. However, since $\cos(\theta_1 - \theta_2)$ is then exactly as likely to be positive as negative, its average value must be 0, and so the observed moment is again $M\sqrt{2}$. Evidently, therefore, we cannot distinguish between the extremes of completely restricted and completely free rotation; and, for a similar reason, we cannot recognize the intermediate case in which the rotation is neither completely restricted nor completely free.

Although no useful information regarding the possible restriction of rotation in aromatic ethers can be obtained from the dipole moments of only anisole and hydroquinone dimethyl ether, a more extended study[36] has led to some fairly definite conclusions. Thus, the dipole moments of 1,4- and 1,5-dimethoxynaphthalene are equal, respectively to 2.09 D and 0.67 D. The first of these values is clearly much greater, whereas the second is much smaller, than that found for the superficially analogous hydroquinone dimethyl ether. The explanation is doubtless the following. With hydroquinone dimethyl ether, there is no reason why the two methoxyl groups cannot be either "cis" with respect to each other, as in configuration XIII, or "trans," as in configuration XIV. On the other hand, the steric interferences between the methyl groups and the hydrogen atoms in the peri positions make impossible both the "trans" configuration XV for the 1,4-diether and the "cis" configuration XVI for the 1,5-diether. Now, if the 1,4-compound were rigidly held in the "cis" configuration XVII, which is a permissible one, its dipole moment ought to be $\sqrt{2}$ times as great as that of hydroquinone dimethyl ether (see the preceding paragraph in fine print and also the one below), and so it ought to be equal to $1.73\sqrt{2}$ D, or 2.45 D. The fact that the observed value is close to, but slightly less than, the predicted one then shows that the molecule spends most of its time near, but does not spend all of its time exactly in, the configuration XVII. Similarly, the further fact that the moment of the 1,5-dimethoxy compound is only slightly greater than zero shows that the configuration XVIII is here favored, but that the methyl groups

are not rigidly held in the plane of the rings.   Two possibilities must now be considered.   The observed appreciable, though incomplete, restriction of rotation may be due to the effects of small contributions from the several quinoid structures that are the analogs of IX, X, and XI, or it may instead be due to large repulsions between the methyl groups and the hydrogen atoms *peri* to them.   There seems, however, to be no way to account for repulsive forces which can act so strongly over such great distances.   One might, in fact, have anticipated that the van der Waals attractions would predominate, so that the bonds between the methyl groups and the oxygen atoms would lie in planes that are more or less perpendicular to that of the rings.   Under such circumstances, however, the observed moment of each of the two above dimethoxynaphthalenes ought to be approximately equal to that of hydroquinone dimethyl ether, 1.73 D.   With 9,10-dimethoxyanthracene, XIX, for example, the methoxyl

groups are necessarily held in the stated positions, and the dipole moment is indeed 1.73 D. Consequently, we can conclude that, in aromatic ethers, the resonance with the quinoid structures imparts a considerable stability to the planar configurations, but that the effect is not powerful enough to overcome either large steric repulsions or the thermal motions at ordinary temperatures.

The foregoing argument was partly based on the assumption that the dipole moment of a molecule with exactly the "*cis*" configuration XVII should be $\sqrt{2}$ times as great as that of hydroquinone dimethyl ether.   The justification for this assumption follows from the discussion in the last one of the above paragraphs in fine print, *provided that* the quantity M has the same value with derivatives of naphthalene as with those of benzene.   This required constancy is, however, supported by the fact that the moment of methyl α-naphthyl ether is equal to 1.28 D and hence is identical with that of anisole; and also by the further fact that the moments of hydroquinone dimethyl ether and of 9,10-dimethoxyanthracene are equal.   Consequently, there seems to be no reason to doubt the correctness of the conclusion that, in the methyl aryl ethers, the carbon atoms of the methyl groups tend to be coplanar with the aromatic rings.

Chapter 6   RESONANCE AND MOLECULAR SPECTRA

6·1 Types of Spectra. Spectroscopic data have long been used in the study of structural problems. Even the most superficial attempt to survey the entire field would here be out of place, however, and so the following discussion, after a preliminary introduction in this section and in the following one, will be limited to a few aspects in which the concept of resonance has proved especially helpful.[1]

Spectra are classified as emission or absorption spectra. (For our purposes, the fluorescence and Raman spectra can be regarded merely as special cases of these general types.) In emission spectra, the molecules of the substance of interest undergo transitions from states of higher to states of lower energy, and the energy lost by the molecules is emitted in the form of light. In absorption spectra, the molecules absorb light and are thereby raised to states of higher energy. In both kinds of spectra, the relation between the energy changes in the molecules and the frequencies of the light emitted or absorbed is given by the Bohr condition:

$$h\nu_{if} = E_f - E_i \qquad (1)$$

where h is Planck's constant, the magnitude of ν_{if} is the frequency, and E_i and E_f are the energies per molecule in the initial and final states, respectively. It will be seen that a positive value of ν_{if} corresponds to absorption, whereas a negative value corresponds to emission, of light.

---

[1] For further details regarding diatomic molecular spectra, see G. Herzberg, *Molecular Spectra and Molecular Structure* I, *Diatomic Molecules* (translated by J. W. T. Spinks), 1st ed., Prentice-Hall, New York, 1939, 2nd ed., D. Van Nostrand Co., New York, 1950. A fairly complete bibliography is given at the end of this book. For polyatomic molecular spectra, see H. Sponer, *Molekülspektren und ihre Anwendung auf chemische Probleme*, Springer, Berlin, vol. I, 1935, vol. II, 1936; E. A. Braude, *Ann. Repts. on Progr. Chem.* (*Chem. Soc. London*) **42**, 105 (1945) and numerous references given there; G. Herzberg, *Infrared and Raman Spectra of Polyatomic Molecules*, D. Van Nostrand Co., New York, 1945. The book by Herzberg again contains an extensive bibliography. Microwave spectroscopy is reviewed by W. Gordy, *Revs. Mod. Phys.* **20**, 668 (1948); E. B. Wilson, Jr., *Ann. Rev. Phys. Chem.* **2**, 151 (1951); W. Gordy, W. V. Smith, and R. F. Trambarulo, *Microwave Spectroscopy*, John Wiley & Sons, New York, 1953.

The following figures are of interest in connection with the orders of magnitude of the quantities involved. A wave length of 4000 A, which lies approximately at the blue end of the visible spectrum, corresponds to an energy change of about 71 kcal per mole, whereas a wave length of 8000 A, which lies approximately at the red end of the visible spectrum, corresponds to an energy change of half that magnitude.

At the present time, it has become fairly common practice in spectroscopic discussions to quote wave lengths in millimicrons (mμ) rather than in angstroms (A). This alternative unit is defined as 10^{-7} cm, and so is equal to 10 A. The wave lengths mentioned in the preceding paragraph are, accordingly, 400 mμ and 800 mμ, respectively. One advantage in employing the millimicron as the unit length is that the wave lengths, when thus stated with one less significant figure, usually give a better indication of the true reliability of the experimental data. In this chapter, however, we shall continue to express wave lengths in angstroms since, for our purposes, there is nothing to be gained by increasing the number of units for the measurement of lengths.

We shall be concerned only with absorption spectra; these can be further classified into three types. The first of these, the pure rotation spectrum, is associated with changes which occur in the rotational states of the molecules without simultaneous changes in the vibrational and electronic states. Since the separations in energy between the various rotational levels are relatively small, it follows from equation 1 that the corresponding frequencies are relatively low or, in other words, that the wave lengths are relatively great. The pure rotation spectra of all substances occur in the far infrared in an experimentally difficult region of the spectrum. Consequently, until the rather recent development of microwave spectroscopy,[1] they had been comparatively little investigated. The second type of spectrum, the rotation-vibration spectrum, is associated with transitions in which the vibrational, and usually also the rotational, states of the molecules are altered, but in which the electronic states remain unchanged. The energy differences are greater here than in the pure rotation spectrum and, accordingly, the absorption occurs at shorter wave lengths, actually in the near infrared region. And finally, the electronic spectrum, in which we shall be principally interested, arises from transitions between electronic states, usually accompanied by simultaneous changes in both the vibrational and rotational levels. (The significance of the term "electronic state" will be explained more fully in Section 6·2.) Relatively large energy differences are involved in the electronic spectra, which therefore occur at relatively short wave lengths, most commonly in the ultraviolet, but sometimes in the visible, region.

The relation among the various energy levels and the corresponding spectra can be seen from Figure 6·1, which schematically represents the two lowest electronic levels of a diatomic molecule. (For polyatomic molecules, the corresponding diagrams would be similar in general nature, but much more complicated.) In this figure, the heights of the various horizontal lines above some appropriate base line represent the energies of the corresponding states of the molecule. The two heavy

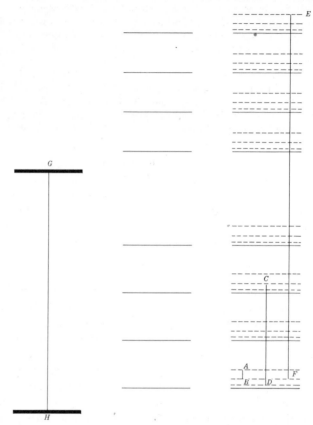

Fig. 6·1. Diagram in which the heights of the various horizontal lines above some arbitrary base line correspond to the energies of a diatomic molecule in the corresponding electronic, vibrational, and rotational states. The heavy lines at the left correspond to two electronic states; the lines in the center correspond to a few of the lowest vibrational states associated with each electronic state; and the lines at the right correspond to a few of the lowest rotational states associated with each of the electronic and vibrational states.

lines at the left of the figure represent the electronic energies of the two states, that is, the energies which would obtain if the nuclei were held in fixed positions. The lines in the center of the figure represent the energies of a few of the lowest vibrational states associated with each electronic state, that is, the energies which would obtain if no rotation of the molecule were allowed.   Since the molecule must have at least the "half quantum" of zero-point vibrational energy, the lowest of these vibrational levels in either electronic state lies above the corresponding electronic level; the remaining levels lie above these at approximately constant intervals.   The lines at the right of the figure represent a few of the lowest rotational levels associated with the various electronic and vibrational levels, that is, the actual energies which the molecule can have when all types of motion are taken into account.   For the sake of clarity, the lowest (nonrotating) levels are represented by full lines, and the other (rotating) levels by broken lines.   (To be rigorously correct, we ought to consider also the motion of the molecule as a whole through space.   This translational motion is of little spectroscopic interest, however, and so we shall ignore it.)

We can now consider the three types of spectrum enumerated above in the light of the energy-level diagram.   The vertical line AB in Figure 6·1, for example, corresponds to one of the transitions in the pure rotation spectrum of the substance, since the electronic and vibrational levels do not change.   The line CD, on the other hand, corresponds to a transition in the vibration-rotation spectrum.   Since CD is longer than AB, the former represents a greater change in energy and, therefore, an absorption of light of shorter wave length.   And finally, the line EF corresponds to a transition in the electronic spectrum.   Since EF is still longer than CD, it represents absorption at still shorter wave lengths.

It is important to observe that each electronic state can be associated with a large number of vibrational and rotational states.   Consequently, a transition between two electronic states does not correspond to only a single change in energy, and it does not result in only a single spectral line.   The *absorption band* resulting from such a transition must therefore consist of a large number of individual lines, which are not widely separated from each other, but which may extend over a range in wave length of several hundred angstrom units.   With a complex molecule, or even with a simple molecule in the liquid phase, these lines may be broadened so that they overlap and are no longer separately distinguishable.   Other factors also may result in a broadening of the lines or even in the production of a true continuous spectrum.   For all these reasons, it is usually difficult to decide, without a detailed analysis of the spectrum, the exact value of the wave length that corresponds to the electronic transition alone.   (In Figure 6·1, for example, the "electronic transition alone" is represented by the length GH.)   In the following sections, we shall make use of the wave length at which the absorption has maximum intensity.

The most commonly used quantitative measure for the intensity of absorption at a given wave length is the *molecular extinction coefficient* ε. This quantity is defined by the equation

$$I = I_0 \cdot 10^{-dc\varepsilon} \tag{2}$$

where I is the intensity of the light after it has passed through d centimeters of either the pure substance or a solution of it in a nonabsorbing solvent; I_0 is the intensity of the light after it has passed through a path which is identical with the foregoing in all respects except that the substance being studied is omitted; and c is the concentration in moles per liter. The more intense the absorption, the larger is the value of ε. All three of the quantities I, I_0, and ε are functions of the wave length, or the frequency, of the light, and so they are uniquely defined only for light of specified wave length, or frequency. Absorption spectra are usually reported in the form of curves, in which the extinction coefficients, or their logarithms, are plotted as ordinates against the wave length, its reciprocal (the so-called wave number), or the frequency as abscissa. Such a method of representation is most useful when the individual lines of the spectrum overlap, so that only a continuous region of absorption of varying intensity is observed. The largest value of ε within any one absorption band will hereafter be designated as ε_{max}, and the corresponding wave length and frequency will be similarly designated as λ_{max} and ν_{max}, respectively.

In accordance with the usual practice, we shall in this chapter speak of molecular extinction coefficients as if they were dimensionless quantities. Actually, however, since the exponent $-dc\varepsilon$ which appears in equation 2 must be a pure number, ε is seen to have the dimensions of an area per mole. More precisely, and as is implied in equation 2, the numerical values that will hereafter be assigned to the extinction coefficients are expressed in units of 1000 cm^2 $mole^{-1}$. It is of interest that the largest observed values of ε are of the order of 10^5 and so correspond to areas of about 10^8 cm^2 per mole, or of about 1.7×10^{-16} cm^2 per molecule. On the other hand, since the linear dimensions of molecules are of the order of 10^{-8} cm, their areas are of the order of 10^{-16} cm^2. The approximate agreement between these two calculated values is not purely fortuitous,[2] but the reason for it is too complex to be given here.

A convenient measure for the intensity of the *total absorption* that is due to an electronic transition is given by the so-called integrated intensity Q, which is defined by the equation[2, 3]

$$Q = \int \varepsilon \, d\nu \tag{3}$$

[2] See, for example, E. A. Braude, *J. Chem. Soc.* **1950**, 379.

[3] For discussion and further references, see T. Förster, *Z. Elektrochem.* **45**, 548 (1939); R. S. Mulliken and C. A. Rieke, *Proc. Phys. Soc. (London) Repts. Progr. in Phys.* **8**, 231 (1941); A. Maccoll, *Quart. Revs. (London)* **1**, 16 (1947).

The molecular extinction coefficient ε is here expressed as a function of the frequency ν, and the integration is extended over the complete range of frequencies that are associated with the band of interest. Since, clearly, a broad band with a comparatively small value of ε_{max} may have a larger integrated intensity than a narrow band with a greater value of ε_{max}, ε_{max} is not, by itself, a sufficient criterion for the strength of an absorption band. However, since the observed values of ε_{max} are available for a great many substances, whereas those of Q are available for relatively few, we shall usually hereafter base our discussion on the former quantities rather than on the latter. This procedure is strictly justified when, as is often approximately true with a series of closely related substances, the absorption bands that are compared with one another have the same shape; and, in any event, there is at present no practical alternative procedure which we might adopt.

Still a further useful measure for the total intensity of an absorption band is the so-called oscillator strength, or f value, which is defined as

$$f = (2300mc/N\pi e^2)\int \varepsilon dv \cong 1.43 \cdot 10^{-19}Q \qquad (4)$$

where m and e are, respectively, the mass and charge of an electron, c is the velocity of light, and N is Avogadro's number.[2,3] It is important to note that here, as in equation 3, the frequency ν has the dimensions of sec^{-1}; indeed, if this point is not borne in mind, serious difficulties may arise since the wave number, with the dimensions of cm^{-1}, is often also designated by the letter ν. Although equation 4 is strictly applicable only to spectra measured on gaseous substances, it is commonly applied also when the substances of interest are in solution.[3] The theoretical significance of the oscillator strength is that, if the classical electromagnetic theory were here valid, an electron oscillating with frequency ν_0 would give rise to an absorption band with $\nu_{max} = \nu_0$, and with $f = 1$. In other words, f is the number of imaginary "classical" electrons which would be required for the production of an absorption band with the observed intensity. Since an actual electron does not behave in the way that the classical theory says it should, the f value need not be equal to 1; most commonly, in fact, f is much smaller than 1, and only for the most intense bands does it approach that value. Although the f value of an absorption band is therefore not equal to the number of electrons responsible for that band, the sum of the f values for all the electronic absorption bands of any given molecule is equal to the total number of electrons in the molecule.[4]

6·2   Ground and Excited Electronic States.   The nature of a transition between two electronic states can be most easily discussed with reference to a specific example, which can be conveniently taken as ethylene. The most stable structures that can be written for this substance are doubtless I, II, and III, of which the first is much more stable than the other two.

$$H_2C{=}CH_2 \qquad H_2C^+{-}CH_2^- \qquad H_2C^-{-}CH_2^+$$
$$\text{I} \qquad\qquad \text{II} \qquad\qquad \text{III}$$

[4] R. Ladenburg and F. Reiche, *Naturwissenschaften* **11**, 584 (1923).

As a result of resonance among these three structures, there arise (as was pointed out on pages 28 and 65f, and as will be discussed further on pages 586f) altogether three states (i.e., electronic states), each of which can possess varying amounts of vibrational and rotational energy. The most stable of these, the ground state, is essentially that represented by the structure I, with small equal contributions from II and III; the two remaining states, the excited states, on the other hand, are essentially resonance hybrids of the structures II and III, with only small contributions from I (but with probably larger contributions from still further structures not considered here).

A superficially rather different description of an electronic transition is provided by the molecular-orbital treatment (cf. Sections 2·9, 2·10, and 9·22–9·26). From the mathematical viewpoint, this alternative picture has proved to be somewhat simpler than the one outlined above and, accordingly, it is in practice more generally useful. If we again consider the ethylene molecule, we can as a first approximation (however, see below) assume that, in the ground state, two electrons are in the bonding orbital of Figure 2·8, Section 2·10; that, in the most stable of the innumerable excited states, only one electron is in this bonding orbital, whereas the second is instead in the antibonding orbital of Figure 2·9, Section 2·10; and that, in a still more highly excited state, both electrons are in the antibonding orbital. A transition from the ground state to the first of these excited states occurs when an electron "jumps" from the bonding to the antibonding orbital; conversely, a transition from this excited state to the ground state occurs when an electron "falls" from the antibonding to the bonding orbital. In general, just as in discussions of *atomic* spectra, any electronic transition can be described as a process in which an electron is transferred from some particular orbital to some different one. (A transition in which two or more electrons are simultaneously transferred is also imaginable, but we may here ignore the possibility of such an occurrence.)

The foregoing picture of an electronic transition is greatly oversimplified and so has only qualitative validity. As was mentioned in Section 2·10 (cf. also Section 2·9), the ground state of the ethylene molecule cannot be exactly described in terms of just the one configuration in which the bonding orbital of Figure 2·8 is doubly occupied. A considerably better, but still only approximate, description can be obtained if there is allowed to be an interaction, or resonance, between this configuration and the less stable one in which the antibonding orbital of Figure 2·9 is doubly occupied. Moreover, even better descriptions can be obtained if the interaction is allowed to include also a large number of additional configurations that involve orbitals which are less stable than either of the ones so far considered, but which need not here be further discussed. Similarly, the most stable *excited* state of ethylene cannot be exactly described in terms of just the one configuration in which the bonding and antibonding orbitals are each singly occupied.   As before, an appreciably better description requires that interaction with numerous additional configurations be taken into account.   However, as long as we are satisfied with merely approximate and qualitative interpretations of the electronic transitions, and as long as we restrict our attention to the absorption bands that occur in the visible or very near ultraviolet part of the spectrum, we can in most instances safely ignore the complication of configuration interaction.   Indeed, it is largely for this reason that the molecular-orbital treatment is mathematically simpler than the valence-bond treatment; for, if the ground and excited states of each molecule had always to be considered as hybrids of all the different configurations that are required for complete accuracy, the subsequent calculations would then be no easier than if these states were instead considered as hybrids of all the corresponding conventional covalent and ionic structures like I, II, and III.   The molecular-orbital treatment with allowance for configuration interaction is, in fact, mathematically indistinguishable from the valence-bond treatment with allowance for the contributions of ionic as well as covalent structures.   The essential distinction between the two treatments is that, when each is carried out in the rather drastically simplified way that is most commonly adopted, the former neglects the configuration interactions whereas the latter neglects the ionic structures.   Now the configuration interactions are seldom extremely important in either the ground or the lowest-lying excited states; consequently, their neglect is frequently permissible.   On the other hand, the ionic structures, although they usually have only small weights in the ground states of molecules, are often of paramount importance in even the lowest of the electronically excited states; consequently, their neglect is seldom permissible in any study in which both the ground and the excited states must be treated. Hence, when we are considering a spectroscopic problem, we may expect that the molecular-orbital treatment in its simplest form can be used with reasonable prospects for success but that the valence-bond method will ordinarily be much less satisfactory unless it is complicated by the explicit · inclusion of the ionic structures.

   The advantages are not entirely, however, in favor of the molecular-orbital method.   In order to illustrate the kinds of additional complication that can arise, let us continue the discussion of the ethylene molecule and, for the sake of simplicity, let us ignore configuration interaction.   In the ground-state configuration in which two electrons are assigned to the bonding orbital, and also in the particular excited configuration in which two electrons are assigned to the antibonding orbital, all electrons are necessarily paired since, in accordance with the Pauli exclusion principle (see Section 9·7), two electrons which occupy the same orbital must have opposite spins. On the other hand, in the less highly excited configuration in which each orbital is singly occupied, the electrons may be either paired or unpaired since the exclusion principle imposes no restriction on the spins of electrons that occupy different orbitals (see also Section 9·10 and page 570). Consequently, this latter configuration, unlike the other two, gives rise not to just one excited state, but to two distinct and far from equivalent excited states. In spectroscopic language, the state in which the electrons are paired is described as a *singlet*, whereas the one in which they are unpaired is described as a *triplet*; in general, the *multiplicity* of any state, or structure, is equal to one plus the number of unpaired electrons.

To the simplest and most usual approximation that the total electronic energy of a molecule is the sum of the energies of the occupied orbitals, the excited singlet and triplet states of ethylene have the same energy. When, however, the electrostatic repulsions between the electrons are more explicitly taken into account, the energies of the two levels are found to be different from each other (see below); morever, they are different also from the calculated value which is obtained by the above treatment (cf. also pages 656f), and which we shall here designate as E_1. In general, the triplet state is more stable than the singlet that arises from the same configuration; and, in a somewhat more refined, but still only approximate, treatment, E_1 is the arithmetic mean of the energies that are associated with these two states. Consequently, if the magnitude of the singlet-triplet separation is ΔE, the energies of the singlet and triplet states are approximately equal to $E_1 + \frac{1}{2}\Delta E$ and $E_1 - \frac{1}{2}\Delta E$, respectively; and, if the energy of the ground state is E_0, the substance should have two electronic absorption bands with frequencies of approximately $[E_1 + \frac{1}{2}\Delta E - E_0]/h$ and $[E_1 - \frac{1}{2}\Delta E - E_0]/h$, respectively (cf. equation 1, Section 6·1). Since, with ethylene, ΔE has been estimated (see the following paragraph) to be about 20–30 kcal per mole,[5, 6] the neglect of this energy term is clearly not permissible in any treatment aiming at even qualitative significance.

The foregoing complication would cause no serious trouble if the singlet-triplet separation ΔE were always known, since then a calculation of E_0 and E_1 would at once lead to predictions of the frequencies, and hence of the wave lengths, of the absorption bands. Unfortunately, however, the simplified treatment that provides the desired approximate

[5] W. J. Potts, Jr., *Thesis*, University of Chicago, 1953.
[6] J. R. Platt, personal communication.

values of E_0 and E_1 gives no information at all about the magnitude of ΔE. Two methods for solving this problem have been employed. On the one hand, by means of detailed and extremely tedious numerical calculation, the value of ΔE can be estimated without reference to the observed spectrum of the substance; on the other hand, by means of a careful study and interpretation of the observed spectrum, the value of ΔE can be obtained empirically from the measured difference, $\Delta E/h$, between the frequencies of the two bands. Neither method is convenient. When the first one is adopted, the attractive simplicity of the treatment is lost, and the procedure becomes about as difficult as that based on the valence-bond approach. If, instead, the second one is adopted, the treatment is no longer entirely theoretical, and it also becomes subject to several additional difficulties. Thus, the intensity of an absorption band is governed by certain so-called selection rules,[1] one of which stipulates that ,a transition between states of different multiplicity is "forbidden." Although this rule is not rigorously valid, it does however ensure that, since the ground state of ethylene is necessarily a singlet, the absorption due to the transition to the excited triplet state is so weak that its observation is difficult, or perhaps even impossible. Consequently, all the empirical data that are required for an application of this procedure may not be available. Even when the selection rules do not present an insurmountable obstacle, there is often considerable uncertainty regarding which one of the innumerable observed absorption bands is to be associated with each of the theoretically predicted electronic transitions. (This difficulty exists also when the alternative valence-bond approach is adopted. See also below.) We shall later, in fact, encounter several specific examples in which this uncertainty prevents satisfactory interpretations of the spectra. And finally, the calculated quantity E_1 is no longer exactly equal to the arithmetic mean of the singlet and triplet energies when the treatment is made more precise, and more complicated, by explicit consideration of configuration interaction in the ground and excited states.

In the foregoing discussion, the difficulty that is introduced by the uncertain magnitude of the singlet-triplet separation ΔE has possibly been somewhat exaggerated. Thus, it seems to be a fairly satisfactory rule of thumb[6] that, when the transition involves the excitation of an electron from a bonding pi orbital to an antibonding one, as in ethylene, ΔE is usually not very different from 20 kcal per mole. On the other hand, when the transition instead involves the excitation of an electron from a nonbonding sigma orbital to an antibonding pi orbital (e.g., the $N \rightarrow A$ bands discussed on pages 278ff), ΔE is likely to be negligibly small.[7] In either event, if the value of ΔE is estimated in the way described, the error in the calculated energy of the singlet-singlet transition will seldom be greater than about 5 kcal per mole. The magnitude of the resulting

[7] C. Reid, *J. Chem. Phys.* **21**, 1906 (1953).

error in the predicted wave length of absorption varies with the region of the spectrum concerned. If, for example, the calculated transition energy is 5 kcal per mole too high, the calculated wave length is about 70 A too small at 2000 A, about 260 A too small at 4000 A, and about 1000 A too small at 8000 A. Consequently, the uncertainties regarding the exact values of the singlet-triplet separations ΔE are probably not large in comparison with the other unavoidable inaccuracies in the treatment.

Let us now return to a discussion of the valence-bond method and, more specifically, let us consider the way in which this method avoids the first, but not all, of the above difficulties. As was pointed out in Section 1·4, there can be no resonance among structures with different numbers of unpaired electrons. Consequently, the hybrids which result from resonance must have definite numbers of unpaired electrons, and hence must have definite multiplicities. If, for example, we wish to obtain the energies of the various singlet states of the ethylene molecule, we consider resonance among only those structures in which, as in I, II, and III,

$$H_2C\!\!=\!\!CH_2 \qquad H_2C^+\!\!-\!\!CH_2^- \qquad H_2C^-\!\!-\!\!CH_2^+$$
$$\text{I} \qquad\qquad\qquad \text{II} \qquad\qquad\qquad \text{III}$$

there are no unpaired electrons; on the other hand, if we instead wish to obtain the energies of the various triplet states, we consider resonance among only those different structures in which, as in IV, there are exactly

$$H_2\overset{\textstyle\cdot}{C}\!\!-\!\!\overset{\textstyle\cdot}{C}H_2$$
$$\text{IV}$$

two unpaired electrons. Since the singlet and the triplet energies are therefore obtained from independent calculations, their respective values are not combined with each other, as they are when the molecular-orbital treatment is used. The advantage which the valence-bond treatment thus enjoys is not sufficient, however, to overcome the disadvantages that have already been described; for, if the ionic structures are ignored, the method becomes too inaccurate to be acceptable whereas, if these structures are not ignored, any quantitative calculations become extremely difficult. Moreover, in the valence-bond treatment, just as in the molecular-orbital treatment, the correlation between the observed absorption bands and the predicted electronic transitions is, as was noted above, often uncertain; and, unless resonance among an impracticably large number of both covalent and ionic structures is taken explicitly into account, the treatment is subject to the same sorts of errors that, in the molecular-orbital treatment, arise from the neglect of configuration interaction.

The situation which has been discussed above with special reference to ethylene is similar to that encountered with all other molecules. In valence-bond language, the ground state can usually be described with sufficient accuracy by means of a single structure or, at worst, as a hybrid of a small number of purely covalent structures; but the electronically excited states can usually be described with comparable accuracy only in terms of resonance among a larger number of both covalent and ionic structures. In molecular-orbital language, the ground state is usually derived from a configuration in which each orbital is occupied by either zero or two electrons, so that all electrons are necessarily paired; but the excited states are instead often derived from configurations in which two orbitals are singly occupied, so that there may be either zero or two unpaired electrons. Whichever method of treatment is adopted, therefore, the calculations of the energies, frequencies, and wave lengths that are associated with electronic transitions is extremely difficult. Indeed, it is so difficult that, except for molecules which are considerably simpler than that of ethylene, it has never been attempted without the introduction of numerous drastic simplifying assumptions; and even then the computations are so tedious and so complex that they cannot readily be described in the same sort of qualitative language that has been employed in the preceding chapters for the interpretation of the properties of molecules in their ground states (however, see Section 6·10). For this reason, we shall here make no attempt to develop anything approaching a comprehensive theory of molecular electronic spectra. Instead, we shall restrict ourselves to the much more modest goal of trying to explain certain regularities which have been observed with groups of closely related substances, and which can be fairly satisfactorily discussed with the aid of only the simple resonance concept. Our reason for thus adopting the valence-bond rather than the molecular-orbital viewpoint is that, although the molecular-orbital treatment is usually more convenient for the purposes of numerical calculation than is its valence-bond analog (see above), it is always farther removed from ordinary chemical experience and, in particular, it can seldom be used at all in the absence of a practical method for estimating the magnitude of the singlet-triplet separation ΔE. Consequently, in most instances, the valence-bond treatment seems more suitable for a qualitative discussion that is designed primarily for chemists.

The resonance and molecular-orbital viewpoints, in exactly the forms outlined above, are not convenient for the interpretation of spectra that occur at wave lengths less than about 1500 A. Since light quanta in this region of the far ultraviolet correspond to energies greater than about 185 kcal per mole, their absorption can result in the rupture of covalent bonds, or in the partial or complete removal of electrons. Often, the absorption spectra here consist of one or more series of so-called *Rydberg bands*, which are explained in the following way. If one electron in a complex molecule is excited to an orbital of sufficiently high energy, then that electron may on the average spend most of its time at a considerable distance from the positive ion formed by the remainder of the molecule. Under such circumstances, the electrostatic interaction between the electron and the residual polyatomic ion may be rather similar to that between an electron and a simple monatomic ion. Consequently, in the region in which the Rydberg series occur, the spectrum of the molecule resembles that of a single atom which has just one electron outside the positively charged kernel. The most significant difference is then that each line of the atomic spectrum is replaced by a complex group of lines, or band, in the molecular spectrum. The reason for this difference is that the polyatomic ion, unlike a monatomic one, has many different vibrational and rotational levels (cf. Figure 6·1, Section 6·1). Now, as is well known, in an atomic spectrum there occur series of lines which have progressively shorter wave lengths, and which are therefore presumed to be due to the jumping of electrons from the orbital that they occupy in the ground state to progressively less stable excited orbitals. In any such series, the lines fall closer together as the wave length decreases, and they finally converge at a limiting wave length that corresponds to the energy required for the complete removal of an electron or, in other words, for the ionization of the atom. Similarly, the bands of a Rydberg series in the spectrum of a polyatomic molecule occur at progressively shorter wave lengths as the electrons jump from the orbital that they occupy in the ground state to the progressively less stable orbitals of the type described above. As with the analogous lines in an atomic spectrum, these bands fall closer together as the wave length decreases, and they finally converge at a limiting wave length that corresponds to the energy required for the ionization of the molecule.

6·3 Spectra of Hydrocarbons. It is found empirically that a hydrocarbon with conjugated double bonds absorbs light of longer wave length than does an analogous compound with only one or more isolated double bonds. Thus, whereas ethylene does not absorb light of wave length greater than about 1900–2000 A, butadiene absorbs at about 2100 A. As the number of double bonds in the conjugated system increases, the absorption comes to progressively greater wave lengths, so that 2,4,6,8,10,12-tetradecahexaene, for example, absorbs in the visible and is, therefore, colored.

The above facts are readily understood when the types of resonance in the various molecules are considered. For ethylene, as we have seen, we can discuss both the ground state and the most stable of the excited ones on the basis of resonance among the structures I, II, and III. Similarly,

$$H_2C{=}CH_2 \qquad\qquad H_2C^+{-}\overset{..}{C}^-H_2 \qquad\qquad H_2\overset{..}{C}^-{-}C^+H_2$$
$$\text{I} \qquad\qquad\qquad\qquad \text{II} \qquad\qquad\qquad\qquad \text{III}$$

for 1,4-pentadiene, which has a pair of isolated double bonds, we can discuss the corresponding states on the basis of resonance among altogether nine structures, IV–XII, since, for each double bond separately, we can

$$H_2C{=}CH{-}CH_2{-}CH{=}CH_2 \qquad H_2C{=}CH{-}CH_2{-}C^+H{-}\overset{..}{C}^-H_2$$
$$\text{IV} \qquad\qquad\qquad\qquad\qquad \text{V}$$

$$H_2C{=}CH{-}CH_2{-}\overset{..}{C}^-H{-}C^+H_2 \qquad H_2C^+{-}\overset{..}{C}^-H{-}CH_2{-}CH{=}CH_2$$
$$\text{VI} \qquad\qquad\qquad\qquad\qquad \text{VII}$$

$$H_2C^+ \text{—} \ddot{C}^- H \text{—} CH_2 \text{—} C^+ H \text{—} \ddot{C}^- H_2 \qquad H_2C^+ \text{—} \ddot{C}^- H \text{—} CH_2 \text{—} \ddot{C}^- H \text{—} C^+ H_2$$

VIII   IX

$$H_2\ddot{C}^- \text{—} C^+ H \text{—} CH_2 \text{—} CH = CH_2 \quad H_2\ddot{C}^- \text{—} C^+ H \text{—} CH_2 \text{—} C^+ H \text{—} \ddot{C}^- H_2$$

X   XI

$$H_2\ddot{C}^- \text{—} C^+ H \text{—} CH_2 \text{—} \ddot{C}^- H \text{—} C^+ H_2$$

XII

write the three structures that are analogous to I, II, and III. As a result, however, of the "insulating" effect of the central methylene group, the two double bonds are nearly as independent as if they were in different molecules. Consequently, we may expect that the near-ultraviolet absorption of this diolefin will occur at about the same wave length as that of the most closely similar monoölefin, 1-pentene, and that the two spectra will have about the same intensity *per double bond*. These expectations are confirmed by the observed spectra of the substances.[8]

With 1,3-butadiene, on the other hand, the conjugation makes it possible for us to write not only the nine structures that are the analogs of IV–XII, but also the three additional structures XIII, XIV, and XV,

$$H_2C \text{—} CH = CH \text{—} CH_2 \qquad H_2C^+ \text{—} CH = CH \text{—} \ddot{C}^- H_2$$

XIII   XIV

$$H_2\ddot{C}^- \text{—} CH = CH \text{—} C^+ H_2$$

XV

which have no close analogs in the unconjugated system. Since the double bonds are therefore less independent of each other in 1,3-butadiene than in 1,4-pentadiene, we may anticipate that the spectra of the two substances will be rather different. Furthermore, by a more careful consideration of the respective possibilities for resonance, we can with some confidence predict the way in which the spectra will differ. Thus, with 1,3-butadiene, the effect of the additional structures XIII–XV must be to lower both the energy of the ground state and that of the lowest excited state. The magnitude of this stabilization in the ground state is given by the familiar resonance energy of the substance (however, see the following paragraph in fine print), and hence is equal to about 3.5 kcal per mole (cf. Table 3·2, Section 3·2). The fact that the stabilization is therefore rather small is entirely consistent with the view that, since the

[8] L. Bateman and H. P. Koch, *J. Chem. Soc.* **1944**, 600.

structures XIII–XV, like the eight others analogous to V–XII, are relatively unstable, the actual state of the normal butadiene molecule is essentially the one represented by the conventional structure XVI, the analog of IV.

$$H_2C\!\!=\!\!CH\!\!-\!\!CH\!\!=\!\!CH_2$$
XVI

On the other hand, the stabilization of the excited state should be appreciably greater than that of the ground state since, in comparison with the high energy of the former state, the structures XIII–XV are not extremely unstable. Consequently, these latter structures should here make significant, and perhaps even predominant, contributions so that the resonance energy is fairly large, and the true state of the excited molecule cannot be satisfactorily described by any individual structure. If, then, we conclude that the energy of the excited state is lowered by the conjugation more than is that of the ground state, we can further conclude that the excitation energy must be decreased by the conjugation, and hence that the absorption must be displaced toward longer wave lengths, as is observed.

Since the atomic nuclei are much heavier, and hence much less mobile, than the electrons, there can be no great change in the positions of the nuclei during an electronic transition. As a consequence of this so-called *Franck-Condon principle*,[9] it is evident that, in the preceding paragraph, we should have based our discussion on the vertical, rather than on the empirical, resonance energies (cf. Section 3·7). The difference between these two quantities is, of course, so great that it cannot legitimately be neglected in any quantitative calculation. We are doubtless justified, however, in ignoring it in the present purely qualitative discussion, since we have used only the assumption that the resonance energy of the excited state is greater than that of the ground state, and since this assumption must surely be as valid for the vertical as for the empirical resonance energies.

Still another feature of the spectra of the unconjugated 1,4-pentadiene and of the conjugated 1,3-butadiene can be interpreted from the above simple and only qualitative viewpoint. With the first of these two substances, there are two excited states with nearly the same energy, i.e., one state for each double bond; and the observed intensity is the sum of the intensities for the two almost completely independent transitions. With the second substance, however, the absorption at 2100 A is presumably due to a transition to only a single electronically excited state; consequently, we might perhaps expect the intensity to be only about half as great as with 1,4-pentadiene. Experimentally, however, the values both of ε_{max} and of the integrated intensity appear to be approximately equal

⁹ J. Franck, *Trans. Faraday Soc.* **21**, 536 (1926); E. U. Condon, *Phys. Rev.* **28**, 1182 (1926); **32**, 858 (1928).

for the two hydrocarbons; and this relation has been found generally valid in other comparisons of analogous conjugated and unconjugated dienes. The explanation for this somewhat unexpected observation can be found in the exceptionally large dipole moments that are associated with structures XIV and XV. Although the complete equivalence of these two structures insures that their effects upon the net dipole moment of the molecule must exactly cancel each other in both the ground and excited states, it can be shown[10] that the large moments of the individual structures or, more precisely, the large *differences* between the corresponding average distributions of charge must lead to intense absorption of light. The fact that the absorption due to the one electronic transition in 1,3-butadiene is considerably more than half as intense as is that due to the two transitions in 1,4-pentadiene can therefore be explained on the ground that the dipole moments of the structures XIV and XV are larger than are those of the corresponding structures V–XII.

Attention may here be called to a common alternative description of an electronic transition. This description is often convenient in that it provides a simple picture of what is taking place but, since it is not strictly correct, it has given rise to much confusion and misunderstanding. If resonance were a form of tautomerism, a molecule of butadiene would be oscillating back and forth among the several contributing structures. Since, in most of these structures, there are formal positive and negative charges, the constant transitions among the structures would then lead to a periodic oscillation of electric charge. Now, according to classical electromagnetic theory, such an oscillation of charge would result in the absorption (or emission) of light. Consequently, we can in this way "explain" the ultraviolet spectrum of the substance. Since the amplitude of the assumed oscillations would be greater in a conjugated olefin than in an unconjugated one, the frequency might well be lower, and the intensity should certainly be greater, in the former substance than in the latter. The present description therefore accounts for all the qualitative features of the spectra as satisfactorily as does the quite different one given above. Clearly, however, the pictures which are thus provided for the respective electronic transitions have little resemblance to the ones which are derived from quantum-mechanical considerations, and which were discussed in Section 6·2. In particular, the supposition that the actually existing molecule of a resonance hybrid, in any specified spectroscopic state, is constantly changing from one purely imaginary contributing structure to another is unacceptable, as is also the further supposition that the ground and excited states of each molecule differ primarily in the amplitudes with which the electric charges oscillate.

With 1,3,5-hexatriene, the number of less stable structures which have formal charges, formal bonds, or both, and which contribute to the ground and excited states, is much greater than with 1,3-butadiene. By an extension of the argument that was used above, we can therefore conclude that the absorption by this triene should occur at longer wave lengths,

---

[10] See, for example, R. S. Mulliken, *J. Chem. Phys.* **7**, 121, 364, 570 (1939); L. Pauling, *Proc. Natl. Acad. Sci. U. S.* **25**, 577 (1939).

and should be more intense (per electronic transition), than that by the diene. Thus, on account of the increased number of structures which individually have high energies, we can anticipate that the difference between the resonance energies of the excited and ground states should be greater here than with the shorter conjugated system; in addition, the dipole moments of the extreme structures XVII and XVIII are doubtless

$$H_2C^+\!\!-\!CH\!\!=\!\!CH\!\!-\!CH\!\!=\!\!CH\!\!-\!\overset{..}{C}{}^-H_2$$
XVII

$$H_2\overset{..}{C}{}^-\!\!-\!CH\!\!=\!\!CH\!\!-\!CH\!\!=\!\!CH\!\!-\!C^+H_2$$
XVIII

greater than even those of XIV and XV. For a similar reason, the trend should continue with 1,3,5,7-octatetraene, 1,3,5,7,9-decapentaene, and so on. The extent to which these inferences are confirmed by experiment can be seen from Table 6·1, in which are listed the observed values, λ_{max},

TABLE 6·1

THE EFFECT OF CONJUGATION ON THE SPECTRA OF OLEFINS[a]

n^b	λ_{max} (angstroms)	ε_{max}	Compound	Solvent[c]
1	1625[d]	15,000	Ethylene	V
2	2170	21,000	1,3-Butadiene	H
3	2650	53,000	2,4,6-Octatrien-1-ol	A
4	2990[e] 3110[e]	64,000	2,4,6,8-Decatetraen-1-ol	A
5	3280	51,000	Vitamin A	A
6	3600	70,000	2,4,6,8,10,12-Tetradecahexaene	C
8	4200	36,000	"Dihydro-β-carotene"	H
9	4700[f]	160,000[f]	5,6-Dihydro-α-carotene	H
10	4450[f]	145,000[f]	α-Carotene	H
11	4500[f]	140,000[f]	β-Carotene	H
15	5090[g]	128,500[g]	Decapreno-β-carotene	CH

[a] Except as noted, the data in this table are taken from E. A. Braude, *Ann. Repts. on Progr. Chem.* (*Chem. Soc. London*) **42**, 105 (1945); *J. Chem. Soc.* **1950**, 379.

[b] The quantity n is here the number of double bonds in the conjugated system.

[c] V = vapor phase; H = hexane; A = ethyl alcohol; C = chloroform; CH = cyclohexane.

[d] J. R. Platt, H. B. Klevens, and W. C. Price, *J. Chem. Phys.* **17**, 466 (1949).

[e] See also G. F. Woods and L. H. Schwartzmann, *J. Am. Chem. Soc.* **71**, 1396 (1949).

[f] L. Zechmeister and A. Polgár, *J. Am. Chem. Soc.* **65**, 1522 (1943).

[g] P. Karrer and C. H. Eugster, *Helv. Chim. Acta* **34**, 28 (1951).

of the wave lengths at which the absorptions by the stated compounds are most intense, and the observed values, ε_{max}, of the molecular extinction coefficients at these wave lengths. Since the required data are not at present available for several of the unsubstituted polyenes, the values of λ_{max} and of ε_{max} are in some instances given for related substances with saturated substituents. Although the presence of these latter groups may be expected to have measurable effects upon the spectra (cf. pages 275ff), the several compounds that are here considered may be presumed not to differ too much to be directly comparable with one another. (However, see below.)

From the data listed in Table 6·1, it can be seen that, as expected, the wave length at which the absorption is most intense becomes progressively greater when the length of the conjugated system is increased. The single exception of 5,6-dihydro-α-carotene is probably not significant since, in the absorption band of this substance, there is at 4400 A an additional maximum that is only slightly less intense than the one at 4700 A. Presumably, therefore, we have incorrectly interpreted the spectrum, and the weaker maximum at the shorter wave length is really the one which is comparable with the maxima cited for the other unsaturated compounds.

Although the values of λ_{max} vary in essentially the way anticipated, those of ε_{max} are more difficult to understand. Instead of continuing to increase with the length of the conjugated system, the intensity of the absorption becomes erratic when the number of double bonds is greater than about four, and often it changes in the direction opposite to the one expected. There are probably several different causes for these discrepancies. In the first place, since the data of Table 6·1 make no allowance for the variations in the number and type of saturated substituents, and since they refer to solutions in several different solvents, they are not strictly comparable with each other. Moreover, as was pointed out on pages 248f, we should have used the integrated intensity Q instead of ε_{max} as the measure of the intensity of the absorption. It hardly seems likely that, by correcting any one or all of these deficiencies in the data, we could bring the observed intensities into satisfactory agreement with the ones expected. There is, however, still another factor which affects the intensity of an absorption band, but which we have not yet explicitly considered. The magnitudes of the dipole moments that are associated with the extreme ionic structures like XIV, XV, XVII, XVIII, etc., must depend not only on the number of carbon atoms lying between the ones with the formal charges, but also on the stereochemical configurations of the molecules. The largest dipoles, and hence the most intense absorptions can be expected to result when the configurations are *trans* about each double bond and *s-trans* (see page 227) about each single bond.

With lycopene, XIX, for example, the value of ε_{max} is more than twice as great when all double bonds are *trans* as it is when all of them are

$$\left[(CH_3)_2C{=}CH{-}CH_2{-}CH_2{-} \left(\begin{array}{c} {-}C{=}CH{-}CH{=}CH{-} \\ | \\ CH_3 \end{array} \right)_2 \begin{array}{c} {-}C{=}CH{-}CH{=} \\ | \\ CH_3 \end{array} \right]_2$$

XIX

instead *cis*;[11] and similar variations have been observed with numerous other similar substances. Since we cannot be sure that, with respect to their configurations, all the substances listed in Table 6·1 are strictly comparable with one another, we cannot be surprised that the intensity of the absorption varies somewhat irregularly with the number of conjugated double bonds. It should, however, be mentioned that the anomalously low value of ε_{max} for vitamin A cannot be explained in this way since the substance has the all-*trans* configuration.[12]

With benzene, as far as the ground state of the molecule is concerned, the most important resonance is doubtless that between the two Kekulé structures. When we consider also the spectroscopically excited states, however, we can no longer, even as a first approximation, ignore either the three Dewar structures or the numerous ionic analogs of the Kekulé and Dewar structures. With the aid of only qualitative arguments of the kind that were used above with the acyclic polyenes, we cannot predict how the wave length in the near-ultraviolet spectrum will compare with that of, say, 1,3,5-hexatriene. The fact that both these substances absorb in the region near 2600 A is, however, not unreasonable. On the other hand, we can fairly confidently predict that the band with the longest wave length will be less intense with benzene than with 1,3,5-hexatriene, since the dipole moments that are associated with the respective ionic structures must be smaller with the former compound than with the latter one. Moreover, if, as seems rather likely, the excited state that is here involved with benzene is the one that can be described approximately as the less stable of the two hybrids resulting from resonance between just the two covalent Kekulé structures, then the various ionic structures must play only small roles, and so again we can conclude that the absorption must be weak. And finally, by a more detailed treatment which cannot be described in nonmathematical terms, and which we shall therefore not attempt here to explain, one can show that the selection rules (see page 253) "forbid" the transition between the two states that arise from the Kekulé structures.[13] In any event, the maximum value of the molecular extinction

---

[11] See L. Zechmeister, *Chem. Revs.* **34**, 267 (1944). Cf. also J. H. Pinckard, B. Wille, and L. Zechmeister, *J. Am. Chem. Soc.* **70**, 1938 (1948).

[12] H. R. Cama, F. D. Collins, and R. A. Morton, *Biochem. J.* **50**, 48 (1952).

[13] A. L. Sklar, *J. Chem. Phys.* **5**, 669 (1937).

coefficient for the first ultraviolet absorption band of benzene is only about $1/250$ times as great as is that of 1,3,5-hexatriene (cf. Tables 6·1 and 6·2).

From the molecular-orbital viewpoint, the spectrum of benzene presents a more than usually complicated problem. The two least stable orbitals that are occupied in the normal molecule correspond separately to the same energy (cf. page 69); consequently, the electron that "jumps" may come from either one of them. Furthermore, the two most stable orbitals that are *not* occupied in the normal molecule similarly correspond to the same energy; consequently, the electron that "jumps" may end up in either one of these. There are, therefore, 2×2, or 4, possible electronic transitions and, since each of them can lead to either a singlet or triplet excited state (see page 252,) there are altogether 2×4, or 8, different excited states. To the usual first approximation (see page 252), these 8 states have the same energy but, when proper allowance is made for the mutual repulsions of the electrons, they are instead found to have rather different energies. The problem of deciding which excited state is the most stable one, and of determining its energy cannot be solved by the present qualitative method of treatment. (For a discussion of the similar problem that arises when the spectrum of benzene is treated from the "free-electron" viewpoint, see page 681.)

The conjugation of benzene rings either with other benzene rings or with ethylenic double bonds may be expected to displace the absorption toward longer wave lengths, and also to increase the intensity of the absorption. This expectation is not, however, confirmed in all details. Although the ultraviolet band with the longest wave length is indeed much more intense with biphenyl ($\varepsilon_{max} \cong 18,000$) than it is with benzene ($\varepsilon_{max} \cong 200$), the predicted change in the value of λ_{max} is here not observed. Both substances absorb in the same region of the spectrum and, to the extent that the small reported difference is trustworthy, λ_{max} is actually a little smaller for biphenyl (2515 A) than for benzene (2550 A). The reason for this failure of the theory is not completely understood, but it is possibly in some way related to the complexities which arise in the spectrum of benzene because of the especially high symmetry of the molecule, and which were briefly described in the preceding paragraph in fine print. One can, in fact, argue that, on account of these complexities, the spectrum of benzene cannot legitimately be compared with that of any less symmetrical derivative like biphenyl. A second possible explanation is that the strong absorption by biphenyl at 2515 A is not the analog of the weak absorption by benzene at 2550 A, but that it is instead more directly related to the strong absorption by benzene at about 2000 A. From this viewpoint, the conjugation of the two rings does after all lead to an appreciable increase in the wave length. On this basis, then, one may further postulate that the weak band at 2550 A in benzene is shifted in biphenyl toward longer wave lengths, but that it is not observed because it is obscured by the much more intense, and quite diffuse, band just discussed. Some evidence for this supposition is provided by the fact that fluorene XX, which differs from biphenyl only in the presence of a

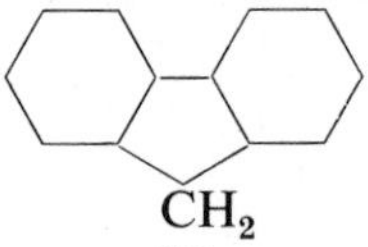

CH_2

XX

saturated o,o'-methylene bridge, shows a secondary peak of rather high intensity at about 3000 A.[14] In any event, there can be no doubt that the conjugation of the two rings in biphenyl has a large and characteristic effect upon the observed spectrum of the substance (cf. also pages 317f).

When three or more benzene rings are directly joined to one another, as in terphenyl, quaterphenyl, etc., the resulting conjugated systems are more extensive than that in biphenyl. Consequently, the ultraviolet absorption spectra can be expected to occur at longer wave lengths and to be more intense. Two rather different situations, however, can arise since the union of the several rings may be either para or meta. (The further possibility of an ortho union may here be ignored inasmuch as the resulting molecules could not then be planar. Cf. Section 6·8.) In p-terphenyl, for example, even the terminal rings can effectively interact with each other since structure XXI, its ionic counterparts XXII and

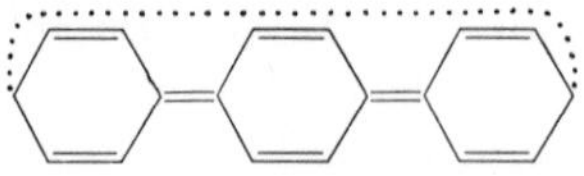

XXI

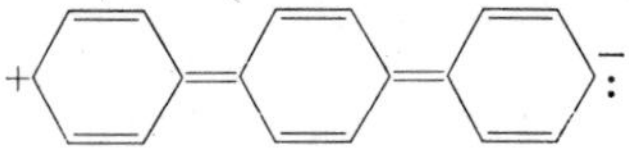

XXII

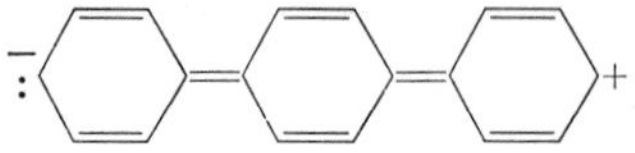

XXIII

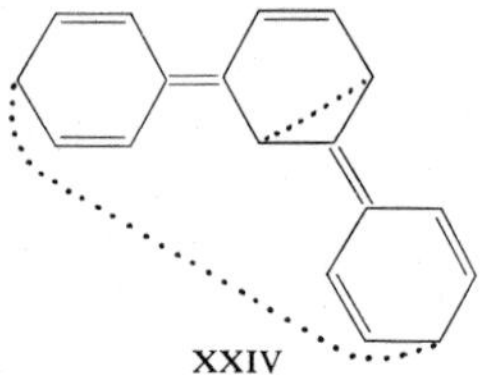

XXIV

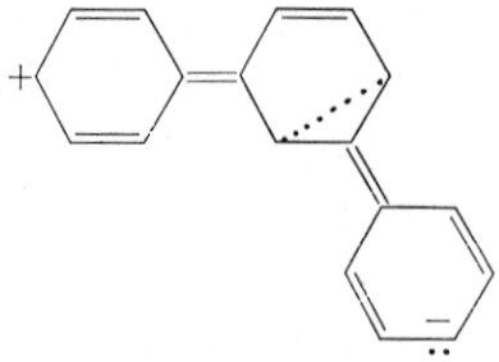

XXV

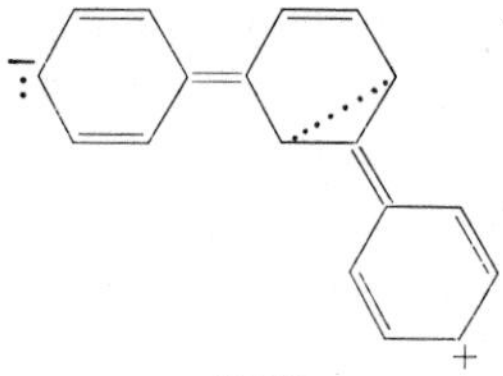

XXVI

[14] See, for example, R. N. Jones, *J. Am. Chem. Soc.* **67**, 2021 (1945). For additional evidence regarding biphenyl itself, see also A. Wenzel, *J. Chem. Phys.* **21**, 403 (1953).

XXIII, and the numerous additional ones that are analogous to these three may be presumed to have significant weights. With *m*-terphenyl, on the other hand, the terminal rings are more effectively insulated from each other, since the structures XXIV, XXV, XXVI, etc., which most closely correspond to XXI, XXII, XXIII, etc., have decreased numbers of effective bonds between adjacent atoms, and so must be relatively unstable.

The observed spectra of the *p*- and *m*-polyphenyls (see Table 6·2) are in fairly satisfactory, although perhaps not complete, agreement with

TABLE 6·2

SPECTRA OF POLYPHENYLS $H-(C_6H_4)_n-H^a$

n	Para Series		Meta Series	
	λ_{max}	ε_{max}	λ_{max}	ε_{max}
	(angstroms)		(angstroms)	
1[b]	2550	213	2550	213
2	2515	18,300	2515	18,300
3	2800	25,000	2515	44,000
4	3000	39,000	—	—
5	3100	62,500	—,	—
6	3175	> 56,000	—	—
9	—	—	2530	184,000
10	—	—	2530	213,000
11	—	—	2530	215,000
12	—	—	2530	233,000
13	—	—	2530	252,000
14	—	—	2530	283,000
15	—	—	2540	309,000
16	—	—	2550	320,000[c]

  [a] The data in this table are taken from A. E. Gillam and D. H. Hey, *J. Chem. Soc.* **1939**, 1170.   Except as noted, the solvent was chloroform.
  [b] The data for benzene refer to solution in absolute ethyl alcohol.
  [c] This figure is uncertain on account of the low solubility of the substance.

what might have been expected on the basis of these considerations. With the *p*-polyphenyls, the wave length λ_{max} of the most intense absorption increases more or less regularly with the number of benzene rings but, with the *m*-polyphenyls, λ_{max} has the nearly constant value of 2530 ± 20 A.   In the former series of compounds, as in the acyclic conjugated polyenes, the effective length of the conjugated system increases with the size of the molecule; in the latter series, as in hydrocarbons with only isolated double bonds, the effective length of the conjugated system is essentially independent of the size of the molecule.   Consequently, both the shift toward longer wave lengths in the *p*-polyphenyls and the

nonexistence of such a shift in the *m*-polyphenyls could have been predicted.   The fact that the values of λ_{max} are smaller for the *p*-polyphenyls
than for comparable acyclic polyenes, and that they converge more
rapidly toward a limiting value, is also not unreasonable.   With the
aromatic compounds, the conjugation of the benzene rings with one
another is due to the weights of such structures as XXI–XXIII in both
the ground and excited states; since the resonance with these structures
must to some extent interfere with the much more important resonance
within each of the individual rings, it cannot be as effective as is that in
an aliphatic polyene in which there is no comparable interference.   In
other words, the conjugation of phenyl groups with one another causes a
smaller change in the properties of the substance than does that of
ethylenic double bonds because, in the former system, it can only slightly
modify the resonance (which is already considerable) whereas, in the
latter, it is responsible for all the important resonance that there is.

Although the difference between the wave lengths at which the various
polyphenyls absorb can therefore be readily understood, the reason why
the intensities increase more rapidly in the meta series than in the more
effectively conjugated para series is not entirely clear.   The values of
ε_{max} (Table 6·2) found for the *m*-polyphenyls are, themselves, rather
reasonable since they are approximately proportional to $n - 1$, where n
is the number of benzene rings, so that $n - 1$ is the number of different,
but partially overlapping, biphenyl groupings.   On account of the essential isolation of each ring from all those others to which it is not directly
linked, the spectrum might in fact be expected to differ only slightly
from that of an equivalent number of independent biphenyl molecules.
The relatively small values of ε_{max} that are found for the *p*-polyphenyls
are, however, more difficult to understand.   Since the spectra of these
compounds have not yet been completely analyzed, we can here state only
a few possibilities that might be considered in any attempted explanation.
In the first place, we may note that the molecules of the *p*-polyphenyls
have higher symmetries than their analogs in the meta series.   For this
reason, there may be selection rules which decrease the probabilities of,
or even "forbid," certain electronic transitions (see pages 262f for mention
of the corresponding situation which arises with the still more symmetrical
benzene).   Moreover, if the light of longest wave length which is absorbed
by a *p*-polyphenyl should be found to be polarized so that its electric
vector is perpendicular to the long axis of the molecule, then the intensity
of the absorption would be determined not by the large magnitudes of
the total dipole moments of the structures like XXII, XXIII, XXVII,
XXVIII, etc., but rather by the much smaller components of these
moments in the direction of the electric vector.   Whether either of these

possibilities is partially or wholly valid, or whether other explanations must still be sought, cannot at present be determined. (See also the comparison of 1,3-butadiene and 1,4-pentadiene, on pages 256ff.)

XXVII   XXVIII

In Table 6·3 are listed data for some of the α,ω-diphenylpolyenes, C_6H_5—$(—CH{=}CH—)_n$—C_6H_5 (of which biphenyl can be considered the

TABLE 6·3

SPECTRA OF α,ω-DIPHENYLPOLYENES C_6H_5—$(—CH{=}CH—)_n$—$C_6H_5{}^a$

n	λ_{max} (angstroms)	ε_{max}
0^b	2515	18,300
1	3060	24,000
2	3340	40,000
3	3580	75,000
4	3840	86,000
5	4030	94,000
6	4200	113,000
7	4350	135,000

[a] Except as noted, the data in this table are taken from K. W. Hausser, W. Kuhn, and A. Smakula, *Z. physik. Chem. B* **29**, 384 (1935), and apply to solution in benzene.

[b] The data for biphenyl are taken from A. E. Gillam and D. H. Hey, *J. Chem. Soc.* **1939**, 1170, and refer to solution in chloroform. Cf. Table 6·2.

first member, with $n = 0$). As with the simple polyenes (cf. Table 6·1), so also with these more complex substances, the absorption shifts toward longer wave lengths and becomes more intense as the length of the conjugated system increases. From a comparison of the values of λ_{max} in Tables 6·1 and 6·3, it is seen that, with respect to the wave length of the most intense absorption, each phenyl group of an α,ω-diphenylpolyene is the equivalent of about $1^1/_2$ double bonds. The continuous and rather rapid increase in the value of ε_{max} suggests that the molecules have predominantly the *trans* configuration[11] (cf. pages 261f), and that the electric vectors of the absorbed light lie in directions that are more or less parallel to the long axes of the respective molecules (cf. the preceding paragraph).

The fusion of benzene rings with one another, as in naphthalene, anthracene, phenanthrene, etc., also usually results in a shift of the ultraviolet absorption toward longer wave lengths. As can be seen from the data listed in Table 6·4, the effect is greater when the molecule is

TABLE 6·4

SPECTRA OF AROMATIC HYDROCARBONS WITH FUSED RING SYSTEMS[a]

Substance	Band[b]					
	L_b		L_a		B_b	
	λ_{max} (ang- (stroms)	ε_{max}	λ_{max} (ang- (stroms)	ε_{max}	λ_{max} (ang- (stroms)	ε_{max}
Benzene	2630[c, d]	220	2080[c]	6,900	1835	4,600
Naphthalene	3125[c]	280	2890[c]	9,300	2200	133,000
Anthracene	—	—	3790[c]	9,000	2560	180,000
Phenanthrene	3535[c]	350	3000[c]	16,000	2540	65,500
Naphthacene	—	—	4740[c]	12,500	2725	180,000
Benz[a]anthracene	3875[c]	1000	3665[c]	8,500	2875	113,000
Benzo[c]phenanthrene	3745[c]	400	3300[c]	12,000	2810	85,000
Chrysene	3635[c]	650	3310[c]	16,000	2690	150,000
Triphenylene	3425[c]	900	3000[c]	20,000	2570	150,000
Pentacene	4170	600	5850[c]	12,000	3095	300,000

[a] The data in this table are taken from H. B. Klevens and J. R. Platt, *J. Chem. Phys.* **17**, 470 (1949), and refer (in most instances) to solutions in *n*-heptane. The wave lengths are rounded off to the nearest 5 A.

[b] The different bands are here designated in the way specified by Klevens and Platt (note *a*). With a few exceptions (pentacene and perhaps also naphthacene and anthracene, for which data are lacking), the order of decreasing wave length is L_b, L_a, B_b.

[c] The value given here is the wave length corresponding to the "onset of absorption."   Ordinarily, λ_{max} may be expected to be about 100–200 A less.

[d] This is the band for which λ_{max} is given as 2550 A in Table 6·2.

linear than when it is angular. Although no simple qualitative explanation for this latter regularity is apparent, more detailed numerical calculations (see Section 6·10) have been in fair agreement with the observations. With most of these hydrocarbons, as with benzene, the absorption at the longest wave length has a very low intensity and so presumably corresponds to a "forbidden" transition. At shorter wave lengths, however, the absorption usually becomes extremely intense. As is evident from the table, the spectrum of each hydrocarbon is greatly complicated by the occurrence of overlapping bands which have different values of λ_{max} and ε_{max}, and which are doubtless due to different electronic transitions.   In accordance with a classification proposed by Klevens and Platt,[15] on the basis of an older and more empirical classification of Clar,[15] the several

[15] H. B. Klevens and J. R. Platt, *J. Chem. Phys.* **17**, 470 (1949).   See also E. J. Clar, *Aromatische Kohlenwasserstoffe*, Springer, Berlin, 1941, and references to earlier papers, given there.

bands which are listed in any one column of Table 6·4 may be correlated with each other in the sense that, although they refer to different substances, they arise from electronic transitions which are as closely analogous as possible. Consequently, in assessing the effect of the structural modifications on the wave length and intensity of absorption, we should compare only the entries within individual columns. In view of the complexity of the spectra, we shall not here attempt to describe the various excited states in detail. We may, however, note that each of these states, like the corresponding ground states, must be a hybrid of numerous structures, of which XXIX, XXX, and XXXI can serve as typical examples.

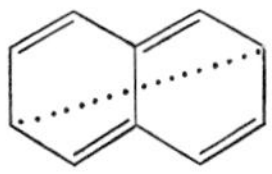

XXIX 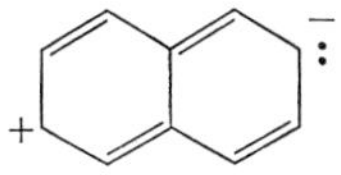   XXX

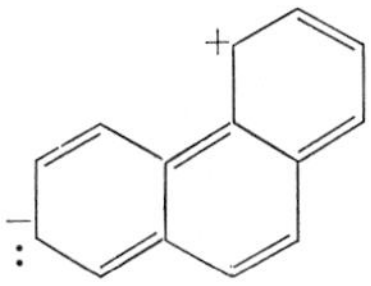

XXXI

The conjugation of *triple* bonds with each other, with double bonds, or with benzene rings has, as might be expected, a characteristic effect upon the ultraviolet absorption spectrum. At wave lengths greater than 2000 A, acetylene itself has only an extremely weak absorption of uncertain origin.[16] Between 1500 and 2000 A, there is a somewhat stronger, but still weak, band with a λ_{max} of about 1725 A. A reasonable assumption is that this band is the analog of the stronger one shown by ethylene at 1625 A (see Table 6·1 on page 260), and hence that it can be discussed in terms of resonance among the structures XXXII, XXXIII, and XXXIV

$$H—C\equiv C—H \qquad H—\overset{..}{C}{}^+=C^-—H \qquad H—\overset{..}{C}{}^-=C^+—H$$
XXXII   XXXIII   XXXIV

(however, see the following paragraph). At still shorter wave lengths, there occurs a very intense absorption which consists at least partially but, as is pointed out below, probably not entirely of Rydberg bands.

In order to account satisfactorily[6] for all the features of the spectra of acetylene and its derivatives, we must explicitly recognize that each of

[16] For a summary of the spectrum of acetylene, and for references to the original literature, see J. R. Platt, H. B. Klevens, and W. C. Price, *J. Chem. Phys.* 17, 466 (1949); C. K. Ingold and G. W. King, *J. Chem. Soc.* 1953, 2702, 2704, 2708, 2725, 2745.

the diagrams XXXIII and XXXIV corresponds to two distinct but equivalent structures (cf. pages 111f), whereas each of the analogous diagrams II and III for ethylene corresponds to only a single structure.

$$H_2C^+\!\!-\!\ddot{C}^-H_2 \qquad\qquad H_2\ddot{C}^-\!\!-\!C^+H_2$$
$$\text{II} \qquad\qquad\qquad\qquad \text{III}$$

Consequently, we can anticipate that the excited state responsible, in ethylene, for the absorption at 1625 A will be replaced, in acetylene, by *two* excited states. Since these latter states can be described as the two hybrids that result from resonance between two equivalent charge distributions which are individually similar to that in the excited state of ethylene, we can further anticipate that one of the excited states of acetylene must be relatively more stable, and the other must be relatively less stable, than the analogous state of ethylene (cf. pages 27f and 285). Hence it follows that, of the two resulting absorption bands, one must occur at longer wave lengths, and the other must occur at shorter wave lengths, than the single corresponding band of ethylene. This prediction is entirely consistent with the observations. The band with the longer wave lengths can be identified with the weak absorption at 1725 A (see above), and the one with the shorter wave length can be considered responsible for part of the strong absorption below about 1500 A. The positions of the bands are therefore as expected. And, although the theoretical basis for this further conclusion cannot here be described, the relation between the observed intensities is also as expected.[6]

The values of λ_{max} and ε_{max} that have been observed for a series of conjugated polyynes are given in Table 6·5. It will be seen that there are two quite different series of bands; one has relatively long wave lengths and very low intensities, whereas the other has shorter wave lengths and extremely high intensities. Both series come to longer wave lengths as the length of the conjugated system is increased. The bands that belong to the first of these groups are doubtless the analogs of the weak absorption by acetylene itself at 1725 A, whereas those that belong to the second group are the analogs of the stronger absorption by acetylene at wave lengths less than about 1500 A.[6] In either event, the excited states can be described as resonance hybrids of such structures as XXXV–XXXVIII, where, it will be remembered, each of the last three diagrams

$$CH_3\!\!-\!C\!\equiv\!C\!-\!C\!\equiv\!C\!-\!CH_3 \qquad CH_3\!\!-\!\ddot{C}\!=\!C\!=\!C\!=\!C\!-\!CH_3$$
$$\text{XXXV} \qquad\qquad\qquad \text{XXXVI}$$

$$CH_3\!\!-\!C^+\!\!=\!C\!=\!C\!=\!\ddot{C}^-\!\!-\!CH_3 \qquad CH_3\!\!-\!\ddot{C}^-\!\!=\!C\!=\!C\!=\!C^+\!\!-\!CH_3$$
$$\text{XXXVII} \qquad\qquad\qquad\quad \text{XXXVIII}$$

corresponds to two different structures (see above). As is not unreasonable, the combined intensity of the absorption resulting from the two transitions with any given polyyne is of the same order of magnitude as twice the intensity of the absorption resulting from the one transition in the corresponding polyene.

TABLE 6·5

SPECTRA OF CONJUGATED POLYYNES $CH_3—(—C{\equiv}C—)_n—CH_3$[a]

n	First Band		Second Band	
	λ_{max} (angstroms)	ε_{max}	λ_{max} (angstroms)	ε_{max}
1[b]	2225	160	1775	10,000
2[c]	2265	360	—	—
3[d]	2680	200	< 2070	> 135,000
	2860			
4[e]	3080	180	2340	281,000
	3260			
5[f]	3245	230	2605	352,000
6[f]	3400	1000	2840	445,000

[a] Except as noted, in solution in ethyl alcohol.
[b] These data apply to 2-octyne in n-heptane. There is also an intermediate band with λ_{max} = "1960?" and ε_{max} = "∼ 2,000." See J. R. Platt, H. B. Klevens, and W. C. Price, *J. Chem. Phys.* **17**, 466 (1949).
[c] J. B. Armitage, C. L. Cook, N. Entwistle, E. R. H. Jones, and M. C. Whiting, *J. Chem. Soc.* **1952**, 1998.
[d] J. B. Armitage, C. L. Cook, E. R. H. Jones, and M. C. Whiting, *J. Chem. Soc.* **1952**, 2010.
[e] J. B. Armitage, E. R. H. Jones, and M. C. Whiting, *J. Chem. Soc.* **1952**, 2014.
[f] C. L. Cook, E. R. H. Jones, and M. C. Whiting, *J. Chem. Soc.* **1952**, 2883.

It may be suggested that the absorption bands of the polyynes have been incorrectly identified and, in particular, that the excited states responsible for the weak bands at the longer wave lengths are in fact triplets, with two unpaired electrons in each. This possibility seems unlikely,[6] however, since the absorptions in question, although indeed relatively weak, are still approximately 100 times as strong as those found generally for the "forbidden" singlet-triplet transitions.[17]

The conjugation of triple bonds with double bonds or with aromatic rings leads similarly to absorption at relatively long wave lengths.[18] As with the purely acetylenic compounds just considered, the bands that are nearest the visible are again weaker than the ones that are more remote. Now, however, even the absorptions at the longest wave lengths are

[17] Cf., for example, J. R. Platt, *J. Chem. Phys.* **18**, 1168 (1950).
[18] See, for example, F. Bohlmann, *Chem. Ber.* **84**, 545, 785 (1951); J. B. Armitage, C. L. Cook, N. Entwistle, E. R. H. Jones, and M. C. Whiting, *J. Chem. Soc.* **1952**, 1998; J. B. Armitage and M. C. Whiting, *ibid.* **1952**, 2005; and further references given in these papers.

rather intense. The explanation for this difference from the polyynes is presumably that here, since the conjugated systems no longer have axial symmetry, each of the diagrams analogous to XXXVI–XXXVIII corresponds to only a single structure. Consequently, the two series of bands encountered in the polyynes is now decreased to just one series, and the intensity becomes similar to that with the analogous polyenes. The stronger bands at the shorter wave lengths are presumably of the Rydberg type. Although a great many different substances with conjugated double and triple bonds have been studied, it will here be sufficient for us to list, in Table 6·6, only the data obtained for one typical group of compounds, the diphenylpolyynes C_6H_5—(—$C{\equiv}C$—)$_n$—C_6H_5.

TABLE 6·6

SPECTRA OF DIPHENYLPOLYYNES C_6H_5—(—$C{\equiv}C$—)$_n$—$C_6H_5{}^a$

n	First Band		Second Band	
	λ_{max} (angstroms)	ε_{max}	λ_{max} (angstroms)	ε_{max}
0^b	2515	18,300	—	—
1	2780	30,000^c	—	—
2	3040	32,000^c	—	—
3	3330	35,000^c	2600^c	75,000^c
4	3650	38,000^c	2800^c	133,000^c
5	3970^d	25,000^c	3100^c	158,000^c
8	—	—	3415^e	300,000^e

^{a} Except as noted, the data in this table are taken from H. H. Schlubach and V. Franzen, *Ann.* **573**, 110 (1951), and refer to solution in methyl alcohol. For more recent and, in some instances, slightly divergent data for most of these substances, see J. B. Armitage, N. Entwistle, E. R. H. Jones, and M. C. Whiting, *J. Chem. Soc.* **1954**, 147.

^{b} The data for biphenyl are taken from A. E. Gillam and D. H. Hey, *J. Chem. Soc.* **1939**, 1170, and refer to solution in chloroform. Cf. Table 6·2.

^{c} This value was estimated from the published curve.

^{d} This value applies to the second maximum, although the third maximum at 3680 A is slightly higher. In the table, the value of λ_{max} for the second maximum is given for the sake of consistency since, with all the other diphenylpolyynes listed, the second maximum is the highest.

^{e} This value is taken from E. R. H. Jones, M. C. Whiting, J. B. Armitage, C. L. Cook, and N. Entwistle, *Nature* **168**, 900 (1951), and refers to solution in ethyl acetate.

With the several classes of hydrocarbon that have been considered above, the values of λ_{max} ordinarily increase with the size of the conjugated system. We are not justified, however, in concluding that the wave lengths at which absorption occurs are determined solely by the number of conjugated double or triple bonds. We have already, in fact, seen that, with the condensed aromatic ring systems, the arrangement of the bonds is often more important than is their number (cf. Table 6·4). Even more striking examples are provided by fulvene, XXXIX, and by azulene, XL, which are, respectively, isomers of benzene and of naphthalene. Although fulvene itself is not known, its 6-methyl-6-isobutyl derivative, XLI, has a

weak absorption with $\lambda_{max} = 3640$ A and $\varepsilon_{max} = 300$, and a strong one with $\lambda_{max} = 2700$ A and $\varepsilon_{max} = 16,000$;[19] since the former band extends into the visible, the substance is colored. Azulene has altogether three bands with wave lengths greater than 2500 A: one with $\lambda_{max} \simeq 7000$ A and $\varepsilon_{max} \simeq 300$; one with $\lambda_{max} \simeq 3600$ A and $\varepsilon_{max} \simeq 4000$; and one with $\lambda_{max} \simeq 2900$ A and $\varepsilon_{max} \simeq 47,000$.[20] On account of the band at about 7000 A, the substance is blue. Clearly, these nonaromatic hydrocarbons absorb at much longer wave lengths than do their aromatic analogs with, apparently, the same extent of conjugation. Still an additional anomaly is provided by the fact that, although the attaching of phenyl substituents to the fulvene skeleton, as in 6,6-diphenylfulvene, XLII, or 1,2,3,4-tetraphenylfulvene, XLIII, has the expected effect of

[19] E. D. Bergmann and Y. Hirshberg, *Bull. soc. chim.* (France) **1950**, 1091. Data for a number of further 6,6-disubstituted fulvenes are given by J. H. Day and J. C. Lukman, *Ohio J. Sci.* **52**, 335 (1952) [*C. A.* **47**, 8658 (1953)].

[20] D. E. Mann, J. R. Platt, and H. B. Klevens, *J. Chem. Phys.* **17**, 481 (1949); E. Clar, *J. Chem. Soc.* **1950**, 1823; J. R. Platt, *J. Chem. Phys.* **18**, 1168 (1950).

shifting the absorption toward still longer wave lengths, the fusing of benzene rings onto the same skeleton, as in benzhydrylidenefluorene, XLIV, has the opposite effect of shifting the absorption toward shorter

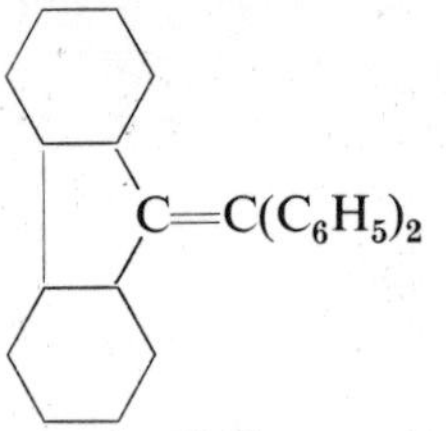

XLIV

wave lengths (and, at the same time, of greatly increasing the intensity).[19, 21] These several irregularities in the relation between the observed spectra and the extents of conjugation are entirely consistent with the results of some approximate numerical calculations which will be more fully discussed in Section 6·10; unfortunately, however, there seems to be no way in which they can be explained as necessary consequences of the purely qualitative theory developed above in this section.

The molecules of the cumulenes contain sequences of two or more carbon-carbon double bonds without any intervening single bonds. The allenes, which form the first members of this series, are well known, but only a few of the higher members have as yet been reported. The possibilities for resonance are here somewhat similar to those present in the conjugated polyenes and polyynes since, for hexapentaene, for example, we can write not only the conventional structure XLV but also such additional less stable ones as XLVI, XLVII, and their respective ionic

XLV

XLVI

XLVII

counterparts. We can therefore expect that both λ_{max} and ε_{max} will increase with the length of the unsaturated system. Although the available data are meager,[22, 23] they are clearly in at least qualitative

[21] For some additional anomalies of this type, see B. Pullman, G. Berthier, and J. Baudet, *J. chim. phys.* **50**, 69 (1953).

[22] R. Kuhn and K. Wallenfels, *Ber.* **71**, 783, 1510 (1938); R. Kuhn and G. Platzer, *ibid.* **73**, 1410 (1940); P. Cadiot and A. Willemart, *Bull. soc. chim.* (*France*) **1951**, 100; R. Kuhn and J. Jahn, *Chem. Ber.* **86**, 759 (1953).

[23] W. M. Schubert, T. H. Liddicoet, and W. A. Lanka, *J. Am. Chem. Soc.* **74**, 569 (1952).

agreement with expectation, since tetraphenylbutatriene, $(C_6H_5)_2C=C=$ $C=C(C_6H_5)_2$, has a rather intense absorption at a wave length slightly greater than 4000 A,[22] and tetraphenylhexapentaene, $(C_6H_5)_2C=C=C=$ $C=C=C(C_6H_5)_2$, has a still more intense absorption at a wave length slightly less than 5000 A.[22] Although the absorptions by the parent compounds, without the phenyl groups, presumably have lower intensities and shorter wave lengths,[23] the values of both λ_{max} and ε_{max} that are found for the tetraphenyl derivatives are nevertheless surprisingly high. Apparently, in fact, the spectroscopic effects which have been attributed above to conjugation are greater with cumulative double bonds than with conjugated ones. The explanation[6] for this quantitative difference is probably that, in the cumulenes, the carbon-carbon distances are at least approximately equal, whereas, in both the conjugated polyenes and polyynes, these distances are doubtless alternately long and short (cf. Table 4·5, Section 4·4). Indeed, if the long bonds in the compounds of the two latter classes could be made much longer than they actually are, the shorter bonds would then become essentially indistinguishable from ordinary isolated multiple bonds, and hence the conjugation should have no spectroscopic effect at all.

Hyperconjugation,[24] like the more familiar conjugation of double (or triple) bonds with one another, can be expected to have characteristic effects upon the electronic spectra. We might therefore anticipate that, when hydrogen atoms which are linked to unsaturated carbon atoms are replaced by saturated alkyl groups, the spectra of the resulting alkylated derivatives will usually be somewhat displaced toward longer wave lengths and will usually become somewhat more intense. This prediction seems to be in satisfactory agreement with the observed spectra. The wave length is almost always increased by alkyl substitution but, possibly because of geometrical factors, the intensity is more erratic. Some typical data, which illustrate these conclusions, are shown in Table 6·7. With the methylbenzenes, the values of both λ_{max} and ε_{max} increase as the number of alkyl groups increases (see also page 277); with the alkylated 1,3-butadienes, λ_{max} again increases, but ε_{max} shows no corresponding regularity. Indeed, with 1,3-cyclohexadiene, which can be considered a 1,4-dialkyl-1,3-butadiene, ε_{max} is only about one-third as great as it is with unsubstituted 1,3-butadiene; and with cyclopentadiene, it is still smaller. The reason for these large variations in intensity is presumably that, although the configurations of the cyclic hydrocarbons are necessarily s-cis, those of their acyclic analogs are predominantly s-trans (cf. page 227). The explanation for the particularly weak absorption by cyclopentadiene may be that, since the geometrical requirements

[24] R. S. Mulliken, C. A. Rieke, and W. G. Brown, *J. Am. Chem. Soc.* **63**, 41 (1941).

of the five-membered ring must here decrease the C—C—C bond angles, the conjugated system is spatially less extended in this compound than in either 1,3-cyclohexadiene or an acyclic diene. Mulliken has also concluded that, for special reasons which cannot be explained in nonmathematical terms, the hyperconjugation in the cyclic dienes is itself partly responsible for the observed low intensities.[25]

TABLE 6·7

SPECTRA OF SOME UNSATURATED HYDROCARBONS WITH HYPERCONJUGATION[a]

Substance	λ_{max} (angstroms)	ε_{max}
Benzene[b]	2540	204
Toluene[b]	2610	225
m-Xylene[b]	2645	300
o-Xylene[b]	2625	300
Mesitylene[j]	2700	300
1,3-Butadiene[c]	2170	20,900
Isoprene[d]	2230	19,000
cis 1,3-Pentadiene[d]	2260	22,000
trans 1,3-Pentadiene[d]	2230	26,000
2,3-Dimethyl-1,3-Butadiene[e, f]	2270	25,000
1,3-Cyclohexadiene[g]	2560	7,940
Cyclopentadiene[e]	2400	3,000
1-Octyne[h]	2225	120
2-Octyne[h]	2225	160
1,3-Pentadiyne[i]	2365	390
2,4-Hexadiyne[i]	2265	360

[a] In solution in various solvents. Data are given for only the one band of longest wave length.

[b] L. Doub and J. M. Vandenbelt, J. Am. Chem. Soc. 69, 2714 (1947); 71, 2414 (1949).

[c] E. A. Braude, Ann. Repts. on Progr. Chem. (Chem. Soc. London) 42, 105 (1945); J. Chem. Soc. 1950, 379.

[d] L. E. Jacobs and J. R. Platt, J. Chem. Phys. 16, 1137 (1948).

[e] V. Henri in International Critical Tables, McGraw-Hill Book Co., New York, 1929, vol. 5, pp. 359ff; L. W. Pickett, E. Paddock, and E. Sackter, J. Am. Chem. Soc. 63, 1073 (1941).

[f] See also A. Smakula, Angew. Chem. 47, 657 (1934); G. Scheibe and R. Pummerer, Ber. 60, 2163 (1927).

[g] V. Henri and L. W. Pickett, J. Chem. Phys. 7, 439 (1939).

[h] J. R. Platt, H. B. Klevens, and W. C. Price, J. Chem. Phys. 17, 466 (1949).

[i] J. B. Armitage, C. L. Cook, N. Entwistle, E. R. H. Jones, and M. C. Whiting, J. Chem. Soc. 1952, 1998.

[j] L. W. Pickett, G. F. Walter, and H. France, J. Am. Chem. Soc. 58, 2296 (1936).

[25] R. S. Mulliken, J. Chem. Phys. 7, 121, 339 (1939).

With the acyclic mono- and dimethyl-1,3-butadienes, the extinction coefficients have approximately the same value as with 1,3-butadiene itself; hence, we may conclude that, with these substances also, the configurations are predominantly *s-trans*. The relatively small variations that are observed are probably the result of two opposing effects. On the one hand, the hyperconjugation may be presumed ordinarily to increase the intensity of the absorption (however, cf. the last sentence of the preceding paragraph); on the other hand, the presence of alkyl groups, especially in the neighborhood of the single bond between the two double ones, can be expected to decrease the intensity by decreasing the fraction of the molecules that have configurations near to *s-trans*. In *cis* 1,3-pentadiene, for example, the configuration should be predominantly *s-trans*, just as in 1,3-butadiene, but the methyl group is in the *cis* position with respect to the double bond; consequently, the hyperconjugation produces only a small increase in intensity. In *trans* 1,3-pentadiene, however, all the geometrical factors are favorable, and so the hyperconjugation produces an appreciably greater increase in intensity. In isoprene and 2,3-dimethyl-1,3-butadiene, the steric repulsions between the methyl groups and the remainders of the respective molecules somewhat decrease the importance of the *s-trans* configurations, so that the increases in intensity, which should otherwise result, may be expected to be small or nonexistent. Clearly, however, as was mentioned above, since ε_{max} is much greater for these substances than for 1,3-cyclohexadiene or for cyclopentadiene, only a small fraction of the acyclic molecules can at any one time have a configuration that is very different from *s-trans*.

It should be observed that, since the data given in Table 6·7 for 1,3-butadiene and its various derivatives were obtained by different investigators at different times and with different apparatus, they are perhaps not strictly comparable. Consequently, we may have here ascribed incorrect signs and magnitudes to some of the smaller variations in intensity. There can, however, be no doubt that ε_{max} is much smaller for 1,3-cyclohexadiene and for cyclopentadiene than for any of the other dienes considered.

When an alkyl group is directly joined to an aromatic ring, as in the alkylbenzenes, the geometrical factors which affect the intensity of absorption are essentially constant. Consequently, with these substances, irregularities of the foregoing types would not be expected (cf. page 275).

Although the data of Table 6·7 are insufficient to permit the drawing of valid conclusions, hyperconjugation of an alkyl group with a triple bond appears to have an appreciably smaller effect than that with a double bond.[26] With 1,3-pentadiyne and 2,4-hexadiyne, in fact, the difference

[26] Cf. also A. D. Walsh, *Ann. Repts. on Progr. Chem.* (*Chem. Soc. London*) **44**, 32 (1947).

between the two spectra is apparently in the direction opposite to that expected. (However, cf. 2-octyne, note b of Table 6·5.)

In the way just outlined, the spectra of the alkyl derivatives of the unsaturated and aromatic hydrocarbons can be considered to provide some evidence for the reality of hyperconjugation. There is reason for believing, however, that there must also be other factors which are at least partly responsible for the observed effects of alkyl substituents.[26, 27] One of these additional factors is electrostatic. Since the attraction that a carbon atom has for electrons increases with its degree of unsaturation (see pages 128f), an ethylenic carbon atom must pull electrons away from any alkyl group that is attached to it. Consequently, the net charge on an unsaturated atom must be made more negative when a hydrogen atom that is bonded to it is replaced by an alkyl group. As a result of this more negative charge, the electron that is excited when the molecule absorbs a quantum of light is less strongly held in the alkylated hydrocarbon than in the corresponding unalkylated one. Less energy is therefore required to excite the electron, and so the absorption occurs at slightly longer wave lengths. Similarly, the intensity of the absorption should also be increased. There is at present no way for deciding the relative importance of the electrostatic effect and of the hyperconjugation, with respect to either the wave length or the intensity of the absorption. Presumably both factors are involved, but either one of them might well be negligible in comparison with the other.

6·4 Spectra of Aldehydes, Ketones, and Their Analogs. The electronically excited states of aldehydes and ketones R_2CO might be expected to resemble those of the corresponding olefins $R_2C{=}CR_2$. With the former substances, however, additional possibilities are introduced by the presence of unshared pairs of electrons on the oxygen atoms. Since the electrons that belong to such unshared pairs are essentially nonbonding (see pages 59f), certain of them are not very firmly held (see below) and so should be excited with relative ease or, in other words, by light of relatively long wave length. For this reason, the transitions that are responsible for the *first* ultraviolet bands of the carbonyl compounds are probably not analogous, after all, to those discussed in the preceding section, but instead involve the excitation of nonbonding electrons.

In the region between about 1500 A and the visible, a *saturated* aldehyde or ketone is ordinarily found to have three different absorption bands which occur at about 2900 A, 1900 A, and 1550 A, and which we shall hereafter designate by the symbols $N \to A$, $N \to B$, and $N \to V$, respectively. As is implied by these symbols, the three bands are due to

---

[27] W. C. Price and W. T. Tutte, *Proc. Roy. Soc.* (*London*) A **174**, 207 (1940); R. S. Mulliken, *Revs. Mod. Phys.* **14**, 265 (1942).

transitions in which the molecules are raised from the normal, or ground, state N to three different, electronically excited states A, B, and V. Although the data which are at present available in regard to the intensities of the several absorptions are seldom both quantitative and comparable, there is general agreement that the band with the longest wave length, $N \to A$, is very weak, that the next band, $N \to B$, is usually somewhat stronger, and that the third band, $N \to V$, is always considerably stronger. To the extent that a valid conclusion can be based on the incomplete and, in some instances, questionable data, it appears that, with an α,β-unsaturated aldehyde or ketone, the wave length of the band $N \to B$ is not greatly altered by the conjugation. In any event, there can be no doubt that the remaining bands, $N \to A$ and $N \to V$, are displaced by the conjugation toward longer wave lengths and become more intense; the band $N \to V$ then often separates into two or more distinct bands which may be called $N \to V_1$, $N \to V_2$, and so on. These several regularities are illustrated by the data listed in Table 6·8 (cf. also the two paragraphs in fine print, below).

A satisfactory interpretation of the above spectra has been found by Mulliken and his co-workers.[28] Since, of the three bands just described, the one designated as $N \to V$ is the most easily discussed, we shall here consider it first. This band, unlike $N \to A$ and $N \to B$, appears to be completely analogous to the ones which occur in the ultraviolet spectra of the corresponding olefins. With a saturated aldehyde or ketone, the relevant excited state can therefore be described as a hybrid of (principally) the three structures I, II, and III; with an α,β-unsaturated aldehyde or

$$R_2C{=}O{:} \qquad\qquad R_2C^+{-}\ddot{O}{:}^- \qquad\qquad R_2\overset{..}{C}{-}O{:}^+$$

$$\text{I} \qquad\qquad\qquad \text{II} \qquad\qquad\qquad \text{III}$$

ketone, the excited state is similarly a hybrid of numerous structures, of which only IV, V, VI, and VII need here be explicitly mentioned. Evidence supporting this interpretation is provided by the fact that corresponding carbonyl compounds and olefins usually exhibit absorptions in

$$R_2C{=}CR{-}CR{=}O \qquad\qquad R_2C{-}CR{=}CR{-}O$$

$$\text{IV} \qquad\qquad\qquad\qquad \text{V}$$

$$R_2C^+{-}CR{=}CR{-}\ddot{O}{:}^- \qquad\qquad R_2\overset{..}{C}^-{-}CR{=}CR{-}O{:}^+$$

$$\text{VI} \qquad\qquad\qquad\qquad \text{VII}$$

[28] See R. S. Mulliken, *J. Chem. Phys.* **3**, 564 (1935); H. L. McMurry and R. S. Mulliken, *Proc. Natl. Acad. Sci. U. S.* **26**, 312 (1940); H. L. McMurry, *J. Chem. Phys.* **9**, 231, 241 (1941).

TABLE 6·8

Spectra of Some Aldehydes and Ketones and Their Analogs

Substance	$N \rightarrow A$		$N \rightarrow B$		$N \rightarrow V^a$	
	λ_{max} (angstroms)	ε_{max}	λ_{max} (angstroms)	ε_{max}	λ_{max} (angstroms)	ε_{max}
Formaldehyde	$\sim 2900^b$	—	1745^b	—	1560^b	—
Acetaldehyde	2850^c	15^c	1800^b	—	1650^b	—
Acetone	2795^d	15^d	1870^e	900^e	1540^f	"strong"^{f}
Propyl ketone	2833^d	—	—	—	—	—
tert-Butyl ketone	2962^d	20^d	—	—	—	—
Cyclopentanone	2954^d	15^d	—	—	—	—
Acrolein	3340^g	18^g	1750^b	—	1935^b	—
Crotonaldehyde	3300^g	18^g	1800^b	—	2120^h	$16,500^h$
2,4-Hexadienal	—	—	—	—	2630^h	$27,000^h$
2,4,6-Octatrienal	—	—	—	—	3060^h	$41,000^h$
3-Penten-2-one	—	—	—	—	2150^f	$10,000^f$
Mesityl oxide	$3270^{d,f}$	$40^{d,f}$	—	—	2150^f	$12,600^f$
3,5-Heptadien-2-one	—	—	—	—	2640^f	$20,800^f$
Phorone	3747^d	82^d	—	—	2630^f	$20,000^f$
Benzaldehyde	3300^c	20^c	—	—	2800^c	$1,800^c$
Acetophenone	$3280^{d,i}$	$40^{d,i}$	—	—	2770^i	$1,000^i$
Benzophenone	$3450^{c,d}$	$112^{c,d}$	—	—	2550^c	$20,000^c$
Biacetyl	$4170^{c,f}$ $2820^{c,f}$	20^c 15^c	$1970^{f,j}$	—	$1750^{f,j}$	"strong"^{f}
p-Benzoquinone	$4450^{c,f}$ $2760^{c,f}$	20^c 300^c	—	—	2400^c	$20,000^c$
Nitromethane	2700^k	15^k	—	—	$\leq 2000^k$	$\gtrless 10,000^k$
Nitrobenzene	3500^l	200^l	—	—	$2600^{l,m}$	$9,000^{l,m}$

^{a} When there are two or more $N \rightarrow V$ transitions, only the one with the longest wave length, $N \rightarrow V_1$, is here recorded.

^{b} See B. Pullman and A. Pullman, *Les Théories électroniques de la chimie organique*, Masson & Cie., Paris, 1952, p. 508.

^{c} V. Henri, in *International Critical Tables*, McGraw-Hill Book Co., New York, 1929, vol. 5, pp. 359ff.

^{d} G. Scheibe and W. Frömel in A. Eucken and K. L. Wolf, *Hand- und Jahrbuch der chemischen Physik*, Akademische Verlagsgesellschaft, Leipzig, vol. 9, 1937, Part IV, pp. 167, 169.

^{e} H. Ley and B. Arends, *Z. physik. Chem.* B **12**, 132 (1931). Cf. also J. R. Platt, I. Rusoff, and H. B. Klevens, *J. Chem. Phys.* **11**, 535 (1943).

^{f} H. L. McMurry, *J. Chem. Phys.* **9**, 231, 241 (1941); A. Smakula, *Angew. Chem.* **47**, 657 (1934).

g F. E. Blacet, W. G. Young, and J. G. Roof, *J. Am. Chem. Soc.* **59**, 608 (1937).

h K. W. Hausser, R. Kuhn, A. Smakula, and M. Hoffer, *Z. physik. Chem.* B **29**, 371 (1935).

i H. Mohler and J. Pólya, *Helv. Chim. Acta* **19**, 1222 (1936).

j V. R. Ells, *J. Am. Chem. Soc.* **60**, 1864 (1938).

k G. Kortüm, *Z. physik. Chem.* B **43**, 271 (1939). Cf. also G. F. Bloomfield and G. A. Jeffrey, *J. Chem. Soc.* **1944**, 120, and the discussion on pages 287f of this book.

l L. Dede and A. Rosenberg, *Ber.* **67**, 147 (1934).

m See page 288.

approximately the same part of the spectrum and with approximately the same intensity (cf. Tables 6·8 and 6·1, Section 6·3). Thus, in the vapor phase, formaldehyde, acetaldehyde, and acetone absorb at about 1560 A, 1650 A, and 1540 A, respectively,[29] whereas monoölefins absorb at about 1600 A (cf. Table 6·1). Although, with the carbonyl compounds, the values of ε_{max} are not available for comparison, the absorptions are reported[28] to be "strong." Moreover, in hexane solutions, λ_{max} and ε_{max} are equal to 2120 A and 16,500, respectively, for crotonaldehyde;[29] and to 2170 A and 21,000, respectively, for 1,3-butadiene (cf. Table 6·1). And, aside from the weak $N \to A$ bands which are present with the carbonyl compounds but absent with the hydrocarbons, the spectra of benzaldehyde, acetophenone, and benzophenone are rather similar to those of their respective analogs styrene, α-methylstyrene, and 1,1-diphenylethylene.[28] (In regard to the $N \to B$ bands of these carbonyl compounds, see the second of the two following paragraphs in fine print.)

With the saturated aldehydes and ketones, the absorptions $N \to V$ occur at such short wave lengths that to some extent they overlap the Rydberg bands (cf. pages 255f). For this reason, the excited states probably cannot be accurately described in terms of only such covalent and ionic structures as I, II, and III, but must instead receive appreciable contributions from Rydberg-type structures in which electrons are raised to large and highly excited orbitals. This complication becomes less important, however, in the conjugated compounds with which the absorptions occur at longer wave lengths.

Benzaldehyde, acetophenone, and benzophenone contain aromatic rings and so present somewhat more complicated examples than their aliphatic analogs. As expected, the weak $N \to A$ bands are observed at relatively great wave lengths (see above), but there are now several different $N \to V$ bands (of which only the first one, $N \to V_1$, is listed in Table 6·8), and these are so intense and cover such a wide range of wave lengths that the $N \to B$ bands are obscured.

The excited states A and B that are responsible for the $N \to A$ and $N \to B$ bands can be most easily described in molecular-orbital language.

[29] See the references given in Table 6·8. Additional data for a number of unsaturated aldehydes and ketones are given by J. F. Thomas and G. Branch, *J. Am. Chem. Soc.* **75**, 4793 (1953).

Thus, the excited state A is considered to be derived from the normal state N by a transition in which an electron belonging to one of the unshared pairs on the oxygen atom is raised to an antibonding pi orbital (cf. page 64) that is associated with the two atoms of the carbonyl group; and the further excited state B is considered to be derived by a transition in which the same electron is raised to an antibonding sigma orbital that is associated with the same two atoms.

In the language of the resonance theory, the description of the two above excited states is rather more difficult, as is not unexpected in view of the relatively great mathematical complexity of this alternative approach to spectroscopic problems. We shall, nevertheless, find it instructive to consider how these states can be represented as hybrids of valence-bond structures. The electrons that belong to the valence shell of the carbonyl carbon atom are associated with altogether four different atomic orbitals (cf. pages 564f). Two of these orbitals, and their electrons, are used in the formation of the two C—R bonds and need not here be further considered. Of the two remaining orbitals, one is involved in the sigma component, and the other in the pi component, of the carbon-oxygen double bond. For the sake of clarity, we may use dots and asterisks to depict the electrons that are associated with the sigma and pi orbitals, respectively. In a similar way, the electrons that belong to the valence shell of the oxygen atom are associated with four different atomic orbitals. As before, the electrons of the sigma and pi orbitals that take part in the carbon-oxygen bonds may again be depicted by dots and asterisks, respectively; we now need, however, further symbols for distinguishing the electrons in the two remaining, doubly occupied orbitals, i.e., the electrons of the two unshared pairs. To at least a good first approximation, one of these latter orbitals is of the type known as $2s$; although we have not yet considered the properties of such an orbital, we need here know only that the $2s$ electrons of the oxygen atom are so firmly held that they can neither take part in the bond formation nor be excited by light in the near ultraviolet. Consequently, these electrons, which may be depicted by small ×'s, require no further explicit attention. The remaining oxygen orbital, on the other hand, is considerably less stable than the $2s$. The electrons which occupy it, and which may be depicted by small open circles, are therefore the ones that, on page 278, were said to be easily excited.

With the rather complicated notation just defined, the conventional structure I of an aldehyde or ketone can now be written more explicitly as VIII; and the excited state A can be described as a hybrid of structures IX and X or, in a completely equivalent way, by the single structure XI with a three-electron bond (cf. Section 2·5). Finally, the further state B

can be similarly described as a hybrid of structures XII and XIII, or by the single structure XIV.   The two electrons which, in structures IX, X, XII, and XIII, are the sole occupants of different orbitals are paired with each other so that, in the structures XI and XIV, the total numbers of

$$R_2C\!:\!{}^*_{\times}O^\circ_\circ$$ $$R_2\overset{*\ **}{C}\!:\!\overset{}{O}{}^\circ$$ $$R_2\overset{**}{C}{}^-\!:\!\overset{*}{O}{}^{\circ+}$$ $$R_2\overset{***}{C}\!:\!O^\circ$$

  VIII   IX   X   XI

$$R_2\overset{\cdot\ ..}{C}{}^*_*O^\circ$$ $$R_2\overset{..}{C}{}^-\!{}^*_*O^{\circ+}$$ $$R_2\overset{...}{C}{}^*_*O^\circ$$

  XII   XIII   XIV

unpaired electrons are zero.   The excited states A and B, like both the further excited state V and the ground state N, are therefore singlets.

The evidence supporting the above interpretation of the near-ultraviolet spectra of the aldehydes and ketones is too complex to be given here in detail.[28]   We may, however, mention some of the more important points. In the first place, we may note that, if the absorption bands $N \rightarrow A$, $N \rightarrow B$, and $N \rightarrow V$ are indeed due to the kinds of transition that have been postulated, then they would be expected to fall in the order that is observed.   In the structure XI, which is assigned to the most stable of the excited states A, there still remains a strong sigma bond between the carbon and oxygen atoms, and the strength of the weaker pi bond should not have been greatly decreased by being changed from a two-electron to a three-electron bond.   On the other hand, in structure XIV, which is assigned to the less stable state B, the two-electron bond that remains between the carbon and oxygen atoms is now of the relatively weak pi type, and the strength of the strong sigma bond should have been greatly decreased by being changed from a two-electron to a three-electron bond. And finally, in the structures II and III, which are considered to make the largest contributions to the still less stable state V, not even weak three-electron bonds of the pi type link the carbon and oxygen atoms, and, in addition, there have been separations of positive and negative charge.

The intensities, as well as the wave lengths of the three bands $N \rightarrow A$, $N \rightarrow B$, and $N \rightarrow V$ are likewise in agreement with the proposed identifications of the respective excited states.   By an application of the selection rules, which we need not here go into, a transition from the normal structure I (or VIII) to the excited structure XI can be shown to be "forbidden," even though both these states are singlets.   Consequently, the absorption should be extremely weak.   Similarly, the absorption resulting from a transition to structure XIV, although not "forbidden," can nevertheless be shown to be rather weak; and that resulting from a transition to a hybrid of structures II and III can be shown to be relatively intense. The calculated intensities[28] are therefore in good qualitative agreement with the ones observed.

The fact that both the $N \to A$ and the $N \to V$ bands move toward longer wave lengths when the carbonyl group is made part of a conjugated system, but that the $N \to B$ bands are possibly somewhat less affected, is also consistent with the proposed interpretation of the spectra.[30]

When two carbonyl groups are present in the same conjugated system, the molecule should have two relatively stable excited states of the type A, two rather less stable excited states of the type B, and, in addition, a number of further excited states that result from the conjugation itself and so are of the type V. Biacetyl will here serve to illustrate the situation that thus obtains. The ground state of this substance can be represented, with an accuracy that is sufficient for our present purposes, by the single structure XV, in which the notation is the same as that employed in the analogous structure VIII. The excited A and B states, on the other hand,

$$
\begin{array}{cccc}
\text{H}_3\text{C} & \text{H}_3\text{C} & \text{H}_3\text{C} & \text{H}_3\text{C} \\
| & | & | & | \\
\text{C:}^*_*\text{O}^\circ_\circ & \text{C:}^{***}\text{O}^\circ & \text{C:}^*_*\text{O}^\circ_\circ & \text{C:}^{***}\text{O}^\circ \\
| & | & | & | \\
\text{C:}^*_*\text{O}^\circ_\circ & \text{C:}^*_*\text{O}^\circ_\circ & \text{C:}^{***}\text{O}^\circ & \text{C:}^{***}\text{O}^\circ \\
\text{H}_3\text{C} & \text{H}_3\text{C} & \text{H}_3\text{C} & \text{H}_3\text{C} \\
\text{XV} & \text{XVI} & \text{XVII} & \text{XVIII}
\end{array}
$$

$$
\begin{array}{ccc}
\text{H}_3\text{C} & \text{H}_3\text{C} & \text{H}_3\text{C} \\
| & | & | \\
\text{C}^*_*\text{O}^\circ & \text{C:}^*_*\text{O}^\circ_\circ & \text{C}^*_*\text{O}^\circ \\
| & | & | \\
\text{C:}^*_*\text{O}^\circ_\circ & \text{C}^*_*\text{O}^\circ & \text{C}^*_*\text{O}^\circ \\
\text{H}_3\text{C} & \text{H}_3\text{C} & \text{H}_3\text{C} \\
\text{XIX} & \text{XX} & \text{XXI}
\end{array}
$$

are more complex since, with a dicarbonyl compound, each of the structures XI and XIV is replaced by a set of three different structures, XVI, XVII, and XVIII, and XIX, XX, and XXI, respectively. If, as seems probable, structures XVIII and XXI are too unstable to have much effect upon the near-ultraviolet spectrum of the substance, then the two A states that were mentioned above are essentially the two hybrids resulting from resonance between structures XVI and XVII, and similarly the two

[30] Cf. B. Pullman and A. Pullman, *Les théories électroniques de la chimie organique*, Masson & Cie., Paris, 1952, pp. 504ff.

B states are essentially the two hybrids resulting from resonance between structures XIX and XX.

Whenever there is resonance between two structures which, like either XVI and XVII or XIX and XX, correspond separately to the same energy, one of the resulting hybrids must be more stable, and the other must be less stable, than the individual contributing structures (cf. pages 27f). Consequently, one of the two $N \to A$ bands of biacetyl should occur at longer wave lengths, and the other should occur at shorter wave lengths, than the single $N \to A$ band of an analogous monocarbonyl compound; for the same reason, a similar relation should exist also among the respective $N \to B$ bands. Experimentally, biacetyl is found (cf. Table 6·8) to have weak absorptions at about 4170 A, 2820 A, and 1970 A, and a much stronger one at about 1750 A. (The first of these is the one responsible for the observed color of the substance.) On the basis of their wave lengths and intensities, the bands at 4170 A and 2820 A can presumably be identified with the two expected $N \to A$ bands. One of them has indeed been displaced, as predicted, toward longer wave lengths; the other, however, has remained very near the position characteristic of the simple ketones like acetone. This apparent discrepancy may have resulted from our neglect of structure XVIII and other less stable structures, but no definite decision is now possible. The band at 1970 A possibly consists of the two (overlapping?) $N \to B$ bands; as usual, the conjugation here has little effect upon either the wave length or the intensity. The strong band at 1750 A is almost certainly the $N \to V$ band $N \to V_1$ that is analogous to the one shown by 1,3-butadiene at 2170 A (see Table 6·1, Section 6·3).

The molecule of p-benzoquinone is considerably more complicated than that of biacetyl. The electronic transitions responsible for the visible and ultraviolet spectra of the two substances may be presumed, however, to be closely analogous. With the former substance, therefore, the weak absorptions at about 4450 A and 2760 A (cf. Table 6·8) are doubtless the two $N \to A$ bands; the further absorptions at shorter wave lengths cannot be so clearly identified, but they must consist of overlapping $N \to B$ and $N \to V$ bands. With other quinones, the situations are so closely analogous that no further discussion should here be necessary.

Thioketones, $R_2C{=}S$, absorb at much longer wave lengths than their oxygen-containing analogs. Thiobenzophenone, for example, is blue, and it has weak bands at about 6000 A and 3100 A,[28] as well as stronger ones at shorter wave lengths. A possible explanation[28] for this striking effect of the replacement of oxygen atoms by sulfur atoms is that, with a decrease in the electronegativity of the atom concerned, the electrons belonging to the unshared pairs become less firmly held and hence more easily excited.   A further, but essentially equivalent, explanation is that the structures XXII and XXIII are more stable, relative to the respective

$$R_2C \overset{***}{\underset{\times\times}{:}} S^\circ \qquad\qquad R_2C \overset{...}{\underset{\times\times}{*}} S^\circ$$

XXII   XXIII

ground states, than are their analogs XI and XIV, because the strength of a three-electron bond increases as the atoms which are linked by it are given more nearly the same electronegativity (cf. Section 2·5).   On the other hand, a quite different explanation, which has also been advanced,[31] is that the especially weak absorptions by these substances at the longest wave lengths are not at all analogous to the $N \to A$ bands, previously considered, but are instead due to transitions to excited *triplet* states. Since such transitions are "forbidden," the observed weakness of the bands finds a logical explanation.   There is, however, excellent reason for believing that this alternative interpretation of the spectra is incorrect.[6] In the first place, although the absorptions are indeed weak, they are apparently much too strong to be attributable to singlet-triplet transitions.[17]   Moreover, additional arguments of the kind discussed more fully below in connection with the nitroso compounds likewise lead to the conclusion that, as initially suggested, the excited states are here singlets of the type A.

Monomeric nitroso compounds, R—N=O, like thioketones, have weak absorptions at relatively long wave lengths.   With nitrosobenzene, for example, the first two bands occur at about 7600 A[31] and about 3000 A.[32] With several other aromatic and aliphatic nitroso compounds, the value of λ_{max} for the first of the two corresponding bands has been found to vary within the limits 6500–6900 A, and that of ε_{max} has been found to vary within the limits 17–24.[33]   The explanation for the existence of *two* absorptions with such relatively long wave lengths may be that, since there is an unshared pair of electrons on each of the two atoms of the nitroso group, and not on just one of them, the electron which is excited may come from either one of these pairs or, as a result of resonance in the excited state, from both of them.   (Cf. the above discussion of biacetyl, in which the electron that jumps may similarly come from either one or both of two different unshared pairs.)   Again, however, the further explanation that the most stable excited state (i.e., the one responsible for the absorption at about 7600 A in nitrosobenzene) is a triplet has also

[31] G. N. Lewis and M. Kasha, *J. Am. Chem. Soc.* 67, 994 (1945).

[32] See H. S. French and D. J. Perkins, *J. Am. Chem. Soc.* 59, 1182 (1937); H. H. Hodgson, *J. Chem. Soc.* 1939, 1807.   These authors differ by more than 200 A in the value of λ_{max}, and by a factor of about 4 in that of ε_{max}.

[33] D. L. Hammick and M. W. Lister, *J. Chem. Soc.* 1937, 489.

been suggested,[31] but is almost certainly incorrect.   As with the analogous absorption by the thioketones, the intensity is too great to be due to a singlet-triplet transition.[17]   Moreover, although the intensities of the absorptions due to genuine singlet-triplet transitions are increased by the proximity of heavy atoms, either in the same molecule or in the surrounding medium,[34] no such effect is observed with nitroso compounds.[33, 35, 36]

Aliphatic nitro compounds have weak absorptions at fairly long wave lengths, and much more intense ones at shorter wave lengths.   With nitromethane,[37] for example, the first ultraviolet band has $\lambda_{max} = 2700$ A and $\varepsilon_{max} = 15$ (see Table 6·8);   and, from the incomplete data that have been published, we may infer that the second band probably has $\lambda_{max} \leqslant 2000$ A and $\varepsilon_{max} \geqslant 10,000$.   The spectrum of nitrocyclohexane[38] appears to be closely similar to that of nitromethane.

Although insufficient data are available for the conclusive identification of the excited states responsible for all the observed bands of the nitro compounds, we can nevertheless make some reasonable guesses.   The ground state of a nitroparaffin is the more stable of the two hybrids resulting from the resonance between the two equivalent structures XXIV and XXV.   The less stable of these hybrids must then be some excited

state, but it can hardly be the particular one involved in the weak band at 2700 A;   for, on account of the large dipole moments of structures XXIV and XXV, the absorption due to a transition between the hybrids should be very intense.   Possibly, the strong band with $\lambda_{max} \leqslant 2000$ A may be the one that arises from such a transition.   The weak band at 2700 A is then presumably the analog of the $N \rightarrow A$ bands of the carbonyl compounds.[36]   Since there are two equivalent oxygen atoms in the molecule, there should be two different $N \rightarrow A$ bands, just as with biacetyl (cf. pages 284f);   perhaps these expected bands occur at so nearly the same wave lengths that they are not resolved, or perhaps one of them occurs at wave lengths shorter than 2000 A and so is obscured by the strong

[34] M. Kasha, *J. Chem. Phys.* **20**, 71 (1952).

[35] D. S. McClure, *J. Chem. Phys.* **17**, 905 (1949).

[36] For still further evidence, see J. R. Platt, *J. Chem. Phys.* **19**, 101 (1951); H. McConnell, *ibid.* **20**, 700 (1952); K. Nakamoto and K. Suzuki, *ibid.* **20**, 1971 (1952); J. R. Platt, *J. Opt. Soc. Amer.* **43**, 252 (1953).

[37] G. Kortüm, *Z. physik. Chem.* B **43**, 271 (1939).

[38] G. F. Bloomfield and G. A. Jeffrey, *J. Chem. Soc.* **1944**, 120.

absorptions in that region. Similarly, there should be two different $N \to B$ bands; these are almost certainly obscured by the foregoing strong bands.

The first ultraviolet band of nitrobenzene is a weak one with $\lambda_{max} =$ 3500 A and $\varepsilon_{max} = 200.$[39] This is possibly an $N \to A$ band, modified by conjugation with the aromatic ring. Another, much stronger band occurs at shorter wave lengths, with a λ_{max} of about 2600 A and an ε_{max} of about 9000.[39] Between these two bands there is probably still a third one of intermediate intensity ($\lambda_{max} \cong 2900$ A and $\varepsilon_{max} \cong 2000$). This additional band is, however, largely obscured by the stronger of its neighbors, so that its existence can only be inferred from the presence of plateaus in the curves obtained for some of the homologs of nitro-benzene.[39] The explanation for the last two of these three bands is presumably that, as a result of the interaction with the nitro group, the characteristic absorptions by the aromatic ring have been brought to longer wave lengths and have been made more intense.[36] This interaction doubtless results not only from the conjugation between the nitrogen-oxygen double bond and the ring, but also from the contributions of the quinoid structures XXVI, XXVII, and XXVIII, which should stabilize

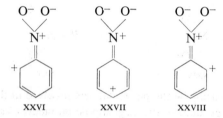

the excited state more than they do the ground state, and which have individually very large dipole moments. The expected $N \to B$ bands are doubtless obscured by these stronger $N \to V$ bands.

6·5 Spectra of Alcohols, Phenols, and Their Analogs. In the ultra-violet part of the spectrum, saturated alcohols are completely transparent down to about 2000 A.[40] The absorptions which occur at still shorter wave lengths possibly involve the excitation of the electrons belonging to the unshared pairs on the oxygen atoms, and so are somewhat analogous to the $N \to A$ and $N \to B$ bands of the aldehydes and ketones. The spectra of the saturated ethers are, as expected, very similar to those of the alcohols.[40]

[39] L. Dede and A. Rosenberg, *Ber.* **67**, 147 (1934); W. G. Brown and H. Reagan, *J. Am. Chem. Soc.* **69**, 1032 (1947).

[40] See M. Pestemer, G. Scheibe, A. Schöntag, and D. Brück in Landolt-Börnstein, *Zahlenwerte und Funktionen*, Springer Verlag, Berlin, 1951, vol. I, Part 3, pp. 78ff.

When a hydroxyl (or alkoxyl) group is directly joined to an aromatic ring, the substance is found to absorb with moderate intensity at wave lengths that are longer than are characteristic of either the related aromatic hydrocarbon or an analogous saturated alcohol (or ether). Thus, the first ultraviolet band of phenol (in aqueous solution) has $\lambda_{max} = 2700$ A and $\varepsilon_{max} = 1460$, and that of anisole has nearly the same value for each of these two quantities.[41] (Cf. Table 6·9 and also Table 6·2, Section 6·3.)

TABLE 6·9

SPECTRA OF SOME PHENOLS AND OF THEIR ANALOGS AND DERIVATIVES[a]

Substance	λ_{max} (angstroms)	ε_{max}
Phenol	2700[b]	1,450[b]
Anisole	2690[b]	1,480[b]
1-Naphthol	3230[c]	2,600[c]
2-Naphthol	3300[c]	2,000[c]
Aniline	2800[b]	1,430[b]
Anilinium ion	2540[b]	160[b]
1-Naphthylamine	3200[d]	5,000[d]
2-Naphthylamine	3400[d]	2,000[d]
Chlorobenzene	2635[b]	190[b]
Bromobenzene	2610[b]	192[b]
Phenoxide ion	2870[b]	2,600[b]
o-Nitrophenol	3500[e]	2,500[e]
m-Nitrophenol	3300[e]	1,800[e]
p-Nitrophenol[f]	3200[b,e]	9,000[b,e]
o-Nitrophenoxide ion	4200[e]	5,000[e]
m-Nitrophenoxide ion	3800[e]	1,500[e]
p-Nitrophenoxide ion	4000[e]	15,000[e]
o-Nitroaniline	4100[e]	5,000[e]
m-Nitroaniline	3600[e]	1,500[e]
p-Nitroaniline	3810[b,e]	13,500[b,e]

[a] In this table, data are given only for the first ultraviolet band.

[b] L. Doub and J. M. Vandenbelt, *J. Am. Chem. Soc.* **69**, 2714 (1947). The data apply to solutions in water containing, at most, 2 per cent methyl alcohol.

[c] C. Daglish, *J. Am. Chem. Soc.* **72**, 4859 (1950). The data refer to solutions in ethyl alcohol.

[d] Y. Hirshberg and R. N. Jones, *Can. J. Research* **27**, 437 (1949). The data refer to solutions in ethyl alcohol.

[e] L. Dede and A. Rosenberg, *Ber.* **67**, 147 (1934). The data refer to solutions in water. In order to decrease the ionization of the nitrophenols, the solutions of these compounds were 0.1 N in perchloric acid.

[f] From the published curve (see Dede and Rosenberg, note *e*), the *first* absorption band of *p*-nitrophenol appears to be a relatively weak, and unresolved, one with a λ_{max} of about 4000 A and an ε_{max} of about 400. The low intensity, however, makes it unlikely that this band is comparable with the ones listed for the remaining substances.

[41] L. Doub and J. M. Vandenbelt, *J. Am. Chem. Soc.* **69**, 2714 (1947).

Two quite different explanations for the observed variations in the spectra of the saturated and the aromatic compounds can be considered. On the one hand, the absorptions by phenol and by anisole, just cited, may be analogous to those by the alcohols and their ethers; and the displacements of the bands toward longer wave lengths may be due to interactions of the type which, in Section 6·4, were considered to affect the $N \rightarrow A$ and $N \rightarrow B$ bands of conjugated aldehydes and ketones. On the other hand, the bands of phenol and of anisole at about 2700 A may instead be more closely related to the absorptions by benzene itself at somewhat shorter wave lengths, and so may be more analogous to the $N \rightarrow V$ bands of the α,β-unsaturated carbonyl compounds. On the basis of general rules which have been formulated by Platt[36] and by McConnell,[36] but which need not here be further described, the evidence in favor of this second alternative seems to be conclusive, not only with phenol and anisole, but also with all the other substances listed in Table 6·9.[6] We shall hereafter, accordingly, ignore the possibility that the absorptions under discussion are of either the $N \rightarrow A$ or the $N \rightarrow B$ type.

The most stable structures that can be written for phenol (or for anisole) are the two Kekulé and three Dewar structures, I–V, with R = H (or CH_3).

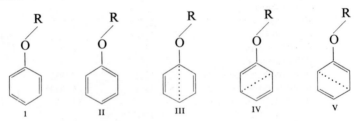

If only these five structures and their respective ionic counterparts had to be considered, the spectrum of each substance should closely resemble that of benzene. The intensity might be slightly increased since, on account of the lowered symmetry of the molecule, the electronic transition is less "forbidden," but no great change in the wave length would be anticipated (cf. the discussion of the anilinium ion on page 291). In Section 3·3, however, it was suggested that a more satisfactory description of the phenol (or anisole) molecule can be obtained if small weights are assigned also to the three quinoid structures VI, VII, and VIII. Although the resonance with these structures is apparently rather unimportant in the ground states of the molecules, we can anticipate that it will have considerably greater effects upon the electronically excited states since, with respect to these latter states, the quinoid structures are not extremely unstable. Consequently, we can predict that the excited states are more effectively stabilized by the resonance than are the ground states, and hence that the absorptions by phenol (and by anisole) will occur at longer wave lengths than does that by the parent hydrocarbon, benzene.   Since the quinoid structures VI, VII, and VIII are characterized by relatively

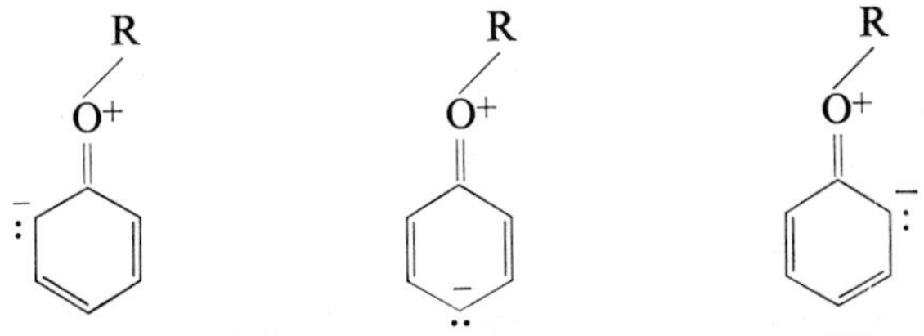

R
O+
VI

R
O+
VII

R
O+
VIII

large dipole moments, we can further predict that the absorption by the oxygen-containing substances will be more intense than that by the hydrocarbon.   As has already been mentioned, these predictions are in complete agreement with the observations.   Some additional data referring to other analogous compounds are given in Table 6·9.

Saturated amines absorb at somewhat longer wave lengths than the corresponding alcohols.[40]   In most instances, diffuse bands start at about 2400 A, but do not become intense until perhaps 2200 A.   As with the alcohols, the electrons which are excited in these transitions presumably originate in the unshared pairs.

With aniline, the first ultraviolet band (in aqueous solution) has $\lambda_{max} = 2800$ A and $\varepsilon_{max} = 1430$.[41]   As with phenol, the fact that both the wave length and the intensity are greater than with benzene can be related to the possibility of writing quinoid structures, which here assume the forms IX, X, and XI.   In an acidic medium, however, the neutral

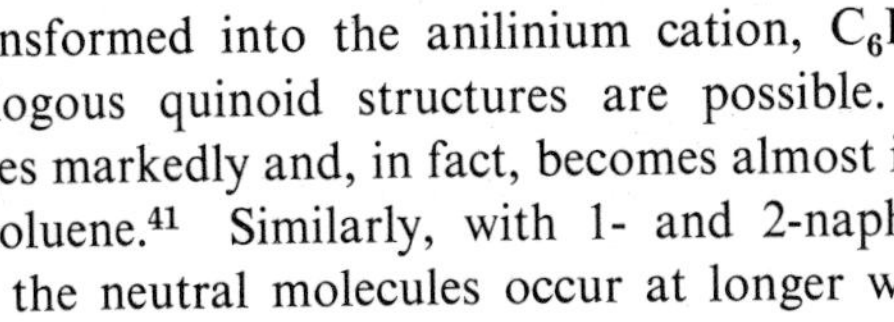

N^+H_2
IX

N^+H_2
X

N^+H_2
XI

molecule is transformed into the anilinium cation, $C_6H_5—N^+H_3$, with which no analogous quinoid structures are possible.   The spectrum therefore changes markedly and, in fact, becomes almost indistinguishable from that of toluene.[41]   Similarly, with 1- and 2-naphthylamines, the absorptions by the neutral molecules occur at longer wave lengths and are more intense than with naphthalene (cf. Tables 6·9 and 6·4, Section 6·3); but those by the respective cations, $C_{10}H_7—N^+H_3$, are similar to that of naphthalene.[42]   Again, therefore, the quinoid structures (such as

[42] E. A. Steck and G. W. Ewing, *J. Am. Chem. Soc.* **70**, 3397 (1948).

XII, XIII, XIV, etc., appear to be important with the amines and impossible with their cations.

XII   XIII   XIV

Saturated alkyl chlorides absorb only at wave lengths shorter than about 2000 A.[40]   Since the chlorine atoms in the molecules of these compounds have unshared pairs of electrons, the diffuse bands which occur in the far ultraviolet are probably again due to the excitation of electrons from these unshared pairs.

With chlorobenzene, the absorption is at slightly longer wave lengths, but is not appreciably more intense, than that of benzene.[41]   Although the evidence is less conclusive here than with the phenols and aromatic amines, we are probably justified in again assuming that the quinoid structures make somewhat larger contributions to the excited state than they do to the ground state.

Since bromine is less electronegative than chlorine, and since iodine is still less electronegative, the wave lengths at which the alkyl halides absorb should increase in the order: alkyl chlorides, alkyl bromides, alkyl iodides.   This expectation is completely confirmed by the observations.[40] In general, the absorption due to an alkyl bromide is fairly intense by about 2500 A, whereas that due to an alkyl iodide has a comparable intensity by about 3000 A.   Since these bands occur in the same part of the spectrum as do those of the aromatic hydrocarbons, the interpretations of the electronic transitions in aryl bromides and iodides are not entirely clear.   In any event, however, the observation that the spectra of chloro-, bromo-, and iodobenzene differ much less than those of methyl chloride, bromide, and iodide[40, 41] is entirely consistent with the supposition (see above) that the electronic transitions in the two groups of compounds are quite dissimilar.

In basic solution, the phenol molecule loses a proton and becomes a phenoxide ion.   Since the quinoid structures XV, XVI, and XVII now

XV   XVI   XVII

require no separation of electric charge, they should be relatively more stable, and hence more important in the resonance, than are their respective analogs, VI, VII, and VIII. Consequently, the difference between the resonance energies of the excited and ground states should be greater in the anion than in the neutral molecule, and so the wave length of the near-ultraviolet absorption should increase with the formation of the ion. Although the quinoid structures XV, XVI, and XVII do not have large dipole moments, they differ rather widely in their distributions of electric charge. Consequently, the intensity of the absorption should be greater with the ion than with the neutral molecule (cf. page 259). As is shown in Table 6·9, each of the foregoing predictions is confirmed by experiment.

With the nitrophenols, significant weights can be assigned to all the different quinoid structures that are analogous either to VI, VII, and VIII or to XVIII, XIX, and XX. With the ortho and para isomers, the additional quinoid structures XXI and XXII can also be involved in the

XVIII   XIX   XX

XXI   XXII   XXIII

resonance. Since these numerous, relatively unstable structures should lower the energies of the excited states more than they lower those of the respective ground states, we may anticipate that the nitrophenols will absorb light at longer wave lengths than either nitrobenzene or phenol. Moreover, as a result of the large dipole moments of the several quinoid structures, the absorptions should have relatively great intensities. And finally, since there is no meta quinoid structure analogous to XXI and XXII (however, see below), the absorption by *m*-nitrophenol may be expected to occur at shorter wave lengths, and to be less intense, than that by either of its isomers. As is shown in Table 6·9, however, these predictions are in no better than fair agreement with the experimental data.[39] In general, the observed intensities of the absorptions are indeed rather great, and they do vary in more or less the way expected. Nevertheless, the value of ε_{max} for the meta isomer is surprisingly large. Perhaps, with this substance, such meta quinoid structures as XXIII (with formal bonds) have significant effects on the spectrum. Much more serious difficulties, however, are encountered with the wave lengths of absorption. The values of λ_{max} are, in fact, smaller, rather than larger, with the nitrophenols than with nitrobenzene, and that for the meta isomer seems out of line with the others. Although no obvious, and entirely satisfactory, explanation for these failures of the simple theory presents itself, there is a possibility that the several absorption bands in the different substances have been incorrectly identified, and that we have accordingly been considering the relations among wave lengths and intensities that are not really comparable with one another.[6] (Cf. also footnote *f* of Table 6·9.) In any event, the problem of correctly accounting for the interactions of the nitro and hydroxyl groups with each other and with the aromatic ring is apparently too complex to be solved by the qualitative and approximate methods here employed.

The spectra of the three isomeric nitrophenoxide ions[39] are in much better agreement with expectation, since the absorptions occur at relatively long wave lengths and are relatively intense, and since that of the meta isomer occurs at the shortest wave lengths and is the least intense. The most surprising feature of these spectra is that ε_{max} is slightly greater for un-ionized *m*-nitrophenol than it is for the corresponding anion. No satisfactory explanation for this unexpected fact can be offered.

Although the predictions which were made above for the un-ionized nitrophenols were found to be rather unsatisfactory, the corresponding ones for the analogously constituted nitroanilines seem to be in complete agreement with the observed spectra.[39] (Cf. Table 6·9.) It is not at all clear, however, why these two groups of compounds should thus differ so markedly. Moreover, we should further note that the spectra of the nitroanilines become just as anomalous as those of the nitrophenols if the solvent is changed from water to hexane.[39] No satisfactory explanation for this effect of the solvent can be offered (however, see Section 6·9).

In acidic media, the nitroanilines are transformed into their respective cations $O_2N-C_6H_4-N^+H_3$. The three spectra then become very similar both to one another and to that of nitrobenzene[39] (cf. pages 291f).

6·6 Spectra of Dyes.[43]   The dyes, as a class, are more interesting than the simpler compounds that have been considered in the preceding sections. Unfortunately, however, the relative complexity of the dyes introduces additional difficulties into any attempt to explain their spectra. Since many quite different types of dye exist, the electronic transitions that are responsible for their observed colors may be expected to vary widely, and often to be poorly understood. We shall here, therefore, limit our attention to only a few important dyes, and, even with this small number of compounds, we shall in most instances give no more than incomplete descriptions and interpretations of the absorption bands that occur in the visible part of the spectrum.

The triphenylmethane dyes are relatively well understood from the theoretical point of view. With crystal violet, for example, the color resides in a cation which can be described as a hybrid of a tremendously large number of structures. If the formal positive charge is placed on the central carbon atom, each of the three rings can have either one of the two Kekulé structures; consequently, there are altogether 2^3, or 8, structures like I. Similarly, if the formal charge is instead placed on any one of the three equivalent nitrogen atoms, each of the two unaffected rings can have either one of the two Kekulé structures; consequently, there are altogether 3×2^2, or 12, structures like II. In addition, there are also

[43] Cf. E. Q. Adams and L. Rosenstein, *J. Am. Chem. Soc.* **36**, 1452 (1914); C. R. Bury, *ibid.* **57**, 2115 (1935); L. Pauling, *Proc. Natl. Acad. Sci. U. S.* **25**, 577 (1939).

12 structures like III, and 24 like IV.   If now we include the innumerable analogs of structures I–IV, in which one or more of the valence bonds

are ionic instead of covalent, and if we include all the further structures with one or more formal bonds, the total number of structures clearly becomes enormous.   The ground state of the cation is the most stable of the hybrids that can be described in terms of the resonance among all these structures, and the first excited state is the next most stable hybrid. From such general and qualitative considerations, we can obviously make no definite predictions regarding the spectrum of the substance.   We can, however, be fairly sure that, since the interaction of so many structures which have the same, or nearly the same, energy must decrease the spacing between the resulting levels, the first electronic band will occur at rather long wave lengths; and we can be quite sure that, since the structures I–IV, etc., differ widely in their distributions of charge, the absorption will be relatively intense.   Although the exact values of λ_{max} and of ε_{max} depend somewhat on concentration (presumably because of dimerization), there can be no doubt that these predictions are in agreement with observation; in an approximately 10^{-5} N aqueous solution, for example, λ_{max} and ε_{max} are equal, respectively, to about 5900 A and 85,000.[44]

The resonance in the cation of crystal violet is sometimes considered to include only the twenty structures of types I and II.   We can easily see, however, that this simplification of the treatment is not legitimate.   As a result of the great difference in the

[44] L. Michaelis and S. Granick, *J. Am. Chem. Soc.* **67**, 1212 (1945).

distributions of electric charge (cf. condition 2, Section 1·4), there can be no effective resonance between any structure of type I and any of type II; similarly, there can be no effective resonance between any two structures of type II if, in these structures, the positive charges are on different nitrogen atoms.   On the other hand, there can be relatively effective resonance between any structure of type I and any of type IV, between any of type IV and the appropriate one of type III; and between any of type III and the appropriate one of type II.   (The significance of the present use of the word "appropriate" is that, in each instance, the resonance under consideration must be between structures in which the positive charges are on atoms that are bonded either to a common third atom or else directly to each other.)   Since the structures of types III and IV are therefore required in order that the resonance may include all the ones of types I and II, it is evident that none of the structures can legitimately be neglected.

When a solution of crystal violet is made basic, the colored cation is changed into the neutral *color base*, V.   Since the three *p*-dimethylamino-

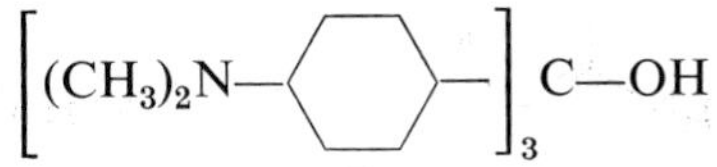

$$\left[(CH_3)_2N-\left\langle \bigcirc \right\rangle - \right]_3 C-OH$$

V

phenyl groups are here "insulated" from each other by a saturated carbon atom, the possibilities for resonance are essentially the same as in dimethylaniline.   Like this simpler amine, therefore, the substance is colorless.   On the other hand, in a strongly acidic solution, the cation of crystal violet acquires an additional proton and is transformed into a divalent cation, which is again a hybrid of a great many structures, but which can here be conveniently represented by the single typical structure VI.   The possibilities for resonance are now essentially the same as with

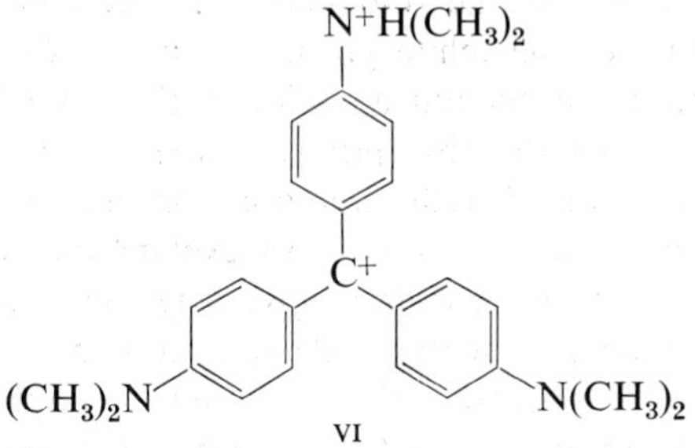

VI

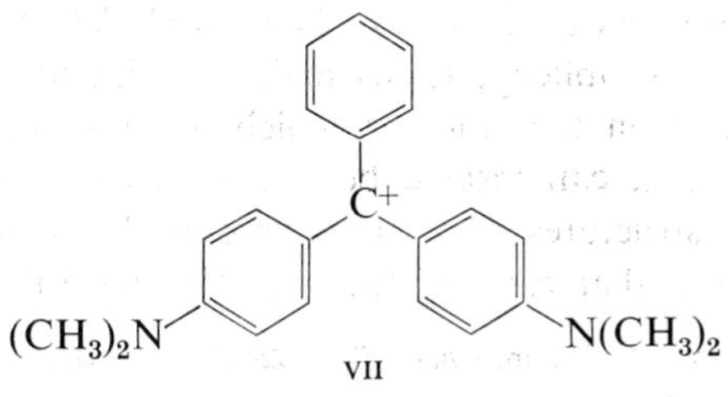

VII

the cation, VII, of malachite green, and so it is not surprising that the two ions have nearly the same color.[44, 45]   Indeed, with each of these dyes, λ_{max} is about 6200 A and ε_{max} is about 90,000–100,000 (see the following paragraph).   In still more acidic solution, the doubly charged cation of crystal violet acquires still another proton and becomes the triply charged cation VIII which, like its analog IX, is yellow.

It appears evident that the resonance must be less important in the univalent ion, VII, of malachite green and in the divalent ion, VI, of crystal violet than it is in the univalent ion, I–IV, of the latter dye.   Consequently, the fact that the absorptions by the first and second of these ions occur at longer wave lengths, and are more intense, than that by the third may be somewhat surprising.   An explanation for this difference among the several spectra has been given by Lewis and Calvin[45] but, since it is based upon an essentially classical approach to the problem, it cannot easily be discussed from the viewpoint employed in this chapter. We shall here, therefore, suggest an alternative explanation which is, however, not unrelated to the one of Lewis and Calvin.

For the sake of simplicity, let us make the drastic, and actually unjustifiable, assumption that the ion which we have represented by the structures I–IV, etc., can instead be described as a hybrid of just the three equivalent structures which are symbolically depicted by the diagrams X–XII, and that each of the ions VI and VII can be similarly

[45] G. N. Lewis and M. Calvin, *Chem. Revs.* **25**, 273 (1939).

described as a hybrid of the two completely analogous structures XIII and XIV. (As should be evident, each of the diagrams X–XIV can be

considered to imply a hybrid of many structures belonging to the several types described above.) Now, in Figure 6·2. the electronic energy W of any individual one of the structures X–XIV is represented by the height of the horizontal line AB above some suitably chosen base line. (The diagram is here simplified by neglect of the rotational and vibrational energies. See Figure 6·1, Section 6·1.) In the ion VI, or VII, the resonance between the structures XIII and XIV leads to two hybrids with the energies represented by the lines CD and EF; the excitation energy associated with the electronic transition between the hybrids is then given by the vertical distance DF.

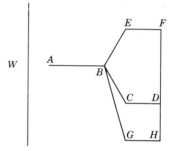

Fig. 6·2. A diagram illustrating the electronic energies W of the individual structures X–XIV (line AB) and of their resulting hybrids (lines CD, EF, and GH).

If, in the more complex univalent cation of crystal violet, the resonance could be restricted to just two of the three structures X–XII, say to XI and XII, then the resulting hybrids would again have the energies CD and EF. When resonance among all three structures is allowed, however, three hybrids must result. Because of the symmetry of the ion, two of these hybrids can be shown (by a method which has been outlined by Pauling,[43] but which is not describable except in mathematical terms) to have the same energy, whereas the third can be shown to have a different energy. To the present crude approximation, the energy of the double level is given by the line EF, whereas that of the single level is given by the line GH, and the excitation energy HF is calculated to be 1.5 times as great as DF. On account of the drastic approximations involved in the treatment, no reliance can be placed in the accuracy of the factor 1.5; and, in fact, the experimental value is more nearly 1.06 (see above). We can, however, have some faith in the qualitative conclusion that the increase in the number of contributing structures from two to three does not decrease the excitation energy, but instead increases it.

The further conclusion that the excited state of the crystal violet cation is a double one is a direct consequence of merely the symmetry of the ion. Since this conclusion is therefore independent of the special assumptions made in the calculation, it also may be considered reliable. Lewis and Bigeleisen[46] have, in fact, obtained good evidence that, as predicted, the observed absorption by crystal violet at 5900 A consists of two different bands which are superimposed on each other; for, when the symmetry of the ion is decreased by suitable substitution, the bands separate and can be individually recognized.

The fact that the absorption by crystal violet is less intense than that by malachite green is possibly due to the greater diffuseness of the ionic charge in the former substance. In terms of the oversimplified models introduced above, this charge is distributed among three equivalent positions (structures X–XII) in the cation of crystal violet, but between only two such positions (structures XIII and XIV) in that of malachite green. Although this ratio of exactly 3:2 would not be quantitatively valid in any less approximate treatment, the qualitative difference thus found between the two dyes must certainly be correct.

If the amino, or substituted amino, groups of crystal violet and its analogs are replaced by hydroxyl groups, we might expect that the colors of the substances would remain more or less unaffected. Although this prediction is indeed essentially correct, the changes in the structures of the compounds lead to changes in their chemical properties. Consequently, the parallelism between the two groups of dyes is not as close as might have been anticipated. A few examples will here be sufficient to illustrate the types of behavior that are encountered.

p-Hydroxytriphenylcarbinol, XV, is colorless since, from the spectroscopic viewpoint, it is equivalent to a mixture of toluene and p-cresol.[47] In basic solution, this phenolic carbinol is transformed into the corresponding anion XVI; in the process, the ultraviolet absorption is slightly

HO—⟨ ⟩—C$(C_6H_5)_2$ $^-$O—⟨ ⟩—C$(C_6H_5)_2$
                | |
               OH   OH
               XV   XVI

displaced toward longer wave lengths, and it becomes slightly more intense. This change is, of course, the same as that observed with phenol (see Table 6·9, Section 6·5, and also the discussion on pages 292f). The substance is, however, easily dehydrated to fuchsone, XVII, which has a

---

[46] G. N. Lewis and J. Bigeleisen, *J. Am. Chem. Soc.* **65**, 2102 (1943).
[47] P. Ramart-Lucas, *Bull. soc. chim. France* [5] **8**, 865 (1941).

strong band with $\lambda_{max} \cong 3900$ A and $\varepsilon_{max} \cong 30,000.$[47]   Since this band extends into the visible, the substance is colored.   The long wave length and high intensity of the absorption are presumably due both to the

$$O=\!\!\left\langle\ \ \right\rangle\!\!=C(C_6H_5)_2$$

XVII

presence of a quinoid system (see page 285) and to the conjugation of this system with the two phenyl groups.

Slightly more complicated analogs of the color base XV and dye XVII are given, respectively, by tri-(p-hydroxyphenyl)-carbinol, XVIII, and aurin, XIX (R = H).[47]   As before, the carbinol is colorless, but its

$$HO\!\!-\!\!\left\langle\ \ \right\rangle\!\!-\!\!\underset{\underset{OH}{|}}{C}(C_6H_4\!\!-\!\!OH\!\!-\!\!p)_2$$

XVIII

$$O=\!\!\left\langle\ \ \right\rangle\!\!=C(C_6H_4\!\!-\!\!OR\!\!-\!\!p)_2$$

XIX

dehydration product is colored.   Since the preparation of pure aurin is relatively difficult, the most significant data are presumably those obtained for its dimethyl ether, XIX (R = CH_3), with which $\lambda_{max} \cong 4300$ A and $\varepsilon_{max} \cong 30,000.$[47]   The fact that aurin thus absorbs light of longer wave length than does fuchsone is doubtless due to the same factors that are responsible for the similar difference between the spectra of anisole and benzene (see pages 290f).   In alkaline solution, aurin is transformed into an anion which is a hybrid of all the many structures analogous to the ones which, on pages 295f, were said to contribute to the states of the crystal violet cation.   The most significant difference between the ions of aurin and of crystal violet is, in fact, that their charges are of opposite sign.   Since, however, the types of resonance are rather similar, we cannot be surprised that the spectra are also rather similar.   The anion of aurin has an absorption band with $\lambda_{max} \cong 5300$ A and $\varepsilon_{max} \cong 70,000.$[47] The reason why each of these values is greater than with neutral aurin is presumably that only with the ion is the particularly effective resonance among equivalent structures possible.   In strongly acidic solution, aurin becomes even more closely analogous to crystal violet for, under these conditions, it is transformed into a cation that must be a hybrid of structures which differ from I–IV, etc., only in the replacement of the three dimethylamino groups by hydroxyl groups.   The value of λ_{max} is about 4800 A,[48] which is less than with the corresponding anion, but greater than with the neutral molecule. The value which is reported[48] for ε_{max} is apparently not directly comparable with the ones given above for either the neutral or the anionic dye, but there can be no doubt that the absorption is again intense.

A dye which is, in a sense, intermediate between fuchsone and aurin, but which is much better known than either, is phenolphthalein. Strangely enough, the considerable amount of work which has been done on this substance and its derivatives has not yet led to complete agreement regarding the interpretation of the different spectra that are observed under different conditions or even, in a few instances, regarding the spectroscopic data themselves. In a neutral medium, phenolphthalein undoubtedly has the lactone structure XX. On the other hand, in a medium which is basic, but not too basic (see below), it is transformed into the red salt that is responsible for the familiar color of the indicator. This salt apparently contains a divalent anion which is a hybrid of structures XXI–XXIV and their numerous analogs, ionic counterparts, etc. Some

[48] W. R. Orndorff, R. C. Gibbs, S. A. McNulty, and C. V. Shapiro, *J. Am. Chem. Soc.* **49**, 1545 (1927).

authors[49] have maintained that the red anion is instead a univalent one that is a hybrid of structures like XXV, etc. It would be difficult, however, to understand how this latter ion could absorb light of such long wave length, since its structure is similar to that of the monomethyl ester, XXVI, which is orange in neutral solution, and red only in the presence of base.[50] The analogous dimethyl derivative, XXVII (R = CH$_3$) is orange red, but its solution in ether is yellow;[50] and the corresponding diethyl compound, XXVII (R = C$_2$H$_5$) is yellow even in the solid state.[51]

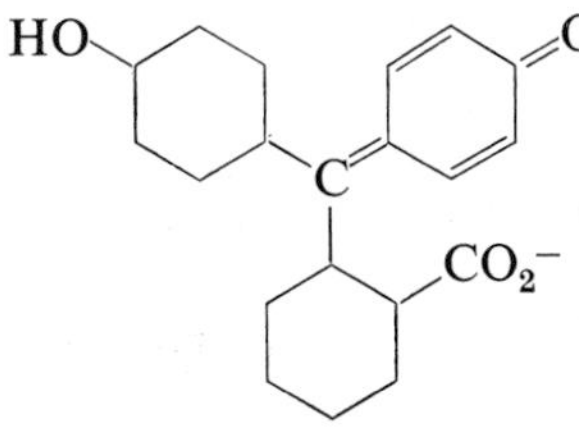

XXV 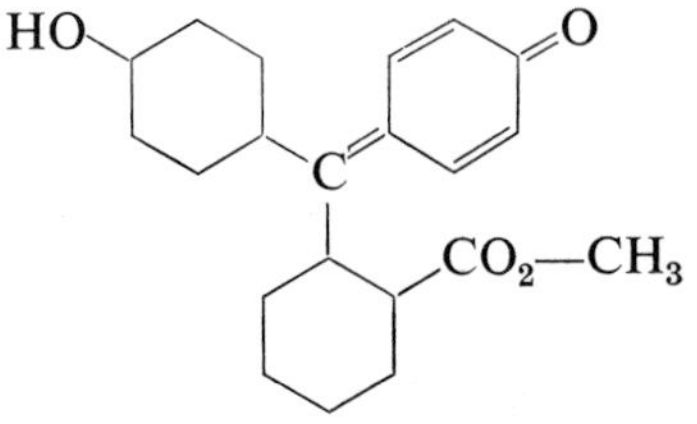   XXVI

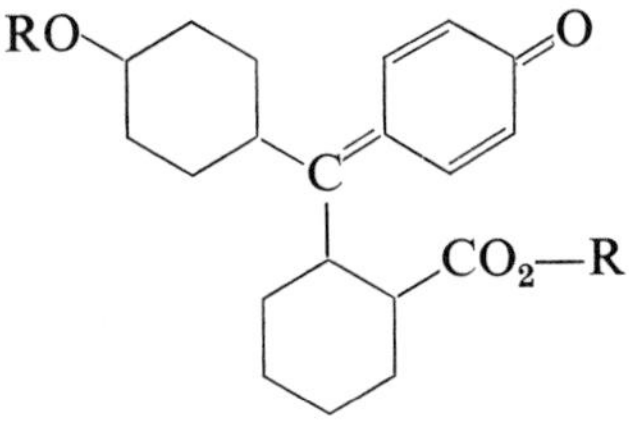

XXVII

Several authors[52] have isolated colorless monosodium and monopotassium salts of phenolphthalein, and these must surely contain the ion XXV. Consequently, the initial statement that the red anion is the divalent one is well supported although, as was implied above, it is not universally accepted.[49]

In extremely basic solution, phenolphthalein again becomes colorless. The explanation for this change is generally agreed to be that a trivalent anion with the structure XXVIII is formed (cf. structure XVI). In strongly acidic solution, red colors are observed both with phenolphthalein itself and with its alkyl derivatives XXVI and XXIX.[50, 53] Presumably,

[49] See, for example, Buu-Hoï, *Bull. soc. chim. France* [5] **8**, 165 (1941).

[50] A. G. Green and P. E. King, *Ber.* **40**, 3724 (1907).

[51] R. Meyer and K. Marx, *Ber.* **40**, 3603 (1907).

[52] See, for example, P. A. Kober, J. T. Marshall, and E. N. Rosenfeld, *J. Am. Chem. Soc.* **34**, 1424 (1912); H. Bassett and P. Halton, *J. Chem. Soc.* **123**, 1291 (1923).

[53] A. Baeyer, *Ann.* **202**, 36 (1880); J. Herzig and H. Meyer, *Ber.* **28**, 3258 (1895); K. H. Meyer and A. Hantzsch, *ibid.* **40**, 3479 (1907).

under these conditions the neutral molecules are transformed into cations which are closely analogous to that of malachite green (cf. the above discussion of aurin in acidic solution).

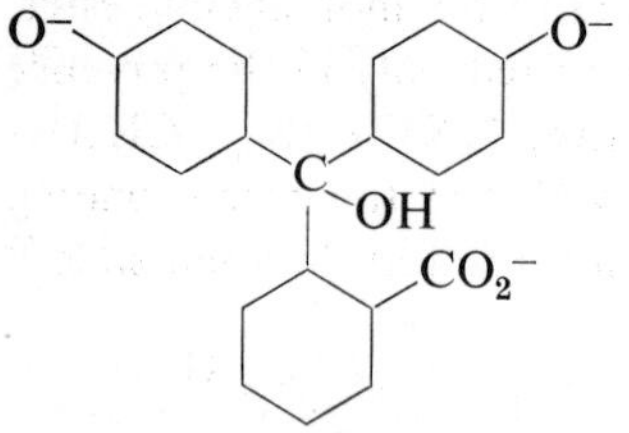

XXVIII 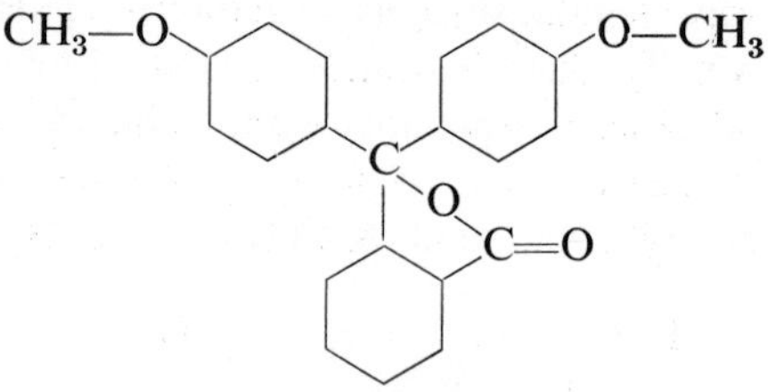   XXIX

As with the most typical of the above triphenylmethane dyes, the members of several other classes of dye are similarly salts, in which either the cations or the anions are intensely colored. With one typical series of *cyanine* dyes, the colors reside in cations which are hybrids not only of the two extreme structures XXX and XXXI, with $n = 0, 1, 2, \cdots$, but also of the numerous intermediate structures in which, as in structure XXXII, the ionic charge is on one of the ring carbon atoms or on an atom

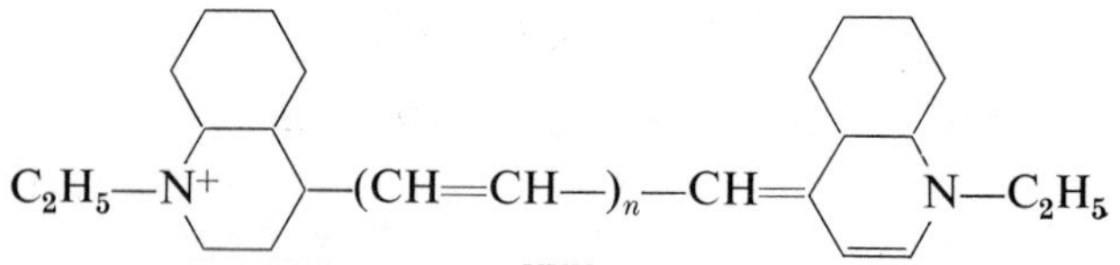

XXX

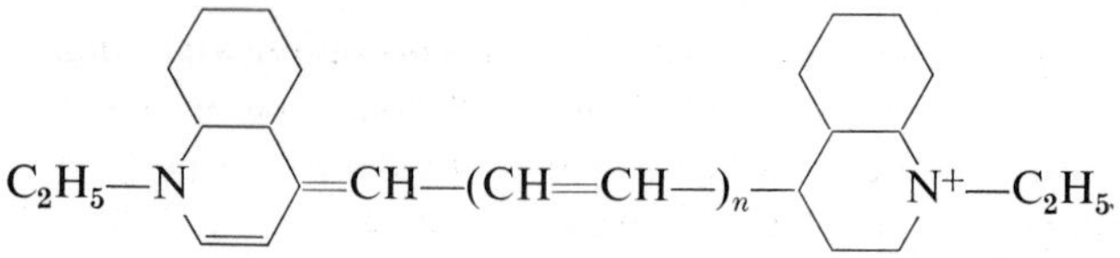

XXXI

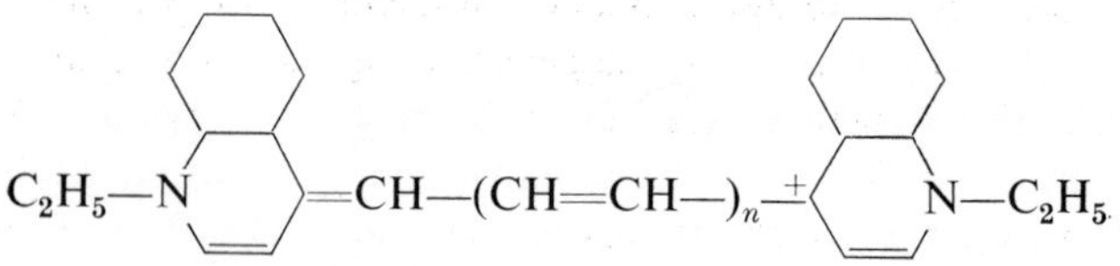

XXXII

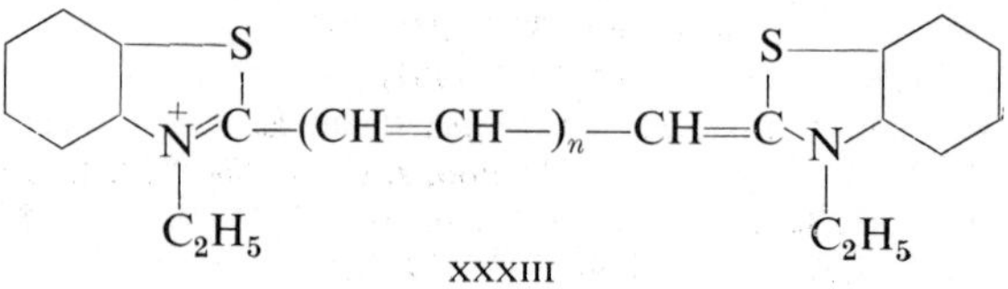

XXXIII

between the two rings; in a second such series, the limiting structures corresponding to XXX and XXXI are, respectively, XXXIII and XXXIV; an intermediate one corresponding to XXXII is XXXV; and so on. For

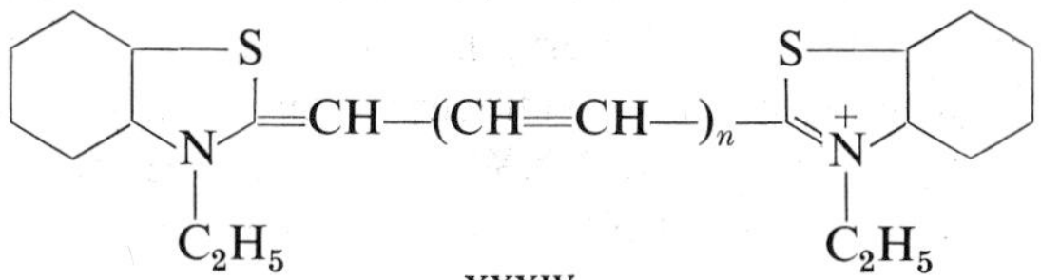

XXXIV

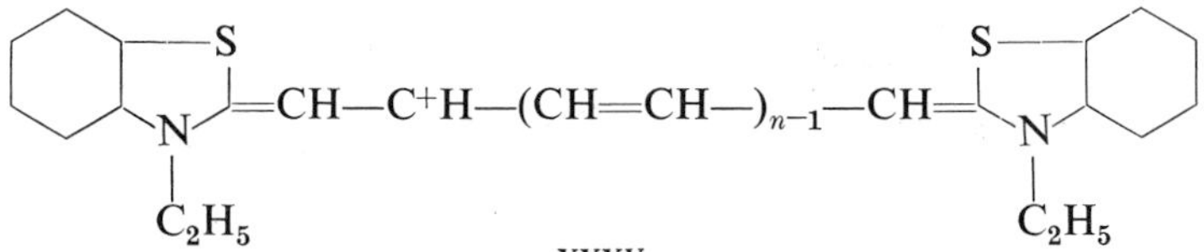

XXXV

the sake of brevity, we have here left implicit both the resonance within the completely aromatic rings and that involving structures which have either formal bonds or more than one formal charge; in the following discussion, we shall continue to use this simplification and, in addition, we shall frequently also represent a cation by only a single typical structure or by only the two extreme structures like XXX and XXXI, or XXXIII and XXXIV. In each instance, however, we must bear in mind that there is resonance with all the additional structures which we thus neglect to mention, and, in fact, that this resonance is of the greatest importance (cf. the paragraph in fine print on pages 296f).

The dyes that are represented by the structures XXX–XXXV are symmetrical since the two ring systems at the ends of the unsaturated chains are completely equivalent, and since the two limiting structures are therefore likewise completely equivalent. In any such series of symmetrical cyanine dyes, the wave length of the first absorption band is found[54] to increase by a nearly constant amount of approximately 1000 A, when the value of n is increased from 0 to 1, from 1 to 2, and so on. In this respect, the dyes are markedly different from the conjugated polyenes, with which the wave lengths are not evenly spaced but instead converge toward a limiting value (cf. pages 260 and 266). A possible reason for this difference is that, although there are two completely equivalent extreme structures (XXX and XXXI, or XXXIII and XXXIV) for each of the above cyanine dyes, there is only one reasonably stable structure for a polyene. Moreover, although the carbon-carbon distances in the

[54] Cf. L. G. S. Brooker, G. H. Keyes, and W. W. Williams, *J. Am. Chem. Soc.* **64**, 199 (1942); L. G. S. Brooker, *Revs. Mod. Phys.* **14**, 275 (1942).

chain of $=$CH— groups ·that connect the terminal ring systems in a symmetrical cyanine dye are doubtless at least approximately equal, the corresponding distances in a polyene must be alternately long and short (cf. page 192). In order to obtain evidence to show whether or not this proposed explanation is satisfactory, Brooker and his associates[54] have examined a large number of unsymmetrical dyes, such as the ones for which the extreme structures are XXXVI and XXXVII, or XXXVIII and XXXIX. With the first of these dyes, there is no obvious reason why

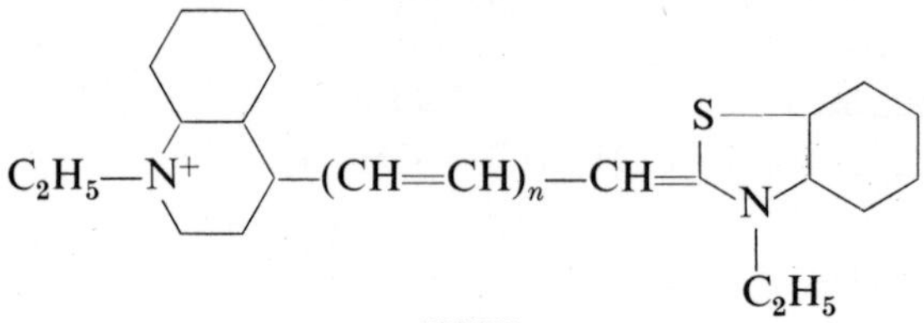

XXXVI

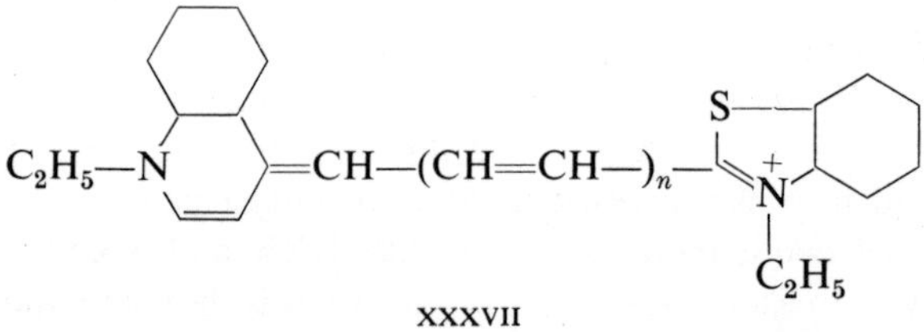

XXXVII

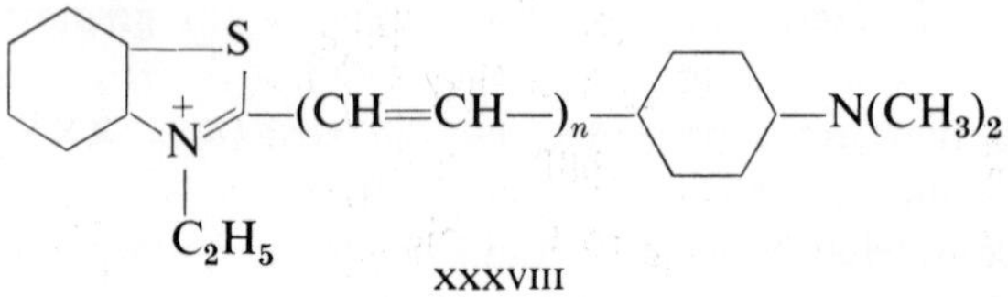

XXXVIII

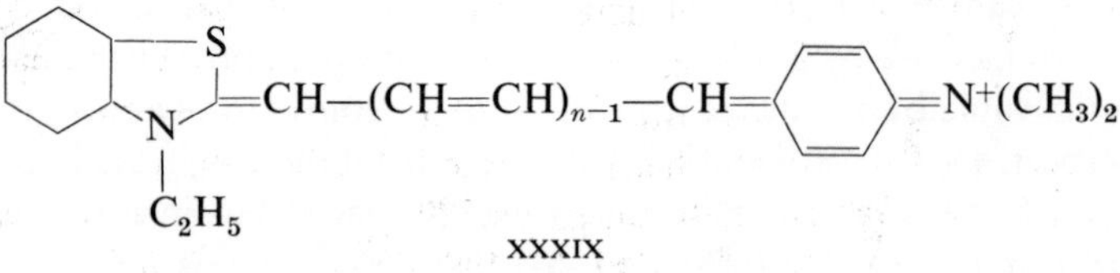

XXXIX

either of the two structures should be much more stable than the other; consequently, although these structures are not exactly equivalent, the dependence of the wave length upon the value of n should be similar to that for a symmetrical cyanine. This expectation has been confirmed by experiment. On the other hand, with the second of the above dyes, the structure XXXIX should be much less stable than XXXVIII because the number of fully aromatic rings is two less in the former structure than in the latter. (The thiazole ring is here considered to be "fully aromatic.") Consequently, the dependence of the wave length upon the value of n should here be similar to that for a polyene. This expectation also has been confirmed by experiment.

The spectrum of an unsymmetrical cyanine dye is affected in still another way by the relative stabilities of the two extreme structures. If these structures have nearly the same energy, then the value of λ_{max} is close to the arithmetic mean of the values for the two corresponding symmetrical dyes; but, if the structures have widely different energies, the value of λ_{max} is appreciably less than the mean.[54] For example, with the symmetrical dyes XXX and XXXIII ($n = 1$), the values of λ_{max} are, respectively, 7050 A and 5575 A; the average of these values is 6313 A, and the value for the corresponding unsymmetrical dye XXXVI ($n = 1$) is 6300 A. On the other hand, with the symmetrical dyes XXXIII ($n = 2$) and XL, the values of λ_{max} are, respectively, 6540 A and 7010 A;

$$(CH_3)_2N-\!\!\left\langle\!\!\bigcirc\!\!\right\rangle\!\!-CH\!\!=\!\!CH\!\!-\!\!CH\!\!=\!\!\left\langle\!\!\bigcirc\!\!\right\rangle\!\!=\!\!N^+(CH_3)_2$$

XL

the average of these values is 6775 A, and the value observed for the unsymmetrical dye XXXVIII ($n = 2$) is 5700 A. As expected, the *deviation* is much greater with the latter dyes than with the former ones. In general, with a given pair of terminal groups, the deviation increases with n; and, with a given value of n, it increases with the difference between the stabilities of the extreme structures. If the particular terminal group that carries the positive charge in the more stable of these structures is described as the more *basic* of the two, then, with the aid of this last regularity, one can arrange the various groups in such an order that each is more basic than any of the others which precede it, but less basic than any of those which follow it.

Azomethane, $CH_3—N\!\!=\!\!N—CH_3$, may be considered the parent compound for all the azo dyes. Its first electronic absorption band, however, occurs[55] in the ultraviolet ($\lambda_{max} = 3400$ A) and is rather weak ($\varepsilon_{max} = 15$). The electronic transition that is responsible for this band is therefore presumably of the type $N \to A$, which was described in Section 6·4. The fact that the wave length is here greater than with an analogous carbonyl compound may be related to the fact that nitrogen is a less electronegative element than oxygen, so that its electrons are relatively easily excited.

The red color of azobenzene is due to a weak band which, with both

[55] G. Kortüm, *Z. physik. Chem.* B **50**, 361 (1941).

stereoisomeric forms, has a λ_{max} of about 4300 A.[56, 57, 58] Perhaps unexpectedly, the intensity for the *cis* isomer, XLI ($\varepsilon_{max} = 1518$) is greater than that for the more extended *trans* isomer, XLII ($\varepsilon_{max} = 510$).

XLI   XLII

XLIII

This fact, together with the comparative weakness of the absorption for both isomers, strongly suggests that the electronic transition which is here involved is not of the $N \rightarrow V$ type; for, if resonance with such quinoid structures (not configurations) as XLIII, etc., were important, the intensity ought to increase when the molecule is made more nearly linear, and it ought also to be considerably greater than is observed. Probably this band at 4300 A is of the $N \rightarrow A$ type,[58, 59] and its wave length is greater than with azomethane because of the conjugation of the benzene rings with the nitrogen-nitrogen double bond. The $N \rightarrow V$ bands are then the more intense ones which occur at shorter wave lengths; with the *cis* and *trans* isomers, λ_{max} is about 2800 A and 3200 A, respectively, and ε_{max} is 5260 and 21,300, respectively. These bands for the two substances differ in at least approximately the way expected, and they closely resemble the corresponding bands of *cis* and *trans* stilbene; these latter compounds can have no $N \rightarrow A$ transitions, and so they do not absorb in the region of 4300 A.[58]

With (*trans?*) p-dimethylaminoazobenzene, XLIV, the first absorption band has $\lambda_{max} = 4100$ A and $\varepsilon_{max} = 30,000$.[57, 60] The high intensity suggests that the transition is of the $N \rightarrow V$ type. If this interpretation is correct, the band is at much longer wave lengths than is its analog with azobenzene itself, and so the presence of the dimethylamino group must

[56] A. Winkel and H. Siebert, *Ber.* **74**, 670 (1941).

[57] J. A. Miller, R. W. Sapp, and E. C. Miller, *J. Am. Chem. Soc.* **70**, 3458 (1948).

[58] P. P. Birnbaum, J. H. Linford, and D. W. G. Style, *Trans. Faraday Soc.* **49**, 735 (1953).

[59] For additional, quite conclusive evidence, see M. Kasha, *Discussions Faraday Soc.* **9**, 14 (1950).

[60] A. Pongratz, G. Markgraf, and E. Mayer-Pitsch, *Ber.* **71**, 1287 (1938).

have markedly decreased the excitation energy. A reasonable explanation for this effect is that the quinoid structures like XLV, etc., are possible

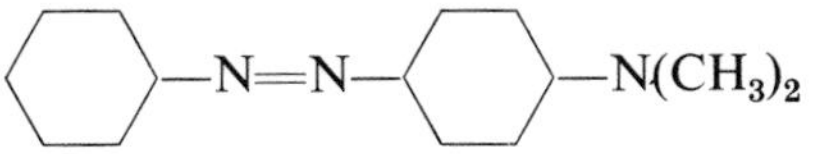

XLIV

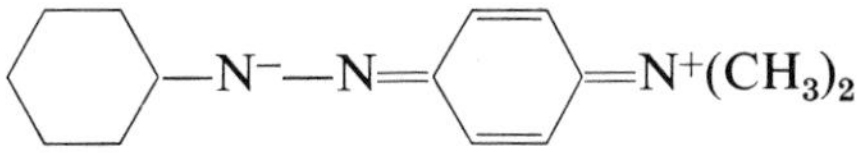

XLV

only for the substituted azo compound, and that these structures stabilize the excited state more than they do the ground state. We may presume that the $N \to A$ band is again relatively weak, as with azobenzene, and that it is hidden by the stronger $N \to V$ band (cf. the discussion of p-hydroxyazobenzene, below). When the neutral molecule XLIV is transformed into the quaternary cation XLVI, the structures like XLV, etc., are no longer possible; the spectrum therefore becomes practically identical with that of unsubstituted azobenzene.[60] In an acidic medium,

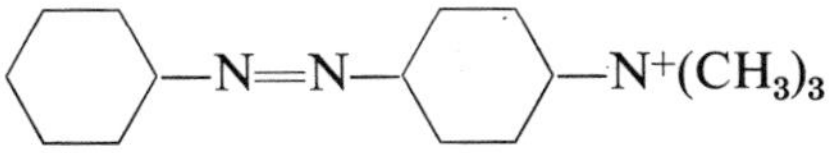

XLVI

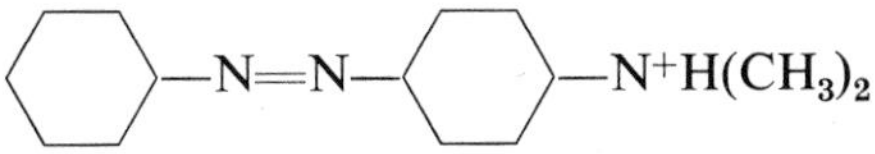

XLVII

on the other hand, the absorption by p-dimethylaminoazobenzene comes to still longer wave lengths ($\lambda_{max} = 5180$ A) and its intensity increases ($\varepsilon_{max} = 38,000$).[57] Clearly, therefore, the cation that is formed cannot have the structure XLVII, analogous to XLVI, but must instead be a hybrid of such structures as XLVIII, XLIX, etc.[60a] Since these latter

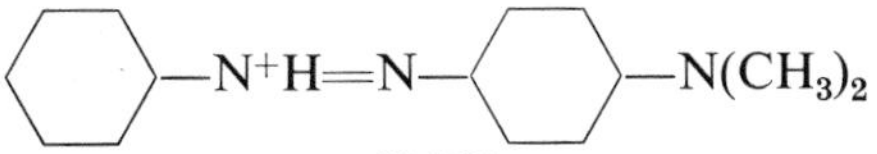

XLVIII

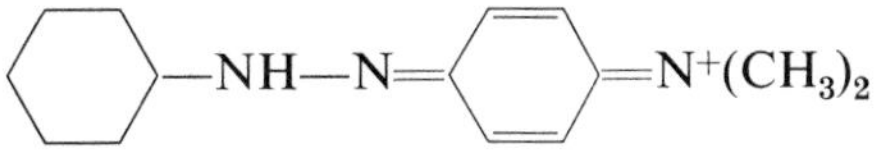

XLIX

[60a] For evidence suggesting that this conclusion is incorrect, however, see I. M. Klotz, H. A. Fiess, J. Y. Chen Ho, and M. Mellody, *J. Am. Chem. Soc.* **76**, 5136 (1954).

structures are individually of about the same stability, and since they have widely different distributions of charge, the resonance among them would be expected to lead to absorption bands that occur at relatively long wave lengths and that have relatively high intensities.

The structures that have the largest weights in the ground and excited states of p-hydroxyazobenzene, L, are closely analogous to the ones that are most important in the corresponding states of p-dimethylaminoazobenzene, XLIV.   Apparently, however, the electrons which, in structure

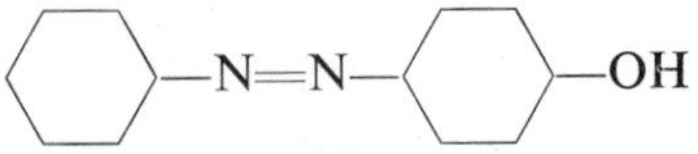

L

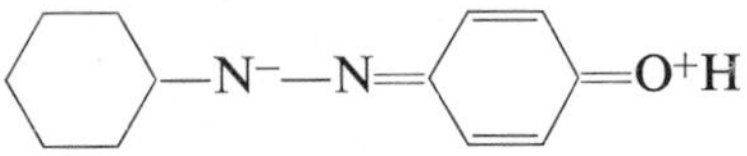

LI

L, belong to unshared pairs on the oxygen atom are less able to be shared with the aromatic rings than are the corresponding electrons in the dimethylaminoazo compound.   Consequently, the quinoid structures LI, etc., should be less important in the resonance than their respective analogs XLV, etc.   It is therefore not surprising that, although the first intense, and completely resolved, band of the hydroxyazo compound has an ε_{max} that is equal to about 25,000, the corresponding value of λ_{max} is only about 3500 A.[60]   From the shape of the published curve, however, this band can be seen partially to overlap a second one that has an ε_{max} of perhaps 1200 and a λ_{max} of perhaps 4300 A.   A reasonable interpretation of the data is that the relatively strong $N \rightarrow V$ band and the relatively weak $N \rightarrow A$ band, which were assumed (see above) to occur at nearly the same wave length with p-dimethylaminoazobenzene, are here more widely separated.   The reason for this difference between the spectra of the two analogous compounds is then presumably that, as has just been noted, the quinoid structures like LI are less important than the ones like XLV.

In a basic medium, the neutral molecule of p-hydroxyazobenzene, L, is transformed into an anion that can be described as a hybrid of such structures as LII, LIII, LIV, etc.   Since the quinoid structures like LIV

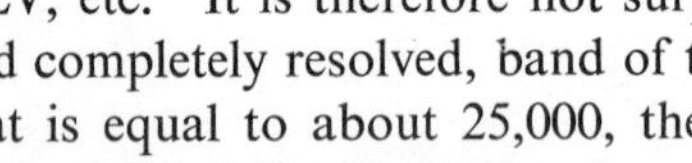

LII

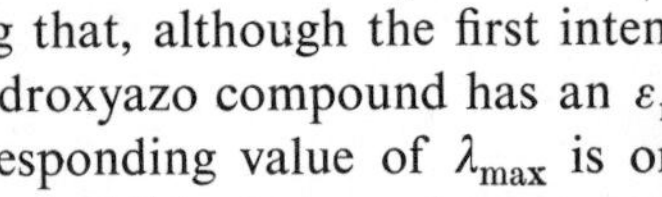

LIII

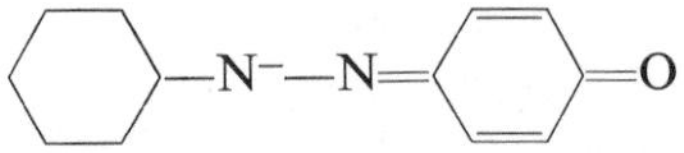

LIV

do not require separations of charge, they can be expected to have greater effects upon the spectrum of the anion than their analogs LI, etc., have upon that of the molecule.　In agreement with expectation, the first intense band, which has an ε_{max} of about 25,000 and so is presumably of the $N \to V$ type, now appears at about 4400 A.[60, 61]　The $N \to A$ band, if it is present at all, is again obscured.

With many of the remaining classes of dye, the interpretations that can at present be given for the observed spectra are even less complete, and more tentative, than they are with the classes already considered.　A single example will here be sufficient to illustrate the kinds of problem that are encountered.　In the molecule of indigo, LV, there is a rather

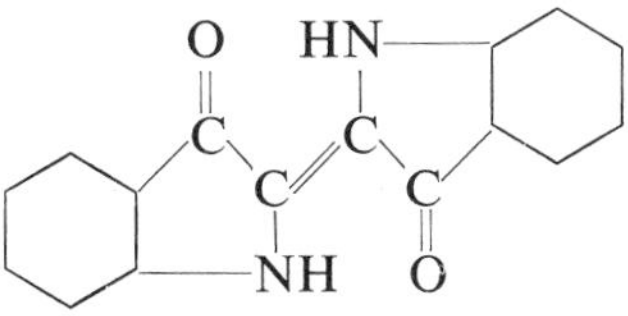

O　HN
C　C
C　C
NH　O

LV

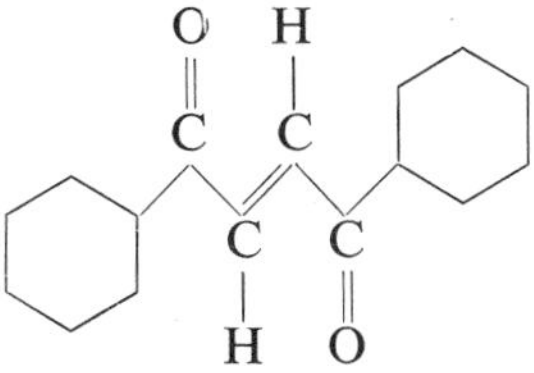

O　H
C　C
C　C
H　O

LVI

extended conjugated system which is similar to that in a quinone.　The absorption by the former substance, however, occurs at such long wave lengths and is so intense that it can hardly correspond to the band that is responsible for the faintly yellow color of, for example, p-benzoquinone (cf. Table 6·8, Section 6·4).　Moreover, the more closely analogous *trans* 1,2-dibenzoylethylene, LVI, is also only yellow, and its first strong absorption ($\varepsilon_{max} \cong 20,000$) occurs at about 2700 A.[62]　Clearly, therefore, the intense blue color of indigo must be dependent upon the presence of the two nitrogen atoms.　Although the electronic transition responsible for the absorption has not been definitely identified, we may presume that it is of the $N \to V$ type and that, since each nitrogen atom in the conventional structure LV has an unshared pair of electrons and is bonded to two different unsaturated atoms, both the ground and excited

[61] W. R. Brode, *Bur. Standards J. Research* **2**, 501 (1929).

[62] L. P. Kuhn, R. E. Lutz, and C. R. Bauer, *J. Am. Chem. Soc.* **72**, 5058 (1950).

states are hybrids in which such structures as LVII–LIX have large weights. From such a qualitative treatment, we can, however, conclude only that

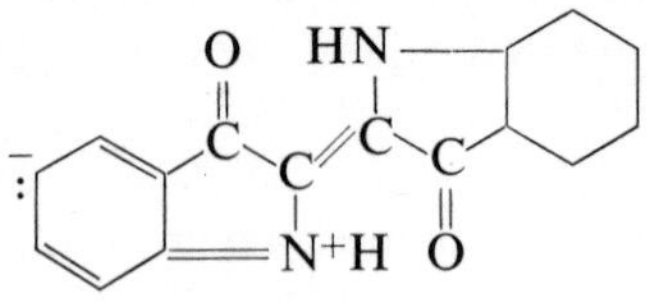

LVII 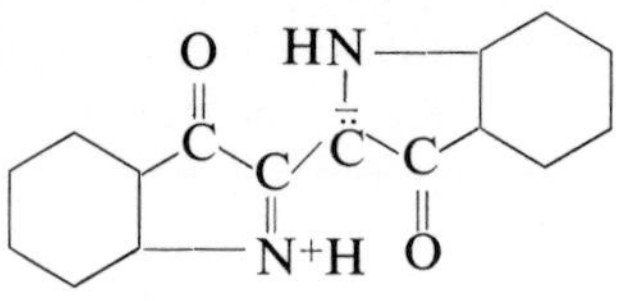   LVIII

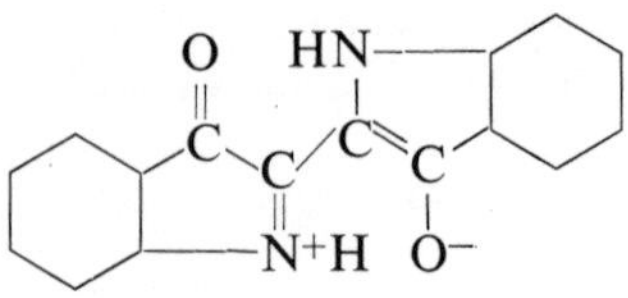

LIX

the strong absorption bands of indigo should occur at longer wave lengths than do those of 1,2-dibenzoylethylene, and we cannot claim that we have explained the color of the dye.

6·7   Spectra of Molecular Compounds.[63]   In Section 2·11, we outlined a plausible interpretation of the attractive forces that act between the components of several important kinds of loose addition compound.   The complex formed between benzene and iodine, for example, was there explained as a hybrid of the two structures I and II.   In the normal state,

I 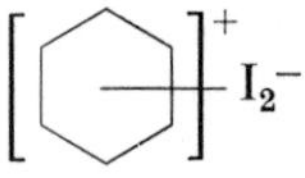   II

the first of these structures must have much the greater weight, so that in some respects the complex differs only slightly from a simple mixture of its two components.   For this reason, the absorption in the visible and near-ultraviolet regions is essentially a superposition of the absorptions that are characteristic of pure benzene and of pure iodine.[64, 65]   The molecular compound has been found,[64] however, to have one strong band which is peculiar to it alone, and which therefore must be explained in some different way.   Mulliken[65] has suggested that this band, for which λ_{max} is 2970 A and ε_{max} is 9800, is a direct consequence of the resonance

[63] Cf. H. McConnell, J. S. Ham, and J. R. Platt, *J. Chem. Phys.* **21**, 66 (1953) and further references given there.

[64] H. A. Benesi and J. H. Hildebrand, *J. Am. Chem. Soc.* **71**, 2703 (1949).   Cf. also J. S. Ham, J. R. Platt, and H. McConnell, *J. Chem. Phys.* **19**, 1301 (1951).

[65] R. S. Mulliken, *J. Am. Chem. Soc.* **74**, 811 (1952).

between structures I and II. From these two structures, there must result two hybrids; the more stable hybrid is the ground state, discussed above, and the less stable hybrid is the excited state for the electronic transition. Since the former hybrid can receive only a small contribution from structure II, whereas the latter can receive only a small contribution from structure I, no great error would be introduced if the transition were described merely as one from structure I to structure II. The original viewpoint is, however, the more accurate and the less likely to cause confusion; it will, accordingly, be adopted in the following discussion. Since structures I and II differ considerably in their distributions of charge, the absorption should be rather intense, as it is indeed observed to be. Mulliken has, in fact, carried through approximate calculations which lead to results in satisfactory agreement with the experimental values for both the wave length and the intensity of the absorption.

The value given above for the molecular extinction coefficient of the benzene-iodine complex is based[64] on the assumption that all the iodine which has been added to the solution is combined with the benzene. Since, however, the complex is doubtless appreciably dissociated into its components, its concentration must be less than that assumed, and the *true* value of ε_{max} must be correspondingly greater than 9800.

Although the above explanation for the spectrum of the benzene-iodine complex appears to be quite satisfactory, there is also an alternative which here requires consideration. Since the intensity of an absorption that is due to a singlet-triplet transition is in general increased by the proximity of heavy atoms,[34] the band at 2970 A may merely be one which is too weak to be readily observed with pure benzene, but which is "enhanced" by the iodine atoms.[66] Such a band has, in fact been discovered by Ham,[67] who has also shown that the relevant excited state is most probably a triplet. There is at present no entirely conclusive way in which a decision between these two conflicting interpretations of the spectrum can be made; on the whole, however, the one given originally seems to be the more generally satisfactory.[66]

The molecular compound that is formed between anthracene and 1,3,5-trinitrobenzene can be represented as a hybrid of the structures III and IV, with the first doubtless having much the greater weight in the ground state (cf. Section 2·11). In solution in carbon tetrachloride, the spectrum of the complex resembles a superposition of the spectra of the components.[68] A significant difference, however, is observed, for, although neither anthracene nor 1,3,5-trinitrobenzene alone has an

[66] H. McConnell, J. S. Ham, and J. R. Platt, *J. Chem. Phys.* **21**, 66 (1953).

[67] J. S. Ham, *J. Chem. Phys.* **21**, 756 (1953).

[68] G. Briegleb and T. Schachowskoy, *Z. physik. Chem. B* **19**, 255 (1932); R. C. Jones and M. B. Neuworth, *J. Am. Chem. Soc.* **66**, 1497 (1944).

appreciable absorption at wave lengths greater than about 4300 A, a solution containing both substances absorbs even at 5000 A.   Although the apparent value of ε_{max} for this new band is only about 30, the true value must be much greater since the complex appears to be almost completely dissociated (cf. the above paragraph in fine print).   The excited state for the electronic transition that is here involved may be the less stable of the two hybrids resulting from resonance between the structures III and IV.   On the other hand, it may instead be a triplet

level, since Reid has shown[69] that, even in the absence of heavy atoms (see above), the formation of molecular complexes may result in markedly increased intensities of bands arising from singlet-triplet transitions. Although no theoretical explanation for this enhancement of the spectrum is now known, the existence of the effect makes uncertain any conclusions regarding the identity of the excited level.   As with the benzene-iodine complex, however, the first of the two alternative interpretations of the spectrum is again considered the more generally satisfactory.[66]

With other molecular complexes, the situations are closely similar to those which we have found above with the benzene-iodine and the anthracene-trinitrobenzene complexes.   In each such system, the observed absorption can be explained in two quite different ways, and in no such system can we conclusively show which way, if either, is correct.   The viewpoint of Mulliken[65] is, however, more generally adopted than is the alternative one.

6·8   Spectroscopic Effects of the Steric Inhibition of Resonance.[70]   In Section 5·5, we saw that, when the presence of bulky substituents forces a conjugated system into a nonplanar configuration, the dipole moment of

[69] C. Reid, *J. Chem. Phys.* **20**, 1212 (1952).

[70] L. G. S. Brooker, F. L. White, R. H. Sprague, S. G. Dent, Jr., and G. Van Zandt, *Chem. Revs.* **41**, 325 (1947).

the substance may be significantly altered.   Consequently, since conjugation influences electronic energy levels as well as charge distributions, we can anticipate that the spectra of conjugated compounds should also be altered when the resonance is thus sterically inhibited.   The situation is here, however, somewhat more complicated than it was in Chapter 5 since conjugation can be expected to have either one of two distinctively different spectroscopic effects.[71]   In order to explain these effects, let us first consider two particularly simple systems, the molecule of 1,3-butadiene and the allyl radical, even though no experimental data that can be related to an inhibition of resonance are at present available for either substance.

The normal state of 1,3-butadiene is a hybrid with which only the single conventional structure I can be assigned a large weight.   The additional, much less stable structures like II, III, IV, etc., have large weights in the several spectroscopically excited states, but only small ones in the ground state.   Since, however, we shall hereafter be interested in only one of the excited states, we can further simplify the discussion by treating the several structures II, III, IV, etc., not individually, but rather as already

$$CH_2\!=\!CH\!-\!CH\!=\!CH_2 \qquad CH_2\!-\!CH\!=\!CH\!-\!CH_2$$

$$I \qquad\qquad\qquad II$$

$$C^+H_2\!-\!CH\!=\!CH\!-\!\ddot{C}^-H_2 \qquad \ddot{C}^-H_2\!-\!CH\!=\!CH\!-\!C^+H_2$$

$$III \qquad\qquad IV$$

combined into a certain hybrid which we shall in the following represent (somewhat loosely) by the single structure V.   The ground state then receives a large contribution from structure I and a small one from structure V; and the excited state of interest receives a large contribution from structure V and a small one from structure I.   In Figure 6·3a, the horizontal lines AB and CD correspond, respectively, to the electronic energies W of the structures I and V for a *planar* molecule, and the lines

$$C^\pm H_2\!-\!CH\!-\!CH\!-\!C^\mp H_2$$

$$V$$

EF and GH correspond to the energies of the two resulting hybrids.   The energy required for a transition from the ground state EF to the excited state GH is then given by the vertical distance FH.   If the molecule is now distorted into a *nonplanar* configuration, the energy of structure I would not be greatly affected and so could still be represented by the line

[71] K. J. Brunings and A. H. Corwin, *J. Am. Chem. Soc.* **64**, 593 (1942).

AB. The energy of structure V, however, must be raised by the rotation about the central carbon-carbon bond since, in each of the component structures II, III, and IV, this bond is a double one. Consequently, the line *CD* must be replaced by *C'D'*, which lies well above *CD*. The energies of the ground and excited states are now represented by the lines *E'F'* and *G'H'*, and the excitation energy is now given by the distance *F'H'*. Since *F'H'* is greater than *FH*, the inhibition of the resonance must displace the absorption toward shorter wave lengths. It can also be shown that, as a result of the decreased overlapping of the orbitals in the nonplanar molecule, the intensity of the absorption should be decreased.

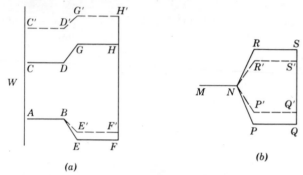

Fig. 6·3.   The energies of the ground and excited states in the planar and nonplanar 1,3-butadiene molecule (*a*) and allyl radical (*b*).

A quite different situation is encountered with the allyl radical, which is a hybrid of (principally) the two structures VI and VII. These structures have the same energy and so must have identical weights. Additional, less stable structure with formal charges, formal bonds, or both

$$CH_2{=}CH{-}\dot{C}H_2 \qquad\qquad \dot{C}H_2{-}CH{=}CH_2$$
VI   VII

are also possible, but these may here be ignored. In Figure 6·3*b*, the line *MN* corresponds to the energy that is associated with either one of the structures VI and VII when the radical is planar, and the lines *PQ* and *RS* correspond, respectively, to the energies of the ground and excited states that result from the resonance. The excitation energy is then given by the vertical distance *QS*. If the radical is now forced to go over from the planar configuration to a nonplanar one, the energies of structures VI and VII must presumably be raised, but they remain equal to each other. Since we are at present interested only in *relative* values, we can therefore continue to represent the energies of the structure VI and VII by the same line *MN* as before. (The different line which corresponds to the arbitrarily chosen zero of energy, but which is not explicitly shown in the figure, should then, however, be lowered.)   As a result of the decreased effectiveness of the resonance, the resonance energy of the ground state is smaller than in the planar radical, and so the total energy of this state is represented by some such line as $P'Q'$; similarly, the energy of the excited state is given by some such line as $R'S'$.   Since the excitation energy $Q'S'$ is less than QS, the inhibition of resonance must displace the absorption toward *longer* wave lengths.   As with 1,3-butadiene, however, the intensity should again be decreased.

Resonance in biphenyl involves altogether the four Kekulé structures VIII–XI, which have the same, or nearly, the same energy and hence also

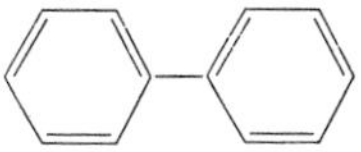

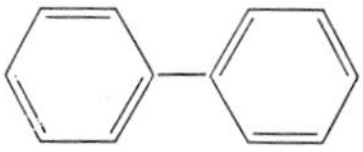

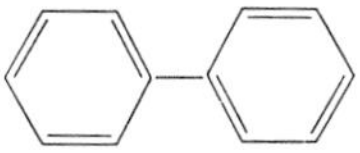

the same, or nearly the same, weights.   Nevertheless, if we are concerned with the reason for the difference between the spectrum of this compound and that of benzene, we must consider that biphenyl is an analog of 1,3-butadiene rather than one of the allyl radical.   The justification for this conclusion is that the conjugation between the two rings in biphenyl is not due to the resonance among the equivalent Kekulé structures, but is instead a result of the small contributions made by the unstable structures in which, as in XII and XIII, the rings are linked by double bonds.

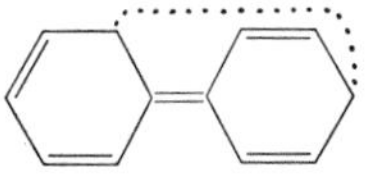

Consequently, when bulky substituents in the *ortho* positions prevent planarity of the molecule, the near-ultraviolet absorption should be displaced toward shorter wave lengths and its intensity should be decreased.   This prediction is only partly in agreement with the observations since, as was pointed out on pages 263f, the conjugation in biphenyl itself does not have exactly the expected effect.   In particular, although the first ultraviolet band of biphenyl is indeed much more intense (per aromatic ring) than is that of benzene, the absorptions by the two compounds occur at nearly the same wave length (cf. Table 6·2, Section 6·3).

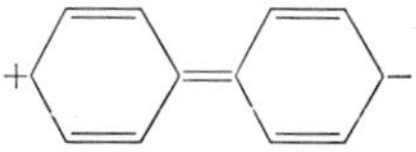

An additional qualitative difference between the spectra is that the absorption band of benzene 'has a rather complex fine structure which is unquestionably due to the vibrations of the atomic nuclei (cf. Figure 6·1, Section 6·1), but which is totally absent with biphenyl.

Whatever the complete explanation of the data may be, there can be no doubt that the spectra of benzene and of biphenyl are in fact quite dissimilar, and that the observed differences are due to the conjugation between the two rings in the molecule of the latter hydrocarbon. This view receives satisfactory confirmation from a study of the steric inhibition of the resonance. With mesitylene, XIV, for example, the values of λ_{max} and ε_{max} are only slightly greater than with benzene (cf. Table 6·7, Section 6·3), and the fine structure, mentioned above, is again apparent. The minor effects of the methyl substituents are possibly due either to hyperconjugation or to the electron-releasing power of the alkyl groups, or to both (cf. page 278). With bimesityl, XV, however, the spectrum is not

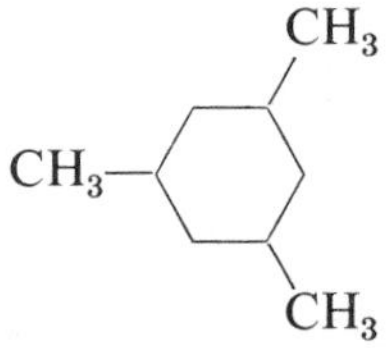

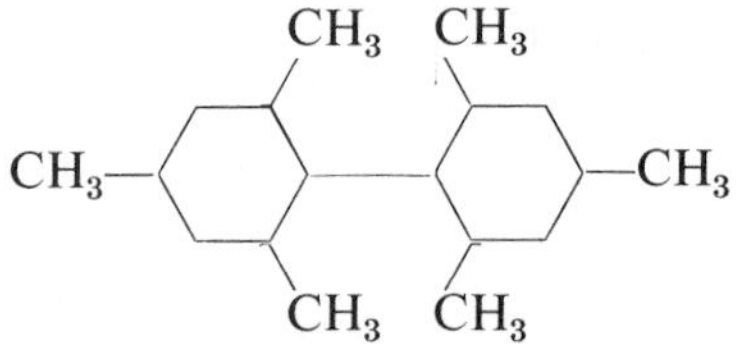

at all like that of biphenyl but is instead almost exactly the same (per aromatic ring) as that of mesitylene.[72]   The only reasonable explanation for the great difference between the effects of the methyl groups in mesitylene and in bimesityl is that, in the latter compound, these groups prevent the rings from being coplanar, as they obviously must do also in such optically active biphenyls as 3,3'-diaminobimesityl, XVI;[73] and that they therefore decrease the effectiveness of the conjugation between the rings.

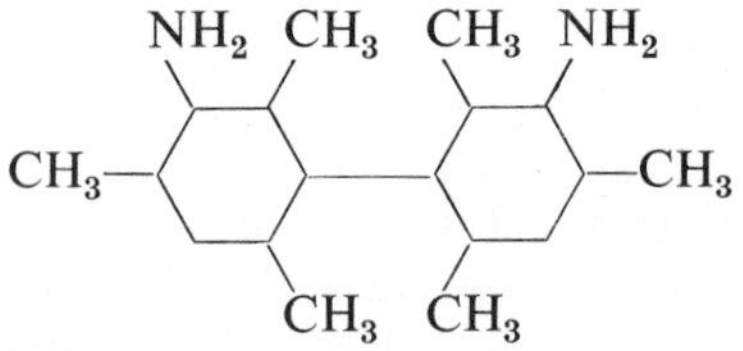

A number of additional examples of the steric inhibition of resonance in suitably substituted derivatives of biphenyl have been given by Rodebush

[72] L. W. Pickett, G. F. Walter, and H. France, *J. Am. Chem. Soc.* **58**, 2296 (1936); M. T. O'Shaughnessy and W. H. Rodebush, *ibid.* **62**, 2906 (1940).

[73] W. W. Moyer and R. Adams, *J. Am. Chem. Soc.* **51**, 630 (1929).

and his co-workers.[72, 74] These authors have also studied the effect of the size of the substituents in the ortho positions, and they have found that, in general, the spectra differ most from that of biphenyl when the blocking groups are largest. These facts lend support to the belief that the planar configuration is necessary in order for the resonance to be completely effective, and also that the molecules do indeed tend to be planar in the absence of steric interference.

Still other authors[75] have investigated the spectra of such more complicated hydrocarbons as 2,2′-binaphthyl, XVII, 1,1′-binaphthyl, XVIII,

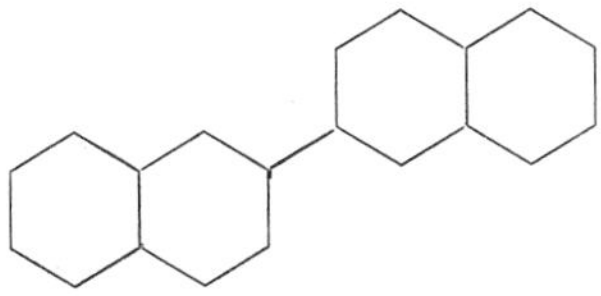

XVII 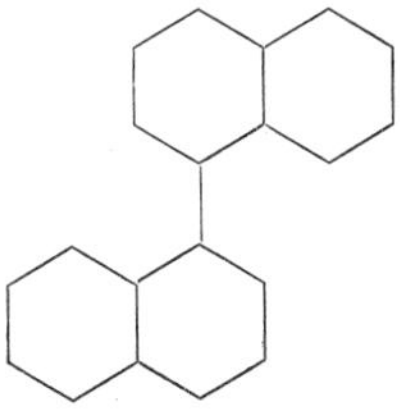   XVIII

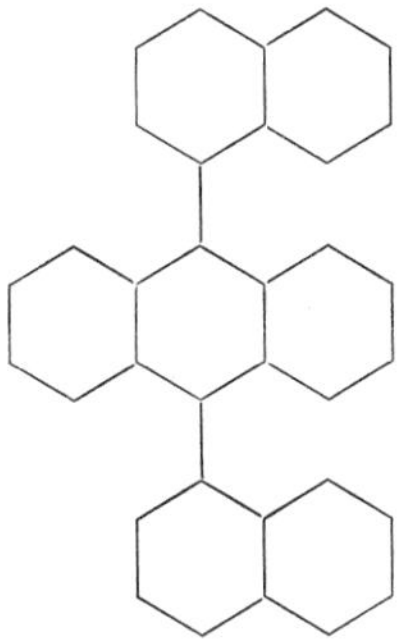

XIX

and 9,10-di-1-naphthylanthracene, XIX. With the first of these compounds, the molecule can be planar as easily as can that of biphenyl; consequently, the absorption is relatively intense and is quite different from that of naphthalene. With 1,1′-binaphthyl, however, planarity is more difficult, although probably not entirely excluded; consequently, the spectrum is much closer to that expected for two independent naphthalene systems. And, with the dinaphthylanthracene, planarity is doubtless quite impossible; consequently, the spectrum is practically identical with that of anthracene plus twice that of naphthalene.

[74] B. Williamson and W. H. Rodebush, *J. Am. Chem. Soc.* **63**, 3018 (1941).

[75] See, for example, R. A. Friedel, M. Orchin, and L. Reggel, *J. Am. Chem. Soc.* **79**, 199 (1948); R. N. Jones, *ibid.* **63**, 313 (1941); **67**, 2127 (1945); *Chem. Revs.* **32**, 1 (1943).

Still an additional modification of the biphenyl structure is illustrated by 4-nitro-4′-aminobiphenyl, XX. Since this substance has a rather strong band with λ_{max} and ε_{max} equal, respectively, to about 3800 A and 16,000, there is doubtless resonance with such quinoid structures as XXI (cf. pages 223ff). In the dimethyl derivative XXII, however, the planar

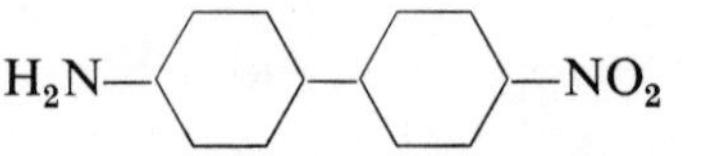

XX

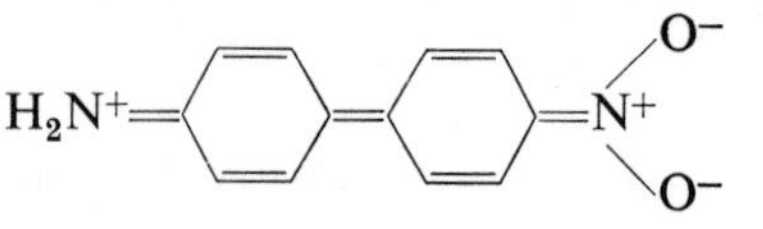

XXI

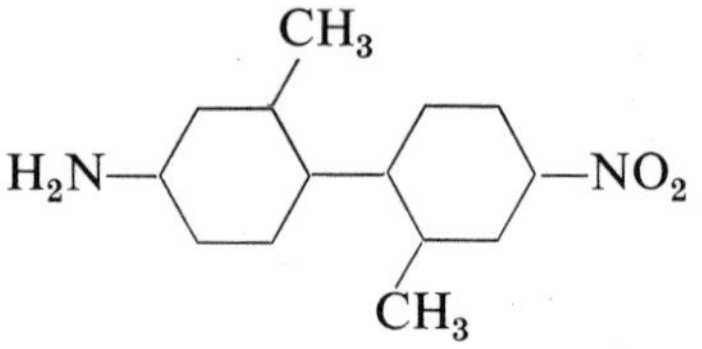

XXII

configuration is made less stable; as a result, the absorption becomes less intense and is shifted to shorter wave lengths.[76]

A somewhat different problem, which can still be considered analogous to those just discussed, is presented by the 1,2-dicarbonyl compounds. As was pointed out on pages 284f, the first electronic absorption bands of these substances are probably of the $N \rightarrow A$ type and so involve excitation of the electrons which, in the conventional structures, are members of unshared pairs on the oxygen atoms. However, since conjugation brings these bands to longer wave lengths, the excited states probably receive significant contributions from some less stable structures in which the carbon atoms of the carbonyl groups are joined by a double bond. Consequently, we may expect that the values of both λ_{max} and ε_{max} will be greatest when the carbonyl groups are most nearly coplanar. Leonard and Mader[77] have studied a series of cyclic 1,2-diketones, including camphorquinone, XXIII, and the several different compounds XXIV, with $n = 2, 3, 4$, and 14; in each of these substances, the complications that could have arisen from the possibility of enolization have been avoided. With camphorquinone, XXIII, the five-membered ring forces the two carbonyl groups to be nearly, if not quite, coplanar; with the

[76] D. W. Sherwood and M. Calvin, *J. Am. Chem. Soc.* **64**, 1350 (1942).

[77] N. J. Leonard and P. M. Mader, *J. Am. Chem. Soc.* **72**, 5388 (1950). For additional, but less conclusive, work leading to the same conclusion, see also N. J. Leonard, R. T. Rapala, H. L. Herzog, and E. R. Blout, *J. Am. Chem. Soc.* **71**, 2997 (1949); N. J. Leonard and E. R. Blout, *ibid.* **72**, 484 (1950).

tetramethylcyclohexanedione and -heptanedione, XXIV, with $n = 2$ and 3, respectively, the larger rings doubtless cause progressively greater deviations from coplanarity; with the tetramethylcycloöctanedione, XXIV, with $n = 4$, the eight-membered ring is large enough so that the

XXIII   XXIV

carbonyl groups can begin to approach the alternative planar, *s-trans* configuration; and, with the tetramethylcycloöctadecanedione, XXIV, with $n = 14$, the eighteen-membered ring permits, but does not require, the carbonyl groups actually to reach the *s-trans* configuration, which is now presumably the most stable one. The observed values of λ_{max} are 4660 A, 3800 A, 3370 A, 3430 A, and 3840 A, respectively, and so are in satisfactory qualitative agreement with expectation. The corresponding values of ε_{max}, on the other hand, can be given no such simple interpretation, since the intensities of the absorptions would be expected to vary with the shapes of the molecules even if the resonance in the conjugated system were not also affected.

When the above 1,2-diketones are treated with *o*-phenylenediamine, they are transformed into the corresponding quinoxalines XXV, or XXVI. Since, with each of these latter compounds, the carbon-nitrogen double bonds are fairly rigidly held in the coplanar configuration, the spectra are no longer very dependent on the sizes of the fused alicyclic rings.[77]

Since the diketones XXIII and XXIV have two carbonyl groups per molecule, each should have two $N \rightarrow A$ bands (see pages 284f). For reasons which should be clear from the above discussion of the allyl radical, any inhibition of the resonance in these conjugated systems should displace the two bands in opposite directions. Although the positions of those $N \rightarrow A$ bands that have the shorter wave lengths do not vary a great deal, this prediction seems to be in agreement with the observations. With camphorquinone, XXIII, the published curve shows that there is a weak absorption with a λ_{max} of about 2800 A, in addition to a strong one for which λ_{max} is less than 2600 A; with the diketones XXIV, with $n = 2$, 3, 4, and 14, λ_{max} is 2975 A, 2990 A, 2955 A, and 2865 A, respectively. If the small differences between these values can be relied upon, their signs and *relative* magnitudes are just as expected;

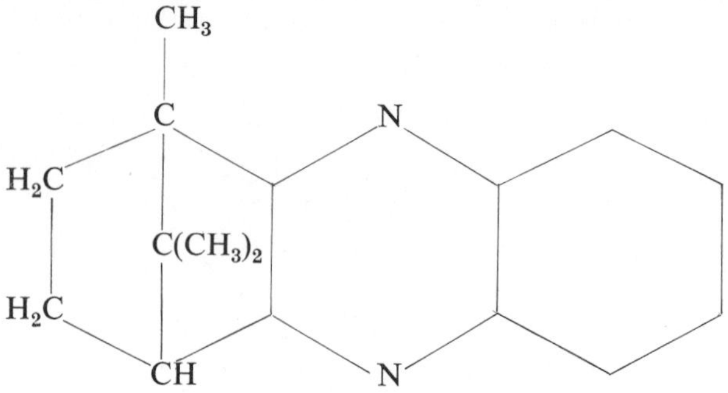

XXV

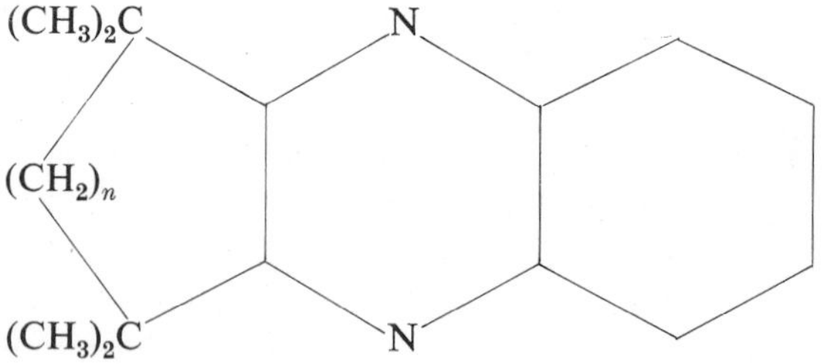

XXVI

this fact provides additional support for the present interpretation of the spectra. As before, however, no entirely satisfactory explanation for the observed intensities can be given.

With aromatic nitro compounds,[76] aromatic amines,[78] unsaturated aldehydes and ketones,[79] and azo dyes,[80] the steric inhibition of resonance may again be expected to displace the first visible or ultraviolet absorptions toward shorter wave lengths and to decrease their intensities. So

[78] W. R. Remington, *J. Am. Chem. Soc.* 67, 1838 (1945); H. B. Klevens and J. R. Platt, *ibid.* 71, 1714 (1949); A. I. Kiprianov and I. N. Zhmurova, *Zhur. Obshcheĭ Khim.* 23, 493, 874 (1953) [*C. A.* 48, 3963 (1954)].

[79] E. A. Braude, E. R. H. Jones, H. P. Koch, R. W. Richardson, F. Sondheimer, and J. B. Toogood, *J. Chem. Soc.* 1949, 1890; L. H. Schwartzmann and B. B. Corson, *J. Am. Chem. Soc.* 76, 781 (1954); G. D. Hedden and W. G. Brown, *ibid.* 75, 3744 (1953).

[80] J. S. P. Blumberger, *Rec. trav. chim.* 63, 127 (1944); 64, 80 (1945); A. I. Kiprianov and I. N. Zhmurova, *Zhur. Obshcheĭ Khim.* 23, 626 (1953) [*C. A.* 48, 6981 (1954)].

far as the limited data that are now available permit a generalization to be made, this prediction has been confirmed by experiment. With each of these different types of substances, departures of the molecules from planarity are found always to be accompanied by profound modifications of the spectra, and the magnitudes of the modifications that are thus produced are found always to increase as the molecules become less nearly planar. Usually, however, the values of ε_{max} are decreased much more than are those of λ_{max}. A possible explanation[79] for this difference is that, unless the forces preventing planarity are extremely great, there must always be at least a small fraction of the molecules in, or near, the planar configuration; and that the absorption by such planar, or nearly planar, molecules is much more intense (per molecule) than is that by the remaining molecules in other configurations.

With an aromatic amine, the most important structures in the resonance are doubtless XXVII–XXXI and their respective analogs with either ionic or formal bonds, or with both. If the nitrogen atom in the actual hybrid is pyramidal, there must always be some strain in each structure in which, as in XXIX–XXXI, this atom takes part in a double bond; on the other hand, if the nitrogen atom is instead planar, then there must be some strain in each structure in which, as in XXVII and XXVIII, this atom takes

XXVII   XXVIII   XXIX   XXX   XXXI

part in three single bonds. In any event, however, the resonance is most effective when the two groups R lie on the same side of the plane of the ring, and it is least effective when, for any reason, one of these groups is forced to lie on each side of that plane. As with the more familiar kinds of conjugation, therefore, the resonance can be sterically inhibited by a rotation about a bond that is represented as single in the most stable structures, but as double in certain of the less stable structures. (For additional, and completely conclusive, spectroscopic evidence for the existence of this effect in an aromatic amine, see page 372.)

In each of the examples so far considered in this section, both the resonance and the spectroscopic effects of its inhibition have been of the particular type which, on pages 315f, we described as characteristic of 1,3-butadiene. There are, however, a number of other substances with which the situation is instead more nearly analogous to that expected for the allyl radical (see pages 316f). Of these additional examples, the ones that have been most carefully studied are doubtless certain cyanine dyes with which, as with the allyl radical, the resonance that is of spectroscopic interest involves more than one relatively stable structure. Thus, the 3,5,3′,5′-tetramethyl-4,4′dicarboethoxydipyrrylmethene cation[71] is a hybrid of the two structures XXXII and XXXIII, and also of several intermediate structures like XXXIV and XXXV. (We shall again ignore the

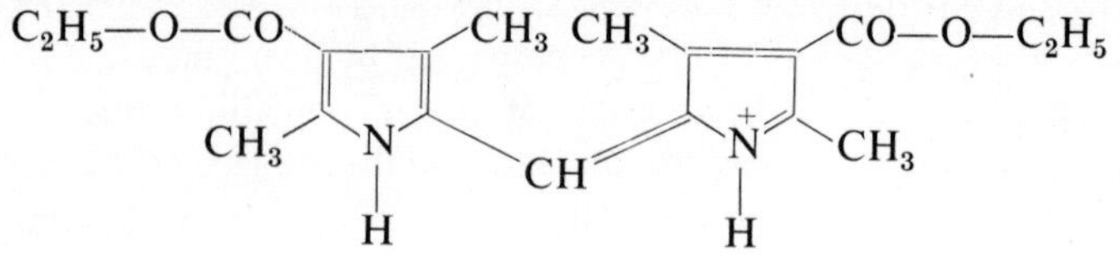

XXXII

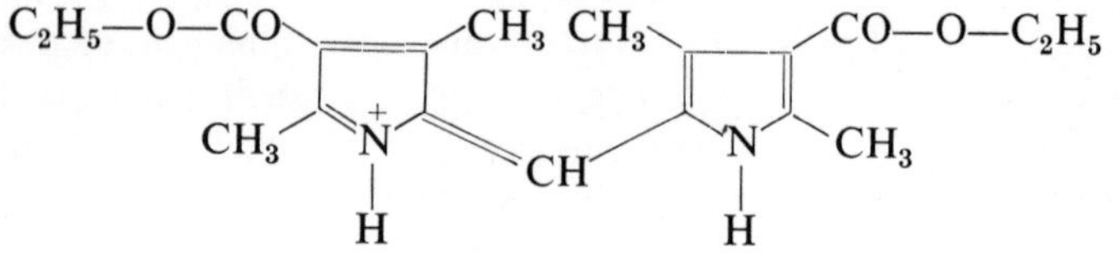

XXXIII

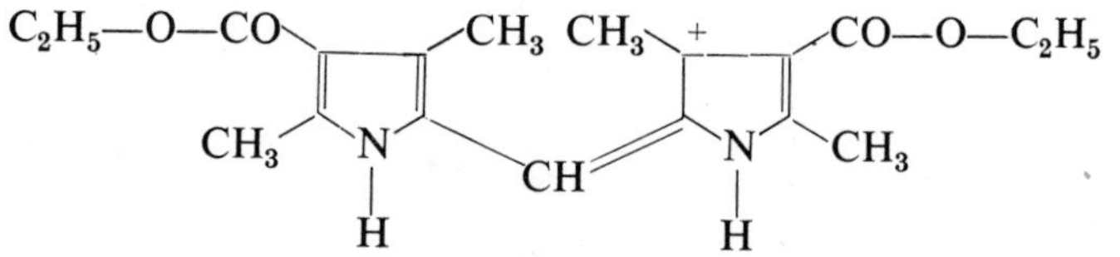

XXXIV

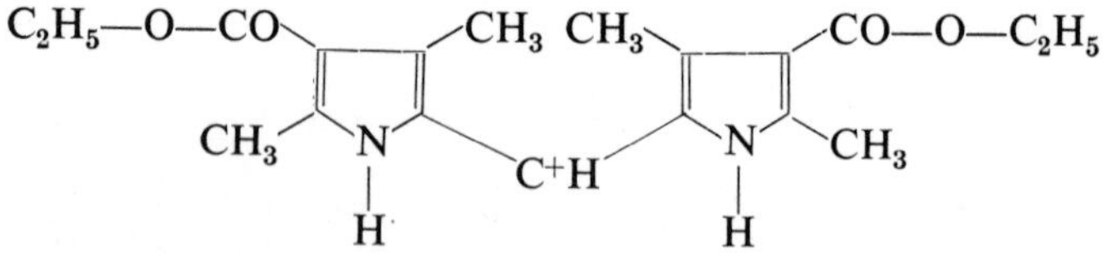

XXXV

less stable structures with formal or ionic bonds.) From models constructed accurately to scale, the conjugated system that is contained in this cation can be shown to be capable of assuming a completely planar configuration. On the other hand, if the hydrogen atoms that are linked to the nitrogen atoms are replaced by methyl groups, the resulting cation, which may here be represented by the single typical structure XXXVI,

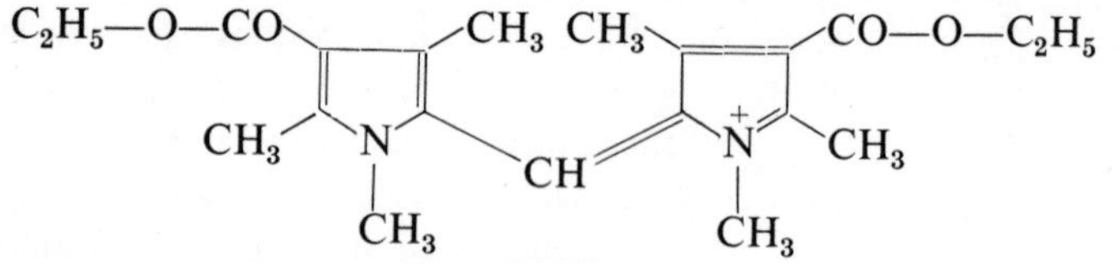

XXXVI

can be shown to be no longer capable of becoming similarly planar. Consequently, the resonance must to some extent be sterically inhibited in the latter compound, but not in the former. Now, when the two additional methyl groups are introduced into the cation, the value of λ_{max} increases from 4700 A to 5100 A (in chloroform), and that of ε_{max} decreases from 135,000 to 57,000 (again in chloroform).[70, 71] The observed changes are therefore in the expected directions.

A number of further, closely similar examples have been given by Brooker and his co-workers,[70] who have found that, in general, the symmetrical cyanines of all types studied behave like the above dipyrrylmethenes; but that the highly unsymmetrical cyanines, with which the extreme structures differ markedly in stability, behave instead in the entirely different way that is observed with the analogs of 1,3-butadiene. With both the symmetrical and the unsymmetrical dyes, a few discrepancies do occur; this fact is hardly surprising, however, since the assumed analogy between the really very complicated cyanine cations and the much simpler allyl radical or 1,3-butadiene molecule, respectively, can be no better than a rough first approximation.

6·9   Solvent Effects.   The relation between the nature of the solvent and the spectrum of the solute dissolved in it presents a problem that is much too complex to be discussed here in detail. We shall therefore restrict the following discussion to a few simple examples with which the resonance concept has proved to be particularly helpful. (A more general treatment of solvent effects has been given by McConnell.[36])

Phenol blue is a hybrid of structures I and II; of the numerous intermediate structures in which, as in III, the electric charges are less widely

separated; and of the innumerable further structures that are analogous to all these but contain ionic bonds, formal bonds, or both. In general, the zwitterionic structures like II and III must be less stable than the formally nonpolar ones like I, and so they can have large weights only in the electronically excited states of the molecule. If, however, the solvent is changed from one of low dielectric constant to one of higher dielectric constant, the energies of the zwitterionic structures should be made significantly lower, but those of the nonpolar structures should remain more or less unchanged. Consequently, under such circumstances, the first electronically excited state, which receives large contributions from the zwitterionic structures, must be stabilized with respect to the ground state, which receives only small contributions from these structures. Since the excitation energy is therefore decreased, the absorption must be displaced toward longer wave lengths. This theoretical prediction is confirmed by experiment;[81] the value of λ_{max}, which is 5520 A in cyclohexane, increases to 5820 A in acetone, to 6120 A in methyl alcohol, and to 6680 A in water.

Bindschedler's green and phenol indophenol, which can here be represented by the single typical structures IV and V, respectively, are superficially analogous to phenol blue; they differ from the latter dye, however,

$$(CH_3)_2N\!-\!\!\left\langle\right\rangle\!\!-\!N\!=\!\!\left\langle\right\rangle\!\!=\!N^+(CH_3)_2$$

IV

$$O^-\!-\!\!\left\langle\right\rangle\!\!-\!N\!=\!\!\left\langle\right\rangle\!\!=\!O$$

V

in the significant respect that each is a hybrid receiving its most important contributions from ionic structures which have the same, or nearly the same, stabilities, and which do not require large separations of charge. If the dielectric constant of the solvent is increased, the energies of these individual structures are doubtless lowered, but by approximately the same amount. Since the *relative* stabilities of the contributing structures are therefore not greatly altered, the change in the solvent should have little effect on the spectra. This prediction also has been confirmed by experiment;[81] the absorption maximum of Bindschedler's green varies only from 7260 A in methyl alcohol to 7290 A in acetone, whereas that of phenol indophenol varies only from 6280 A in water to 6420 A in acetone. (Neither dye is sufficiently soluble in cyclohexane to be studied in that solvent.)

If, with some given dye, the zwitterionic structures are more, and not less, stable than the formally nonpolar ones, the effect of a change in the dielectric constant of the solvent should be the opposite of that observed

[81] L. G. S. Brooker and R. H. Sprague, *J. Am. Chem. Soc.* **63**, 3214 (1941).

with phenol blue; for, then, an increase of the dielectric constant should lower the energy of the ground state more than it lowers that of the excited state. Examples confirming this prediction are provided by the *merocyanine* dyes, for which the extreme zwitterionic and nonpolar structures are, respectively, VI and VII, with $n = 0$, 1, 2, and 3.[82] When $n = 1$,

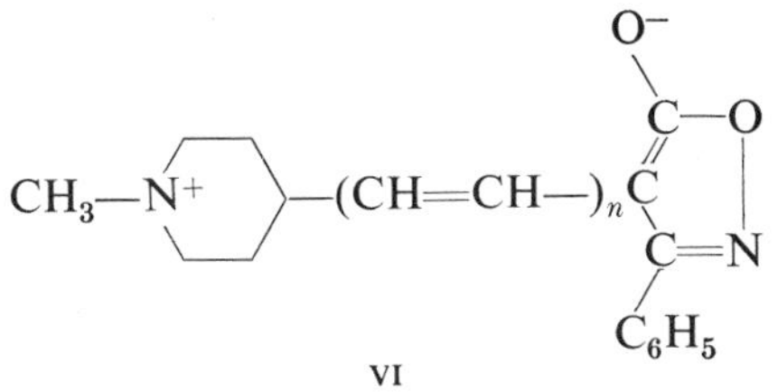

VI

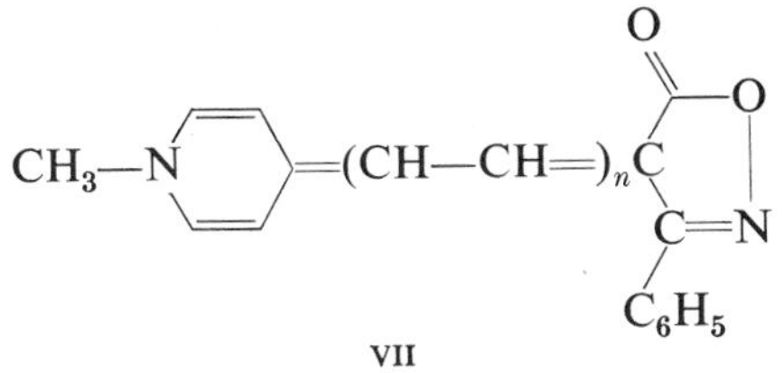

VII

the value of λ_{max} decreases from 5150 A in pyridine to 4700 A in methyl alcohol and to 4350 A in water. The effect becomes even greater when the length of the conjugated chain that links the terminal rings is increased; thus, when $n = 3$, λ_{max} is 7100 A in pyridine, but only 4875 A in water.

Further evidence supporting the above interpretation of solvent effects has been obtained from a comparison of spectra and dipole moments.[83] With the dye for which the extreme structures are VIII and IX, the

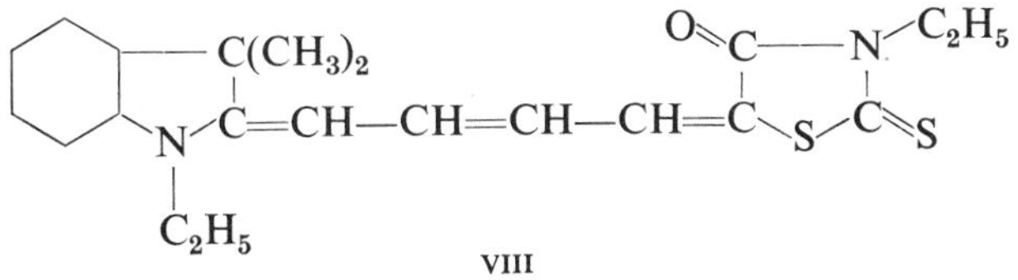

VIII

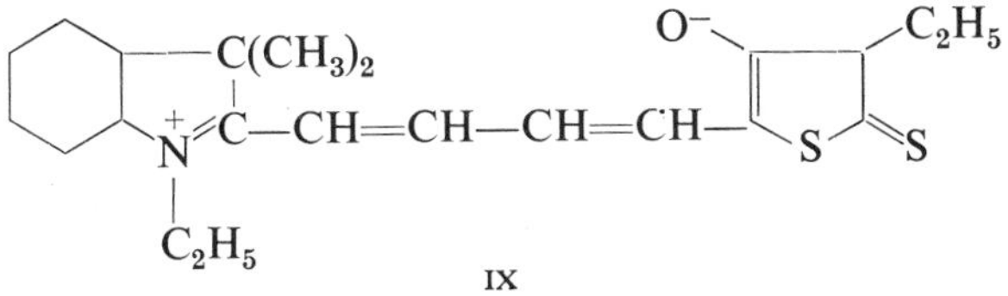

IX

[82] L. G. S. Brooker, G. H. Keyes, R. H. Sprague, R. H. VanDyke, E. VanLare, G. VanZandt, F. L. White, H. W. J. Cressman, and S. G. Dent, Jr., *J. Am. Chem. Soc.* **73**, 5332 (1951).

[83] L. M. Kushner and C. P. Smyth, *J. Am. Chem. Soc.* **71**, 1401 (1949).

nonpolar structures should be more stable than the zwitterionic ones. Accordingly, the value of λ_{max} increases from 5475 A in phenylcyclohexane to 5880 A in aqueous ethanol;[82] and the dipole moment is 6.91 D.[83]   On the other hand, with the further dye for which the corresponding structures are X and XI, the nonpolar and zwitterionic structures should be

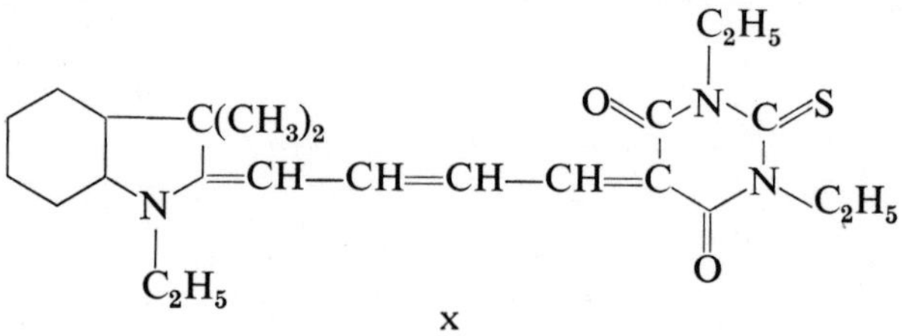

X

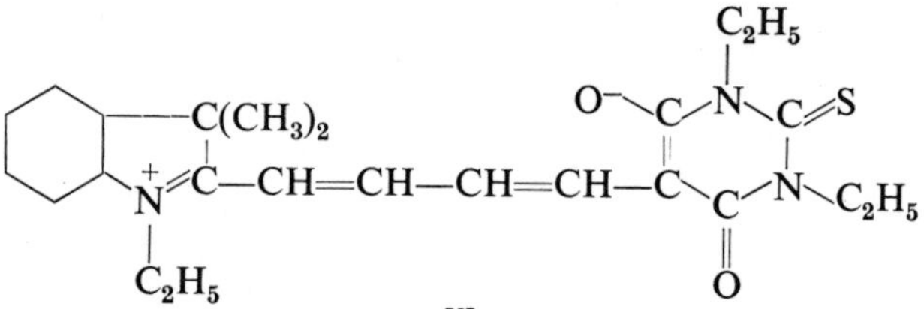

XI

about equally stable.   Accordingly, the value of λ_{max} increases only from 5845 A in phenylcyclohexane to 5895 A in aqueous ethanol;[82] and the dipole moment is 9.7 D.[83]   Finally, with the dye for which the extreme structures are XII and XIII, the zwitterionic structures should now be more stable than the nonpolar ones.   Accordingly, the value of

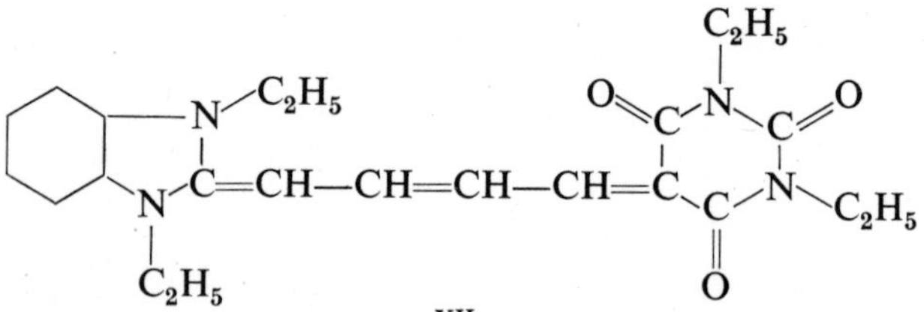

XII

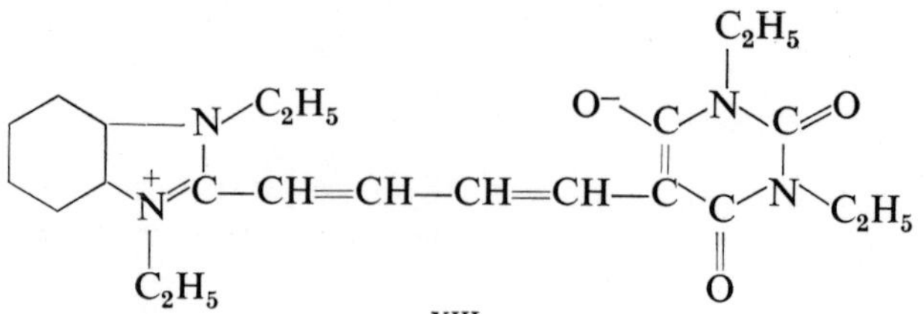

XIII

λ_{max} now *decreases* from 5550 A in phenylcyclohexane to 4265 A in aqueous ethanol;[82] and the dipole moment is 17.7 D.[83]

With an unsymmetrical cyanine cation, the deviation (cf. page 307) has been found to be an approximate measure of the difference between the energies of the extreme structures. Consequently, with an electrically neutral merocyanine dye, with which one of the extreme structures is zwitterionic whereas the other is formally nonpolar, the deviation should vary in a predictable way with the dielectric constant.[82] In general, an increase in the dielectric constant ought to increase, or decrease, the deviation when the zwitterionic structures are more stable, or less stable, respectively, than the nonpolar ones. In agreement with expectation, a change in the solvent from pyridine to methyl alcohol increases the deviation from 115 A to 440 A with the dye for which the extreme structures are XIV and XV, but decreases it from 545 A to 455 A with the dye for which the extreme structures are instead XVI and XVII.

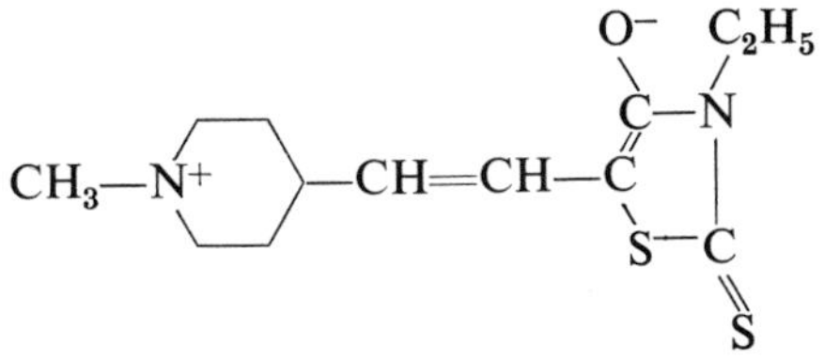

XIV

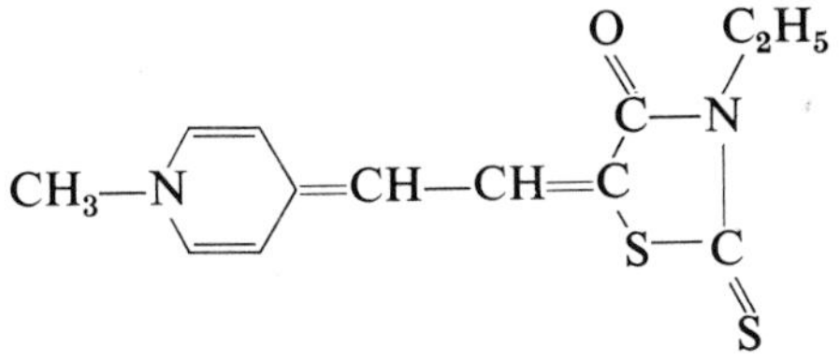

XV

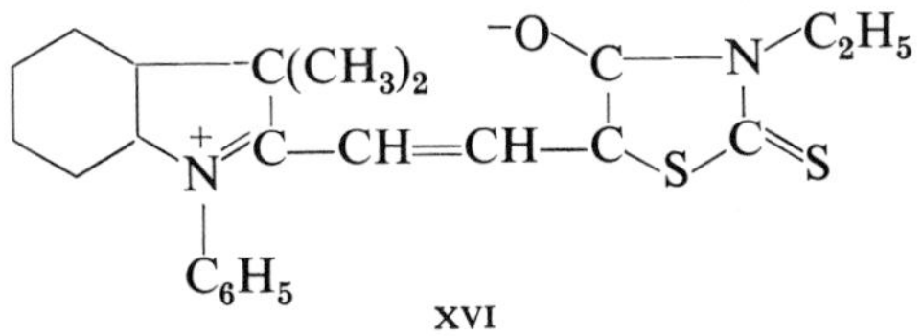

XVI

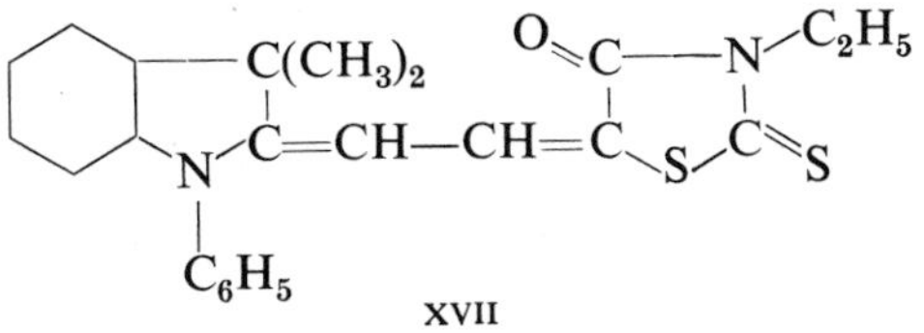

XVII

Numerical calculations by Simpson[84] have led to at least qualitative agreement with the observed solvent effects. On the other hand, Bayliss and McRae,[85] on the basis of additional experimental data, have concluded that the approach adopted in this section is somewhat oversimplified and, in particular, that other properties of the solvent besides its dielectric constant are also important. The problem would doubtless repay further study.

6·10 Theoretical Calculations of the Spectra of Unsaturated and Aromatic Hydrocarbons. Since the wave lengths at which molecules absorb light are determined by the differences between the energies of the pertinent initial and final states (cf. equation 1, Section 6·1), and since the required energies can always in principle be calculated by quantum-mechanical methods, only mathematical difficulties prevent us from predicting, as accurately as may be desired, the complete spectrum of any given substance. These difficulties are in practice, however, so great that no such calculations have ever been made for organic molecules without the introduction of drastic simplifying assumptions. Consequently, the results which have been obtained can be quantitatively correct only if there have been extensive cancellations of errors; frequently, in fact, they are not even qualitatively reliable.

Several different kinds of treatment have been employed in the attempts to calculate the positions of the electronic absorption bands of unsaturated and aromatic hydrocarbons. Many of these treatments are based on obvious extensions of the methods which have been used in the calculations of resonance energies, and which have already been briefly described in Section 3·8 (see also Sections 9·19, 9·20, and 9·25). In general, the excitation energies are obtained as numerical multiples of certain parameters, J or β, which are assigned such values that the agreement between the calculated and observed wave lengths is the best possible. As might have been anticipated, satisfactory results can often be obtained only if the value of J, or of β, is allowed to vary somewhat with the type of compound under consideration.

In one respect, the calculations of excitation energies are theoretically sounder than are those of resonance energies. Since, during an electronic transition, the relatively heavy atomic nuclei must remain in, or near, their initial positions, the interatomic distances must be essentially the same in each excited state as in the corresponding ground state (cf. the paragraph in fine print on page 258). Consequently, there is here no error analogous to the one resulting from the neglect of the distinction between the vertical and empirical resonance energies (cf. page 133). Since the values of the parameters J and β are not obtained from theoretical

[84] W. T. Simpson, *J. Am. Chem. Soc.* **73**, 5359 (1951).

[85] N. S. Bayliss and E. G. McRae, *J. Am. Chem. Soc.* **74**, 5803 (1952).

calculations but are instead estimated by comparison with the experimental data, we may assume that they to some extent compensate for the errors inherent in the procedures used; there is, therefore, no reason why these parameters must be assigned exactly the same values in the calculations of excitation energies and of resonance energies.

A rather serious difficulty which is encountered with each of the calculations described in this section is that there is often no completely unambiguous way for deciding which particular one of all the bands in the observed spectrum of a given substance is to be correlated with each of the calculated transitions. Consequently, even if a substance does indeed absorb light in some region that has been predicted, this fact does not, by itself, show that the calculation is correct; for, in the absence of additional information, we cannot be sure that the electronic transition which has been treated theoretically is the one which is responsible for the observed band. We shall later see an example in which the apparently satisfactory agreement between the calculated and observed wave lengths is almost certainly invalidated by such an erroneous identification of the band.

The first method of calculation which will here receive explicit mention is one originally due to Sklar.[86] When this method is employed, the hydrocarbon of interest is treated as a hybrid of all the purely covalent structures that can be obtained by pairing the pi electrons on the carbon atoms in all possible ways. Thus, 1,3-butadiene is considered to be a hybrid of structures I and II, benzene is considered to be one of structures III–VII, and so on. Structures which, like VIII and IX, have ionic

$$CH_2{=}CH{-}CH{=}CH_2 \qquad CH_2{-}CH{=}CH{-}CH_2$$
$$\text{I} \qquad\qquad\qquad\qquad \text{II}$$

III   IV   V   VI

VII   VIII   IX

$$C^+H_2{-}CH{=}CH{-}C^-H_2$$

bonds are not taken into account; this neglect doubtless forms the most serious defect of Sklar's approach to the problem (see the paragraph

[86] A. L. Sklar, *J. Chem. Phys.* **5**, 669 (1937).

following the one in fine print below).   By application of the extremely approximate valence-bond method (see Sections 3·8, 6·2, 9·19, and 9·20), the energies of all the electronic states that result from the resonance are first calculated.   The difference between the energy of each excited state and that of the ground state is then the calculated value of the corresponding excitation energy.

Sklar also described[86] an approximate method for taking into account the ionic structures like VIII and IX.   However, since this method is relatively unsatisfactory, and since it has not been accepted by the other workers in the field, it will hereafter be ignored.

The results of several calculations that have been made by the method of Sklar are listed in Table 6·10.   Although the agreement between the calculated and experimental values of λ_{max} is, in general, rather good, this success of the theory is probably more apparent than real.   In several instances, in fact, the observed absorption band is probably quite different from the one to which the calculation refers.   With 1,3-butadiene, for example, the high intensity of the absorption at 2100 A makes it practically certain that the excited state receives large contributions from such ionic structures as VIII, which are not included in the theoretical treatment (cf. pages 259f).   The band arising from a transition to the excited state in which the covalent structure II has a large weight must instead be a very weak one, and its value of λ_{max} is not at present known.   Presumably, therefore, the agreement between the calculated and observed wave lengths is fortuitous.   There is, moreover, no assurance that similar accidents may not be responsible also for the agreements that are found with many of the remaining hydrocarbons.

A second method of calculation, which is due to Förster,[87] is essentially identical with that of Sklar.   It is, however, more approximate since it neglects all structures with formal bonds; for this reason, it permits no prediction at all for any simple conjugated polyene like 1,3-butadiene, with which there is then only a single structure to be considered.   Similarly, it leads to the same predicted value of λ_{max} for any polyphenyl as for benzene.   As is shown in Table 6·10, however, it is about as satisfactory as the method of Sklar with the condensed aromatic hydrocarbons like naphthalene, anthracene, etc.   The fact that a slightly different value must now be used for the exchange integral J is, of course, only to be expected (cf. page 330).

The method of Platt[88] differs from those of Sklar and Förster in that it is based on the molecular-orbital approach (see Sections 3·8, 6·2, and

[87] T. Förster, *Z. physik. Chem. B* **41**, 287 (1938).
[88] J. R. Platt, *J. Chem. Phys.* **18**, 1168 (1950).

TABLE 6·10

CALCULATIONS OF THE SPECTRA OF HYDROCARBONS

λ_{max}

(angstroms)

Substance	Observed[a, b]	S^c	F^d	P^e
1,3-Butadiene	2100	1900	—	2,500
1,3,5-Hexatriene	2500	2460	—	3,500
Fulvene	3700	3645	—	5,400
Benzene	2550	2470	2450	2,000[f]
	2100[f]			
Styrene	2900	2570	2450	3,200
Biphenyl	2550	2570	2450	3,000
Azulene	6900	6914	7800	5,000
Naphthalene	2850	2680	2950	3,450
Anthracene	3750	—	3650	5,300
Phenanthrene	3400	—	3000	3,500
Pyrene	3300	—	3450	4,800
Naphthacene	4800	—	4500	7,400
Pentacene	5800	—	5450	10,000
Coronene	3450[f]	—	3700[g]	4,000

[a] J. R. Platt, *J. Chem. Phys.* **18**, 1168 (1950).

[b] B. Pullman and A. Pullman, *Les Théories électroniques de la chimie organique*, Masson et Cie, Paris, 1952, pp. 481ff.

[c] Calculated by the valence-bond method with the exchange integral J set equal to -44 kcal per mole. See A. L. Sklar, *J. Chem. Phys.* **5**, 669 (1937). The values for a few of the compounds listed were calculated by the present author.

[d] Calculated by the valence-bond method with neglect of all structures containing formal bonds, and with the exchange integral J set equal to -48.5 kcal per mole. See T. Förster, *Z. physik. Chem.* B **41**, 287 (1938). The values listed for a few of the compounds were calculated by the present author.

[e] Calculated by the molecular-orbital method with the overlap integral between adjacent orbitals set equal to 0.25, and with the parameter β set equal to -91 kcal per mole for short polyenes, but to -65.4 kcal per mole for ring systems. See J. R. Platt, reference *a*. The values listed for a few of the compounds were calculated by the present author.

[f] This value applies to the "center of gravity" of all the singlet-singlet transitions, and not to any individual band.

[g] Cf. G. R. Baldock, *Proc. Phys. Soc.* (*London*) A **63**, 585 (1950).

9·25). It therefore avoids the error of ignoring the contributions from the structures with ionic bonds, but it introduces the quite different one of ignoring the singlet-triplet separations in the excited electronic configurations (see pages 251ff). These separations may be rather large and they may vary considerably in magnitude; consequently, even when the value of the parameter β is adjusted so as to give the best possible agreement with the experimental data, there can be no assurance that the calculations have more than qualitative significance.   As is shown in Table 6·10, the predicted values of λ_{max} are indeed no better than rough first approximations to the ones observed.   Although Platt's method of calculation thus seems relatively unsatisfactory with respect to the wave lengths at which the absorptions occur, it is probably more reliable, with respect to the identifications of the electronic transitions, than either of the above valence-bond methods.   For example, in agreement with the conclusion reached on page 332, it unambiguously predicts that the excited state responsible for the first strong absorption by 1,3-butadiene is largely ionic.

The method of calculation which has proved most satisfactory is doubtless the one based on the so-called *free-electron model* (see Section 9·28).   However, since this method is dependent upon approximations that are rather different from those underlying the procedures just discussed, we shall postpone any discussion of this additional treatment.

6·11   Force Constants.   The near-infrared spectrum of a molecule is due to changes in its state of vibration.   One is often able to calculate from the observed frequencies of absorption the various *force constants* that describe the resistance offered by the molecule to deformation from its most stable geometrical configuration.   In the simplest treatments, the force constants are considered to be of only two kinds, known as the bending and the stretching force constants, respectively.   Of these, the former refer to alterations in the values of bond angles, whereas the latter refer to alterations in the values of bond lengths.

In the following discussion, we shall be interested only in the stretching force constants k, which are defined by the equation[89]

$$W_d = \tfrac{1}{2}k(r - r_e)^2 \tag{1}$$

W_d here represents the energy of distortion that is necessary to stretch (or to contract) the bond in question from its most stable length r_e to the length r.   It is found that the force constant, k, like the bond length, r_e, is roughly constant for a bond of given type and varies only slightly from molecule to molecule.   The value of k is dependent, however, upon the atoms bonded, and it is more or less proportional to the bond order for pure single, double, and triple bonds between atoms of the same two elements.

When a bond is not a pure single, double, or triple bond, but is of intermediate character as a result of resonance, its force constant may be

---

[89] This equation is only roughly approximate and is not closely obeyed when r is very different from r_e.   For better, but more complicated, expressions for k and W_d, see P. M. Morse, *Phys. Rev.*, **34**, 57 (1929).

TABLE 6·11

STRETCHING FORCE CONSTANTS[a]

· Substance	Atoms Bonded				
	CC	CN	CO	CCl	NN
(Pure single bond)	4.9	—	4.98	4.38	—
(Pure double bond)	9.5	—	13.0	—	—
(Pure triple bond)	15.8	18.10	—	—	22.9[h]
Cyanogen chloride	—	16.65	—	5.15	—
Carbon monoxide	—	—	18.6	—	—
Carbon dioxide	—	—	15.24	—	—
Tetrachloroethylene	5.8	—	—	5.2	—
Cyanogen[b]	6.69	17.51	—	—	—
Carbon suboxide	14.87	—	14.15	—	—
Biacetylene[c]	6.6[d]	—	—	—	—
	15.5[e]				
Benzene[f]	7.6	—	—	—	—
Isocyanic acid[g]	—	14.0	15.0	—	—
Isothiocyanic acid[g]	—	13.2	—	—	—
Hydrogen azide[g]	—	—	—	←	10.1[i]
					17.3[j]

[a] The quantities listed in the body of the table are the stretching force constants, expressed in units of 10^5 dynes per centimeter, for the bonds which, in the molecules given at the left of the row, link the atoms specified at the top of the column. Except as noted, the values are taken from H. W. Thompson and J. W. Linnett, *J. Chem. Soc.* **1937**, 1291, 1384; J. W. Linnett and H. W. Thompson, *ibid.* **1937**, 1399; *Nature* **139**, 509 (1937).

[b] Additional, but only slightly different, values for the force constants in cyanogen are given by A. Langseth and C. K. Møller, *Acta Chem. Scand.* **4**, 725 (1950).

[c] The values for biacetylene are taken from S. M. Ferigle, F. F. Cleveland, and A. G. Meister, *J. Chem. Phys.* **20**, 526 (1952).

[d] This value applies only to the bond which, in the conventional structure, is represented as single.

[e] This value applies only to the bonds which, in the conventional structure, are represented as triple.

[f] The value for benzene is taken from F. M. Garforth, C. K. Ingold, and H. G. Poole, *J. Chem. Soc.* **1948**, 508.   According to these authors, the force constants for pure single and pure double bonds between carbon atoms are, respectively, 4.5 and 9.8 × 10^5 dynes per centimeter.

[g] W. J. O. Thomas, *Trans. Faraday Soc.* **49**, 853 (1953).

[h] W. Gordy, *J. Chem. Phys.* **14**, 305 (1946).

[i] This value applies to the bond nearer the hydrogen atom.

[j] This value applies to the bond farther from the hydrogen atom.

expected to have an intermediate value. Although a more careful examination of the problem[90] has suggested that this conclusion need not always be valid, the data which are now available seem usually to be in satisfactory agreement with the simple intuitive prediction. Considerable caution should, however, be exercised in the use of these data since, except with the very simplest molecules, the interpretations of the spectra are always difficult and often uncertain. Not infrequently, in fact, the published values of the force constants are seriously in error because the types of vibration that are responsible for the various Raman and infrared lines have been incorrectly identified. Even when this pitfall is successfully avoided, the number of observed frequencies, or wave lengths, may be insufficient to determine all the force constants; and, in addition, the exact numerical values which are finally obtained for these constants are necessarily somewhat dependent upon the mathematical form of the initially assumed relation between the total distortional energy of the molecule and the several interatomic distances and bond angles. We shall here, therefore, give only the few typical examples that are listed in Table 6·11. The variations are seen to be always in the expected directions; they are sometimes too small, however, to be of certain significance in view of the above-mentioned sources of error, and in view also of the possibility that the changes in the valence states of the atoms concerned may, by themselves, be responsible for at least a part of the observed effects.

[90] C. A. Coulson and H. C. Longuet-Higgins, *Proc. Roy. Soc.* (*London*) *A* **193**, 456 (1948).

Chapter 7   RESONANCE AND CHEMICAL EQUILIBRIUM

7·1 General Discussion. The study of chemical equilibrium and of the way in which it is related to the structures of the various reactants involved has long attracted the attention of both practical and theoretical chemists. The great interest in this problem has been due partly to the rigor and elegance of the thermodynamic methods that can be used in such a study, and partly also to the intrinsic importance of the subject itself. From the practical point of view, a knowledge of the values of equilibrium constants is of the utmost importance, because it enables one to know whether or not the reactions are capable of proceeding to appreciable extents in the desired directions under any realizable experimental conditions, and it shows how the most favorable conditions are to be chosen. From the theoretical point of view, such knowledge is of equal importance, because it aids in the understanding of the *reasons why* structural changes have their observed effects, and it often makes possible a prediction of the effects of changes which have not yet been investigated. These theoretical aspects provided part of the impetus for the development of the prequantum-mechanical theories of intermediate stages and of mesomerism (Section 1·2) and will form the basis for most of the discussion in this chapter.

In the reversible reaction

$$A + B \rightleftarrows X + Y \tag{1}$$

the equilibrium constant K and the standard free-energy change ΔF° are given by the familiar thermodynamic equations[1]

$$K = \frac{[X][Y]}{[A][B]} = \frac{(X)(Y)\gamma_X\gamma_Y}{(A)(B)\gamma_A\gamma_B} \tag{2}$$

and
$$\Delta F^\circ = -RT \ln K \tag{3}$$

The expressions in square brackets are the activities of the stated substances; the ones in parentheses are the respective concentrations; the

---

[1] See, for example, I. M. Klotz, *Chemical Thermodynamics*, Prentice-Hall, New York, 1950, or any textbook of physical chemistry.

γ's are the activity coefficients; and R and T are the gas constant and the absolute temperature, respectively. Similarly, in a second reaction

$$A' + B' \rightleftarrows X' + Y' \tag{4}$$

the corresponding equations

$$K' = \frac{[X'][Y']}{[A'][B']} = \frac{(X')(Y')\gamma_{X'}\gamma_{Y'}}{(A')(B')\gamma_{A'}\gamma_{B'}} \tag{5}$$

and

$$\Delta F^{\circ\prime} = -RT \ln K' \tag{6}$$

also obtain. From equations 2, 3, 5, and 6, it follows that

$$\Delta\Delta F^{\circ} \equiv \Delta F^{\circ} - \Delta F^{\circ\prime} = -RT \ln \frac{K}{K'} = -RT \ln \frac{[X][Y][A'][B']}{[A][B][X'][Y']}$$

$$= -RT \ln \frac{(X)(Y)(A')(B')}{(X')(Y')(A)(B)} \frac{\gamma_X\gamma_Y\gamma_{A'}\gamma_{B'}}{\gamma_{X'}\gamma_{Y'}\gamma_A\gamma_B} \tag{7}$$

If the reactions of equations 1 and 4 are very similar in type (for example, if each of them is the neutralization of a monocarboxylic acid by a certain specified base in a certain specified solvent) then two simplifications in the treatment are immediately suggested. In the first place, it seems reasonable that the distinction between the activities and the concentrations can be ignored, and that the quantity $\Delta\Delta F^{\circ}$ can be expressed directly in terms of concentrations without reference to activities or activity coefficients. The justification for this first simplification is that the activity coefficients of A, B, X, and Y should not differ significantly from those of A', B', X', and Y', respectively, so that the expression involving the activity coefficients at the extreme right of equation 7 should be very nearly unity. This approximation, which considerably simplifies all the subsequent discussion of equilibria, is probably a fairly good one, although it is of course not rigorously correct.

The second simplification which we shall make is a much less justifiable one. Equation 7 relates the ratio K/K' of the equilibrium constants of the two reactions to the difference $\Delta\Delta F^{\circ}$ between the standard free-energy changes. However, from a consideration of the resonance in the various molecules we can usually draw conclusions only in regard to the differences $\Delta\Delta E \equiv \Delta E - \Delta E'$ between the corresponding changes in internal energy (not free energy). Since

$$\Delta\Delta F^{\circ} = \Delta\Delta E + P \Delta\Delta V - T \Delta\Delta S^{\circ} \tag{8}$$

for reactions at constant pressure P and temperature T, we can identify $\Delta\Delta E$ and $\Delta\Delta F^{\circ}$ only if the remaining terms are negligible. The first of these, $P \, \Delta\Delta V$, is probably sufficiently small to be ignored, since the volume changes ΔV and $\Delta V'$ for the two reactions must be not only small individually but also approximately equal to each other. The second term, $T \, \Delta\Delta S°$, which involves the difference between the entropy changes, may be rather large, however. In fact, in some series of apparently very similar reactions that have been carefully studied, this term has been found to be more important than $\Delta\Delta E$ in determining the relative values of the equilibrium constants.[2]

For the reasons just outlined, it would seem to be highly dangerous for us to assume that variations in the positions of chemical equilibria can be predicted by a method requiring the identification of $\Delta\Delta F°$ and $\Delta\Delta E$. Nevertheless, we are often forced to make this assumption if we wish to discuss these variations at all, because we do not have sufficient experimental data to attempt a more rigorous treatment, except for a few extremely restricted groups of reactions. To as great an extent as possible, therefore, we shall limit ourselves to comparisons of reactions for which $\Delta\Delta F°$ is large, with the hope that thereby we can be fairly certain of the *direction* of the effect due to resonance, even though we cannot predict its exact magnitude. We shall find that we are often able in this way to obtain simple and logical explanations of the sometimes striking variations in the positions of equilibrium in analogous reactions.[3]

The reasoning which underlies the arguments in the following sections can be illustrated with the reactions of equations 1 and 4. First, let us suppose that X' is the only one of all the reactants and products in these equations that is stabilized to any appreciable extent by resonance. If the two reactions are so similar that all further factors cancel in the comparison, then it follows that ΔE is algebraically greater than $\Delta E'$. Since $\Delta\Delta E$ is therefore positive, as presumably $\Delta\Delta F°$ is also, reaction 4 goes farther to the right than reaction 1. Conversely, if A' is the only substance so stabilized, reaction 1 goes farther to the right than reaction 4; and, in general, the reaction for which the gain in resonance energy is largest, or for which the loss in resonance energy is smallest, goes the most nearly to completion. These conclusions are justified, of course, only in so far as all further factors capable of affecting the equilibrium actually do cancel in the comparison.

In certain classes of reaction the difficulties in the treatment, which were described above, can be shown to be negligible. This favorable

[2] For one example taken from the many that could have been cited, see L. F. Fieser and C. C. Price, *J. Am. Chem. Soc.* **58**, 1838 (1936).

[3] For a more complete and more rigorous discussion of the difficulties referred to above, see L. P. Hammett, *Physical Organic Chemistry*, McGraw-Hill Book Co., New York, 1940, Chapter III.

situation seems to occur fairly generally, for example, when the substances A, B, X, and Y of equation 1 differ from A', B', X', and Y', respectively, only with regard to substitution at points far removed from the reaction centers. Thus, for the equilibrium between, on the one hand, meta- or para- (but not ortho-) substituted anilines plus formic acid and, on the other hand, the corresponding formanilides plus water, we might expect $\Delta\Delta S°$ to be small, so that $\Delta\Delta F°$ and $\Delta\Delta E$ are approximately equal. This expectation is apparently in accord with experiment.[4]

A more complicated situation of a rather different type, in which the value of $\Delta\Delta S°$ again causes no trouble, arises in, for example, a comparison of the ionization constants of meta- and para-substituted benzoic acids. The major effect of substituents here seems to consist in an electrostatic interaction with the ionizable proton. Since this coulombic energy is a form of "reversible work," it contributes directly to the free energies, rather than to the internal energies, of the substances. Consequently, it can legitimately be used in the discussion of the changes in ionization constant, without apology for the neglect of entropy terms. It can be shown theoretically, and it has been verified experimentally,[3] that the temperature dependence of the dielectric constant of the solvent introduces a variation in the entropy of ionization. As a result, $\Delta\Delta F°$ and $\Delta\Delta E$ are not equal, but this fact causes no difficulty because $\Delta\Delta F°$ (or, rather, that part of it which is directly due to the electrostatic interactions under discussion) is the quantity that is being dealt with in the theoretical treatment. As in the previous example of the formanilides, substituents that are close to the centers of reaction introduce further effects that cannot at present be allowed for, so that, for example, no treatment of the ortho-substituted benzoic acids can be carried through with any assurance.

7·2   Acid Strengths.[5]   There are at least two independent factors that cause variations in the strengths of acids of the same general type. The first of these, which has been recognized and understood for many years,[6] is electrostatic in nature. In α-chlorobutyric acid, for example, the ionizable proton is in a region of relatively high positive potential, since it is closer to the positive than it is to the negative end of the large carbon-chlorine dipole. For this reason, less work is required to remove the proton to infinity (or, in other words, to ionize the molecule) than in unsubstituted butyric acid, in which no such effect exists. As a result, α-chlorobutyric acid is a stronger acid than butyric acid, the ionization

[4] O. C. M. Davis, *Z. physik. Chem.* **78**, 353 (1911). See also L. P. Hammett, *Physical Organic Chemistry*, McGraw-Hill Book Co., New York, 1940, p. 190.

[5] Cf. G. Schwarzenbach and K. Lutz, *Helv. Chim. Acta* **23**, 1162 (1940).

[6] For example, see N. Bjerrum, *Z. physik. Chem.* **106**, 219 (1923).

constants[7] being 1.45×10^{-3} and 1.50×10^{-5}, respectively. In a similar manner, the facts that β-chlorobutyric acid, with a constant of 8.8×10^{-5}, is weaker than its α isomer, and that γ-chlorobutyric acid, with a constant[8] of 3×10^{-5}, is still weaker, find a ready explanation in the steadily increasing distance between the proton and the carbon-chlorine dipole in the un-ionized molecule. Similar qualitative interpretations of the empirical data can be made, by obvious extensions of the reasoning, for a large number of further acids; and with many acids a semiquantitative approach has led to completely satisfactory results.[9] However, in spite of the great importance of this treatment, we shall have little further to say about it, except incidentally, since it does not directly involve the idea of resonance.

It should be apparent that, just as in the meta- and para-substituted benzoic acids which were mentioned at the end of Section 7·1, these purely electrostatic effects contribute directly to the free energy of ionization. Consequently, unless the polar group is close to the ionizable proton, no complications are introduced by the fact that the entropy of ionization is not known.

The second important factor influencing acid strength directly involves the theory of resonance. Phenol, for example, is an acid with a dissociation constant of 1.02×10^{-10} (see page 367). The fact that this value is tremendously greater than that of any comparable alcohol cannot be explained on the basis of electrostatic interactions of the type that are important in the chlorobutyric acids. A consideration of the possibilities for resonance, however, leads at once to a simple interpretation of the observations. Thus, with a saturated alcohol, neither the undissociated molecule, ROH, nor the negative ion, RO⁻, is stabilized by resonance to any appreciable extent, since only one reasonable structure can be written for each. With phenol, on the other hand, both the undissociated molecule and the negative ion are hybrids of the Kekulé and the ortho- and paraquinoid structures, of which I, II, III, and IV represent typical examples. (As usual, the Dewar and other similar structures with formal bonds also have small weights. They will here be ignored, however,

---

[7] Except as otherwise noted, all dissociation constants cited in this and the following sections are taken from *International Critical Tables*, McGraw-Hill Book Co., New York, 1929, vol. VI, pp. 259ff. They refer to 25°C and to aqueous solutions.

[8] This value is taken from Landolt-Börnstein, *Physikalisch-Chemische Tabellen*, Springer, Berlin, 1923, vol. II, p. 1125.

[9] J. G. Kirkwood and F. H. Westheimer, *J. Chem. Phys.* **6**, 506 (1938); F. H. Westheimer and J. G. Kirkwood, *ibid.* **6**, 513 (1938). A simpler, but almost purely empirical, method of calculation has been given by C. G. Derick, *J. Am. Chem. Soc.* **33**, 1152 (1911). For a detailed discussion of this latter method, see G. E. K. Branch and M. Calvin, *The Theory of Organic Chemistry*, Prentice-Hall, New York, 1941, pp. 217ff.

because they would merely complicate the following discussion without leading to anything essentially new and without altering the conclusions in any significant way.) The Kekulé structures I and III are the most stable and hence the most important in the resonance, but the quinoid structures II and IV are of particular interest in the present connection

and require special consideration. It will be observed that in structure II a wide separation of charges has been effected, whereas in IV the negative ionic charge has merely been transferred from the oxygen to a carbon atom. As a result, IV is doubtless considerably more stable, relative to its corresponding Kekulé structure III, than II is relative to I. This implies that structure IV must have a larger weight in the ion than structure II has in the neutral molecule, and that the resonance energy of the ion must be greater than that of the neutral molecule. It follows then that the resonance facilitates ionization, and that phenol should be a stronger acid than a saturated alcohol, in which no such resonance can be postulated.

This same conclusion can be obtained in a different, but more or less equivalent, way which does not make explicit use of the idea of resonance energy. In the quinoid structure II of the undissociated molecule, the oxygen atom carries a positive formal charge. The effect of this charge is to make the oxygen atom more positive, or less negative, than a corresponding oxygen atom in a saturated alcohol. The resonance, therefore, creates an electrostatic effect, which then increases the degree of ionization just as in the chlorobutyric acids. In most, but not all, of the remaining examples discussed in this and in the succeeding sections, these same two points of view can be adopted. The second of these possible points of view has the advantage of relating the effect to a purely electrostatic interaction and so of decreasing to some extent the difficulty regarding the changes in entropy. However, we shall make use of only the former one, based upon the idea of resonance energy, because it is the more general of the two and can be applied to a wider variety of problems.

The structural feature of the phenol molecule which gives rise to the above-described effects is the enolic grouping, $C{=}C{-}OH$. It is evident, then, that the relatively great acidities of the various substituted phenols, the naphthols, and so on can be explained in an entirely analogous way. The same type of reasoning leads also to the further conclusion that the nonphenolic enols should likewise be considerably more acidic than comparable saturated alcohols. This prediction cannot be tested directly by comparison with experiment, because the simplest enols, like vinyl alcohol, V, rearrange immediately, and for all practical purposes irreversibly, to the corresponding aldehydes or ketones; the more complex ones like the enol forms of acetoacetic ester, VI, and of acetylacetone, VII, contain highly polar groups which exert large independent effects

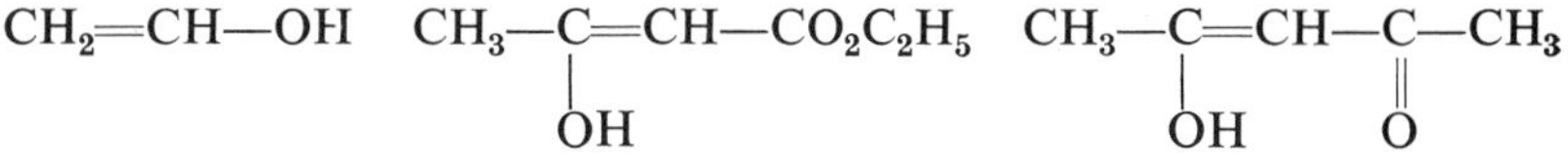

$$CH_2{=}CH{-}OH \qquad CH_3{-}\underset{\underset{OH}{|}}{C}{=}CH{-}CO_2C_2H_5 \qquad CH_3{-}\underset{\underset{OH}{|}}{C}{=}CH{-}\underset{\underset{O}{\|}}{C}{-}CH_3$$

V   VI   VII

upon the acid strengths; and, with the still more complex ones like 1,2-dimesityl-1-propene-1-ol, VIII, with which steric hindrance has greatly decreased the rate of ketonization,[10] the ionization constants have not been measured.

From the evidence which is available, however, it seems evident that the predicted effect does exist.[5, 11] In the enol form of acetylacetone,

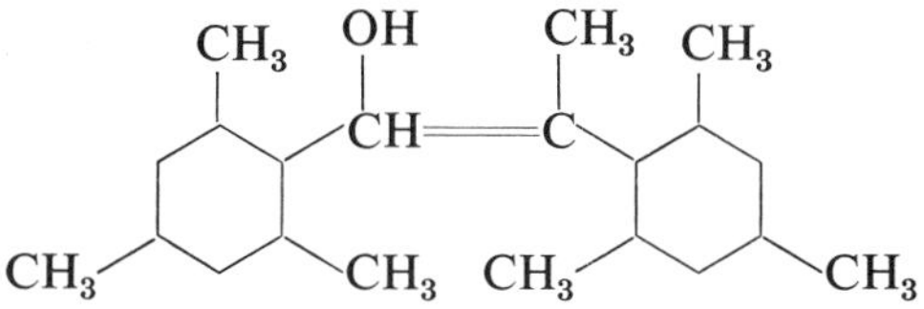

VIII

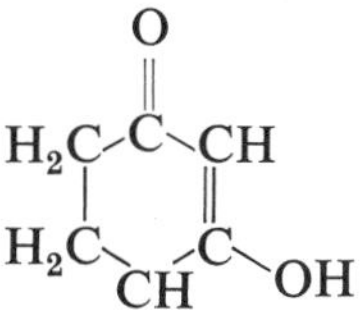

IX 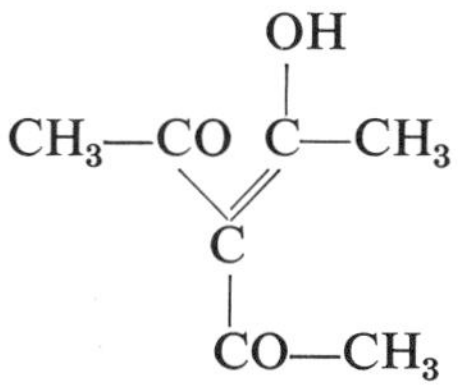   X

VII, for example, the reported ionization constant of 5.8×10^{-9} is definitely too large to be due merely to an electrostatic interaction with the adjacent carbonyl group. Moreover, in the enol forms of 1,3-cyclohexanedione (dihydroresorcinol), IX, and of triacetylmethane, X, with

---

[10] R. C. Fuson, J. Corse, and C. H. McKeever, *J. Am. Chem. Soc.* **62**, 3250 (1940).

[11] G. Schwarzenbach and K. Lutz, *Helv. Chim. Acta* **23**, 1147 (1940). See also, G. Schwarzenbach and E. Felder, *ibid.* **27**, 1701 (1944); M. L. Eidinoff, *J. Am. Chem. Soc.* **67**, 2072 (1945).

constants of 5.5×10^{-6} and 1.55×10^{-6}, respectively, the acid strengths are even greater. And finally, in the enol form of glutaconic dialdehyde, XI, the observed constant of 1.75×10^{-6} is of the same order of magnitude, although the electrostatic interaction should be considerably

$$HO—CH\!\!=\!\!CH—CH\!\!=\!\!CH—CH\!\!=\!\!O$$

XI

smaller. It is of interest that acetylacetone, dihydroresorcinol, glutaconic dialdehyde, and triacetylmethane give rise to negative ions in which the resonance should be especially effective, since it involves two equivalent structures in the first three ions, and three such structures in the last one. This difference from the simple enols like phenol may be partly responsible for the somewhat greater acidity of the di- and tricarbonyl compounds.

The values of the ionization constants of the above enols are based upon the assumptions that, in aqueous solution, acetylacetone is 19.6 per cent enolic,[12] whereas 1,3-cyclohexanedione, triacetylmethane, and glutaconic dialdehyde are each 100 per cent enolic. If the last three of these substances contain some of the keto forms in aqueous solution, the true ionization constants of the enol forms are correspondingly greater than the values given.

The foregoing discussion of the phenols and enols can be generalized to include all other types of substance containing the characteristic grouping $X = Y—\ddot{Z}—H$. The atoms X, Y, and Z can be of any kind, the only essential restriction being that the hydrogen, H, must be joined to an atom Z, which has an unshared pair of electrons and is linked by a single bond to a doubly bound atom Y. Thus, thiophenol, XII, and

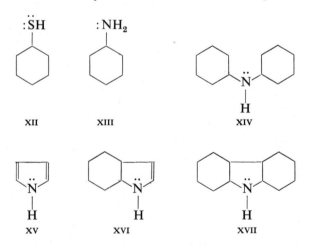

[12] F. C. Nachod, *Z. physik. Chem.* A **182**, 193 (1938).

aniline, XIII, should be stronger acids than saturated aliphatic mercaptans, RSH, and primary amines, RNH_2, respectively. Since the values of the ionization constants are not known, the correctness of these predictions can only be inferred from the chemical behaviors of the substances. In particular, thiophenol can be titrated with sodium hydroxide to a sharp end-point when phenolphthalein is used as an indicator, but an aliphatic mercaptan cannot.[13] No corresponding data seem to be available, however, for the amino compounds. Similarly, in diphenylamine, XIV, with an increased number of possible quinoid structures, and in pyrrole, XV, indole, XVI, and carbazole, XVII, the acid strengths should be still greater, as they do indeed appear to be. With pyrrole and its derivatives, the presence of an aromatic sextet is doubtless an additional important factor, just as with cyclopentadiene and its derivatives (see pages 347f).

In a carboxylic acid, XVIII, resonance of the present type may make a considerable contribution to the relatively great acid strength, although the closeness of the large carbonyl group moment makes a decision

XVIII   XIX   XX

difficult. Both the electrostatic and the resonance factors operate here to increase the acidity, and we cannot be sure how much of the observed effect must be attributed to each cause. The same situation is encountered also in the amide of a carboxylic acid, XIX, and in the imide of a dicarboxylic acid, XX.

A different type of example in which the electrostatic and resonance factors produce effects in the same direction is provided by the nitrophenols. These substances are more acidic than the simple phenols, as could have been predicted from the fact that nitro groups, like chlorine atoms, seem always to increase the acidities of any compounds in which they are present. This effect is due at least partly to the purely electrostatic interactions of the large nitro group moments. Here, however,

[13] P. Klason and T. Carlson, Ber. 39, 738 (1906). Some numerical values for the ionization constants of both aliphatic and aromatic mercaptans in a mixture of ethanol and water are given by J. Maurin and R. A. Pâris, Compt. rend. 232, 2428 (1951).

the fact that the ortho- and paranitrophenols, XXI and XXIII, respectively, are stronger acids than their meta isomer, XXII,[14] makes it seem

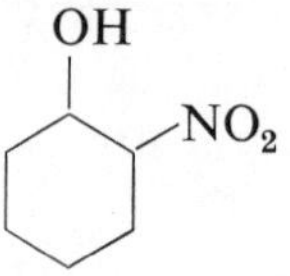

OH   OH   OH

—NO$_2$

NO$_2$

NO$_2$

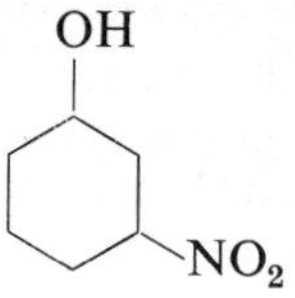

$K_a = 5.6 \times 10^{-8}$ $K_a = 5.3 \times 10^{-9}$ $K_a = 6.2 \times 10^{-8}$

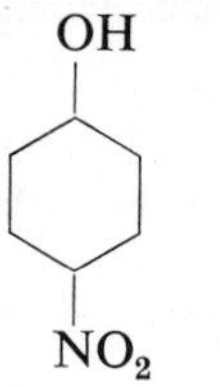

XXI   XXII   XXIII

probable that resonance also is involved. In the *para* compound, for example, there is resonance not only with the structures analogous to those with significant weights in phenol and in nitrobenzene, but also with such further ones as XXIV for the neutral molecule and XXV for the ion. Consideration of the charge distributions makes it apparent that the second of these structures is relatively more stable than the first, and consequently that the resonance should increase the acid strength. In the ortho isomer, the corresponding orthoquinoid structures, XXVI and XXVII, lead similarly to an increase in acid strength. In the meta

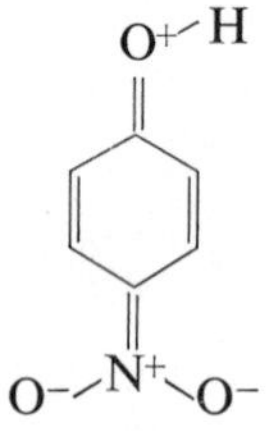

XXIV 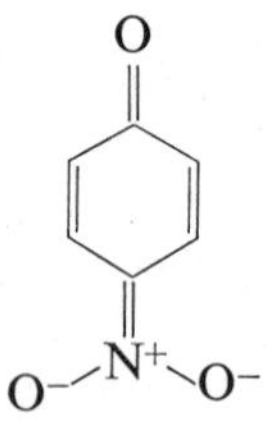   XXV 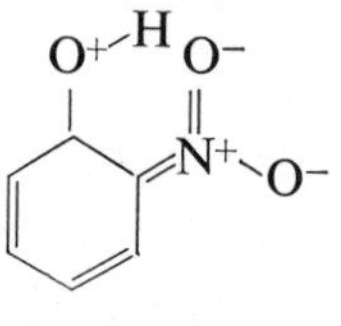   XXVI

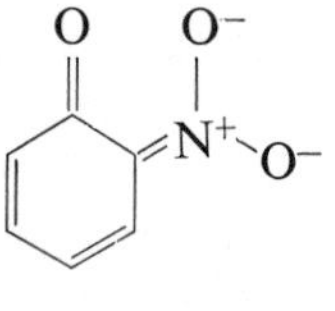

XXVII 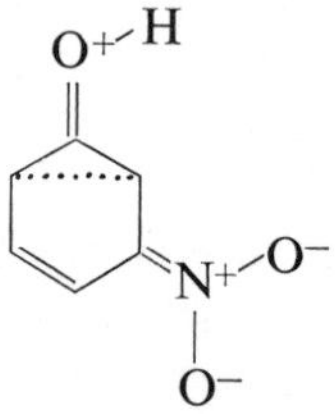   XXVIII 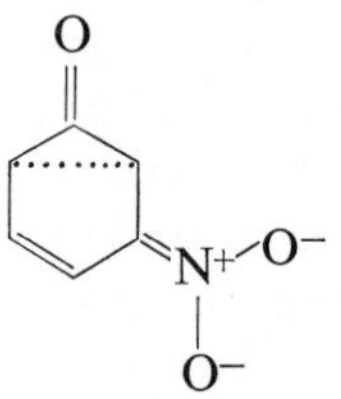   XXIX

isomer, on the other hand, the metaquinoid structures, XXVIII and XXIX, have formal bonds and so are too unstable to have great effect. Further evidence confirming this interpretation will be given in Section 7·4.

[14] G. W. Wheland, R. M. Brownell, and E. C. Mayo, *J. Am. Chem. Soc.* **70**, 2492 (1948).

Resonance can frequently exert an appreciable effect upon the acid strength even of a substance which possesses no enolic or similar grouping. In the neutral molecule of cyclopentadiene, XXX, for example,

XXX	XXXI	XXXII
XXXIII	XXXIV	XXXV
XXXVI	XXXVII	XXXVIII

there is only the small stabilization due to the simple conjugated system, whereas, in the corresponding negative ion, there is in addition the much more effective resonance among the five equivalent structures XXXI–XXXV. It is only reasonable, then, that this substance should be much more strongly acidic than a saturated hydrocarbon like cyclopentane, although it is still an extremely weak acid when compared with, say, a phenol. In indene, XXXVI, the acidity is also comparatively great, but it has probably been reduced somewhat from that of cyclopentadiene itself, since the resonance energy is already so great in the neutral molecule (on account of the presence of the fused benzene ring) that it is increased to a smaller extent by the formation of the ion.[15] With a second fused benzene ring, this trend continues, and fluorene, XXXVII, is known to be more weakly acidic than indene.[16] On the other hand, phenyl groups which are present as substituents upon the carbon atom carrying the acidic hydrogen atom have the opposite effect and increase the acid strength. Thus, phenylfluorene, XXXVIII, is an acid of about the same strength as indene, and the strengths of triphenylmethane, diphenylmethane, toluene, and methane decrease in the order named.[16] The reason for this effect

[15] G. W. Wheland, *J. Chem. Phys.* **2**, 474 (1934).

[16] J. B. Conant and G. W. Wheland, *J. Am. Chem. Soc.* **54**, 1212 (1932); W. K. McEwen, *ibid.* **58**, 1124 (1936).

of phenyl groups becomes apparent from a consideration of the structures which may be expected to have significant weights in toluene and in the benzyl anion. For the un-ionized molecule there are only the two Kekulé structures to be considered (structures with formal bonds being neglected); but, for the ion there are, in addition to the Kekulé structures,

XXXIX   XL   XLI

also the three quinoid structures XXXIX, XL, and XLI. Since, therefore, the resonance energy of the ion is greater than that of the neutral molecule, the effect of the phenyl group is to increase the acid strength. When there are two phenyl groups, as in diphenylmethane, or three phenyl groups, as in triphenylmethane, the acidity must be increased still more. The theoretical expectations, accordingly, are in complete agreement with the experimental facts. A more quantitative treatment of this problem has been given, but the results are only moderately satisfactory.[15]

On the basis of the above discussion, it might be expected that cycloheptatriene should be more acidic than even cyclopentadiene, since here the ion is a hybrid of altogether *seven* equivalent structures. Although no numerical data are available, the chemical properties of the two substances show that the expectation is *not* realized and that, in fact, cycloheptatriene is considerably the weaker acid of the two. There are probably two reasons for this discrepancy. In the first place, the seven-membered ring probably is not completely planar, and so the seven structures for the ion are not actually equivalent after all. (See the analogous discussion of cycloöctatetraene on page 143.) In the second place, theoretical calculations have shown that, even if the ion were planar, the resonance should be much less effective here than with cyclopentadiene.[15, 17] The reason for this possibly surprising result is that the cyclopentadiene anion contains six "aromatic" electrons, whereas the cycloheptatriene anion contains eight (cf. page 136).

Perinaphthene is a hybrid receiving large contributions from the structures XLII–XLIV, and smaller contributions from numerous other, less stable structures which, like XLV and XLVI, have either formal or ionic bonds (or both). Since the molecule therefore consists essentially of a naphthalene ring system that is conjugated with an ethylenic double bond, the resonance energy should be slightly greater than that of naphthalene itself (cf. Table 3·7, Section 3·3). When, however, a proton is removed from the methylene group, the resulting anion contains three

---

[17] E. Hückel, *Z. Elektrochem.* **43**, 752 (1937).

completely equivalent six-membered rings; hence, it is a hybrid not only of the structures that are analogous to XLII–XLVI, etc., but also of all

XLII   XLIII   XLIV

XLV   XLVI

XLVII   XLVIII   XLIX

the additional structures which, like XLVII–XLIX, are related to these by rotation about the threefold axis or by reflection in one of the planes of symmetry. The resonance energy of the ion should therefore be considerably greater than that of the neutral molecule, and so the substance should be relatively acidic. The chemical properties of perinaphthene are in agreement with this prediction, and the acid strength of the substance has been found to be greater than that of triphenylmethane, but less than that of cyclopentadiene.[18]

In p,p',p''-trinitrotriphenylmethane, L, as in the nitrophenols, the nitro groups increase the acid strength both by their electrostatic interactions and also by their making possible, *in the ion alone*, resonance with such additional structures as LI. The effect here is so great that, although

L   LI

triphenylmethane has been assigned[16] an ionization constant smaller than 10^{-33}, the alkali metal salts of its trinitro derivative are not completely

[18] V. Boekelheide and C. E. Larrabee, *J. Am. Chem. Soc.* **72**, 1240, 1245 (1950).

solvolyzed even in aqueous alcoholic solution. It is difficult to assess the relative importance of the electrostatic and resonance factors, but evidence that the latter plays an important, even though not a decisive, role will be given in Section 7·4.

The relatively acidic nature of acetylene and of its monosubstitution products is apparently not a resonance effect but is due to a quite different cause. The explanation is probably that the carbon atom which carries the acidic hydrogen is linked by a triple bond to its adjacent carbon atom. In fact, it can be shown on theoretical grounds that, when an atom is joined to another by a multiple bond, it may be expected to hold its remaining electrons more firmly than usual. (See page 221.) Thus, as far as the electrons taking part in a carbon-hydrogen bond in acetylene are concerned, the carbon atom is acting like an atom of a more electronegative element, such as nitrogen. Consequently, acetylene is more acidic than ethane, just as ammonia is more acidic than methane. A similar, but smaller, effect should operate also in ethylenic compounds, so that a hydrogen atom joined to a doubly bonded carbon atom should show an intermediate acidity. This prediction is borne out by the fact that benzene is a stronger acid than a paraffin hydrocarbon,[16] but a much weaker one than acetylene.

An acetylenic hydrocarbon is ordinarily considered to be acidic only if it has at least one hydrogen atom that is directly linked to a triply bonded carbon atom. 6,9-Pentadecadiyne, LII, however, has been found[19] to contain active hydrogen, in the Zerevitinov sense, and so to be slightly acidic. Presumably, the anion is here stabilized by resonance among the structures LIII–LV.

$$CH_3—(CH_2)_4—C\equiv C—CH_2—C\equiv C—(CH_2)_4—CH_3$$
$$LII$$

$$CH_3—(CH_2)_4—C\equiv C—\overset{..}{C}^-H—C\equiv C—(CH_2)_4—CH_3$$
$$LIII$$

$$CH_3—(CH_2)_4—\overset{..}{C}^-=C=CH—C\equiv C—(CH_2)_4—CH_3$$
$$LIV$$

$$CH_3—(CH_2)_4—C\equiv C—CH=C=\overset{..}{C}^-—(CH_2)_4—CH_3$$
$$LV$$

There is reason to believe that at least part of the relatively great acidity of phenol and related compounds is due to an effect of the kind just discussed in connection with acetylene and benzene. In phenol, for

[19] Tchao, Y. L., *Bull. soc. chim. France* [4] **53**, 1537 (1933).

example, the oxygen atom must have given up a larger than usual share of its electrons to the carbon atom to which it is joined, merely as a result of the increased electronegativity of the latter. Consequently, for this additional reason also, the oxygen atom should be more positive, and the acid strength should be greater, in phenol than in a saturated alcohol. There is no way for estimating whether this additional effect is less or more important than the effect of the resonance. That it is by no means negligible is strongly suggested, however, by the following considerations,[20] which are taken from the field of the organic boron compounds. The equilibrium

$$R_3B + NH_3 \rightleftarrows R_3B^- - N^+H_3$$

is similar to the more familiar one

$$H^+ + NH_3 \rightleftarrows H - N^+H_3$$

because, in each reaction, a new valence bond is formed with the aid of the unshared pair of electrons originally possessed by the ammonia. In order to call attention to similarities of this sort, Lewis has proposed that the terms "acid" and "base" be generalized so that an acid becomes any substance with a vacant place into which a pair of electrons can be placed, and a base becomes any substance with an unshared pair of electrons which can be put into such a vacant place.[21] It is of interest now to consider the acid strength of the substance R_3B, in this generalized sense, in relation to the nature of the group R. The facts are that these acids follow the same regularities as the hydroxy compounds, and, in particular, that phenyl groups lead to stronger acids than do alkyl groups. For example, the addition compound of ammonia with trimethyl boron is 90 per cent dissociated at about 55°,[22] whereas the corresponding addition compound with triphenyl boron is not noticeably dissociated at temperatures much below its melting point of 212°.[23]

Although a direct comparison of the dissociation constants of these two substances is impossible on account of lack of data, the greater acidity of the triphenyl compound seems beyond question. However, there is no obvious way in which this fact can be related to resonance, because no structures analogous to II or IV, above, can be drawn; the boron atom just does not have the necessary electrons. Consequently, it appears necessary to suppose that the much greater acidity of triphenyl boron, as

[20] H. C. Brown, personal communication.

[21] G. N. Lewis, *Valence and the Structure of Atoms and Molecules*, Chemical Catalog Co., New York, 1923, pp. 141f; *J. Franklin Inst.* **226**, 293 (1938).

[22] A. Stock and F. Zeidler, *Ber.* **54**, 531 (1921); H. C. Brown, H. Bartholomay, Jr., and M. D. Taylor, *J. Am. Chem. Soc.* **66**, 435 (1944).

[23] E. Krause, *Ber.* **57**, 813 (1924).

compared with trimethyl boron, must be a result only of the greater electronegativity of the aromatic carbon atoms. If so, then the same effect should increase also the acid strength of phenol and its analogs to a considerable, but indeterminate, extent. The exact extent to which the resonance is responsible for the increased acid strengths of these latter substances is therefore uncertain. Evidence supporting the belief that resonance is a significant factor will be given, however, in Section 7·4.

Additional insight into the effects of resonance on the acidities of certain types of aromatic compounds can be gained from the consideration of an important general relationship that has been discovered by Hammett.[24]   The equation

$$C_6H_4XY + A \rightleftarrows \text{Products} \tag{1}$$

describes a reaction in which a benzene derivative C_6H_4XY reacts with a reagent A to give products that depend upon the identities of X, Y, and A, and possibly also upon the experimental conditions. For example, the ionization of phenol in aqueous solution is represented by equation 1 if X is H, Y is OH, and A is H_2O, and if the products are the ions C_6H_5—O^- and H_3O^+. Similarly, the esterification of p-nitrobenzoic acid with ethyl alcohol is represented by this same equation if X is p-NO_2, Y is CO_2H, and A is C_2H_5OH, and if the products are p-O_2N—C_6H_4—CO_2—C_2H_5 and H_2O. Hammett's relationship can now be written in the form

$$\log k_z - \log k_h = \rho\sigma_z \tag{2}$$

where k_z is the value of either the equilibrium constant or the rate constant for reaction 1 when the substituent X is some specified atom or group Z; k_h is the value of the equilibrium or rate constant for the same reaction when the substituent X is a hydrogen atom; and ρ and σ_z are, respectively, the so-called *reaction constant* and *substituent constant*. The value of ρ is determined by the type of reaction that is involved. In other words, this parameter depends upon the identities of Y and A, and upon the experimental conditions, but it is the same for all substituents Z. The value of σ_z, on the other hand, depends only upon the identity of Z, and so is the same for all Y, for all A, and for all experimental conditions. (However, see page 354.) With any individual reaction, the ρ that applies when the k's are equilibrium constants is different from the one that applies when the k's are instead rate constants; the same σ's can, however, be used for both the equilibrium and the rate constants. Since

---

[24] L. P. Hammett, *Chem. Revs.* **17**, 125 (1935); *Physical Organic Chemistry*, McGraw-Hill Book Co., New York, 1940, pp. 186ff.   Cf. also H. H. Jaffé, *Chem. Revs.* **53**, 191 (1953).

equation 2 defines only the ratios of the values of ρ for different reactions, and the differences between the values of σ_z for different substituents, Hammett has adopted the convention of setting $\rho = 1.000$ when this equation relates to the ionization constants of different benzoic acids in water at 25°C, and $\sigma_z = 0.000$ when $Z = H$. In general, equation 2 can be used only when the substituents X and Y are meta or para to each other; when they are instead ortho, relatively large deviations occur because of the entropy effects which were mentioned in Section 7·1.

We can now apply Hammett's relation to some ionization constants. Since $\sigma_z = 0.710$ when $Z = m\text{-NO}_2,$[24] we see from equation 2 that m-nitrobenzoic acid must be stronger than benzoic acid and, more precisely, that the logarithm of the ratio of the ionization constants should be about 1.000×0.710, or 0.710. The experimental value[25] is 0.709. Similarly, since $\sigma_z = 0.778$ when $Z = p\text{-NO}_2,$[24] p-nitrobenzoic acid must be even stronger than the meta isomer. For the logarithm of the ratio of the ionization constants of p-nitrobenzoic acid and benzoic acid, the expected and experimental[25] values are both equal to 0.778. In a qualitative way, the resonance concept leads to a simple interpretation of these variations in acid strength, since the two nitrobenzoic acids may be expected to receive small contributions from such relatively unstable quinoid structures as LVI–LIX. The positive charges which these structures place on the carbon atoms then facilitate the removal of the ionizable

LVI   LVII   LVIII   LIX

protons and so increase the values of the ionization constants (cf. the discussion of the chlorobutyric acids on pages 340f). Since the effect of these charges must clearly be greater when the carboxyl group is para to the nitro group than when it is meta, p-nitrobenzoic acid should be stronger than its meta isomer.

When the above treatment is applied to the acid strengths of the nitrophenols, it is found to be relatively unsatisfactory. Since the value of ρ that must now be used is 2.008 instead of 1.000,[24] the logarithm of the ratio of the ionization constants of the nitrophenol and of phenol

[25] J. F. J. Dippy and F. R. Williams, *J. Chem. Soc.* **1934**, 1888; J. F. J. Dippy and R. H. Lewis, *ibid.* **1936**, 644.

ought to be about 2.008×0.710, or 1.426, with the meta compound, and about 2.008×0.778, or 1.662, with the para compound. The observed values are 1.716 and 2.784, respectively (cf. pages 346 and 367). These discrepancies are not at all unreasonable, however, and they might even have been anticipated; for, as was suggested on pages 345f, the nitrophenols are doubtless hybrids of the structures XXIV and XXVIII as

well as of the ones analogous to LVI–LIX, etc. Since these additional structures must increase the acid strengths, and since the paraquinoid structure XXIV must have a considerably greater effect than its closest analog XXVIII, the observed values of the logarithms of the ratios are larger than the calculated ones, and the difference is considerably greater with p-nitrophenol than with m-nitrophenol.

In order to minimize the difficulties caused by such especially large interactions between the groups that are joined to the same aromatic ring, Hammett has proposed[24] that, for any given substituent Z, the value of the parameter σ_z be allowed sometimes to depend upon the natures of any additional substituents that may be present. Thus, when a nitro group is para to either a hydroxyl group or an amino group, $\sigma_{p\text{-NO}_2}$ is changed from 0.778 to 1.27. The value that is calculated for the logarithm of the ratio of the ionization constants of p-nitrophenol and of phenol is then increased from 1.662 to 2.55; although the discrepancy is not completely eliminated, its magnitude is so decreased that the treatment is reasonably satisfactory. Similar variations in the substituent constants σ_z seem to be necessary also when acyl,[24] carboxyl,[24] cyano,[24] and sulfonyl[26] groups are para to hydroxyl or amino groups. Since, however, the interactions between substituents that are meta to each other are always relatively small, they are ordinarily ignored, and hence no corresponding variations in the σ's are introduced.

From the above extremely brief discussion of the reaction and substituent constants, it may appear that the number of parameters which must be empirically evaluated is at least as great as the number of data which are to be fitted. As would have been immediately apparent, however, if more of the pertinent experimental evidence had been

[26] F. G. Bordwell and G. D. Cooper, *J. Am. Chem. Soc.* **74**, 1058 (1952).

cited, this view is quite incorrect. In fact, with the use of only a relatively few independent parameters, the equilibrium and rate constants for an incomparably larger number of reactions can be calculated, and the agreement between the predicted and observed values is usually rather close. Although the especially satisfactory results which were obtained above for the nitrobenzoic acids merely reflect that fact that σ_{m-NO_2} and σ_{p-NO_2} were themselves obtained from the ionization constants of these acids, discrepancies as large as those found with the nitrophenols are seldom encountered.

Additional examples illustrating the usefulness of equation 2 will be mentioned later in this chapter and also in Chapter 8.

7·3 Base Strengths. The same two factors which influence acid strengths, namely, the electrostatic interaction and the resonance, give rise also to characteristic variations in base strength. An example of a molecule in which only the resonance effect appears to be important is provided by aniline. (However, see below.) This substance, with an ionization constant[27] of 3.8×10^{-10}, is much more weakly basic than any of the comparable aliphatic amines, which have ionization constants in the range 10^{-3} to 10^{-5}. A reasonable explanation for this difference is that the resonance energy is here greater in the neutral molecule than in the corresponding positive ion. Aniline is a hybrid not only of the Kekulé (and Dewar) structures, but also of such ortho- and paraquinoid structures as I. The anilinium ion, however, can receive no contributions

I

from structures analogous to these latter, because the unshared pair of electrons, which is on the nitrogen atom in the conventional structure of aniline itself, has been used up in forming the new nitrogen-hydrogen bond and so cannot be placed upon the ortho or para carbon atoms as in I. The resonance, therefore, stabilizes the molecule with respect to the ion (however, see the next paragraph). Just as with the acid strength of phenol (see page 342), the effect of the resonance can here also be referred to a change in the distribution of electric charge. Thus, the contribution of structure I to the neutral molecule increases the positive charge (or decreases the negative charge) on the nitrogen atom, and so makes it more difficult for a proton to come up.

Although the explanation which has just been offered for the low base strength of aniline is qualitatively satisfactory, it seems to be quantitatively

[27] N. F. Hall and M. R. Sprinkle, *J. Am. Chem. Soc.* **54**, 3469 (1932).

inadequate. Reference to Table 3·7, Section 3·3, suggests that the difference between the resonance energies of aniline and of benzene can hardly be greater than about 2–4 kcal per mole, whereas ΔF° of ionization of aniline is greater than that of, say, ethylamine by 8 kcal per mole. Two possible explanations for the discrepancy can be proposed. In the first place, as a result of the difficulties which are encountered in the interpretation of the measured heats of combustion, and which were described in Section 3·3, the difference between the resonance energies of aniline and of benzene may be somewhat greater than the 2–4 kcal per mole, cited above. In the second place, the relatively great electronegativity of the aromatic carbon atoms may decrease the base strength of aniline, just as it increases the acid strength of phenol (cf. pages 350f). Indeed, if the electrons which are responsible for the carbon-nitrogen bond are, on the average, closer to the carbon atom in aniline than in an analogous saturated amine, then the magnitude of the net negative charge remaining on the nitrogen atom must be smaller in the aromatic compound than in the aliphatic. Consequently, the phenyl group must decrease the attraction of the amino group for a proton. As with phenol, so also with aniline it is impossible to determine exactly how much of the total effect is due to resonance and how much is instead due to the change in the electronegativity of the carbon atoms. In Section 7·4, however, we shall advance evidence to support the belief that both factors are important.

A useful alternative way for stating the value of the basic ionization constant K_b of an amine B is in terms of the acid ionization constant K_a of the conjugate acid[28] BH+. Thus

$$K_a = \frac{[B][H^+]}{[BH^+]} = \frac{[B][H^+][OH^-]}{[BH^+][OH^-]} = \frac{K_w}{K_b} \tag{1}$$

where K_w is equal to $[H^+][OH^-]$, the ion product of water, which has a value of approximately 10^{-14} at ordinary temperatures. In place of the constants K_a and K_b themselves, we shall frequently find it convenient to employ the respective quantities pK_a and pK_b, which are defined by the equations

$$pK_a = -\log K_a \cong 14 - pK_b \tag{2}$$

and

$$pK_b = -\log K_b \cong 14 - pK_a \tag{3}$$

For example, Hall and Sprinkle[27] reported that the pK_a of aniline is 4.58. Hence, the ionization constants are $K_a = 10^{-4.58} = 2.63 \times 10^{-5}$, and $K_b \cong 10^{-14}/2.63 \times 10^{-5} = 3.8 = 10^{-10}$. It is important to bear in mind that the stronger an amine is as a base, the smaller are the values of K_a and pK_b, and the larger are the values of K_b and pK_a.

Pyrrole, II, is like aniline in being a very weak base because resonance with such structures as III is possible in the neutral molecule but impossible

[28] J. N. Brönsted, Rec. trav. chim. 42, 718 (1923); T. M. Lowry, Chemistry & Industry 42, 43 (1923).

in the positive ion, and also because the nitrogen atom is joined to two carbon atoms which, being unsaturated, must have relatively great electronegativities. For the same reasons, diphenylamine, IV, triphenylamine, V, indole, VI, and carbazole, VII, are also extremely weak bases.

With pyrrole, indole, and carbazole, with which the nitrogen atoms are members of unsaturated five-membered rings, the base strengths are doubtless still further reduced by an additional factor; for, with each of these substances, the neutral molecule contains an aromatic sextet that is no longer present in the cation. (See pages 347f for a discussion of the analogous problem presented by the acidity of cyclopentadiene.)

The fact that pyridine is a much weaker base than any of its aliphatic analogs probably has little relation to the resonance in the molecule, but is instead primarily due to the increased electronegativities of the unsaturated carbon and nitrogen atoms in each of the Kekulé-like structures of the type VIII (see page 350). The situation is therefore analogous to that discussed in Section 7·2 in connection with the acid strengths of acetylene and of benzene. The relation between the two problems is easily seen if it is borne in mind that, since pyridine is a relatively weak base, the pyridinium ion, which has a structure analogous to that of benzene, must be a relatively strong acid. (See equations 1–3.)

The resonance effect in some substances *increases* the base strength. Guanidine, for example, is a strong base with a pK_a of 13.5,[29] presumably because the resonance among the three equivalent structures IX, X, and XI in the ion is much more effective than that between the corresponding

[29] N. F. Hall, *J. Am. Chem. Soc.* **52**, 5115 (1930).

nonequivalent structures XII, XIII, and XIV in the neutral molecule. The electrostatic effect due to the carbon-nitrogen dipoles should tend to *decrease* the base strength, as should also the effect of the double bond

$$
\begin{array}{ccc}
\overset{\displaystyle N^{+}H_2}{\overset{\|}{\underset{H_2N \quad NH_2}{C}}} &
\overset{\displaystyle NH_2}{\overset{|}{\underset{H_2N \quad N^{+}H_2}{C}}} &
\overset{\displaystyle NH_2}{\overset{|}{\underset{H_2N^{+} \quad NH_2}{C}}} \\
IX & X & XI
\end{array}
$$

$$
\begin{array}{ccc}
\overset{\displaystyle NH}{\overset{\|}{\underset{H_2N \quad NH_2}{C}}} &
\overset{\displaystyle N^{-}H}{\overset{|}{\underset{H_2N \quad N^{+}H_2}{C}}} &
\overset{\displaystyle N^{-}H}{\overset{|}{\underset{H_2N^{+} \quad NH_2}{C}}} \\
XII & XIII & XIV
\end{array}
$$

between the nitrogen and carbon atoms. The observed increase therefore shows that the resonance effect must here be large. In spite of an earlier report to the contrary,[30] all the alkyl-substituted guanidines appear to have about the same base strength as guanidine itself.[31] Since the replacement of one or more hydrogen atoms by alkyl groups cannot be expected greatly to modify the resonance in either the ion or the neutral molecule, this fact is completely consistent with the above interpretation.

With the amidines, the two principal structures for the ions, XV and XVI, are equivalent, whereas those for the neutral molecule, XVII and XVIII,

$$
\begin{array}{cccc}
R-\overset{\displaystyle N^{+}H_2}{\underset{\displaystyle NH_2}{C}} &
R-\overset{\displaystyle NH_2}{\underset{\displaystyle N^{+}H_2}{C}} &
R-\overset{\displaystyle NH}{\underset{\displaystyle NH_2}{C}} &
R-\overset{\displaystyle N^{-}H}{\underset{\displaystyle N^{+}H_2}{C}} \\
XV & XVI & XVII & XVIII
\end{array}
$$

are not. The base strengths, accordingly, are increased by the resonance. Although the electrostatic interactions and electronegativities again operate in the opposite direction, the substances are fairly strong bases. The pK_a of acetamidine (structure XVII or XVIII with R = CH_3) has been reported to be 12.41.[5] An interesting analog of the amidines is given by the substance XIX, which has a pK_a of 12.13; the relatively great base strength can be explained as resulting from resonance similar to that in the amidines.[5]

A further, rather similar example is given by 2-aminopyridine. The structures that have the greatest weights in the neutral molecule are here

[30] T. L. Davis and R. C. Elderfield, *J. Am. Chem. Soc.* **54**, 1499 (1932).
[31] B. Neivelt, E. C. Mayo, J. H. Tiers, D. H. Smith, and G. W. Wheland, *J. Am. Chem. Soc.* **73**, 3475 (1951); S. J. Angyal and W. K. Warburton, *J. Chem. Soc.* **1951**, 2492.

XX and XXI, whereas the ones with the largest weights in the cation are XXII–XXIV. Since the resonance energy is doubtless rather large even

XIX   XX   XXI

XXII   XXIII   XXIV

in the free amine, it should not be greatly increased by the addition of the proton. Consequently, the substance should be a weaker base than either of the above amidines. In agreement with expectation, the observed value of pK_a (in water at 20°C) is only about 7.[32] That the effect of the resonance is not negligible, however, is evident since the base strength is much greater than with either aniline ($pK_a = 4.58$)[27] or pyridine ($pK_a = 5.21$).[32]

4-Aminopyridine, XXV, ought to be a somewhat stronger base than 2-aminopyridine since, although the resonance and electronegativity effects should be approximately the same in the two amines, the electrostatic interactions which are due to the carbon-nitrogen dipoles, and which decrease the base strengths, ought to be appreciably smaller in the former substance. This prediction is confirmed by the observation that pK_a is 9.1.[32] 3-Aminopyridine, XXVI, on the other hand, ought to be a

XXV   XXVI   XXVII

[32] A. Albert and R. Goldacre, *Nature* **153**, 467 (1944). See also A. Albert and R. Goldacre, *J. Chem. Soc.* **1946**, 706; P. H. Gore and J. N. Phillips, *Nature* **163**, 690 (1949).

relatively weak base since, for its cation, no quinoid structure analogous to XXIV is possible. The observed value of pK_a is indeed only 6.6.[32] Although this substance is therefore the least basic of all the isomeric aminopyridines, it is still considerably more basic than pyridine itself; we may accordingly conclude that even such unstable structures as XXVII and its analogs are able to stabilize the cation with respect to the neutral molecule.

With those aminoquinolines in which the amino groups are joined to the carbon atoms of the heterocyclic ring, the base strengths vary in more or less the same way as with the corresponding derivatives of pyridine. The values of pK_a for quinoline, 2-aminoquinoline, 3-aminoquinoline, and 4-aminoquinoline are, respectively, 4.94, 7.34, 4.95, and 8.46.[32] Even when the amino group is joined to an atom of the benzenoid ring, the interactions between the two nitrogen atoms have appreciable effects. With 7-aminoquinoline, for example, pK_a is raised to 6.65,[32] and so the

XXVIII   XXIX

structure XXVIII may be assumed to contribute to the state of the corresponding cation. With some of the remaining isomers, however, the interpretation is less clear. Although the cation of 5-aminoquinoline should receive a contribution from structure XXIX, which is analogous to XXVIII, the value of pK_a is[32] only 5.51 and so is slightly smaller than that of 6-aminoquinoline ($pK_a = 5.62$),[32] with which a structure analogous to XXVIII and XXIX is impossible. No satisfactory explanation for this discrepancy can be given. It is of interest, however, that no similar difficulty is encountered with the aminoacridines, the base strengths of which vary in the way expected.[32]

The carboxylic acids also are analogous to the amidines and so might be expected to have pronounced basic character. Probably as a result of the electrostatic effect, however, these substances are slightly weaker bases than simple ketones.[33]

In urea and in the amides of carboxylic acids, the situations are similar to those encountered in guanidine and in the amidines, respectively.

[33] L. P. Hammett, *Physical Organic Chemistry*, McGraw-Hill Book Co., New York, 1940, p. 271.

With these substances, however, the structures XXX–XXXIX are completely equivalent in neither the ions nor the neutral molecules; consequently, the resonance effects are of less importance, and the base

$$
\begin{array}{ccc}
\text{XXX} & \text{XXXI} & \text{XXXII} \\
\text{XXXIII} & \text{XXXIV} & \text{XXXV} \\
\text{XXXVI} & \text{XXXVII} & \text{XXXVIII} \quad \text{XXXIX}
\end{array}
$$

strengths of the substances are smaller. It is to be noted that in these positive ions the protons are considered to be attached to oxygen, and not to nitrogen atoms as might perhaps have been anticipated in view of the fact that amines are in general stronger bases than ketones. This assumption is made because the resonance *increases* the ease of attachment of a proton to oxygen in these substances and *decreases* that to nitrogen. In the amides, for example, the structures XXXVI and XXXVII are more nearly of the same energy than are XXXVIII and XXXIX, and so the resonance favors the ion; the structure XL for the

XL

other possible ion, however, has no possibility for resonance with a structure analogous to XXXVII or XXXIX, and so here the resonance favors the neutral molecule.

We have already seen that, when a carboxylic acid, a urea, or an amide acts as a base, the proton which is taken up probably becomes attached to an oxygen atom. There are, in addition, a number of further examples in which "oxonium salts" of greater or less stability are formed in analogous reactions. The halochromic salts obtained from α,β-unsaturated ketones, for example, are more stable than the corresponding derivatives of saturated ketones. In dibenzalacetone, for example, the resonance includes the normal structure XLI, and several relatively unstable ones like XLII. In the ion, on the other hand, the corresponding structures, XLIII and XLIV, respectively, are more nearly of the same

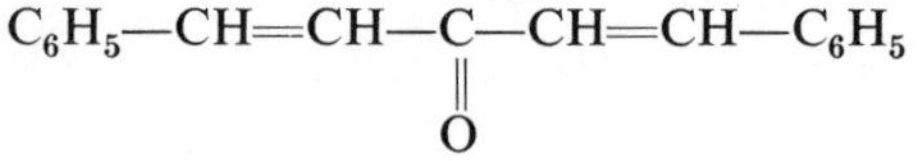

$$C_6H_5—CH{=}CH—\underset{\substack{\| \\ O}}{C}—CH{=}CH—C_6H_5$$

XLI

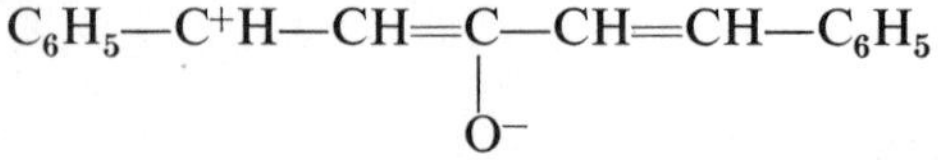

$$C_6H_5—C^+H—CH{=}\underset{\substack{| \\ O^-}}{C}—CH{=}CH—C_6H_5$$

XLII

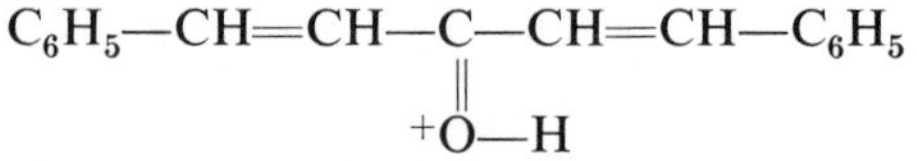

$$C_6H_5—CH{=}CH—\underset{\substack{\| \\ {}^+O—H}}{C}—CH{=}CH—C_6H_5$$

XLIII

$$C_6H_5—C^+H—CH{=}\underset{\substack{| \\ O—H}}{C}—CH{=}CH—C_6H_5$$

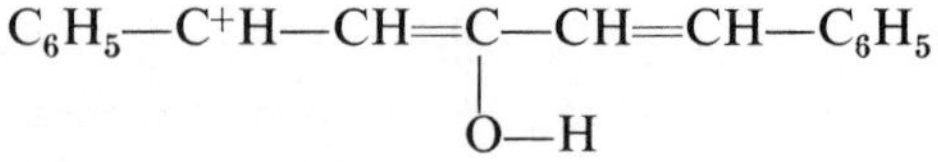

XLIV

stability since there is no separation of charge in either. The resonance, therefore, is more effective in the ion, and so the base strength is increased.[34] An extreme example of this effect is provided by dimethyl-γ-pyrone, XLV. In this substance, the positive ion is stabilized to a particularly great extent by resonance between the equivalent Kekulé-like structures XLVI and XLVII, as well as with such structures as XLVIII, which are

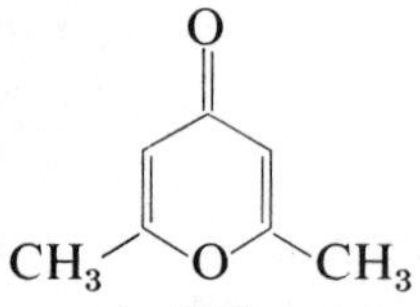

XLV 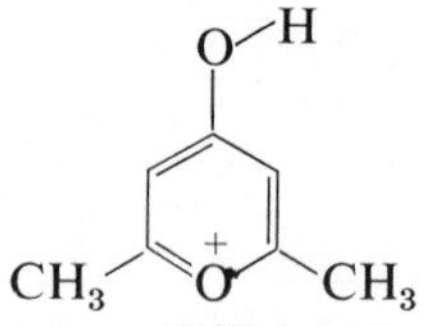   XLVI 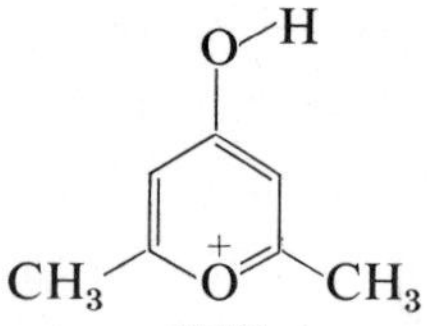   XLVII

[34] For quantitative data obtained for several analogous unsaturated aldehydes and ketones, see J. F. Thomas and G. Branch, *J. Am. Chem. Soc.* **75**, 4793 (1953); and for the basic ionization constants of some flavones, see C. T. Davis and T. A. Geissman, *ibid.* **76**, 3507 (1954).

analogous to XLIV. As a result, the substance is a particularly strong base for an oxygen compound. (In *International Critical Tables*[7] the ionization constant of this substance is given as $K_b = 6 \times 10^{-9}$. However, in the original paper from which this value was taken, the author states that the pyrone is a much weaker base than aniline and has an ionization constant of $K_b = 3 \times 10^{-14}$.)

With flavone, XLIX, the situation is entirely similar, in consequence of the γ-pyrone ring which the molecule contains.[34] Pelargonidin, L, is an example of a somewhat different type, but its corresponding positive

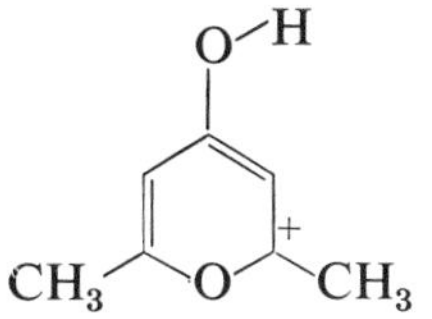

XLVIII 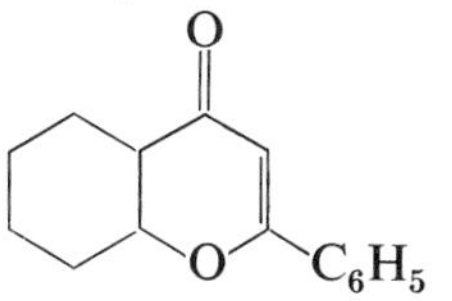   XLIX

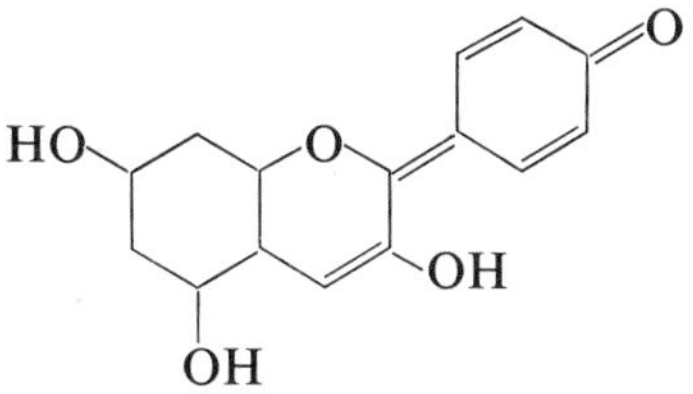

L 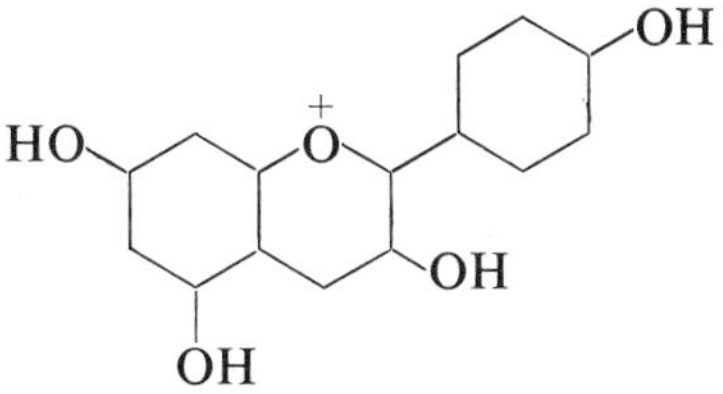   LI

ion, LI, also is of the oxonium type and is stabilized by the presence of an oxygen-containing ring with aromatic character.

Just as hydrocarbons can be regarded as extremely weak acids, so alcohols can be regarded as extremely weak bases, not only in the sense that such substances are capable of forming oxonium salts of the type $(ROH_2)^+X^-$, but also in the sense that positive ions, R^+, can be derived from them by the removal of hydroxide ions. The simple aliphatic alcohols do not behave as bases in this way, but the triarylcarbinols do. Triphenylcarbinol, for example, dissolves in concentrated sulfuric acid to give an intensely yellow solution containing the triphenylmethyl cation,[35] and triphenylmethyl chloride ionizes spontaneously in a number of solvents, including especially liquid sulfur dioxide.[36] Some salts, such

---

[35] A. Hantzsch, *Z. physik. Chem.* **61**, 257 (1907); L. P. Hammett and A. J. Deyrup, *J. Am. Chem. Soc.* **55**, 1900 (1933).

[36] For extensive studies of this problem, see, for example, K. Ziegler and E. Boye, *Ann.* **458**, 229 (1927); K. Ziegler and H. Wollschitt, *ibid.* **479**, 90 (1930); N. N. Lichtin and P. D. Bartlett, *J. Am. Chem. Soc.* **73**, 5530 (1951); N. N. Lichtin and H. Glazer, *ibid.* **73**, 5537 (1951).

as triphenylmethyl perchlorate, are colored, and hence presumably ionized, even in the solid state; and the yellow addition compound between triphenylmethyl chloride and aluminum chloride is doubtless a salt composed of the ions $(C_6H_5)_3C^+$ and $AlCl_4^-$. The reason for this behavior is presumably that the positive ion here is stabilized by resonance not only with the Kekulé structures of each ring separately, but also with ortho- and paraquinoid structures, like LII, which have no analogs

LII

in the un-ionized molecule.   Since the additional resonance energy of the cation should decrease as the number of aromatic rings decreases, benzohydrol should be a weaker base than triphenylcarbinol, and benzyl alcohol should be a still weaker one.   The experimental evidence is, however, not entirely clear.   From cryoscopic studies of several mono-, di-, and triarylcarbinols in 100 per cent sulfuric acid, and from parallel spectroscopic studies, Newman and Deno[37] have concluded that the second and third aryl groups have little or no effect upon the basicity of the carbinol; and they have accordingly suggested that, as a result of a steric inhibition of the resonance (cf. Section 7·4), no more than two, and possibly only one, of the aryl groups can aid in the stabilization of the cation.   Although benzohydryl chloride is rapidly polymerized by aluminum chloride, it gives an orange color when it is treated with stannic chloride;[38] and even benzyl chloride, in some of its reactions, shows transient colors which may be presumed to indicate the formation of intermediate benzyl cations.   On the other hand, solutions of benzohydryl or benzyl halides in liquid sulfur dioxide have conductivities which are only very slightly greater than that of the pure solvent;[38, 39] clearly, therefore, these substances are much less ionized than triphenylmethyl chloride under the same conditions.   The most reasonable conclusion which can be drawn from these confusing data is probably that, as is

[37] M. S. Newman and N. C. Deno, *J. Am. Chem. Soc.* **73**, 3644 (1951).

[38] F. Straus and A. Dützmann, *J. prakt. Chem.* [2] **103**, 1 (1921).

[39] P. Walden, *Bes.* **35**, 2018 (1902); *Z. physik. Chem.* **43**, 385 (1903).   For a somewhat more recent review of the subject, see P. Walden in *Handbuch der allgemeinen Chemie*, Akademische Verlagsgesellschaft, Leipzig, 1924, vol. IV, Part III, pp. 139ff.

expected on theoretical grounds, the base strengths of the several carbinols increase with the number of aryl groups, but that the effects of the second and third aryl groups are much smaller than is that of the first.

Since the relatively great electronegativity of the carbon atoms in aromatic rings ought, in the absence of other factors, to *decrease* the base strengths of aryl carbinols, any net increase indicates that the resonance is playing a predominant role. The distinction between these two effects of an aryl group is made especially clear by some results obtained by Lichtin and Glazer[36] in a study of certain phenyl-substituted triphenylmethyl chlorides. Thus, the ionization constant of triphenylmethyl chloride in liquid sulfur dioxide is slightly decreased if the hydrogen atom in a meta position is replaced by a phenyl group, but it is greatly increased if the hydrogen atom in one of the para positions is similarly replaced. In the former case, no meta quinoid structure without formal bonds can be written, and so the only important effect of the fourth phenyl group is that due to the electronegativity of its carbon atoms; in the latter, the cation can be stabilized by the contributions of such

C_6H_5 OH

LIII   LIV

additional structures as LIII, and the effect of the resonance is more than sufficient to counterbalance that of the electronegativity.

In 9-phenyl-9-fluorenol, LIV, the hydroxyl group is joined to a carbon atom that is part of a (modified) cyclopentadiene ring. Consequently, the same factors that make 9-phenylfluorene more acidic than the superficially analogous triphenylmethane (cf. page 347) should here operate to make the phenylfluorenol less basic than the superficially analogous triphenylcarbinol. As has been shown by Ziegler and Wollschitt,[36] this prediction is confirmed by the behavior of the corresponding chloride.

Hydroxy, alkoxy, amino, alkylamino, and other similar groups greatly increase the stabilities of triarylmethyl cations when they are present as substituents in the para positions of the benzene rings. This effect is probably due to the possibility of resonance in the ion with a number of still further structures, such as LV for crystal violet, for example. (See Section 6·6.) These structures contain more bonds, and so are more stable, than structures like LVI, analogous to LII for the triphenylmethyl cation itself. Since their weights must therefore be large, they are

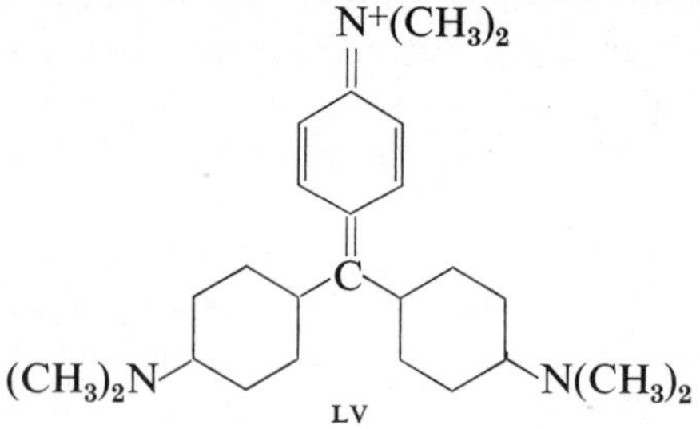

$$N^+(CH_3)_2$$

$$(CH_3)_2N \qquad C \qquad N(CH_3)_2$$

LV

$$N(CH_3)_2$$

$$(CH_3)N_2 \qquad C \qquad N(CH_3)_2$$

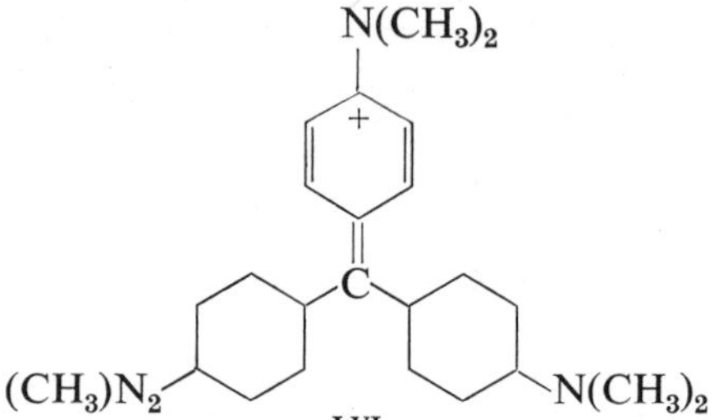

LVI

doubtless particularly effective in increasing the base strength of the carbinol.

Several authors have attempted to apply the molecular-orbital method[15, 40] or, less commonly, the valence-bond method[15] to the calculation of the differences between the resonance energies of carbinols and of their corresponding cations. The correlation between the results thus obtained and the observed basicities of the substances has usually been qualitatively satisfactory, but quantitatively inexact. (For mention of the analogous calculations for the acidities of hydrocarbons, see page 348.)

Hammett's reaction and substituent constants, ρ and σ, respectively, provide information regarding the effect of resonance on base strengths, as well as on acid strengths (cf. pages 352ff). Since the value of ρ that applies to the equilibrium in the ionization of an anilinium ion is equal to 2.73,[24] the logarithm of the ratio of the ionization constants of aniline and p-nitroaniline should be approximately 2.73×0.778, or 2.12, if $\sigma_{p\text{-}NO_2}$ is assumed to have its usual value of 0.778. Experimentally, however, the logarithm of the ratio is instead 3.47,[41] so that the nitro group decreases the base strength much more than might have been expected.

[40] See, for example, A. Streitwieser, Jr., J. Am. Chem. Soc. 74, 5288 (1952).
[41] L. P. Hammett and M. A. Paul, J. Am. Chem. Soc. 56, 827 (1934).

On the other hand, if $\sigma_{p\text{-}NO_2}$ is assumed to have the value 1.27, which applies when the nitro group is para to an amino or hydroxyl group, then the calculated logarithm of the ratio of ionization constants is increased to 2.73 × 1.27, or 3.47, and so is brought into agreement with experiment. As with p-nitrophenol, therefore, a particularly strong interaction must here also act between the two substituents that are para to each other. Consequently, the base strength of p-nitroaniline provides additional

$$N^+H_2$$

$$-O{\sim}N^+{\sim}O-$$

LVII

evidence for the belief (cf. pages 223f and 233f) that the quinoid structure LVII must be assigned a fairly large weight in the resonance.

7·4 Steric Inhibition of Resonance in Acids and Bases. It was pointed out in Section 7·2 that the relatively great acidities of ortho- and para-nitrophenol are partly due to resonance with quinoid structures. It is evident, then, that the acid strengths should be reduced if the resonance with these structures could in some way be prevented. Such an inhibition of the resonance can be effected, as was shown in Section 5·5, by the placing of methyl groups in the two positions ortho to the nitro group (in the para isomer only, of course). Methyl groups themselves, however, exert direct effects upon the acidities of phenols, and so a rather detailed study of the problem is necessary.[14] Since m-2-xylenol, I, is a weaker acid than m-5-xylenol, II, which in turn is a weaker acid than phenol, III,

OH	OH	OH
CH₃...CH₃	CH₃...CH₃	
$pK_a = 10.58$	$pK_a = 10.18$	$pK_a = 9.99$
I	II	III

itself, it follows that the methyl groups, even in the absence of any other factors, decrease the acidity of the compound, and are more effective when ortho, than when meta, to the hydroxyl group. On the other hand, 2-nitro-m-5-xylenol, V, is a weaker acid than 5-nitro-m-2-xylenol, IV. The order here is the opposite of that observed in the simple xylenols and so can hardly be due to any direct interaction of the methyl groups. The explanation is presumably that the nitro group in V can exert only its electrostatic, and not its resonance, effect, whereas that in IV can exert

OH
CH$_3$ CH$_3$

NO$_2$
$pK_a = 7.22$
IV

OH

CH$_3$ CH$_3$
NO$_2$
$pK_a = 8.25$
V

OH

NO$_2$
$pK_a = 7.16$
VI

both effects.   If the data are taken at their face value, it would appear that the·resonance is responsible for between one-third and one-half of the total effect.   (However, see the following paragraph.)

It is interesting that 5-nitro-*m*-2-xylenol, IV, is almost as strong an acid as *p*-nitro-phenol, VI, although a much larger difference of about half a *pK* unit might have been expected from analogy with *m*-2-xylenol and phenol.   A possible explanation of this fact is as follows.[42]   The comparatively great acidity of all the nitrophenols must be partly due to the direct electrostatic interaction between the nitro group moments and the ionizable protons.   Coulomb's law shows that this interaction is increased in magnitude if the dielectric constant of the medium is lowered.   Now the methyl groups in the nitroxylenol increase the size of the molecule, so that more of the electrostatic lines of force between the nitro group and the proton must pass through the molecule, and less must pass through the solvent, than is true in *p*-nitrophenol.   Since the volume occupied by the molecule must be a region of low dielectric constant (possibly about 2) whereas the aqueous solvent has a much higher dielectric constant (about 80), it follows that the methyl groups in the nitroxylenol lower the *effective* dielectric constant and therefore increase the electrostatic interaction.   A similar effect should presumably operate also in 2-nitro-*m*-5-xylenol, V, so that the actual decrease of the acid strength of this substance by the inhibition of resonance is somewhat greater than appears at first sight; consequently the effect of the resonance alone in increasing the acid strength of the nitrophenols may be somewhat greater than estimated above.   It should be noted, however, that the shielding by the methyl groups should be less effective here than in the examples treated by Westheimer and Shookhoff, because the electrostatic interaction is here of the dipole-ion, and not of the ion-ion, type.

Cyano groups increase the acid strengths of phenols nearly as much as do nitro groups.   Two independent factors are again involved since the cyano group, like the nitro group, has a large dipole moment with its positive end pointing toward the remainder of the molecule; and since the resonance with structures like VII must stabilize the anion more than the resonance with the corresponding structures like VIII stabilizes the neutral molecule (cf. page 346).   On the other hand, since the linear form of the cyano group makes impossible any steric inhibition of the resonance, the effects of methyl substituents should be rather different

[42] Cf. F. H. Westheimer and M. W. Shookhoff, *J. Am. Chem. Soc.* **61**, 555 (1939).

with the cyanophenols and with the nitrophenols. More particularly, methyl groups in the former compounds should uniformly decrease the acid strengths, and they should be more effective when they are ortho to the hydroxyl group than when they are instead ortho to the cyano group. The observed[14] values of pK_a for 5-cyano-m-2-xylenol, IX, 2-cyano-m-5-xylenol, X, and p-cyanophenol, XI, do indeed fall in the predicted order.

Although the difference between the acidities of the first two of these compounds is somewhat smaller than might have been anticipated, there can be no doubt that the data are in complete agreement with the view that, as expected, the resonance is sterically inhibited in the nitrophenols, but not in the cyanophenols.

An example which is somewhat similar to that of the nitrophenols, but for which the data are less complete, is given by a comparison of 4,4′,4″-trinitrotriphenylmethane and 3,3′,3″,5,5′,5″-hexamethyl-4,4′,4″-trinitrotriphenylmethane. As was mentioned in Section 7·2, the first of these two substances is sufficiently acidic so that its sodium salt is stable in aqueous alcoholic solution and, in fact, its pK_a in absolute ethanol has the relatively low value of 17.44.[43] The second substance, however, is much less acidic,[44] although the numerical value of its dissociation constant is not known. The direct effect of the methyl groups is presumably in the observed direction, as in m-5-xylenol, II, but it is probably rather small in magnitude. The explanation of the facts is to be found

[43] R. S. Stearns and G. W. Wheland, J. Am. Chem. Soc. 69, 2025 (1947).
[44] G. W. Wheland and A. A. Danish, J. Am. Chem. Soc. 62, 1125 (1940).

rather in an inhibition of resonance in the trinitrotrixylylmethane. In this substance, the quinoid structures like XII are rendered unstable by

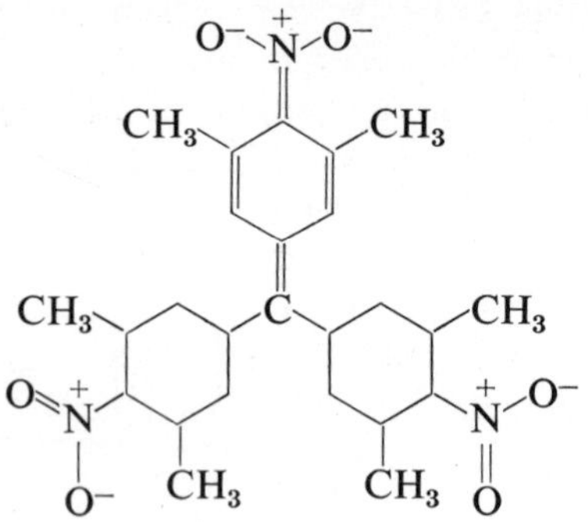

XII

the twisting of each nitro group out of the plane of the benzene ring to which it is joined; these structures, therefore, can have only small weights in the ion, and so they can increase its stability to only a small extent. The electrostatic effect of the nitro groups remains, however, so that the trinitrotrixylymethane is still a much stronger acid than trixylylmethane itself.

In tri-o-tolylmethane, the hydrogen atoms of the side-chain methyl groups have been found to be more acidic than the one attached to the central carbon atom.[45] This fact is somewhat surprising, since triphenyl-methane is known to be much more acidic than toluene.[16] A possible explanation is that, in the ion of the tritolyl compound, the resonance with structures like XIII is inhibited by the bulky methyl groups, which

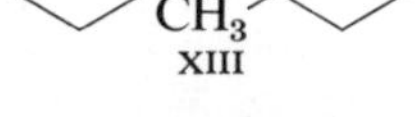

XIII

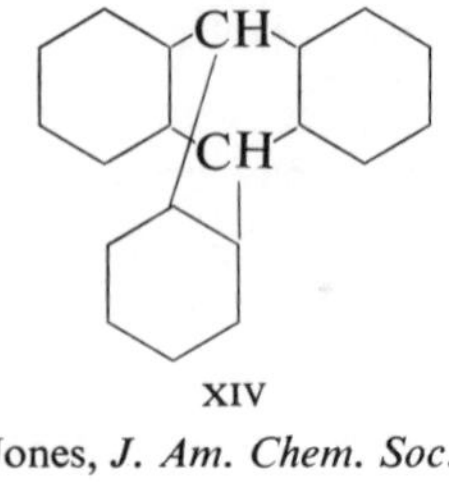

XIV

[45] P. D. Bartlett and J. E. Jones, *J. Am. Chem. Soc.* **64**, 1837 (1942).

prevent the achievement of the completely planar configuration. As a matter of fact, such a configuration is impossible also in the corresponding ion formed from triphenylmethane itself, because even the hydrogen atoms in the ortho positions are large enough to interfere with each other. However, the methyl groups must lead to considerably greater departures from planarity and, therefore, to an appreciably decreased acid strength.

Still a further example of a slightly different kind of steric inhibition of resonance is possibly given by the hydrocarbon triptycene, XIV.[46]   From analogy with triphenylmethane, this substance might be expected to have weakly acidic properties, so that it should react with phenylisopropyl potassium in accordance with the equation

$$C_{20}H_{14} + C_6H_5C(CH_3)_2K \rightarrow C_{20}H_{13}K + C_6H_5CH(CH_3)_2$$

Triptycene

Actually, however, no such reaction occurs here even in 21 hours, although the corresponding reaction with triphenylmethane is complete almost instantaneously.   The explanation of this difference in behavior may be merely that the reaction requires a Walden inversion about the carbon atom at which substitution occurs.   This proposal would mean that perhaps the hydrogen atom which is replaced cannot leave the triptycene molecule (either as a solvated proton or in combination with the phenyl-isopropide ion) unless the potassium cation has already approached the carbon atom from the opposite side.   Such an inversion is, however, impossible in consequence of the ring structure.   Under these circumstances, the rate of the reaction would be practically zero, and the failure of the reaction to occur sheds no light either on the position of the equilibrium or on the acidity of the hydrocarbon.   On the other hand, triptycene may actually be a much weaker acid than isopropylbenzene, so that the equilibrium in the above reaction is far to the left.   The potassium salt of triptycene could then never be formed in the above manner, regardless of rates.   If this second possibility is correct, the fact that triptycene is so much weaker as an acid than is the analogous tri-phenylmethane could be accounted for as the result of an inhibition of resonance.   On account of the presence of the rings, the triptycene negative ion would be held rigidly in a configuration which is even farther from the completely planar one than is that of the corresponding tri-o-tolylmethide negative ion.   As a result, the former ion cannot be stabilized by the resonance to any appreciable extent, and consequently the hydro-carbon has no apparent acid character.   It seems necessary to suppose that this second factor is important, whether the rates of reaction are fast or slow.

[46] P. D. Bartlett, M. J. Ryan, and S. G. Cohen, *J. Am. Chem. Soc.* **64**, 2649 (1942).

There have been reported a few examples in which the base strength of an amine is increased by an inhibition of resonance. Dimethyl picramide, XV, for example, has a pK_a of -4.69, as compared with -9.29 for unsubstituted picramide.[41]   The former substance is therefore a stronger base by a factor of about 4×10^4 in the ionization constant. Since the corresponding factor for dimethylaniline and aniline[27] is only about 3, it seems apparent that in dimethylpicramide the base strength must be greatly increased by an inhibition of the resonance with such structures as XVI.   This explanation is a reasonable one, since the dimethylamino group is large enough to interfere sterically with the orthonitro groups, whereas the amino group is not.

XV

Benzoquinuclidine, XVII, is a substituted aniline in which the amino group must be more or less rigidly held out of the plane of the aromatic ring.   Consequently, such quinoid structures as XVIII must be extremely

XVI   XVII   XVIII

unstable, and so can be assigned only small weights in the resonance. Direct evidence confirming the belief that the resonance is thus sterically inhibited has, in fact, been obtained from a spectroscopic study,[47] in which it was found that the near-ultraviolet spectrum of benzoquinuclidine is rather different from that of aniline, but is closely similar to that of benzene.   Furthermore, the transformation of the free base into the ammonium cation is here accompanied by only a slight change in the spectrum (cf. pages 291f).   The substance is therefore ideally suited for testing the relative importance of the effects which electronegativity and resonance have upon the base strength of aniline and its derivatives.   If only the former factor is important, benzoquinuclidine should be as weak

[47] B. M. Wepster, *Rec. trav. chim.* **71**, 1159 (1952).

as a typical aromatic amine; if, on the other hand, only the second factor is important, benzoquinuclidine should be as strong as a typical aliphatic amine. Since the observed value of pK_a, 7.79,[48] is about halfway between the two extremes, the two factors must be about equally important.

There is some ambiguity in the choice of the aromatic and aliphatic amines to be compared with benzoquinuclidine. If dimethyl-p-toluidine and quinuclidine, XIX,

$$\begin{array}{c} \text{CH} \\ \text{H}_2\text{C} \quad \text{CH}_2\,\text{CH}_2 \\ \text{H}_2\text{C} \quad \text{CH}_2\,\text{CH}_2 \\ \text{N} \end{array}$$

XIX

are arbitrarily taken as standards, then the corresponding values of pK_a are, respectively, 5.50[27] and 10.65,[49] so that the resonance effect is slightly the less important of the two; if different substances had instead been taken, however, the opposite conclusion might have been reached. It is of interest that the difference of $2.3pK$ units between benzoquinuclidine and dimethyl-p-toluidine corresponds to a difference of about 3 kcal per mole in ΔF° of ionization (cf. equation 3, Section 7·1). If the resonance were the only cause for the observed difference between the base strengths of these compounds, then the additional stabilization which the latter gains from the contributions of the quinoid structures must likewise be about 3 kcal per mole. This value is a reasonable one, but it cannot be confirmed by any independent determination.

Some further, much less striking, and much less conclusively established examples of the steric inhibition of resonance in aromatic amines are given in Table 7·1. In the derivatives of aniline in which methyl groups

TABLE 7·1

STERIC INHIBITION OF RESONANCE IN AROMATIC AMINES

Substituents in Ring	pK_a			
	Aniline		Dimethylaniline	
	In Water[a]	In 50% Aqueous Ethanol[b]	In Water[a]	In 50% Aqueous Ethanol[b]
None	4.58	4.25	5.06	4.26
o-Methyl	4.39	3.98	5.86	5.07
m-Methyl	4.69	—	—	—
p-Methyl	5.07	—	5.50	—
2,6-Dimethyl	—	3.42	—	4.69
2,4-Dimethyl	—	4.61	—	5.28
3,5-Dimethyl	—	4.48	—	4.48
2,5-Dimethyl	—	4.17	—	5.19

[a] N. F. Hall and M. R. Sprinkle, *J. Am. Chem. Soc.* **54**, 3469 (1932).
[b] G. Thomson, *J. Chem. Soc.* **1946**, 1113.

[48] B. M. Wepster, *Rec. trav. chim.* **71**, 1171 (1952).
[49] V. Prelog and Ingold, quoted by B. M. Wepster, reference 48.

are attached to one or more of the carbon atoms of the ring, substitution at the meta position is seen to produce a slight increase in pK_a, and hence also in the base strength; substitution at the para position is seen to produce a larger increase; and substitution at the ortho position is seen to produce a considerable decrease. The first two of these regularities could have been predicted; for, since a methyl group releases electrons to the ring (cf. page 226), it must increase the attraction of the nitrogen atom for a proton; furthermore, it should have a greater effect when it is para to the amino group than when it is meta. The effect of substitution at the ortho position is, however, somewhat unexpected since ortho derivatives are ordinarily analogous to their para isomers. We cannot explain the data by assuming a steric inhibition of resonance, since the amino group is probably too small to be forced away from a planar configuration in these compounds, and since, in any event, an inhibition of the resonance ought not to decrease the base strength but ought instead to increase it. A different suggestion has been made by Brown and Cahn,[50] who point out that the —NH$_3^+$ group must be somewhat larger than the —NH$_2$ group and, in addition, must be much more dependent on the stabilization that results from solvation. Consequently, since the volume that is available for the amino group must be decreased when bulky substituents are present in the ortho positions, the equilibrium between the free amine and its cation should then be displaced in favor of the neutral base.

The explanation proposed by Brown and Cahn seems to be in satisfactory agreement with the data for all the compounds with simple —NH$_2$ groups. However, when the various N,N—dimethyl derivatives are considered, the observed variations in the values of pK_a require that the steric inhibition of the resonance be also taken into account. Thus, although pK_a (in 50 per cent alcohol) is essentially the same for dimethylaniline as for aniline, it is about 1 pK unit greater for dimethyl-o-toluidine than for o-toluidine. That the presence of methyl substituents in the ring cannot, by itself, cause such an increase in base strength is indicated by the fact that pK_a (again in 50 per cent alcohol) for 5-dimethylamino-m-xylene is identical with that for 5-amino-m-xylene. When the measurements are made in aqueous solution, similar regularities are observed; for example, the replacement of the amino group by a dimethylamino group increases pK_a by about 0.5 unit with both aniline and p-toluidine, but by about 1.5 units with o-toluidine. In each of the instances cited here, and in each of the other ones which are contained in Table 7·1, the dimethylaniline is a stronger base than the corresponding aniline if, and

[50] H. C. Brown and A. Cahn, *J. Am. Chem. Soc.* **72**, 2939 (1950); cf. also B. M. Wepster, reference 48.

only if, there is at least one orthomethyl group. It will be noted that the effect of the inhibition of the resonance is much smaller here than with either N,N—dimethylpicramide or benzoquinuclidine. The explanation is presumably that, even with a methyl group in each ortho position, the dimethylamino group is not forced entirely out of the plane of the ring.

3,5,4′-Trimethyl-4,3′,5′-tricarboethoxydipyrrylmethene hydrobromide is a salt, of which the orange-red cation is a hybrid of structure XX and its numerous analogs[51] (cf. pages 323f).   Both the color of this cation and its stability are doubtless related to the possibility of resonance among such a large number of approximately equivalent structures. The N,N′—dimethyl derivative, on the other hand, is almost colorless in the solid state and so presumably has the covalent structure XXI.   The reason for

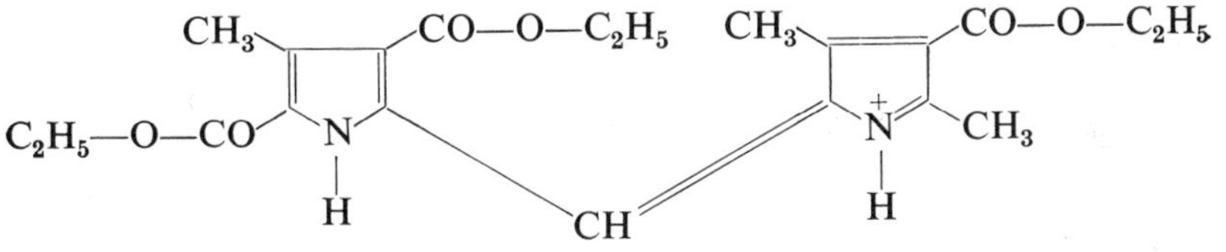

XX

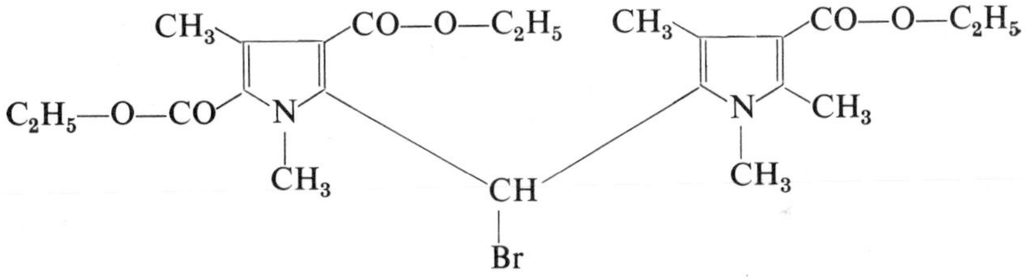

XXI

the difference between the two substances is possibly that, when the methyl groups are joined to the nitrogen atoms, the cation can no longer achieve the planar configuration which is required for the most effective resonance.   The substance forms a blood-red liquid, however, when it is melted, and it shows brilliant colors when it is dissolved in concentrated sulfuric or perchloric acid, and when it is treated with anhydrous stannic chloride in chloroform. Apparently, therefore, it ionizes under these more extreme conditions and gives rise to a cation that is completely analogous to the one that is a hybrid of structures XX, etc.

The above examples of steric inhibition are of interest not only for their own sakes, but also for the light which they shed upon the effects of resonance upon acid and base strengths in general.   It seems difficult, for example, to explain the data for the xylenols, nitroxylenols, and so

[51] K. J. Brunings and A. H. Corwin, *J. Am. Chem. Soc.* **66**, 337 (1944).

on, on any basis other than an inhibition of resonance. If this interpretation is correct for these substances, then, we have little choice but to assume that the corresponding interpretations which, in Sections 7·2 and 7·3, were given for the acid and base strengths of analogous compounds are also essentially correct. In this way, we have some reason for believing that the difficulties that arise from the unknown entropy changes do not completely invalidate the present method of treatment.

7·5 Addition to Double Bonds. The equilibrium in the reaction between ethylene and bromine is greatly in favor of the addition product,

$$CH_2{=}CH_2 + Br_2 \rightleftharpoons \underset{\underset{Br}{|}}{CH_2}{-}\underset{\underset{Br}{|}}{CH_2}$$

ethylene bromide. On the other hand, bromine does not add at all to tetraphenylethylene, I. Although this failure to add may be due merely to an unexpectedly slow rate of reaction, it appears that here the equilibrium between the ethylene and its bromide, II, has probably been

$$
\begin{array}{cc}
H_6C_5 & C_6H_5 \\
\diagdown\!\!\!\!\diagup & \\
C{=}C & \\
\diagup\!\!\!\!\diagdown & \\
H_5C_6 & C_6H_5 \\
& I
\end{array}
\qquad
\begin{array}{ccc}
H_5C_6 & Br & C_6H_5 \\
\diagdown & | & \diagup \\
C & {-} & C \\
\diagup & | & \diagdown \\
H_5C_6 & Br & C_6H_5 \\
& II &
\end{array}
$$

considerably displaced toward the ethylene. If the possibility of resonance were ignored, the difference in behavior between these two unsaturated substances could not be related to a difference in the natures of the bonds broken and formed in the reactions, because the two systems would then be identical in that respect. The explanation may therefore be that tetraphenylethylene is stabilized to an appreciable extent by the conjugation of the four phenyl groups with the ethylenic linkage. This stabilization would be lost if addition occurred, because then the central double bond would have been destroyed and so the conjugation would no longer exist. In ethylene itself, no such resonance effect is involved, since there is no conjugation in either the unsaturated compound or its addition product. The correctness of the above interpretation is supported by the fact that hydrogen and chlorine, which have greater intrinsic tendencies than bromine to add to double bonds, react even with tetraphenylethylene in the usual ways to give tetraphenylethane and tetraphenylethylene chloride, respectively. An alternative explanation, which also seems to be in agreement with the facts, is that the addition of bromine may be prevented by the steric repulsions which are exerted by the bulky phenyl groups. The fact that the atoms of hydrogen and chlorine are smaller than those of bromine is then partly responsible for the ability of hydrogen and chlorine to react.   Probably both the resonance and steric factors are involved to some extent.

In the reaction of an alkali metal with an olefin, the situation is the exact reverse of that discussed in the preceding paragraph.   Sodium adds readily to tetraphenylethylene to form a disodium salt, but it does not add to ethylene at all.   The reason for this difference in behavior is presumably that, in the negative ion of the salt derived from the tetra-phenyl compound, there is resonance with structures like III and IV; the second of these is analogous to structure V for the benzyl anion.

III   IV   V

(See Section 7·2.)   This resonance in the ion should be more important than that resulting from the conjugation in the original tetraphenyl-ethylene, because the additional structures (IV and the like) have neither formal bonds nor separated charges of opposite sign, and so are relatively stable.   In this way, the resonance, which is impossible both in ethylene itself and in its corresponding ion, facilitates the addition in the tetraphenyl compound and so displaces the equilibrium in the observed direction.

The further type of addition that occurs in the Diels-Alder reaction[52] can be treated more or less quantitatively.   The essential change that is here involved is shown in the equation

diene   dienophile   addition
product

As is indicated by the use of the two arrows, the reaction is often reversible so that, at a sufficiently high temperature, the product at the right breaks

[52] For discussions of the Diels-Alder reaction, see M. C. Kloetzel in R. Adams, *Organic Reactions*, John Wiley & Sons, New York, vol. IV, 1948, Chapter 1; H. L. Holmes, *ibid.*, vol. IV, 1948, Chapter 2; L. W. Butz and A. W. Rytina, *ibid.*, vol. V, 1949, Chapter 3; K. Alder, C. V. Wilson, and J. A. VanAllan in *Newer Methods of Preparative Organic Chemistry*, Interscience Publishers, New York, 1948, pp. 381ff.

down to regenerate the reagents at the left.   In a few instances,[53] the positions of the equilibria have been quantitatively measured; most commonly, however, the maximum available information is merely that the addition does, or does not, proceed far enough to give a satisfactory yield of the desired product.   By the use of either Klages's or Franklin's method for calculating heats of combustion (see Tables 3·4 and 3·6, Section 3·3), one can estimate that, in the absence of resonance, the reaction should be exothermic, and that $-\Delta H$ should be something like 15–20 kcal per mole; consequently, even when the conjugation is taken into account (cf. Table 3·2, Section 3·2), the value of $-\Delta H$ should still be about 12–18 kcal per mole with a simple aliphatic diene.   Although the entropy is doubtless unfavorable, the fact that, for example, the addition of maleic anhydride (the dienophile) to cyclopentadiene (the diene) seems to go essentially to completion to give the product VI is

therefore quite reasonable.   On the other hand, the further fact that the analogous reaction between maleic anhydride and benzene does not occur is also quite reasonable for, if it did, the product would have the structure VII, and so the stabilization resulting from the resonance in the aromatic ring would have been lost.   Since the resonance energy of benzene is about 36 kcal per mole (Table 3·2), the reaction would, in fact, not be exothermic but strongly endothermic.

Naphthalene is intermediate between cyclopentadiene and benzene for, in the reaction with maleic anhydride to give the product VIII, the loss of resonance energy should be approximately equal to the difference between the resonance energies of naphthalene and of benzene.   Since this difference is about 25 kcal per mole (cf. Table 3·7, Section 3·3), the reaction should be neither strongly exothermic nor strongly endothermic.   It is therefore not surprising that, although naphthalene itself reacts to the extent of less than 1 per cent with even a thirtyfold excess of maleic anhydride, some of its more reactive alkyl derivatives are more nearly completely converted into the respective addition compounds.[54]

For a number of more complex aromatic hydrocarbons, similar treatments lead to results that are qualitatively, and even semiquantitatively,

[53] See, for example, W. E. Bachmann and M. C. Kloetzel, *J. Am. Chem. Soc.* **60**, 481 (1938).

[54] M. C. Kloetzel, R. P. Dayton, and H. L. Herzog, *J. Am. Chem. Soc.* **72**, 273 (1950);   M. C. Kloetzel and H. L. Herzog, *ibid.* **72**, 1991 (1950).

satisfactory. A few of these results, together with the ones already discussed, are shown in the third column of Table 7·2. The quantities

TABLE 7·2

DECREASES IN RESONANCE ENERGY ACCOMPANYING
DIELS-ALDER REACTIONS

Compound	Structure (and Points of Attack[a])	Estimated Decrease in Resonance Energy[b]	
		Empirical[c]	Theoretical[d]
Benzene		36	37
Naphthalene		25	28
Anthracene		24	26
		12	16
Phenanthrene		31	30
		49	44
		49	45
Naphthacene		26	25
		13	14

TABLE 7·2 (*contd.*)

Compound	Structure (and Points of Attack[a])	Estimated Decrease in Resonance Energy[b]	
		Empirical[c]	Theoretical[d]
Benz[a]anthracene		28	31
		15	20
		20	25
Chrysene		25	29
Triphenylene		27	30[e]

[a] The asterisks show the carbon atoms of the diene component to which the dienophile would become attached if the reaction under consideration should occur.

[b] In kilocalories per mole.

[c] The values in this column are derived from the empirical resonance energies listed in Table 3·2, Section 3·2, and in Table 3·7, Section 3·3.

[d] The values in this column were obtained by R. D. Brown, *J. Chem. Soc.* **1950**, 691, by the molecular-orbital method with the parameter β set equal to −34 kcal per mole.

[e] This value was obtained by the method of Brown (note *d*) with use of data cited by B. Pullman and A. Pullman, *Les Théories électroniques de la chimie organique*, Masson et Cie., Paris, 1952, pp. 632f.

that are given here are the estimated decreases in resonance energy, which would result if additions occurred at the pairs of carbon atoms designated by the asterisks in the structures listed in the second column. The data required for the calculations are taken from Tables 3·2 and 3·7. In general, appreciable reactions are observed only when the losses of resonance energy are smaller than about 15 kcal per mole. Moreover, the fact that the equilibrium is somewhat less favorable for the addition with benz[a]anthracene than with anthracene[53] is also accounted for.

With use of the approximate molecular-orbital method (see pages 131ff and Section 9·25), Brown[55] has directly calculated the decreases of resonance energy which would accompany the Diels-Alder reactions of a great many dienes belonging to varied types. Some of the results which he has thus obtained are shown in the last column of Table 7·2. It will be seen that, in general, Brown's theoretical values are in fairly good agreement with the foregoing, more empirical ones. The small discrepancies which do occur are, in fact, no greater than could have been anticipated in view of the approximations inherent in the two treatments. The *qualitative* disagreement regarding the relative tendencies of anthracene and naphthacene to enter into the additions is possibly, however, somewhat unexpected. Although precise data regarding the positions of the respective equilibria are not available, it seems reasonable to suppose that, since naphthacene reacts with maleic anhydride "much faster" than does anthracene,[56] the reaction with naphthacene may go more nearly to completion than the reaction with anthracene. If this inference is correct, then the theoretical difference in resonance energy is here more reliable than the empirical one.

The quantities that were listed by Brown[55] in his paper were not the decreases in resonance energy, but were instead the so-called *para-localization energies*. The two sets of values are, however, readily interconverted since they differ by a constant amount. Although we need not here consider the precise definition of the para-localization energies, we may note that these quantities are 54.4 kcal per mole greater than the corresponding decreases in resonance energy.

7·6　Free Radicals.　The energy of dissociation of ethane into methyl radicals is about 80–85 kcal per mole,[57] whereas that of hexaphenylethane into triphenylmethyl radicals is only about 11.5 kcal per mole.[58] These two values are not strictly comparable because the first refers to the gas phase and the latter to solution; however, the difference between them must be real because it is much too large to be due merely to solvent

[55] R. D. Brown, *J. Chem. Soc.* **1950**, 691, 2730; **1951**, 1612.

[56] See E. Clar, *Ber.* **64**, 2194 (1931).

[57] H. C. Andersen, G. B. Kistiakowsky, and E. R. Van Artsdalen, *J. Chem. Phys.* **10**, 305 (1942); H. C. Andersen and G. B. Kistiakowsky, *ibid.* **11**, 6 (1943); D. P. Stevenson, *ibid.* **10**, 291 (1942).

[58] K. Ziegler and L. Ewald, *Ann.* **473**, 163 (1929); E. Müller and I. Müller-Rodloff, *ibid.* **521**, 89 (1936); R. Preckel and P. W. Selwood, *J. Am. Chem. Soc.* **63**, 3397 (1941).

effects.   Evidently, therefore, the six phenyl groups in hexaphenylethane have in some way greatly decreased the strength of the central carbon- carbon bond.   In consequence of this weakening of the bond, the substance is appreciably dissociated into radicals in solution at ordinary temperatures, whereas ethane itself shows no detectable dissociation except at extremely high temperatures.

Attention may here be called to the fact that, as was more fully explained on page 119, the bond energies which were discussed in Section 3·4 are not directly related to the energies required for the rupture of the individual bonds.   Consequently, although D(C—C) was found on page 117 to be 83.6 kcal per mole, the apparently gratifying agreement between this value and the observed dissociation energy of ethane must be largely accidental.

It seems probable that at least two factors are involved in the marked decrease in the stability of the central carbon-carbon bond in hexa- phenylethane.   In the first place, the phenyl groups are quite bulky, and they doubtless interfere with each other in such a way that the two triphenylmethyl radicals cannot come close enough together for a strong bond to be formed between them.   This suggestion receives some support from the observation[59] that the central bond in hexamethylethane is slightly longer, and so presumably somewhat weaker, than usual; con- sequently, it appears that in this substance an analogous steric interaction actually produces the postulated effect.   More direct evidence pointing in the same direction has been provided by the fact that the heat of hydrogenation of hexaphenylethane, to give two molecules of triphenyl- methane, is greater by 27 kcal per mole than that of ethane, to give two molecules of methane.[60]   In neither hydrogenation is there any significant change in the possibilities for resonance, and so the most reasonable explanation of the difference in the heats of the reactions is the steric one. A similar study of the reactions with oxygen to form peroxides has led to the conclusion that the central bond in hexaphenylethane has been weakened to the extent of about 35 kcal per mole;[60] this value is probably less reliable, however, than the one of 27 kcal per mole, which was obtained from the heats of hydrogenation.   As with the heats of dissoci- ation, the heats of hydrogenation and oxidation of ethane are not exactly comparable with those of hexaphenylethane, because the former refer to the gas phase and the latter to solution; again, however, the observed effects are so large that they must surely be real.

The second factor weakening the bond in hexaphenylethane is a reso- nance effect.   In the undissociated molecule, there is resonance among

[59] S. H. Bauer and J. Y. Beach, *J. Am. Chem. Soc.* **64**, 1142 (1942).   See also the Appendix.
[60] H. E. Bent and G. R. Cuthbertson, *J. Am. Chem. Soc.* **58**, 170 (1936).

the various Kekulé and Dewar structures of all the benzene rings separately, but these rings are not conjugated with one another. The total resonance energy is therefore just six times that of benzene itself. In the triphenylmethyl radical, however, the resonance must be assumed to include also such *ortho* and *para* quinoid structures as I. The resonance

I

energy per radical is, accordingly, greater than three times that of benzene, and so the resonance facilitates the dissociation.

An idea of the order of magnitude of the resonance effect can be obtained with the use of the approximate method of calculation described in Section 3·8. Equation 1 of that section gives a resonance energy of 180 kcal per mole for hexaphenylethane and of 240 kcal for two moles of the triphenylmethyl radical. The difference of 60 kcal per mole between these two quantities is then an approximate measure of the extent to which the resonance weakens the central carbon-carbon bond in the ethane. This figure is presumably an upper limit since, in order for the resonance in the radical to be completely effective, the radical would have to be planar, on account of the various quinoid structures of the type of I. As was mentioned above, however, in connection with the triphenylmethyl cation and anion (see pages 364 and 371), complete planarity is impossible because it would require that the orthohydrogen atoms of the different phenyl groups lie unreasonably close together. Consequently, there must be some twisting about the bonds linking the phenyl groups to the methyl carbon atom, and the resonance energy must be somewhat reduced. It is significant, however, that the calculated resonance effect, when combined with the steric effect, is of at any rate the correct order of magnitude to account for the observed weakening of the bond.

Calculations of the above simple type for any of the remaining hexaarylethanes lead always to identical answers, namely, that the resonance favors dissociation by 60 kcal per mole of ethane (or by a somewhat smaller amount when the lack of planarity is considered). As is shown in Table 7·3, however, more elaborate calculations distinguish among the various aryl groups. It is interesting that the order of increasing calculated resonance effect is usually the same as that of increasing observed degree of dissociation. This agreement is possibly fortuitous, however, since there seem to be rather wide variations in the entropies of dissociation.[61] (See Section 7·1.) Also, the surprisingly large effects that

TABLE 7·3

FREE-RADICAL RESONANCE ENERGIES OF PHENYL-SUBSTITUTED ETHANES

	Calculated Free-Radical Resonance Energy[b]		
Ethane[a]	I[c]	II[d]	III[e]
Diphenylethane (bibenzyl)	20	37	30
Di-m-biphenylylethane	20	37	30
Di-β-naphthylethane	20	45	33
Di-p-biphenylylethane	20	47	33
Di-α-naphthylethane	20	54	37
Bifluoryl (dibiphenyleneëthane)	40	58	59
Tetraphenylethane	40	61	52
Diphenylbifluoryl	60	78	75
Hexaphenylethane	60	80	70
Tetraphenyldi-p-biphenylylethane	60	84	71
Hexa-m-biphenylylethane	60	80	70
Tetraphenyldi-α-naphthylethane	60	89	77
Hexa-p-biphenylylethane	60	93	74

[a] The ethanes are listed in the approximate order of increasing dissociation. Cf. W. E. Bachmann in H. Gilman, *Organic Chemistry*, John Wiley & Sons, New York, 1st ed., 1938, vol. I, p. 504; 2nd ed., 1943, vol. I, pp. 587ff; G. W. Wheland, *Advanced Organic Chemistry*, John Wiley & Sons, New York, 2nd ed., 1949, Section 15·9.

[b] The "free-radical resonance energy" is defined as the resonance energy of 2 moles of the radical (in kilocalories per mole) minus that of 1 mole of the ethane. It is, therefore, a measure of the extent to which the resonance favors dissociation into radicals.

[c] Calculated from equation 1 of Section 3·8.

[d] Calculated by the valence-bond method, with the integral J set equal to -36 kcal per mole. See G. W. Wheland, *J. Am. Chem. Soc.* 63, 2025 (1941).

[e] Calculated by the corrected molecular-orbital method with the parameter β set equal to -38 kcal per mole. See G. W. Wheland, note d. In the values given here for di-β-naphthylethane and for di-α-naphthylethane, small numerical errors appearing in Table II of the original paper have been corrected.

saturated alkyl groups exert upon the extent of dissociation cannot be accounted for on the basis of resonance.[62] (Hyperconjugation involving

---

[61] C. B. Wooster, *J. Am. Chem. Soc.* 58, 2156 (1936); R. Preckel and P. W. Selwood, *ibid.* 63, 3397 (1941).

[62] C. S. Marvel, M. B. Mueller, C. M. Himel, and J. F. Kaplan, *J. Am. Chem. Soc.* 61, 2771 (1939).

structures like II might be used to explain the effects of ortho- and para-alkyl groups, but it cannot be of much importance with meta groups,

$\cdot$H

CH$_2$

CH$_3$ C   CH$_3$

II

which seem to be the most effective of all.)   The further fact that the *m*-biphenylyl group promotes dissociation to a considerably greater extent than the simple phenyl group is also difficult to understand.[63]   It seems evident, therefore, that, although resonance is probably the major factor responsible for the stability of the triarylmethyl radicals, some additional factors as well must play important roles in determining the relatively small differences among the various hexaarylethanes.   The steric effect, for example, must vary within rather wide limits, and possibly still other factors, which are not as yet understood, would have to be considered in a completely satisfactory theory.

The tetraarylethanes, on the whole, are much less highly dissociated into radicals than are the hexaarylethanes.   This difference could have been expected on the resonance theory, since the gain in resonance energy on dissociation decreases rapidly as the number of aryl groups decreases.   (However, see below.)   Indeed, equation 1 of Section 3·8 leads to the result that the resonance effect facilitates the dissociation of a tetraaryl compound by only 40 kcal per mole, as compared with 60 kcal per mole for a hexaaryl compound; and the more elaborate calculations reported in Table 7·3 lead to similar conclusions.   The steric factor also should in general become less important as the number of aryl groups decreases.   Consequently, appreciable dissociation is possible only when the steric effects are exceptionally large as, for example, in tetraphenyldi-*tert*-butylethane,[64] tetra-*p*-biphenylyldi-*tert*-butylethane,[65] and decaphenyl-butane.[66]   (This last compound, although it contains altogether ten

[63] C. S. Marvel, E. Ginsberg, and M. B. Mueller, *J. Am. Chem. Soc.* **61**, 77 (1939).
[64] J. B. Conant and N. M. Bigelow, *J. Am. Chem. Soc.* **50**, 2041 (1928).
[65] J. B. Conant and R. F. Schultz, *J. Am. Chem. Soc.* **55**, 2098 (1933).
[66] W. Schlenk and H. Mark, *Ber.* **55**, 2285 (1922).

phenyl groups, belongs to the class of tetraarylethanes and, for our present purposes, might better be called tetraphenyldi(triphenylmethyl)ethane. This is because the triphenylmethyl groups do not increase the possibilities for resonance any more in the radical than in the undissociated molecule.) In these various substances, the *tert*-butyl and triphenylmethyl groups, which are certainly very bulky, probably serve to lengthen, and so to weaken, the central carbon-carbon bond. The fact that tetramesitylethane and several analogous tetraarylethanes also appear to dissociate into radicals comparatively readily may also be due to steric interactions of the same sort.[67]

In diphenylethane, the resonance effect should be still less important, as is shown in Table 7·3. No compound of this type is known to dissociate appreciably into radicals at ordinary temperatures, regardless of the sizes of any substituents that may be present upon either the ethane carbon atoms or the benzene rings. The steric effect is apparently, therefore, insufficient here to produce a measurable dissociation, even though it is augmented by a rather powerful resonance effect (cf. the following paragraph).

Since the calculations leading to the values listed in Table 7·3 were obtained on the assumption that the radicals are completely planar, they must exaggerate the effect of the resonance in any radical which is, in fact, nonplanar. The error that is thus introduced should be especially serious with a triarylmethyl, somewhat less serious with a diarylmethyl, and probably negligible with a monoarylmethyl. Consequently, the fact that hexaphenylethane is much more highly dissociated than bibenzyl may be due more to the greater steric hindrance in the former ethane than it is to the difference between the resonance stabilizations of the triphenylmethyl and benzyl radicals. Some quantitative data bearing out this supposition have been obtained by Szwarc.[68] Thus, the heat of dissociation of hexaphenylethane (in solution) is 11.5 kcal per mole[58] (see page 381), so that the total weakening of the central carbon-carbon bond is about 70 kcal per mole.[57] Since approximately 30 kcal per mole of this weakening is due to steric hindrance,[60] only something like 40 kcal per mole can be attributed to the resonance. On the other hand, the heat of dissociation of bibenzyl (in the vapor state) is 47 kcal per mole,[68] so that the total weakening of the carbon-carbon bond is about 35 kcal per mole. Since the steric hindrance should here be little, if any, greater than with ethane, the effect of the resonance must be nearly as important with bibenzyl as with hexaphenylethane. These calculations are, of

---

[67] W. T. Nauta and P. J. Wuis, *Rec. trav. chim.* **57**, 41 (1938). See also J. Coops, W. T. Nauta, M. J. E. Ernsting, and A. C. Faber, *ibid.* **59**, 1109 (1940).

[68] M. Szwarc, *Chem. Revs.* **47**, 75 (1950).

course, only approximately valid, since they are based upon the supposition that data which apply to solutions can be directly compared with data which apply to the gaseous state; and since also there is some uncertainty regarding the magnitude of the effect due to steric hindrance in hexaphenylethane.[60] Although we must therefore realize that the numerical values which we have obtained have large probable errors, we can nevertheless be quite confident that, as was originally suggested, the increase in resonance energy which accompanies the dissociation into free radicals is not much larger with hexaphenylethane than with bibenzyl. Consequently, the figures which are given in Table 7·3, and which were obtained with neglect of the steric inhibition of the resonance in the nonplanar radicals, can have, at most a qualitative significance.

The dissociation of the tetraarylethanes into diarylmethyl radicals is paralleled by the dissociation of the tetraarylhydrazines into radicals containing "divalent nitrogen"; thus

$$(C_6H_5)_2\ddot{N}—\ddot{N}(C_6H_5)_2 \rightleftarrows 2(C_6H_5)_2\ddot{N}\cdot$$

(On account of resonance with quinoid structures in which the odd electrons are on ortho or paracarbon atoms, these radicals could be equally well described as containing trivalent carbon.) The reason for the greater dissociation of compounds of this latter type even in the absence of especially large steric interactions, is presumably that less work is required to break a nitrogen-nitrogen than a carbon-carbon bond, so that a given stabilization of the radical by resonance produces a greater net effect. The hexaaryltetrazanes dissociate similarly into triarylhydrazyls; thus

$$(C_6H_5)_2\ddot{N}—\underset{\underset{C_6H_5}{|}}{N}———\underset{\underset{C_6H_5}{|}}{N}—\ddot{N}(C_6H_5)_2 \rightleftarrows 2(C_6H_5)_2\ddot{N}—\underset{\underset{C_6H_5}{|}}{\ddot{N}}\cdot$$

Again, the relative stabilities of the radicals can be related to their greater possibilities for resonance. For one group of related compounds, dipole moment measurements[69] have shed light upon the nature of the electronic changes accompanying dissociation. Hydrazine, III, phenylhydrazine, IV, 1,1-diphenylhydrazine, V, and 1,2-diphenylhydrazine, VI, all have dipole moments in the range 1.53–1.87 D. Consequently, 1,1,2-triphenylhydrazine, VII, might be expected to have a moment of about the same magnitude, as might also 1-picryl-2,2-diphenylhydrazine, VIII, if resonance interactions were ignored, since then the three nitro group moments in the ortho and para positions should cancel each other. For VII, no measurements have been made, but there is no reason to doubt that the

[69] J. Turkevich, P. F. Oesper, and C. P. Smyth, *J. Am. Chem. Soc.* **64**, 1179 (1942).

prediction is essentially correct. For VIII, however, the observed moment is actually 3.59 D, which is about 2 D greater than anticipated.

$$H_2\ddot{N}-\ddot{N}H_2 \qquad C_6H_5-\ddot{N}H-\ddot{N}H_2 \qquad (C_6H_5)_2\ddot{N}-\ddot{N}H_2$$

III   IV   V

VI   VII   VIII

The explanation is presumably that there is resonance with structures like IX. (Compare the discussion of *p*-nitroaniline in Section 5·4.) In the 1-picryl-2,2-diphenylhydrazyl radical, X, the moment is still further

IX   X

XI   XII

XIII   XIV   XV

increased to 4.92 D. Structures like XI thus appear to be more important with the radical than are those like IX with the hydrazine.

A further type of free radical which has received a great deal of attention[70] is illustrated by the semiquinone XII. This substance has considerable stability.[71] It shows a relatively small tendency to disproportionate into a mixture of duroquinone, XIII, and the doubly charged durohydroquinone ion XIV; and it shows only an extremely slight tendency to dimerize to give either a quinhydrone or any ion derivable from a quinhydrone. Steric and resonance effects are doubtless both important in preventing the dimerization, but only the latter effect can account for the failure of the substance to disproportionate. This interpretation is supported by the further fact that the semiquinone is stable only in rather strongly alkaline solution, in which it can exist as the ion XII. On account of the possibility of resonance between the two equivalent structures, XII and XV (together with several others in which the unpaired electron is on a carbon atom of the ring), the stabilization by resonance should therefore be relatively great. In neutral solution, however, the semiquinone would presumably acquire a proton; it could then be a hybrid of only such nonequivalent, electrically neutral structures as XVI and XVII, and so should be much less stabilized. It disproportionates, therefore, practically completely into duroquinone, XIII, and

[70] For general discussions, see L. Michaelis, *Chem. Revs.* **16**, 243 (1935); L. Michaelis and M. P. Schubert, *ibid.* **22**, 437 (1938). Experimental papers by Michaelis and co-workers, which are too numerous to list here, are to be found in the *Journal of the American Chemical Society.* (See also references 71, 72, and 73.)

[71] L. Michaelis, M. P. Schubert, R. K. Reber, J. A. Kuck, and S. Granick, *J. Am. Chem. Soc.* **60**, 1678 (1938); L. Michaelis and S. Granick, *ibid.* **66**, 1023 (1944).

durohydroquinone, XVIII. We might expect that the present semi-quinone, XII, should again become stable in strongly acid solution, as a result of the equivalence of the structures XIX and XX. This question does not seem to have been investigated, but the somewhat analogous semiquinone that is obtained by the oxidation of p,p'-dihydroxydiphenyl-amine, XXI, is reported to be more stable in either alkaline or acid solution that it is in neutral solution.[72]

An interesting example of steric inhibition of resonance is apparently given by a comparison of the semiquinone XXII, with its lower homologs XXIII, XXIV, and XXV.[73] Since these last three radicals are all relatively

XXI   XXII

XXIII   XXIV   XXV

stable, it appears that methyl groups as such have no adverse effect. The radical XXII, however, is so unstable that it is not formed at all. The explanation is apparently that, in this substance, the planarity necessary for the quinoid structure, and hence for the resonance, is impossible.

The foregoing discussion by no means exhausts the known types of free radical. Since nothing essentially new is to be learned, however, from a detailed consideration of the remaining types, we shall content ourselves here with calling attention to Table 7·4, in which are listed examples of a number of the most important kinds of radicals. The reader should now be able without difficulty to see for himself the nature of the steric interactions that operate, and to write down the various structures that are involved in the resonance.

[72] G. Schwarzenbach and L. Michaelis, J. Am. Chem. Soc. 60, 1667 (1938).
[73] L. Michaelis, M. P. Schubert, and S. Granick, J. Am. Chem. Soc. 61, 1981 (1939).

TABLE 7·4

SOME IMPORTANT TYPES OF FREE RADICAL OF LONG LIFE

Characteristic Structure	Reference[a]
$(C_6H_5)_3C\cdot$	M. Gomberg, *Ber.* **33**, 3150 (1900); *J. Am. Chem. Soc.* **22**, 757 (1900).
	K. Ziegler and C. Ochs, *Ber.* **55**, 2257 (1922).
	K. Ziegler and B. Schnell, *Ann.* **445**, 266 (1925).
$[(C_6H_5)_2\overset{\cdot}{C}—\overset{\cdot\cdot}{O}:]^-$	W. Schlenk and T. Weickel, *Ber.* **44**, 1182 (1911).
$(C_6H_5)_2{}^+\overset{\cdot}{N}—\overset{\cdot\cdot}{O}:^-$	H. Wieland and M. Offenbächer, *Ber.* **47**, 2111 (1914).
$[(C_6H_5)_3N\cdot]^+$	E. Weitz and H. W. Schwechten, *Ber.* **59**, 2307 (1926).
	L. Michaelis, M. P. Schubert, and S. Granick, *J. Am. Chem. Soc.* **61**, 1981 (1939).
	L. Michaelis, M. P. Schubert, R. K. Reber, J. A. Kuck, and S. Granick, *J. Am. Chem. Soc.* **60**, 1678 (1938).
$(C_6H_5)_2\overset{\cdot\cdot}{N}\cdot$	H. Wieland, *Ann.* **381**, 200 (1911).

TABLE 7·4 (*contd.*)

Characteristic Structure	Reference[a]
$(C_6H_5)_3C\cdot$	M. Gomberg, *Ber.* **33**, 3150 (1900); *J. Am. Chem. Soc.* **22**, 757 (1900).
$(C_6H_5)_2\overset{..}{N}\!-\!\overset{..}{N}\!-\!C_6H_5$	S. Goldschmidt, *Ber.* **53**, 44 (1920).

S. Goldschmidt, A. Vogt, and M. A. Bredig, *Ann.* **445**, 123 (1925).

L. F. Fieser and W. Y. Young, *J. Am. Chem. Soc.* **54**, 4095 (1932).

D. Lipkin, D. E. Paul, J. Townsend, and S. I. Weissman, *Science* **117**, 535 (1953); S. I. Weissman, J. Townsend, D. E. Paul, and G. E. Pake, *J. Chem. Phys.* **21**, 2227 (1953); T. L. Chu and S. C. Yu, *J. Am. Chem. Soc.* **76**, 3367 (1954).

[a] These references are not intended to be complete. For further references and for a more detailed discussion of free radicals of long life, see W. E. Bachmann in H. Gilman, *Organic Chemistry*, John Wiley & Sons, New York, 1st ed., 1938, vol. I, Chapter 5; 2nd ed., 1943, vol. I, Chapter 6; G. W. Wheland, *Advanced Organic Chemistry*, John Wiley & Sons, New York, 2nd ed., 1949, Section 2·7 and Chapter 15.

Additional information regarding a few of the above radicals has been obtained from studies of the nuclear hyperfine structures in the microwave magnetic resonance absorptions by the respective substances (see pages 183 and 396f). The quantities that are directly measured in these experiments are the average values of $1/r^3$, where r is the distance between the unpaired electron and any atomic nucleus which has a spin. The cube roots of the reciprocals of these quantities are then defined (somewhat loosely) as the average distances themselves. By examining a sample of triphenylmethyl in which the methyl carbon atom is enriched in the isotope C^{13}, Weissman and Sowden[74] have found that the average distance of the unpaired electron from the nucleus of the methyl carbon atom is only about 0.7 A. The most obvious interpretation of this value is that

[74] S. I. Weissman and J. C. Sowden, *J. Am. Chem. Soc.* **75**, 503 (1953).

the unpaired electron has a negligibly small probability of being on any of the carbon atoms in the aromatic rings, and hence that the quinoid structures like I can have no

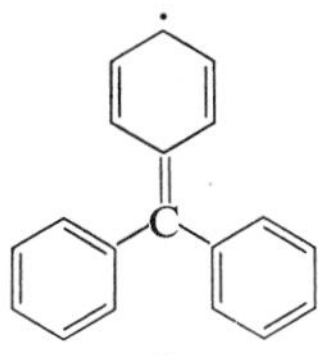

I

more than negligibly small weights in the hybrid. This interpretation is, however, inconsistent with the conclusions which were reached on pages 382ff, and which seem to be firmly established. Quite possibly, therefore, some different interpretation, the nature of which is not yet apparent, will be found to bring the seemingly discordant data into satisfactory agreement. Similarly, with 1-picryl-2,2-diphenylhydrazyl, the average distances of the unpaired electron from the two nitrogen atoms of the hydrazyl grouping have been found[75] to be equal, and considerably shorter than would have been

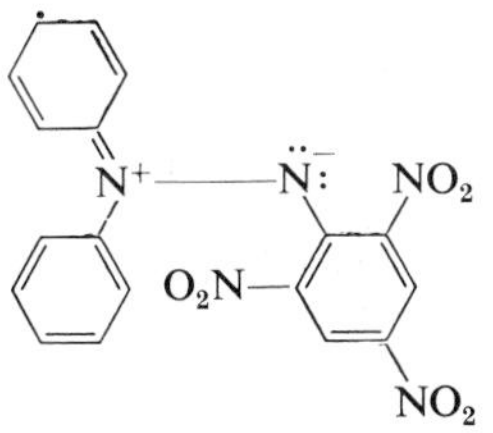

XXVI 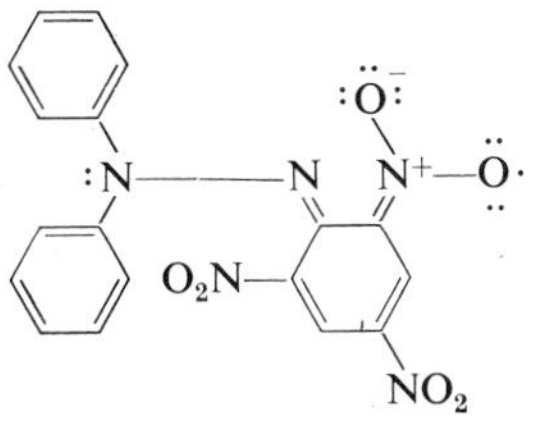   XXVII

expected if this radical receives important contributions from structures like XXVI and XXVII. Again, the interpretation of the data is at present obscure.

7·7 Biradicals. The free radicals discussed in Section 7·6 contain odd numbers of electrons per molecule, so that each must have (at least) one unpaired electron. (See Section 1·4.) It is of interest now to consider the question whether a molecule with an even number of electrons can have two of them unpaired and so be a biradical. This question cannot be answered experimentally on the basis of chemical evidence alone, because there is no necessary correlation between the chemical properties of a substance and the presence or absence of unpaired electrons. Although it is true that color and a high degree of reactivity are often taken as characteristics of free radicals, many colored and very reactive substances, such as triphenylmethyl sodium, $(C_6H_5)_3CNa$, are not free radicals; and some free radicals, such as oxygen, O_2, which is a true biradical, are colorless and not exceptionally reactive. The most nearly

[75] C. A. Hutchison, Jr., R. C. Pastor, and A. G. Kowalsky, *J. Chem. Phys.* **20**, 534 (1952); C. A. Hutchison, Jr., personal communication.

rigorous method for showing the presence of unpaired electrons in a molecule is doubtless by a detailed analysis of its spectra. This procedure, however, is difficult and laborious for even the simplest molecules, and becomes impracticable for the more complicated ones in which we shall be interested. It is fortunate, therefore, that an alternative method provides trustworthy information, except under certain special circumstances[76] that are not likely to be encountered in complex organic molecules. This second method is based upon the fact that molecules without unpaired electrons are almost invariably *diamagnetic*, whereas those with unpaired electrons are normally *paramagnetic*. A measurement of the *magnetic susceptibility* of a substance thus shows with almost complete certainty whether unpaired electrons are present or not. The actual number of unpaired electrons can be determined from the numerical value of the magnetic susceptibility, so that, for example, the degree of dissociation of a molecule like hexaphenylethane can be measured magnetically.[61, 62, 63, 77]

A substance is said to be diamagnetic if it is repelled by an inhomogeneous magnetic field, and paramagnetic if it is attracted by such a field. It will be sufficient for our purposes to define the magnetic susceptibility simply as a quantitative measure of the force by which the substance is attracted by the inhomogeneous field. A positive value of the susceptibility corresponds to paramagnetism, whereas a negative value corresponds to diamagnetism.[76, 77]

In the way sketched briefly above, it has been found that certain molecules with even numbers of electrons do indeed exist as biradicals, but that many others, which had previously been considered biradicals on account of their color and chemical behavior, are actually normal molecules with no unpaired electrons. The situation can be conveniently summarized by the following rule.[78] A molecule is a biradical if, and only if, no structure of the conventional type, and without formal bonds, can be written for it. For example, since structure I and five other structures analogous to it are possible for pentacene, the substance should not be a biradical even though it is both colored and sensitive to oxygen. In agreement with the rule, pentacene is indeed diamagnetic[78] and hence a hybrid of structures without unpaired electrons. Similarly, rubrene, for which the symbol II represents altogether sixty-four structures, is also diamagnetic[78] even though, like pentacene, it is colored and sensitive to oxygen. On the other hand, *m,m'*-biphenylene-bis(diphenylmethyl), III,

[76] J. H. Van Vleck, *The Theory of Electric and Magnetic Susceptibilities*, Oxford University Press, Oxford, 1932, pp. 272ff.

[77] Cf. G. W. Wheland, *Advanced Organic Chemistry*, John Wiley & Sons, New York, 2nd ed., 1949, pp. 691ff.

[78] E. Müller and I. Müller-Rodloff, *Ann.* **517**, 134 (1935).

is paramagnetic[78] and a true biradical, because no structure without either unpaired electrons or formal bonds can be written for it.

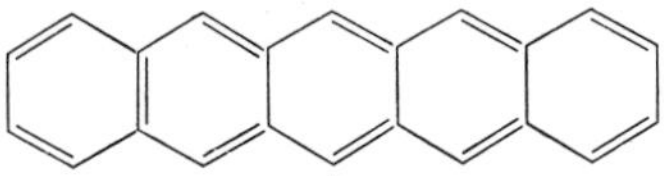

I

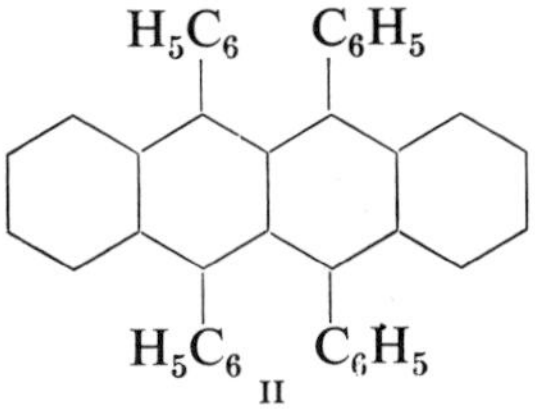

II

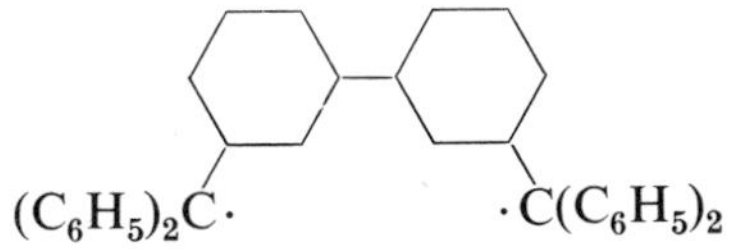

III

A number of apparent exceptions to the rule of Müller and Müller-Rodloff have been encountered. One of the most puzzling examples of such compounds has been the p,p'-isomer of the biradical III. Since the quinoid structure IV is here possible, the substance should have no unpaired electrons and should be diamagnetic. As is demanded by the rule, the substance is, in fact, diamagnetic,[78] but it also catalyzes the ortho-para-hydrogen interconversion.[79] Since in general only paramagnetic substances have such catalytic effect, the substance thus behaves in this respect as if it exists partly in a biradical form. In an attempt to explain this discrepancy, it has been suggested[79] that the molecule might be represented by either one of the two equivalent structures V and VI

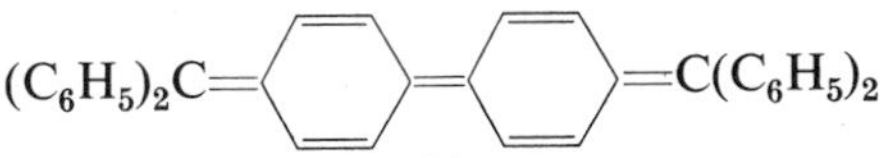

IV

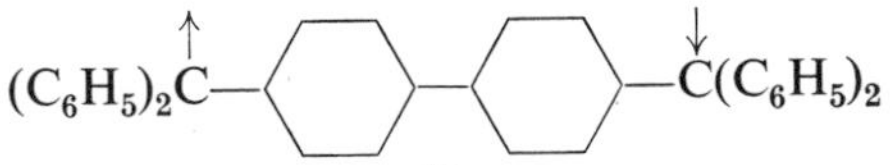

V

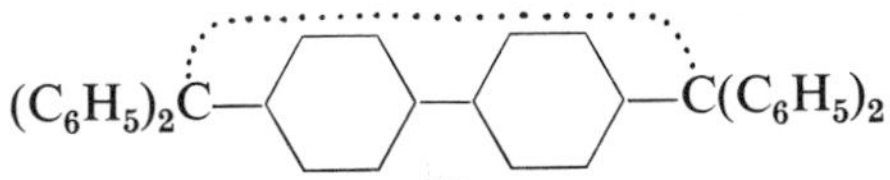

VI

[79] G. M. Schwab and N. Agliardi, *Ber.* **73**, 95 (1940).

(cf. page 19). According to this explanation, the two electrons, although they are thus paired with each other, are so far apart in space that each can act as if alone and unpaired in catalyzing the interconversion. The situation would thus be somewhat analogous to that in, say, *p*-dinitrobenzene, where localized *electric* dipoles exist even though the molecule as a whole is nonpolar. This· suggestion, however, cannot possibly be correct, because the molecule must be a hybrid of a great many structures. Although structures like V or VI must certainly be assigned finite weights, they are less stable, on account of their formal bonds, and so are probably of less importance than IV. (However, see pages 23f and 639.) In any event, no significance can be attached to the statement that there are odd electrons upon *any* two *specified* atoms. A more complete analysis which cannot be given here, shows that the suggested explanation (to the extent that it has any meaning at all) is equivalent to the supposition that the difference in energy between the forms with no, and with two, unpaired electrons is small compared with the energy of interaction between the molecule and the ortho- or para-hydrogen. If such were correct, however, the substance should be paramagnetic, because then a large fraction of the molecules would exist in the biradical form even at ordinary temperatures. More recently, Müller[80] has re-examined the problem and has concluded that neither his own measurement of the magnetic susceptibility[78] nor Schwab and Agliardi's study of the ortho-para-hydrogen interconversion[79] excludes the possibility that the compound is a mixture of two different forms in equilibrium with each other. According to this view, most of the molecules have no unpaired electrons and are diamagnetic, but a small fraction of them have two unpaired electrons and are paramagnetic. In confirmation of Müller's suggestion, Hutchison and his co-workers[81] have indeed found, by a study of the microwave paramagnetic resonance absorption (see the following paragraph) that p,p'-biphenylene-bis(diphenylmethyl) contains about 4–5 per cent biradical. Since the equilibrium is therefore greatly in favor of the diamagnetic form, we may conclude that, *in their ground states*, the molecules have no unpaired electrons and, accordingly, that the rule of Müller and Müller-Rodloff is here obeyed.

The principle of the method based upon microwave magnetic resonance absorption is the following.[82] If a molecule has a spin (i.e., a magnetic moment) which is due to the presence of one or more unpaired electrons, then, in a static magnetic field, the

[80] E. Müller, *Fortschr. chem. Forsch.* **1**, 325 (1949).

[81] C. A. Hutchison, Jr., A. Kowalsky, R. C. Pastor, and G. W. Wheland, *J. Chem. Phys.* **20**, 1485 (1952).

[82] For further details, see C. J. Gorter, *Physica* **3**, 995 (1936); J. B. M. Kellogg and S. Millman, *Revs. Mod. Phys.* **18**, 323 (1946); C. A. Hutchison, Jr., *Tech. Rept.* No. 1, Contract N6ori–20, Office of Naval Research, 1951, pp. 47ff.

spin must be oriented in some particular one of two or more different directions. (In general, the number of possible orientations is one greater than the number of unpaired electrons, and so is equal to the *multiplicity*. Cf. page 252.) Since, as a result of the interaction with the field, the different orientations of the spin correspond to slightly different energies, a transition from any orientation to any other must be accompanied by the absorption or emission of light (cf. equation 1 of Section 6·1). If the magnetic field is of the order of 3000–10,000 gauss, the wave length of the light absorbed, or emitted, is of the order of 3–1 cm and so falls within the microwave region. Consequently, one can detect the presence of a free radical by observing that the expected absorption does occur; and one can determine the amount of the free radical by measuring the intensity of the absorption. Since the total energy of the radical, in each of its orientations, must be slightly affected by the magnetic interaction between the spin of the electron and that of any nucleus which has a spin, the microwave absorption should then show a fine structure or, more precisely, a hyperfine structure; and, from a study of this hyperfine structure, one can obtain information regarding the average distance between the unpaired electron and the nucleus with the spin (cf. pages 392f). This last effect is different from, and in addition to, the one that is due to the electrostatic interaction between the electronic charge distribution and the nuclear quadrupole moment (discussed on page 211), and which can also lead to a hyperfine structure.

A second, rather similar, apparent exception to the rule of Müller and Müller-Rodloff is presented by porphyrindine, which is paramagnetic[83] although the structure VII without formal bonds can be written for it. The paramagnetism increases with the temperature, however, and so there is apparently something like a tautomeric equilibrium between the diamagnetic form VII and an isomeric (or electromeric) paramagnetic form VIII. From the temperature coefficient of the magnetic susceptibility, it has been concluded that the form VII is more stable than VIII

$$
\begin{array}{c}
\text{O}^- \qquad\qquad\qquad {}^-\text{O} \\
| \qquad\qquad\qquad\qquad | \\
(\text{CH}_3)_2\text{C}\!-\!-\!\text{N}^+ \qquad\qquad {}^+\text{N}\!-\!-\!\text{C}(\text{CH}_3)_2 \\
| \qquad \diagdown\text{C}\!-\!\text{N}\!=\!\!\text{N}\!-\!\text{C}\!\diagup \qquad | \\
\text{HN}\!=\!\text{C}\!-\!-\!\text{N} \qquad\qquad \text{N}\!-\!-\!\text{C}\!=\!\text{NH} \\
| \qquad\qquad\qquad\qquad | \\
\text{H} \qquad\qquad\qquad\qquad \text{H}
\end{array}
$$

VII

$$
\begin{array}{c}
\text{O}^- \qquad\qquad\qquad {}^-\text{O} \\
| \qquad\qquad\qquad\qquad | \\
(\text{CH}_3)_2\text{C}\!-\!-\!\text{N}^+ \qquad\qquad {}^+\text{N}\!-\!-\!\text{C}(\text{CH}_3)_2 \\
| \qquad \diagdown\text{C}\!=\!\text{N}\!-\!\!\text{N}\!=\!\text{C}\!\diagup \qquad | \\
\text{HN}\!=\!\text{C}\!-\!-\!\text{N} \qquad\qquad \text{N}\!-\!-\!\text{C}\!=\!\text{NH} \\
| \qquad\qquad\qquad\qquad | \\
\text{H} \qquad\qquad\qquad\qquad \text{H}
\end{array}
$$

VIII

[83] E. Müller and I. Müller-Rodloff, *Ann.* **521**, 81 (1936).

by about 0.5 kcal per mole.   The ground state of the molecule is therefore diamagnetic, in agreement with the rule.

Still a further type of molecule which appears to violate the rule is illustrated by the compound IX, which exists as a biradical.[84]   Here,

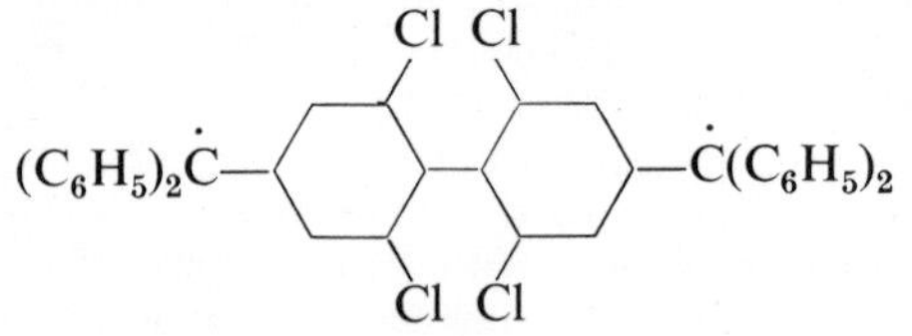

$$(C_6H_5)_2\dot{C}-\text{[ring system with Cl Cl above and Cl Cl below]}-\dot{C}(C_6H_5)_2$$

IX

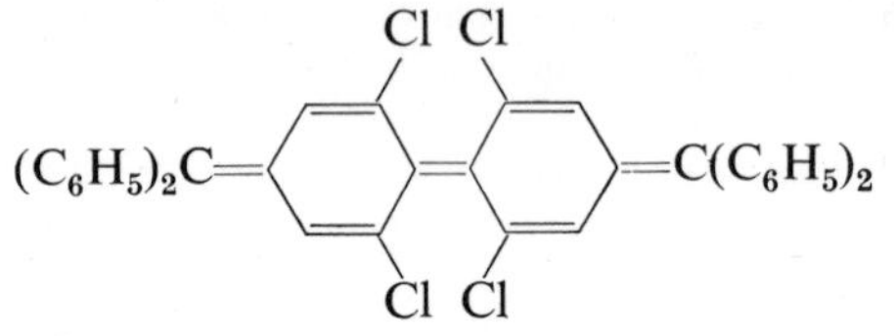

$$(C_6H_5)_2C=\text{[quinoid ring system with Cl Cl above and Cl Cl below]}=C(C_6H_5)_2$$

X

$$HO_2C\quad Cl\ Cl\quad CO_2H$$
$$Cl-\text{[ring system with Cl Cl below]}-Cl$$

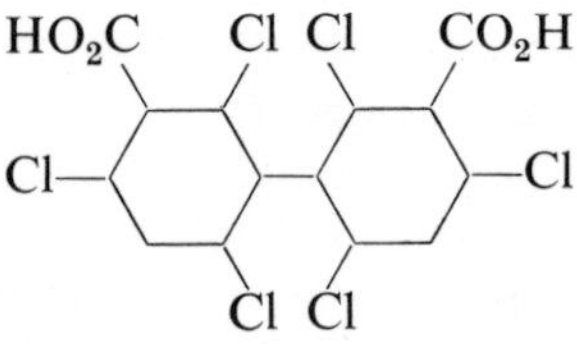

XI

however, the quinoid structure X, although it can be written on paper, does not represent a possible state of the molecule, because it requires that the two central phenyl groups be coplanar.   The existence of optically active biphenyls like 2,2',4,4',6,6'-hexachloro-3,3'-dicarboxybiphenyl, XI, for example, shows that the bulky substituents make such coplanarity impossible.[85]   This example is of particular interest since it provides evidence in support of the belief that, in the absence of large steric interference, the molecules of biphenyl and related substances tend to assume the planar configuration.   Indeed, it is only on this basis that the striking difference in properties between p,p'-biphenylene-bis(diphenylmethyl) and its tetrachloro derivative IX is at all understandable.

In addition to the above apparent exceptions, a small number of simple inorganic substances form genuine exceptions.   The most important of these is the oxygen

[84] E. Müller and H. Neuhoff, Ber. 72, 2063 (1939).
[85] J. White and R. Adams, J. Am. Chem. Soc. 54, 2104 (1932).

molecule, O_2, which, as has already been mentioned several times, has two unpaired electrons and so is a biradical, even though the structure $:\overset{\cdot\cdot}{O}\!\!=\!\!\overset{\cdot\cdot}{O}:$ can be written for it. The explanation for this exceptional behavior is well understood, but cannot be discussed here.[86]

7·8 Radicals of Short Life. The free radicals which have been discussed in Sections 7·6 and 7·7 are commonly described as *long lived*, since they can be kept for extended periods of time, either in the pure state or in equilibrium with other substances in which all electrons are paired. There exist, however, other free radicals which are instead described as *short lived*, since they can be obtained only in extremely low concentrations, as unstable intermediates in certain reactions. We shall encounter a number of these latter radicals in Chapter 8; here, however, we shall consider only the factors responsible for the variations in their stabilities.

As a convenient measure for the stability of any radical $R\cdot$, we shall use the energy that is required for its production by removal of a hydrogen atom from a molecule of the compound RH. Since we are therefore dealing directly with changes in either internal energy or enthalpy, and not with changes in free energy, the fact that we ordinarily do not know the entropies does not now introduce any difficulties.

In order to produce methyl radicals by breaking the carbon-hydrogen bonds in methane, one has to supply an amount of energy equal to about 101 kcal per mole.[68] On the other hand, in order to produce ethyl radicals by a similar reaction from ethane, one has to supply only an energy of about 98 kcal per mole;[68] and, in order to produce *n*-propyl, isopropyl, *n*-butyl, and *tert*-butyl radicals, the corresponding energies are, respectively, 95, 89, 94, and 86 kcal per mole.[68] Although the values given here for (especially) the secondary and tertiary radicals are of rather uncertain accuracy, the foregoing data are probably good enough to show the existence of certain unmistakable trends. Thus, the *bond-dissociation energy* decreases, and hence the relative stability of the resulting radical increases, when a hydrogen atom is replaced by an alkyl group; and the effect is especially large when the replacement is made at the atom that carries the unpaired electron.

With the short-lived free radicals, just as with their long-lived analogs, the observed variations in stability are probably due to both a steric and a resonance effect. In the *tert*-butyl radical, for example, the three methyl groups are so bulky that they doubtless make more difficult the linking of a fourth substituent to the central carbon atom. Furthermore,

[86] J. E. Lennard-Jones, *Trans. Faraday Soc.* **25**, 668 (1929); G. W. Wheland, *ibid.* **33**, 1499 (1937).

since these groups must also to some extent interfere with one another, the system should be most stable when the angles between the bonds by which they are linked to the central atom are as large as possible.[87]   Now, in a normal molecule like one of isobutane, the bond angles must have very nearly the tetrahedral value of 109° 28' but, in the radical, they can increase to as much as 120°. Consequently, this second steric factor, like the first one, should stabilize the free radical. With a secondary alkyl radical like isopropyl, both effects should be somewhat smaller than with the tertiary one; and, with a primary radical, they should be still smaller.

Brown and his coworkers[87] have suggested that the two types of steric interference which were considered in the preceding paragraph be designated as *F-strain* (for front-strain, or face-strain) and *B-strain* (for back-strain), respectively. From what has already been said, the significance of these terms should be obvious. Brown has also shown, in a large number of additional papers, that the concepts of *F-strain* and *B-strain* are valuable in many other fields of organic chemistry besides that of the short-lived free radicals. However, since these concepts are only indirectly related to that of resonance, we shall here consider them no further.

As was mentioned above, the relative stabilities of the free alkyl radicals are increased not only by steric strains but also by resonance. The *tert*-butyl radical, for example, can receive contributions from the conventional structure I and also from such additional "no-bonded" structures as II, III, etc.[15]   Since all these structures contain the same total

$$\begin{array}{ccc}
\underset{\text{I}}{\overset{\displaystyle CH_3}{\underset{\displaystyle CH_3 \, \cdot \, \overset{|}{C} \diagdown CH_3}{\big|}}} &
\underset{\text{II}}{\overset{\displaystyle CH_3}{\underset{\displaystyle \underset{H\cdot}{CH_2} \! = \! \overset{|}{C} \diagdown CH_3}{\big|}}} &
\underset{\text{III}}{\overset{\displaystyle \cdot H \ \ CH_2}{CH_3 \diagup \overset{\|}{C} \diagdown CH_3}}
\end{array}$$

$$\begin{array}{cc}
\underset{\text{IV}}{\overset{\displaystyle CH_3}{\underset{\displaystyle \underset{H\cdots H}{CH_2} \! = \! \overset{|}{C} \diagdown CH_3}{\big|}}} &
\underset{\text{V}}{\overset{\displaystyle CH_3}{\underset{\displaystyle \underset{H}{CH_3 \diagup \overset{|}{C} \diagdown CH_3}}{\big|}}}
\end{array}$$

number of *effective* bonds between adjacent atoms, they should have comparable energies, and so the resonance should here lead to an appreciable stabilization. No equally advantageous hyperconjugation is

[87] For further discussion of the principles which are here involved, see, for example, H. C. Brown, H. Bartholomay, Jr., and M. D. Taylor, *J. Am. Chem. Soc.* **66**, 435 (1944); H. C. Brown, *Science* **103**, 385 (1946); A. E. Remick, *Electronic Interpretations of Organic Chemistry*, John Wiley & Sons, New York, 2nd ed., 1949, pp. 298ff, 314.

possible, however, with the analogous isobutane, for which each of the structures like IV has one less effective bond than the conventional structure V. Consequently, the resonance must stabilize the *tert*-butyl radical more than it does the isobutane molecule. With a secondary radical, the resonance effect should be smaller than with a tertiary one; and, with a primary radical, it should be still smaller. Since the steric and resonance effects therefore always act in the same direction, there is no reliable method for estimating how much of the observed stabilizations of the radicals is due to each factor.

The energy required to remove a hydrogen atom from a propylene molecule corresponds to only about 77 kcal per mole.[68] The resulting allyl radical is therefore even more stable than the *tert*-butyl radical. Since the steric factor is probably rather small, the considerable decrease in the bond dissociation energy must be due primarily to the resonance in the radical; indeed, a large effect would here be expected in view of the complete equivalence of the two structures VI and VII. Similarly,

$$CH_2\!\!=\!\!CH\!\!-\!\!\overset{\cdot}{C}H_2 \qquad\qquad \overset{\cdot}{C}H_2\!\!-\!\!CH\!\!=\!\!CH_2$$
$$\text{VI} \qquad\qquad\qquad\qquad \text{VII}$$

for the production of the benzyl radical from the toluene molecule, the bond dissociation energy is about 77.5 kcal per mole.[68] The stabilization of the radical by resonance among the structures VIII–XII is therefore clearly indicated.

It should be evident from the above discussion of the allyl and benzyl radicals that the distinction between the short-lived and the long-lived radicals is quite arbitrary. The former class of radicals shades imperceptibly into the latter as the bond dissociation energy decreases; and, in fact, the benzyl radical has been discussed in exactly the same way, as a member of each class.

7·9 Tautomerism.[88] In a simple keto-enol system, such as acetaldehyde, the equilibrium is greatly in favor of the keto form I; and the enol

$$CH_3\!\!-\!\!CH\!\!=\!\!O \qquad\qquad CH_2\!\!=\!\!CH\!\!-\!\!OH$$
$$\text{I} \qquad\qquad\qquad\qquad \text{II}$$

[88] For a more comprehensive and more detailed discussion of tautomerism, see, for example, G. W. Wheland, *Advanced Organic Chemistry*, John Wiley & Sons, New York, 2nd ed., 1949, Chapter 14.

form II is present only in minute traces.[89]   In phenol, on the other hand, the situation is exactly reversed, and the substance is, for all practical purposes, completely enolic.   In each of these extreme cases, the essential structural change involved in the tautomerism can be expressed by the same equation:

$$-\overset{\displaystyle |}{\underset{\displaystyle H}{C}}-C{=}O \rightleftharpoons -C{=}C-OH$$

The striking difference in the positions of equilibrium is, therefore, not due to a corresponding difference in the energies of the bonds broken and formed, but must be a result of resonance.   In acetaldehyde, neither the keto nor the enol form is stabilized to any great extent by resonance, so that the observed position of the equilibrium expresses merely the greater intrinsic stability of the keto grouping.   In phenol, however, the two possible keto forms, III and IV, are stabilized to small extents by the resonance resulting from the conjugated systems, whereas the enol form, V, is stabilized to a much greater extent by resonance between the two

III   IV   V

Kekulé structures.   (The relatively unstable Dewar structures also have small effects, but they can here be ignored.)   The result of the resonance is therefore to favor the enol form of this substance and to shift the equilibrium in the observed direction.

An explanation somewhat similar to the above was proposed by Thiele[90] on the basis of his theory of partial valence.   It has, of course, long been realized that the stability of the enol form of phenol must be due to the same factors which account for the stability of benzene itself.

In the various substituted phenols (such as the cresols, nitrophenols, and so on) and in 1- and 2-naphthol, 1- and 2-anthrol, and the like, the

[89] For numerical data referring to the equilibria with acetone, cyclopentanone, and cyclohexanone, see G. Schwarzenbach and C. Wittwer, *Helv. Chim. Acta* **30**, 669 (1947). The much more extensive evidence supporting the reality of the tautomeric equilibrium with simple ketones has been discussed in many places; see, for example, G. W. Wheland, *Advanced Organic Chemistry*, John Wiley & Sons, New York, 2nd ed. 1949, pp. 255ff, 590f.

[90] J. Thiele, *Ann.* **306**, 87 (1899).

resonance stabilizes the fully aromatic ring systems in similar fashion, and so displaces the equilibria toward the enol forms. With 9-anthrol, VI, however, the keto form, VII, is the more stable of the two forms,

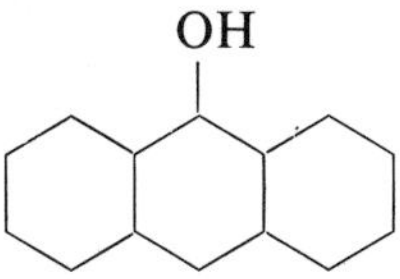

OH

O

VI

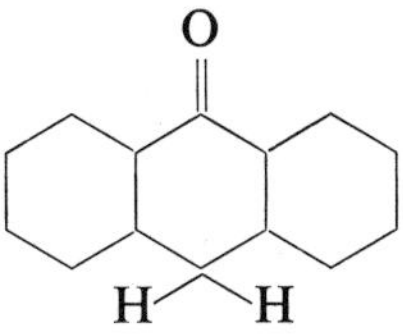

VII

although both can be isolated.[91] This difference from phenol exists because the resonance energy of the anthrol form, VI, is only slightly greater than that of anthracene, which is less than three times that of benzene, whereas in the anthrone form, VII, the resonance energy should be about the same as that of benzophenone, which is itself about twice that of benzene. Consequently, the gain in resonance energy in passing from the keto to the enol form is less here than in phenol, and so the keto form is relatively more stable (see below). On the other hand, 9-phenanthrol, VIII, resembles the remaining phenanthrols in being largely enolic; the reason for this difference from 9-anthrol is presumably that the resonance energy of phenanthrene is greater than that of anthracene, so that more resistance is offered to any modification of the completely aromatic ring system. (See below.)

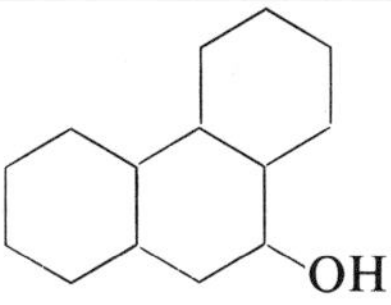

OH

OH

O

H_2 H_2

OH   HO   OH   O   O

H_2

VIII

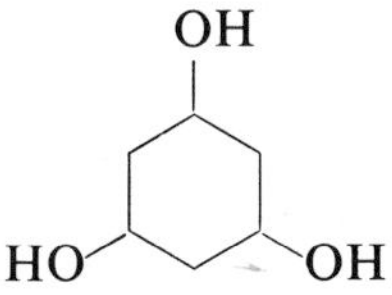

IX

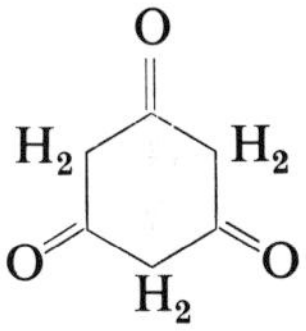

X

OH

O

H_2

OH

H_2 O

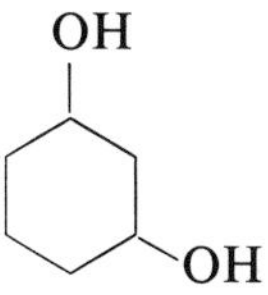

XI

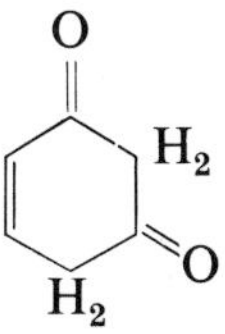

XII

In phloroglucinol, the trienolic form, IX, is stabilized by the resonance in the benzenoid ring, whereas the triketo form, X, no longer has even the small stabilization, resulting from conjugation. Nevertheless, the

[91] K. H. Meyer, *Ann.* **379**, 37 (1911).

substance shows many of the reactions of a triketone, and the equilibrium is apparently less one-sided than with phenol. The reason for this difference in behavior is probably that here, with *three* keto-enol groupings in the molecule, the greater intrinsic stability of the keto form is more nearly able to counterbalance the resonance effect. Resorcinol, XI, is intermediate in structure between phenol and phloroglucinol and, as expected, is intermediate in properties as well. This substance shows some of the reactions of the diketonic form, XII, but the equilibrium seems to be more in favor of the completely enolic form than with phloroglucinol.

The qualitative explanations which have just been offered for the positions of the tautomeric equilibria in phenols can be shown also to have some semiquantitative significance.[92]   With the use of either Klages's method (Table 3·4, Section 3·3) or Franklin's method (Table 3·6, Section

3·3) for calculating heats of combustion, the keto grouping $-\overset{|}{C}H-\overset{|}{C}=O$, is found to be perhaps 10–16 kcal per mole more stable than the enol

grouping $-\overset{|}{C}=\overset{|}{C}-OH$. The exact value of this difference, which we shall hereafter designate as ΔB, is not uniquely determined, since it depends upon the way in which we make certain arbitrary decisions. Thus, we may consider the enol to be either a primary, a secondary, or a tertiary alcohol (see pages 106f); and we may either include or omit a small correction for the resonance which, in the enol, is made possible by the presence of unshared pairs of electrons on the oxygen atom (cf. pages 85 and 106f). We shall here, however, set ΔB equal to 13 kcal per mole, and we shall assume that any errors which we thus introduce are no greater than those which arise from our neglect of all entropy terms.

Table 7·5 shows the results of the calculations that can be made for several different phenols. With phenol itself, for example, the resonance energy R_e of the enol form can be assumed equal to that of benzene, 36 kcal per mole (cf. Tables 3·2, Section 3·2, and 3·7, Section 3·3), since, as was mentioned in the preceding paragraph, the effect of any interaction between the hydroxyl group and the aromatic ring is included in the term ΔB. In either one of the two nonequivalent keto forms, III and IV, however, the resonance energy R_k is much smaller; from the data of Table 3·2, in fact, a value of about 5 kcal per mole appears reasonable. Consequently, the estimated difference ΔE between the energies of the enol and keto forms is $\Delta B - (R_e - R_k)$, or -18 kcal per mole. The

---

[92] For a somewhat premature and overoptimistic attempt to calculate the positions of keto-enol equilibria, see G. W. Wheland, *J. Chem. Phys.* **1**, 731 (1933).

negative sign here shows that the enol is the more stable form; the large magnitude shows that the equilibrium must be greatly in favor of that form.

TABLE 7·5

CALCULATIONS OF THE DIFFERENCES BETWEEN THE ENERGIES OF THE KETO AND ENOL FORMS OF PHENOLS[a]

Substance	ΔB [b]	R_e [c]	R_k [d]	$R_e - R_k$	ΔE [e]
Phenol	13	36	5	31	−18
1-Naphthol	13	61	38	23	−10
2-Naphthol	13	61	38	23	−10
1-Anthrol	13	84	63	21	−8
2-Anthrol	13	84	63	21	−8
9-Anthrol	13	84	72	12	1
1-Phenanthrol	13	92	63	29	−16
9-Phenanthrol	13	92	73	19	−6
Resorcinol	26	36	5	31	−5
Phloroglucinol	39	36	0	36	3

[a] All energies are in kilocalories per mole.
[b] ΔB is the estimated energy of all the enol groupings, —C=C—OH, present in the completely enolic form minus that of all the keto groupings, —CH—C=O, present in the completely ketonic form. Cf. Tables 3·4 and 3·6, Section 3·3.
[c] R_e is the estimated resonance energy of the enol form. Cf. Tables 3·2, Section 3·2, and 3·7, Section 3·3.
[d] R_k is the estimated resonance energy of the keto form. Cf. Tables 3·2 and 3·3, Section 3·2, and 3·7, Section 3·3.
[e] ΔE, the estimated total energy of the enol form minus that of the keto form, is equal to $\Delta B - (R_e - R_k)$.

With most of the remaining substances that are considered in Table 7·5, the estimated values of ΔE are again negative, but they are smaller in magnitude than with phenol. The calculations are therefore in agreement with the observation that, with these more complex substances, the equilibria seem to be definitely, but somewhat less completely, in favor of the enol forms. With 9-anthrol and phloroglucinol, however, ΔE is positive, so that the keto forms should now be the more stable; and, with resorcinol, although ΔE is negative, its magnitude is relatively small. Consequently, the treatment is as satisfactory for these latter, rather exceptional phenols as for the above more typical ones. We should, however, bear in mind that the calculations are, at best, only semiquantitative, and hence that no reliance can be placed in the exact numerical values which are obtained for ΔE. Indeed, when the magnitude of ΔE is small, even its true sign may be the opposite of that found.

In acetylacetone, XIII and XIV, as in 9-anthrol, the keto-enol equilibrium is evenly enough balanced so that both forms can be isolated. In the gas phase, the equilibrium mixture contains 91–93 per cent enol.[93] The stabilization of the enolic form, XIV, seems here to be due to at

$$CH_3-\overset{\overset{O}{\|}}{C}-CH_2-\overset{\overset{O}{\|}}{C}-CH_3 \qquad CH_3-\overset{O-H-----O}{\underset{|}{C}=CH-----\overset{\|}{C}-CH_3}$$

XIII   XIV

least two factors. In the first place, the hydrogen bond which is present between the two oxygen atoms in this, but not in the keto form, XIII, must have an energy of 5–10 kcal per mole. (See Section 2·8.) The energies of the bonds (now including the hydrogen bond) are therefore not so unfavorable for the enol form as in, say, acetaldehyde. In the second place, the resonance effect must displace the equilibrium further in the same direction. Whereas the keto form has no possibilities for resonance, the enol form is stabilized by resonance with the structures

$$CH_3-\overset{O-H----O}{\underset{|}{C}---CH=C-CH_3} \qquad CH_3-\overset{^+O-H----O}{\overset{\|}{C}---C^-H---\overset{\|}{C}-CH_3}$$

XV   XVI

$$CH_3-\overset{^+O-H----O^-}{\overset{\|}{C}---CH=\underset{|}{C}-CH_3}$$

XVII

XV, XVI, and XVII. Structure XV is of the type encountered in conjugated systems in general. The role of conjugation in keto-enol tautomerism seems to have been discussed first by Thiele.[90] Structures analogous to XVI play a role in the phenols too, but there they are of negligible importance in comparison with the Kekulé structures, which produce such a large stabilization. (Cf. the discussion of vinyl ether in Section 3·2.) On the other hand, structures like XVII have no close analogs in any of the enols discussed heretofore.

In acetoacetic ester, XVIII and XIX, the conjugation is less able to stabilize the enol form, since, as was shown in Section 3·2, little or no

$$CH_3-\overset{\overset{O}{\|}}{C}-CH_2-\overset{\overset{O}{\|}}{C}-OC_2H_5 \qquad CH_3-\overset{O-H--O}{\underset{|}{C}=CH-\overset{\|}{C}-OC_2H_5}$$

XVIII   XIX

[93] Data for the equilibrium in the gas phase for this and other keto-enol systems are taken from J. B. Conant and A. F. Thompson, Jr., *J. Am. Chem. Soc.* **54**, 4039 (1932). See also W. Strohmeier and I. Höhne, *Z. Naturforsch.* **7b**, 184 (1952); **8b**, 53 (1953).

resonance energy results from the conjugation of an ethylenic linkage with a carboalkoxy group. The equilibrium is, accordingly, less favorable to the enol form than it is in acetylacetone, and the equilibrium mixture in the gas phase contains only 45.3–46.9 per cent enol. In malonic ester, XX and XXI, the amount of enol form present at equilibrium is too small to be measured. This decreased stability of the enol is not unreasonable since, in the structure XXI, one of the two carboethoxy

$$
\underset{\text{XX}}{C_2H_5O-\overset{\overset{\displaystyle O}{\|}}{C}-CH_2-\overset{\overset{\displaystyle O}{\|}}{C}-OC_2H_5}
\qquad
\underset{\text{XXI}}{C_2H_5O-\overset{\overset{\displaystyle O-H--O}{|\qquad\quad\|}}{C}=CH-\overset{}{C}-OC_2H_5}
$$

groups is no longer intact and has presumably therefore lost part of its own resonance energy. (See Table 3·7, Section 3·3.)

Triacetylmethane, XXII and XXIII, seems to be somewhat more enolic than acetylacetone. The reason is presumably that, whereas there are still no possibilities for resonance in the keto form, XXII, the conjugation in the enol form, XXIII, has been increased. (For this substance, the

equilibrium has not been studied in the gas phase. Schwarzenbach and Lutz[11] consider that it is 100 per cent enolic in aqueous solution, whereas Nachod[12] has found acetylacetone to be only 19.6 per cent enolic in the same solvent. On the other hand, it has been reported that, in alcoholic solution, triacetylmethane is about 89 per cent enolic[94] and acetylacetone is about 83 per cent enolic.[93]) Even tricarbomethoxymethane, XXIV and

XXV, in which the enol form necessarily contains a carbomethoxy group that is no longer intact, is 8–16 per cent enolic in the gas phase.[93]

[94] F. Seidel, W. Thier, A. Uber, and J. Dittmer, *Ber.* **69**, 650 (1936).

Acyclic 1,2-diketones, like biacetyl, XXVI, exist largely in the keto form, probably because their corresponding enol forms, XXVII, are

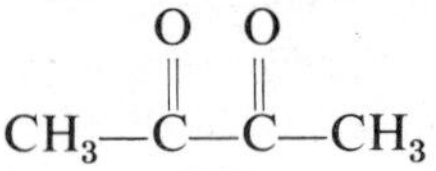

$$CH_3-\overset{\overset{\displaystyle O}{\|}}{C}-\overset{\overset{\displaystyle O}{\|}}{C}-CH_3$$
XXVI

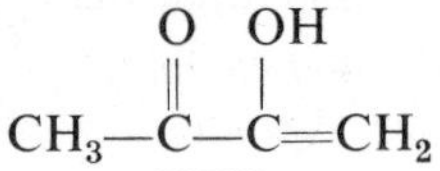

$$CH_3-\overset{\overset{\displaystyle O}{\|}}{C}-\overset{\overset{\displaystyle OH}{|}}{C}=CH_2$$
XXVII

prevented by steric requirements from having hydrogen bonds between the oxygen atoms, and because the conjugation is not increased in extent by enolization. On the other hand, cyclic 1,2-diketones, like 1,2-cyclo-hexanedione, XXVIII and XXIX, for example, are largely enolic. It has been suggested[92] that the reason for the difference between the acyclic and cyclic compounds is that the former are free, whereas the latter are not free, to assume the stable *s-trans* arrangement of the carbonyl groups. In the cyclic 1,2-diketones, the electrostatic repulsions of the carbonyl group moments must be very large in the keto form, XXVIII, but are considerably smaller in the enol form, XXIX. This explanation may be

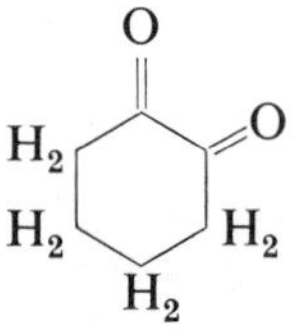

XXVIII 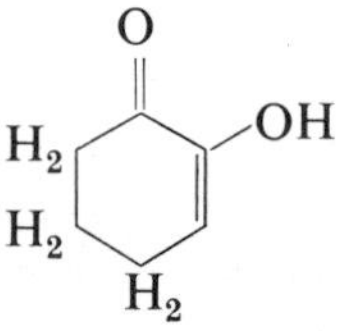   XXIX

partly correct, but it should be noted that there seems to be a definite tendency, which is not yet satisfactorily explained, for a double bond to take up positions *in* certain rings. Brown[95] has, to be sure, suggested that this tendency may be the result of internal strains (*I*-strains) in the rings. The application of these ideas to the present problem is, however, not clear. Brown states, as one of the conclusions drawn from his theory, that a double bond which is adjacent to (exo to) a ring is more stable when the ring is five membered than when it is six membered. In many instances, this generalization does indeed seem to be valid.[88] For example, cyclopentanone is considerably less enolic than cyclohexanone,[89] and the two closely analogous β-keto esters, XXX and XXXI, are,

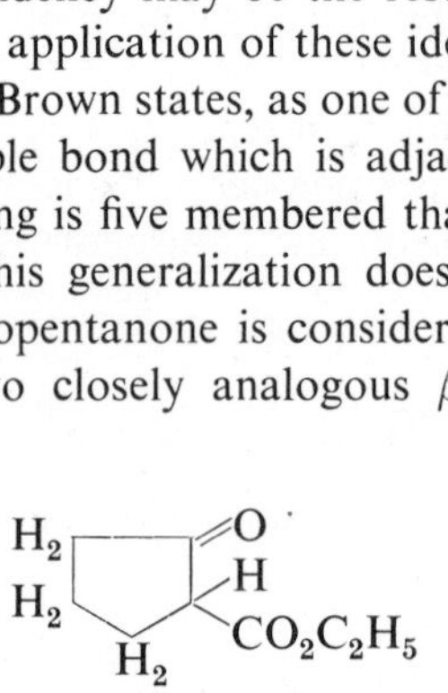

XXX 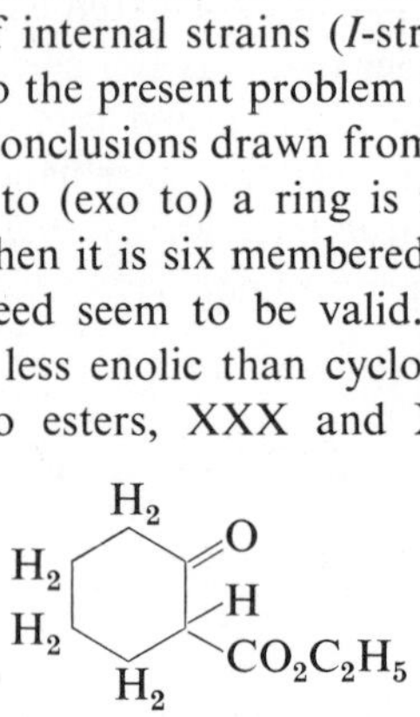   XXXI

[95] H. C. Brown, *Record Chem. Progr.* (*Kresge-Hooker Sci. Lib.*), **14**, 83 (1953); H. C. Brown, J. H. Brewster, and H. Schecter, *J. Am. Chem. Soc.* **76**, 467 (1954).

respectively, about 28 per cent and about 90 per cent enolic in the vapor phase.[93, 96] On the other hand, with the cyclic 1,2-diketones, the dependence of the keto-enol equilibrium upon the size of the ring is just the opposite of that predicted. Cyclopentane-1,2-dione and cyclohexane-1,2-dione are, respectively, 100 per cent and 40 per cent enolic in dilute aqueous solution.[97] No explanation for these confusing variations can here be offered.

Keto-enol tautomerism is known to occur also in substances in which the two carbonyl groups involved are farther apart than in those considered hitherto. For example, glutaconic dialdehyde, XXXII and XXXIII, seems to be largely enolic.[11] As with the 1,3-diketones like

$$
\begin{array}{cc}
\overset{O}{\overset{\|}{HC}}-CH_2-CH=CH-\overset{O}{\overset{\|}{CH}} & \overset{OH}{\overset{|}{HC}}=CH-CH=CH-\overset{O}{\overset{\|}{CH}} \\
\text{XXXII} & \text{XXXIII}
\end{array}
$$

acetylacetone, the enolization results in an increase in the length of the conjugated system and hence in the resonance energy. It seems unlikely, however, that a strong hydrogen bond could here be formed between the two oxygen atoms, because the necessary eight-membered ring is not commonly encountered. The reason for the stability of the enol is probably that, in general, aldehydic carbonyl groups are enolized with relative ease.

If cyclobutadiene were a typical aromatic compound that is greatly stabilized by resonance between the two equivalent Kekulé-like structures XXXIV and XXXV, its hydroxy derivatives should be close analogs of

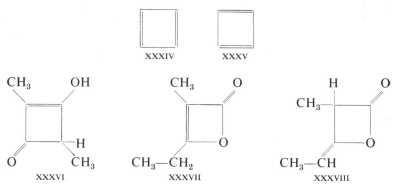

the phenols, and so should be largely enolic. However, since the parent hydrocarbon doubtless has little or no aromatic character (cf. pages

[96] R. Schreck, *J. Am. Chem. Soc.* **71**, 1881 (1949).
[97] G. Schwarzenbach and C. Wittwer, *Helv. Chim. Acta* **30**, 663 (1947).

144ff), its hydroxy derivatives should presumably be more similar to the above aliphatic and alicyclic enols. Although there is at present no completely decisive evidence which either confirms or contradicts this prediction, Woodward and Small[98] have concluded that one of the two known dimers of methylketene is a monoenol with the structure XXXVI. (The other dimer is considered to contain a heterocyclic four-membered ring, as in structures XXXVII and XXXVIII.) Since an intramolecular hydrogen bond is as unlikely here as with the analogous enol XXIX, the high stability of the enol form again seems anomalous.

As should be evident from the foregoing discussion, no satisfactory semiquantitative treatment of the type applied to the phenols can at present be given for the nonaromatic enols. The reason for the present difficulty is largely that we are now interested in *small* variations in the energy differences ΔE, whereas, in the earlier treatment, we dealt only with much larger variations. Consequently, the errors and uncertainties in the calculations are now of greatly increased importance since they are doubtless at least as large as are the quantities that we should like to estimate. We shall here, therefore, make no attempt to outline any more quantitative approach to the problem.

Lactam-lactim tautomerism of the type shown in the equation

$$
\begin{array}{cc}
\overset{\displaystyle O}{\underset{\displaystyle }{\|}} & \overset{\displaystyle OH}{\underset{\displaystyle }{|}} \\
-C-NH_2 & -C=NH \\
\text{Lactam} & \text{Lactim}
\end{array}
\qquad \rightleftarrows
$$

is analogous to the keto-enol tautomerism just considered. The equilibrium is commonly considered to lie far toward the lactam form, but we might expect it to be appreciably displaced toward the lactim with such compounds as α-hydroxypyridine, XXXIX. Even here, however, the substance seems actually to have the lactam, or α-pyridone, structure XL.

XXXIX   XL   XLI   XLII   XLIII

Apparently, therefore, the difference, ΔB, between the intrinsic stabilities of the lactam and lactim groupings (cf. Table 7·5) is so great that the

---

[98] R. B. Woodward and G. Small, Jr., *J. Am. Chem. Soc.* **72**, 1297 (1950); see also E. B. Reid and S. J. Groszos, *ibid.* **75**, 1655 (1953).

resonance in the aromatic pyridine ring is insufficient to overcome it. Similarly, γ-hydroxy-pyridine, XLI, is more correctly described as γ-pyridone, XLII, and so, although it is not strictly a lactam, it is a *vinylog*[99] of one. With β-hydroxypyridine, XLIII, on the other hand, the tautomerism is of the keto-enol type; accordingly, the substance, like a typical phenol, has the enol structure.

With α-aminopyridine, there is a similar possibility of tautomerism between the two forms XLIV and XLV. With this compound, however,

XLIV　　　　　　　XLV　　　　　　　XLVI　　　　　　　XLVII

the energy difference ΔB should be essentially zero, and so the position of the equilibrium should be determined principally by the greater resonance energy of the form XLIV. Although the chemical properties are somewhat different from those of a typical aromatic amine like aniline, the evidence[100] supporting the belief that the substance does indeed have structure XLIV appears to be conclusive. Similarly, the γ- and β-amino-pyridines must be assigned the respective structures XLVI and XLVII.

Primary and secondary nitroso compounds are in general unstable and rearrange to the corresponding oximes, thus:

$$\text{R}'—\overset{\overset{\displaystyle R}{|}}{\underset{\underset{\displaystyle H}{|}}{C}}—N\!=\!O \rightarrow \text{R}'—\overset{\overset{\displaystyle R}{|}}{C}\!=\!N—OH \qquad (R, R' = H, \text{ alkyl, or aryl})$$

On the other hand, primary and secondary nitro compounds are the stable forms, and the aci nitro compounds, although their existence can be shown, and although they can occasionally be isolated, are ordinarily present at equilibrium only in traces;[101] thus:

$$\text{R}'—\overset{\overset{\displaystyle R}{|}}{\underset{\underset{\displaystyle H}{|}}{C}}—NO_2 \rightleftharpoons \text{R}'—\overset{\overset{\displaystyle R}{|}}{\underset{\underset{\displaystyle OH}{|}}{C}}\!=\!\overset{\overset{\displaystyle O^-}{|}}{N^+} \qquad (R, R' = H, \text{ alkyl, or aryl})$$

[99] Cf. R. C. Fuson, *Chem. Revs.* **16**, 1 (1935).

[100] C. L. Angyal and R. L. Werner, *J. Chem. Soc.* **1952**, 2911.

[101] See D. Turnbull and S. H. Maron, *J. Am. Chem. Soc.* **65**, 212 (1943) for numerical values of the equilibrium constants for a few simple aliphatic nitro compounds.

As far as the natures of the bonds broken and formed are concerned, these two equilibria would be identical if resonance were ignored, since the essential change in each would then be simply

$$-\overset{\displaystyle |}{\underset{\displaystyle H}{C}}-N{=}O \rightleftarrows -\overset{\displaystyle |}{C}{=}N-OH$$

The reason for the striking difference in the position of equilibrium is apparently that the nitro, but not the nitroso, compound is stabilized by resonance between the two equivalent structures XLVIII and XLIX,

$$R-\overset{+}{N}\overset{\displaystyle \nearrow O}{\underset{\displaystyle \searrow O^-}{}} \qquad\qquad R-\overset{+}{N}\overset{\displaystyle \nearrow O^-}{\underset{\displaystyle \searrow O}{}}$$

XLVIII   XLIX

whereas no important resonance is possible in either the aci nitro compound or the oxime. The argument is perhaps not completely free from objection because the presence of the formal positive charge on the nitrogen atom of the nitro compound makes the two situations not exactly comparable. There is unfortunately no way for predicting the magnitude, or even the direction, of the effect produced upon the equilibrium by that formal charge. However, since the structures which have the greatest weights in the nitro compound are equivalent to each other, it seems certain that the resonance energy must be large and, in fact, must be the dominating factor.

In some substances, the nitro-aci-nitro equilibrium is affected by resonance with still further structures in such a way that it is shifted back again part of the way toward the aci form. In phenylnitromethane, for example, the phenyl group is conjugated with a carbon-nitrogen double bond in the aci form L, but is isolated in the nitro form LI. The

$$C_6H_5-CH{=}\overset{+}{N}\overset{\displaystyle \nearrow O^-}{\underset{\displaystyle \searrow OH}{}} \qquad\qquad C_6H_5-CH_2-NO_2$$

L   LI

equilibrium might, therefore, be expected to be less unfavorable for the aci form than in, say, nitromethane, in which no such conjugation is possible. The actual position of equilibrium is not known for the former substance, but the fact that its aci form can be isolated, whereas that of the latter cannot, suggests that the expectation is in accord with the facts. In p-nitrophenylnitromethane, LII and LIII, the effect of the conjugation

$$p\text{-}O_2N\text{—}C_6H_4\text{—}CH_2\text{—}NO_2 \qquad p\text{-}O_2N\text{—}C_6H_4\text{—}CH{=}N^+\begin{smallmatrix}\nearrow O^-\\ \searrow OH\end{smallmatrix}$$

LII   LIII

appears to be still greater, since the equilibrium mixture contains measurable amounts of the aci form LIII, varying from 0.18 per cent in ethyl alcoholic solution to 16 per cent in pyridine solution.[102] In ω-nitroacetophenone, LIV and LV, similarly, the conjugation favors the aci form, which is present to the extent of 10.3 per cent in toluene and of 2.7 per cent in 67 per cent aqueous methyl alcohol.[102] Since the equilibrium in this last example is shifted *away* from the aci form in hydroxylic solvents, it appears that a hydrogen bond between the carbonyl and nitro oxygen atoms, as in LV, must be responsible for at least a part of the

$$\underset{\text{LIV}}{C_6H_5\text{—}\overset{\displaystyle O}{\overset{\|}{C}}\text{—}CH_2\text{—}NO_2} \qquad\qquad \underset{\text{LV}}{C_6H_5\text{—}\overset{\displaystyle O\,\text{-}\,\text{-}\,H\text{—}O}{\overset{\|}{C}}\text{—}CH{=}N^+\text{—}O^-}$$

observed effect.[103] It is also possible that the substance is more accurately described as an *enol* with the alternative structure LVI, or that it is a tautomeric mixture of the two forms LV and LVI.

$$\underset{\text{LVI}}{C_6H_5\text{—}\overset{\displaystyle O\text{—}H\,\text{-}\,\text{-}\,O}{\overset{|\qquad\quad\|}{C}}{=}CH\text{—}N^+\text{—}O^-}$$

[102] K. H. Meyer and P. Wertheimer, *Ber.* **47**, 2374 (1914).
[103] Cf. N. V. Sidgwick, T. W. J. Taylor, and W. Baker, *The Organic Chemistry of Nitrogen*, Oxford University Press, Oxford, 1937, p. 233.

Chapter 8   RESONANCE AND CHEMICAL REACTION

8·1 The Activated Complex and the Rates of Reaction. As was pointed out in Chapter 1, the theory of resonance can be considered an outgrowth of the theories of intermediate stages and of mesomerism. Since these earlier theories were concerned largely with the relative speeds of chemical reactions, it is to be expected that the more modern point of view also should be applicable to this important problem. This expectation has indeed been realized, as we shall see in the following sections of the present chapter. It will be advantageous, however, for us first to consider in some detail the more fundamental question of the actual nature of the reaction process.

It will be convenient to discuss a rather simple reaction, in which a bromide ion collides with an alkyl bromide molecule and replaces the bromine atom which the latter contains; thus:

$$Br^- + RBr \rightarrow BrR + Br^-$$

The products of the reaction are the same as the reactants, so that there is no net change, but the course of the reaction can be followed experimentally by observation of the racemization of an optically active alkyl bromide or by the use of radioactive bromide ion.[1] If we represent the bromine atoms as Br and Br*, we can write the two independent structures, I and II, for the system. For our present purposes, we may ignore

$$Br^{*-} \quad R{-}Br \qquad\qquad Br^*{-}R \quad Br^-$$
$$\text{I} \qquad\qquad\qquad\qquad \text{II}$$

the distinction between real and formal bonds, because we shall wish to consider the distances between the atoms as capable of continuous variation within wide limits. The structure I can be taken as that of the original reactants when the ion Br^{*-} is at a large distance from the molecule RBr, and the structure II can be taken as that of the final

---

[1] E. D. Hughes, F. Juliusburger, S. Masterman, B. Topley, and J. Weiss, *J. Chem. Soc.* **1935**, 1525; E. D. Hughes, F. Juliusburger, A. D. Scott, B. Topley, and J. Weiss, *ibid.* **1936**, 1173; W. A. Cowdrey, E. D. Hughes, T. P. Nevell, and C. L. Wilson, *ibid.* **1938**, 209.

products when the ion Br⁻ is at a large distance from the molecule RBr*. The reaction itself, therefore, is to be regarded as a transition—we might perhaps say a rearrangement—between the two structures.

The course of the reaction can be visualized with the aid of Figure 8·1, in which the energies, E, of the two structures and of the system are plotted schematically against a parameter r. This parameter may be defined by the equation

$$r = r_{CBr} - r_{CBr*}$$

where r_{CBr} and r_{CBr*} are the distances between the nucleus of the carbon atom at which the reaction occurs and the nuclei of the appropriate

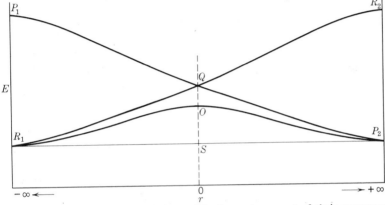

FIG. 8·1.   Energies E of the initial and final structures, and of their resonance hybrid, during the course of a chemical reaction.

bromine atoms or ions.   At the outset, when r has a large negative value, structure I has a low energy, since the ion Br*⁻ is at a great distance from the normal molecule RBr.   As the ion approaches the molecule, however, the energy of this structure rises along the curve R_1QR_2.   As far as the midpoint Q, the increase in energy is due largely to the mutual repulsion of the atoms which are not bonded to each other but are forced to come close together; from the midpoint on, it is due largely to the stretching of the bond between the radical R and the atom Br as the latter goes off to infinity.   Conversely, the energy of structure II starts at a high value and decreases along the curve P_1QP_2 as the reaction proceeds.   Since the reactants and the products are identical, it follows that the curves R_1QR_2 and P_1QP_2 are symmetrical about the vertical broken line, and also that, at the point Q, the carbon atom at which the replacement occurs is equidistant from Br and Br*, so that $r = 0$.   The fact that a Walden inversion is known to occur in the reaction[1] shows, furthermore, that the ion Br*⁻ must have approached the molecule from the side opposite the atom Br; when $r = 0$, the three bonds which the central carbon atom forms with atoms other than Br and Br* are therefore in, or approximately in, a plane at right angles to a line passing through the carbon and the two bromine nuclei. In the course of the reaction, the molecule is therefore "turned inside out," like an umbrella in a high wind. The situation is shown graphically in structures III, IV, and V,

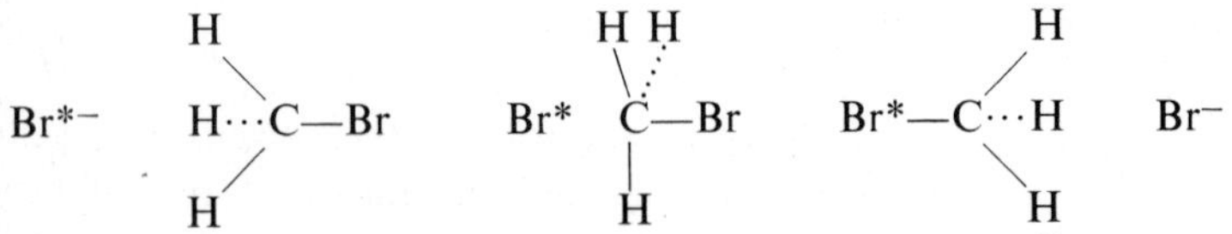

$$
\begin{array}{ccc}
\text{H} & \text{H H} & \text{H} \\
\backslash & \backslash\colon & / \\
\text{Br*}^- \quad \text{H}\cdots\text{C—Br} & \text{Br*} \quad \text{C—Br} & \text{Br*—C}\cdots\text{H} \quad \text{Br}^- \\
/ & | & \backslash \\
\text{H} & \text{H} & \text{H} \\
\text{III} & \text{IV} & \text{V}
\end{array}
$$

in which the geometrical arrangements of the atoms are given for the beginning, the midpoint, and the end of the reaction with $R = CH_3$ ($r \ll 0$, $r = 0$, and $r \gg 0$, respectively of Figure 8·1). The dotted lines in structures III, IV, and V do not represent formal bonds but are intended to indicate that the hydrogen atoms concerned lie behind the plane of the paper.

So far, no account has been taken of resonance. At the outset and at the conclusion of the reaction, this neglect is justified because the two structures differ widely in distribution of electric charge (condition 2 of Section 1·4) and also in stability (condition 4). The actual structures of the system at the extremes are therefore simply I and II, respectively. The situation is different, however, at intermediate values of r, for then the charge distributions become more nearly alike. The stabilities of the structures also differ less widely and become equal when $r = 0$. Resonance is important, accordingly, when r is small in magnitude. That is to say, the actual structure of the system is neither I nor II but something intermediate; in fact, it changes in a continuous manner from I to II as the reaction proceeds, and is just halfway between these structures when $r = 0$. The energy of the system is lower, on account of the resonance, than would correspond to either of the two structures, and so it follows a curve $R_1 O P_2$ that lies below the broken curve $R_1 Q P_2$ and becomes coincident with it at the extremes.

At the point O, at which the actual energy is highest, the system is, as we have just seen, a resonance hybrid of the structures I and II. It is commonly referred to as the *activated complex*, or as the *transition state*, for the reaction.[2] Its energy is greater than that of the reactants by the

---

[2] The following treatment follows the discussions of H. Pelzer and E. Wigner, *Z. physik. Chem. B* **15**, 445 (1932); H. Eyring, *J. Chem. Phys.* **3**, 107 (1935); M. G. Evans and M. Polanyi, *Trans. Faraday Soc.* **31**, 875 (1935). See also H. Eyring, J. Walter, and G. E. Kimball, *Quantum Chemistry*, John Wiley & Sons, New York, 1944, Chapter XVI.

amount SO, which is known as the *energy of activation* $\Delta E^{\ddagger}$ of the reaction. Like an ordinary molecule, it can be considered to have other thermodynamic properties in addition to internal energy, so that we may speak of a *heat*, a *free energy*, and an *entropy* of activation, $\Delta H^{\ddagger}$, $\Delta F^{\ddagger}$, and $\Delta S^{\ddagger}$, respectively.

According to the theory of absolute reaction rates,[2] the velocity of the forward reaction is given by the equation

$$-\frac{d(\mathrm{Br}^{*-})}{dt} = -\frac{d(\mathrm{RBr})}{dt} = \frac{kT}{h}(\mathrm{Br}^{*}\mathrm{RBr}) \tag{1}$$

where k is Boltzmann's constant, T is the absolute temperature, h is Planck's constant, Br*RBr stands for the activated complex, and the quantities in parentheses represent the concentrations of the substances specified. With the aid of the thermodynamic relations

$$K^{\ddagger} = \frac{[\mathrm{Br}^{*}\mathrm{RBr}]}{[\mathrm{Br}^{*-}][\mathrm{RBr}]} = \frac{(\mathrm{Br}^{*}\mathrm{RBr})}{(\mathrm{Br}^{*-})(\mathrm{RBr})}\frac{\gamma_{\mathrm{Br}^{*}\mathrm{RBr}}}{\gamma_{\mathrm{Br}^{*}}\cdot\gamma_{\mathrm{RBr}}} = e^{-\Delta F^{\ddagger}/RT} \tag{2}$$

where the quantities in the square brackets represent the activities of the appropriate substances, and the γ's are the activity coefficients, equation 1 can be put into the form

$$-\frac{d(\mathrm{Br}^{*-})}{dt} = \frac{kT}{h}K^{\ddagger}(\mathrm{Br}^{*-})(\mathrm{RBr})\frac{\gamma_{\mathrm{Br}^{*}}\cdot\gamma_{\mathrm{RBr}}}{\gamma_{\mathrm{Br}^{*}\mathrm{RBr}}}$$

$$= \frac{kT\gamma_{\mathrm{Br}^{*}}\cdot\gamma_{\mathrm{RBr}}}{h\gamma_{\mathrm{Br}^{*}\mathrm{RBr}}}(\mathrm{Br}^{*-})(\mathrm{RBr})e^{-\Delta F^{\ddagger}/RT} \tag{3}$$

The specific rate constant k is therefore

$$k = \frac{kT\gamma_{\mathrm{Br}^{*}}\cdot\gamma_{\mathrm{RBr}}}{h\gamma_{\mathrm{Br}^{*}\mathrm{RBr}}}e^{-\Delta F^{\ddagger}/RT}$$

$$= \frac{kT\gamma_{\mathrm{Br}^{*}}\cdot\gamma_{\mathrm{RBr}}}{h\gamma_{\mathrm{Br}^{*}\mathrm{RBr}}}e^{\Delta S^{\ddagger}/R}e^{-\Delta H^{\ddagger}/RT} \tag{4}$$

The right sides of equations 1, 3, and 4 are sometimes multiplied by a constant factor κ, which is called the *transmission coefficient*, and which is related to the probability that the activated complex will proceed to the final products instead of reverting to the original reagents. However, since the value of κ is considered ordinarily to be close to unity, and since almost nothing is known about the way in which it varies from reaction to reaction, we shall hereafter follow the most usual practice of simply ignoring this complication of the theory.

From the foregoing brief discussion, it is evident that the nature and properties of the activated complex are of the utmost importance in determining the rate of a chemical reaction. We shall, accordingly, center our attention upon it throughout the present chapter. We shall find that certain of the features encountered above in the discussion of the reaction between a bromide ion and an alkyl bromide molecule are common to all reactions, but that others are special and do not obtain generally. The activated complex is always a resonance hybrid among several structures, and the specific rate constant is always given by an equation analogous to equation 4. On the other hand, unless the reactants and products are identical, the points corresponding to R_1 and P_2 of Figure 8·1 need not lie at the same value of the energy E; the points corresponding to P_1 and R_2 need not lie at the same value of E; and the activated complex need not receive equal contributions from the initial and final structures.

In the way described above, the problem of reaction rates has been reduced to one of equilibria. The present situation differs from those considered in Chapter 7 only in that here the "reaction product" which is in equilibrium with the reactants is not an ordinary molecule capable of isolation, but is instead an activated complex. Just as before, therefore, we may feel that, as long as we restrict ourselves to qualitative comparisons of the rates of very similar reactions, we may safely ignore the distinctions both between concentration and activity, and between internal energy and free energy. This assumption is valid, however, only if certain conditions are satisfied. First, the activity coefficients of all the corresponding reactants and of the activated complexes that are involved in the reactions to be compared (but now not necessarily those of the final products) must be respectively equal to each other; second, the entropies of activation of the reactions to be compared must similarly be equal; and finally, the changes in the pressure-volume products during activation must be equal, so that the distinction between the energy and the heat of activation may be ignored. The first and third of these conditions are probably satisfied with sufficient accuracy in all the cases in which we shall be interested, but the second is much more dubious.[3] In some reactions (for example, in the substitution reactions of aromatic systems) this second condition also seems to be sufficiently well satisfied, but in others (for example, in the side-chain reactions of the ortho-substituted benzyl halides) it may be in more or less serious conflict with the facts. However, *to the extent that the above basic assumptions are*

[3] See, for example, L. P. Hammett, *Physical Organic Chemistry*, McGraw-Hill Book Co., New York, 1940, Chapters IV and VII. For a discussion of several series of reactions (semicarbazone formation) in which the relative rates are determined by entropy rather than by energy differences, see, for example, F. P. Price, Jr., and L. P. Hammett, *J. Am. Chem. Soc.* **63**, 2387 (1941).

actually valid, we can predict that, of two similar reactions, the one involving the activated complex which is stabilized to the greater extent with respect to the reactants (by factors like electrostatic interactions or resonance) will proceed at the faster rate.   In the subsequent sections, we shall see that such predictions are indeed in agreement with experiment in a considerable number of reactions.   As might be expected, the theory does not always permit the interpretation of small differences in the rates of reaction, but it does often lead to an understanding of the larger and more striking differences.   It seems probable, therefore, that the various activity coefficients, entropies of activation, and pressure-volume products, although not strictly constant, are nevertheless nearly enough constant in many series of reactions to permit valid qualitative conclusions to be drawn.   A *quantitative* theory of reaction rates is, however, still a goal for future achievement,[4] as indeed is also a completely unimpeachable qualitative one.

As in the discussion of equilibria, the difficulty in connection with changes in entropy does not enter if the reactions to be compared with each other differ only in electrostatic effects exerted by polar groups situated far from the reaction centers.   (See Section 7·1.) Under such circumstances, the theoretical treatment refers directly to the free energy, and not to the internal energy, of activation, so that the entropy of activation does not matter.   As before, however, structural changes near to the reaction centers often produce large and unpredictable effects which make a satisfactory discussion impossible. A further point of interest is that Evans and Polanyi[5] have given theoretical reasons for supposing that the rate constant itself (or, what amounts to the same thing, the free energy of activation) is actually the quantity which is directly related to structure in series of related reactions.   If this conclusion is correct, then the internal energy and entropy of activation are separately of little interest, and the present method of treatment is justified for qualitative discussions.   Until this question has received further clarification, however, it would seem safer to consider that errors of uncertain magnitude and sign may always be introduced by unpredictable variations in (especially) the entropy of activation.

8·2   Reactions of Resonance Hybrids.   If a substance is a hybrid of two or more structures, we might naturally suppose that its chemical reactions would be those characteristic of, at any rate, all the structures which have large weights.   This expectation is frequently, but not always, borne out by the facts.   Thus, the addition of one mole of chlorine to one of 1,3-butadiene leads not only to 3,4-dichloro-1-butene, I, the product to be expected from the conventional structure, II for the original hydrocarbon, but also to 1,4-dichloro-2-butene, III, the product to be expected

---

[4] However, see F. H. Westheimer and M. W. Shookhoff, *J. Am. Chem. Soc.* **62,** 269 (1940), for a semiquantitative theoretical interpretation of electrostatic effects upon the rates of certain hydrolytic reactions.

[5] M. G. Evans and M. Polanyi, *Trans. Faraday Soc.* **32,** 1333 (1936).

from the less stable structure IV.[6]   On the other hand, 2,7-dihydroxy-naphthalene couples with a diazonium salt at the 1 and 8 positions, in accordance with the Erlenmeyer structure V, but it cannot be made to couple at the 3 or 6 positions,[7] even though it doubtless receives large

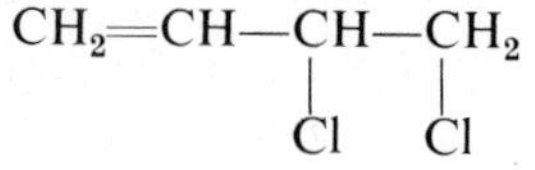

$$CH_2\!\!=\!\!CH\!-\!\!CH\!-\!\!CH_2$$
$$\qquad\quad |\quad\; |$$
$$\qquad\quad Cl\quad Cl$$

I

$$CH_2\!\!=\!\!CH\!-\!\!CH\!\!=\!\!CH_2$$

II

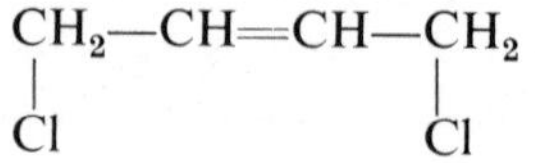

$$CH_2\!-\!\!CH\!\!=\!\!CH\!-\!\!CH_2$$
$$|$$
$$Cl\qquad\qquad\quad Cl$$

III

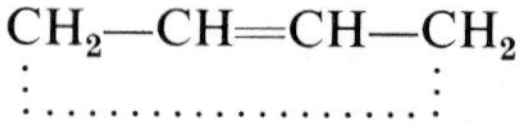

$$CH_2\!-\!\!CH\!\!=\!\!CH\!-\!\!CH_2$$

IV

HO⟨naphthalene⟩OH   HO⟨naphthalene⟩OH   HO⟨naphthalene⟩OH

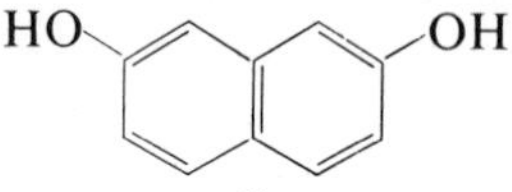

V 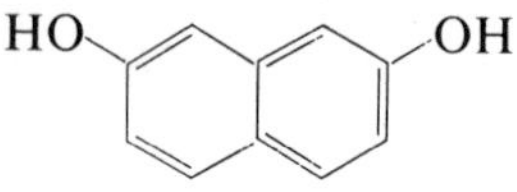   VI 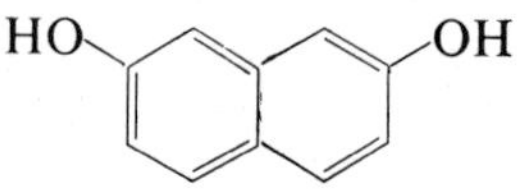   VII

contributions also from the two Erdmann structures VI and VII (cf. page 104).   And finally, N-methyl-γ-pyridone does not behave like either a tertiary amine or an unsaturated ketone, even though structure VIII must surely have a larger weight in the resonance than any other, such as IX or X.[8]

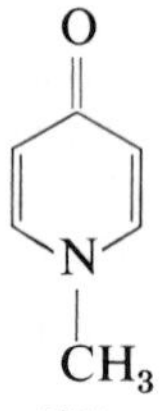

VIII 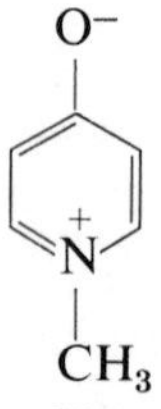   IX 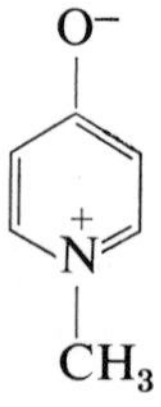   X 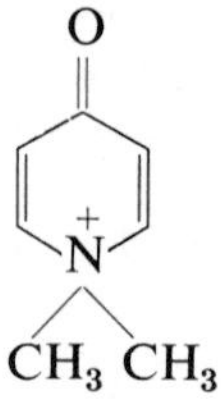   XI

As is shown by the three examples which have just been cited, knowledge of the structures which make the largest contributions to the states of specified hybrids does not necessarily enable us to predict the chemical behaviors of the substances.   Ordinarily, in fact, we need additional information regarding the detailed mechanisms of the reactions and, more particularly, regarding the natures of the respective activated complexes.   When the required information is available, however, we often can predict or, at any rate, explain the orders of increasing, or decreasing,

[6] I. E. Muskat and H. E. Northrup, *J. Am. Chem. Soc.* **52**, 4043 (1930).

[7] L. F. Fieser and W. C. Lothrop, *J. Am. Chem. Soc.* **57**, 1459 (1935).

[8] See, for example, N. V. Sidgwick, T. W. J. Taylor, and W. Baker, *The Organic Chemistry of Nitrogen*, Oxford University Press, Oxford, 1937, pp. 530ff.

rates in series of closely similar reactions.   The remainder of this chapter will accordingly be devoted to a consideration of such problems.

Although further discussion of the reactions of 1,3-butadiene and of 2,7-dihydroxynaphthalene must be postponed until pages 458ff and 496f, respectively, we can here outline a fairly satisfactory, but incomplete, explanation for the failure of N-methyl-γ-pyridone to react in the ways that might be expected for its most important structure, VIII. If, for example, this substance combined with methyl iodide to form a quaternary ammonium salt, the resulting cation, XI, could no longer receive even small contributions from any Kekulé-like structures analogous to IX and X. Consequently, since the reaction would therefore be accompanied by an appreciable decrease in the resonance energy, the equilibrium might possibly be unfavorable for the production of the quaternary salt.   Moreover, since the neutral molecule of N-methyl-γ-pyridone is considerably stabilized by the resonance, whereas the activated complex must be appreciably less stabilized (cf. the following paragraph), the activation energy is larger, and so the reaction is slower, than with a more typical tertiary amine like trimethylamine.

The argument leading to the conclusion that the resonance should thus decrease the rate of the reaction between N-methyl-γ-pyridone and methyl iodide is, in somewhat greater detail, the following.   Let us, for the moment, suppose that Figure 8·1 refers to a purely imaginary reaction which involves these two reagents, but in which the Kekulé-like structures of type IX and X (see also below) are in some way prevented from playing any role in either the original amine or the activated complex.   (Since we shall not be interested in the part of this figure which lies to the right of the central vertical line, the fact that the points P_2 and R_2 are at the same levels as R_1 and P_1, respectively, is here of no moment.)   Now, let us consider how the diagram must be modified in order to allow for the resonance which we have arbitrarily, and incorrectly, assumed to be impossible.   In the first place, each of the points R_1 and S must be lowered by a distance corresponding to the additional resonance energy that is due to the structures IX and X.   In the second place, the points Q and O must also be lowered since the activated complex must be a hybrid not only of such structures as XII and XIII, but also of such

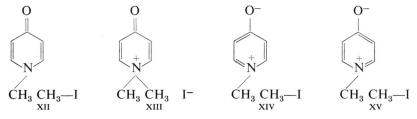

Kekulé-like structures as XIV and XV. If R_1 and S are lowered by exactly the same amount as O, then the activation energy SO is not changed; but, if R_1 and S are lowered by a larger amount than O, then the activation energy is increased. The latter alternative is almost certainly the correct one since, in the original N-methyl-γ-pyridone, there is only the one especially stable structure VIII whereas, in the activated complex, there are two such structures, XII and XIII. Consequently, the relatively unstable Kekulé-like structures IX and X must be more important in the resonance in the former system than their analogs XIV and XV are in the resonance in the latter system. Moreover, this conclusion should be valid even if our assumption regarding the nature of the activated complex is incorrect for, regardless of the exact mechanism of the reaction, there must be structures which have large weights in the activated complex, and in which, as in both the structure XIII and the final product XI, the nitrogen atom is linked by single bonds to four different atoms.

If N-methyl-γ-pyridone should react with, say, hydroxylamine in the way characteristic of an α,β-unsaturated ketone, the product might have either one of the two structures XVI and XVII (cf. pages 463f). The

reaction leading to the first of these products should, however, be slow since, just as in the one leading to the quaternary cation XI, the activated complex must receive large contributions from structures in which an atom of the ring (now a carbon atom) forms four single bonds, and since the resonance with the Kekulé-like structures must therefore stabilize the activated complex less than it does the original reagent. Similarly, the reaction leading to the alternative product XVII should also be slow for, although the structures XVIII and XIX may here be as important with the oxime as their analogs IX and X are with the ketone VIII, the activated complex in the rate-determining step probably involves some such structure as XX.

Apparently as a corollary of the common misconception that a resonance hybrid passes successively through all the contributing structures, many chemists seem to assume that such a substance can enter into reaction with a second reagent only if the molecule happens to be momentarily in a suitable structure at the time of collision. This view is absolutely erroneous, however, since, as was pointed out in Chapter 1, a resonance hybrid does not actually undergo the assumed transitions among the structures. Indeed, if the above picture were correct, then the failure of 2,7-dihydroxy-naphthalene to couple at the 3 and 6 positions would be completely inconsistent with the data which were cited in previous chapters, and which show that the resonance must include the structures VI and VII as well as V. On the other hand, if the correct view in regard to the nature of resonance is instead adopted, the above difficulty ceases to exist, because there is then no reason why a resonance hybrid has to exhibit the reactions expected for all, or even for any, of the structures involved.

8·3   General Formulation of the Theory.   The structures which have the greatest weights in the activated complex for any given reaction can be grouped into two classes.   In those structures which we shall hereafter describe as belonging to Class A, no covalent bond has been formed between the two reacting molecules; in those which we shall describe as belonging to Class B, such a bond has been formed.   For example, structure I of Section 8·1 and structures XII, XIV, and XV of Section 8·2 are of Class A, whereas structures II of Section 8·1 and XIII of Section 8·2 are of Class B.   The Class A and Class B structures are seen to be closely related to the original reactants and to the final products, respectively.

The relative stability of a structure of Class A must be determined largely by the distributions of electric charge in the two reagents.   Thus it is clear that such a structure is most stable when the most negative center of one reagent is close to the most positive center of the other.   It therefore follows that, if these Class A structures were the only ones involved in the activated complex, then any reagent which either is a positive ion or else has its own reactive center at the positive end of a dipole must attack its reaction partner preferentially at the latter's most negative available position; and, conversely, that any reagent which either is a negative ion or else has its reactive center at the negative end of a dipole must attack *its* reaction partner at the latter's most positive available position.   (The meaning of the word "available," as used here, is discussed on page 426.)

The relative stability of a structure of Class B, on the other hand, is not primarily dependent upon the net distribution of electric charge in the two reagents, but rather upon certain other factors which we shall need to consider in some detail.   Before we take up this problem, however, we shall first discuss two points which are fundamental to an understanding of the subsequent theoretical development.   In the first place, we must now call attention, more strongly than we have done hitherto, to the fact that our interest is centered upon the stabilities of the activated complexes *after* they have been formed, and hence upon the stabilities of the contributing structures *after* all the various atoms have assumed the positions which they occupy in the respective complexes.   Nevertheless, it proves to be convenient to discuss these stabilities in relation to the changes which must have occurred in the individual reagent molecules *before* the structures in question could be set up.   This manner of speaking must not be taken as implying that we are concerned with the processes by which the activated complexes are formed (although, as a matter of fact, an independent and roughly equivalent treatment of reaction rates can be obtained on such a basis).[9]   Instead, whenever we refer, for example, to the polarization of one of the reagent molecules by the other in the course of the reaction, we shall do so only for the sake of the light which can thereby be shed upon the stabilities of the Class B structures and of the complex itself.

The second point to be considered here is of a rather different nature from the first, but it is equally essential to an understanding of the theory.   According to the definition given above, any structure of Class B contains a new covalent bond, which is formed by the sharing of two electrons.   Of these two electrons, both may have come originally from one reagent and none from the other, or else one may have come from each reagent.   There are, therefore, three distinct types of reagent to be considered: the so-called *electrophilic*, *radical*, and *nucleophilic* reagents, which are defined as contributing zero, one, and two electrons, respectively, to the bond in question.   Clearly, every bimolecular reaction must be either between one electrophilic and one nucleophilic reagent, or else between two radical reagents.   The problem of determining the type to which any given reagent belongs is a matter for experimental investigation along lines that will be discussed in greater detail in later sections in connection with specific reactions.   For the present, we need mention only that a given reagent may be of different types in different reactions.   We shall find, for example, in Section 8·11 that pyridine is electrophilic when it is aminated with sodamide, radical when it enters into the Gomberg reaction, and nucleophilic when it is nitrated.

[9] For a discussion of the so-called collision theory of reaction rates, see L. P. Hammett, *Physical Organic Chemistry*, McGraw-Hill Book Co., New York, 1940, pp. 112ff; S. Glasstone, K. J. Laidler, and H. Eyring, *The Theory of Rate Processes*, McGraw-Hill Book Co., New York, 1941, pp. 5ff.

Electrophilic and nucleophilic reagents have often been defined as attacking preferentially the most negative and most positive centers, respectively. This definition is implicitly based upon the exclusive consideration of the Class A structures. It is usually equivalent to that adopted here, however, as will be shown later in this section.

The terms *kationoid* (or *cationoid*) and *anionoid* are used by some authors in place of electrophilic and nucleophilic, respectively.[10] It should be noted also that an electrophilic (or kationoid) reagent is an "acid," whereas a nucleophilic (or anionoid) reagent is a "base" in the generalized sense of Lewis.[11] Still further terms which have been suggested include *electron-deficient*, *electron-attracting*, and *electron-accepting*,[12] which are synonymous with electrophilic; and *electrodotic*,[13] *electron-repelling*, and *electron-donating*,[12] which are synonymous with nucleophilic. In this chapter, however, we shall continue to use the terms originally defined, since they seem to be the ones most widely accepted and generally understood.

We are now in position to return to the original problem of establishing criteria for the relative stabilities of the structures of Class B. From what has already been said, it would appear that the relative stabilities of the various structures of this type which can be derived from any one given reagent should be determined largely by the relative ease with which the necessary zero, one, or two electrons (as the case may be) can be brought by polarization to the various possible points of attack in that reagent. We thus implicitly assume that the behavior of the reagent is determined primarily by whether it is electrophilic, radical, or nucleophilic, and only incidentally by the exact identity of its reaction partner. In this way, the treatment can be greatly simplified.

Let us examine more closely this criterion for the relative stabilities of the Class B structures. We can think of such a structure as having been established in two steps, which may have been either simultaneous or successive. (The question whether the steps are simultaneous or successive is of no significance here, because, as was pointed out above, we are not primarily interested in the process by which the structure is produced, but only in its stability after it has been established.) In the first of these steps, the two reagent molecules are polarized by each other in such a way that the electronic configurations necessary for the formation of the new bond are produced. In other words, an incomplete valence shell (usually an open sextet of electrons or else the completely empty valence

---

[10] See, for example, R. Robinson, *Two Lectures on an "Outline of an Electrochemical (Electronic) Theory of the Course of Organic Reactions,"* The Institute of Chemistry of Great Britain and Ireland, London, 1932; *J. Soc. Dyers and Colourists, Jubilee Issue,* 65 (1934).

[11] G. N. Lewis, *Valence and the Structure of Atoms and Molecules,* Chemical Catalog Co., New York, 1923, pp. 141f; *J. Franklin Inst.* **226**, 293 (1938).

[12] Cf. C. R. Noller, *Textbook of Organic Chemistry,* W. B. Saunders Co., Philadelphia, 1951, pp. 97f.

[13] N. F. Hall, *J. Am. Chem. Soc.* **63**, 883 (1941).

shell of the hydrogen ion), which is capable of accommodating an un-shared pair of electrons, is produced at the reactive center of an electro-philic reagent; a single, unpaired electron is produced at the reactive center of a radical reagent; and an unshared pair of electrons is produced at the reactive center of a nucleophilic reagent. In the second step, the bond is formed by the sharing of the two electrons produced in the first step. To the extent, then, that all other factors can be ignored, a structure of Class B must be most stable when the new covalent bond which it contains joins the two reagents at the points at which the necessary electron configurations can be most easily provided. Therefore, if these Class B structures were the only ones contributing to the activated com-plex, the most reactive center of any electrophilic, radical, or nucleophilic reagent would be at that one of its available positions at which an incom-plete valence shell of the specified type, a single unpaired electron, or an unshared pair of electrons, respectively, could be most easily created.

The significance of the word "available," as it was used in the preceding discussion, can be made clear by an example. We shall find in Section 8·11 that, in the nitration of chlorobenzene, the organic molecule acts as a nucleophilic reagent. However, even though its chlorine atom already possesses three unshared pairs of electrons even in the Kekulé structures, the reaction takes place upon a carbon atom of the ring. The reason for this apparent discrepancy is that any reaction taking place upon the chlorine atom would have to be of an entirely different type from, and hence would not be directly comparable with, the one which occurs. The situation can be expressed by the statement that, as an experimental fact, the chlorine atom is not an *available position* for the particular reaction under discussion. The foregoing remarks would not need to be altered in any essential way if attention were centered upon the structures of Class A, and therefore upon the especially great concentration of negative charge at the chlorine atom.

In the above discussion, we have employed two extreme points of view in deriving qualitative rules for the prediction of relative reactivity; if the Class A structures alone are considered, the distribution of electric charge is the determining factor; if, on the other hand, the Class B structures alone are considered, the ease of the appropriate electronic displacements is the determining factor. Actually, the truth lies indefi-nitely somewhere between the extremes, and it is not legitimate for us to restrict our attention to either limiting type of structure alone. Fortu-nately, however, this difficulty appears not to be serious in any of the examples in which we shall be interested. The reason for this fact can be seen in the following way. A position at which an unshared pair of electrons can be easily provided is ordinarily also a position with a net negative charge, and so it is a center of nucleophilic activity from either point of view; conversely, a position at which the required kind of incomplete valence shell can be easily provided is ordinarily also a position with a net positive charge, and so it is a center of electrophilic activity from either point of view.   Consequently, if each of the reagents in a given reaction has a charge distribution such that its available positions are appreciably positive or negative, considerations of the Class A and of the Class B structures usually lead to the same qualitative conclusions regarding reactivity.   On the other hand, in many reactions, the available positions in one or both of the reagents may have no appreciable charges.   This situation is fairly generally encountered in reactions between radical reagents and occasionally also in those between electrophilic and nucleophilic reagents.   Under such circumstances, the Class A structures permit no definite conclusions at all to be drawn regarding reactivity.   However, since the relative ease of producing the required polarizations may still vary widely, the Class B structures can differ considerably in energy, and so be the decisive factor.   Consequently, in these latter types of reaction as well, there is no conflict between the two points of view.

From the above discussion, it follows that we can safely ignore the structures of Class A, since these provide no additional information regarding the reactions either between electrophilic and nucleophilic reagents or between radical reagents.   We shall, accordingly, center our attention in the following sections more upon the structures of Class B, although we shall nevertheless have occasion from time to time to treat certain problems from both points of view.   This procedure, which is adopted here for the sake of convenience, is not to be taken as implying that the relatively neglected structures of Class A are of secondary importance.   For all we know at present, these may indeed have the largest weights in the activated complexes for many, if not for all, reactions. The point is merely that they have no effect, which we need to consider explicitly, upon the conclusions reached.

8·4   Symbols for Describing Resonance.   Up to the present time, in discussing any given molecule, we have indicated the various structures which are presumed to be involved in the resonance by explicitly writing either all of them or else a few representative examples.   Especially in the discussion of the reactions of electrophilic and nucleophilic reagents, we shall now find it convenient to make use of a more compact, but less generally applicable, system of representation, which has been devised and used largely by the English organic chemists.[14]   The fundamental principle of this system is that one first writes down the most stable structure in the customary manner, and then introduces certain conventional symbols to show the direction in which that structure needs to

[14] See, for example, J. Allan, A. E. Oxford, R. Robinson, and J. C. Smith, *J. Chem. Soc.* **1926**, 401.   Cf. also the further references given in reference 6 of Chapter 1.

be modified. These symbols are of two different types, i.e., straight arrows and curved arrows, which will be discussed separately.

A bond between two atoms of different kinds is usually associated with a dipole moment, so that one of the atoms is relatively positive and the other is relatively negative. (See Chapter 5.) The situation can be represented graphically if the bond is written not simply as a straight line but as an arrow with its head and tail at the more negative and more positive atoms, respectively. The direction of the arrow is accordingly in agreement with the usual convention for dipole moments; it is also the same as that in which the electrons have, on the average, been displaced. The symbol I, for example, implies that the most important structure of the molecule is II, with a pure covalent bond, but that a small weight must also be assigned to structure III. The further structure IV

$$H \rightarrow Cl \qquad H—Cl \qquad H^+ \quad Cl^- \qquad H^- \quad Cl^+$$
$$\text{I} \qquad\qquad \text{II} \qquad\qquad \text{III} \qquad\qquad \text{IV}$$

has a still smaller weight, and is ignored. The head of an arrow therefore marks a negative center, at which an unshared pair of electrons could be provided with relative ease; accordingly, it is a center of nucleophilic activity and a point at which an electrophilic reagent might attack. In a similar way, the tail of an arrow marks a center of electrophilic activity and a point at which a nucleophilic reagent might attack. It is to be noted that these conclusions follow unambiguously, whether the problem is regarded from the viewpoint of the Class A or from that of the Class B structures.

This first type of displacement of electric charge is known as the inductive effect, or the I-effect. Although, as was shown above, it can be described as due to resonance, it can instead be discussed in purely classical terms; the idea of resonance is not essential to its understanding, since the more electronegative atom can be thought of as merely pulling the electrons toward itself as a result of its greater intrinsic attraction for them. The I-effect can be relayed down a saturated chain (with rapid damping) as is indicated in the structure $H_3C \rightarrow CH_2 \rightarrow CH_2 \rightarrow Cl$ for n-propyl chloride.

A second way in which the distribution of electric charge in a molecule can be altered is illustrated by vinyl chloride. If, for simplicity, we ignore the I-effect, we can write for this substance the two structures V and VI, of which the former is much the more important. Resonance between these two can be represented by the single symbol VII. Each

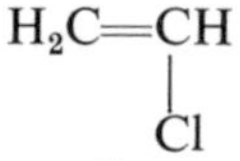

$$\begin{array}{ccc}
H_2C{=}CH & H_2C{-}{-}CH & H_2\overset{\frown}{C}{=}CH \\
| & \| & | \\
Cl & Cl^+ & Cl \\
\text{V} & \text{VI} & \text{VII}
\end{array}$$

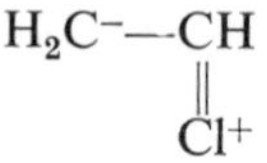

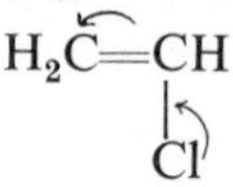

curved arrow corresponds here to a transference of a pair of electrons from a position at its tail to a position at its head. If this transference went to completion, the original structure V would have been changed into VI; the symbolism implies, however, that any such transference is only a minor correction or, in other words, that the structure VI has only a small weight. In a similar way, the symbol VIII for chlorobenzene signifies that structure IX is most important, but that the ortho- and paraquinoid structures X and XI make small contributions. The additional Kekulé structure XII and the additional orthoquinoid structure XIII are also implied, since the general principles of resonance require

that the weights of these structures be equal to those of IX and X, respectively, to which they are equivalent. And finally, the symbol XIV for nitrobenzene signifies large weights for the structures XV–XVIII and much smaller ones for the less stable structures XIX–XXI.

This second type of displacement of electrons was named the tautomeric effect, or T-effect, before the essential distinction between resonance and tautomerism was recognized; we shall refer to it hereafter as the resonance effect, or R-effect. As with the I-effect, the heads and tails of the arrows mark the centers of nucleophilic and electrophilic activity, respectively. This conclusion again follows unambiguously from either of the two extreme points of view regarding the nature of the activated complex. Frequently, the head or the tail of a curved arrow is placed not at a definite atom but on the bond between two atoms. Under such circumstances, the electrophilic or nucleophilic activity is possessed by only such atoms as show a net loss or gain of electrons, respectively. For example, in the structure VII for vinyl chloride, nucleophilic activity is possessed only by the carbon atom to which the chlorine atom is not attached, because it alone shows a net gain of electrons.

As was pointed out in Sections 5·2 and 5·3, the existence of dipole moments and of polarization can be considered results of resonance, so that the *I*-effect becomes merely a special case of the *R*-effect. For example, the symbols I and XXII for hydrogen

$$H—\overset{\frown}{Cl}$$
XXII

chloride are essentially equivalent since both imply resonance between the structures II and III. It is usually more convenient, however, to retain the distinction between the two effects and between their respective methods of representation.

8·5 Proton-Initiated Additions of Acids to Carbon-Carbon Double Bonds. The familiar rule of Markovnikov states that an unsymmetrical reagent of the type HX adds to a carbon-carbon double bond in such a way that the hydrogen atom becomes attached to the carbon atom which is already linked to the larger number of hydrogen atoms. Some exceptions to this rule, which are now recognized, will be mentioned on pages 437–440 and in Section 8·6; we shall begin the discussion, however, by considering some "normal" additions, that is, reactions in which the rule is obeyed. As in all the applications of the present theory to actual reactions, we shall find it necessary to make assumptions regarding detailed mechanisms. We shall attempt, however, to express these mechanisms in such general terms that no modifications, which may be required later by the acquisition of further experimental knowledge, will be likely to invalidate the fundamental principles involved.

In the addition of hydrogen chloride to an olefin, we shall assume that the reaction is initiated by the attack of the proton upon the organic molecule. This assumption is supported by the fact that strong acids, in general, enter into such reactions, but that, except for the hydrogen halides, substances capable of providing halide ions do not ordinarily give rise to corresponding reactions.[15] The proton, therefore, is probably

[15] For some possible exceptions to this statement, see K. Nozaki and R. Ogg, Jr., *J. Am. Chem. Soc.* **63**, 2583 (1941); **64**, 697, 704, 709 (1942). Cf. also F. R. Mayo and J. J. Katz, *ibid.* **69**, 1339 (1947); F. R. Mayo and M. G. Savoy, *ibid.* **69**, 1348 (1947).

involved in an essential step of the reaction.   It is, however, not entirely free but must be combined in some way.   In an ionizing solvent, it is solvated; in a nonpolar solvent, such as benzene, or in the absence of a solvent, it is presumably still combined with chlorine in an un-ionized molecule of hydrogen chloride; and in the presence of a catalyst, such as ferric chloride, it may be present in some sort of complex.   In any event, however, the hydrogen is assumed to be transferred to the olefin as a proton, and not as either a hydrogen atom with one electron or as a negative hydride ion with two electrons.   The initial product is then an organic positive ion, which immediately, or perhaps simultaneously, picks up a chloride ion from the solution to form the final product.   This chloride ion may not be, and in fact probably is not, the same one that was originally combined with the proton.   (If the reaction is carried out in an ionizing solvent, this last statement is obvious; if in a non-ionizing solvent, it seems reasonable on geometrical grounds.)

Regardless of the exact state of combination of the proton, and regardless of the source of the chloride ion, the essential features of the reaction will be reproduced well enough for our purposes if we treat the proton as completely free.   Moreover, we can ignore the chloride ion, since it is apparently not involved in an essential way in the primary reaction that determines the mode of addition.   With these simplifications, then, we are in position to consider the structures which make the largest contributions to the transition state.

The role of the chloride ion in the reaction may not be quite so simply that of an innocent bystander as is stated above, because the presence of such a negative ion in the fairly immediate neighborhood of the olefin molecule may be required for the easy formation of the organic positive ion.[15]   If so, the rate of reaction could then be dependent upon the concentration of chloride, as well as of hydrogen, ion.   It is doubtful, however, if such refinements in the treatment would necessarily alter the present admittedly oversimplified discussion in any significant way.

It will be necessary for us to consider separately the two different activated complexes that are involved in the formation of the two possible products.   In the reaction between hydrogen chloride and styrene, for example, these products are 1-chloroethylbenzene, C_6H_5—CHCl—CH_3, and 2-chloroethylbenzene, C_6H_5—CH_2—CH_2Cl, for the normal and abnormal additions, respectively.   With the first of these reactions, the activated complex is presumably a hybrid of principally the structures I–VII, of which I and II are of Class A whereas III–VII are of Class B; with the second of the reactions, however, the only structures which can have large weights in the activated complex are VIII–XI, since here no quinoid structures analogous to V–VII, and without formal bonds, are possible. If only the eight structures I–IV and VIII–XI had to be considered, we would expect the two activated complexes to be of about the

$$
\text{(I)}\quad C_6H_5\text{—CH=CH}_2 \cdot H^+ \qquad
\text{(II)}\quad C_6H_5\text{—CH=CH}_2 \cdot H^+ \qquad
\text{(III)}\quad C_6H_5\text{—C}^+H\text{—CH}_2\text{—H}
$$

$$
\text{(IV)}\quad C_6H_5\text{—C}^+H\text{—CH}_2\text{—H} \qquad
\text{(V)}\quad {}^+C_6H_5\text{=CH—CH}_2\text{—H} \qquad
\text{(VI)}\quad {}^+C_6H_5\text{=CH—CH}_2\text{—H}
$$

$$
\text{(VII)}\quad C_6H_5{}^+\text{=CH—CH}_2\text{—H} \qquad
\text{(VIII)}\quad C_6H_5\text{—CH=CH}_2 \cdot H^+ \qquad
\text{(IX)}\quad C_6H_5\text{—CH=CH}_2 \cdot H^+
$$

$$
\text{(X)}\quad C_6H_5\text{—CH—C}^+H_2\text{, H} \qquad
\text{(XI)}\quad C_6H_5\text{—CH—C}^+H_2\text{, H}
$$

same stability since there should then be no great difference between either the electrostatic interactions or the resonance stabilizations. The resonance cannot, however, be restricted in the way postulated, since the additional structures V–VII must also be involved and, in particular, must further stabilize the complex for normal addition. Since this complex is therefore considerably more stable than is the one for abnormal addition, we can conclude that the addition should occur predominantly in agreement with Markovnikov's rule, as, in fact, it does.

It is important to note that the above argument was not based merely on the assumption that the activated complex leading to normal addition is a hybrid of a larger total number of structures than is the one leading to abnormal addition. The point is rather that the resonance in the former activated complex includes not only a structure which is *essentially equivalent to each* of the ones important in the latter complex, but also some additional structures which have no close analogs. If this one-to-one correspondence between the structures I–IV and VIII–XI had not existed, we could not have drawn any conclusion from a consideration of only the total numbers of contributing structures. (See page 82.)

The foregoing example has been discussed in some detail because it was desired that the essential features of the rather complex problem should be made as clear as possible. The treatment could have been carried through with considerably less labor, however, with the aid of the general considerations of Sections 8·3 and 8·4. The necessary argument proceeds along the following lines. The proton is clearly an electrophilic reagent, since it has no electrons to contribute to the new covalent bond. The styrene must therefore be nucleophilic, and its role in the reaction must be to provide an unshared pair of electrons at the point of attack. Consequently, the reaction is initiated at that position of the hydrocarbon molecule at which such an unshared pair can be most easily produced. Since the dipole moment of styrene is small, the I-effect also is small and presumably negligible, but the R-effect remains to be considered. As a result of the conjugation, the required unshared pair of electrons can be brought to the terminal carbon atom by means of the polarization shown in structure XII, but it can be brought to the central carbon atom only by the polarization shown in the different structure XIII. The first of these two polarizations should be much easier than

$$C_6H_5{-}CH{=}CH_2 \qquad C_6H_5{-}\overset{..}{C}H{=}CH_2$$

$$\text{XII} \qquad\qquad\qquad \text{XIII}$$

$$\overset{+}{C_6H_5}{-}\overset{..}{C}H{-}CH_2 \qquad \overset{+}{C_6H_5}{-}CH{-}\overset{..}{C}H_2$$

$$\text{XIV} \qquad\qquad\qquad \text{XV}$$

the second, since it permits the residual positive charge to be distributed over a larger region of space or, in other words, since it provides a greater number of places from which the electrons can be drawn. There is, in fact, no practical way in which the central carbon atom can acquire an unshared pair of electrons at the expense of the benzene ring, except as a result of resonance with such unstable structures as XIV; and, even if we should consider this relatively unlikely type of resonance, we would learn nothing new because, for every structure like XIV which favors attack at the central carbon atom, there is an equally good (or equally poor) one like XV which instead favors attack at the terminal carbon atom. Consequently, we are justified in assuming that the structures XII and XIII depict the only kinds of polarization that need here to be considered.

There remains one additional point which must be explained before our discussion of the addition of hydrogen chloride to styrene is complete. We have advanced reasons why, in the first step of the reaction, the proton attacks the terminal carbon atom in preference to the central one. We can therefore infer that the resulting intermediate organic cation is a hybrid of (principally) the five structures III–VII. We have not yet, however, considered why, in the concluding step (which may be simultaneous with the first one), the chloride ion becomes attached to the particular carbon atom that has the formal positive charge in structures III and IV, in preference to any of the other atoms that have the formal charge in structures V–VII. One reason why the alternative products XVI and XVII are not, in fact, formed is doubtless that, since these latter

substances no longer contain intact aromatic rings, they are less stable than are the original reagents, so that the equilibria are unfavorable for the assumed additions. Indeed, since the heat liberated in the addition of hydrogen chloride to ethylene is only about 16 kcal per mole (cf. Table 3·5, Section 3·3), whereas the resonance energy of a benzene ring is more nearly 36 kcal per mole (cf. Tables 3·2 and 3·7, Section 3·3), any reaction leading from styrene to a product like XVI or XVII would doubtless be strongly endothermic. Furthermore, a consideration of the probable activation energies for the respective reactions shows that the rate must be greater when the chloride ion comes up to the carbon atom of the side chain than when it comes up to an ortho or para atom; for, only in the former event will the resonance with the structures of Class B allow the ring in the activated complex to retain its fully aromatic character.

When hydrogen chloride adds to propylene, the initial step of the reaction should consist in an attack by a proton upon either the terminal or the central unsaturated carbon atom. If the reaction follows the first of these two courses, the activated complex must be a hybrid to which the three structures XVIII–XX make the largest contributions; if, however, it follows the second course, the activated complex must be a hybrid to which only the two structures XXI and XXII can make comparably large contributions. (For the sake of clarity, the proton which comes initially from the hydrogen chloride is here designated by an asterisk.) Unless the electrostatic interactions are especially large (see the following paragraphs), the two Class A structures XVIII and XXI should be about equally stable, as should also the two Class B structures XIX and XXII. Moreover, the stabilization resulting from the resonance between structures XVIII and XIX must be approximately the same as that resulting from the resonance between the closely similar structures XXI and XXII. Consequently, if we could legitimately ignore the further Class B structure XX, there should be no great difference between the energies of the two activated complexes, or between the rates of the normal and abnormal additions. When, however, the effect of the resonance with structure XX is also taken into account, the first activated complex is seen to be the more stable (cf. the paragraph in fine print on page 432). Since the terminal carbon atom is therefore the favored point of attack for the proton, and since there can here be no uncertainty with respect to the concluding step of the reaction (cf. the preceding paragraph), the addition must be normal and must lead to the production of isopropyl chloride.

In discussing the additions of hydrogen chloride to styrene and to propylene, we have so far ignored any effects which may be due to electrostatic interactions. With styrene, the error which we have thereby introduced is probably negligible because all the carbon atoms, being equally unsaturated, may be presumed to have about the same net charge. Consequently, there is no reason why the energies of structures I–IV should differ appreciably from those of structures VIII–XI, respectively. With propylene, however, the central carbon atom is more electronegative than the carbon atom of the methyl group to which it is linked (cf. pages 128f). Consequently, although the conventional structure XXIII is the only one which has a large weight, the relatively unimportant structure XXIV must have a somewhat larger weight than the still less stable one XXV. Since the central carbon atom thereby acquires a small net nega-

$$CH_3—CH{=}CH_2 \qquad C^+H_3 \quad \ddot{C}^-H{=}CH_2 \qquad \ddot{C}^-H_3 \quad C^+H{=}CH_2$$

XXIII   XXIV   XXV

$$CH_3—C^+H—\ddot{C}^-H_2 \qquad CH_3—\ddot{C}^-H—C^+H_2$$

XXVI   XXVII

$$CH_3 \rightarrow CH{=}\overset{\frown}{C}H_2$$

XXVIII

tive charge and hence has a slightly decreased electronegativity, structure XXVI must similarly have a somewhat larger weight than XXVII. These several displacements of charge can be conveniently summarized by the single structure XXVIII, with both a straight and a curved arrow (cf. Section 8·4). In this final structure, each of the unsaturated atoms is at the head of an arrow and so is a possible center of nucleophilic activity. We are therefore unable, from these considerations alone, to predict which carbon atom will be successful in capturing the proton. Some authors, in attempting to solve this problem, have proposed the general rule that the R-effect, which is here represented by the curved arrow, is always more effective than the I-effect, which is represented by the straight arrow; and hence that, when the two effects are in opposition, the former will determine the structure of the major product.

Although the above rule does indeed lead to the correct prediction that the addition of hydrogen chloride to propylene should be predominantly normal, its theoretical justification is not clear. Structure XXVIII suggests that, of the two unsaturated carbon atoms, the one which is linked to the methyl group has the more negative charge; for, if the opposite were true, the curved arrow ought instead to be drawn as in structure XXIX. Consequently, structure XVIII should be less stable

$$CH_3 \rightarrow \overset{\frown}{CH}=\!=\!CH_2$$
$$\text{XXIX}$$

than XXI, but structure XIX should be more stable than XXII. As far as just these four structures are concerned, therefore, the two of Class A favor abnormal addition, whereas the two of Class B favor normal addition. Consequently, the rule which we are now considering implies that the Class B structures are more important than the Class A structures. However, unless the additional Class B structure XX is also taken into account, there is no obvious reason for this important difference. The rule, in the form in which it was originally stated, therefore seems somewhat incomplete.

In the Class B structure XX, which is considered to make the decisive contribution to the state of the activated complex for normal addition, one of the three hydrogen atoms of the methyl group is represented as not bonded to the carbon atom to which, in the actual system, it is in fact linked. Consequently, the inclusion of this structure in the resonance implies that hyperconjugation, or no-bond resonance, here plays an important role. Indeed, just as the polarizations which are required for the normal and abnormal additions of hydrogen chloride to styrene are represented by the respective structures XII and XIII (see page 433), so also the corresponding polarizations with propylene can be similarly represented by the structures XXX and XXXI. (The first of these latter structures can be written also in the alternative and approximately equivalent form XXXII.)   The treatment of styrene, with which there is

$$H_3\!\!=\!\!C\!\!-\!\!CH\!\!=\!\!CH_2 \qquad H_3\!\!=\!\!C\!\!-\!\!CH\!\!=\!\!CH_2 \qquad \overset{H}{\underset{}{CH_2\!\!-\!\!CH\!\!=\!\!CH_2}}$$

XXX   XXXI   XXXII

conjugation of the classical type, and that of propylene, with which there is instead only hyperconjugation, are therefore seen to be essentially identical.   With each hydrocarbon, the electrostatic interactions are apparently too small, or too evenly balanced, to be decisive, and so the proton attacks the unsaturated atom at the *end* of the conjugated system, since that is the atom to which the required unshared pair of electrons can be brought most easily.

In the molecule of *tert*-butylethylene, the net charges on the unsaturated carbon atoms should not be greatly different from those on the corresponding atoms in the molecule of propylene.   Since the electrostatic interaction should therefore again be less important than the resonance, the relative stabilities of the activated complexes for the normal and abnormal additions of hydrogen chloride should here also be determined largely by hyperconjugation or, in other words, by the contribution of the particular structure XXXIII to the former complex.   The addition

$$^+CH_3$$

$$(CH_3)_2C\!\!=\!\!CH\!\!-\!\!\underset{H}{\overset{|}{C}H_2}$$

XXXIII

should therefore be normal.   This prediction is confirmed by the observation[16] that the major product is, as expected, pinacolyl chloride, XXXIV. The reaction is, however, complicated[16] by the formation of rather large quantities of the rearrangement product, 2,3-dimethyl-2-chlorobutane, XXXV, together with traces of the abnormal addition product, 3,3-dimethyl-1-chlorobutane, XXXVI.   The occurrence of the rearrangement

$$(CH_3)_3C\!\!-\!\!CHCl\!\!-\!\!CH_3 \qquad (CH_3)_2CH\!\!-\!\!\underset{Cl}{\overset{|}{C}(CH_3)_2} \qquad (CH_3)_3C\!\!-\!\!CH_2\!\!-\!\!CH_2Cl$$

XXXIV   XXXV   XXXVI

is here of special interest since it provides further evidence for the essential correctness of the mechanism which is here postulated and, in particular,

[16] G. G. Ecke, N. C. Cook, and F. C. Whitmore, *J. Am. Chem. Soc.* **72**, 1511 (1950).

for the existence of the intermediate cation **XXXVII** (cf. Section 8·14). (However, see the following paragraph.)

$$(CH_3)_3C-C^+H-CH_3$$
XXXVII

Although the rearrangement accompanying the addition of hydrogen chloride to *tert*-butylethylene gives some support for the reality of the postulated intermediate cation XXXVII, there is no necessity for us to believe that this ion is ever completely free. Indeed, the further reaction in which this ion becomes linked to a chloride ion, or in which it rearranges, may be simultaneous with the addition of the proton to the molecule of the olefin. There is, in fact, evidence that in certain closely analogous reactions the intermediate cation can have at most a transient existence. When hydrogen bromide is added to 1,2-dimethylcyclohexene, XXXVIII, to 2,3-dimethylcyclohexene, XXXIX, and to 2-methylmethylenecyclohexane, XL, in acetic acid at 25°C,

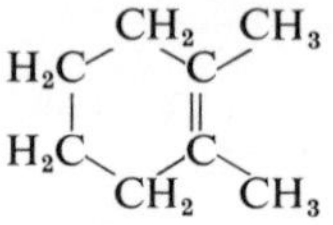

XXXVIII 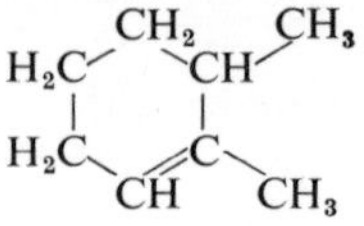   XXXIX 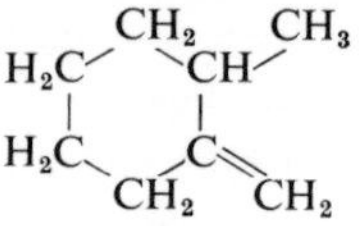   XL

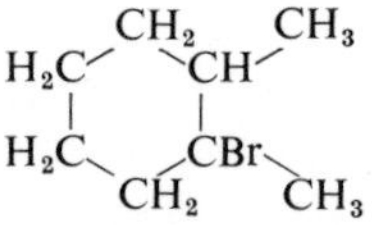

XLI 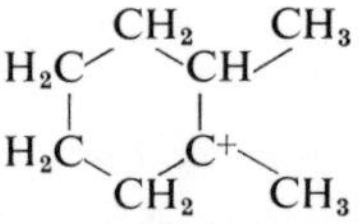   XLII

the relative amounts of the stereoisomeric bromides XLI are quite different.[17] If all these reactions went through the same cation, XLII, the relative amounts of the isomeric products would have to be identical. Since clearly, therefore, there is no such common intermediate, the cation in at least two of the three reactions must never be entirely free. This conclusion, however, merely confirms our original knowledge that our assumed mechanism is greatly oversimplified, and it does not invalidate the above interpretations of the several reactions considered.

With a trisubstituted propylene of the type **XLIII**, where the letter X represents a halogen atom, prediction is much more difficult than with the foregoing olefins, since the importance of the hyperconjugation must here be considerably decreased, whereas that of the electrostatic interactions must be considerably increased. Although we can still write the structure **XLIV**, which is the analog of **XX** and **XXXIII**, we cannot

$$CX_3-CH{=}CH_2 \qquad\qquad X^+$$

$$CX_2{=}CH-CH_2$$
$$|$$
$$H$$

XLIII   XLIV

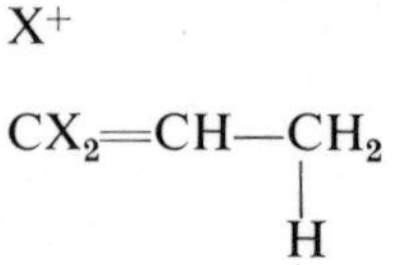

[17] G. S. Hammond and T. D. Nevitt, *J. Am. Chem. Soc.* **76**, 4121 (1954).

expect that the resulting resonance will greatly stabilize the activated complex for normal addition.   Consequently, we can anticipate that the normal addition will be rather slow, but we cannot be equally certain whether it will now be slower or faster than the abnormal addition.   The central carbon atom undoubtedly has a fairly large net positive charge since, by the I-effect, the substituted methyl group must have pulled electrons away from it; the methylene carbon atom, on the other hand, probably has a somewhat smaller net positive charge since, by the R-effect, it must also have lost a share of its electrons.   The initial structure XLIII

$$CX_3 \leftarrow \overset{\curvearrowleft}{C}H{=}CH_2$$
XLV

can therefore be written more fully as XLV.   Since only the central carbon atom is here at the head of an arrow, and since this arrow is a curved one, we might perhaps predict that the addition will be abnormal.

A further, and roughly equivalent, argument leading to the same conclusion can be based on a more detailed consideration of the four remaining structures, XLVI–XLIX, which must be given significant weights in the two possible activated complexes.   Although the Class A structures XLVI and XLVIII favor normal addition whereas the Class B structures XLVII and XLIX favor abnormal addition, the effects operating

$$
\begin{array}{llll}
X & X & X & X \\
| & | & | & | \\
CX_2{-}CH{=}CH_2 & CX_2{-}C^+H{-}CH_2 & CX_2{-}CH{=}CH_2 & CX_2{-}CH{-}C^+H_2 \\
& \quad\quad\quad\;| & & \quad\quad\quad| \\
H^+ & \quad\quad\quad\;H & H^+ & \quad\quad\quad H \\
\text{XLVI} & \quad\text{XLVII} & \text{XLVIII} & \quad\text{XLIX}
\end{array}
$$

in opposite directions should not exactly cancel.   Since the difference between the energies of structure XLVII and XLIX is probably greater than is that between the energies of structures XLVI and XLVIII, the former difference should outweigh the latter.   Consequently, the relative rates of addition should be determined primarily by the structures of Class B; and hence the addition is again found to be predominantly abnormal.   The argument is, however, inconclusive since it ignores the effect of the hyperconjugation, which favors normal addition.   The empirical data[18, 19] are that the addition of hydrogen chloride is always extremely slow, as predicted; and that it is abnormal when X is F,[18] but normal when X is Cl.[19]   Although these facts could hardly have been

[18] A. L. Henne and S. Kaye, *J. Am. Chem. Soc.* **72**, 3369 (1950).
[19] M. S. Kharasch, E. H. Rossin, and E. K. Fields, *J. Am. Chem. Soc.* **63**, 2558 (1941).

predicted in complete detail, they are not unreasonable. In particular, the observed difference between the trifluoro- and the trichloropropene is in the expected direction, since the effect of the electrostatic interactions should be larger, and that of the hyperconjugation should be smaller, with the more electronegative halogen.

A closely analogous example in which the large electron-attracting power of the substituent in a monosubstituted ethylene results in a reversal of the usual direction of addition is presented by the neurine cation L.

$$(CH_3)_3N^+—CH{=}CH_2 \qquad\qquad (CH_3)_3N^+—CH_2—CH_2I$$
$$\text{L} \qquad\qquad\qquad\qquad\qquad\qquad \text{LI}$$

The reaction with hydrogen iodide here proceeds only with considerable difficulty, and the product is the trimethyl-β-iodoethylammonium ion, LI.[20]

Let us now consider a slightly different sort of example, the addition of hydrogen chloride to vinyl chloride; and, for the sake of brevity, let us confine our remarks to the second, and shorter, of the two treatments illustrated above with reference to propylene and certain of its trisubsti-tuted derivatives. The reader should now be able without difficulty to fill in the missing details of the more complete discussion. In vinyl chloride, the I-effect cannot be neglected, as in propylene and in *tert*-butylethylene, because the dipole moment of the molecule is rather large (cf. Table 5·3, Section 5·4). Consequently, we must write the structure as LII. There is here no ambiguity about the directions of the arrows,

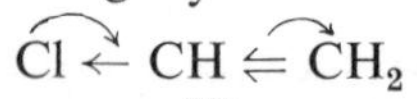

$$\overset{\frown}{Cl} \xleftarrow{} CH \xleftarrow{} \overset{\frown}{C}H_2$$
$$\text{LII}$$

either straight or curved, because the indicated displacements can occur in only the ways specified. The course of the reaction, however, cannot be definitely predicted, because the I-effect and the R-effect oppose each other, and we cannot be sure, without recourse to experiment, which one will predominate. The I-effect (the straight arrows) makes the carbon atom carrying the chlorine the more nucleophilic center, whereas the R-effect (the curved arrows) gives nucleophilic activity only to the terminal carbon atom. We have here, therefore, a more extreme example of the same kind of conflict that we encountered on pages 435ff, in our discussion of propylene. Since the general rule which was there stated seems usually, in spite of its incompleteness, to lead to a correct answer, we may anticipate that the reaction will be initiated at the methylenic carbon atom, and hence that the addition will be in accordance with Markovni-kov's rule. The reaction does indeed follow this course, which is the one favored by the R-effect, but we should note that the I-effect nevertheless

20 E. Schmidt, *Ann.* **267**, 300 (1892).

exerts a noticeable influence, in that it makes this reaction proceed more slowly than the corresponding one with unsubstituted ethylene.[21] The addition of hydrogen chloride to vinyl chloride can, in fact, be effected only in the presence of catalysts like ferric chloride. The situation may be described thus: the I-effect decreases the nucleophilic activity of both carbon atoms, whereas the R-effect increases that of the terminal carbon atom only; this increase is great enough to make the terminal atom the more reactive of the two, but it is not great enough to bring the reactivity back to the level obtaining in ethylene itself.

The discussion so far has been limited almost entirely to the addition of hydrogen chloride to a few rather simple ethylene derivatives. The present treatment, however, is not restricted to these reactions but can be extended to a large number of others. It should be evident, for example, that other acids, such as hydrogen bromide, hydrogen iodide, sulfuric acid, and so on, ought also to react in completely analogous manners to form analogous products. This expectation is indeed borne out by the facts since, in so far as the reactions have been studied, all strong acids add to olefins in the same way that hydrogen chloride does and hence, with only a few exceptions, in agreement with Markovnikov's rule. The treatment can also be extended in an obvious way to include other unsymmetrical olefins, so that it is quite general. (For further discussion of "abnormal" additions and of the reactions of conjugated systems, however, see Sections 8·6 and 8·9, respectively.)

The hydration of olefins also can be discussed from the present viewpoint. For example, if propylene is treated with fairly concentrated sulfuric acid, the organic cation CH_3—C^+H—CH_3 is presumably formed as above (however, see the following paragraph). This ion has several possibilities for subsequent reaction. It could acquire a bisulfate ion from the solution to give isopropyl sulfuric acid or, on the other hand, it could take up a molecule of water to give the oxonium ion LIII. Since

$$CH_3—CH—CH_3$$
$$\overset{|}{{}^+OH_2}$$
LIII

this latter ion could readily lose a proton, the product isolated from the reaction mixture would be isopropyl alcohol. The net result of this second possible course of the reaction is therefore addition of water to the olefin in accordance with Markovnikov's rule. It is to be noted that an intermediate formation, and subsequent hydrolysis, of isopropyl sulfuric acid does not need to be postulated.

[21] M. S. Kharasch and C. W. Hannum, *J. Am. Chem. Soc.* **56**, 712 (1934).

RESONANCE AND CHEMICAL REACTION

Just as in the addition of a hydrogen halide to an olefin, so also in the analogous hydration the postulated intermediate cation need never be entirely free (cf. the paragraph in fine print on page 438). Evidence bearing on this question has been obtained from a study of the hydration of trimethylethylene, LIV, and of *unsym*-methylethylethylene, LV, in aqueous nitric acid.[22] In each reaction, the sole product is, as expected,

$$CH_3—C=CH—CH_3$$
$$\qquad |$$
$$\qquad CH_3$$
$$\qquad LIV$$

$$CH_2=C—CH_2—CH_3$$
$$\qquad |$$
$$\qquad CH_3$$
$$\qquad LV$$

$$CH_3—C(OH)—CH_2—CH_3$$
$$\qquad\quad |$$
$$\qquad\quad CH_3$$
$$\qquad\quad LVI$$

$$CH_3—C^+—CH_2—CH_3$$
$$\qquad\; |$$
$$\qquad\; CH_3$$
$$\qquad\; LVII$$

tert-amyl alcohol LVI. Now, if the formation of the cation LVII were rapid and reversible, as in the scheme

$$CH_3—C=CH—CH_3 \qquad\qquad CH_3—C^+—CH_2—CH_3 \qquad\qquad CH_2=C—CH_2—CH_3$$
$$\qquad |\qquad\qquad + H_3O^+ \rightleftarrows \qquad |\qquad\qquad + H_2O \rightleftarrows \qquad |\qquad\qquad + H_3O^+$$
$$\qquad CH_3 \qquad\qquad\qquad\qquad\qquad CH_3 \qquad\qquad\qquad\qquad\qquad CH_3$$
$$\qquad LIV \qquad\qquad\qquad\qquad\qquad\; LVII \qquad\qquad\qquad\qquad\qquad LV$$

then there should be a perceptible interconversion of the two isomeric hydrocarbons LIV and LV, into each other before the hydration has occurred. This expectation, however, is not realized; for, in each instance, the olefin that is recovered when the reaction is half complete is found to have undergone no appreciable rearrangement. Apparently, therefore, the cation LVII reacts with the solvent as fast as it is formed and so has no independent existence. As before, this complexity of the mechanism does not invalidate the above theoretical discussion.

8·6 Free-Radical Additions to Carbon-Carbon Double Bonds.[23] When hydrogen bromide adds to styrene, the reaction can follow either one of two quite different courses, depending upon the experimental conditions. If oxygen and peroxides are rigorously excluded from the reaction mixture, or if an "antioxidant" like diphenylamine or thiocresol is added, only 1-bromoethylbenzene, C_6H_5—CHBr—CH_3 (the normal product), is obtained; but, if oxygen is present, 2-bromoethylbenzene, C_6H_5—CH_2—CH_2Br (the abnormal product), may also be formed in varying amounts. In fact, if peroxides are added, the latter bromide may become the major product. Clearly, therefore, there must be two entirely different mechanisms for the addition. Of these, the one leading to normal addition has

[22] J. B. Levy, R. W. Taft, Jr., and L. P. Hammett, *J. Am. Chem. Soc.* **75**, 1253 (1953).
[23] For surveys of the free-radical additions to olefins and for references to the original literature, see F. R. Mayo and C. Walling, *Chem. Revs.* **27**, 351 (1940); W. A. Waters, *The Chemistry of Free Radicals*, Oxford University Press, Oxford, 1946, Chapter IX; D. H. Hey, *Ann. Repts. on Progr. Chem.* (*Chem. Soc. London*) **45**, pp. 149ff (1948); G. W. Wheland, *Advanced Organic Chemistry*, John Wiley & Sons, New York, 2nd ed., 1949, Section 15·5.

already been discussed in Section 8·5, but the one leading to abnormal addition remains to be considered.

It appears at the present time that the addition of hydrogen bromide to styrene in the presence of oxygen or peroxides is probably a chain reaction proceeding through the steps:

$$HBr + O_2 \rightarrow (H \cdot O_2) + Br$$

or $$HBr + Peroxide \rightarrow (H \cdot Peroxide) + Br$$ (1)

$$Br + C_6H_5CH{=}CH_2 \rightarrow C_6H_5\overset{\cdot}{C}H{-}CH_2Br \qquad (2)$$

$$C_6H_5\overset{\cdot}{C}H{-}CH_2Br + HBr \rightarrow C_6H_5CH_2CH_2Br + Br \qquad (3)$$

The purpose of the oxygen or peroxide is thus to start the chain by producing a bromine atom in reaction 1. This atom is used up in reaction 2, but a new one is produced in reaction 3 to take its place and to carry on the chain. The sequence of reactions can therefore continue indefinitely, or until the chain is broken by some such reaction as

$$H + Br \rightarrow HBr \qquad (4)$$

(at the wall, or in the presence of some other "third body"), or the like.

We need now to consider why in step 2 the bromine atom, which is clearly a radical reagent, attacks the terminal unsaturated atom of the styrene in preference to the central one. The activated complex for the predominant (abnormal) reaction can be a hybrid of the structures I–VII, whereas that for the alternative (normal) reaction can be a hybrid of only the structures VIII–XI. It is difficult to see how the distribution of charge in the styrene molecule could have any significant effect upon the relative stabilities of the Class A structures I, II, VIII, and IX, or of the Class B

$$\text{IX} \qquad\qquad \text{X} \qquad\qquad \text{XI}$$

structures III, IV, X, and XI, because the bromine atom is electrically neutral. It is to be expected, therefore, that the possibility of resonance with the further Class B structures V–VII will make the activated complex for abnormal addition the more stable of the two, so that the product should be predominantly 2-bromoethylbenzene, as it actually is.

When a bromine atom attacks a molecule of propylene, the activated complex can be a hybrid either of the three structures XII, XIII, and XIV or of the two structures XV and XVI. Since structures XII and XIII are essentially equivalent to XV and XVI, respectively, and since, with the former complex, the additional Class B structure XIV must also be

$$\text{XII} \qquad\qquad\qquad \text{XIII} \qquad\qquad\qquad \text{XIV}$$

$$\text{XV} \qquad\qquad\qquad \text{XVI}$$

involved, we can conclude that the attack will occur more rapidly at the terminal carbon atom than at the central one, and hence that the addition will be predominantly abnormal. The reaction in the presence of added peroxides has, in fact, been found[23] to yield only *n*-propyl bromide. As in the proton-initiated additions which were discussed in Section 8·5, therefore, the effect of the hyperconjugation in propylene upon the course of the reaction is analogous to that of the more familiar kind of conjugation in styrene. With each of these hydrocarbons, the bromine atom, like a proton, preferentially attacks the *end* of the conjugated system.

The addition of hydrogen bromide to vinyl chloride in the presence of peroxides also occurs abnormally and gives 1-chloro-2-bromoethane as the major product. In this reaction, the activated complex for abnormal addition receives its largest contributions from structures XVII, XVIII, and XIX, whereas that for normal addition is a hybrid of only XX and XXI. The structure XIX cannot be expected to stabilize the former

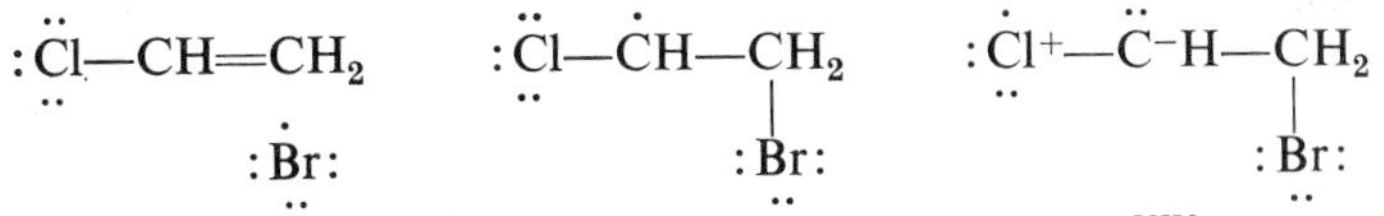

$$\overset{..}{:}\overset{.}{Cl}-CH{=}CH_2 \qquad \overset{..}{:}\overset{.}{Cl}-\overset{.}{C}H-CH_2 \qquad :Cl^+-\overset{..}{C^-}H-CH_2$$

$$\overset{.}{:}Br: \qquad\qquad :Br: \qquad\qquad :Br:$$

XVII   XVIII   XIX

$$\overset{..}{:}\overset{..}{Cl}-CH{=}CH_2 \qquad\qquad \overset{..}{:}\overset{.}{Cl}-\overset{.}{C}H-CH_2$$

$$:Br: \qquad\qquad\qquad :Br:$$

XX   XXI

activated complex a great deal, for, although it has the same number of bonds as the remaining structures, its charge distribution is unfavorable. (The effect of resonance between structures XVIII and XIX is to produce a three-electron bond between the carbon and chlorine atoms, in addition to the two-electron bond. Since these atoms are not equivalent, the three-electron bond can therefore be expected to be weak. See Section 2·5.) However, the addition does in fact take place predominantly in the abnormal manner, so that structure XIX is apparently decisive nevertheless.

It is possible that the highly electronegative character of the chlorine atom in vinyl chloride might also favor the abnormal addition. To be sure, our present qualitative point of view gives us no reason to anticipate such an effect, but a more quantitative approach might lead to a definite prediction. See, for example, the somewhat analogous case of the orientation in chlorobenzene for substitution by a radical reagent (Section 8·11).

The above-described mechanism of abnormal addition is not restricted to the three reactions considered, the addition of hydrogen bromide to styrene, to propylene, and to vinyl chloride. It is instead quite general and can be considered operative whenever a radical reagent attacks an olefin. There is, however, an important limitation to which it is subject: hydrogen bromide is ordinarily the only one of all the common acids that can be made to enter into an abnormal addition. (However, see the paragraph following the one in fine print, below.) The reason for this fact is probably that, with the remaining acids, one or more of the reactions corresponding to the steps 1, 2, and 3 in the above scheme for hydrogen bromide can occur only rarely, if at all. For example, hydrogen chloride and sulfuric acid appear to be so stable that they are ordinarily unable to react in the necessary ways with either a peroxide (in step 1) or an organic radical (in step 3); and an iodine atom, although it can be produced from hydrogen iodide (in step 1) is probably not sufficiently reactive to attack a molecule of the olefin (in step 2). Aside from hydrogen bromide, the only acids which generally enter into abnormal additions, and which have been carefully studied, seem to be the mercaptans, the thioacids, and certain bisulfites. For example:

$$CH_3CH{=}CH_2 + C_6H_5SH \rightarrow CH_3CH_2CH_2SC_6H_5$$

$$(CH_3)_2C{=}CH_2 + CH_3COSH \rightarrow (CH_3)_2CHCH_2SCOCH_3$$

$$CH_3CH{=}CH_2 + NaHSO_3 \rightarrow CH_3CH_2CH_2SO_3Na$$

In all these reactions, the abnormal addition occurs only in the presence of oxygen, or other oxidizing agent, and is inhibited by "antioxidants." Presumably, therefore, chain mechanisms, involving radicals like C_6H_5S, CH_3COS, and HSO_3 or SO_3^-, respectively, are again involved.

Mercaptans add *normally* also, in the presence of certain catalysts, including fairly strong sulfuric acid, elementary sulfur, strong bases, and so on. The nature of these reactions is not clearly understood at present. Bisulfites, on the other hand, appear to add only in the abnormal manner, and only under oxidizing conditions.

As is perhaps not very surprising, there are a few exceptions to the above generalization that hydrogen chloride does not enter into abnormal additions. One of these exceptions has already, in fact, been discussed on pages 438ff, where it was mentioned that the addition of hydrogen chloride to 3,3,3-trifluoro-1-propene gives 1-chloro-3,3,3-trifluoropropane rather than 2-chloro-1,1,1-trifluoropropane.[18] There is here, however, no reason for us to suppose that the reaction follows a radical-chain mechanism of the type illustrated in equations 1, 2, and 3. Evidence that free-radical additions of hydrogen chloride to such olefins as ethylene and propylene may occur in the gas phase and at high temperatures has, to be sure, been obtained by Raley, Rust, and Vaughan;[24] and, under similar conditions, the addition of hydrogen chloride to allyl chloride has been found to yield the abnormal product, 1,3-dichloropropane.[25] In these reactions, however, the experimental conditions are so different from those commonly employed in the corresponding abnormal additions of hydrogen bromide that no significant comparison is possible. Finally, as was also mentioned earlier (see page 437), the addition of hydrogen chloride to *tert*-butylethylene under the usual conditions gives a small amount of the abnormal product, 3,3-dimethyl-1-chlorobutane. The belief that this reaction is of the radical-chain type is supported by the

[24] J. H. Raley, F. F. Rust, and W. E. Vaughan, *J. Am. Chem. Soc.* **70**, 2767 (1948). Cf. also W. E. Hanford and J. Harmon, U.S. **2,418,832** [*C. A.* **42**, 581 (1948)].

[25] F. R. Mayo, *J. Am. Chem. Soc.* **76**, 5392 (1954).

fact that the yield of the abnormal product is increased by the presence of peroxides.[16]   There is, however, no obvious reason why, with this particular olefin, hydrogen chloride thus behaves anomalously.

Unlike hydrogen chloride, hydrogen iodide has never been found to add abnormally to any olefin under any experimental conditions.   Although the reaction between this latter acid and 3,3,3-trifluoro-1-propene might reasonably be expected to yield the abnormal product 1-iodo-3,3,3-trifluoropropane, the reaction has apparently not been reported. On the other hand, rearrangements leading to changes in the carbon skeleton have been observed.[16]   Thus, the addition of hydrogen iodide to *tert*-butylethylene gives not only pinacolyl iodide but also a small amount of 2,3-dimethyl-2-iodobutane (cf. page 437).

Several *nonacidic* reagents have been found to add to olefins by what appear to be free-radical mechanisms.   The most important of these further reactions are doubtless the ones which are involved in the polymerizations of olefins, and which are more fully discussed in Section 8·10. Here, however, we shall describe only some of the simpler, closely related reactions.   In the presence of a few mole per cent of acetyl peroxide, bromotrichloromethane adds to styrene to give 1,1,1-trichloro-3-bromo-3-phenylpropane.[26]   A possible mechanism for the reaction is that shown in the equations

$$CH_3—CO—O—O—CO—CH_3 \rightarrow 2\overset{\cdot}{C}H_3 + 2CO_2 \qquad (5)$$

$$\overset{\cdot}{C}H_3 + BrCCl_3 \rightarrow CH_3Br + \overset{\cdot}{C}Cl_3 \qquad (6)$$

$$\overset{\cdot}{C}Cl_3 + C_6H_5—CH{=}CH_2 \rightarrow C_6H_5—\overset{\cdot}{C}H—CH_2—CCl_3 \qquad (7)$$

$$C_6H_5—\overset{\cdot}{C}H—CH_2—CCl_3 + BrCCl_3 \rightarrow C_6H_5—CHBr—CH_2—CCl_3$$
$$+ \overset{\cdot}{C}Cl_3 \qquad (8)$$

(However, see the following paragraph.)   The sequence can continue by repetition of the last two steps, until at last the chain is broken by some such reaction as

$$2\overset{\cdot}{C}Cl_3 \rightarrow Cl_3C—CCl_3 \qquad (9)$$

In the particular step that determines the structure of the product isolated, the trichloromethyl radical attacks the styrene molecule and, like a bromine atom (cf. equation 2, Section 8·6), it goes to the terminal carbon atom.   The reason for this orientation is again presumably that the activated complex for the actual reaction is more effectively stabilized by resonance than the one for the alternative reaction would be.   Indeed,

[26] M. S. Kharasch, O. Reinmuth, and W. H. Urry, *J. Am. Chem. Soc.* **69**, 1105 (1947).

the same argument that was based upon a consideration of structures I–XI (pages 443f) can be applied here also without essential change, if only the bromine atoms in these structures are replaced by trichloromethyl groups.

The mechanism outlined above in equations 5–9 is only one of a large number that could have been proposed. Thus, equation 5 might be replaced by

$$CH_3—CO—O—O—CO—CH_3 \rightarrow 2CH_3—CO—O \qquad (5')$$

Similarly, equation 6 might be replaced by

$$CH_3—CO—O + BrCCl_3 \rightarrow CH_3Br + CO_2 + \overset{\cdot}{C}Cl_3 \qquad (6')$$

and so on. Although there is at present no conclusive way for deciding among these alternatives, the resulting uncertainty causes no serious difficulty. The only feature of the mechanism that is essential to the foregoing argument is the assumption that the structure of the product is determined by a step in which the trichloromethyl group is transferred to the styrene molecule with just one electron for the new carbon-carbon bond. Any mechanism embodying this assumption would for our purposes be as satisfactory as the one originally stated.

When bromotrichloromethane adds to propylene, the product is, as expected, 1,1,1-trichloro-3-bromobutane.[26] Hence, in the step which is analogous to that shown in equation 7, the trichloromethyl radical must attack the terminal unsaturated atom in preference to the central one. Since the more complex radical thus again behaves in the same way as a bromine atom, we may assume that the activated complexes for the two alternative reactions are here hybrids of structures which differ from XII–XVI (page 444) only in the replacement of bromine atoms by trichloromethyl groups. As in the reactions already considered in this and the preceding sections, therefore, the effect of the hyperconjugation in propylene is similar to that of the conjugation in styrene.

The addition of bromotrichloromethane to vinyl chloride has not been reported. We may, however, infer that it would lead to 1,1,1,3-tetra-chloro-3-bromopropane since, with the presumably analogous unsaturated compound, vinyl acetate, the product is 1-bromo-3,3,3-trichloropropyl acetate.[26] Again, therefore, the trichloromethyl radical attacks the same unsaturated atom as does a bromine atom.

In the presence of acetyl peroxide, other halogen compounds besides bromotrichloromethane can add to olefins. The substances that have been found to react in this way include chloroform, bromoform, carbon tetrachloride, carbon tetrabromide,[27] iodotrifluoromethane,[28] and others.[28a]

[27] M. S. Kharasch, E. V. Jensen, and W. H. Urry, *J. Am. Chem. Soc.* **69**, 1100 (1947).

[28] A. L. Henne and M. Nager, *J. Am. Chem. Soc.* **73**, 5527 (1951); R. N. Haszeldine and B. R. Steele, *J. Chem. Soc.* **1953**, 1199.

[28a] See, for example, P. Tarrant and A. M. Lovelace, *J. Am. Chem. Soc.* **77** 768 (1955).

Moreover, many unsaturated compounds besides the ones already mentioned can enter into such reactions; ethylene, 1-octene,[26] and ethyl acrylate,[27] for example, have been thus employed. And finally, the acetyl peroxide can be omitted if the reaction mixture is illuminated with ultraviolet light or, in some but not in all instances, if iodine and either magnesium or Raney nickel are present.[26, 27] Presumably, under these latter conditions, there are produced free radicals which replace the ones represented in equations 6 and 6′ as, respectively, methyl and acetate. In many of the reactions that have been mentioned both in this paragraph and in the preceding ones, the addition of the halide to the olefin is accompanied by the formation of further products with higher molecular weights. When bromotrichloromethane adds to styrene, for example, this polymeric material is only a minor by-product; on the other hand, when carbon tetrachloride adds to the same olefin, the polymer is the major product, and only a little of the expected 1,3,3,3-tetrachloro-1-phenylpropane is obtained. In each of these reactions, the polymerization doubtless proceeds by a mechanism which differs in no essential way from the one that is more fully described in Section 8·10.

In order correctly to predict the structure of the product that is formed in any of the above free-radical additions, one ordinarily needs to consider two independent problems: the identity of the radical that attacks the olefin molecule, and the point at which, in the latter molecule, the attack occurs. The first of these problems will be briefly discussed in the following paragraph; the second is, however, the subject that has already been most carefully considered in this section. In general terms, the conclusion to which we have thus come is that, ordinarily, a radical reagent may be expected to go to the unsaturated carbon atom that is joined to the larger number of hydrogen atoms (however, see below), since this position is the one at the end of the most extensive conjugated, or "hyperconjugated," system. With any unsymmetrical olefin in which the unsaturated atoms are linked to the same number of hydrogen atoms, a mixture of the two possible products may be expected; as yet, however, no experimental studies of this question have been reported, except for the peroxide-induced additions of hydrogen bromide.[23]

Of the two problems which were stated at the beginning of the preceding paragraph, the first still remains to be considered. For the sake of definiteness, let us assume that, in each addition, the reaction is initiated by methyl radicals that result from the decomposition of acetyl peroxide (cf. equations 5 and 6). Now, since a carbon-hydrogen bond is always stronger than an analogous carbon-halogen bond,[29] this methyl radical may be expected to react with a hydrogen halide HX in such a way as to

[29] See, for example, Table A3 on p. 172 of M. Szwarc, *Chem. Revs.* **47**, 75 (1950).

produce a molecule of methane CH_4 plus a halogen atom X, rather than a molecule of the methyl halide CH_3X plus a hydrogen atom H. Consequently, in agreement with the mechanism postulated above (equations 1, 2, and 3), the radical that attacks the olefin must be a halogen atom. On the other hand, in the additions of bromotrichloromethane and of its several analogs, prediction is more difficult since ordinarily the atom that is captured by the methyl radical in the chain-initiating step merely transfers its attachment from one carbon atom to another. In all the reactions which have as yet been reported, however, the structures of the products isolated can be explained if the methyl radical is assumed to remove a bromine atom in preference to either a hydrogen or a chlorine atom, a hydrogen atom in preference to a chlorine atom,[26, 27] and an iodine atom in preference to either a hydrogen[30] or a fluorine[28] atom. These empirical generalizations are illustrated in the following reactions:

$$CHBr_3 + CH_2{=}CH{-}n\text{-}C_6H_{13} \xrightarrow{(CH_3{-}CO)_2O_2} CHBr_2{-}CH_2{-}CHBr{-}n\text{-}C_6H_{13}$$

$$CBrCl_3 + C_6H_5{-}CH{=}CH_2 \xrightarrow{(CH_3{-}CO)_2O_2} C_6H_5{-}CHBr{-}CH_2{-}CCl_3$$

$$CHCl_3 + CH_2{=}CH{-}n\text{-}C_6H_{13} \xrightarrow{(C_6H_5{-}CO)_2O_2} CCl_3{-}CH_2{-}CH_2{-}n\text{-}C_6H_{13}$$

$$\underset{\text{limonene}}{CHI_3 + C_{10}H_{16}} \xrightarrow{(CH_3{-}CO)_2O_2} \underset{\substack{\text{limonene-iodoform} \\ \text{addition product}[30, 31]}}{I{-}C_{10}H_{16}{-}CHI_2}$$

$$CIF_3 + CF_3{-}CH{=}CH_2 \xrightarrow[\text{122 hr.}]{\text{Hg, 215°C}} CF_3{-}CHI{-}CH_2{-}CF_3$$

As is shown in the last of the foregoing equations, the trifluoromethyl radical must attack the terminal unsaturated atom of 3,3,3-trifluoro-1-propene. Apparently, therefore, hyperconjugation involving structure XXII for the activated complex is here of sufficient importance to determine the course of the reaction, even though the corresponding structure XXIII, does not lead to normal addition of hydrogen chloride.[18] (Cf. pages 438ff.) The reason for this difference is probably that the especially great electronegativity of fluorine makes structure XXIII extremely unstable, but has no

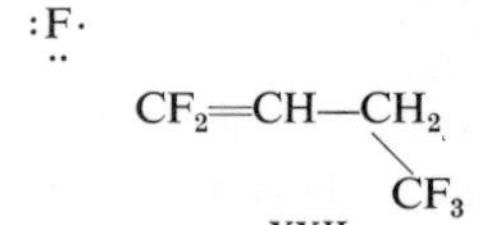

$$:\overset{..}{\underset{..}{F}}\cdot \qquad\qquad\qquad\qquad :\overset{..}{\underset{..}{F}}:^+$$

$$\underset{XXII}{\overset{\displaystyle CF_2{=}CH{-}CH_2}{\underset{\displaystyle \searrow}{}\,CF_3}} \qquad\qquad \underset{XXIII}{\overset{\displaystyle CF_2{=}CH{-}CH_2}{\underset{\displaystyle \searrow}{}\,H}}$$

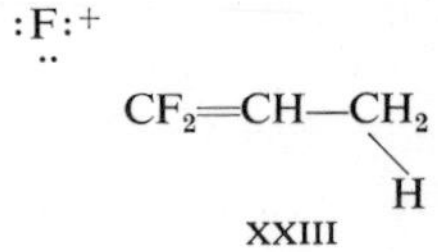

comparable adverse effect upon structure XXII. A particularly interesting feature of the reaction is that the trifluoromethyl radical does not here attack the same carbon atom that is attacked by the proton in the addition of a strong acid. In this respect,

[30] M. Weizmann, S. Israelashvili, A. Halevy, and F. Bergmann, *J. Am. Chem. Soc.* **69**, 2569 (1947).

[31] The positions of the iodine atom and CHI_2 group were not determined.

3,3,3-trifluoro-1-propene differs from all the other olefins that have been considered above since, with each of these, the radical and the electrophilic reagents have been found to attack the same position. Clearly, therefore, we cannot accept the view, which has been advanced by some authors, that, since both radical and electrophilic reagents have deficiencies of electrons, each goes to the carbon atom with the larger net negative charge. An additional reason for rejecting this view is that, as was shown on page 436, the central carbon atom in propylene is probably more negative than the terminal one, at which the reactions actually occur.

A reaction in which there seem to be still further important factors in addition to the ones already discussed is the addition of iodotrifluoromethane to 1,1-difluoro-1-propene, XXIV. Since the product has been identified[32] as 1-iodo-1,3,3,3-pentafluoro-2-methylpropane, XXV, the trifluoromethyl radical must here attack the central unsaturated atom in preference to the terminal one. Although the reaction is therefore

$$CH_3—CH{=}CF_2$$

$$\begin{array}{c} CH_3—CH—CF_2I \\ | \\ CF_3 \end{array}$$

XXIV   XXV

in agreement with the above rule that the primary attack is upon the carbon atom that is bonded to the larger number of hydrogen atoms, it nevertheless appears somewhat anomalous. Indeed, the orientation is here contrary to what might have been expected either on the basis of the hyperconjugating effect of the methyl group or on the basis of steric hindrance. Perhaps the activated complex is a hybrid not only of structures XXVI and XXVII, but also of such additional ones as XXVIII and XXIX, no analogs of which are possible with the alternative complex. Since resonance among the structures XXVII–XXIX is equivalent to the formation of three-electron bonds between

$$CH_3—CH{=}CF_2$$
$$\overset{\centerdot}{C}F_3$$
XXVI

$$\begin{array}{c} CH_3—CH—\overset{\centerdot}{C}F_2 \\ | \\ CF_3 \end{array}$$
XXVII

$$\begin{array}{c} CH_3—CH—C \overset{\displaystyle \ddot{F}\cdot +}{\underset{\displaystyle \ddot{F}:}{\Big\backslash}} \\ | \\ CF_3 \end{array}$$
XXVIII

$$\begin{array}{c} CH_3—CH—C \overset{\displaystyle \ddot{F}:}{\underset{\displaystyle \ddot{F}\cdot +}{\Big\backslash}} \\ | \\ CF_3 \end{array}$$
XXIX

the carbon and fluorine atoms of the CF_2 group (see Section 2·5), the resulting stabilization ought to be small. The observed orientation, however, suggests that this stabilization is nevertheless more than sufficient to counterbalance the effect of the hyperconjugation in the other possible complex. (See pages 444f for a discussion of the similar situation that arises in the peroxide-induced addition of hydrogen bromide to vinyl chloride.)

The reaction between benzenediazonium chloride and acrylonitrile, in the presence of cupric chloride, leads to a fair yield of α-chlorohydrocinnamonitrile, XXX.[33] Although this reaction is rather different from any of the foregoing additions, it seems to be initiated by the attack of a radical reagent, namely, the phenyl radical, upon the unsaturated atom at the end of a conjugated system. Similarly, the reaction between

[32] R. N. Haszeldine, *J. Chem. Soc.* **1953**, 3565.
[33] C. F. Koelsch, *J. Am. Chem. Soc.* **65**, 57 (1943); see also C. F. Koelsch and V. Boekelheide, *ibid.* **66**, 412 (1944).

2,4-dichlorobenzenediazonium chloride and methyl crotonate gives methyl α-chloro-β-(2,4-dichlorophenyl)-butyrate, XXXI.[33] In each of

$$C_6H_5—CH_2—CHCl—CN$$
XXX

$$CH_3—CH—CHCl—CO_2CH_3 \qquad\qquad C_6H_5—CHCl—CH—CO_2CH_3$$

Cl

Cl

XXXI   Cl

XXXII

these two instances, the aryl radical becomes linked to the carbon atom that is β to the modified carboxyl group. When, however, the ethylenic double bond in the initial unsaturated reagent is conjugated also with a benzene ring, the entering aryl group goes to the α position. Thus, the reaction between p-chlorobenzenediazonium chloride and methyl cinnamate gives methyl β-chloro-α-(p-chlorophenyl)-hydrocinnamate, XXXII.[33] Clearly, therefore, the radical reagent here attacks the end of the conjugated system C_6H_5—C=C, rather than that of the alternative conjugated system C=C—C=O. This behavior, although we could not have predicted it, is at any rate not unreasonable.

8·7 Addition of Halogens to Carbon-Carbon Double Bonds. When bromine adds to even an unsymmetrical olefin like styrene or propylene, only a single product is possible, regardless of the mechanism. We shall find it interesting, however, to consider the nature of the activated complex, because, in doing so, we can obtain an understanding of several related phenomena. Just as the initial step in the normal addition of an acid to an olefin is considered to be a reaction with a positive hydrogen ion, so also the initial step in the addition of bromine is considered to be a reaction with a positive bromine ion.[34] This ion, like the hydrogen ion in the addition of an acid, HX, need not be, and probably is not, completely free; it may be combined with a negative bromide ion in a polarized bromine molecule, Br^+Br^-, or it may be combined in some way with a catalyst molecule. In any event, however, we can carry through the following discussion as if the ion were actually free, because its exact state of combination is not essential to the argument.

[34] An excellent survey of this problem is given by L. P. Hammett, *Physical Organic Chemistry*, McGraw-Hill Book Co., New York, 1940, pp. 147ff. See also C. K. Ingold, *Structure and Mechanism in Organic Chemistry*, Cornell University Press, Ithaca, N. Y., 1953, pp. 658ff.

The treatment of the addition of bromine to propylene, for example, is completely analogous to that of the addition of hydrogen chloride to this same olefin, since in both reactions the inorganic reagent is clearly electrophilic. The only essential change is the replacement of the positive hydrogen ion, H^+, by the positive bromine ion, Br^+. The effect of the electrostatic interactions in the Class A structures is then qualitatively the same as before; and, since the bromine ion, just like the hydrogen ion, is able to accommodate a pair of electrons provided by the unsaturated hydrocarbon, the relation among the Class B structures is also unaltered. It follows, therefore, that the attack must be initiated at the end of the molecule, as before, so that the initial product has structure I and not II. The completion of the reaction is then effected immediately,

$$CH_3-C^+H-CH_2 \qquad\qquad CH_3-CH-C^+H_2$$
$$\quad\ \ \big| \qquad\qquad\qquad\qquad\qquad \big|$$
$$\quad\ \ Br \qquad\qquad\qquad\qquad\qquad Br$$
$$\quad\ \ \text{I} \qquad\qquad\qquad\qquad\qquad\ \ \text{II}$$

or simultaneously with the first step, by the capture of a negative ion from the solution (however, see below). If the reaction is carried out in, say, carbon tetrachloride as solvent, this negative ion can be only a bromide ion, Br^-, so that the final product is necessarily propylene bromide, III. On the other hand, if the reaction is carried out in water, hydroxide ions also are available, so that propylene bromohydrin, IV, is a further possible product. Under such circumstances, the net effect of the reaction is the addition of the unsymmetrical hypobromous acid,

$$CH_3-CH-CH_2 \qquad CH_3-CH-CH_2 \qquad CH_3-CH-CH_2$$
$$\quad \big|\quad\ \ \big| \qquad\qquad\quad \big|\quad\ \ \big| \qquad\qquad\quad \big|\quad\ \ \big|$$
$$\quad Br\ \ \ Br \qquad\qquad\ HO\ \ \ Br \qquad\qquad\ Br\ \ \ OH$$
$$\quad \text{III} \qquad\qquad\qquad\quad \text{IV} \qquad\qquad\qquad\quad \text{V}$$

HOBr. Although the two products IV and V are conceivable in this reaction, only the former is actually produced, as we have just seen.

The above treatment has, of course, been drastically oversimplified. As a result, it is able only with some difficulty to account for the stereochemical features of certain completely analogous reactions. For example, cis and trans stilbene, $C_6H_5CH{=}CHC_6H_5$, give rise on bromination to diastereomeric dibromides, $C_6H_5CHBr-CHBrC_6H_5$ (presumably by trans addition in both reactions). This fact would be hard to explain if the reactions proceeded through intermediate positive ions of the type $C_6H_5C^+H-CHBrC_6H_5$, because rotation about the central carbon-carbon bonds and inversion of the carbonium carbon atoms should occur freely in such ions, and the stereochemical configurations should be lost.

Tarbell and Bartlett[35] have suggested that the concluding phase of the reaction (the capture of a bromide ion from solution) occurs so rapidly that the rotation does not have time to occur.   Roberts and Kimball,[36] on the other hand, have made an alternative proposal that the intermediate positive ion contains a three-membered ring, as in structure VI. A slightly different suggestion is that the intermediate is a hybrid of structure VI and of such additional ones as VII–IX. In any event, the rigidity of

$$C_6H_5CH\text{---}CHC_6H_5$$
$$\diagdown \diagup$$
$$Br^+$$
VI

$$C_6H_5\text{---}CH\text{---}C^+H\text{---}C_6H_5$$
$$\diagdown$$
$$Br$$
VII

$$C_6H_5\text{---}C^+H\text{---}CH\text{---}C_6H_5$$
$$\diagup$$
$$Br$$
VIII

$$C_6H_5\text{---}CH\text{=}CH\text{---}C_6H_5$$
$$Br^+$$
IX

the cation would then make possible the maintenance of the configuration. The attack by the bromide ion in the concluding step would presumably be accompanied by a Walden inversion, so that the addition of the bromine should be trans, as it probably is.   The possibility of a mechanism of this type receives further strong support from an extensive series of investigations of related reactions.[37, 38]   The work of Nozaki and Ogg[15] also suggests a more complex mechanism in which, at any rate under some circumstances, the negative bromide ion plays a more essential role than is here assumed.   Regardless of the exact nature of the intermediate, however, we shall continue to treat the problem from the above simpler point of view.   It is doubtful if we shall thereby be led into any errors that are important for our present purposes.

Several further reactions analogous to the formation of the halohydrins have been reported.   For example, the addition of bromine to stilbene in methyl alcoholic solution leads to the methoxybromide X,[39] and the

[35] D. S. Tarbell and P. D. Bartlett, *J. Am. Chem. Soc.* **59**, 407 (1937).

[36] I. Roberts and G. E. Kimball, *J. Am. Chem. Soc.* **59**, 947 (1937). For a more recent and somewhat conflicting view, however, see P. B. D. de la Mare and J. G. Pritchard, *J. Chem. Soc.* **1954**, 3990.

[37] S. Winstein and H. J. Lucas, *J. Am. Chem. Soc.* **60**, 836 (1938); **61**, 1576 (1939); H. J. Lucas and C. W. Gould, Jr., *ibid.* **63**, 2541 (1941); S. Winstein and R. E. Buckles, *ibid.* **64**, 2780, 2787 (1942); S. Winstein, *ibid.* **64**, 2791, 2792 (1942); S. Winstein, H. V. Hess, and R. E. Buckles, *ibid.* **64**, 2796 (1942); S. Winstein and R. B. Henderson, *ibid.* **65**, 2196 (1943).

[38] For further discussion of the cationic intermediate, with particular reference to its stereochemical implications, see G. W. Wheland, *Advanced Organic Chemistry*, John Wiley & Sons, New York, 2nd ed., 1949, Section 7·9.

[39] P. D. Bartlett and D. S. Tarbell, *J. Am. Chem. Soc.* **58**, 466 (1936).

addition of bromine to ethylene in the presence of a large concentration of chloride ion or of nitrate ion leads to the bromochloride XI, or to the bromonitrate XII, respectively.[40] None of these reactions involves the

$$C_6H_5\text{—}CH\text{—}CH\text{—}C_6H_5 \qquad H_2C\text{—}CH_2 \qquad H_2C\text{—}CH_2$$
$$\quad\ \ \ |\qquad\ \ |\qquad\qquad\qquad\ |\quad\ \ |\qquad\qquad\ \ |\quad\ \ |$$
$$\quad\ \ \ Br\quad\ OCH_3\qquad\qquad\ Br\ \ Cl\qquad\qquad Br\ \ ONO_2$$

$$\qquad\qquad X \qquad\qquad\qquad\qquad\quad XI \qquad\qquad\qquad XII$$

problem of orientation, because in each the olefin is symmetrical. We could, however, predict that under comparable conditions propylene should give the substances XIII, XIV, and XV. The only one of these

$$CH_3\text{—}CH\text{—}CH_2 \qquad CH_3\text{—}CH\text{—}CH_2 \qquad CH_3\text{—}CH\text{————}CH_2$$
$$\quad\ \ |\qquad\ \ |\qquad\qquad\qquad\ |\quad\ \ |\qquad\qquad\qquad\ |\qquad\qquad |$$
$$CH_3\text{—}O\quad\ Br\qquad\qquad Cl\quad\ Br\qquad\qquad O\text{—}NO_2\quad\ Br$$

$$\qquad\quad XIII \qquad\qquad\qquad\quad XIV \qquad\qquad\qquad\qquad XV$$

reactions that has been studied seems to be the addition of bromine in the presence of chloride ion;[41] the major product is here indeed the bromochloride XIV, although about one-fourth as much of the isomeric product in which the chlorine and bromine atoms are interchanged is also obtained.

When the mixed halogen iodine chloride, ICl, adds to an unsymmetrical olefin, the question of orientation again arises. Thus, with styrene, the product could be either 1-chloro-2-iodo-1-phenylethane, XVI, or 2-chloro-1-iodo-1-phenylethane, XVII (or a mixture of the two). Presumably,

$$C_6H_5\text{—}CHCl\text{—}CH_2I \qquad\qquad C_6H_5\text{—}CHI\text{—}CH_2Cl$$
$$\qquad\qquad XVI \qquad\qquad\qquad\qquad\qquad\ XVII$$

$$CH_3\text{—}CHCl\text{—}CH_2I \qquad\qquad CH_3\text{—}CHI\text{—}CH_2Cl$$
$$\qquad\qquad XVIII \qquad\qquad\qquad\qquad\qquad XIX$$

however, the reaction is initiated by a positive halogen ion, which is more likely to be I^+ than it is to be Cl^+; consequently, the predominant product should have the structure XVI. This expectation has been confirmed by Ingold and Smith,[42] who have found that not less than 95 per cent of the product does indeed have the predicted structure. Similarly, the addition of iodine chloride to propylene should lead principally to 2-chloro-1-iodopropane, XVIII; here, however, the orientation is less one-sided than with styrene since Ingold and Smith[42] have found that the two products XVIII and XIX are formed in a ratio of approximately 2 to 1.

[40] A. W. Francis, *J. Am. Chem. Soc.* 47, 2340 (1925); see also F. N. Hayes, H. K. Suzuki, and D. E. Peterson, *ibid.* 72, 4524 (1950).

[41] W. C. Stickler, personal communication.

[42] C. K. Ingold and H. G. Smith, *J. Chem. Soc.* 1931, 2742; see also H. Ingle, *J. Soc. Chem. Ind. (London)* 21, 587 (1902).

Evidence that bromine chloride, BrCl, adds to styrene with formation of 2-bromo-1-chloro-1-phenylethane, XX, has also been obtained.[43]

$$C_6H_5—CHCl—CH_2Br$$
XX

It was suggested above that the cationic intermediate in the addition of a halogen to an olefin contains a three-membered ring. This possibility somewhat complicates the interpretation of every reaction in which two structurally isomeric products might be formed. In the concluding step of the addition of iodine chloride to styrene, for example, the chloride ion might attack the terminal carbon atom of the ion (which is here represented by the single typical structure XXI) to give 2-chloro-1-iodo-1-phenylethane XVII; or it might instead attack the central carbon atom to give 1-chloro-2-iodo-1-phenylethane, XVI. Since the reaction is observed[42] to go predominantly in the

$$C_6H_5—CH—CH_2$$
\\ /
I+
XXI

second of these two directions, the attack must be considerably easier at the more hindered position than at the less hindered one. Some explanation for this rather unexpected result is clearly required. One possibility is that the ion XXI is never completely free; or, in other words, that the iodine atom is unable to become attached to the styrene molecule unless a chloride ion is coming up at the same time. A second possibility is that the carbon-iodine bond at the left of structure XXI is more readily broken than is the one at the right. This difference in reactivity might, in fact, be anticipated, since our earlier conclusion that a radical reagent will preferentially attack the end of a conjugated system may be considered to imply that the terminal atom of such a system forms a stronger bond than the central one. (Still another view regarding the properties of the ionic intermediate is given by de la Mare and Pritchard.[36])

8·8   Addition to Carbon-Oxygen Double Bonds.[44]   Whereas the reagents which can add to carbon-carbon double bonds have been found to be either electrophilic or radical, those which can add to carbon-oxygen double bonds are on the whole nucleophilic.   In an aldehyde or ketone, for example, the distribution of electric charge is that represented by either of the equivalent structures, I and II.   The carbon atom, therefore,

$$
\begin{array}{cc}
R\diagdown & R\diagdown \\
\quad C \rightrightarrows O & \quad C = O \\
R'\diagup & R'\diagup \\
\text{I} & \text{II}
\end{array}
$$

[43] R. E. Buckles and J. W. Long, *J. Am. Chem. Soc.* **73**, 998 (1951).

[44] For detailed discussions of these reactions, see L. P. Hammett, *Physical Organic Chemistry*, McGraw-Hill Book Co., New York, 1940, Chapter XI; W. F. Luder and S. Zuffanti, *The Electronic Theory of Acids and Bases*, John Wiley & Sons, New York, 1946, pp. 127f, Chapter 11; E. R. Alexander, *Principles of Ionic Organic Reactions*, John Wiley & Sons, New York, 1950, Chapters 8 and 9; C. K. Ingold, *Structure and Mechanism in Organic Chemistry*, Cornell University Press, Ithaca, N. Y., 1953, pp. 676ff.

is a center of electrophilic activity and a point of attack by a nucleophilic reagent.

A characteristic example of a nucleophilic reagent is given by the cyanide ion, CN^-, which not only has an unshared pair of electrons upon the carbon atom but also is negatively charged. The initial product in the reaction with, say, acetaldehyde is presumably the ion III, which then acquires a proton from the solution and becomes the cyanohydrin, IV.

$$CH_3—\overset{\displaystyle CN}{\underset{\displaystyle O^-}{CH}} \qquad\qquad CH_3—\overset{\displaystyle CN}{\underset{\displaystyle OH}{CH}}$$

$$\text{III} \qquad\qquad\qquad\qquad\qquad \text{IV}$$

The formation of an oxime presents a more complex problem. The nucleophilic reagent in this reaction is hydroxylamine, H_2NOH, which has an unshared pair of electrons upon the nitrogen atom. Since the reaction is acid catalyzed, the electrophilic reagent is presumably not the free carbonyl compound, $RR'CO$, but is instead the more actively electrophilic ion $[RR'COH]^+$. The initial product is therefore V. The reaction can now be completed in either one of two ways. With chloral (R = CCl_3, R' = H) a proton is lost to the solution to give the product VI, and with a few other negatively substituted carbonyl compounds the reactions are similar. With acetaldehyde (R = CH_3, R' = H), however, and in general with most remaining aldehydes and ketones, the concluding step consists in the loss of both a proton and a water molecule, with the consequent formation of the oxime VII. Although acids catalyze the

$$\overset{\displaystyle R}{\underset{\displaystyle R'}{}}\!\!\!\!\!>\!\!C\!\!<\!\!\overset{\displaystyle N^+H_2OH}{\underset{\displaystyle OH}{}} \qquad \overset{\displaystyle R}{\underset{\displaystyle R'}{}}\!\!\!\!\!>\!\!C\!\!<\!\!\overset{\displaystyle NHOH}{\underset{\displaystyle OH}{}} \qquad \overset{\displaystyle R}{\underset{\displaystyle R'}{}}\!\!\!\!\!>\!\!C\!\!=\!\!NOH$$

$$\text{V} \qquad\qquad\qquad \text{VI} \qquad\qquad\qquad \text{VII}$$

reaction, as was stated above, they can also act in the opposite sense by changing the hydroxylamine into the ion H_3N^+OH, which can have no nucleophilic activity at all, since it has no unshared pair of electrons. (Similarly, the fact that the cyanohydrin reaction, discussed above, does not occur in too acid solution is to be related to the transformation of the nucleophilic cyanide ion into the nonnucleophilic hydrogen cyanide molecule.) Consequently, the reaction of oxime formation has an optimum pH, at which its rate reaches a maximum value. In strongly basic solution, the rate again increases, doubtless as a result of the transformation of the hydroxylamine into the ion H_2NO^-, which is strongly enough nucleophilic to react rapidly with the carbonyl compound $RR'CO$

itself.   This complex problem has been discussed elsewhere[44] in consider-able detail, and nothing further need be said about it here.

8·9   1,4-Addition to Conjugated Systems.   We have already considered the additions of several different reagents to compounds in which, as with styrene, the multiple bond at which the reaction occurs is part of a conjugated system.   In all the above examples, however, the conjugation has been of importance only in determining the position at which the second reagent attacks, and it has introduced no essential change in the type of reaction that ensues.   More particularly, the additions have involved only individual multiple bonds, even when two or more such bonds are present.   In this section, on the contrary, we shall turn our attention to a group of reactions in which entire conjugated systems are involved so that, in the product that is isolated, more than one multiple bond has been affected.

The addition of bromine to 1,3-butadiene, for example, doubtless proceeds by a mechanism similar to that outlined in Section 8·7 for the addition to propylene.   That is to say, the active reagent is probably a positive bromine ion (or its equivalent) which is necessarily electrophilic. The attack therefore occurs at that point of the butadiene molecule at which an unshared pair of electrons can be most easily provided.   The structures I and II indicate the ways in which an unshared pair can be

$$CH_2{=}CH{-}CH{=}CH_2 \qquad\qquad CH_2{=}CH{-}CH{=}CH_2$$
$$\text{I} \qquad\qquad\qquad\qquad\qquad \text{II}$$

brought to one of the terminal, or to one of the central carbon atoms, respectively, as the molecule is polarized in the reaction.   Clearly, the former process is the easier of the two, because it permits the electrons to be brought from either or both of two atoms instead of from only one. Consequently, the reaction must commence at the terminal atom, so that the initial product is a resonance hybrid of structures III and IV (however, see below).

$$CH_2{=}CH{-}C^+H{-}CH_2 \qquad\qquad C^+H_2{-}CH{=}CH{-}CH_2$$
$$\qquad\qquad\qquad\overset{|}{Br} \qquad\qquad\qquad\qquad\qquad\qquad \overset{|}{Br}$$
$$\text{III} \qquad\qquad\qquad\qquad\qquad\qquad \text{IV}$$

This same conclusion could have been obtained from a completely equivalent but more laborious treatment along the lines followed in Section 8·5.   Thus, the activated complex for reaction at one of the terminal carbon atoms is a hybrid of the structures V, VI, and VII,

$$CH_2{=}CH{-}CH{=}CH_2 \qquad\qquad CH_2{=}CH{-}C^+H{-}CH_2$$
$$\qquad\qquad Br^+ \qquad\qquad\qquad\qquad\qquad\qquad \overset{|}{Br}$$
$$\text{V} \qquad\qquad\qquad\qquad\qquad\qquad \text{VI}$$

whereas that for reaction at one of the central atoms is a hybrid of only VIII and IX. The former complex, therefore, is the more stable and is the one actually formed.

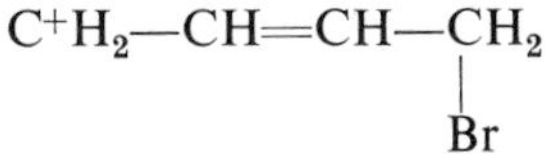

$$C^+H_2—CH\!=\!CH—CH_2$$
$$\underset{\text{VII}}{\overset{|}{Br}}$$

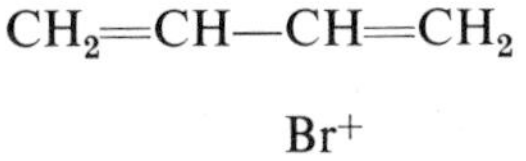

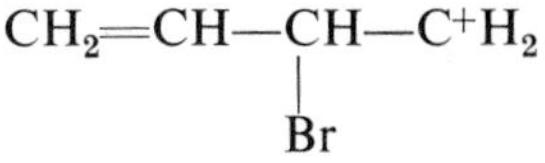

$$CH_2\!=\!CH—CH\!=\!CH_2 \qquad CH_2\!=\!CH—CH—C^+H_2$$
$$\underset{\text{VIII}}{Br^+} \qquad\qquad\qquad \underset{\text{IX}}{\overset{|}{Br}}$$

The foregoing discussion has ignored all structures with formal bonds. Such structures are less stable than the ones considered and make contributions which, for our present purposes, are negligible.

In order to complete the reaction, a negative bromide ion must now come up to produce either the product X (related to the structure III of the intermediate) or else the product XI (related to the structure IV of

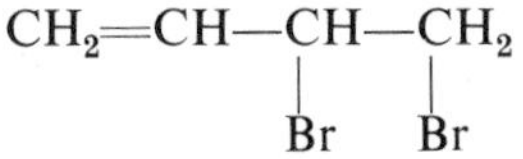

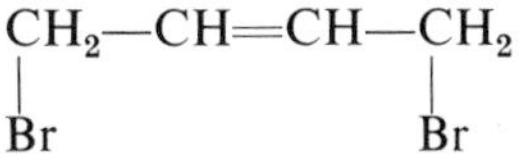

$$CH_2\!=\!CH—CH—CH_2 \qquad CH_2—CH\!=\!CH—CH_2$$
$$\underset{\text{X}}{\overset{|}{Br}\quad\overset{|}{Br}} \qquad\qquad \underset{\text{XI}}{\overset{|}{Br}\qquad\qquad\overset{|}{Br}}$$

the intermediate). In the former event, the net result of the reaction is 1,2-addition to one of the double bonds, whereas, in the latter event, it is 1,4-addition to the conjugated system. We are unable to predict which of the two possible products will predominate, but our discussion has been of value nevertheless in that it has provided a simple and logical explanation for the *possibility* of 1,4-addition.

The proportion of 1,4-dibromo-2-butene, XI, has been reported[45] to vary from 38.4 per cent of the total dibromides isolated, when the addition is carried out in hexane as solvent, to 70.0 per cent, when it is carried out in acetic acid. Although the first of these reactions was performed at $-15°$ and the second at $4°$, the above figures are subject to some small uncertainty, because an equilibrium between the 1,2- and the 1,4-products is established at a rate which increases with temperature. Further experiments[46] on the addition of chlorine to butadiene have shown that, in this completely similar reaction, the 1,4-dichloro-2-butene amounts to about 30 per cent of the total dichlorides isolated, when the addition is carried out in carbon disulfide as solvent. This figure is possibly somewhat more reliable than the corresponding ones for the addition of bromine, because the equilibrium between the two dichlorides is not mobile at the temperature of the experiments.[46, 47]

[45] E. H. Farmer, C. D. Lawrence, and J. F. Thorpe, *J. Chem. Soc.* **1928**, 729.

[46] I. E. Muskat and H. E. Northrup, *J. Am. Chem. Soc.* **52**, 4043 (1930).

[47] K. Mislow and H. M. Hellman, *J. Am. Chem. Soc.* **73**, 244 (1951). Cf. also Ya. M. Slobodin and S. A. Zaboev, *Zhur. Obshcheĭ Khim.* (*J. Gen. Chem.*) **22**, 603 (1952) [*C. A.* **46**, 7433 (1952)]; K. Mislow, *J. Am. Chem. Soc.* **75**, 2512 (1953).

The above discussion has again been greatly oversimplified since it has ignored the cyclic structure of the intermediate cation (see page 454). In a more nearly complete treatment, two possibilities would have to be considered since the ring that contains the halogen atom might be either three-membered, as in structure XII, or five-membered, as in structure XIII. Although, on the basis of the strain theory, we might perhaps

$$CH_2\!\!=\!\!CH\!-\!\!CH\!-\!\!CH_2$$
$$\diagdown\;\diagup$$
$$Br^+$$

$$CH_2$$
$$HC\diagdown$$
$$\|\quad\quad Br^+$$
$$HC\diagup$$
$$\diagdown$$
$$CH_2$$

            XII   XIII

prefer the latter alternative, the former seems to be the correct one;[47] for, in the 1,4-addition of chlorine to 1,3-butadiene, only *trans* 1,4-dichloro-2-butene, $Cl\!-\!CH_2\!-\!CH\!\!=\!\!CH\!-\!CH_2Cl$, is formed. This product could hardly have arisen if the reaction had passed through the necessarily *cis* intermediate XIII; moreover, the observations cannot be explained on the assumption that the *cis* dichlorobutene is initially formed but immediately rearranges to its more stable *trans* isomer for, under the conditions of the experiment, no such interconversion occurs.[47] We cannot, however, be extremely surprised that the smaller ring should thus be preferred over the larger one, since we have no evidence that the strain theory applies to structures like XII, in which the halogen atoms, and possibly also the carbon atoms (cf. page 454 and also below), are in exceptional valence states.

If, as has just been concluded, the intermediate cation that is involved in the reaction between bromine and 1,3-butadiene has the cyclic structure XII, our earlier interpretation of the 1,4-addition needs to be reexamined and made more precise. Since the carbon-bromine bonds within the three-membered ring are doubtless extremely weak, the intermediate may be presumed to be a hybrid receiving large contributions not only from structure XII but also from structures V, VI, VII, and IX, which should now be rewritten in the modified forms V*a*, VI*a*, VII*a*, and IX*a*, respectively.

$$CH_2\!\!=\!\!CH\!-\!\!CH\!\!=\!\!CH_2$$
$$Br^+$$
      V*a*

$$CH_2\!\!=\!\!CH\!-\!C^+H\!-\!CH_2$$
$$\diagup$$
$$Br$$
      VI*a*

$$C^+H_2\!-\!CH\!\!=\!\!CH\!-\!CH_2$$
$$\diagup$$
$$Br$$
      VII*a*

$$CH_2\!\!=\!\!CH\!-\!CH\!-\!C^+H_2$$
$$\diagdown$$
$$Br$$
      IX*a*

Since, in the concluding step of the reaction, a bromide ion may become attached to the carbon atom that carries the formal positive charge in any one of these structures, either 1,2- or 1,4-addition should be possible. Again, however, just as in our original treatment, we cannot predict the relative amounts of the two products formed.

In the addition of hydrogen chloride to 1,3-butadiene, the proton should initiate the reaction by attacking one of the terminal carbon atoms to give a cation that is a hybrid of structures XIV and XV. The isolable product should therefore be either 3-chloro-1-butene, XVI, or 1-chloro-2-butene, XVII, or a mixture of the two. Both of these unsaturated

$$CH_2{=}CH{-}C^+H{-}CH_3 \qquad\qquad C^+H_2{-}CH{=}CH{-}CH_3$$
$$\text{XIV} \qquad\qquad\qquad\qquad\quad \text{XV}$$

$$CH_2{=}CH{-}CHCl{-}CH_3 \qquad\qquad CH_2Cl{-}CH{=}CH{-}CH_3$$
$$\text{XVI} \qquad\qquad\qquad\qquad\quad\ \text{XVII}$$

chlorides are, in fact, obtained;[48] the former accounts for about 75–80 per cent of the total product, the latter for about 25–20 per cent. In the corresponding reaction of isoprene, the two ends of the conjugated system are not equivalent, and so the proton need not attack both with equal ease. If the hyperconjugation that is made possible by the methyl group is taken into account, the polarizations which bring the required pairs of electrons to the terminal unsaturated atoms can be represented by the structures XVIII and XIX; since the first of these polarizations should be

$$\overset{\curvearrowleft}{C}H_2{=}C\overset{\curvearrowleft}{-}CH{=}CH_2 \qquad\qquad CH_2{=}C\overset{\curvearrowright}{-}CH\overset{\curvearrowright}{=}CH_2$$
$$\underset{\text{XVIII}}{\overset{|}{\underset{}{C}}H_2{-}H} \qquad\qquad\qquad \underset{\text{XIX}}{\overset{|}{C}H_2{-}H}$$

more effective than the second, the proton may be expected to attack the methylene group that is nearer to the methyl group. Consequently, the product should be either 3-chloro-3-methyl-1-butene, XX, or 4-chloro-2-methyl-2-butene, XXI, or both. Jones and Chorley have reported[49] that only the latter substance is formed, and hence that the addition is exclusively 1,4. Although the interpretation of this observation is made somewhat obscure by the possibility of a ready interconversion of the two allylic chlorides XX and XXI (cf. Section 8·14), the nonoccurrence of

$$CH_3{-}CCl{-}CH{=}CH_2 \qquad\qquad CH_3{-}C{=}CH{-}CH_2Cl$$
$$\underset{\text{XX}}{\overset{|}{C}H_3} \qquad\qquad\qquad\qquad \underset{\text{XXI}}{\overset{|}{C}H_3}$$

[48] M. S. Kharasch, J. Kritchevsky, and F. R. Mayo, *J. Org. Chem.* **2**, 489 (1937).
[49] W. J. Jones and H. W. T. Chorley, *J. Chem. Soc.* **1946**, 832.

either 3-chloro-2-methyl-1-butene, XXII, or 1-chloro-2-methyl-2-butene, XXIII, shows that the initial attack by the proton must have been at the position predicted.

$$CH_2=C-CHCl-CH_3 \qquad\qquad CH_2Cl-C=CH-CH_3$$
$$| \qquad\qquad\qquad\qquad\qquad\qquad\qquad |$$
$$CH_3 \qquad\qquad\qquad\qquad\qquad\qquad CH_3$$
$$\text{XXII} \qquad\qquad\qquad\qquad\qquad \text{XXIII}$$

When hydrogen chloride adds to an α,β-unsaturated acid, such as acrylic acid, the reaction doubtless begins as usual with the addition of a proton at the end of the conjugated system. In this reaction, two possibilities exist, as is shown in the structures XXIV and XXV for the original

$$CH_2=CH-C=O \qquad\qquad CH_2=CH-C=O$$
$$| \qquad\qquad\qquad\qquad\qquad\qquad |$$
$$OH \qquad\qquad\qquad\qquad\qquad OH$$
$$\text{XXIV} \qquad\qquad\qquad\qquad \text{XXV}$$

acrylic acid. Since oxygen is a more electronegative element than carbon, the first of these modes of polarization must presumably be the more easily effected, and consequently the initial product should be a hybrid of the three structures XXVI, XXVII, and XXVIII. (Here, and

$$CH_2=CH-C=O^+H \quad CH_2=CH-C^+-OH \quad C^+H_2-CH=C-OH$$
$$| \qquad\qquad\qquad\qquad | \qquad\qquad\qquad\qquad |$$
$$OH \qquad\qquad\qquad\qquad OH \qquad\qquad\qquad\qquad OH$$
$$\text{XXVI} \qquad\qquad\qquad \text{XXVII} \qquad\qquad\qquad \text{XXVIII}$$

below, the resonance within the carboxyl group itself may be ignored as not affecting the final conclusions reached.) When this ion acquires a chloride ion, to complete the reaction, the resulting neutral molecule might be either XXIX, by 1,2-addition, or XXX, by 1,4-addition. The former structure, however, is of a type known to be unstable. If such a molecule were formed, it would presumably break up again immediately to regenerate the hydrogen chloride and acrylic acid; we therefore need consider it no further. A molecule with the second structure, XXX, would also be unstable but, if it were formed, it could rearrange irreversibly to the stable keto form XXXI, and it would not be restricted to merely

$$CH_2=CH-C-OH \quad CH_2-CH=C-OH \quad CH_2-CH_2-C=O$$
$$\diagup \diagdown \qquad\qquad | \qquad\qquad | \qquad\qquad | \qquad\qquad |$$
$$Cl \quad OH \qquad Cl \qquad OH \qquad Cl \qquad OH$$
$$\text{XXIX} \qquad\qquad\quad \text{XXX} \qquad\qquad\quad \text{XXXI}$$

decomposing into the original reactants. This is apparently what happens, since the product that is obtained is indeed the β-chloropropionic acid XXXI. It is to be noted that the addition has occurred in violation of

Markovnikov's rule, but that the mechanism is probably entirely different from that involved in the peroxide-induced addition of hydrogen bromide to an olefin. With the remaining α,β-unsaturated acids, and with the α,β-unsaturated aldehydes and ketones, the reaction would be expected to follow the same course as with acrylic acid; in all these reactions the chlorine atom (or, in general, the halogen atom) actually ends in the β position, regardless of Markovnikov's rule, and in agreement with expectation.

The above discussion of acrylic acid may seem inconsistent with the conclusion, reached in Section 3·2, that the carbonyl part of a carboxyl group cannot be effectively conjugated with an ethylenic double bond. This conclusion was derived, however, only for normal, unreacting molecules, and may not be valid when applied to activated complexes. Indeed, the structures XXVI, XXVII, and XXVIII, above, seem to be of not very different energy, so that resonance among them might be expected to produce an appreciable stabilization. In any event, there can be little doubt that an oxonium cation which is a hybrid of structures XXVI, XXVII, and XXVIII is actually formed to some extent in strongly acid solution.

In the addition of hydrogen chloride to cinnamic acid, the proton should again initiate the reaction by attacking the oxygen atom of the carbonyl group. The product should therefore be β-chlorohydrocinnamic acid, C_6H_5—CHCl—CH_2—CO_2H, as it is indeed found to be. It is of interest that there is here no uncertainty analogous to the one regarding the point of attack by a radical reagent upon the closely related methyl cinnamate (cf. page 452).

Nucleophilic reagents also have a tendency preferentially to attack the end of a conjugated system, unless other factors intervene. An α,β-unsaturated carbonyl compound is seen from structure XXXII to have

$$R-CH\!\!=\!\!CH-C\!\!=\!\!O$$
$$\mid$$
$$R$$

XXXII

centers of electrophilic activity at the carbonyl carbon atom and at the β position. (A phenyl group is sometimes included in the conjugated system, as with benzalacetophenone and cinnamic aldehyde, discussed below. Addition to such compounds would hardly be expected to be initiated in the ring, however, since then the large stabilization resulting from resonance between the Kekulé structures would necessarily be lost. Consequently, reactions proceeding in such a way, although occasionally encountered are not the general rule.) The β position is at the end of the conjugated system, but the carbonyl carbon atom is closer to the electronegative oxygen atom that provides the driving force for the electronic shift (which was found in Section 5·4 to be appreciable even in the unreacting, unpolarized molecule). Apparently, the two factors are fairly evenly balanced. Benzalacetophenone, XXXIII, for example, can react with a nucleophilic reagent either at the carbonyl carbon atom or at the β position, depending upon the reagent and upon the conditions.

$$C_6H_5—CH{=}CH—C{=}O \qquad\qquad C_6H_5—CH{=}CH—CH{=}O$$
$$\underset{\displaystyle C_6H_5}{|}$$
$$\text{XXXIII} \qquad\qquad\qquad\qquad\qquad \text{XXXIV}$$

With hydroxylamine, it forms an oxime in the usual way in acid solution, but it behaves in a much more complex manner in basic solution and reacts at least partially at the β position.[50]   Cinnamic aldehyde, XXXIV, reacts by 1,2-addition with sodium malonic ester to form the compound XXXV, whereas benzalacetophenone reacts by 1,4-addition with the same reagent to give the product XXXVI.   The actual nucleophilic reagent in

$$C_6H_5—CH{=}CH—CH{=}C(CO_2C_2H_5)_2$$
$$\text{XXXV}$$

$$C_6H_5—CH—CH_2—CO—C_6H_5$$
$$\underset{\displaystyle CH(CO_2C_2H_5)_2}{|}$$
$$\text{XXXVI}$$

these last two reactions is doubtless the negative ion $[HC(CO_2C_2H_5)_2]^-$. Just as in the addition of bromine to butadiene, the present theory does not make possible a prediction of the actual mode of addition, but it does account for the possibility of 1,4- as well as 1,2-addition.

The addition of Grignard reagents to α,β-unsaturated compounds seems to be analogous to the addition of sodium malonic ester, since a negative organic ion, or its equivalent, may be assumed to be involved.   Such an obviously nucleophilic reagent would be expected to attack either the carbon atom of the carbonyl group or the one in the β position, so that either 1,2- or 1,4-addition could result as before.   This conclusion is in agreement with experiment.[51]   However, a detailed discussion of the complex problem would seem especially dangerous, in view of the surprisingly great, and not yet completely understood, effect which traces of metal salts have been found to exert upon the courses of such reactions.[52]

When a radical reagent reacts with a conjugated system, it also should attack the terminal position since, as we showed in Section 8·6, this

[50] K. v. Auwers and H. Müller, *J. prakt. Chem.* **137**, 57 (1933).

[51]For examples, see E. P. Kohler, *Am. Chem. J.* **38**, 511 (1907); C. F. H. Allen and A. H. Blatt in H. Gilman, *Organic Chemistry*, John Wiley & Sons, New York, 1st ed., 1938, vol. I, pp. 581ff; 2nd ed., 1943, vol. I, pp. 672ff.

[52] M. S. Kharasch and P. O. Tawney, *J. Am. Chem. Soc.* **63**, 2308 (1941); M. S. Kharasch and D. C. Sayles, *ibid.* **64**, 2972 (1942).

position is the one at which a single unpaired electron can be most easily provided. The additions which are of this type, and which have been most carefully studied, are those leading to the polymerization of the unsaturated compounds (cf. Section 8·10). Since, however, these latter reactions seem relatively seldom to involve 1,4-addition, we shall here consider only a few miscellaneous examples in which polymerization is not the important feature.

The addition of hydrogen bromide to acrylic acid (as to any other α,β-unsaturated acid, aldehyde, or ketone) is unaffected by the presence of peroxides. This fact is easily accounted for by the present theory. Under peroxide-free conditions, the hydrogen bromide presumably acts as an electrophilic reagent and so behaves in exactly the same way as hydrogen chloride, which has been considered previously. The product of the addition is therefore β-bromopropionic acid. In the presence of peroxides, the hydrogen bromide may act as a radical reagent, and, if so, the reaction should be initiated by the attack of a bromine atom at the end of the conjugated system to give either XXXVII or XXXVIII. There

$$CH_2-\overset{\bullet}{C}H-\underset{\underset{\displaystyle OH}{|}}{C}=O \qquad\qquad CH_2=CH-\underset{\underset{\displaystyle OH}{|}}{\overset{\bullet}{C}}-OBr$$
$$\underset{\displaystyle Br}{|}$$

$$\text{XXXVII} \qquad\qquad\qquad \text{XXXVIII}$$

can be little question that the first of these must be the one actually formed, since the second could hardly lead to any stable final product. The result of the addition must therefore be again β-bromopropionic acid, just as in the absence of peroxides. It is interesting that in this reaction a change in mechanism cannot reverse the direction of addition, as it does with propylene or even with such conjugated systems as styrene. (In regard to the question of conjugation in acrylic acid, see the paragraph in fine print on page 463.)

A rather different kind of reaction between a radical reagent and a conjugated olefin is presented by the addition of hexaphenylethane to butadiene.[53] The first step is undoubtedly the addition of a triphenylmethyl radical to one end of the butadiene molecule to form an initial product that is a hybrid of structures XXXIX and XL. The reaction is

$$(C_6H_5)_3C-CH_2-\overset{\bullet}{C}H-CH=CH_2 \qquad (C_6H_5)_3C-CH_2-CH=CH-\overset{\bullet}{C}H_2$$
$$\text{XXXIX} \qquad\qquad\qquad\qquad \text{XL}$$

$$(C_6H_5)_3C-CH_2-CH=CH-CH_2-C(C_6H_5)_3$$
$$\text{XLI}$$

[53] J. B. Conant and B. F. Chow, *J. Am. Chem. Soc.* **55**, 3475 (1933).

then completed by a second triphenylmethyl radical. As might have been anticipated on steric grounds, the addition is 1,4 instead of 1,2 so that the final product is XLI.

Still another reaction which possibly involves a 1,4-addition to a conjugated system is that between benzenediazonium chloride and methyl cinnamalacetate, XLII.[33] Although the initial product was here not fully characterized, it was doubtless either methyl 5-chloro-2,5-diphenyl-3-pentenoate, XLIII, or methyl 3-chloro-2,5-diphenyl-4-pentenoate, XLIV, since, on dehydrochlorination by the action of potassium hydroxide,

$$C_6H_5—CH\!=\!CH—CH\!=\!CH—CO_2CH_3 \qquad\qquad C_6H_5—CHCl—CH\!=\!CH—CH—CO_2CH_3$$

$$\underset{\text{XLII}}{} \qquad\qquad\qquad\qquad\qquad \overset{|}{\underset{\underset{\text{XLIII}}{C_6H_5}}{}}$$

$$C_6H_5—CH\!=\!CH—CHCl—CH—CO_2CH_3 \qquad\qquad C_6H_5—CH\!=\!CH—CH\!=\!C—CO_2CH_3$$

$$\overset{|}{\underset{\underset{\text{XLIV}}{C_6H_5}}{}} \qquad\qquad\qquad\qquad\qquad \overset{|}{\underset{\underset{\text{XLV}}{C_6H_5}}{}}$$

it was transformed into a methyl α-phenylcinnamalacetate, XLV. In either event, the phenyl radical must have attacked the position that is α to the carbomethoxy group and hence at the end of the conjugated system $C_6H_5—C\!=\!C—C\!=\!C$ (cf. page 452).

8·10   Polymerization of Olefins.[54]   When isobutylene is treated with sulfuric acid, it is changed into a complex mixture of polymers containing the two isomeric diisobutylenes I and II, a number of isomeric triisobutylenes, and also some higher polymers. Since the original isobutylene

$$CH_2\!=\!\overset{\overset{\displaystyle |}{}}{\underset{\underset{\displaystyle I}{CH_3}}{C}}—CH_2—C(CH_3)_3 \qquad\qquad CH_3—\overset{\overset{\displaystyle |}{}}{\underset{\underset{\displaystyle II}{CH_3}}{C}}\!=\!CH—C(CH_3)_3$$

is an unsymmetrical olefin, there exist several conceivable ways in which the molecules could be linked to each other in the polymerization. For example, the carbon skeleton of a diisobutylene might be that represented by either III or IV, and the further skeleton V, although impossible for an olefin, might appear in a derived alcohol, sulfate, or the like. The fact that only the first of these skeletons seems to be formed means that

[54] See C. S. Marvel and E. C. Horning, in H. Gilman, *Organic Chemistry*, John Wiley & Sons, New York, 2nd ed., 1943, vol. I, pp. 739ff; G. Egloff, *ibid.*, pp. 10ff. See also *The Chemistry of Large Molecules* (R. E. Burk and O. Grummitt, editors), Interscience Publishers, New York, 1943; the chapters by H. Mark (pp. 1ff) and by C. S. Marvel (pp. 219ff) are of particular interest with respect to the present discussion. More recent surveys of the field include C. C. Price, *Mechanisms of Reactions at Carbon-Carbon Double Bonds*, Interscience Publishers, New York, 1946, Chapters IV–VII; C. E. H. Bawn, *The Chemistry of High Polymers*, Interscience Publishers, New York, 1948; M. J. S. Dewar, *The Electronic Theory of Organic Chemistry*, Oxford University Press, Oxford, 1949, Chapter XIV. See also the comprehensive series of monographs entitled High Polymers, published by Interscience Publishers, New York, 1940–.

the reaction leading to this particular arrangement of atoms is much faster than is either of those leading to the other two. We shall find it interesting to consider the reason for this difference in rates.

The first step in the polymerization of isobutylene by sulfuric acid presumably consists in the acquisition of a proton, which is an electrophilic reagent, by the organic molecule. The resulting positive ion could be either VI or VII, but, as should be apparent from the discussion in

$$(CH_3)_2C^+\!\!-CH_3 \qquad\qquad (CH_3)_2C\!-\!C^+H_2$$
$$\qquad\qquad\qquad\qquad\qquad\qquad\qquad\quad |$$
$$\qquad\qquad\qquad\qquad\qquad\qquad\qquad\quad H$$

VI   VII

Section 8·5, the first of these must be formed in preference to the second. On being changed into the ion VI, the molecule of isobutylene, which was originally a nucleophilic reagent, becomes a powerful electrophilic one. Its center of electrophilic activity is situated at the central carbon atom, since this has an open sextet of electrons. Consequently, in the subsequent reaction between the ion and a second molecule of isobutylene, the more complex ion VIII must be formed by union of the two reagents

$$(CH_3)_2C^+\!\!-CH_2\!-\!C(CH_3)_3$$

VIII

at their most electrophilic and nucleophilic positions, respectively. Several possibilities now arise. On the one hand, the ion VIII may lose a proton to give one or the other of the two neutral diisobutylenes I and II; on the other hand, this ion may react further with unchanged isobutylene to yield ultimately either a triisobutylene or else a still more highly polymerized product.

The known structures of the triisobutylenes, 2,2,4,6,6-pentamethyl-3-heptene and 1,1-di-neopentylethylene, suggest that these substances are formed by the attack of the *tert*-butyl cation VI upon the diisobutylene I, and not by further reaction of the ion VIII.

The polymerization of styrene has been studied rather more carefully than that of isobutylene. It is of particular interest in that it can be brought about not only by an electrophilic but also by either a radical or a nucleophilic reagent as well.   For example, stannic chloride, the phenyl radical, and triphenylmethyl sodium are effective (together with numerous further reagents of all three types).   The first of these is electrophilic, because the octet of electrons about the tin atom can be expanded to include as many as twelve electrons; the second, which can be generated in the reaction mixture (along with the benzoate, or benzoyloxy, radical, C_6H_5—CO—O) by the thermal decomposition of benzoyl peroxide, is obviously a radical reagent; and the last is a powerfully nucleophilic reagent because it contains the triphenylmethyl anion.   The mechanism of the polymerization and the essential part of the structure of the polymer are probably very similar for the three different types of reaction and can be discussed together.   We shall let the symbol R represent the stannic chloride molecule, the phenyl (or the benzoate) radical, or the triphenylmethyl anion, as the case may be; and we shall let the letter z represent a vacancy (capable of accommodating a pair of electrons), a single unpaired electron, or an unshared pair of electrons, respectively. (When R is electrophilic or nucleophilic, the letter z may imply in addition a positive or negative charge, respectively.)   In each of the reactions, the first step is presumably an attack by the reagent R upon the terminal carbon atom of a styrene molecule, to give the product IX.   The electrophilic, radical, or nucleophilic activity, which is indicated by the latter z,

$$C_6H_5—\overset{z}{C}H—CH_2—R$$
$$\text{IX}$$

is thereby transferred to the carbon atom attached directly to the benzene ring in this initial product.   (See the paragraph following the one in fine print below.)   Consequently, the second and subsequent steps should lead successively to the products X, XI, XII, and so on.   The polymerization is therefore presumably of the "head-to-tail" type, regardless of the

$$zCH—CH_2—CH—CH_2R \qquad zCH—CH_2—CH—CH_2—CH—CH_2R$$
$$\;\;\;|\qquad\qquad\;\;|\qquad\qquad\qquad\;\;|\qquad\qquad\;\;\;|\qquad\qquad\;\;\;|$$
$$\;\;C_6H_5\qquad\;\;C_6H_5\qquad\qquad\;\;C_6H_5\qquad\;\;C_6H_5\qquad\;\;C_6H_5$$
$$\qquad\qquad\text{X}\qquad\qquad\qquad\qquad\qquad\qquad\text{XI}$$

$$zCH—CH_2—CH—CH_2—CH—CH_2—CH—CH_2R$$
$$\;\;\;|\qquad\qquad\;\;|\qquad\qquad\;\;\;|\qquad\qquad\;\;\;|$$
$$\;\;C_6H_5\qquad\;\;C_6H_5\qquad\;\;C_6H_5\qquad\;\;C_6H_5$$
$$\qquad\qquad\text{XII}$$

nature of the reagent which induces it.   On the whole, this conclusion seems to be in satisfactory agreement with the facts.   The dimer that is formed when the polymerization is brought about by an electrophilic reagent like sulfuric acid has been identified[55] as the "head-to-tail" product XIII; and the polymers of high molecular weight that are formed

$$CH{=}CH{-}CH{-}CH_3$$
$$\underset{C_6H_5}{|} \qquad \underset{C_6H_5}{|}$$

XIII

with various different reagents seem also to be predominantly "head-to-tail," although, in these, some randomness of orientation may possibly exist.[54] (See, however, the discussion of the polymerization by sodium below in this section.)

Several features of the above mechanism merit further discussion. In the first place, each styrene molecule is considered to react initially at its terminal carbon atom or, in other words, at the end of its conjugated system, whether the polymerization is induced by an electrophilic, radical, or nucleophilic reagent. The reason for this identical behavior has already been given in the preceding sections and need not be repeated here. It is of especial interest, however, that electrophilic and nucleophilic reagents attack styrene at the same position; this fact could hardly have been explained on the basis of the Class A structures of the activated complex, because the two types of reagent would be expected to be affected differently by the distribution of charge (whatever it may be) in the styrene molecule.

Although independent experimental evidence was advanced in Sections 8·5 and 8·6 to show that electrophilic and radical reagents actually do attack styrene in the manner indicated above, similar evidence showing the behavior of nucleophilic reagents is more difficult to obtain, because a reagent of this type, if it is active enough to react at all, ordinarily polymerizes the styrene. A close analogy, however, is provided by the reaction[56]

$$(C_6H_5)_2C{=}CH_2 + C_6H_5C(CH_3)_2K \rightarrow (C_6H_5)_2C{-}CH_2{-}C(CH_3)_2C_6H_5$$
$$\underset{K}{|}$$

in which the nucleophilic phenylisopropyl anion attacks the 1,1-diphenylethylene molecule at the terminal position, as expected. Bartlett, Friedman, and Stiles have also obtained evidence that, when propylene is treated with isopropyl lithium, the primary attack by the isopropyl anion is upon the carbon atom of the methylene group.[57]

[55] R. Stoermer and H. Kootz, *Ber.* **61**, 2330 (1928); J. Risi and D. Gauvin, *Can. J. Research* **14**, 255 (1936).

[56] K. Ziegler and K. Bähr, *Ber.* **61**, 253 (1928). For additional related reactions, see W. D. McPhee and E. G. Lindstrom, *J. Am. Chem. Soc.* **65**, 2177 (1943), and further references given there.

[57] P. D. Bartlett, S. Friedman, and M. Stiles, *J. Am. Chem. Soc.* **75**, 1771 (1953).

A second feature which here requires comment is that the unstable intermediate which was represented above by the structure IX must be a hybrid also of certain additional quinoid structures in which the center of electrophilic, radical, or nucleophilic activity (represented by the letter z) is upon an ortho or para position of the ring. There can, however, be no doubt that the subsequent reaction of this intermediate will take place at the atom which is designated by the z in structure IX; for, if any alternative course were followed, the aromatic character of the ring would have to be destroyed, or else the carbon-hydrogen bond at the point of reaction would have to be broken. Since neither of these possibilities seems likely, we can therefore be confident that the polymerization will occur in the way originally stated. Similarly, with the more complex intermediates that were represented by structures X, XI, and XII, there must again be resonance with quinoid structures; as before, however, this resonance does not require any modification of the foregoing discussion.

A further point of interest in connection with the proposed mechanism of polymerization of styrene is that the reagent R is not necessarily regenerated but instead may be contained in the final polymer. In the latter event, it is therefore not strictly a catalyst, even though only a trace of it may be required to polymerize a large quantity of styrene. This is because a molecule of the polymer may contain an enormous number of styrene residues but only a single R. And finally, it should be noted that the polymerization must terminate in some way, since it cannot continue forever. Clearly, therefore, there must be a further reaction which we have not considered, and which destroys the active electrophilic, radical, or nucleophilic center. The nature of this reaction, and hence of the "end group," is not completely established; it doubtless varies with the substance being polymerized and with the experimental conditions. This uncertainty has no direct bearing, however, upon the problems in which we are at present primarily interested, namely, the mechanisms of the polymerizations themselves and the structures of the polymers, exclusive of the end groups.

When the product that is formed from styrene contains both the group R which initiated the reaction and also some second end group at the other end of the chain, it cannot in general have exactly the same composition as the original unsaturated compound. Consequently, such a product is not strictly a polymer, and the reaction by which it is formed is not strictly a polymerization. For this reason, some authors[58] have adopted the alternative words *telomer* and *telomerization*, respectively. We shall here, however, retain the older, less precise but more familiar expressions.

[58] M. D. Peterson and A. G. Weber, U.S. **2,395,292**, Feb. 19, 1946 [*C. A.* **40**, 3463 (1946)].

The polymerization of styrene by metallic sodium may be of the radical type inasmuch as a sodium atom has a single unpaired electron. An alternative mechanism is possible, however. The first step in the polymerization may consist in the addition of two atoms of sodium to a molecule of styrene to give the substance XIV. This can now induce

$$C_6H_5-CH-CH_2$$
$$\underset{Na}{|} \quad \underset{Na}{|}$$
XIV

polymerization in the same way as the nucleophilic triphenylmethyl sodium, which it closely resembles. If this interpretation is correct, the next step in the polymerization should be the reaction of the disodium compound XIV with a second molecule of styrene to give the product XV. The reason for this "head-to-head," instead of the usual "head-to-tail," polymerization is that the terminal carbon atom of the disodium

$$C_6H_5-CH-CH_2-CH_2-CH-C_6H_5$$
$$\underset{Na}{|} \qquad\qquad \underset{Na}{|}$$
XV

compound XIV must be the seat of its greatest nucleophilic activity, inasmuch as sodium methyl is more strongly nucleophilic than sodium benzyl. This second phase of the reaction is therefore analogous to the well-known "dimerizing addition" of sodium to 1,1-diphenylethylene, to yield the product XVI.[59] When once the substance XV has been formed,

$$(C_6H_5)_2C-CH_2-CH_2-C(C_6H_5)_2$$
$$\underset{Na}{|} \qquad\qquad \underset{Na}{|}$$
XVI

the subsequent reactions, which can proceed in both directions simultaneously, should be "head-to-tail" as in the polymerization by triphenylmethyl sodium, so that the structure of the final polymer can be expressed as XVII. This interpretation provides a possible way of reconciling the

$$\cdots-CH-CH_2-CH-CH_2-CH_2-CH-CH_2-CH-\cdots$$
$$\underset{C_6H_5}{|} \quad \underset{C_6H_5}{|} \qquad \underset{C_6H_5}{|} \qquad \underset{C_6H_5}{|}$$
XVII

chemical evidence supporting a predominantly "head-to-tail" arrangement in polystyrene[54] with the fact that, when the polymerization by sodium is stopped at the dimeric stage by being conducted in alcoholic

[59] W. Schlenk, J. Appenrodt, A. Michael, and A. Thal, *Ber.* **47**, 473 (1914).

solution, the substance isolated is the "head-to-head" product, 1,4-diphenylbutane.[60]

Isobutylene and styrene are not the only unsaturated compounds that can be polymerized by the action of electrophilic, radical, or nucleophilic reagents. 1,3-Butadiene, vinyl chloride, acrylonitrile, methyl methacrylate, and others that are too numerous to be listed here (however, see below) behave in very much the same way as the two substances already considered; and, in many instances, they lead to technically important rubber-like polymers and plastics. In all such reactions that have as yet been studied, the mechanisms of the polymerizations of the resulting polymers can easily be interpreted by suitable extensions of the treatments outlined above. Consequently, since no further discussion of the general principles that are here involved should now be necessary, we shall devote the remainder of this section to a consideration of certain special complications that are encountered only when the material which is to be polymerized is not a single pure substance but is instead a mixture of two or more different substances.[61]

In the polymerization of a mixture, several quite dissimilar types of reaction can be imagined, and examples illustrating many of these types have been found. Thus, it is conceivable that each monomer which is present may react only with itself; the product is then a mixture of polymers each of which is derived from only a single monomer. This first possibility can be realized, for example, in the radical-induced polymerization of a mixture containing styrene and vinyl acetate. The explanation for this behavior is here that the first of the two substances is polymerized much faster than the second, and that, consequently, the reaction of the styrene is essentially complete before that of the vinyl acetate has more than started. A further situation that would also lead to a mixture of polymers is one in which the different monomers are polymerized at comparable rates but just do not react with each other; no examples of such polymerization have as yet been encountered.

A quite different type of polymerization, to which the term *copolymerization* is commonly applied, occurs when a mixture of monomers gives rise to a single homogeneous polymer that contains units derived from each monomer present. This is the most common situation, and the only one of practical importance. Even when the reaction follows this course, there are several possibilities that require consideration since, in the polymer chain, the monomer units may be arranged either at random or

[60] T. Midgley, Jr., A. L. Henne, and H. M. Leicester, *J. Am. Chem. Soc.* **58**, 1961 (1936).

[61] For a comprehensive survey of the field, and for references to the original literature, see F. R. Mayo and C. Walling, *Chem. Revs.* **46**, 191 (1950).

in accordance with some fairly definite pattern. Since the experimental methods which have been devised[61] for distinguishing between these two possibilities are complicated, and since they are not really pertinent to the present discussion, we shall here, after noting that such methods exist, merely consider a few of the more interesting conclusions to which they have led.

When a mixture of styrene and p-methoxystyrene is polymerized under free-radical conditions, the two monomers enter the polymer chain almost at random. In other words, if a single step in the polymerization is represented in general terms by the equation

$$CH{=}CH_2 \qquad \overset{\cdot}{C}H{-}CH_2{-}\cdots \qquad \overset{\cdot}{C}H{-}CH_2{-}CH{-}CH_2{-}\cdots$$

$$\underset{X}{\bigcirc} \quad + \quad \underset{Y}{\bigcirc} \quad \rightarrow \quad \underset{X}{\bigcirc} \quad \underset{Y}{\bigcirc}$$

(cf. pages 468f), the rate is approximately the same if $X = Y = H$, if $X = Y = O{-}CH_3$, if $X = H$ and $Y = O{-}CH_3$, and if $X = O{-}CH_3$ and $Y = H$. Apparently, therefore, the p-methoxyl group has little effect either upon the reactivity of the free radical at the left of the arrow in the above equation or upon that of the styrene molecule. This approximate equality of rates is, however, a relatively rare occurrence. One might, in fact, expect that, with any group of monomers, some of the compounds should be more reactive than others, but that the order of increasing reactivity should be more or less independent of the identity of the attacking free radical. Within the rather important limitations that are more fully described below, this expectation is in fair agreement with the observations. Thus, under free-radical conditions, the rate at which styrene units enter a copolymer is usually greater than that at which allyl chloride units enter. Consequently, in the copolymerization of these two monomers, the radicals both of the type XVIII and of the type XIX

$$C_6H_5{-}\overset{\cdot}{C}H{-}CH_2{-}\cdots \qquad\qquad Cl{-}\overset{\cdot}{C}H{-}CH_2{-}\cdots$$
$$\text{XVIII} \qquad\qquad\qquad\qquad \text{XIX}$$

combine with styrene more rapidly than with allyl chloride. If equivalent quantities of these monomers are initially present, therefore, the more reactive one is preferentially removed, so that the mixture becomes progressively richer in the less reactive monomer, and the composition of the polymer that is being formed changes as the reaction proceeds.

Although the idea that monomers can be arranged in an order of increasing (or decreasing) reactivity therefore has some validity, its usefulness is limited by the existence of certain rather specific interactions which often lead to discrepancies. An extreme example of this behavior is provided by maleic anhydride and stilbene. Under (free-radical) conditions under which neither of these substances is polymerized by itself, a mixture of the two can readily be converted into a copolymer of high molecular weight. Regardless of the composition of the original mixture, the copolymer always contains exactly equivalent amounts of the two monomers. The only reasonable explanation for these observations is that a radical of the type XX can combine with a molecule of stilbene but not with one of maleic anhydride, whereas a radical of the type XXI can

$$HC\!\!-\!\!-\!\!CH\!\!-\!\!\cdots \qquad\qquad C_6H_5\!\!-\!\!CH\!\!-\!\!CH\!\!-\!\!\cdots$$

$$\underset{O}{\overset{}{}}C\!\!-\!\!O\!\!-\!\!C\!\!\underset{O}{\overset{}{}} \qquad\qquad\qquad C_6H_5$$

$$\text{XX} \qquad\qquad\qquad\qquad \text{XXI}$$

combine with a molecule of maleic anhydride but not with one of stilbene. In the copolymer, therefore, there must be a strict alternation of stilbene and maleic anhydride units. A less extreme example is provided by styrene and methyl methacrylate. In a mixture containing equivalent quantities of these monomers, a radical of the type XXII is about twice

$$CH_3\!\!-\!\!O\!\!-\!\!CO\!\!-\!\!C\!\!-\!\!CH_2\!\!-\!\!\cdots$$

$$CH_3$$

$$\text{XXII}$$

as likely to attack a molecule of styrene as it is to attack one of methyl methacrylate, and a radical of the type XVIII is about twice as likely to attack a molecule of methyl methacrylate as it is to attack one of styrene. Consequently, although there is clearly an appreciable tendency toward alternation, identical monomer units must fairly frequently be adjacent to each other in the chain. Since such alternating effects seem rather generally to prevail, any entirely satisfactory treatment of copolymerization must take them explicitly into account. Consequently, although the relative intrinsic reactivities of the different monomers (see the preceding paragraph) are important factors that must always be borne in mind, they are often insufficient by themselves to determine the courses of the reactions.[61]

In the above discussion, copolymerization has been described in some detail, so that the significance of the alternating effect might be made quite clear. We are now, therefore, in position to consider some of the explanations that have been offered for the existence of this effect. One of the first such explanations was that, with any two monomers that have a pronounced tendency to alternate, the copolymerization is preceded by the formation of a 1:1 molecular compound. This explanation is now believed, however, to be incorrect or, at any rate, to be of only minor importance, since there is seldom any positive evidence supporting the reality of the assumed complexes, and since the alternation is not appreciably affected by dilution.[61] A second, and more successful explanation is one based upon the idea of steric hindrance. Thus, let us suppose that, of two monomers R—CH=CH_2 and R'—CH=CH_2, the former has the greater intrinsic reactivity, but offers the greater steric resistance to polymerization. A radical of the type R'—$\overset{\cdot}{C}H$—CH_2— · · ·, with its reactive center located in a small group, would then combine more rapidly with the more reactive monomer R—CH=CH_2; but a radical of the type R—$\overset{\cdot}{C}H$—CH_2— · · ·, with its reactive center located in a large group, would combine more rapidly with the less hindered monomer R'—CH=CH_2. Although this steric factor seems to be important in some copolymerizations, it is at present considered inadequate to account for all the available data.[61]

The explanation that is now favored[61] is that the alternating effect is ordinarily due primarily to electrostatic interactions of one kind or another. Let us consider a reaction between a free radical R—$\overset{\cdot}{C}H$—CH_2— · · · and a monomer CH_2=CH—R', in which the groups R and R' may be either the same or different and in which neither needs to be identical with the group designated by the same symbol in the preceding paragraph. If, for the sake of simplicity, we ignore the structures in which the unpaired electron is on any atom within the groups R and R', the activated complex can be described as a hybrid in which structures XXIII and XXIV have

$$CH_2 = CH - R'$$
$$R - \overset{\cdot}{C}H - CH_2 - \cdots$$
XXIII

$$CH_2 - \overset{\cdot}{C}H - R'$$
$$R - \overset{|}{C}H - CH_2 - \cdots$$
XXIV

particularly large weights (see also below). Now, if the group R withdraws electrons from the vinyl group to which it is attached, whereas the group R' releases electrons to its attached vinyl group (or vice versa), the electrostatic interactions clearly increase the stabilities of the contributing structures XXIII and XXIV, and also that of their hybrid, the activated complex. On the other hand, if R and R' are either both electron withdrawing or both electron releasing, the electrostatic interactions must decrease the stabilities of the structures and also that of the activated complex. Moreover, if the resonance in the transition state is assumed to include further structures like XXV and XXVI, as well as their analogs

$$C^+H_2—\overset{..}{C}H—R' \qquad\qquad \overset{..}{C}^-H_2—\overset{.}{C}H—R'$$

$$R—\overset{..}{C}^-H—CH_2—\cdots \qquad\qquad R—C^+H—CH_2—\cdots$$

$$\text{XXV} \qquad\qquad\qquad \text{XXVI}$$

in which the formal charges are on atoms in the groups R and R', then the effect of the electrostatic interactions should be still greater. In any event, we may conclude that a difference in the electron-withdrawing or electron-releasing characters of the groups R and R' should be an important factor contributing to the observed alternating effect. This conclusion receives considerable support from the fact that, in general, the observed tendency toward alternation increases as the groups R and R' become electrically more dissimilar. Thus, the alternation is much more pronounced in the copolymerization of styrene and acrylonitrile than it is in that of styrene and vinyl chloride.

Copolymerizations induced by electrophilic or nucleophilic reagents are also known, but have been comparatively little studied.[61] In general, the relative reactivities of the different monomers vary widely and depend not only on the structures of the monomers, but also on the conditions employed. No evidence, however, for an alternating effect in these polar reactions has as yet been found. The belief that, as has been assumed throughout this section, there are three essentially different mechanisms of polymerization receives strong confirmation from the fact that the composition of a copolymer may be altered by a change in the nature of the reagent which induces its formation. With, for example, a mixture containing equivalent quantities of styrene and of methyl methacrylate, the polymer that is produced is a 1 : 1 copolymer if the reaction is initiated by a peroxide, but it contains almost exclusively methyl methacrylate if the reaction is initiated by a metal halide, and almost exclusively styrene if the reaction is initiated by an alkali metal. Under these three conditions, the reagents that attack the monomer molecules are doubtless radical, electrophilic, and nucleophilic, respectively.

8·11 Orientation of Substituents in Aromatic Systems. It has been found that substitution in benzene and in other aromatic ring systems can be effected by reagents of all three possible types, electrophilic, radical, and nucleophilic. In most of the common reactions, such as halogenation, nitration, sulfonation, and diazo coupling, the substituting reagent is electrophilic, so that the aromatic compound itself must be nucleophilic. On the other hand, in the Gomberg reaction,[62] both of the

[62] M. Gomberg and W. E. Bachmann, *J. Am. Chem. Soc.* **46**, 2339 (1924).

reagents are apparently radical;[63] and in the hydrolysis, alcoholysis, and aminolysis of aryl halides, amines, ethers, and the like, the substituting reagent is nucleophilic.[64]   This list of reactions is intended to be illustrative rather than exhaustive; several further reactions belonging to these three types will be mentioned later.

In the most familiar of the reactions in which a nucleophilic reagent attacks an aromatic molecule, a stable anion such as chloride or nitrite is displaced by the entering substituent; a few examples of such reactions are in fact given in the preceding paragraph.   There have been found,[64] however, a number of further reactions in which a hydrogen atom, presumably in the form of a negative hydride ion, is displaced instead. This hydride ion is, of course, immediately, or perhaps simultaneously, transformed into either molecular hydrogen, H_2, by interaction with one of the reagents, or into water in the presence of the air or other oxidizing agent; easily reducible substances are often, accordingly, added to the reaction mixture in order to remove the hydride ion.   Since the reactions of this latter type are relatively little known, a brief digression for the purpose of summarizing the pertinent facts would here seem desirable.[65]

A hydrogen atom can sometimes be directly replaced by a hydroxyl group by the action of sodium or potassium hydroxide.   In this way, o- and a trace of p-nitrophenol can be made from nitrobenzene; α-pyridone can be made from pyridine; phloroglucinol can be made from phenol or from resorcinol; and alizarin (1,2-dihydroxyanthraquinone) can be made from 1- or 2-hydroxyanthraquinone.   In a similar way, by the action of sodium or potassium amide, α-aminopyridine can be made from pyridine;[66] 2- and 4-aminoquinoline can be made from quinoline;[66] 4-amino-2,6-dimethylpyridine can be made from 2,6-dimethylpyridine;[66] and α-naphthylamine and 1,5-diaminonapthalene can be made from naphthalene.   (Strangely enough, however, neither o- nor p-nitroaniline can be made in this way from nitrobenzene, because the reaction leads only to sodium benzene diazotate in small yield.[67])   By the action of hydroxylamine and sodium ethoxide, 1-amino-2-nitronaphthalene can be made from 2-nitronaphthalene; and 2,4-dinitroaniline and 2,4-dinitro-m-phenylenediamine can be made from m-dinitrobenzene.   Similarly, by the action of potassium cyanide, 2-nitro-6-ethoxybenzonitrile can be made from m-dinitrobenzene (in alcoholic solution); and isopurpuric acid (2-hydroxylamino-3,5-dicyano-4,6-dinitrophenol) can be made from picric acid, with reduction of one of the three nitro groups by the hydride ion

[63] For comprehensive surveys of substitutions by radical reagents, see D. H. Hey and W. A. Waters, *Chem. Revs.* **21**, 169 (1937); D. H. Hey, *Ann. Repts. on Progr. Chem.* (*Chem. Soc. London*) **37**, pp. 268ff (1940); W. A. Waters, *The Chemistry of Free Radicals*, Oxford University Press, 1st ed., 1946, 2nd ed., 1948, Chapter VIII.

[64] For detailed discussions of substitutions by nucleophilic reagents, see J. F. Bunnett and R. E. Zahler, *Chem. Revs.* **49**, 273 (1951); C. K. Ingold, *Structure and Mechanism in Organic Chemistry*, Cornell University Press, Ithaca, N. Y. 1953, Chapter XV.

[65] Reactions of this type are surveyed by J. F. Bunnett and R. E. Zahler on pp. 372ff of the paper cited in reference 64.   The nucleophilic substitutions listed without reference in the present group of paragraphs in fine print are taken from this review and from *Beilsteins Handbuch der organischen Chemie.*

[66] For a general discussion of reactions of this type, see M. T. Leffler in R. Adams, *Organic Reactions*, John Wiley & Sons, New York, vol. I, 1942, Chapter 4.

[67] F. W. Bergstrom and J. S. Buehler, *J. Am. Chem. Soc.* **64**, 19 (1942).

liberated (see above). In the Piria reaction,[68] 1-nitronaphthalene is transformed by the action of sodium bisulfite into naphthionic acid and 1-naphthylamine-2,4-disulfonic acid. And finally, the reaction between quinoline and lithium phenyl leads to a quantitative yield of 2-phenylquinoline.[69] The actual reagents in these different groups of reactions are doubtless the hydroxide ion, the amide ion, the hydroxylamine anion, the cyanide ion, the bisulfite ion, and the phenyl anion, respectively. In several of the reactions cited, the product that is isolated has clearly undergone a more or less extensive reduction, presumably by the hydride ion or its equivalent (see above); and, in the reaction between quinoline and lithium phenyl, the *initial* product seems to be a dihydro-2-phenylquinoline, which is dehydrogenated during its isolation.

The nucleophilic displacement of hydrogen from an aromatic molecule, and the concurrent reduction by the hydride ion that is released, may possibly explain certain anomalous substitutions which have recently been observed. Thus, by the action of sodamide in liquid ammonia, *o*-chloroanisole is converted principally into *m*-anisidine,[70] and 1-chloronaphthalene is converted principally into 2-naphthylamine.[71] In each of these reactions, the amino group becomes linked to a carbon atom adjacent to the one that initially carried the chlorine atom. Since a considerable number of additional, completely analogous rearrangements are also known,[72] the reaction appears to be a rather general one. Although it is still too early for a definitive explanation of the problem thus presented, a not unreasonable guess is that, as a result of the specific orienting and activating effects that obtain in the molecules concerned, the amide anion displaces a hydride ion in preference to a halide ion, and then, either simultaneously or subsequently, this hydride ion (or its equivalent) removes the halogen atom by reduction. Since too little is now known regarding orientation and activation in nucleophilic substitutions, we cannot at present have much confidence in this proposed explanation. Some support for the hypothesis is, however, given by the fact that aromatic halides can indeed be reduced, in the way postulated, by the action of lithium aluminum hydride, which presumably here acts as a source of hydride ion.[73] An explanation which is not essentially different from the foregoing has been given by Bunnett, Cormack, and McKay[72] and by Elderfield.[72] On the other hand, from a study of the reaction between chlorobenzene and potassium amide in liquid ammonia, with C^{14} as an isotopic tracer, Roberts and his co-workers[72] have concluded that the carbon atom to which the halogen atom was initially linked becomes equivalent, at some time during the reaction, with one of its neighbors in the ring. On the basis of this evidence,

[68] R. Piria, *Ann.* **78**, 31 (1851). See also W. H. Hunter and M. M. Sprung, *J. Am. Chem. Soc.* **53**, 1432, 1443 (1931).

[69] K. Ziegler and H. Zeiser, *Ann.* **485**, 174 (1931).

[70] H. Gilman and S. Avakian, *J. Am. Chem. Soc.* **67**, 349 (1945).

[71] R. S. Urner and F. W. Bergstrom, *J. Am. Chem. Soc.* **67**, 2108 (1945).

[72] For fairly complete references to the original literature, see H. Gilman and R. H. Kyle, *J. Am. Chem. Soc.* **74**, 3027 (1952). For discussion of the probably analogous von Richter reaction, see V. von Richter, *Ber.* **4**, 21, 459, 553 (1871); **7**, 1145 (1874); **8**, 1418 (1875); J. E. Bunnett, J. F. Cormack, and F. C. McKay, *J. Org. Chem.* **15**, 481 (1950). See also R. C. Elderfield, *Record Chem. Progr.* (*Kresge-Hooker Lib.*) **13**, 119 (1952); pp. 382ff of J. F. Bunnett and R. E. Zahler, *Chem. Revs.* **49**, 273 (1951); J. D. Roberts, H. E. Simmons, Jr., L. A. Carlsmith, and C. W. Vaughan, *J. Am. Chem. Soc.* **75**, 3290 (1953); R. A. Benkeser and W. E. Buting, *ibid.* **74**, 3011 (1952); J. F. Bunnett, M. M. Rauhut, D. Knutson, and G. E. Bussell, *ibid.* **76**, 5755 (1954).

[73] See, for example, W. G. Brown in R. Adams, *Organic Reactions*, John Wiley & Sons, New York, vol. VI, 1951, Chapter 10.

they suggested the transient existence of a "benzyne" intermediate in which, by loss of a molecule of hydrogen chloride, there has been produced a triple bond between the two equivalent carbon atoms. It is not yet possible, however, to draw any definite conclusions from the information that is now available.

The above discussion of nucleophilic substitutions is far from complete, but it should be sufficient to illustrate the nature and scope of the reactions concerned. As the reader has possibly already observed, the aromatic substances which undergo the substitutions by these nucleophilic reagents are usually of rather special types and, more frequently than not, are relatively inert toward the usual electrophilic reagents (at any rate, at the points at which the substitutions occur). The reasons for these facts, and also for the observed orientations, should become apparent from the following discussion in this section.

It appears that the difficulty referred to in Section 8·1 in connection with the entropy of activation is relatively unimportant in the substitution reactions of aromatic compounds (at any rate, when the second reagent is electrophilic). In other words, if the two reactions being compared with each other are substitutions by the same reagent at two different positions in the same molecule, then $\Delta\Delta S^{\ddagger}$ is found experimentally to be small.[74] Contrary to what might have been expected, this generalization seems often to be valid even when one of the reactions that are being compared occurs at a position that is ortho to a substituent already present.

As in the discussions of the addition reactions of unsaturated substances, we shall find it necessary here also to make rather detailed assumptions regarding the natures of the effective reagents, and regarding the mechanisms of the various reactions. As before, however, the exact forms in which we express these assumptions are of minor importance, provided only that they are not at variance with the fundamental principles upon which the treatment is based. In the bromination of benzene, for example, we shall consider that the reaction is initiated by the attack of a positive bromine ion upon the organic molecule. Actually, just as in the addition of bromine to an olefin, the bromine may instead enter into the activated complex in the form of a polarized molecule, $Br^+ Br^-$, or, more probably, of a complex with a catalyst molecule, such as $Br—Br^+—Fe^-Br_3$, or the like. The essential point, however, is that the bromine atom is transferred to the product as a positive ion with only six electrons in its valence shell or, in more general terms, that it behaves as an electrophilic reagent. Similarly, we shall consider that in chlorination, iodination, nitration, sulfonation, and diazo coupling the attacking reagents are, respectively, the ions or molecules Cl^+, I^+, NO_2^+, SO_3, and

[74] F. E. C. Sheffer and W. F. Brandsma, *Rec. trav. chim.* **45**, 522 (1926); A. E. Bradfield and B. Jones, *J. Chem. Soc.* **1928**, 1006; L. P. Hammett, *Physical Organic Chemistry*, McGraw-Hill Book Co., New York, 1940, pp. 124ff; B. Jones, *J. Chem. Soc.* **1942**, 418, 676.

ArN_2^+. All these are clearly electrophilic since each either is a positive ion or has its reactive center at a relatively positive position, and since, in addition, each has an open sextet of electrons at its reactive center in at least one of the important contributing structures. Furthermore, we shall also consider that, in the Gomberg reaction and its analogs, the effective reagent is a free aryl radical, which has an odd electron and so is clearly a radical reagent; that, in the hydrolysis, alcoholysis, and aminolysis reactions the reagents are, respectively, the clearly nucleophilic hydroxide ion, alkoxide ion, and amine molecule (or amide anion); and that, in all further reactions that we shall have occasion to consider, the reagents are similar to the ones just listed.

In addition to the foregoing assumptions regarding the reagents which attack the aromatic molecules, we shall have to make further assumptions regarding the natures of the activated complexes. A single example will suffice to illustrate the general principles that are common to all the reactions being considered. For the bromination of benzene, it seems probable that the structures which have the largest weights in the activated complex are I–VII. (For the sake of simplicity, only the hydrogen atom

being replaced in the reaction is written explicitly.) Of these, structures I and II are of Class A, whereas the others are of Class B. It is to be noted, however, that III and IV resemble the Class A structures in that their relative stabilities are determined largely by charge distributions rather than by the ease with which a pair of electrons can be brought by polarization to the point of attack; consequently, any further reference to Class B structures is to be considered to apply only to the ones like V, VI, and VII in which the carbon atom attacked is joined by single bonds to four different atoms, and in which the benzene ring has an ortho or para quinoid structure.

In discussing the relative stabilities of the activated complexes for various substitution reactions, we have the same two choices as in the previous discussions of the addition reactions. On the one hand, we can center our attention upon the Class A structures (including now those like III and IV) and thereby emphasize the importance of the electrostatic interactions; or, on the other hand, we can center our attention upon the Class B structures (exclusive of III and IV) and thereby emphasize the importance of the ease with which the necessary polarizations can be produced. As before, these two points of view seem always to lead to identical conclusions, except for certain reactions like those between radical reagents, for which the former leads again to no very definite conclusions at all. We shall, accordingly, lay the greater emphasis upon the second point of view in order to be able to treat in a unified manner as large a number of reactions as possible. In other words, we shall consider that an aromatic substance will react the more easily with an electrophilic, radical, or nucleophilic reagent, the more easily an unshared pair of electrons, a single unpaired electron, or an open sextet of electrons can be provided at the point of attack.

It would be out of place here to attempt an adequate discussion of the experimental evidence that can be advanced in support of the essential features of the mechanisms postulated in this section. We can, however, state some of the most important conclusions that have been reached, and we can briefly indicate the nature of the evidence upon which these conclusions are based. After this short digression, we shall, on page 484, return to our discussion of orienting effects.[75]

The most carefully studied substitution reactions of aromatic systems are doubtless the nitrations, which seem now to be quite well understood. When the solvent is sulfuric acid, the nitric acid is known, from a cryoscopic measurement of its apparent molecular weight,[76] to be completely, or almost completely, ionized in accordance with the equation

$$HNO_3 + 2H_2SO_4 \rightarrow NO_2^+ + 2HSO_4^- + H_3O^+$$

Since the nitronium ion, NO_2^+, is therefore present in large amount, the belief that it is the effective reagent for the attack upon the organic molecule is entirely reasonable. If the nitric acid is present in large excess, so that the concentration of nitronium ion remains constant, the rate of the reaction is, as expected, proportional to the concentration of the substance nitrated.[77]

More conclusive evidence regarding the mechanism of aromatic nitration has been obtained from studies in which the solvent is nitromethane.[77] Under these conditions, the ionization of the nitric acid is only slight, and so the concentration of the nitronium ion is small. Consequently, if the aromatic compound is a rather reactive one, so that it combines very rapidly with the trace of nitronium ion that is available, the measured rate of nitration should be simply the rate at which the nitronium ion is formed by ionization of the nitric acid. The rate of nitration should then be independent of the concentration of the substance nitrated, and it should be the same for all sufficiently reactive substances. Both of these expectations are realized with benzene and with

[75] For a more general and more complete discussion, see C. K. Ingold, *Structure and Mechanism in Organic Chemistry*, Cornell University Press, Ithaca, N. Y., 1953, Chapter VI.

[76] R. J. Gillespie, J. Graham, E. D. Hughes, C. K. Ingold, and E. R. A. Peeling, *J. Chem. Soc.* **1950**, 2504.

[77] E. D. Hughes, C. K. Ingold, and R. I. Reed, *J. Chem. Soc.* **1950**, 2400.

toluene,[77] even though, in competitive experiments, in which a mixture of the two hydrocarbons is nitrated, toluene is always found to react about twenty-five times as fast as benzene, regardless of the solvent. On the other hand, with the considerably less reactive p-dichlorobenzene, the slow step in the nitration is now the attack of the nitronium ion upon the aromatic molecule, and so the reaction is slower than with benzene and toluene, and its rate is proportional to the concentration of the aryl halide.[77]

In aqueous solution, nitration is relatively slow, except with such especially reactive substances as phenols, phenol ethers, and aromatic amines, with which the complications that are mentioned in the two following paragraphs require special consideration. With 2-phenylethane-1-sulfonic acid, which behaves more normally than the substances just named, the rate of reaction is proportional to the concentration of the substance nitrated, but it increases with the acidity of the medium.[78] These facts are consistent with the view that the rate-determining step consists in an attack by an un-ionized nitric acid molecule or by either one of the two cations NO_2^+ and $H_2NO_3^+$. The first of these possibilities is excluded, however, by the observation that, on the addition of a strong acid like sulfuric or perchloric acid, the rate increases much faster than can reasonably be explained by an increase in the concentration of the nitric acid. Of the remaining possibilities, an attack by nitronium ion, although not impossible, seems unlikely since no evidence for the existence of this ion under the stated conditions has been found. Consequently, the attacking reagent is here most probably the ion $H_2NO_3^+$.[78]

The nitration of phenols and phenol ethers proceeds by two independent paths which, by choice of the substances studied and of the experimental conditions, can be kinetically separated from each other.[79] On the one hand, there is a mechanism which is essentially identical with those described above, and which involves attack by the nitronium ion or, in aqueous solution, by the ion $H_2NO_3^+$. On the other hand, there is also a second mechanism that is dependent on the presence of nitrous acid. This latter reagent acts by first nitrosating the organic substance; the resulting nitroso compound is then oxidized by the nitric acid to the nitro compound that is finally isolated and, in the process, the nitrous acid that is consumed in the first step is replaced by the reduction of the nitric acid. The initial nitrosation is considered to involve attack by the nitrosonium ion, NO^+, which, like the nitronium ion, is clearly electrophilic.[79]

With an aromatic amine, the nitration proceeds by the same two mechanisms that are observed with a phenol or phenol ether, but it is further complicated by the occurrence of additional reactions in which the attack is upon the nitrogen atom of the amino group. This more complex behavior has probably not yet been completely elucidated.[80]

One other feature of the most typical mechanism of aromatic nitration has now been established. In the course of the reaction, a nitronium ion becomes attached to a carbon atom of the organic molecule, and the proton that was originally linked to that carbon atom breaks away in combination with some base present in the medium. These two steps may be either simultaneous or successive and, if they are successive, either one may be the slow, rate-controlling step. The kinetic evidence, however, has shown that the departure of the proton has no effect on the rate of the reaction. In the first place, when the nitration is carried out in nitromethane as solvent, the addition of a small amount of water only slightly decreases the rate; if the removal of the proton

[78] E. S. Halberstadt, E. D. Hughes, and C. K. Ingold, J. Chem. Soc. 1950, 2441.

[79] C. A. Bunton, E. D. Hughes, C. K. Ingold, D. I. H. Jacobs, M. H. Jones, G. J. Minkoff, and R. I. Reed, J. Chem. Soc. 1950, 2628.

[80] J. Glazer, E. D. Hughes, C. K. Ingold, A. T. James, G. T. Jones, and E. Roberts, J. Chem. Soc. 1950, 2657.

were rate controlling, the water should increase the rate by virtue of its basic character.[77] In the second place, if some of the hydrogen atoms in a sample of benzene are replaced by the heavier isotope tritium, and if the substance is then dinitrated in sulfuric acid solution, the rates at which the hydrogen and tritium atoms are displaced by nitro groups are, within the rather small experimental uncertainty, identical.[81]   If the rupture of the carbon-hydrogen or carbon-tritium bond were involved in the rate-controlling step, hydrogen should be replaced considerably faster than tritium since a carbon-hydrogen bond is somewhat weaker than a carbon-tritium bond.   We can, therefore, conclude that the two steps are successive, and that the slow step is the one in which the new carbon-nitrogen bond is formed.[81]

No other aromatic substitutions have been so carefully studied as has nitration. The existence of the positive chlorine ion, Cl^+, and its role as the effective reagent in certain chlorinations has, however, been demonstrated by kinetic studies.[82]   The reactions which have provided the most conclusive evidence are those carried out in dilute aqueous solutions of hypochlorous acid, containing either sulfuric acid and silver sulfate or perchloric acid and silver perchlorate.   (The function of the silver salts is to remove chloride ion and hence to prevent the formation of molecular chlorine.   The kinetic results are not affected by small changes in the concentrations of these salts.) Under the conditions specified, the rates at which phenol, anisole, and the dimethyl ether of hydroquinone are chlorinated are equal to each other and are independent of the concentrations of the organic reagents.   They are also equal to the rates of the addition of hypochlorous acid to allyl fluoride and to allyl ethyl ether.   The most satisfactory explanation for these observations is that, in each of the reactions cited, the rate-determining step is the production of the chlorine cation in accordance with the equation

$$HOCl + 2H_2SO_4 \rightarrow Cl^+ + H_3O^+ + 2HSO_4^-$$

or

$$HOCl + 2HClO_4 \rightarrow Cl^+ + H_3O^+ + 2ClO_4^-$$

(Cf. the equation on page 481.)   This interpretation receives further support from the fact that the rate is proportional to the concentration of hypochlorous acid and rapidly increases with increasing acidity of the medium.   With less reactive aromatic compounds, the rate of chlorination becomes proportional to the concentration of the organic reagent;   the rate-controlling step then probably involves an attack by the different cation H_2OCl^+, although the possibility that the Cl^+ ion is still the effective reagent cannot be definitely excluded.   The above evidence relating to the mechanism of chlorination is so closely parallel to the previously described, and more complete, evidence relating to the mechanism of nitration that no further comment should here be necessary.

The data which have been discussed in the preceding paragraphs are sufficient to show that *some* aromatic substitutions proceed by mechanisms that differ in no important way from the ones postulated in this section.   Clearly, however, they are not sufficient to show that *all* such reactions proceed by the same mechanisms, or even by analogous mechanisms.   Especially in the substitutions by radical and nucleophilic

[81] L. Melander, *Arkiv Kemi* **2**, 211 (1951).   See also T. G. Bonner, F. Bowyer, and · G. Williams, *J. Chem. Soc.* **1953**, 2650.   For an analogous study in which deuterium was used instead of tritium, see W. M. Lauer and W. E. Noland, *J. Am. Chem. Soc.* **75**, 3689 (1953).   For an analogous study (in which tritium was again used) of aromatic sulfonation, see U. Berglund-Larsson and L. Melander, *Arkiv Kemi* **6**, 219 (1953).

[82] P. B. D. de la Mare, E. D. Hughes, and C. A. Vernon, *Research (London)* **3**, 192, 242 (1950).

reagents, conclusive experimental evidence regarding the mechanisms is lacking. We shall, however, continue to discuss the theory from the viewpoint that was stated on pages 479ff, even though many details of the treatment may have little or no direct experimental support. The reason why this apparently arbitrary procedure leads to rather satisfactory results is that complete knowledge of all details of the mechanism is seldom necessary. Most commonly, in fact, if we know that, in a given reaction, the attacking reagent is electrophilic, radical, or nucleophilic, we can predict the orientation without making an explicit assumption in regard to the structure of that reagent. In a nitration, for example, it is for our purposes immaterial whether the attacking reagent is NO_2^+, $H_2NO_3^+$, or even HNO_3, so long as there is no uncertainty that this reagent, whatever it is, is electrophilic and has its reactive center at the nitrogen atom. Similarly, the identity of the rate-controlling step, however interesting and important it may be to a kineticist, is also rather immaterial in an explanation of the orienting effects.

The first aromatic compound to which we shall apply the general treatment that was described on pages 479–481 is pyridine. Although not a benzene derivative, this substance, on account of its simplicity, provides a particularly convenient introduction to the subject. For our purposes, we may think of a molecule of pyridine as being just like one of benzene, except that one of the atoms of the ring (the nitrogen atom) is distinguished from the remaining five by having a greater intrinsic attraction for electrons. In order to show the resulting polarization, the Kekulé structures therefore need to be modified in the way indicated in the structure VIII.

VIII

(The I-effect is also operative. It could be represented in the above structure by replacing each valence bond in it with a straight arrow pointing toward the nitrogen atom. The figure would then, however, be unnecessarily cluttered. We shall, therefore, ignore the I-effect for the moment, but we shall soon return to it.) The effect of the resonance in pyridine, as is indicated by the curved arrows in structure VIII, is to bring electrons from the α and γ positions to the nitrogen atom. As a result, the attack by an electrophilic reagent will be made more difficult at the α and γ positions, and that by a nucleophilic reagent will be made more easy. Since, to the present approximation, the β position is not affected, the orientation must be β for an electrophilic, and α, γ for a nucleophilic reagent. Since the I-effect, which has heretofore been neglected, removes electrons also from the β position, we can draw the further conclusion that substitution by an electrophilic reagent should be more difficult, even in the favored β position, than in benzene. All these predictions are in agreement with experiment; nitration of pyridine, for example, occurs with great difficulty and leads to the β-nitro derivative, whereas the reaction with sodamide (in which the actual reagent must be the strongly nucleophilic ion, NH_2^-, or its equivalent), occurs with comparative ease and leads to the α-amino derivative.[66]   A further, and it is assumed completely comparable, example of orientation with respect to a nucleophilic reagent is given by the fact that α- and γ-chloropyridine can be hydrolyzed by a base much more readily than can either β-chloropyridine or chlorobenzene.

The nitration of pyridine is carried out in a strongly acidic medium, so that the substance which is nitrated must be the ion $C_5H_6N^+$.   On account of the positive charge upon the nitrogen atom in this ion, the electrons are drawn to the nitrogen from the rest of the molecule even more strongly than in the electrically neutral pyridine molecule itself.   Consequently, the reactivity of all the positions, and especially of the α and γ positions, toward the electrophilic reagent is decreased to an even greater extent.   The reality of this expected effect has been demonstrated[83] by a comparison of the reactions of pyridine and of 2,6-di-*tert*-butylpyridine with sulfur trioxide in liquid sulfur dioxide as solvent.   The unsubstituted pyridine forms a complex, $C_5H_5N^+$—S^-O_3, which is structurally analogous to the cation $C_5H_6N^+$, and which is not sulfonated under the conditions employed.   On the other hand, the di-*tert*-butyl derivative is prevented by steric hindrance from forming an analogous complex, and it is accordingly sulfonated (in the 4 position?) about as easily as nitrobenzene, i.e., with only moderate difficulty. The effect of the alkyl groups is here doubtless due partly to their usual activating influence upon electrophilic substitutions (cf. page 489); a more important cause for the observed difference in rates of sulfonation must surely, however, be the difference between the net charges on the nitrogen atoms in the two substances.

A further point of interest in connection with the substitution reactions of pyridine is that sometimes the rule of orientation appears to change with temperature.   For example, bromination leads largely to β-bromopyridine, as expected, at 300°, but to α-bromopyridine at 500°.   The explanation may be that, at the higher temperature, the bromine dissociates into bromine atoms, so that the substituting agent becomes radical instead of electrophilic.   (See below.)

The purely qualitative arguments employed in the preceding paragraphs for the interpretation of the reactions of electrophilic and nucleophilic reagents with pyridine are no longer able to lead to a definite prediction when applied to the reactions of radical reagents.   This limitation applies even when the problem is considered from the viewpoint of the Class B structures.   There is, indeed, no immediately obvious reason why a single unpaired electron could be provided more easily at any one position in this molecule than at any other.   However, some semiquantitative calculations, which are based on the molecular-orbital approach (see Sections 9·22–9·26), have led to more useful conclusions.[81]   Although the

[83] H. C. Brown and B. Kanner, *J. Am. Chem. Soc.* **75**, 3865 (1953); *Tech. Rept. to the Office of Naval Research*, Project NR 056127, July 1, 1953.

[84] G. W. Wheland, *J. Am. Chem. Soc.* **64**, 900 (1942).   In this paper references are given to several earlier calculations of similar type.   For analogous calculations based on the valence-bond approach, but applied only to substitutions by electrophilic and nucleophilic reagents, see A. L. Green, *J. Chem. Soc.* **1954**, 3538.

justification for these conclusions cannot be explained in terms of the simple qualitative concept of resonance, which is being used in this section, we shall nevertheless find it profitable here to state, without proof, the predictions that follow from the mathematical treatment. The results of the calculations are expressed in terms of two parameters, δ_1 and δ_2, which may be thought of as measures of the amounts by which the electronegativities of the nitrogen atom and of the α carbon atoms, respectively, exceed those of the β and γ carbon atoms. Since the exact values of the δ's are not known, the treatment is not as complete as might be desired. However, since nitrogen is a more electronegative element than carbon, both δ's must be positive; and, since, in particular, the nitrogen atom must be more electronegative than the α carbon atom, δ_1 must be greater than δ_2. If, for the sake of definiteness, δ_2 is assumed to be equal to $1/3\delta_1$,[85] the α position in pyridine is found to be the most reactive toward a radical reagent, and the β and γ positions are found to be about equally reactive; all three positions are more reactive than any of those in benzene. Essentially these same conclusions have subsequently been reached also by a different, closely related but simpler and more approximate method of calculation.[86]

In general, the above predictions for attack by radical reagents are in quite satisfactory agreement with experiment.[87]   In the Gomberg reaction between sodium benzenediazotate and pyridine, for example, the major product is α-phenylpyridine, and the β and γ isomers are produced in approximately equal amount. With other diazotates besides the one just mentioned, the major product is again usually the α-arylpyridine[87] but, most commonly, the yield of the β isomer is significantly greater than is that of the γ isomer. Similar, but less conclusive, results have been obtained also in the formation of phenylpyridines by the decomposition of benzoyl peroxide in pyridine, a reaction which, like the Gomberg reaction, can be considered to go through phenyl radicals, or their equivalent, as reactive intermediates.[88] In evaluating all these data, however, one should bear in mind that the total yield is seldom good, and hence that the relative amounts of the three products which are isolated in the pure state may give a misleading idea of the relative rates of the reactions at the α, β, and γ positions.

A further simple example is provided by the trimethylanilinium ion,

[85] Cf. G. E. K. Branch and M. Calvin, *The Theory of Organic Chemistry*, Prentice-Hall, New York, 1941, pp. 217ff; H. H. Jaffé, *J. Chem. Phys.* **21**, 415 (1953).

[86] M. J. S. Dewar, *J. Am. Chem. Soc.* **74**, 3357, (1952).

[87] J. W. Haworth, I. M. Heilbron, and D. H. Hey, *J. Chem. Soc.* **1940**, 349; E. C. Butterworth, I. M. Heilbron, and D. H. Hey, *ibid.* **1940**, 355.

[88] D. H. Hey and E. W. Walker, *J. Chem. Soc.* **1948**, 2213.

$[C_6H_5N(CH_3)_3]^+$. The effect of the positively charged substituent must here be to pull electrons away from, and hence to increase the electron affinity of, the carbon atom to which it is attached. The aromatic ring is accordingly qualitatively similar to that of pyridine, and the rules of orientation can be expected to be the same. Substitution by an electrophilic reagent should therefore be difficult and should occur at the meta position, which is analogous to the β position in pyridine; substitution by a radical reagent should occur predominantly at the ortho position, which is analogous to the α position; and substitution by a nucleophilic reagent should occur with relative ease at the ortho and para positions, which are respectively analogous to the α and γ positions. The first of these predictions is confirmed by the fact that, for example, nitration of phenyltrimethylammonium bisulfate proceeds slowly and gives only the meta product; the second prediction has not yet been experimentally tested; and the third is supported by the observation[89] that, in the reaction between an aromatic chloride and sodium methoxide, the rate at which the halogen atom is replaced by methoxyl is greatly increased by the presence of a quaternary ammonium group in the para position.

Structure IX for nitrobenzene shows that, just as with pyridine, an electrophilic reagent should attack the meta position with deactivation, and a nucleophilic reagent should attack the ortho and para positions with activation. (The terms "deactivation" and "activation" are applied to reactions which proceed less, or more, rapidly, respectively, than the corresponding reactions with benzene itself.) In considering the orientation with respect to a radical reagent, we can note first that the situation is somewhat analogous to that in pyridine, with the nitrogen atom in the

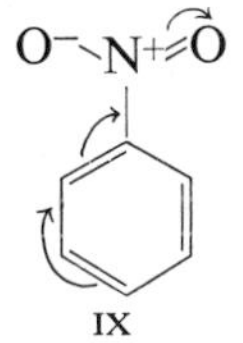

IX

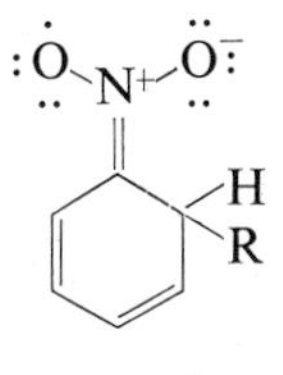

X 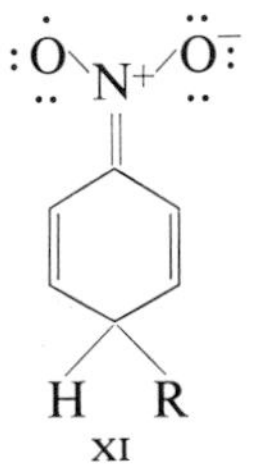   XI 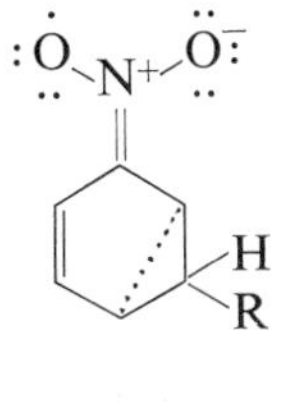   XII

[89] Cf. Table 4 on p. 309 of J. F. Bunnett and R. E. Zahler, Chem. Revs. 49, 273 (1951).

ring of the latter substance being replaced here by the carbon atom which carries the nitro group. This analogy exists because the nitro group removes electrons from, and so increases the electron affinity of, the carbon atom to which it is attached. Consequently, we may expect a radical reagent to attack principally the ortho positions. A further factor which leads to ortho, and also to para, orientation is that the Class B structures X and XI (where R represents the radical reagent) should be much more stable than the corresponding one, XII, which would be required for meta substitution, but which contains a formal bond. As should be apparent, the situation here is closely analogous to that encountered in Section 8·6, where it was found that a radical reagent preferentially attacks the *end* of a conjugated system. Again, all these predictions are in agreement with experiment. Nitration of nitrobenzene, for example, does indeed occur with some difficulty, and it leads predominantly to the meta derivative; the hydrolysis of *o*- or *p*-nitrochlorobenzene occurs much more readily than that of either *m*-nitrochlorobenzene or chlorobenzene; and the decomposition of sodium benzenediazotate, of benzoyl peroxide, or of N-nitrosoacetanilide in the presence of nitrobenzene gives a mixture of nitrobiphenyls containing 60–70 per cent of the ortho, 0–10 per cent of the meta, and 30–40 per cent of the para isomer.[90]

The mechanism which we have assumed for the radical substitutions may be considerably oversimplified since there is no assurance that the attacking radical displaces the hydrogen atom in a single step. Thus, the formation of a phenylpyridine by the reaction between, say, benzoyl peroxide and pyridine may perhaps proceed by a chain mechanism[91] that is based upon some such steps as

$C_6H_5-CO_2-CO_2-C_6H_5$ $\rightarrow 2C_6H_5-CO_2*$

$C_6H_5-CO_2* + C_5H_5N$ $\rightarrow C_6H_5-CO_2H + C_6H_4N*$

$C_6H_4N* + C_6H_5-CO_2-CO_2-C_6H_5 \rightarrow C_5H_4N-C_6H_5 + C_6H_5-CO_2* + CO_2$

where the free radicals which initiate and carry on the chains are denoted by asterisks. Similar sequences can be suggested also for the further reactions in which the initial reagents are diazotates or nitrosoanilides instead of peroxides, or in which other aromatic compounds besides pyridine take part. There can, however, be little doubt that these substitutions are radical for, if they were instead either electrophilic or nucleophilic, they could not lead to the observed relative proportions of isomeric products (cf. also the orientations with the remaining substances that are considered below in this section). In any event, therefore, the orientations are presumably determined by reactions in which free radicals attack the aromatic molecules; the points at which these attacks occur should not be primarily dependent either upon the identities of the free radicals concerned, or upon any subsequent steps that may occur. Consequently, since we will come to the same conclusions regarding orientation, no matter what detailed mechanisms we assume for the reactions, we shall here retain the simple viewpoint that was initially adopted.

[90] D. F. DeTar and H. J. Scheifele, Jr., *J. Am. Chem. Soc.* **73**, 1442 (1951).
[91] D. F. DeTar and S. V. Sagmanli, *J. Am. Chem. Soc.* **72**, 965 (1950).

In toluene, if hyperconjugation of the methyl group with the benzene ring is neglected, the rules of orientation might be expected to be just the opposite of those applying to the trimethylanilinium ion. The reason for this conclusion is that here the substituent does not remove electrons from, but instead gives them up to, the benzene ring, as is shown by the observed direction of the dipole moment of the molecule.[92]   Accordingly, electrophilic reagents should attack the ortho and para positions with activation; nucleophilic reagents should attack the meta position with deactivation; and radical reagents should attack the para position somewhat less readily than the meta position, and the ortho position least readily of all.   The predictions for the electrophilic and nucleophilic reagents are correct, but that for the radical reagents appears to be incorrect.   For example, nitration of toluene gives largely the ortho and para isomers, and the reaction takes place more easily than the nitration of benzene.[75]   On the other hand, methyl groups make the replacement of a halogen atom by the action of a nucleophilic reagent more difficult, and are especially effective in that regard when ortho or para to the point of attack.[64]   With a radical reagent, the evidence is somewhat conflicting. According to one early report,[93] the decomposition of benzoyl peroxide in the presence of toluene gives mostly p-methylbiphenyl; but, according to a much more extensive, and more recent study,[94] the orientation in the Gomberg reaction is predominantly ortho with a considerable number of different diazo compounds and, in at least one instance, no para product could be found at all.   One reason for the discrepancy is probably that, since the yields are always small, the products which are *isolated* in the largest amounts may be only minor constituents of the complex mixtures that are formed.   The evidence strongly suggests, however, that a methyl group directs a radical reagent principally to the ortho position.   The reason why the above theoretical approach to the problem led to exactly the opposite conclusion is possibly to be found in the neglect of hyperconjugation.   In reactions with radical reagents at the ortho and para positions, structures XIII and XIV (where R represents a radical reagent) can contribute to the activated complex, whereas, in a reaction at the meta position the only analogous structures that are possible are some relatively unstable ones with formal bonds, like XV.   Consequently, as a result of the hyperconjugation, the activated complexes for reaction at the ortho and para positions are stabilized more than is the one for reaction at the meta position.   The supposition that the effect of hyperconjugation is sufficient to outweigh the opposing effect of the transfer

[92] J. W. Williams, *Fortschr. Chem. u. Physik physik. Chem.* **20**, 257 (1930), Table 11.
[93] W. Dietrich, *Helv. Chim. Acta* **8**, 149 (1925).
[94] R. H. Wilson, *J. Appl. Chem. (London)* **3**, 37 (1953).

of the electrons to the ring is consistent with approximate calculations.[84] It is to be noted that the hyperconjugation does not necessarily alter the conclusions reached for the reactions with electrophilic and nucleophilic

| XIII | XIV | XV | XVI |

reagents, as is evident from a consideration of structure XVI. In this, the arrows are drawn in the direction suggested by the observed direction of the dipole moment of the molecule.

In benzyl chloride, XVII, benzal chloride, XVIII, and benzotrichloride, XIX, the electronegative chlorine atoms oppose the shift of electrons

| XVII | XVIII | XIX |

toward the ring. As a result, the proportion of meta isomer formed in the reactions with electrophilic reagents increases progressively when the number of chlorine atoms increases, as is shown in Table 8·1. The

TABLE 8·1

PER CENTS OF META ISOMER FORMED IN NITRATIONS

Substance Nitrated	$n = 0$	$n = 1$	$n = 2$	$n = 3$
C_6H_5—CCl_nH_{3-n} [a]	4.4	4.2	33.8	64.5
		11.6	32.8–33.3	48.3–48.6
C_6H_5—$(CH_2)_nN^+(CH_3)_3$ [b]	100	88	19	5

[a] For this series of substances, the figures in the top row are those of M. A. F. Holleman, *Rec. trav. chim.* **33**, 1 (1914); the ones in the second row are those of B. Flürscheim and E. L. Holmes, *J. Chem. Soc.* **1928**, 1607.

[b] These figures are taken from the compilation of C. K. Ingold, *Rec. trav. chim.* **48**, 797 (1929).

trifluoromethyl group, like the trichloromethyl group in benzotrichloride, is also meta directing and deactivating. A further steady transition between the two types of orientation is illustrated by the series of ions XX–XXIII. The trimethylanilinium ion XX is attacked in the meta

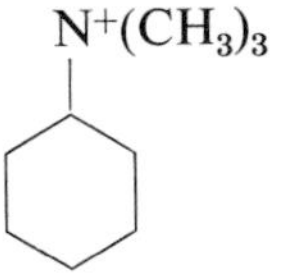

$N^+(CH_3)_3$ $CH_2-N^+(CH_3)_3$ $CH_2-CH_2-N^+(CH_3)_3$

XX 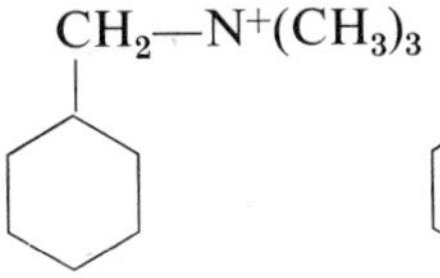   XXI 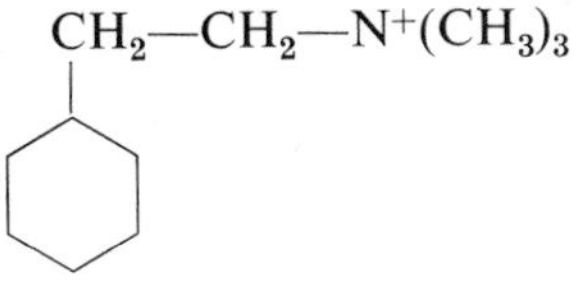   XXII

position by an electrophilic reagent, as we have already seen, but the ion XXIII is attacked predominantly in the ortho and para positions, and the intermediate ions XXI and XXII exhibit intermediate behaviors.

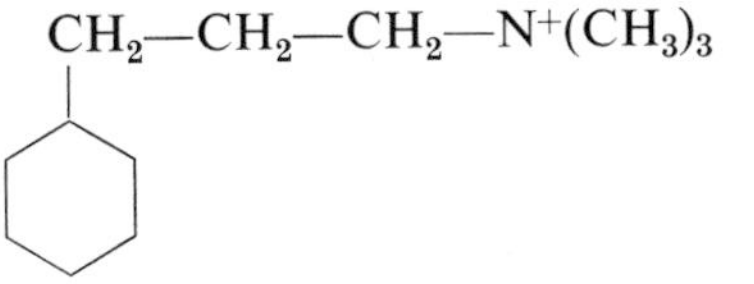

$CH_2-CH_2-CH_2-N^+(CH_3)_3$

XXIII 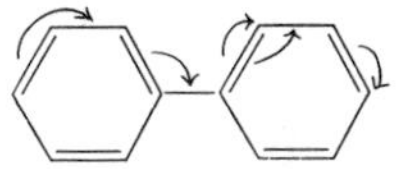   XXIV

(See Table 8·1.) Apparently here, the inductive effect which results from the attraction of the positively charged nitrogen atom for the electrons is damped fairly rapidly as it is transmitted along the saturated chain. The natural tendency of alkyl groups to produce ortho, para orientation with respect to electrophilic reagents, therefore, gradually assumes greater importance as the chain is lengthened, and it finally becomes predominant.

With respect to nucleophilic substitutions, the halogen-substituted alkyl groups have been relatively little investigated. The trifluoromethyl group has been shown, however, to be ortho, para directing and activating.[95] Although the effect of replacing hydrogen atoms by fluorine atoms is therefore in the expected direction, the transition between the two extreme types of orientation has not been studied in any quantitative way. There are also no data regarding the attack by radical reagents upon the substances considered in this paragraph and in the preceding one.[95a]

Aryl, like alkyl, groups are ortho, para directing toward electrophilic reagents. The structure XXIV for biphenyl, for example, shows that the required unshared pair of electrons can be readily provided at the ortho and para positions (of the ring at the right of the figure as drawn) in consequence of the polarization during the reaction. The same structure shows also that open sextets of electrons can also be readily provided at

[95] Cf. Table 11 on p. 314 of J. F. Bunnett and R. E. Zahler, *Chem. Revs.* **49**, 273 (1951).
[95a] However, see R. L. Dannley and M. Sternfeld, *J. Am. Chem. Soc.* **76**, 4543 (1954) for data showing predominant meta orientation in the radical substitutions of certain benzotrihalides.

the ortho and para positions (of the ring at the left of the figure in this case). Consequently, the phenyl group should be ortho, para directing for substitution by a nucleophilic reagent as well. Experimental confirmation of this prediction is, however, insufficient to establish its correctness. In Bunnett and Zahler's exceptionally detailed and comprehensive survey of nucleophilic substitutions,[64] there is mention of only one reaction that sheds light upon the behavior of biphenyl derivatives. Thus, the rate of the reaction between o-bromonitrobenzene and piperidine is slightly increased if a phenyl group is introduced into the position that is para to the halogen atom;[96] no data showing the effects of phenyl groups in the ortho and meta positions, however, are available. (The foregoing discussion is not to be taken as implying that the two rings in biphenyl are not equivalent. The direction of the polarization in the molecule is determined by the nature of the reagent and by its point of attack.) Finally, for reaction with a radical reagent, the possibility of writing such structures as XXV and XXVI shows that the orientation should again be ortho, para. The justification for this prediction is that, since a formal bond makes no contribution to the stability of the structure containing it, an atom linked by such a bond can easily contribute a single electron to a new bond with the attacking reagent. Structures in which meta carbon atoms are joined by formal bonds can also be drawn; these, however, are either of the type represented by XXVII, in which the two atoms joined by the formal bond are in the same ring, or of the type represented by XXVIII, which is relatively unstable in consequence of

XXV   XXVI

XXVII   XXVIII

the additional formal bond. In neither event, however, could these further structures be expected to have as great an effect upon the orientation as those like XXV and XXVI. This prediction is verified by the fact that the decomposition of benzoyl peroxide in biphenyl as solvent leads to p-terphenyl,[97] and that, in the Gomberg reaction between biphenyl and either diazotized aniline or diazotized p-nitroaniline, the orientation is again para.[98]

    [96] N. Campbell, W. Anderson, and J. Gilmore, J. Chem. Soc. 1940, 446.
    [97] H. Gelissen and P. H. Hermans, Ber. 58, 285 (1925).
    [98] W. S. M. Grieve and D. H. Hey, J. Chem. Soc. 1938, 108.

Naphthalene is another substance which can be expected to exhibit the same orientation for all three types of reagents. The arguments leading to this conclusion are somewhat more complicated than those outlined above in connection with biphenyl (without, however, being essentially different), and they will be left for the interested reader to work out for himself. Experimentally, it has been found that nitric acid, diazotized methyl anthranilate[98, 99] (in the Gomberg reaction), and sodamide[66] all attack at the α position. It is of particular interest that the identical orientation for these widely different reagents could hardly have been explained on the basis of any assumed distribution of charge in the unreacting naphthalene molecule.

The sulfonation of naphthalene at the β position at high temperatures seems to be a matter of equilibrium rather than of rate, since the α-sulfonic acid is apparently formed first, just as at low temperatures; the initial product then "rearranges" by a mechanism involving desulfonation and subsequent resulfonation to the more stable β isomer. An additional, and perhaps again only apparent, anomaly in the reactions of naphthalene derivatives occurs with the nucleophilic displacements of the halogen atoms from the halonaphthalenes. In the isotopic exchange reactions between the monobromonaphthalenes and radioactive bromide ion, the beta isomer reacts appreciably faster than the alpha isomer;[100] and, in the reactions of the chloro-, bromo-, and iodonaphthalenes with piperidine, the beta isomers are again the more reactive.[101] The isotopic exchanges were, however, carried out at temperatures higher than 200°C, and the aminations were carried out at 165°C and at 200°C. The several reactions were therefore not strictly comparable with the more familiar ones studied at much lower temperatures. Indeed, from the temperature coefficients of the rate constants, Berliner, Quinn, and Edgerton[101] were able to show that, as expected, the activation energies are higher for the displacements of the halogen atoms in the beta positions; and hence that, if the reactions could be observed at sufficiently lower temperatures, the alpha isomers would then be the more reactive. In the 1-halo-2-nitro- and 2-halo-1-nitronaphthalenes, with which the reactions with piperidine proceed with measurable speeds at room temperature or below, the halogen atoms are displaced from the alpha positions more rapidly than from the beta positions.[101] Although the complete explanation for these observations is not apparent, steric hindrance may be one of the contributing factors.

An interesting variation in the radical substitution reactions of naphthalene is illustrated by the observation[102] that, when benzoyl peroxide is decomposed in the presence of 1-chloro-, 1-bromo-, or 1-nitronaphthalene, the products consist not of substituted phenylnaphthalenes but of substituted naphthyl benzoates. Apparently, therefore, the benzoyl peroxide decomposes to benzoate radicals C_6H_5—CO_2, which attack the aromatic

[99] For the analogous formation of (principally) α-phenylnaphthalene from naphthalene and N-nitrosoacetanilide, see R. Huisgen and G. Sorge, *Ann.* **566**, 162 (1950).

[100] B. Pullman, P. Rumpf, and F. Kieffer, *J. chim. phys.* **45**, 150 (1948).

[101] E. Berliner, M. J. Quinn, and P. J. Edgerton, *J. Am. Chem. Soc.* **72**, 5305 (1950).

[102] R. L. Dannley and M. Gippin, *J. Am. Chem. Soc.* **74**, 332 (1952).

molecules; and the phenyl radicals, if they are formed at all, are ultimately transformed into the benzene that is also found among the
products.   In any event, the orientation is, as expected, predominantly
alpha since the positions occupied by the entering benzoate group are,
in order of decreasing preference, 4, 5, and 2.   Since the reactions occur
most rapidly in the ring that is already substituted, we can further conclude
that the chlorine and bromine atoms and the nitro group are all activating
for radical attack.   An additional reaction which is clearly analogous to
the foregoing is the one between benzoyl peroxide and anthracene; the
product is here the benzoate of 9-anthrol.[103]

In chlorobenzene, there are two different effects that need to be considered separately.   The first of these effects exists because the chlorine
atom is strongly electronegative, and so pulls electrons away from the
carbon atom to which it is attached.   If this displacement of charge were
the only factor to be considered, the orientation should be just as in
pyridine or in the trimethylanilinium ion—meta with deactivation for
electrophilic reagents, predominantly ortho for radical reagents, and
ortho, para with activation for nucleophilic reagents.   The situation
could then be represented by the structure XXIX.   The second effect to
be considered results because the chlorine atom has an unshared pair of
electrons, so that the R-effect symbolized by the structure XXX can play
a significant role.   If this displacement of charge were the only factor
involved, the orientation would be ortho, para with activation for an
electrophilic reagent, indeterminate for a radical reagent, and meta with
deactivation for a nucleophilic reagent. (However, resonance with
structures like XXXI might favor ortho, para orientation for a radical
reagent R.   Cf. the somewhat analogous situation in the peroxide-induced

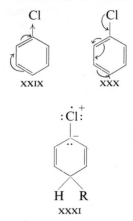

[103] I. M. Riott and W. A. Waters, *J. Chem. Soc.* **1952**, 2695.

addition of hydrogen bromide to vinyl chloride, discussed in Section 8·6.) The two effects, which are due, respectively, to the electronegativity and to the unshared pair of electrons of the chlorine atom, are largely in conflict with each other.   We therefore cannot predict with any assurance what the actual orientation will be for any of the different types of reagent. Experimentally, it is found that the orientation is ortho, para with de-activation for an electrophilic reagent.   When benzoyl peroxide is decomposed in the presence of chlorobenzene, the rates at which the resulting radical reagent attacks the ortho, meta, and para positions are, respectively, 2.7, 1.03, and 1.2 times that at which the same reagent attacks any one of the six equivalent positions in unsubstituted benzene.[104] The observed orientation is therefore ortho, para; and all positions are slightly activated.   Closely similar values for the relative rates have been found also for fluorobenzene, bromobenzene, and iodobenzene.[104]   With respect to nucleophilic substitution, the chlorine atom activates all positions, but especially meta.[105]   In each of the three types of reaction, therefore, a compromise between the opposed effects is reached, so that each determines some features of the total picture.   This result, although it could not have been foreseen in its entirety, is not unreasonable.[84]

For phenols, phenol ethers, and aromatic amines, the theoretical treatments are the same as for chlorobenzene.   Here also, there are two opposed effects, and we cannot tell a priori which will predominate.   In these substances, however, the R-effect wins out completely, at any rate as far as substitution by an electrophilic reagent is concerned, so that the orientation for such a reagent is ortho, para, with very great activation. There is also evidence[106] that, with anisole, even the relatively unfavored meta position is slightly activated.   With respect to nucleophilic substi-tution, the little evidence which is available suggests that the hydroxyl, alkoxyl, and amino groups deactivate both the meta and para positions, but it is insufficient to show the relative degrees of deactivation at the different positions.[107]   These several observations, although they could not have been foreseen, are nevertheless again quite reasonable.[84]

[104] D. R. Augood, J. I. G. Cadogan, D. H. Hey, and G. H. Williams, *J. Chem. Soc.* **1953**, 3412; D. H. Hey and G. H. Williams, *Discussions Faraday Soc.* **14**, 216 (1953); R. L. Dannley, E. C. Gregg, Jr., R. E. Phelps, and C. B. Coleman, *J. Am. Chem. Soc.* **76**, 445 (1954).   For some earlier and less complete evidence pointing to similar conclusions, see M. Gomberg and W. E. Bachmann, *J. Am. Chem. Soc.* **46**, 2339 (1924); W. S. M. Grieve and D. H. Hey, *J. Chem. Soc.* **1934**, 1797; D. F. DeTar and H. J. Scheifele, Jr., *J. Am. Chem. Soc.* **73**, 1442 (1951).   See also R. L. Dannley and M. Gippin, reference 102.
[105] Cf. p. 315 of J. F. Bunnett and R. E. Zahler, *Chem. Revs.* **49**, 273 (1951).
[106] P. B. D. de la Mare and C. A. Vernon, *J. Chem. Soc.* **1951**, 1764.
[107] Cf. pp. 317ff of J. F. Bunnett and R. E. Zahler, *Chem. Revs.* **49**, 273 (1951).

In connection with the present difference in behavior between chlorobenzene on the one hand and the phenols, phenol ethers, and aromatic amines on the other, it is of interest to recall a conclusion reached in Section 5·4. We found there that the dipole moment of p-nitroaniline requires a relatively large contribution from a structure like XXXII, whereas the moment of p-nitrochlorobenzene requires only a small contribution from the analogous structure XXXIII. It therefore appears that the unshared

N^+H_2 Cl^+

$O^-N^+O^-$ $O^-N^+O^-$

XXXII   XXXIII

pair of electrons, which is required at the point of attack in an electrophilic substitution, should be provided more easily in the amine than in the halogen compound. On this basis, the difference in orienting effect under discussion is seen to be, at any rate, in the expected direction.

We are now in position to consider in greater detail the problem that was briefly mentioned in Section 8·2, in connection with the reactions of 2,7-dihydroxynaphthalene. The point of interest is that this substance couples readily with a diazonium compound at the 1 (or 8) position, but cannot be forced to couple at the 3 (or 6) position.[7] In order to understand this striking experimental result, let us consider the natures of the activated complexes that would be involved in the reactions at the 1 and at the 3 position. As usual, we shall center our attention principally upon the Class B structures; and, since the R-effect, which is made possible by the hydroxyl group, seems to be an essential feature of the coupling reaction, we shall consider only those structures in which the oxygen atom is joined to the naphthalene nucleus by a double bond. In any event, structures of this type would be expected to be especially stable, and so especially important, since they contain one more bond than any of the others. With these simplifications, then, we can write the structures XXXIV and XXXV for coupling in the 1 position, but only the single structure XXXVI for coupling in the 3 position. It will be remembered

R   H

HO⟍   ⟋O$^+$H

XXXIV

that in diazo coupling the active reagent, which is presumably the diazonium cation and which is abbreviated as simply "R" in structures XXXIV–XXXVI, is electrophilic and so contributes no electrons to the

C—R bond.   (The situations for coupling in the 8 and 6 positions are equivalent to the two above and need not be discussed further.)

It is now apparent that the activated complex for coupling at the 1 position must be much the more stable of the two, since it alone retains the full resonance energy of an intact benzene ring.   If, for example, the activation energies for the two reactions differed by just this resonance energy, say 36 kcal per mole, the ratio of the rate constants would be about $10^{26}:1$.   This enormous value is, however, only an upper limit and cannot be taken seriously.   Since the ignored Class A structures must be important in the activated complexes and since the numerous Class B structures with merely single bonds between the oxygen and carbon atoms are also involved, the ratio must be much smaller.   There can be no reasonable doubt, however, that it still is very large, so that the coupling should occur with much greater ease at the 1 (or 8) position than at the 2 (or 6) position, as is observed.   In fact, a value of about 10.4 kcal per mole for the difference in energy of activation, and hence of about 3×10^7 for the ratio of rate constants, has been derived[84] by a semi-quantitative method, in which all the Class B structures (but not the Class A structures) are taken into account.   This figure cannot be relied upon as even approximately correct numerically, but the fact that it is still very large is significant.   It is especially to be noted that the conclusion that 2,7-dihydroxynaphthalene should couple only in the 1 (or 8) position has been derived without the necessity of postulating that the unreacting molecule is rigidly fixed in the Erlenmeyer structure XXXVII.

A possibly somewhat similar situation, in which a fixation of bonds in an aromatic molecule has been postulated, is encountered in 5-hydroxyhydrindene, XXXVIII.   In this substance, coupling with a diazonium compound occurs readily at position 6, but only with difficulty at position 4.[108]   The original interpretation of the experimental data was that the molecule is more or less rigidly held in structure XXXIX, and that the further structure XL is involved to only a minor extent, if at all.   We can now,

108 W. H. Mills and I. G. Nixon, *J. Chem. Soc.* **1930**, 2510.   See also L. F. Fieser and W. C. Lothrop, *J. Am. Chem. Soc.* **58**, 2050 (1936); **59**, 945 (1937).

however, suggest a different interpretation, which makes no such drastic assumption regarding the unreacting molecule.   If, as before, we neglect all Class A structures and also all those Class B structures in which there is only a single bond between the oxygen and carbon atoms, we can write the structures XLI and XLII for the activated complexes

XXXVIII

XXXIX

XL

XLI

XLII

involved in the reactions at positions 6 and 4, respectively.   There is no obvious difference in resonance energy possible here to make one activated complex more stable than the other, but a difference in bond energies seems reasonable.   In structures XLI and XLII, the bond between carbon atoms 8 and 9 is represented as single and double, respectively.   Mills and Nixon[108] suggested that the bond angles that are enforced by the fused five-membered ring are such as to make the structure XLI, in which the bond in question is single, more stable than XLII, in which it is double.   Still a further possibility[84] is that the C_8—C_9 bond is stretched by a spring-like action of the five-membered ring, so that its length is nearer to the single-bond value than in, say, phenol. In either event, structure XLI is more stable than XLII, and consequently the coupling can be expected to occur more readily in position 6 than in position 4, as is observed. Again this prediction must be modified by the inclusion of the Class A, and of the remaining Class B, structures.   On the other hand, Longuet-Higgins and Coulson[109] have concluded, on the basis of a detailed, but still only approximate, calculation which cannot be described here, that any changes in bond angles are of secondary importance, and that the C_8—C_9 bond is not stretched, as was assumed above, but is instead shortened.   In view of the complexity of the problem and of the many drastic approximations that are therefore required in any attempted theoretical treatment, a completely satisfactory understanding of the problem seems now to be impossible.   Since the observed effect is a relatively small one, a fairly precise evaluation of each contributing factor would be required before a reliable conclusion could be reached.

When the problem of orientation in aromatic systems is considered, as in this section, from the viewpoint of the resonance theory, the ortho and

[109] H. C. Longuet-Higgins and C. A. Coulson, *Trans. Faraday Soc.* **42**, 756 (1946). Cf. also M. J. S. Dewar, *The Electronic Theory of Organic Chemistry*, Oxford University Press, Oxford, 1949, pp. 197ff.

para positions seem always to be equally activated, or deactivated. Since there are two equivalent ortho positions but only one para position, we might therefore anticipate that, when a second substituent is introduced into a monosubstituted benzene, the resulting mixture of products should contain twice as much of the ortho isomer as of the para. This statistical ratio, however, is seldom, if ever, exactly realized. Clearly, therefore, there must be additional factors which are independent of the ones already considered, and which determine the ortho-para ratio. One of these factors is doubtless steric hindrance,[110] which makes it relatively difficult for a reagent to attack a position that is ortho to a bulky atom or group. In the nitration of alkylbenzenes, for example, the ortho-para ratio is approximately 1.4 for toluene, 1.2 for ethylbenzene, 0.16 for isopropylbenzene, and 0.15 for tert-butylbenzene.[111, 112] Although these data are perhaps not strictly comparable since they were obtained by different workers under different experimental conditions, the trend toward smaller values with increasing complexity of the alkyl group is unmistakable. Moreover, the size of the attacking reagent seems also to have the expected effect. With chlorobenzene, for example, the ortho-para ratio is approximately 0.7 for chlorination, 0.4 for nitration, 0.13 for bromination, and 0.0 for sulfonation.[111] Even though the exact dimensions of the inorganic molecules or ions are not known, the observed order of decreasing values is here reasonable.

Steric hindrance cannot, however, be the only factor that is responsible for the observed deviations of the ortho-para ratio from the value 2.[110] In the nitration of the halogenobenzenes, for example, this ratio is approximately 0.1 with fluorobenzene, 0.4 with chlorobenzene, 0.6 with bromobenzene, and 0.7 with iodobenzene;[111] the order is here, therefore, the exact opposite of the one expected from steric effects alone. Although, as was noted above, the simple resonance approach provides no satisfactory explanation either for these data or for the corresponding data that have been obtained for many other groups of substances, a more quantitative treatment, which is based on molecular-orbital calculations,[113] has proved rather more successful (cf. also the discussion of radical substitution in pyridine, pages 485f). The details of these

[110] For a recent summary of the evidence, see, for example, C. K. Ingold, *Structure and Mechanism in Organic Chemistry*, Cornell University Press, Ithaca, N. Y., 1953, pp. 257ff.

[111] These data are taken from the compilation of Ingold, reference 110.

[112] See also K. L. Nelson and H. C. Brown, *J. Am. Chem. Soc.* **73**, 5605 (1951); H. C. Brown and W. H. Bonner, *ibid.* **76**, 605 (1954); J. H. Lamneck, Jr., *ibid.* **76**, 1106 (1954).

[113] M. J. S. Dewar, *J. Chem. Soc.* **1949**, 463. For a treatment of the ortho-para ratio from the valence-bond point of view, see A. L. Green, *J. Chem. Soc.* **1954**, 3538.

calculations cannot be given here, but three general rules to which they have led, and which apply to attack by electrophilic reagents, can profitably be stated without proof. (1) If the substituent that is responsible for the orientation merely withdraws electrons from, or releases electrons to, the aromatic ring, the ortho-para ratio decreases with increasing electronegativity of that substituent; (2) if the structure of the aromatic compound contains the grouping Ar—X, where X is any atom with an unshared pair of electrons, the ortho-para ratio (with respect to the substituent containing the atom X) decreases with increasing electronegativity of X; and (3), if the structure of the aromatic compound contains the grouping Ar—X=Y, the ortho-para ratio increases with increasing electronegativity of the atom Y. These rules, which had previously been derived from a more empirical viewpoint,[114] are in satisfactory agreement with the observations. The above data for the halogenobenzenes, for example, illustrate the second, and perhaps also the first, of the rules; the fact that, in nitrations, the ortho-para ratio is approximately 1.4 for toluene, 0.6 for benzyl chloride, 0.5 for benzal chloride, and 0.2 for benzotrichloride[110] illustrates the first rule, and perhaps also the effect of steric hindrance; and the fact that aromatic aldehydes, acids, nitriles, nitro compounds, and the like give much more of the ortho-disubstituted product than of the para[110, 113] illustrates the third rule.

Hammett's concept[115] of reaction constants ρ and substituent constants σ (cf. pages 352ff), provides an interesting alternative approach to the problem of orientation. Since σ is generally negative for any substituent which, like the amino and hydroxyl groups, facilitates electrophilic substitution, ρ for this type of reaction must also be negative (cf. equation 2, Section 7·2), even though its numerical value has not been definitely established. Conversely, ρ for nucleophilic substitution must be positive, even though its exact value is again not known. A few examples will here be sufficient to illustrate how this method for treating some simple problems of orientation can be applied. Since $\sigma_{p\text{-}NH_2} = -0.660$, whereas $\sigma_{m\text{-}NH_2} = -0.161$,[115] electrophilic reagents will attack the para position of aniline in preference to the meta position, and the meta position in preference to any of the six equivalent positions in unsubstituted benzene; since $\sigma_{p\text{-}Cl} = 0.227$, whereas $\sigma_{m\text{-}Cl} = 0.373$,[115] electrophilic reagents will attack the para position of chlorobenzene in preference to the meta position, but even the favored para position is deactivated; and since

[114] See C. K. Ingold, *Ann. Repts. on Progress Chem.* (*Chem. Soc. London*) **23**, 140 (1926).
[115] L. P. Hammett, *Chem. Revs.* **17**, 125 (1935); *Physical Organic Chemistry*, McGraw-Hill Book Co., New York, 1940, pp. 186ff; H. H. Jaffé, *Chem. Revs.* **53**, 191 (1953).

$\sigma_{p\text{-}NO_2} = 1.27$, $\sigma_{m\text{-}NO_2} = 0.710$, $\sigma_{p\text{-}CN} = 1.00$, and $\sigma_{m\text{-}CN} = 0.678$,[115] nucleophilic reagents will attack the para positions of nitrobenzene and of benzonitrile in preference to the meta positions, all positions are activated, and the nitro group is more effective in promoting the reactions than the cyano group.

The above values of $\sigma_{p\text{-}NO_2}$ and $\sigma_{p\text{-}CN}$ are the ones which apply when the substituents are para to amino or hydroxyl groups. Although this choice is not ideal, it is here required by a lack of reliable and consistent data. Hammett[115] gives no value for $\sigma_{p\text{-}CN}$ for use when the cyano group is not para to an amino or hydroxyl group; Jaffé[115] gives the value 0.628 but states that this is the average of values ranging from 0.232 to 0.756. In view of these uncertainties, the comparisons made in the preceding paragraph seem to be the least objectionable ones now possible.

It is possibly somewhat surprising that Hammett's substituent constants can thus be correlated with the orienting and activating (or deactivating) effects of the atoms or groups concerned. Since these constants were originally evaluated from a study of reactions that occur at some distance from the aromatic rings (for example, the ionization of substituted benzoic acids or the hydrolysis of substituted benzoate esters),[115] they presumably refer primarily to the distributions of electric charge.[116] Since $\sigma_{p\text{-}NO_2} > \sigma_{m\text{-}NO_2}$, the carbon atom which is para to the nitro group in, say, nitrobenzene, must be more positive, or less negative, than the one which is meta to that group; and the remaining differences between pairs of σ values can be interpreted in completely similar ways. We have found in this section, however, that most features of the observed orientation effects can be satisfactorily explained in terms of the polarization of the organic molecules by the attacking reagents, and without explicit reference to the charge distributions in the isolated and unreacting molecules. Some explanation for the success of Hammett's relations is therefore required. In the first place, it may be noted that, on the basis of some approximate molecular-orbital calculations, a certain measure of correlation between charge distribution and polarizability may be expected.[86, 117] In the second place, the observed correlation is not, in fact, perfect. The most clearly established example in which the application of Hammett's substituent constants to aromatic substitution reactions leads to an incorrect conclusion has been encountered in studies of the —$N^+(CH_3)_3$ group.[118] Since this group is meta directing and deactivating for electrophilic substitution, and ortho, para directing and activating for nucleophilic substitution, the inequalities $\sigma_{p\text{-}N^+(CH_3)_3} > \sigma_{m\text{-}N^+(CH_3)_3}$

[116] Cf. H. H. Jaffé, *J. Chem. Phys.* **20**, 279, 778, 1554 (1952); **21**, 415 (1953).

[117] H. C. Longuet-Higgins, *J. Chem. Phys.* **18**, 283 (1950).

[118] J. D. Roberts, R. A. Clement, and J. J. Drysdale, *J. Am. Chem. Soc.* **73**, 2181 (1951).

> 0 might be expected to hold.   Now, when the σ's are evaluated from the ionization constants of the benzoic acids or of the anilinium ions, or from the rate constants for the reactions of the benzoic acids with diphenyldiazomethane,[118] both the σ's are indeed found to be positive; however, $\sigma_{m\text{-}N^+(CH_3)_3}$ is appreciably greater than $\sigma_{p\text{-}N^+(CH_3)_3}$.   The most logical explanation[118] for this discrepancy is that the σ's, when determined in the ways cited, refer to the net charges on the carbon atoms that are meta and para to the $-N^+(CH_3)_3$ group, whereas the orienting and activating effects are determined by the relative ease with which the required charges can be brought to the points of attack during the courses of the substitutions.   In the nitration of the trimethylanilinium ion at the para position, for example, the activated complex is especially un-stable, not because the para carbon atom has an exceptionally large positive charge, but rather because the energy of the Class B structure XLIII, which is one of those contributing to the state of the hybrid, is

$$N^+(CH_3)_3$$

H   NO$_2$
XLIII

very high on account of the proximity of the two positive charges.   (For discussion of a somewhat analogous situation which likewise arises when the effect of the resonance becomes comparable with that of the normal charge distribution, see the paragraphs preceding the ones in fine print at the end of Section 7·2.)

In each of the problems that have so far been discussed, we have found it unnecessary to consider either the competition or the interaction between different substituents that are present in the same molecule.   Let us now, however, turn to the more complex problem that arises when this simplification is no longer possible.   In 3-nitrophenol, for example, the hydroxyl group directs an electrophilic reagent to positions 2, 4, and 6, whereas the nitro group directs such a reagent to position 5.   When there is a competition of this type, the empirical rule that any substituent which orients ortho and para will predominate over any other which orients meta seems to be generally valid.   With 3-nitrophenol, accord-ingly, chlorination and bromination give, respectively, 2-chloro- and 2-bromo-3-nitrophenol.   In each instance, therefore, the observed orientation is largely, or entirely, determined by the hydroxyl group.   Similarly, in 3-nitrotoluene, the orientation is largely determined by the methyl group; in 3-chloronitrobenzene, it is largely determined by the chlorine atom; and so on.

When the orientations in the above disubstituted derivatives of benzene are considered from the qualitative viewpoint of the simple resonance theory, no entirely satisfactory explanations for the observed behaviors seem to be possible. When, however, the problem is treated in the more quantitative way[84] that is permitted by the molecular-orbital approach (cf. also page 499), rather reasonable results can be obtained.[119] Although the approximations that must be introduced into these latter treatments are extremely drastic, the fairly good agreements with the empirical data are gratifying, and probably significant.

A different type of competition or, more precisely, interaction between substituent groups is displayed in the alkaline hydrolysis of 2,7-dichloro-phenazine-5-oxide, XLIV.[120] Since the amine oxide grouping in position 5 has here a close structural similarity to a nitro group, it ought to be strongly activating and ortho, para directing for attack by a nucleophilic reagent like the hydroxide ion. On the other hand, the trivalent nitrogen atom at position 10 ought to be slightly deactivating, but to have an uncertain orienting effect (cf. page 495). We might therefore perhaps expect that there will be a net activation, and that the chlorine atom at position 2 will be the one replaced. Pachter and Kloetzel, however, have shown that, although there is indeed a net activation, the chlorine atom which is displaced is the one at position 7. The product, accordingly, has structure XLV instead of the expected XLVI. A satisfactory explanation for the observed orientation can be obtained from a consideration

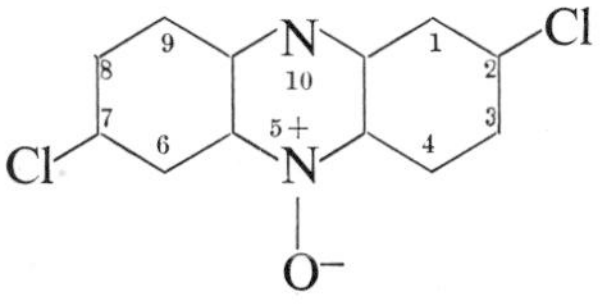

XLIV

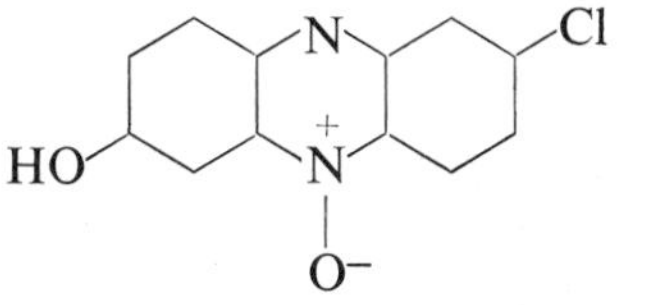

XLV

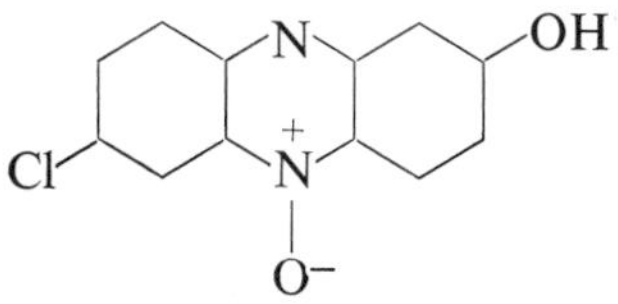

XLVI

[119] S. L. Matlow and G. W. Wheland, *J. Am. Chem. Soc.* **77**, 3653 (1955).

[120] I. J. Pachter and M. C. Kloetzel, *J. Am. Chem. Soc.* **74**, 971 (1952). See also H. H. Jaffé, *J. Am. Chem. Soc.* **76**, 3527 (1954) for discussion of both nucleophilic and electrophilic substitution in the analogous, but simpler, pyridine 1-oxide.

of the resonance within the two possible activated complexes. If the hydroxide ion attacks the molecule of the phenazine oxide at position 2, only such Class B structures as XLVII, XLVIII, etc., with extensive separations of charge can be involved; but, if the attack is instead at position 7, there are not only all the Class B structures which, like XLIX and L, are analogous to XLVII, XLVIII, etc., but also the doubtless

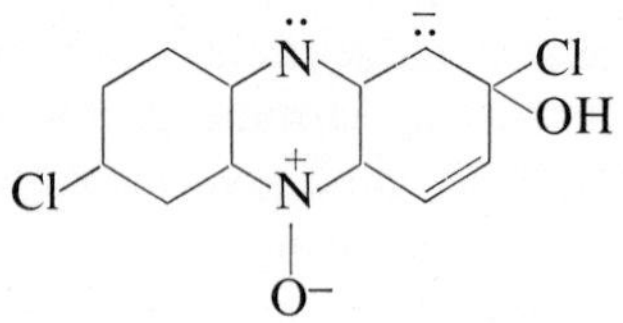

XLVII

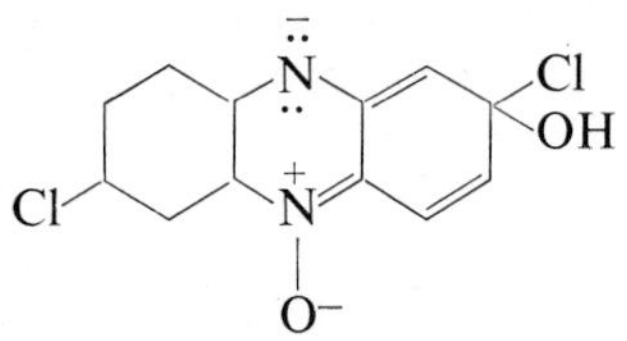

XLVIII

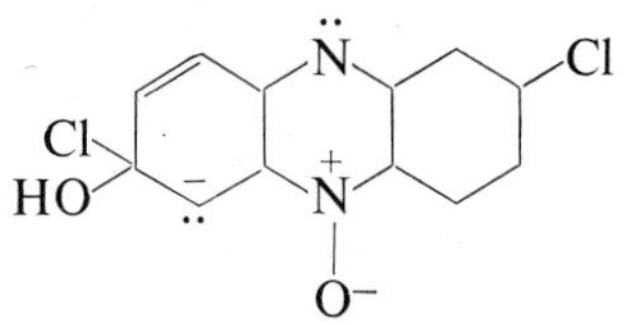

XLIX

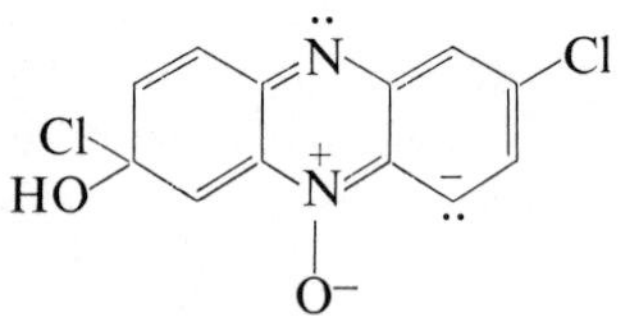

L

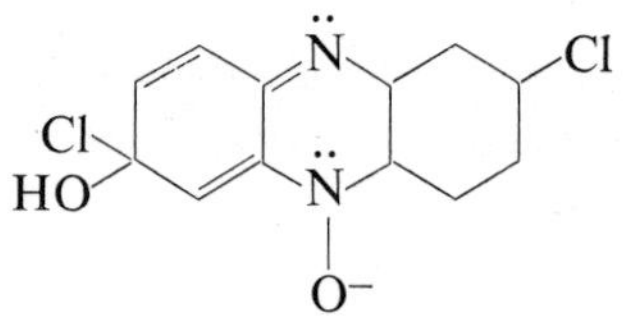

LI

much more stable structure LI. Consequently, the fact that reaction occurs at position 7, rather than at position 2, is reasonable and, indeed, could have been predicted.[120]

Veratraldehyde, LII, provides a further example of a substance with which the observed orientation appears at first sight to be anomalous.

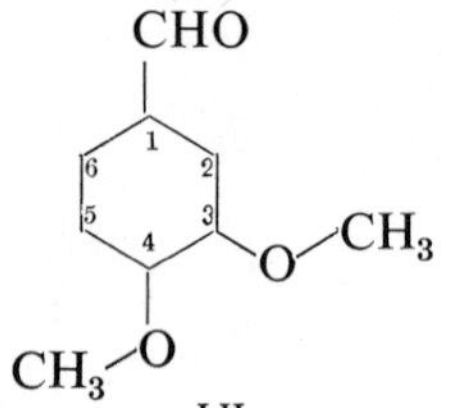

LII

The methoxyl group in position 3 should here direct an electrophilic attack to positions 2 and 6, whereas the one in position 4 should instead direct the attack to position 5. Since the effects of these two groups ought therefore to cancel each other, we might naturally expect that the orientation will be determined by the formyl group, and hence that the substitution will occur most rapidly at position 5. Experimentally, however, bromination leads to 6-bromoveratraldehyde, LIII, and nitration leads to 6-nitroveratraldehyde, LIV. Similarly, with piperonal, LV, bromination gives 6-bromopiperonal, LVI, and nitration gives 6-nitro-piperonal, LVII. In each of these reactions, the orientation is therefore

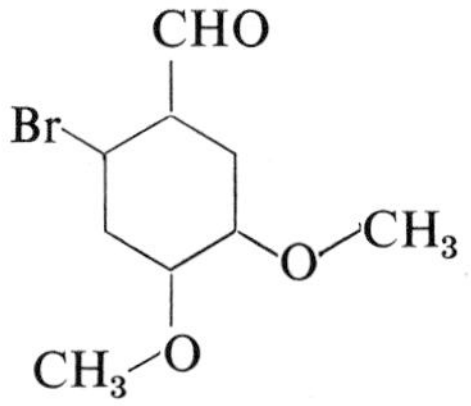

LIII 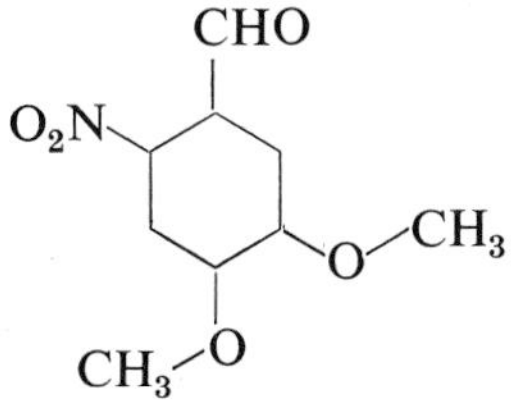   LIV

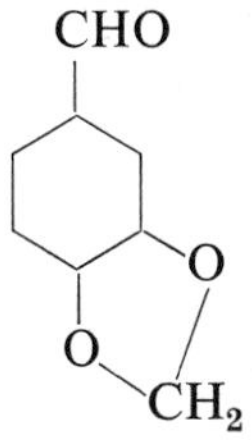

LV 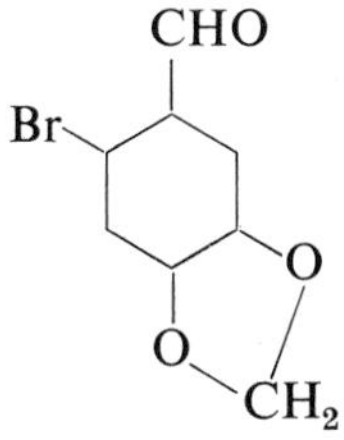   LVI 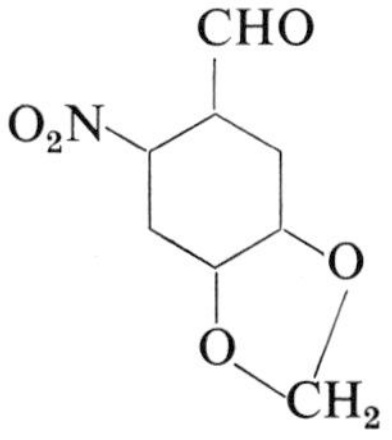   LVII

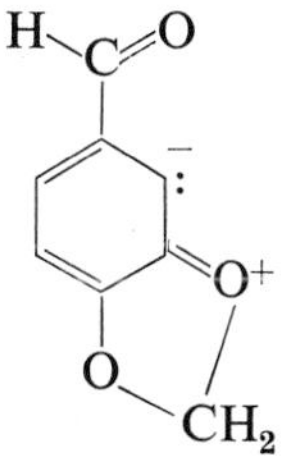

LVIII 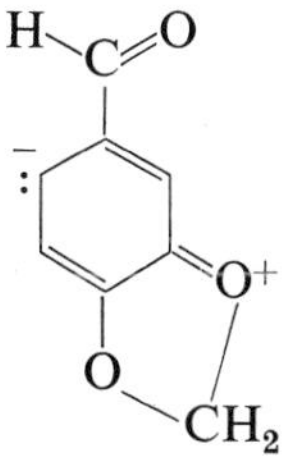   LIX 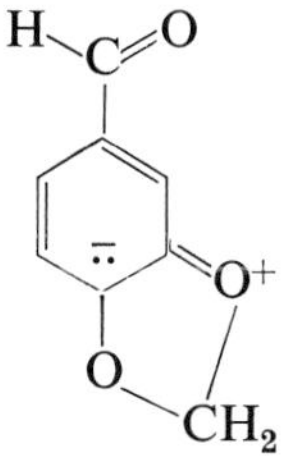   LX 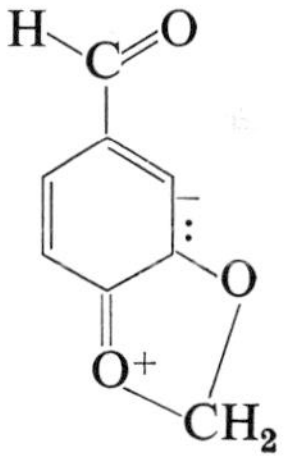   LXI

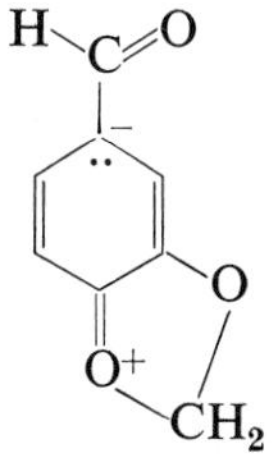

LXII 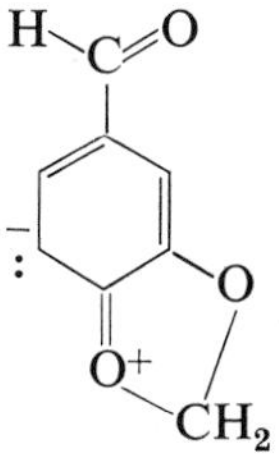   LXIII 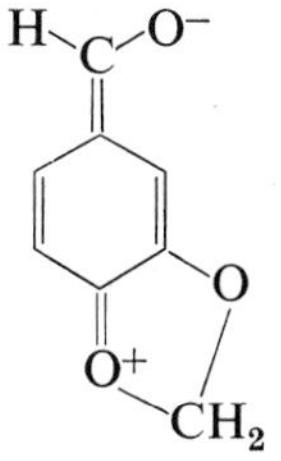   LXIV

quite different from that expected. A possible, but probably inadequate, explanation for these anomalies is that electrophilic reagents prefer the 6 positions in veratraldehyde and in piperonal simply because alkoxyl groups activate para positions more effectively than they do ortho positions. There is, in fact, evidence that such a difference exists, since the bromination of phenol gives mostly *p*-bromophenol; and the nitration, especially when it proceeds by an initial nitrosation (cf. page 482), likewise gives mostly the para isomer.[121]

An additional and perhaps more important factor has been suggested by Râmy and Robinson.[122] When re-expressed in terms of the resonance theory, the explanation that is due to these latter authors takes the following form. In piperonal, for example, the resonance doubtless includes not only the two Kekulé structures which are implied in the structure LV, but also the seven quinoid structures LVIII–LXIV. As a result of the contribution from structure LXIV, only the methoxyl group that is in position 3 remains unmodified and hence able to exert its full activating effect. Consequently, the reactions occur at the position that is para to this group. Although the argument of Râm y and Robinson thus leads to the correct answers, a more careful examination shows that, in the form just stated, it is unjustifiably oversimplified. The difficulty arises because the resonance with the quinoid structure LXIV affects only the initial reagent, which is common to the reactions at the 5 and 6 positions, but does not directly affect the activated complexes, which are different for the two reactions. The only factor which can favor one point of attack over the other is therefore ignored.

If we instead center our attention upon the activated complexes, we find little obvious difference between them. For attack at the 5 position of piperonal, for example, the most significant contributing structures are possibly LXV, LXVI, and LXVII, where R^+ represents the effective electrophilic reagent; and for attack at the 6 position, the corresponding

    LXV   LXVI   LXVII

[121] Cf. C. K. Ingold, *Structure and Mechanism in Organic Chemistry*, Cornell University Press, Ithaca, N. Y., 1953, p. 265.

[122] J. N. Râm y and R. Robinson, *J. Chem. Soc.* **127**, 1618 (1925).

structures are the closely analogous LXVIII, LXIX, and LXX.   The
latter hybrid may be somewhat the more stable since, in it, the positive

charge that originally comes from the reagent R$^+$ is more evenly distributed
between the oxygen atoms of the two methoxyl groups; from the present
qualitative considerations, however, we are hardly justified in concluding
that the difference in stability is necessarily great enough to account for
the observed difference in rate of reaction.   Again, therefore, we must
rely on the results obtained from some more quantitative molecular-
orbital calculations,[119] which have shown that the second of the above
activated complexes should indeed be more stable than the first.

Although the explanation to which we thus finally come is superficially
rather different from that originally proposed by Rây and Robinson, the
two interpretations are nevertheless closely related; and the more recent
one can be considered a logical development of the earlier one.   The
complete solution to the problem is still, however, quite obscure since
there seems to be little consistency in the behaviors of different compounds
with closely analogous structures.   Although, as was stated above, both
bromination and nitration of veratraldehyde, LII, lead to substitution at
position 6, each of the corresponding reactions with vanillin, LXXI,

occurs instead at position 5; and, with 4-nitroveratrole, LXXII, bromination occurs at position 6 but nitration occurs at position 5.   A satisfactory explanation for these conflicting observations will probably be
possible only with the aid of additional experimental data.

8·12 Steric Inhibition of Resonance and Rates of Reaction. The hydrolysis and other similar reactions of an aryl halide, such as chlorobenzene, for example, proceed with greater difficulty than the corresponding reactions of any comparable alkyl halide. A partial explanation of this relative inertness may be that the unreacting molecule is stabilized by resonance with structures, of which I is a typical example, in which the chlorine atom is joined to the ring by a double bond. The activated complex, however, has smaller possibilities for resonance, since no Class B structures analogous to I can be written. Consequently, the activation

$$Cl^{+}$$

I

energy should be somewhat higher and the rate should be somewhat lower, than for the corresponding reaction of an alkyl halide, in which no resonance at all of the present type is involved. (This same explanation may be partly responsible also for the inertness of the unsaturated aliphatic halides of the vinyl chloride type.) However, the stabilization of the unreacting molecules by the resonance under consideration can amount at most to only a very few kilocalories per mole, so that this present effect is much too small to be responsible for all of the great difference in reactivity. A further factor which may be involved in the reactions of the aromatic halides (but which cannot be in those of the vinyl halides) is that the resonance within the benzene ring must be largely destroyed in the Class B structures of the activated complexes, and that the stabilities of these complexes are accordingly decreased. And finally, we should note that the mechanism of substitution at an unsaturated atom is doubtless so different from that at a saturated atom that a direct comparison between the rates of the two types of reaction is of questionable significance (cf. Section 8·1).

Whatever the complete explanation for the relative inertness of the aryl halides may be, however, it is an important empirical fact that a nitro group in a position ortho or para with respect to the halogen atom enables the reactions under discussion to take place much more easily. In Section 8·11 we accounted for this activating effect of a nitro group (for substitution by a nucleophilic reagent) on the basis of resonance with quinoid structures like II. Since such structures are most stable when the nitro group lies in the plane of the benzene ring, we can anticipate that the activating effect of the nitro group would be decreased if the molecule could be forced out of the planar configuration. A certain amount of experimental evidence is available in confirmation of this

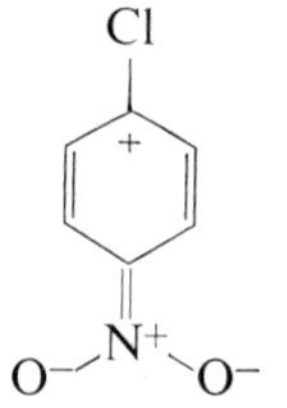

II

expectation. The data quoted below are of varying types, but all of them are directly comparable since they refer to reactions in which substitution by a nucleophilic reagent is facilitated by an ortho- or paranitro group.

When 2,5-dinitro-*m*-xylene, III, is heated in a sealed tube with aqueous ammonia, the nitro group in position 2 is replaced by an amino group to give the nitroxylidine, IV.[123]   At first sight, this reaction seems anomalous,

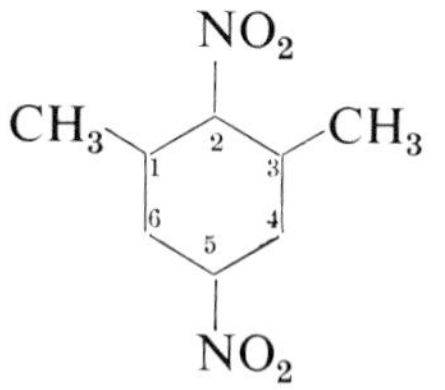

III 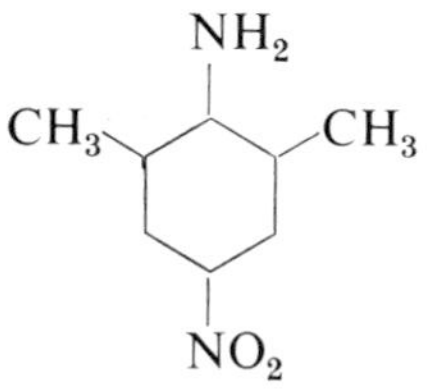   IV

because one might have predicted that the nitro group in position 5 ought to be the more easily replaced of the two.   In the first place, the nitro group in position 5 is less surrounded by the methyl radicals and so is more open to attack by the ammonia molecule; and, in the second place, methyl groups are known to be more effective in deactivating an aromatic molecule for substitution by a nucleophilic reagent when they are ortho or para, than when they are meta, to the position at which the reaction occurs.[64]   The fact that the nitro group in position 2 is actually the one replaced, in spite of the steric hindrance and in spite of the unfavorable positions of the methyl groups, is readily understandable, however, on the basis of an inhibition of resonance.   Position 2 is, in fact, activated to the full extent for reaction with a nucleophilic reagent because the nitro group in position 5 is free to assume the necessary coplanar configuration; position 5, on the other hand, is activated to a smaller extent, because the nitro group in position 2 is effectively held out of the plane of the ring by the bulky methyl groups.   The observed course of the

[123] K. Ibbotson and J. Kenner, *J. Chem. Soc.* **123**, 1260 (1923).

reaction, although it could hardly have been predicted in advance, is therefore entirely reasonable.

Several further reactions, which likewise appear anomalous at first sight, but which can be interpreted in a similar manner, have been reported. For example, in 2,3-dinitrotoluene, V, and 2,5-dinitrotoluene, VI, the

nitro group which is ortho to the methyl group, and which is apparently, therefore, the more hindered, is the one that is replaced the more rapidly by an amino group on treatment with aqueous ammonia.[124] In each of these reactions, the group replaced is ortho or para to the nitro group that encounters the less hindrance to taking up the coplanar configuration.

A somewhat more detailed kinetic study of the problem has been made by Spitzer and Wheland,[125] who investigated the rates at which a number of nitro and cyano aryl bromides react with piperidine:

$$RBr + (CH_2)_5NH \rightarrow [(CH_2)_5NHR]^+Br^-$$

They found, for example, that the rate constant for 2-nitro-5-bromo-*m*-xylene, VII, was only about one-thirty-fifth as great as that for *p*-nitro-bromobenzene, VIII. In order to exclude the possibility that this result might be due merely to the recognized deactivating effect of the methyl groups, they studied also the corresponding reactions of 2-cyano-5-bromo-*m*-xylene, IX, and *p*-cyanobromobenzene, X. The rate constant for the first of these two substances was found to be about one-third as

[124] H. Burton and J. Kenner, *J. Chem. Soc.* **119**, 1047 (1921); J. Kenner and M. Parkin, *ibid.* **117**, 852 (1920). For a number of additional examples in which reactions similarly occur at the apparently more hindered positions, see Tables 45, 47, and 50 on pp. 354ff of J. F. Bunnett and R. E. Zahler, *Chem. Revs.* **49**, 273 (1951).

[125] W. C. Spitzer and G. W. Wheland, *J. Am. Chem. Soc.* **62**, 2995 (1940).

great as that for the second. Inasmuch as resonance of the type summarized in structure XI cannot be sterically inhibited (on account of the

linearity of the cyano group), this figure provides a measure of the direct
deactivating effect of the methyl groups. Since the deactivation in the
nitro compound was considerably greater, it appears that, in this substance, the inhibition of resonance must be important. The proof is not
as complete as might be desired, however, because it was found that
2-bromo-5-nitro-m-xylene, XII, reacted much more slowly than its isomer,
VII. For this discrepancy, Spitzer and Wheland offered the explanation
that the steric hindrance caused by the methyl groups ought to be large
in view of the size of the piperidine molecule. In examining this possibility, they showed that, even toward hydroxide ion, the bromonitroxylene
XII was less reactive than its isomer VII. The significance of this result
is not completely clear, however, since the hydroxide ion in solution (in
aqueous dioxane) might also be large in consequence of solvation.

Just as the activating effect of nitro groups toward nucleophilic reagents
can be sterically inhibited, so also can that of amino groups toward
electrophilic reagents. This possibility exists because a Class B structure,
like XIII, for the reaction between aniline and bromine, is most stable

when the two amino hydrogen atoms lie in the plane of the benzene ring.
On account of the small size of the hydrogen atoms, an observable effect
of this sort could hardly be expected in substances possessing only the
unsubstituted amino group —NH_2, but it should be demonstrable in
analogous substances with, say, a dimethylamino group —$N(CH_3)_2$.

It should perhaps be mentioned that the present discussion does not require complete coplanarity of the nitrogen atom and the three atoms joined to it, since an appreciable (though probably smaller) effect could result from any reasonably close approximation to coplanarity. The essential point at issue is that the hydrogen atoms of the amino group (or the radicals which replace them) should lie on the same side of the benzene ring if the resonance under discussion is to have a great effect upon the rates. (Cf. also page 323.)

There is in the literature considerable evidence which confirms the above expectation. For example, dimethyl-*vic-m*-xylidine, XIV, is reported[126] not to react with nitrous acid, aldehydes, or diazonium com-

$$\text{N(CH}_3)_2$$

$$\text{CH}_3 \underset{}{\bigcirc} \text{CH}_3$$

XIV

pounds. Since these three types of reaction are characteristic of highly activated aromatic substances, a small inhibition of the resonance might be sufficient to produce the observed result.

Brown and his co-workers[127] have made a careful study of hydrogen exchange in aromatic amines. In the reaction

$$(\text{CH}_3)_2\text{NC}_6\text{H}_5 + \text{D}^+ \rightarrow (\text{CH}_3)_2\text{NC}_6\text{H}_4\text{D} + \text{H}^+$$

the deuteron D^+ must be an electrophilic reagent, since it can attack only at those positions at which an unshared pair of electrons can be provided. This conclusion is confirmed by the fact that exchange reactions of the above type have been found[128] to obey the customary rules of orientation for electrophilic reagents. Consequently, the rate of exchange should decrease if the resonance of the dimethylamino group with the ring is inhibited. For example, the rate could be expected to decrease in the order: *o*-fluorodimethylaniline > *o*-chlorodimethylaniline > *o*-bromodimethylaniline, as the size of the ortho substituent increases. This prediction has been experimentally confirmed.[127] More conclusive evidence pointing in the same direction can be derived from the further order of decreasing rate of reaction: N-methylindoline, XV > N-methyltetrahydroquinoline, XVI > N-methyl-homo-tetrahydroquinoline, XVII.[127] With the first of these substances, the five-membered ring holds the molecule rigidly in, or near, the planar configuration; with the second,

[126] P. Friedlaender, *Monatsh.* **19**, 627 (1898). See also C. D. Nenitzescu and V. Vântu, *Ber.* **77**, 705 (1944).

[127] W. G. Brown, A. H. Widiger, and N. J. Letang, *J. Am. Chem. Soc.* **61**, 2597 (1939).

[128] A. P. Best and C. L. Wilson, *J. Chem. Soc.* **1938**, 28.

the puckered six-membered ring prevents planarity from being achieved; and, with the third, the seven-membered ring makes the departure from planarity still greater.   The observed decrease in rate of reaction therefore parallels the decrease in resonance.

Still another reaction in which resonance seems markedly to increase the rate, and in which an inhibition of the resonance should therefore lead to a considerable decrease in the rate, is the deacylation of an o- or p-nitroacetanilide, in the presence of methoxide ion, to form methyl acetate and the free nitroaniline.[129]   Since this reaction probably involves an attack by the methoxide ion upon the carbon atom of the carbonyl group, it should be facilitated by the contributions of such quinoid structures as XVIII and XIX.   From this conclusion, two different

corollaries immediately follow.   In the first place, a nitro group that is meta to the acetylamino group should have relatively little effect upon the rate; and, in the second place, the reactions should become much slower when bulky substituents are introduced into the positions that are ortho to either the nitro or the acetylamino group.   Both these predictions have been experimentally confirmed.[129]   In order, however, to be

[129] B. M. Wepster and P. E. Verkade, Rec. trav. chim. 67, 411, 425 (1948); 68, 77, 88 (1949); 69, 1393 (1950); H. J. B. Biekart, H. B. Dessens, P. E. Verkade, and B. M. Wepster, ibid. 71, 1245 (1952).

entirely sure that the effects which are thus found to be caused by the bulky substituents are actually due to an inhibition of the resonance, one must first exclude the alternative possibility that they are instead due to a classical steric hindrance. With those derivatives in which the substituents are ortho to the nitro group but are more distant from the acetylamino group, steric hindrance seems out of the question; but, with those other derivatives in which the substituents are ortho to the acetylamino group, it provides an explanation that is superficially attractive.

A more careful study[129] has, however, shown that even here the inhibition of the resonance is the more important effect. Since the carbonyl group, at which the attack occurs, is not directly joined to the aromatic ring, but is separated from the ring by a nitrogen atom, the deacylation of a 2,6-disubstituted p-nitroacetanilide, XX, for example, should be compared not with the saponification of a 2,6-disubstituted methyl benzoate, XXI, but rather with that of a 2,6-disubstituted methyl phenylacetate, XXII; of the last two reactions, only the first is appreciably

affected by steric hindrance. Furthermore, although the methyl group that is joined to the nitrogen atom in N-methyl-o-nitroacetanilide, XXIII, causes a considerable decrease in the rate of deacylation,[130] the corresponding methyl group in the para isomer XXIV causes an appreciable *increase* in the rate;[129] with each of these compounds, the methyl group should increase the steric hindrance, but only with the first should it increase the inhibition of the resonance. And finally, if bulky substituents are introduced into the acetyl group, the rate of deacylation is not greatly

[130] P. J. Witjens, B. M. Wepster, and P. E. Verkade, *Rec. trav. chim.* **62**, 523 (1943).

affected. For all these reasons, therefore, steric hindrance appears here to be relatively unimportant.

In the examples considered so far, the resonance that is inhibited is of such nature that it would otherwise have facilitated reaction. The

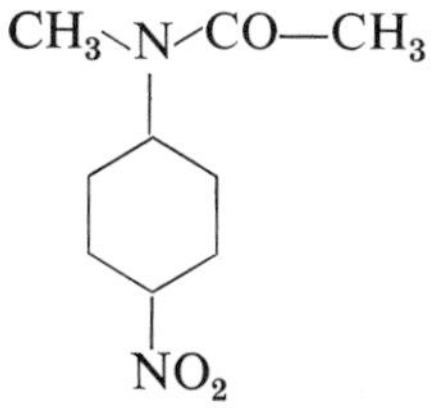

$$CH_3 \diagdown N \diagup CO—CH_3$$

XXIV

inhibition therefore has the result of slowing the reaction. One can, however, imagine the opposite situation, in which the resonance would have made the reaction more difficult. In such an event, an inhibition of resonance must make the reaction faster. It is possible, for example, that the relative ease of dinitrating mesitylene (as compared with benzene) is due not only to the direct activating effect of the methyl groups for the reaction with the electrophilic reagent but also to a decrease in the deactivating effect of the first nitro group after it has been introduced.[131] This situation is clearly just the converse of the one considered above in which the methyl groups decrease the activating effect of a nitro group for substitution by a nucleophilic reagent.

A further example, which has been more carefully examined, has to do with the rates of saponification of the esters of aminobenzoic acids.[132] In the alkaline hydrolysis of an ester, an important structure contributing to the activated complex is supposed to be one in which a hydroxide ion has become attached to the carbonyl carbon atom.[133] Consequently, although the unreacting molecule of ethyl p-dimethylaminobenzoate is a hybrid of structures like XXV (along with the other more important ones), no corresponding resonance is possible in the activated complex, for which only such Class B structures as XXVI can be drawn (in addition to those with normal Kekulé structures of the ring). The resonance with structure XXV therefore increases the activation energy and so lowers the rate of hydrolysis. As expected, the introduction of methyl groups in the two positions ortho to the dimethylamino group, as is shown in structure XXVII, markedly increases the rate of hydrolysis[132] by inhibiting the

[131] G. Baddeley, *Nature* **144**, 444 (1939). Several further examples of the present type are given in this paper.

[132] F. H. Westheimer and R. P. Metcalf, *J. Am. Chem. Soc.* **63**, 1339 (1941).

[133] See, for example, L. P. Hammett, *Physical Organic Chemistry*, McGraw-Hill Book Co., New York, 1940, pp. 354ff; M. L. Bender, *J. Am. Chem. Soc.* **73**, 1626 (1951).

foregoing type of resonance. It is significant that, in the absence of the dimethylamino group, as in the ester XXVIII, the methyl groups have

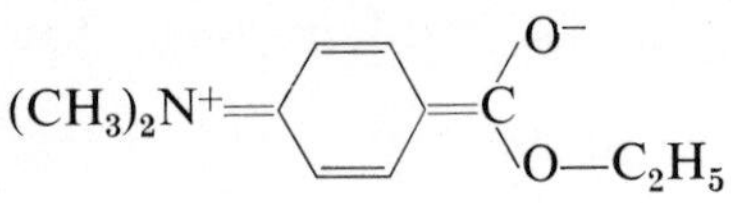

XXV

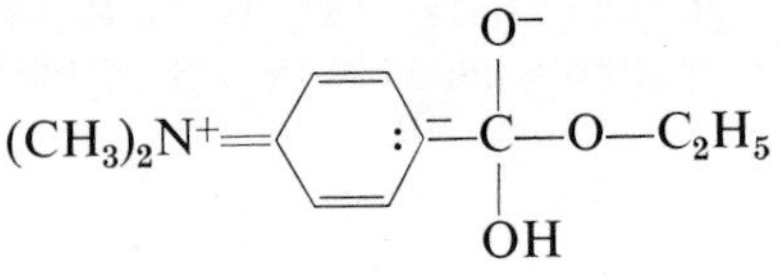

XXVI

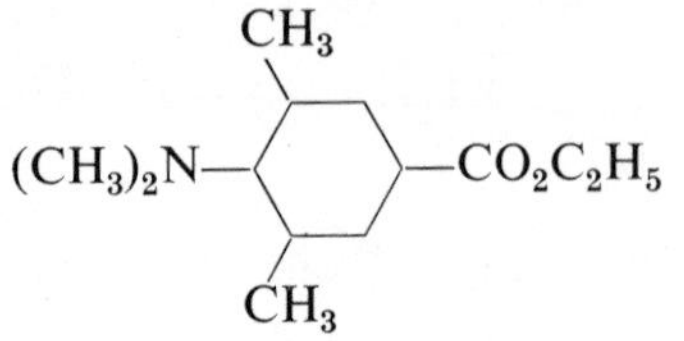

XXVII

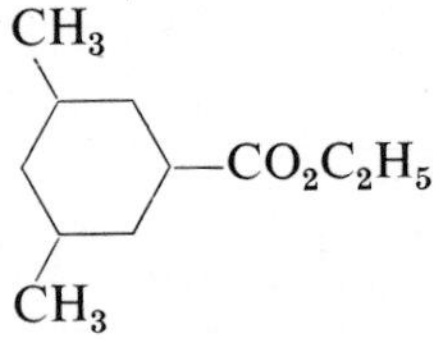

XXVIII

no such striking effect upon the rate of hydrolysis. We have here, there-fore, an example in which an interaction that might be regarded as a special type of "steric hindrance" makes a reaction go faster.

8·13 Some Additions to Aromatic Systems. In Section 7·5, we con-sidered several reactions in which aromatic hydrocarbons act as the diene components in Diels-Alder reactions. Although we were there primarily concerned with the positions of the equilibria in the several additions, we shall here be more interested in the factors that determine the points at which the dienophiles attack the aromatic molecules, and hence in the structures of the products that are formed.

The mechanism of the Diels-Alder reaction has not yet been definitely established. Consequently, before we can predict the relative rates of the competing reactions that might occur between a given aromatic hydrocarbon and a given dienophile, we must first make some fairly detailed assumptions regarding the courses of the additions and, more particularly, regarding the natures of the activated complexes. If the predictions to which we are ultimately led are then in uniformly good agreement with the observations, we can conclude that the original assumptions are not too far from correct to be useful; on the other hand, - if the predictions are in poor agreement with the observations, we can conclude that the assumptions must be discarded.

Following a suggestion made by Brown,[134] we shall presume that, in the reaction in which, for example, a molecule of maleic anhydride (the dienophile) becomes linked to the 1 and 4 positions of anthracene (the diene), the activated complex is a hybrid of principally the Class A

[134] R. D. Brown, *J. Chem. Soc.* **1950**, 691, 2730.

structure I and the Class B structure II (see the following paragraph in fine print).   Similarly, we shall presume that, in the different reaction in which the attack is at the 9 and 10 positions, the activated complex is a hybrid of principally the corresponding structures III and IV.   The first

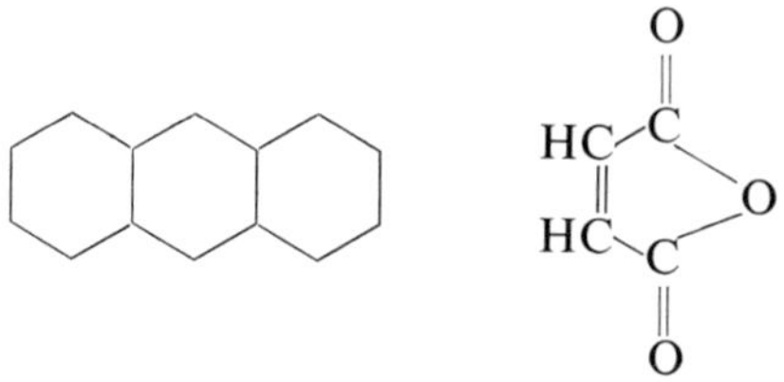

I

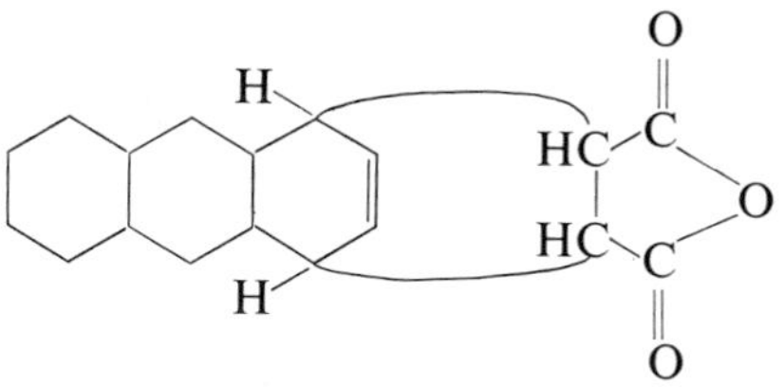

II

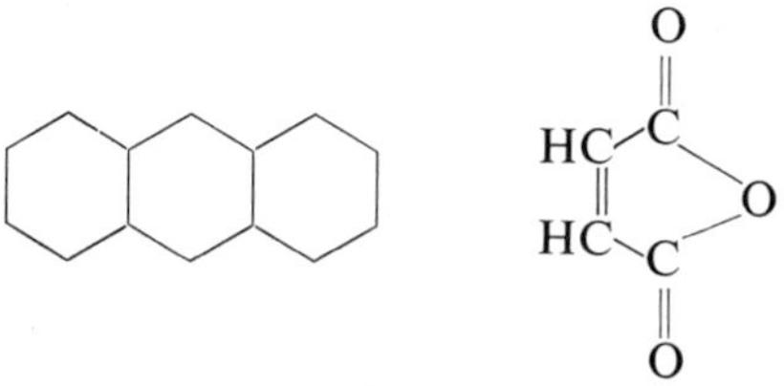

III

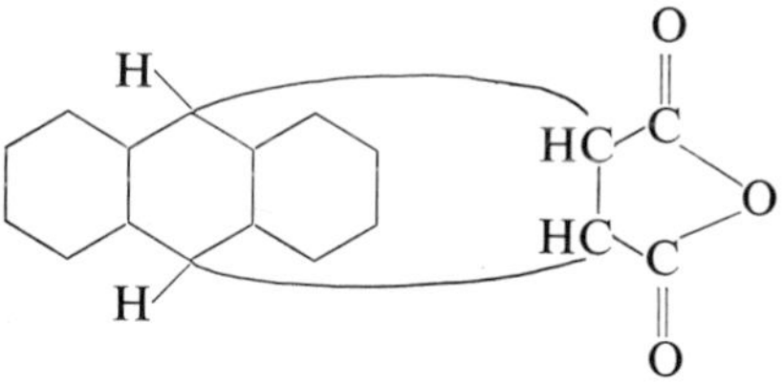

IV

of these complexes is doubtless the less stable of the two since, although structure I should be roughly equivalent to structure III, from which it differs only in the relative positions of the two reactant molecules in space, structure II must correspond to an appreciably higher energy than does structure IV since the resonance energy of naphthalene is appreciably less than twice that of benzene (cf. Table 3·7, Section 3·3, and Table 7·2, Section 7·5).   Moreover, all further imaginable activated complexes, such as the one in which structures V and VI have the greatest weights, can similarly be seen to be relatively unstable. (Structure V differs both

$$
\begin{array}{c}
\text{O} \\
\parallel \\
\text{HC}^{\diagup}\text{C} \\
\parallel \quad \quad \diagdown \text{O} \\
\text{HC}_{\diagdown}\text{C}^{\diagup} \\
\parallel \\
\text{O}
\end{array}
$$

V

$$
\begin{array}{c}
\text{O} \\
\parallel \\
\text{HC}^{\diagup}\text{C} \\
\mid \quad \quad \diagdown \text{O} \\
\text{HC}_{\diagdown}\text{C}^{\diagup} \\
\parallel \\
\text{O}
\end{array}
$$

VI

from I and from III in the relative positions of the reactant molecules.) Consequently, we can conclude that the addition of maleic anhydride and of all other dienophiles to anthracene will occur across the 9 and 10 positions. The fact that these reactions do indeed lead to the expected products lends some support to the assumed mechanism.

In structures I–V, the resonance within each completely aromatic ring is not explicitly represented, but is implied by the use of the conventional simple hexagon. This procedure, which is here adopted for the sake of simplicity, will be followed also in the remainder of the section. In structures I–VI, no effort has been made to depict the true three-dimensional forms of the respective activated complexes; consequently, the shapes of all the structures are unavoidably distorted; and, as was noted above, the geometrically different structures I, III, and V appear identical.

The above treatment of the additions to anthracene can easily be extended to other aromatic hydrocarbons since, in general, the reaction may be expected to occur most rapidly at the positions which, in Table 7·2, correspond to the smallest possible "estimated decrease in resonance energy." The product that is formed should always, therefore, be the most stable one. Although this prediction is completely confirmed by experiment, the observed reversibility of the Diels-Alder reaction makes the interpretation of the data less clear. There is a possibility that the addition compound which is isolated is not necessarily the product that is most rapidly formed but is instead merely the one that predominates in the equilibrium mixture of all the isomers. Fortunately, however, as Brown has shown,[134] there is an excellent qualitative agreement between the predicted stabilities of the activated complexes and the relative rates of addition.   Consequently, although there is a lack of quantitative data, the evidence which is now available does support the belief that the present treatment of the Diels-Alder reaction is kinetically, as well as thermochemically, significant.

In certain other addition reactions of aromatic hydrocarbons, the attacking reagent becomes attached to *adjacent* carbon atoms.   For example, when anthracene is treated with osmium tetroxide in the presence of pyridine,[135] there is formed a loose complex between the pyridine and an osmic ester that, for the moment, we shall represent by the noncommittal structure VII.   Although the mechanism of the reaction is again

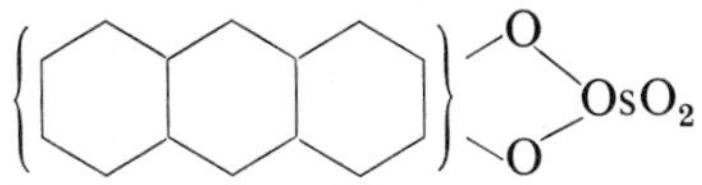

$$\left\{ \text{anthracene} \right\} \begin{matrix} O \\ \diagdown OsO_2 \\ O \end{matrix}$$

VII

unknown, we may as before make a rather definite assumption regarding the nature of the activated complex;[136, 137] and then, on the basis of this assumption, we may predict the structure of the product.   Thus it seems not unreasonable to suppose that the activated complex for attack at the 1 and 2 positions is essentially a hybrid of structures VIII and IX, whereas that for attack at the 2 and 3 positions is essentially a hybrid of structures X and XI (cf. the paragraph in fine print, above).   Since the first of these

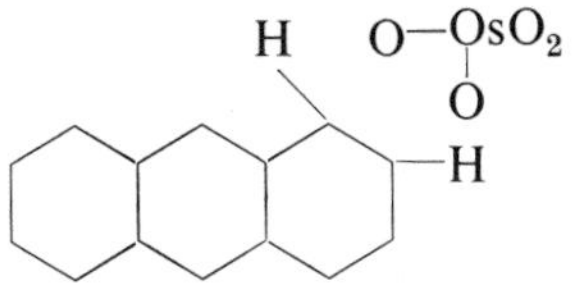

VIII 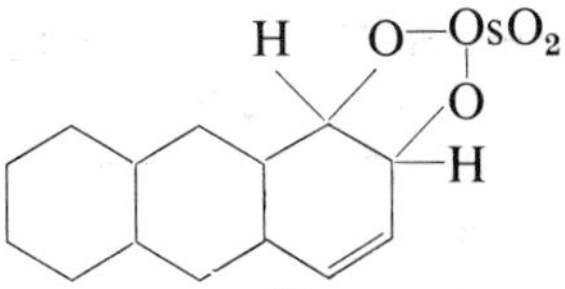   IX

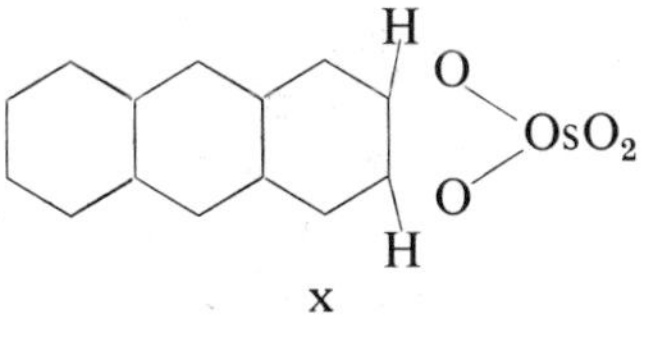

X 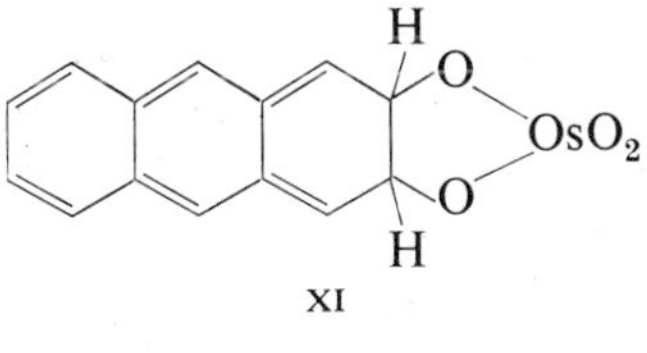   XI

complexes is clearly the more stable of the two, it must be the one actually formed, and so the structure of the ester VII must be the one that is more precisely shown as IX.   This prediction is confirmed by the fact that hydrolysis of the ester yields 1,2-dihydro-1,2-dihydroxyanthracene, XII.[135]

[135] J. W. Cook and R. Schoental, *Nature* 161, 237 (1948).

[136] G. M. Badger, *J. Chem. Soc.* 1950, 1809.

[137] G. M. Badger, *Quart. Revs. (London)* 5, 147 (1951); *Roy. Australian Chem. Inst. J. & Proc.* 17, 14 (1950).

Similarly, and again in agreement with expectation, phenanthrene is transformed by an analogous series of reactions into 9,10-dihydro-9,10-dihydroxyphenanthrene, XIII.[138]   So far as is now known, the addition

XII

XIII

of osmium tetroxide to an aromatic hydrocarbon always occurs, as in the two above examples, at the positions which the present simple treatment would lead us to expect.   Although the product that is isolated is always therefore the most stable one possible, no uncertainty of the kind that was encountered above in our discussion of the Diels-Alder reaction arises here, since the addition of osmium tetroxide is apparently irreversible.

The additions of several other reagents to aromatic hydrocarbons are possibly analogous to those of osmium tetroxide.[137]   Since, however, the experimental data referring to these further reactions are extremely meager, we shall here merely mention that both ozone[139] and diazoacetic ester[140] attack naphthalene at the 1 and 2 positions, which are the positions to be expected if the activated complexes are at all similar to the ones represented above by the structures VIII–XI.

8·14   Molecular Rearrangements.[141]   The field of molecular rearrangements is nearly as broad as that of organic chemistry itself.   Consequently, we shall make no attempt here to cover the whole subject, but we shall instead content ourselves with a brief discussion of a limited number of special problems in which the concept of resonance is particularly helpful.

A large number of rearrangements appear to take place by what is frequently called the Whitmore mechanism.[142]   Although the details necessarily vary to some extent from example to example, the essential features that are common to all the rearrangements of this class can be

[138] N. L. Drake and T. R. Sweeney, *J. Org. Chem.* **11**, 67 (1946).

[139] C. Harries and V. Weiss, *Ann.* **343**, 311 (1905); see also J. P. Wibaut and J. van Dijk, *Rec. trav. chim.* **65**, 413 (1946); G. M. Badger, *ibid.* **71**, 468 (1952).

[140] E. Buchner and S. Hediger, *Ber.* **36**, 3502 (1903).

[141] For general surveys of molecular rearrangements, see E. S. Wallis in H. Gilman, *Organic Chemistry*, John Wiley & Sons, New York, 1st ed., 1938, vol. I, Chapter 8, 2nd ed., 1943, vol. I, Chapter 12; G. W. Wheland, *Advanced Organic Chemistry*, John Wiley & Sons, New York, 1949, Chapters 12 and 13.

[142] F. C. Whitmore, *J. Am. Chem. Soc.* **54**, 3274 (1932).

stated with reference to the type structure I.   In this structure, B and C represent single atoms, whereas A may represent either an atom or (more

$$A\overset{..}{\underset{..}{—}}\overset{..}{B}\overset{..}{\underset{..}{—}}\overset{..}{C}$$

I

frequently) a radical.   The dots indicating electrons are written to show that atom B has its full octet, but that C has only a sextet, of electrons in the valence shell; these electrons are usually, but not necessarily, shared with further atoms or groups which are not explicitly represented in the structure.   Now the essential feature of the Whitmore mechanism of rearrangements is that a structure of the general type I is produced in some way in an initial step of the reaction.   The instability produced by the presence of only a sextet of electrons on the atom C is then partially relieved by the migration of A, *together with its pair of electrons*, to produce the structure II, in which the sextet is now upon the atom B.

$$\overset{..}{\underset{..}{B}}—\overset{..}{\underset{..}{C}}—A$$

II

In the concluding step, the instability which still remains in the structure II is relieved by an appropriate redistribution of the valence electrons, with or without the loss of an ion to, or the acquisition of an ion from, the solution.   The various steps need not take place successively, since all of them could occur simultaneously.

   The principles of the above mechanism can be made clearer by a discussion of specific examples.   When pinacol is treated with sulfuric acid, it is transformed into pinacolone.   The first step in the rearrangement is considered to be the removal, by the acid, of a hydroxyl group.   The organic cation III, which is thereby formed, is then changed into a hybrid of structures IV and V by the migration of a methyl group with its pair

$$
\begin{array}{ccc}
\underset{\underset{III}{\displaystyle CH_3-\overset{\displaystyle CH_3}{\underset{\displaystyle OH}{\overset{|}{\underset{|}{C}}}}---\overset{\displaystyle CH_3}{\overset{|}{C^+}}—CH_3} &
\underset{\underset{IV}{\displaystyle CH_3-\overset{|}{\underset{\displaystyle OH}{C^+}}---\overset{\displaystyle CH_3}{\underset{\displaystyle CH_3}{\overset{|}{\underset{|}{C}}}}—CH_3} &
\underset{\underset{V}{\displaystyle CH_3-\overset{|}{\underset{\displaystyle ^+OH}{C}}---\overset{\displaystyle CH_3}{\underset{\displaystyle CH_3}{\overset{|}{\underset{|}{C}}}}—CH_3}
\end{array}
$$

of electrons.   In the concluding step, this latter ion loses a proton to the solution and becomes the final product, pinacolone, which is a resonance hybrid, receiving a small contribution from VI and doubtless a much larger one from the conventional structure VII.   Similarly, in the Hofmann rearrangement of the acid amide VIII to an isocyanate by the action of bromine and sodium hydroxide, the reaction is considered to proceed through the phases represented by structures IX–XIII. The first two of these structures (IX and X) correspond to stable substances which

$$
\begin{array}{cc}
& CH_3 \\
& | \\
CH_3\!-\!C^+\!\!-\!C\!-\!CH_3 \\
& | \quad | \\
& O^- \; CH_3 \\
& \text{VI}
\end{array}
\qquad
\begin{array}{cc}
& CH_3 \\
& | \\
CH_3\!-\!C\!-\!C\!-\!CH_3 \\
& \| \quad | \\
& O \; CH_3 \\
& \text{VII}
\end{array}
$$

$$
\underset{\text{VIII}}{\overset{O}{\overset{\|}{R\!-\!C\!-\!NH_2}}}
\qquad
\underset{\text{IX}}{\overset{O}{\overset{\|}{R\!-\!C\!-\!NHBr}}}
\qquad
\underset{\text{X}}{\overset{O}{\overset{\|}{[R\!-\!C\!-\!NBr]^-Na^+}}}
$$

$$
\underset{\text{XI}}{\overset{O}{\overset{\|}{R\!-\!C\!-\!\ddot{N}\!\!:}}}
\qquad
\underset{\text{XII}}{O\!=\!C^+\!-\!\ddot{N}^-\!\!-\!R}
\qquad
\underset{\text{XIII}}{O\!=\!C\!=\!\ddot{N}\!=\!R}
$$

can be isolated. The last two (XII and XIII) are structures which contribute through resonance to the state of the isocyanate. (Structure XII is unstable and so is unimportant; it is mentioned here only because of its logical position in the present interpretation of the reaction.) The Lossen rearrangement of the hydroxamic ester XIV and the Curtius

$$
\begin{array}{c}
\overset{O}{\overset{\|}{R\!-\!C\!-\!N}}\diagdown^{H}\diagup \\
\diagdown \\
O\!-\!CO\!-\!C_6H_5 \\
\text{XIV}
\end{array}
\qquad\qquad
\underset{\text{XV}}{\overset{O}{\overset{\|}{R\!-\!C\!-\!N_3}}}
$$

rearrangement of the azide XV likewise lead to the isocyanate and probably proceed through essentially the same mechanism. These two substances, by the loss of a molecule of benzoic acid or of nitrogen, respectively, can, in fact, produce the same hypothetical intermediate XI as above, and then the remaining steps can proceed exactly as in the Hofmann rearrangement of the amide.

It would carry us too far afield to discuss at length the experimental evidence that can be brought forward in support of the mechanism described above,[141, 142] or to attempt to account for the driving forces that cause the rearrangements to proceed at all. The question which we shall consider here is that of the mechanism by which the migrating group A (of structure I) and its associated pair of electrons lose contact with atom B and become joined instead to C (as in structure II). In the first place, we may note that A apparently does not break off from the rest of the molecule, in the form of either a radical or an ion, and then recombine again at a different position. The most conclusive experimental evidence pointing toward this conclusion is derived from a study of the Hofmann rearrangement of the amide XVI.[143] This substance can

XVI

be obtained in an optically active form in consequence of the restricted rotation about the bond between the benzene and naphthalene rings. If the amide which is subjected to the rearrangement is optically active, the resulting isocyanate is found also to be active and not appreciably racemized. This fact shows conclusively that the molecule cannot have broken up into two parts during the rearrangement, because, if it had done so, rotation about the bond in question would have been possible during the time that the two parts were separate, and so more or less racemization should have occurred. It therefore follows that the group, as it migrates, must already have become attached to the nitrogen atom, as in the isocyanate, before it entirely loses its connection with the carbon atom to which it was originally joined in the amide.

On the basis of the classical valence theory, this conclusion is not easily understandable because the radical which migrates does not have sufficient valence electrons to be bonded to both the nitrogen and carbon atoms at the same time. In the past, such vague and poorly defined terms as residual, secondary, or partial valence have been used for the description of situations of this kind. At the present time, however, the theory of resonance permits a more precise picture of the rearrangement to be drawn. If, for simplicity, we return to the structures I and II, we can visualize the transition between them in the following way. At the outset, the hypothetical intermediate which has hitherto been described by the structure I must receive also a negligibly small contribution from XVII. (As in Section 8·1, and for the same reason, we shall here ignore the distinction between formal and effective bonds.) Similarly, at the conclusion of the transition, the intermediate which has been described by the structure II must receive a negligibly small contribution from XVIII. At some intermediate time while the group A is in the process of migrating, the resonance is between the two equally stable structures XIX and XX. The further structure XXI may then also have a significant

[143] E. S. Wallis and W. W. Moyer, *J. Am. Chem. Soc.* **55**, 2598 (1933).

weight, but, since this additional resonance in no way affects the subsequent discussion, we shall hereafter ignore it. (For the sake of maximum generality, the formal charges are omitted from structures I, II, and
XVII–XXI. Cf. also structures VII–IX, Section 8·7.) Now structures

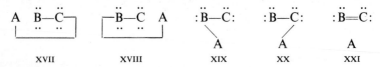

I, XIX, and XVIII can be regarded merely as successive phases, corresponding to different atomic positions, of a single structure, which we may
call R, since the electrons are paired in the same way in each; similarly,
the structures XVII, XX, and II can likewise be regarded as successive
phases of a second single structure, which we may call S. As group A
migrates from atom B to atom C, structure R, which was originally *the*
structure of the system, becomes less important in a continuous manner
and ultimately becomes negligible. Conversely, structure S, which was
originally negligible, achieves greater importance in a continuous manner
and ultimately becomes *the* structure. At no time is group A free from
the remainder of the molecule. The similarity between the present
situation and that discussed in Section 8·1 in connection with the reaction
between a bromide ion and an alkyl bromide should be too obvious to
require comment. (However, see the following paragraph.)

At the midpoint of the step in which atom or group A changes its
attachment from atom B to atom C, the system is, as we have seen, a
hybrid of structures XIX and XX (and possibly also of structure XXI).
The question now arises whether this hybrid is to be regarded as merely
an activated complex, or instead as a more or less ordinary molecule
which, although unstable and short lived, has a real existence. The
distinction between these two alternatives is most easily seen from a
consideration of the ways in which the total energy of the system might
vary during the course of the migration. One of the possible behaviors
is shown in Figure 8·1, Section 8·1 (except that the permissible values of
the parameter r now cover only a small part of the complete range from
$-\infty$ to $+\infty$); a second is shown in Figure 8·2, in which the several
curves have the same significance as the corresponding ones in Figure 8·1.
The important difference between the two figures is that, whereas 8·1
shows the hybrid to have only a single configuration with maximum
energy (point O), 8·2 shows the hybrid to have two such configurations
(points M and M') and, in addition, an intermediate configuration with
minimum energy (point O). If the energy varies in the way shown in
Figure 8·1, there is no configuration in which the system can remain for

any length of time; consequently, the intermediate can be described only as an activated complex.   On the other hand, if the energy varies in the different way shown in Figure 8·2, the system can perhaps remain for a short time in the configurations near the minimum at point O.   While it is in this "energy valley," it may undergo several collisions with other molecules; and when it leaves the valley, it can either return to the configuration of the original reactant at point R_1 or continue to that of the product at point P_2.   Consequently, the intermediate is here not merely an activated complex but is instead a real, though unstable, molecule.

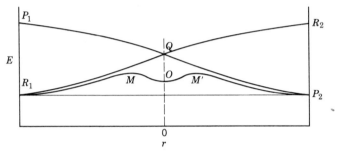

Fig. 8.2. An alternative way in which the energies E of the initial and final structures, and of their resonance hybrid, may vary during the course of a chemical reaction.

The two extreme situations are, however, not sharply distinguished from each other, since they gradually become identical as the valley at point O in Figure 8·2 is made more and more shallow.

The discussion in the preceding paragraph was not completely general since, both in Figure 8·1 and in Figure 8·2, points R_1 and P_2 lie at the same level and hence correspond to the same total energy of the system.   Although such a situation is occasionally encountered (see, for example, the following paragraph), the product is usually more stable than the reactant, and so point P_2 ordinarily lies well below the point R_1.   There is, however, no need for us to "correct" the figures, since the relative heights of P_2 and R_1 are not involved in the discussion.

There is rather convincing evidence that, in some rearrangements, the systems pass through configurations with minimum energy, as in Figure 8·2.   The most carefully studied example of such a reaction is doubtless the conversion of 3-phenyl-2-butyl p-toluenesulfonate, XXII, into the corresponding acetate, XXIII.[144]   This transformation, which occurs

[144] D. J. Cram, *J. Am. Soc.* **71**, 3863 (1949).   Cf. also D. J. Cram, *ibid.* **71**, 3871, 3875, 3883 (1949); **74**, 2129, 2137, 2149, 2152, 2159 (1952); S. Winstein and K. C. Schreiber, *ibid.* **74**, 2165 (1952).   For more recent work showing that the conclusions reached by Cram are not generally valid for even closely analogous reactions, see W. A. Bonner and C. J. Collins, *J. Am. Chem. Soc.* **75**, 5372 (1953), **77**, 99 (1955); C. J. Collins and W. A. Bonner, *ibid.* **77**, 92 (1955).

when the sulfonate is dissolved in glacial acetic acid containing small amounts of acetic anhydride and of potassium acetate, may appear to be a simple replacement of one acyl group by another; but its stereochemical features, which have been worked out in complete detail, show that it is in fact much more complicated than might have been expected. Since each of the structures XXII and XXIII contains two nonequivalent

$$
\begin{array}{cc}
\overset{\displaystyle C_6H_5}{|} & \overset{\displaystyle C_6H_5}{|} \\
CH_3\!-\!CH\!-\!CH\!-\!CH_3 & CH_3\!-\!CH\!-\!CH\!-\!CH_3 \\
\underset{\text{XXII}}{|} & \underset{\text{XXIII}}{|} \\
O\!-\!SO_2\!-\!C_6H_4\!-\!CH_3\text{-}p & O\!-\!CO\!-\!CH_3
\end{array}
$$

asymmetric carbon atoms, each must correspond to two different pairs of enantiomorphs. All eight of the predicted optically active forms have been prepared, as well as the four racemic modifications. The inter-conversions which have been effected are shown, together with their interpretations (see below), in the equations

in which the phenyl, methyl, p-toluenesulfonyl (tosyl), and acetyl groups are designated by the respective abbreviations ϕ, Me, Ts, and Ac; the heavy lines represent bonds which project in front of the paper; and the broken lines represent bonds which project behind the paper. The cations XXIV*a* and XXIV*b* are postulated intermediates, which are more fully described in the following paragraphs; each is, more explicitly, a hybrid of structures XXV and XXVI (the counterparts of XIX and XX),

$$CH_3—CH—C^+H—CH_3 \qquad CH_3—C^+H—CH—CH_3$$

XXV   XXVI

$$CH_3—CH—CH—CH_3 \quad CH_3—CH—CH—CH_3 \quad CH_3—CH—CH—CH_3$$

XXVII   XXVIII   XXIX

and presumably also of the three additional structures XXVII, XXVIII, and XXIX.

The observations which must be explained are, first, that either member of one enantiomorphic pair of sulfonates gives a completely racemic acetate, in each molecule of which there has been either an inversion of the configuration about each asymmetric atom or else no inversion about either atom; and, second, that either member of the other enantiomorphic pair of sulfonates gives an optically active acetate without inversion of configuration about either asymmetric atom. No satisfactory interpretation of these observations can be based on the assumption that the reactions are simple displacements, either with or without Walden inversions. If an inversion always occurred, the sulfonate XXII*a* would give only the optically active acetate XXIII*d* (or XXIII*c*), rather than the racemic mixture of XXIII*a* and XXIII*b*; and the sulfonate XXII*b* would give only the acetate XXIII*b*, rather than its diastereomer XXIII*c* (or XXIII*d*). On the other hand, if an inversion never occurred, the sulfonate XXII*a* would give only the acetate XXIII*b*, although the sulfonate XXII*b* would then indeed give the acetate XXIII*d* (or XXIII*c*). Even the assumption that an inversion occurs in some reactions, but not in others, is here of no help, since it does not explain how, in the formation of the acetate XXIII*a* from the sulfonate XXII*a*, there is an inversion at *each* asymmetric atom, and not merely at the one atom at which the reaction occurs.

The most satisfactory interpretation for the above solvolyses of the 3-phenyl-2-butyl sulfonates is the one shown in equations 1 and 2. With the ester XXII*a*, for example, the migration of the phenyl group is considered to be simultaneous with the departure of the sulfonate anion. Since there must therefore be a Walden inversion at the asymmetric atom at the right of the structure, the resulting intermediate cation will have the *cis* configuration XXIV*a*. If, in the succeeding step, an acetate ion attacks, again with inversion, the carbon atom on the left side of this cation, the acetate XXIII*a* is formed; if it instead attacks the carbon atom on the right side of the cation, the enantiomorphic acetate XXIII*b* is formed. Since the two enantiomorphs are found to be produced at equal rates, the attacks at the two positions must be equally probable. This conclusion then strongly suggests the further one that the cation XXIV*a* must persist for an appreciable time for, only if it does so, are the two carbon atoms completely equivalent, so that the intermediate XXIV*a* has a plane of symmetry and is optically inactive. In the overall reaction, then, there is a net inversion either at both or at neither of the asymmetric centers. Similarly, the sulfonate XXII*b* is transformed into the *trans* intermediate XXIV*b*, which, when attacked by acetate ion at either one of the two available positions, gives the same optically active acetate XXIII*c* or XXIII*d*. This latter reaction is consistent with the belief that the intermediate XXIV*b*, like its analog XXIV*a*, has an appreciable lifetime; it provides no additional evidence, however, since the observations are equally consistent with the assumption that the system has only one configuration with maximum energy, as in Figure 8·1, and even with the view that the reaction is a simple substitution without inversion.

A further rearrangement, in which the nature of the intermediate is still not entirely clear, occurs in the reaction between cyclopropanemethylamine, XXX, and nitrous acid. Of the several products of this reaction, the ones in which we shall here be interested are cyclopropylcarbinol, XXXI, and cyclobutanol, XXXII. When the carbon atom to which the

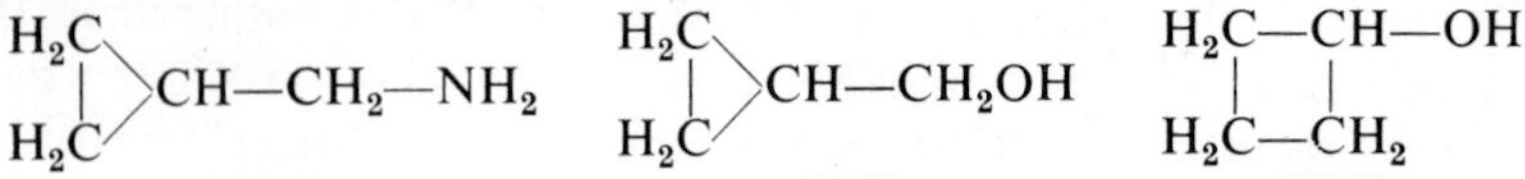

$$\begin{array}{ccc}
\underset{\text{XXX}}{\substack{H_2C \\ | \\ H_2C}}\!\!\!\!\diagdown\!\!\!\!\diagup CH\!-\!CH_2\!-\!NH_2 & \underset{\text{XXXI}}{\substack{H_2C \\ | \\ H_2C}}\!\!\!\!\diagdown\!\!\!\!\diagup CH\!-\!CH_2OH & \underset{\text{XXXII}}{\substack{H_2C\!-\!CH\!-\!OH \\ | \quad | \\ H_2C\!-\!CH_2}}
\end{array}$$

amino group is bonded in the original amine, XXX, is enriched in the radioactive isotope C^{14}, the radioactivity in each of the resulting alcohols XXXI and XXXII is found to be more or less equally divided among the three methylene groups even though with cyclopropylcarbinol the occurrence of a rearrangement is not immediately obvious.[145] A possible

[145] J. D. Roberts and R. H. Mazur, *J. Am. Chem. Soc.* **73,** 3542 (1951). For discussion of a somewhat similar reaction, see also J. D. Roberts and C. C. Lee, *ibid.* **73,** 5009 (1951); S. Winstein and D. Trifan, *ibid.* **74,** 1154 (1952); C. C. Lee and J. W. T. Spinks, *Can. J. Chem.* **31,** 761 (1953).

sequence of reactions, which accounts for the formation of the observed products, is shown in the equations

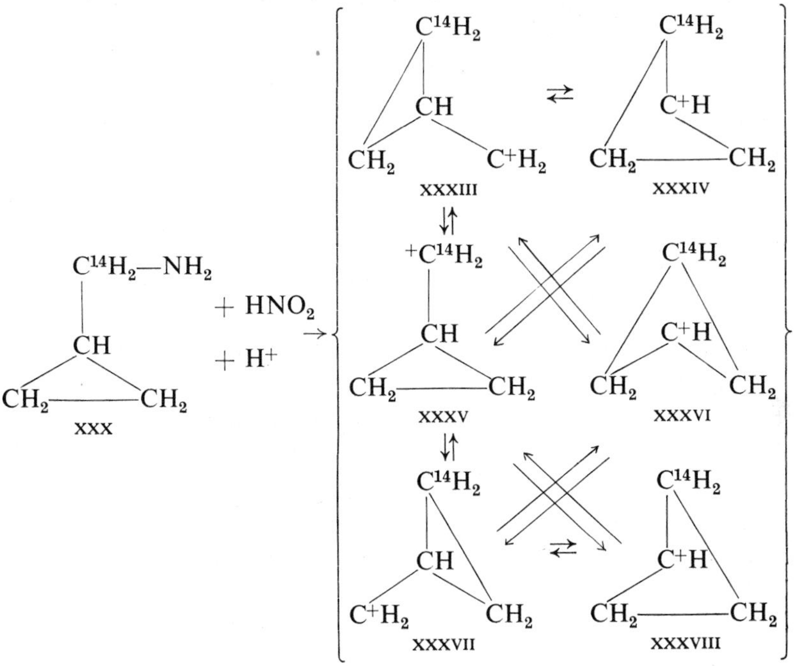

$$C^{14}H_2\text{—}NH_2 \text{, } CH \text{, } CH_2\text{——}CH_2 \quad (\text{XXX}) \quad \xrightarrow[+\ H^+]{+\ HNO_2} \Bigg\{ \text{(XXXIII} \rightleftarrows \text{XXXIV, XXXV} \rightleftarrows \text{XXXVI, XXXVII} \rightleftarrows \text{XXXVIII)} \Bigg\} + N_2 + 2H_2O \quad (3)$$

Structures shown in the bracketed scheme:

XXXIII: $C^{14}H_2$ / CH / CH_2 — C^+H_2 (cyclopropane with $C^{14}H_2$ substituent and C^+H_2)

XXXIV: $C^{14}H_2$ / C^+H / CH_2——CH_2

XXXV: $^+C^{14}H_2$ / CH / CH_2——CH_2

XXXVI: $C^{14}H_2$ / C^+H / CH_2 CH_2

XXXVII: $C^{14}H_2$ / CH / C^+H_2 CH_2

XXXVIII: $C^{14}H_2$ / C^+H / CH_2——CH_2

and

$$R^+ + H_2O \rightarrow ROH + H^+ \quad (4)$$

in which R^+ represents any one of the cations XXXIII–XXXVIII. In equations 3, the several structures are written in such a way that their mutual relations are made as clear as possible; no stereochemical significance is at present to be attached to the locations of the letters which designate the different atoms (however, see below). As is implied by the use of the double arrows, $\rightleftarrows$, each of the rearrangements proper is here assumed to be reversible. This assumption suggests, but perhaps does not require, the further one that each of the several intermediates is a molecule occupying an energy valley of the type depicted in Figure 8·2.

An alternative interpretation of the observations is that all the rearrangements shown in the equations 3 have a common "nonclassical" intermediate, which is a hybrid of structures XXXIII–XXXVIII, and in which the four carbon atoms lie at the corners of a nearly regular tetrahedron. In view of the considerable stabilization which should result from the resonance among such a large number of more or less equivalent structures, the abbreviation R^+ of equation 4 may refer not to six different cations with the structures XXXIII–XXXVIII but rather to a single cation which is a hybrid of all these structures, and which reacts with water to give the six products that are observed. The invariance of the relative positions of all the atoms in the diagrams XXXIII–XXXVIII would then be stereochemically significant, and each pair of double arrows, ⇄, would have to be replaced by a double-headed arrow, ↔. We do not at present have sufficient information to decide between the two above alternatives. In any event, however, the complete equivalence of the structures XXXIII, XXXV, and XXXVII, and also of the structures XXXIV, XXXVI, and XXXVIII, leads at once to the observed uniform distribution of the radioactivity among the three methylenic carbon atoms in each of the alcohols formed in the reaction.

In still other rearrangements, the intermediates seem to be more like activated complexes than like reactive molecules; the evidence is insufficient, however, to exclude the possibility that plots of the total energies E against the parameter r that defines the configurations, as in Figures 8·1 and 8·2, would have very shallow minima at the points O. In, for example, the reaction between ethylamine-1-C^{14}, XXXIX, and nitrous acid, the major alcoholic product is the unrearranged ethanol-1-C^{14}, XL; and only a trace of the rearranged ethanol-2-C^{14}, XLI, is obtained.[146] If there were here a symmetrical intermediate which receives equal contributions from the two equivalent structures XLII and XLIII,

$$CH_3-C^{14}H_2-NH_2 \qquad CH_3-C^{14}H_2-OH \qquad HO-CH_2-C^{14}H_3$$

XXXIX   XL   XLI

$$CH_2-C^{14+}H_2 \qquad\qquad C^+H_2-C^{14}H_2$$

H   H

XLII   XLIII

and which has an appreciable lifetime, exactly half the radioactivity in the resulting ethanol would have to reside in each carbon atom. Consequently, the intermediate must here be essentially an activated complex and not an unstable, but real, molecule.

In the rearrangements which we have considered above, the group which migrates takes with it its two bonding electrons, and it goes to a position at which there was originally only a sextet of electrons. One can, however, imagine two other types of reaction, since the migrating group might take either only one or else none of its bonding electrons,

[146] J. D. Roberts and J. A. Yancey, *J. Am. Chem. Soc.* **74**, 5943 (1952). For a somewhat similar, but less clear-cut, example, see J. D. Roberts, W. Bennett, R. E. McMahon, and E. W. Holroyd, Jr., *ibid.* **74**, 4283 (1952).

and since it might then go to a position that has, respectively, either a deficiency of just one electron or else an unshared pair of electrons. Although rearrangements belonging to these further types are relatively rare, they are not unknown.

A reaction which apparently illustrates the first of these additional types of rearrangement occurs when triphenylmethyl peroxide, XLIV, is isomerized at the temperature of boiling xylene into benzopinacol

$$(C_6H_5)_3C \overset{..}{\underset{..}{-O}} \overset{..}{\underset{..}{-O}} -C(C_6H_5)_3 \rightarrow 2(C_6H_5)_3C \overset{..}{\underset{..}{-O}} \cdot$$
$$\text{XLIV}$$

$$\rightarrow 2(C_6H_5)_2 \overset{.}{C} \overset{..}{\underset{..}{-O}} -C_6H_5 \rightarrow \begin{array}{c} (C_6H_5)_2 C \overset{..}{\underset{..}{-O}} -C_6H_5 \\ | \quad :: \\ (C_6H_5)_2 \overset{}{C} \overset{..}{\underset{..}{-O}} -C_6H_5 \end{array} \qquad (5)$$
$$\text{XLV}$$

diphenyl ether, XLV.[147]   The most reasonable explanation for this transformation is the one contained in the sequence of reactions 5, in the second step of which a phenyl group migrates with a single valence electron.   A somewhat similar free-radical rearrangement occurs when β-phenylisovaleraldehyde, XLVI, is heated with a small amount of *tert*-butyl peroxide.   In this reaction, there is obtained an excellent yield of an approximately 1:1 mixture of *tert*-butylbenzene and isobutylbenzene.[148] Presumably, the original peroxide decomposes to some free radicals which attack the aldehyde and degrade it to the neophyl radical XLVII.   This latter radical then either extracts a hydrogen atom from a second molecule of aldehyde and forms a molecule of *tert*-butylbenzene; or else it rearranges to the isomeric radical XLVIII, which similarly extracts a

$$C_6H_5-C(CH_3)_2-CH_2-CHO \qquad C_6H_5-C(CH_3)_2-\overset{.}{C}H_2$$
$$\text{XLVI} \qquad\qquad\qquad \text{XLVII}$$

$$\overset{.}{C}(CH_3)_2-CH_2-C_6H_5$$
$$\text{XLVIII}$$

hydrogen atom and forms a molecule of isobutylbenzene.   In either event, there is always produced a new radical to carry on the chain.

The Stevens rearrangement provides the clearest example of a reaction in which the migrating group leaves both its bonding electrons behind

[147] H. Wieland, *Ber.* **44**, 2550 (1911).   For a recent discussion of this and related reactions, see M. S. Kharasch, A. C. Poshkus, A. Fono, and W. Nudenberg, *J. Org. Chem.* **16**, 1458 (1951).

[148] S. Winstein and F. H. Seubold, Jr., *J. Am. Chem. Soc.* **69**, 2916 (1947).   Some similar, but more complex, reactions are reported also by W. H. Urry and M. S. Kharasch, *ibid.* **66**, 1438 (1944); W. H. Urry and N. Nicolaides, *ibid.* **74**, 5163 (1952).

and goes to an adjacent atom with an unshared pair of electrons.[149] When benzyldimethylphenacylammonium bromide, XLIX, is heated with aqueous sodium hydroxide, it is transformed into ω-dimethylamino-ω-benzylacetophenone, L.[150] The function of the base is here doubtless to

$$C_6H_5—CH_2—\overset{\displaystyle |}{\underset{\displaystyle CH_2—CO—C_6H_5}{N^+(CH_3)_2}} \quad Br^- \qquad\qquad C_6H_5—CH_2—\overset{\displaystyle N(CH_3)_2}{\underset{\displaystyle |}{CH}}—CO—C_6H_5-$$

$$\text{XLIX} \qquad\qquad\qquad\qquad\qquad\qquad \text{L}$$

$$C_6H_5—CH_2—\overset{\displaystyle |}{\underset{\displaystyle ^-:CH—CO—C_6H_5}{N^+(CH_3)_2}}$$

$$\text{LI}$$

remove a proton from the ammonium ion; the benzyl group in the resulting fragment LI then migrates, without its electrons, from the nitrogen atom to the adjacent carbon atom. As expected, this rearrangement occurs only with such quaternary cations, and under such experimental conditions, that an unshared pair of electrons can be provided by the removal of a proton. Most commonly, in fact, the migration is to a position that is alpha to a carbonyl group, as in the foregoing example. Under the influence of the extremely strong base, lithium phenyl, however, the migration may instead be to a position that is alpha only to a less effectively activating phenyl group, as in the transformation of the

$$C_6H_5—CH_2—N^+(CH_3)_3 \qquad\qquad C_6H_5—\overset{\displaystyle |}{\underset{\displaystyle CH_3}{CH}}—N(CH_3)_2$$

$$\text{LII} \qquad\qquad\qquad\qquad\qquad \text{LIII}$$

benzyltrimethylammonium cation, LII, into 1-dimethylamino-1-phenylethane, LIII.[151]

Little is now known in regard to the detailed mechanisms of the above rearrangements in which the migrating groups take with them less than their full complements of electrons. Analogy, however, suggests that these reactions can be satisfactorily interpreted with the aid of an obvious generalization of the Whitmore mechanism. Thus, the second step in the conversion of triphenylmethyl peroxide, XLIV, into benzopinacol diphenyl ether, XLV (cf. equation 5) may be considered to involve an

[149] For a recent review of the Stevens rearrangement, see C. K. Ingold, *Structure and Mechanism in Organic Chemistry*, Cornell University Press, Ithaca, N. Y., 1953, pp. 523ff.

[150] T. S. Stevens, E. M. Creighton, A. B. Gordon, and M. MacNicol, *J. Chem. Soc.* **1928**, 3193.

[151] G. Wittig, R. Mangold, and G. Felletschin, *Ann.* **560**, 116 (1948).

intermediate that is a hybrid of structures LIV and LV, with perhaps contributions also from LVI, LVII, and LVIII; and the Stevens rearrangement

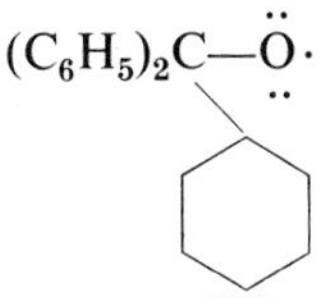

$(C_6H_5)_2C\ddot{-}\ddot{O}\cdot$

LIV

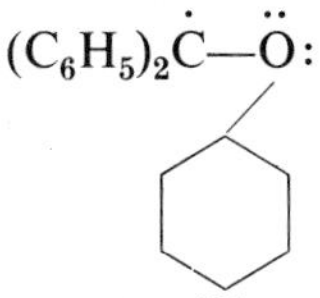

$(C_6H_5)_2\overset{\cdot}{C}\ddot{-}\ddot{O}:$

LV

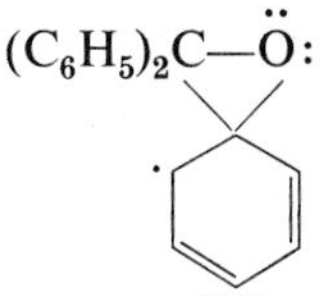

$(C_6H_5)_2C\ddot{-}\ddot{O}:$

LVI

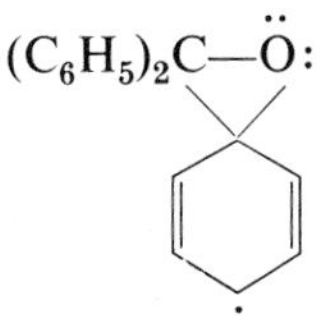

$(C_6H_5)_2C\ddot{-}\ddot{O}:$

LVII

$(C_6H_5)_2C\ddot{-}\ddot{O}\cdot$

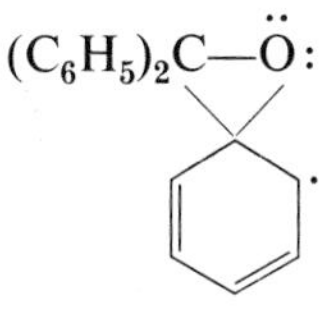

LVIII

of the benzyltrimethylammonium ion LII to 1-dimethylamino-1-phenylethane, LIII, may be considered to involve an intermediate that is a hybrid of structures LIX and LX. There is at present no evidence,

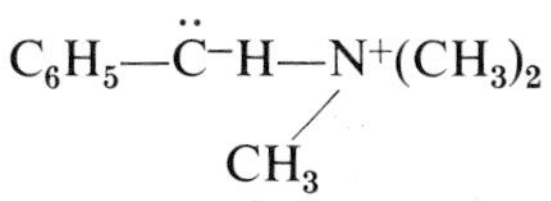

$C_6H_5\ddot{-}\overset{-}{C}\ddot{-}H\ddot{-}N^+(CH_3)_2$
$\qquad\diagdown$
$\qquad CH_3$
LIX

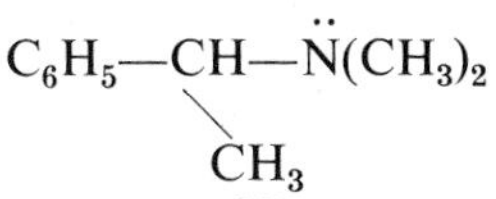

$C_6H_5\ddot{-}CH\ddot{-}\ddot{N}(CH_3)_2$
$\qquad\diagdown$
$\qquad CH_3$
LX

however, to show whether, in these migrations, the energies of the systems vary in the way shown in Figure 8·1 or in that shown in Figure 8·2.

Not all rearrangements can occur either by the Whitmore mechanism or by any simple extension of it. The truth of this statement is made particularly clear by the fact that the migrating group does not always ultimately become attached to an atom adjacent to the one to which it was originally joined, but instead often goes farther to a more distant atom. An important additional type of rearrangement, which involves a so-called 1, 3 shift instead of the 1, 2 shift common to all the previous examples, is given by the allylic rearrangement, which can be illustrated by the reaction between phenylvinylcarbinol, LXI, and hydrogen bromide. The product is not the expected secondary bromide LXII but the primary cinnamyl bromide LXIII.[152] The most reasonable explanation for this

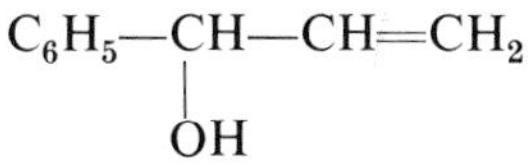

$C_6H_5\ddot{-}CH\ddot{-}CH\text{=}CH_2$
$\qquad|$
$\qquad OH$
LXI

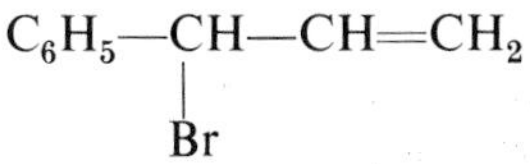

$C_6H_5\ddot{-}CH\ddot{-}CH\text{=}CH_2$
$\qquad|$
$\qquad Br$
LXII

$C_6H_5\ddot{-}CH\text{=}CH\ddot{-}CH_2Br$
LXIII

[152] J. Meisenheimer and J. Link, *Ann.* **479**, 211 (1930).

rearrangement is that the strong acid removes a hydroxide ion from the carbinol and leaves a positive organic ion which is a hybrid of the structures LXIV and LXV. The resonance between these structures then

$$C_6H_5—C^+H—CH{=}CH_2 \qquad C_6H_5—CH{=}CH—C^+H_2$$

LXIV   LXV

$$C_6H_5—CH{=}CH—CH_2OH$$

LXVI

stabilizes the ion in the usual way and so is presumably responsible in large part for its relatively easy formation. A bromide ion now comes up from the solution to complete the reaction; it could in principle approach the carbon atom which carries the positive charge in either of the two structures LXIV and LXV, to give either LXII or LXIII, respectively. We could hardly have predicted in advance that the reaction would follow only the second of these two conceivable courses, but we have at any rate come to an understanding of how the observed facts are *possible*. Moreover, on the basis of the above mechanism, we can now predict that cinnamyl alcohol, LXVI, must also give the same product, cinnamyl bromide, LXIII, as phenylvinylcarbinol does under the same experimental conditions, because the same organic cation is an intermediate in both reactions. There should therefore be no rearrangement in this reaction. This prediction is in agreement with experiment.[152]

The situation is not always so clear cut as in the preceding example. When either methylvinylcarbinol, LXVII, or crotyl alcohol, LXVIII, is

$$CH_3—CH—CH{=}CH_2 \qquad CH_3—CH{=}CH—CH_2OH$$
$$\quad\;\; |$$
$$\quad\;\; OH$$

LXVII   LXVIII

treated with hydrogen bromide, the product is a mixture of the two bromides LXIX and LXX.[153] However, these two bromides are not

$$CH_3—CH—CH{=}CH_2 \qquad CH_3—CH{=}CH—CH_2Br$$
$$\quad\;\; |$$
$$\quad\;\; Br$$

LXIX   LXX

obtained in exactly the same proportions from the two alcohols. Methylvinylcarbinol gives a somewhat higher proportion of its related bromide LXIX than crotyl alcohol does; and, conversely, crotyl alcohol gives a somewhat higher proportion of *its* related bromide LXX than methylvinylcarbinol does. This observation appears to be in conflict with the

[153] W. G. Young and J. F. Lane, *J. Am. Chem. Soc.* **60**, 847 (1938).

belief that both reactions proceed through a common intermediate cation which is a hybrid of structures LXXI and LXXII (analogous to LXIV

$$CH_3—C^+H—CH{=}CH_2 \qquad\qquad CH_3—CH{=}CH—C^+H_2$$
$$\text{LXXI} \qquad\qquad\qquad\qquad \text{LXXII}$$

and LXV, respectively). However, Young and Lane have shown[153] that the data can be quantitatively explained if it is assumed that each reaction occurs by two independent mechanisms. On the one hand, most of the reaction proceeds by the mechanism already outlined, and gives identical products from the two alcohols; but, on the other hand, a small amount of reaction occurs simultaneously by a different mechanism in which a bromide ion directly displaces a hydroxide ion in the un-ionized molecule, without any rearrangement. This second mechanism is presumably of the Walden inversion type described in Section 8·1.

The evidence supporting the correctness of the above mechanism seems now to be quite conclusive.[154] Although we shall here make no attempt to describe even a fair sampling of all this evidence, we may nevertheless mention that the rates of the reactions have been found in general to increase with increasing stabilities of the migrating anions, with increasing stabilities of the allylic cations, and in the presence of such solvents or catalysts as might be expected to favor the required ionizations. Much additional support has also been obtained from extensive kinetic studies.

A reasonable alternative mechanism for the allylic rearrangement is one in which the two steps that were outlined above are not successive, but instead simultaneous. If, for example, an ethoxide ion should attack a molecule of crotyl bromide, LXX, at the unsaturated carbon atom that is joined to the methyl group, and if the bromine atom should at the same time break away as an anion, the product would be 3-ethoxy-1-butene, LXXIII, and no crotyl ethyl ether, LXXIV, would be formed. Similarly,

$$CH_3—CH—CH{=}CH_2 \qquad\qquad CH_3—CH{=}CH—CH_2OC_2H_5$$
$$\;\;|$$
$$OC_2H_5$$
$$\text{LXXIII} \qquad\qquad\qquad\qquad\qquad \text{LXXIV}$$

the corresponding reaction with 3-bromo-1-butene, LXIX, if it occurred, would give only crotyl ethyl ether, LXXIV, but no 3-ethoxy-1-butene, LXXIII. The activated complex for the first of these two reactions would then be a hybrid of structures LXXV and LXXVI, whereas that

[154] For a summarizing discussion, and for many references to the original literature, see C. K. Ingold, *Structure and Mechanism in Organic Chemistry*, Cornell University Press, Ithaca, N. Y., 1953, pp. 586ff.

for the second would be a hybrid of structures LXXVII and LXXVIII. Although this mechanism might seem more advantageous than the one

$$CH_3—CH=CH—CH_2$$
$$|$$
$$C_2H_5—O^- \quad Br$$

LXXV

$$CH_3—CH—CH=CH_2$$
$$|$$
$$C_2H_5—O \quad Br^-$$

LXXVI

$$CH_3—CH—CH=CH_2$$
$$|$$
$$Br \quad ^-O—C_2H_5$$

LXXVII

$$CH_3—CH=CH—CH_2$$
$$|$$
$$Br^- \quad O—C_2H_5$$

LXXVIII

requiring the production of an unstable organic cation as an intermediate, it appears in fact to be of negligible importance, and only indirect evidence for its reality has been obtained.[155, 156]   The difficulty is here that the simple replacement of the halogen atom by the ethoxy group, without rearrangement, occurs much faster than the alternative replacement, with rearrangement.

In certain other, closely analogous reactions, however, the existence of the two independent mechanisms has been experimentally demonstrated. When crotyl bromide LXX in acetone solution is treated with lithium bromide containing radioactive bromide ion, Br^{*-}, the two reactions

$$CH_3—CH=CH—CH_2Br + Br^{*-} \rightleftarrows CH_3—CH=CH—CH_2Br^* + Br^- \quad (6)$$

and

$$CH_3—CH=CH—CH_2Br + Br^{*-} \rightleftarrows CH_3—CHBr^*—CH=CH_2 + Br^- \quad (7)$$

occur at measurable rates.[155]   Although the first of these reactions is again much faster (actually 28,000 times faster) than the second, this fact here causes no trouble since only the second reaction leads to a product that is *chemically* different from the original reagent.   Similarly, when 3-bromo-1-butene, LXIX, is treated with radioactive bromide ion, the two corresponding reactions

$$CH_3—CHBr—CH=CH_2 + Br^{*-} \rightleftarrows CH_3—CHBr^*—CH=CH_2 + Br^- \quad (8)$$

$$CH_3—CHBr—CH=CH_2 + Br^{*-} \rightleftarrows CH_3—CH=CH—CH_2Br^* + Br^- \quad (9)$$

occur at measurable rates, with the direct substitution (equation 8) now only sixty times faster than the indirect one (equation 9).   However, merely from the fact that radioactive 3-bromo-1-butene is produced from crotyl bromide, and that radioactive crotyl bromide is produced from 3-bromo-1-butene, we cannot conclude that the mechanisms of the

[155] B. D. England and E. D. Hughes, *Nature*, **168**, 1002 (1951).
[156] P. B. D. de la Mare, E. D. Hughes, and C. A. Vernon, *Nature* **169**, 672 (1952).

reactions are of the type postulated; for, without further information, we cannot exclude the possibility that the rearrangements are largely, or entirely, the results of initial ionizations. The additional evidence which is thus required has been obtained from a study of the kinetics of the reactions. The rates at which the radioactive, rearranged bromides are formed are proportional both to the concentrations of the original organic bromides and to that of the radioactive bromide ion; the rate-controlling steps must therefore be the ones in which the ions attack the molecules of the unsaturated halides, and they cannot be simply the dissociation of the latter molecules.

A further example of an allylic rearrangement that has been shown not to involve an unstable organic cation occurs when 3,3-dichloro-1-propene, LXXIX, is treated with ethanolic sodium ethoxide.[156] Here again, there are two competing reactions

$$CH_2\!\!=\!\!CH\!\!-\!\!CHCl_2 + C_2H_5\!\!-\!\!O^- \rightarrow CH_2\!\!=\!\!CH\!\!-\!\!CHCl\!\!-\!\!OC_2H_5 + Cl^-$$

LXXIX

and

$$CH_2\!\!=\!\!CH\!\!-\!\!CHCl_2 + C_2H_5\!\!-\!\!O^- \rightarrow C_2H_5\!\!-\!\!O\!\!-\!\!CH_2\!\!-\!\!CH\!\!=\!\!CHCl + Cl^-$$

LXXIX   LXXX

which now, however, occur with comparable speed, so that both organic products can be isolated. The rate at which the rearranged product LXXX is formed is proportional to the concentration of the 3,3-dichloro-1-propene and also to that of ethoxide ion. As before, therefore, the rate-controlling step must be an attack by the ion upon the neutral molecule; in any event, it cannot be an ionization of the dihalide.

The Claisen rearrangement doubtless proceeds by a mechanism that is analogous to the second of the two that have just been proposed for the allylic rearrangement. When allyl vinyl ether, LXXXI, for example, is heated to about 250°, it is transformed into the isomeric allylacetaldehyde LXXXII.[157] The activated complex for this reaction is presumably a hybrid of structures LXXXIII and LXXXIV.[158] Similarly, in the more

$$CH_2\!\!=\!\!CH\!\!-\!\!CH_2\!\!-\!\!O\!\!-\!\!CH\!\!=\!\!CH_2 \qquad\qquad CH_2\!\!=\!\!CH\!\!-\!\!CH_2\!\!-\!\!CH_2\!\!-\!\!CHO$$

LXXXI   LXXXII

typical rearrangement of allyl phenyl ether, LXXXV, to o-allylphenol, LXXXVI, the activated complex can be considered a hybrid of structures LXXXVII and LXXXVIII.[158] In this latter example, however, the product would seem to be not o-allylphenol, LXXXVI but rather its keto form LXXXIX. We must therefore make the additional assumption

[157] C. D. Hurd and M. A. Pollack, *J. Am. Chem. Soc.* **60**, 1905 (1938).
[158] Cf. C. D. Hurd and M. A. Pollack, *J. Org. Chem.* **3**, 550 (1939).

that the foregoing rearrangement proper is immediately followed, or perhaps accompanied, by a migration of a proton from the carbon atom to which it is linked in structure LXXXIX to the oxygen atom in which

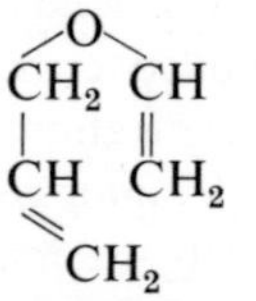

LXXXIII 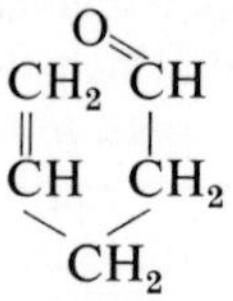   LXXXIV

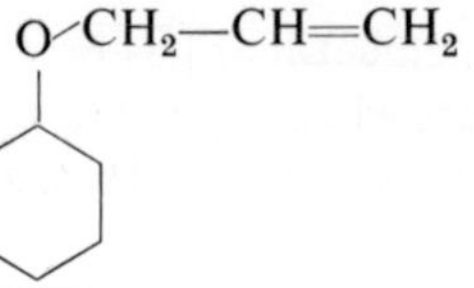

LXXXV 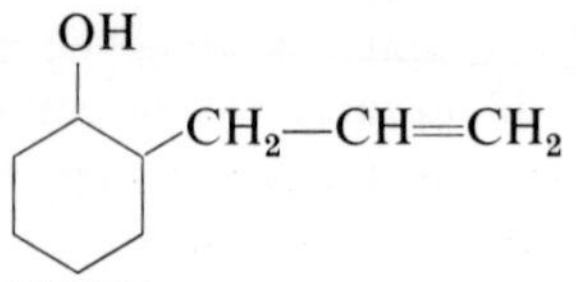   LXXXVI

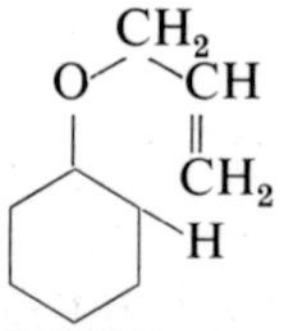

LXXXVII 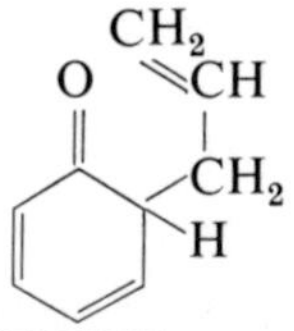   LXXXVIII 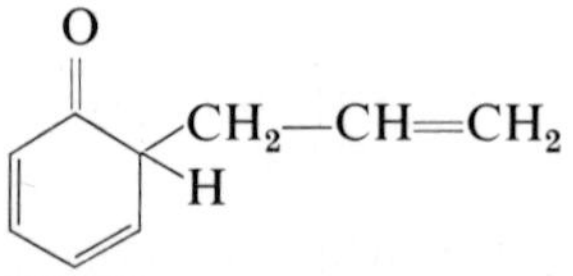   LXXXIX

it is linked in structure LXXXVI. This concluding step, however, is probably not a true rearrangement, but is instead a process dependent upon the presence of both an acid and a base in the surrounding medium; the acid gives up a proton to the oxygen atom, and the base removes a different proton from the carbon atom.

From structures LXXXIII, LXXXIV, LXXXVII, and LXXXVIII, it is seen that the allyl group is not linked to the remainder of the molecule by the same carbon atom in the final product as in the original ether. This so-called "inversion" of the allyl group has been confirmed in numerous reactions. Cinnamyl phenyl ether, XC, for example, gives only *o*-(1-phenylallyl)-phenol, XCI, whereas phenyl 1-phenylallyl ether, XCII, gives only *o*-cinnamylphenol, XCIII.

When, in a Claisen rearrangement, a substituted allyl group migrates to the *para* position, rather than to the *ortho* position, it is apparently not inverted.[159] (However, see below in this paragraph.) The most conclusive evidence supporting this belief has been obtained by Ryan

[159] For earlier work suggesting that this lack of inversion is not general, see O. Mumm, H. Hornhardt, and J. Diederichsen, *Ber.* **72**, 100 (1939); O. Mumm and J. Diederichsen, *ibid.* **72**, 1523 (1939). See, however, S. J. Rhoads, R. Raulins, and R. D. Reynolds, *J. Am. Chem. Soc.* **75**, 2531 (1953); **76**, 3456 (1954).

and O'Connor,[160] who found that the rearrangement of the radioactive allyl 2,6-dimethylphenyl ether XCIV gives only the 4-allyl-2,6-dimethyl-phenol XCV.   The mechanism of this reaction has been the subject of

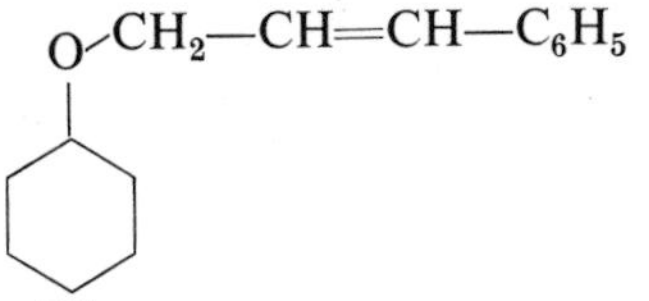

XC

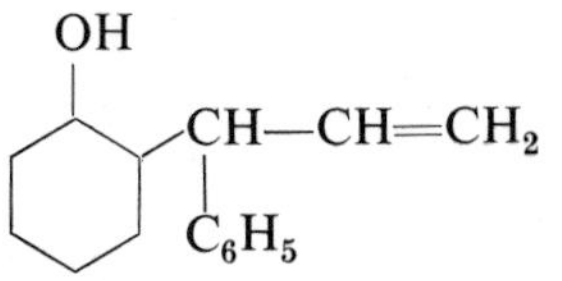

XCI

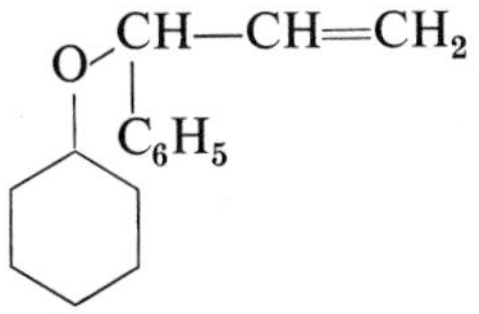

XCII

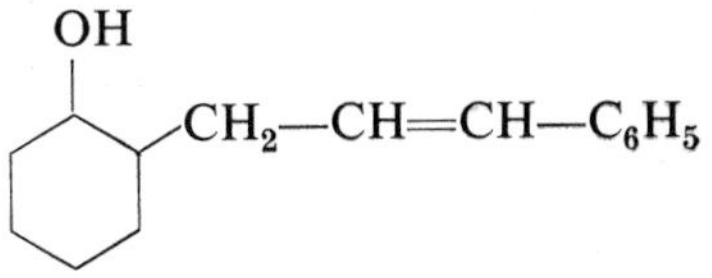

XCIII

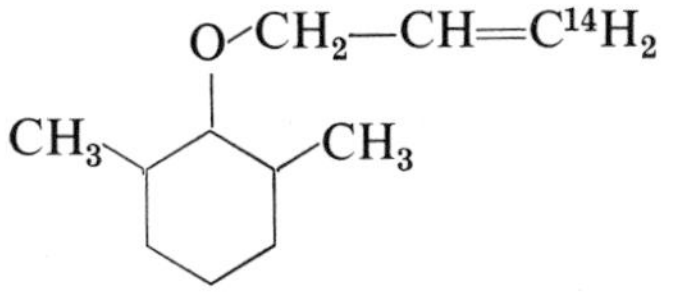

XCIV

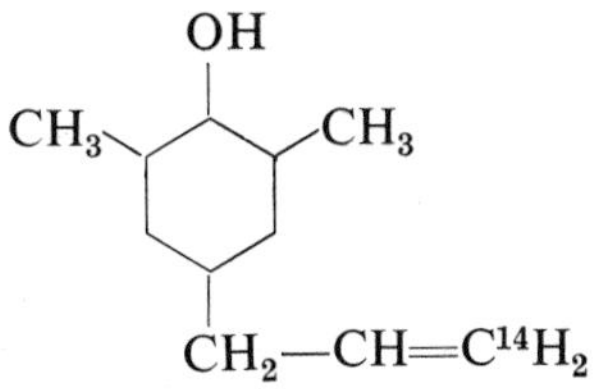

XCV

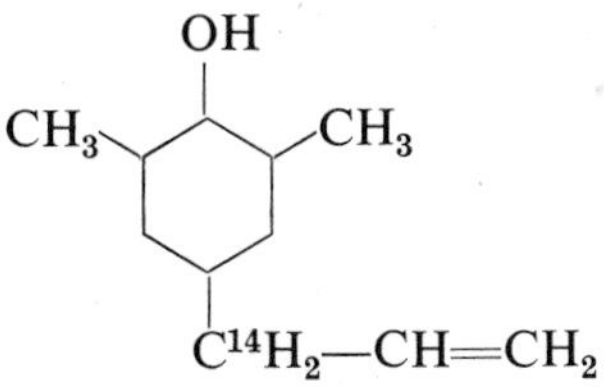

XCVI

much speculation.   If the allyl group broke away as any sort of reactive fragment, which might be a cation, an anion, or a free radical, and which subsequently attacked the aromatic ring, equal quantities of the two products XCV and XCVI would necessarily be formed, since the fragment would then be a hybrid of the equivalent structures XCVII and XCVIII,

$$CH_2{=}CH{-}\overset{z}{C}H_2 \qquad\qquad \overset{z}{C}H_2{-}CH{=}CH_2$$
XCVII   XCVIII

[160] J. P. Ryan and P. R. O'Connor, *J. Am. Chem. Soc.* **74**, 5866 (1952).   See also H. Schmid and K. Schmid, *Helv. Chim. Acta* **36**, 489 (1953).   A similar conclusion has also been reached by more conventional chemical methods by E. N. Marvell, A. V. Logan, L. Friedman, and R. W. Ledeen, *J. Am. Chem. Soc.* **76**, 1922 (1954).

in which z represents, respectively, a positive formal charge, a negative formal charge and associated unshared pair of electrons, or a single unpaired electron.   Although such a mechanism is therefore impossible for the reaction under the usual experimental conditions, there is nevertheless evidence that it may be involved in the superficially analogous *photochemical* rearrangement; for, under these latter conditions, the ether XCIV gives approximately equal quantities of the two products XCV and XCVI.[161]

A further possibility for the thermal (i.e., conventional) *p*-Claisen rearrangement is that the reaction occurs first in the way which leads to an *o*-allylphenol (see above).[158]   The initial product, which would here have the structure XCIX, is extremely unstable since it has lost most of

XCIX   C

its resonance energy; it cannot, however, be stabilized by the gain and loss either of a proton, as with the analogous product LXXXIX, or of an entire methyl group; consequently, the allyl group moves on to the para position by a repetition of its first migration.   Since there is an inversion in each step, the new unstable product has the structure C which, by gain and loss of a proton, is transformed into XCV.   Very convincing evidence for the correctness of this suggested mechanism has recently been obtained;[162] for, from either of the two ethers CI and CII, there is obtained a mixture of the two rearranged products CIII and CIV. This observation is clearly consistent with the view that both reactions proceed through a common intermediate with the structure CV (analogous to XCIX).   Moreover, the alternative possibility that the formation of the products CIII and CIV from the ethers CII and CI, respectively, is unrelated to the rearrangement proper, but is instead due to the establishment of a reversible equilibrium among the substances CI, CV, and CII,

---

[161] K. Schmid and H. Schmid, *Helv. Chim. Acta* **36**, 687 (1953).

[162] D. Y. Curtin and H. W. Johnson, Jr., *J. Am. Chem. Soc.* **76**, 2276 (1954).   Earlier, very convincing evidence leading to the same conclusion has been given also by H. Conroy and R. A. Firestone, *J. Am. Chem. Soc.* **75**, 2530 (1953).   For additional work confirming that of Curtin and Johnson, see E. N. Marvell and R. Teranishi, *J. Am. Chem. Soc.* **76**, 6165 (1954); K. Schmid, W. Haegele, and H. Schmid, *Experientia* **9**, 414 (1953) [*C. A.* **49**, 1626 (1955)].

has been excluded by the demonstration that, under the conditions of the experiment, there is no significant interconversion of the ethers CI and

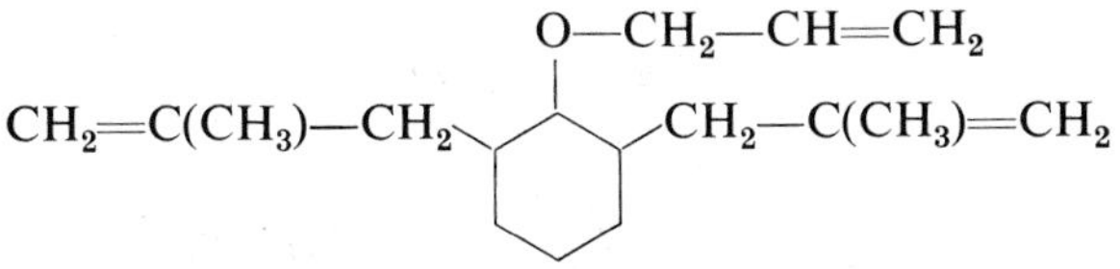

$$O—CH_2—CH=CH_2$$

$$CH_2=C(CH_3)—CH_2\diagdown \quad \diagup CH_2—C(CH_3)=CH_2$$

CI

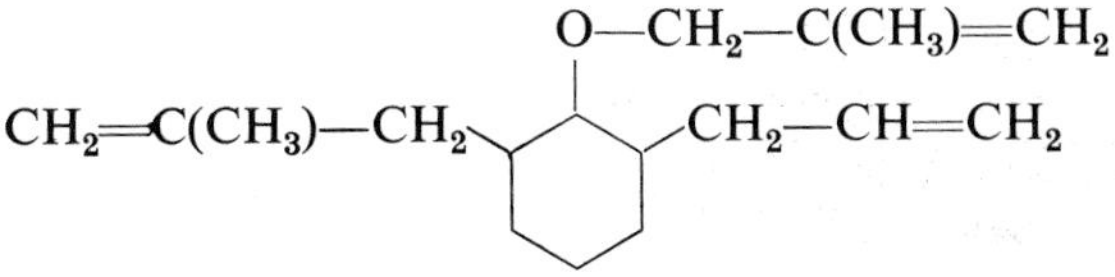

$$O—CH_2—C(CH_3)=CH_2$$

$$CH_2=C(CH_3)—CH_2\diagdown \quad CH_2—CH=CH_2$$

CII

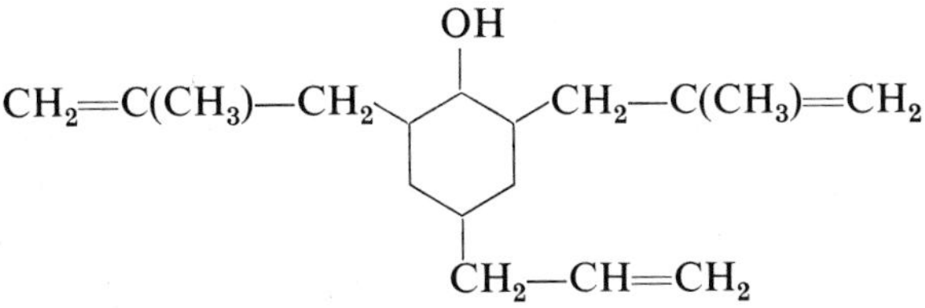

$$OH$$

$$CH_2=C(CH_3)—CH_2\diagdown \quad \diagup CH_2—C(CH_3)=CH_2$$

$$CH_2—CH=CH_2$$

CIII

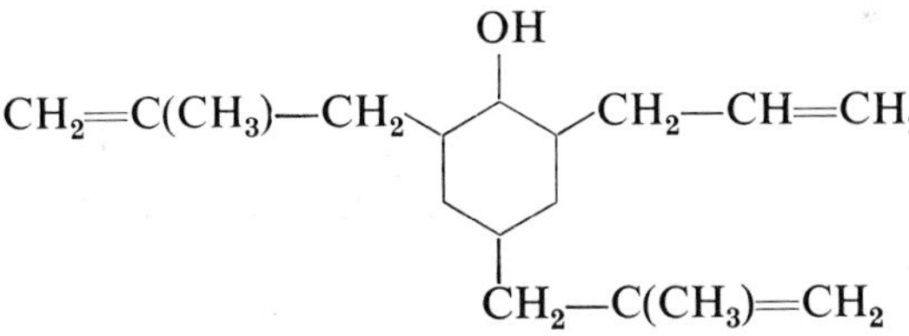

$$OH$$

$$CH_2=C(CH_3)—CH_2\diagdown \quad \diagup CH_2—CH=CH_2$$

$$CH_2—C(CH_3)=CH_2$$

CIV

$$O$$

$$CH_2=C(CH_3)—CH_2\diagdown \quad \diagup CH_2—C(CH_3)=CH_2$$
$$-CH_2—CH=CH_2$$

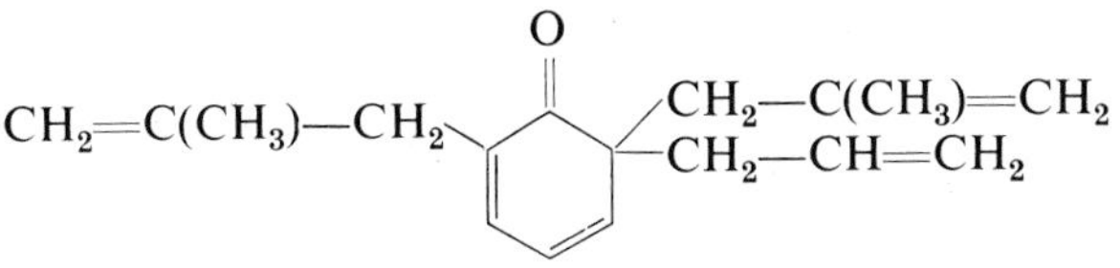

CV

CII. Consequently, only the mechanism of Hurd and Pollack[158] is consistent with all the data now available.

When either 3-chloro-1-butene, CVI, or crotyl chloride, CVII, is treated with diethylamine, the sole product that is obtained is 1-diethylamino-2-butene, CVIII.[163]   The rearrangement that occurs in the first of these

$$CH_3-CHCl-CH=CH_2 \qquad CH_3-CH=CH-CH_2Cl$$
CVI   CVII

$$CH_3-CH=CH-CH_2-N(C_2H_5)_2$$
CVIII

two reactions is certainly of the allylic type, considered above, but, as we shall see below, it may also have some analogy with the Claisen rearrangement.   Although the same product CVIII is formed from both of the unsaturated halides CVI and CVII, the existence of a common intermediate cation, which is a hybrid of structures LXXI and LXXII

$$CH_3-C^+H-CH=CH_2 \qquad CH_3-CH=CH-C^+H_2$$
LXXI   LXXII

(cf. page 535), has been definitely excluded, since the rate of the reaction has been found to be proportional to the concentration of each reagent.

The further possibility that the rearrangement occurs either before or after, rather than during, the replacement of the chlorine atom by the diethylamino group has also been definitely excluded, since neither 3-chloro-1-butene, CVI, nor 3-diethylamino-1-butene, CIX, is transformed

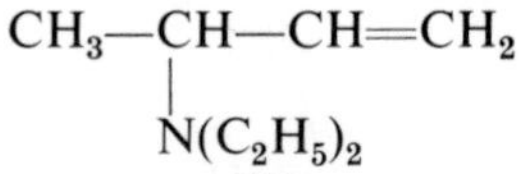

$$CH_3-CH-CH=CH_2$$
$$|$$
$$N(C_2H_5)_2$$
CIX

into its isomer under the experimental conditions employed.   Clearly, therefore, the amine must directly attack the unsaturated carbon atom at position 1 in the molecule of 3-chloro-1-butene.   Young, Webb, and Goering,[163] accordingly, concluded that the reaction proceeds by the mechanism outlined on pages 535ff; Ingold,[164] on the other hand, has made the alternative suggestion that the hydrogen atom of the NH group in the secondary amine plays an essential role; and that, in analogy with

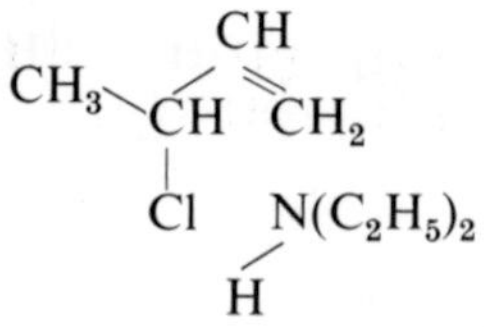

CX 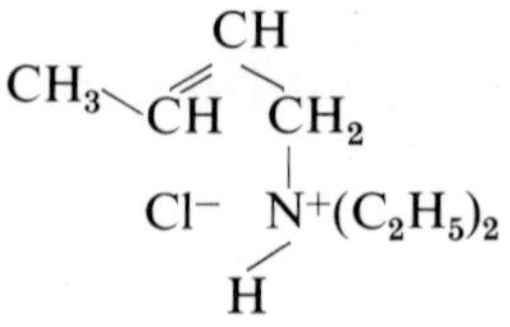   CXI

[163] W. G. Young, I. D. Webb, and H. L. Goering, *J. Am. Chem. Soc.* **73**, 1076 (1951).
[164] C. K. Ingold, *Structure and Mechanism in Organic Chemistry*, Cornell University Press, Ithaca, N. Y., 1953, pp. 592f.

the Claisen rearrangement, the activated complex is here a hybrid of the cyclic structures CX and CXI.   We cannot at present be certain which of the two mechanisms is the more satisfactory; in any event, however, the difference between them is slight, and possibly trivial.

Still another mechanism for the allylic rearrangement has apparently been encountered in the transformation of 3-chloro-3-methyl-1-butene, CXII, into 1-chloro-3-methyl-2-butene, CXIII.[165]   This isomerization,

$$(CH_3)_2CCl—CH=CH_2 \qquad\qquad (CH_3)_2C=CH—CH_2Cl$$
CXII   CXIII

which accompanies the solvolysis of the original halide in glacial acetic acid, has been found from a careful kinetic study to be intramolecular. The activated complex is therefore presumably a hybrid of structures CXIV and CXV.[166]   If such a cyclic intermediate is indeed involved, the reaction again has some analogy with the Claisen rearrangement.

$$(CH_3)_2C \underset{Cl}{\overset{CH}{<}} CH_2 \qquad\qquad (CH_3)_2C \underset{Cl}{\overset{CH}{<}} CH_2$$
CXIV   CXV

[165] W. G. Young, S. Winstein, and H. L. Goering, *J. Am. Chem. Soc.* **73**, 1958 (1951).
[166] Cf. E. D. Hughes, *Trans. Faraday Soc.* **34**, 185 (1938).

Chapter 9   MATHEMATICAL BASIS OF RESONANCE

9·1   Introduction. As has been shown in the preceding chapters, a great many aspects of the theory of resonance can be discussed in purely qualitative and descriptive terms.   Nevertheless, to most persons who are unfamiliar with wave mechanics, this theory must appear not only quite arbitrary, but also rather abstruse.   Consequently, with the hope of correcting this unfortunate impression, we shall here present, as simply as possible and without any attempt to achieve either completeness or rigor, those parts of the mathematical development which are necessary for an adequate understanding of the theory.   In addition, the superficially different but more or less parallel line of reasoning which has led to the molecular-orbital treatment of valence will also be briefly described.

The reader will be assumed to know enough calculus to have a clear understanding of what a partial differential equation means, but not necessarily enough to be able to solve such an equation without help; and he will be assumed to be familiar with the more elementary properties of determinants.   He will also frequently be called upon either to accept certain essential parts of the argument on faith, or else to consult other sources for the empirical data and mathematical proofs which must here be omitted.[1]

9·2   The Schrödinger Equation. The theory of resonance is based upon that particular form of quantum mechanics which is known as *wave mechanics*, and which has as its primary postulate the so-called *Schrödinger equation*, or *wave equation*.   For one particularly simple type of system, this equation can be derived directly from experimental data. Although the treatment in this instance is neither entirely rigorous nor completely general, it will nevertheless be outlined here since it will help

---

[1] Of the many excellent introductions to quantum mechanics which are now available, only a few can be mentioned here.   See, for example, L. Pauling and E. B. Wilson, Jr., *Introduction to Quantum Mechanics*, McGraw-Hill Book Co., New York, 1935; H. Eyring, J. Walter, and G. E. Kimball, *Quantum Chemistry*, John Wiley & Sons, New York, 1944; H. Margenau and G. M. Murphy, *The Mathematics of Physics and Chemistry*. D. Van Nostrand Co., New York, 1943, Chapter 11; L. I. Schiff, *Quantum Mechanics*, McGraw-Hill Book Co., New York, 1949; K. S. Pitzer, *Quantum Chemistry*, Prentice-Hall, New York, 1953.

to dispel the otherwise almost unavoidable impression that the wave equation is simply "pulled out of a hat." The system to be considered is one consisting of a single particle (electron, proton, atom, or the like), which has a mass m, and which is acted upon by an external field (electric, gravitational, or the like) so that the potential energy is a function $V(x, y, z)$ of the Cartesian coordinates x, y, and z of the particle. For such a system, the Schrödinger equation takes the special form

$$-\frac{h^2}{8\pi^2 m}\left(\frac{\partial^2 \psi}{\partial x^2} + \frac{\partial^2 \psi}{\partial y^2} + \frac{\partial^2 \psi}{\partial z^2}\right) + V\psi = W\psi \tag{1}$$

which it is now our task to derive. (The significance of the letters h, ψ, and W will be explained as we proceed.) As a result of diffraction studies,[2] we must apparently admit, as an experimental fact, that a particle of the type described is associated with some sort of wave phenomenon. If the particle is moving with velocity v, its wave length λ has been shown by the same diffraction studies to be[3]

$$\lambda = h/mv \tag{2}$$

where h is Planck's constant. Even though we may have no idea what it is that is thus "waving," we may nevertheless assume that the wave has not only a wave length λ but also an amplitude, which can be expressed as a function $\psi(x, y, z)$ of the coordinates x, y, and z. As is true in all kinds of wave motion (cf. also the following paragraph in fine print), this amplitude must satisfy the partial differential equation[4]

$$\frac{\partial^2 \psi}{\partial x^2} + \frac{\partial^2 \psi}{\partial y^2} + \frac{\partial^2 \psi}{\partial z^2} + \frac{4\pi^2}{\lambda^2}\,\psi = 0 \tag{3}$$

When the wave length given by equation 2 is inserted in equation 3, we find that

$$\frac{\partial^2 \psi}{\partial x^2} + \frac{\partial^2 \psi}{\partial y^2} + \frac{\partial^2 \psi}{\partial z^2} + \frac{4\pi^2 m^2 v^2}{h^2}\,\psi = 0 \tag{4}$$

In order to specify the dependence of the velocity v upon the coordinates, we now make use of the fact that the total energy W, which is a constant, can be expressed as

$$W = \text{Kinetic energy} + \text{Potential energy} = \tfrac{1}{2}mv^2 + V(x, y, z)$$

so that $m^2 v^2 = 2m[W - V(x, y, z)]$

[2] See, for example, C. J. Davisson and L. H. Germer, *Phys. Rev.* **30**, 705 (1927); *Proc. Natl. Acad. Sci. U. S.* **14**, 317 (1928); G. P. Thompson, *Proc. Roy. Soc. (London)* A **117**, 600 (1928); E. Rupp, *Ann. Physik* **85**, 981 (1928).

[3] Cf. also L. de Broglie, *Nature* **112**, 540 (1923); Thesis, Paris, 1924; *Ann. phys.* [10] **3**, 22 (1925).

[4] See, for example, H. Margenau and G. M. Murphy, *The Mathematics of Physics and Chemistry*, D. Van Nostrand Co., New York, 1943, pp. 223ff.

Equation 4 can therefore be written as

$$\frac{\partial^2 \psi}{\partial x^2} + \frac{\partial^2 \psi}{\partial y^2} + \frac{\partial^2 \psi}{\partial z^2} + \frac{8\pi^2 m}{h^2} [W - V(x, y, z)]\psi = 0 \tag{5}$$

or, often more conveniently, as equation 1.

Although we need not here discuss the derivation of the classical wave equation 3, we may nevertheless find it instructive to consider its one-dimensional analog

$$\frac{d^2 \psi}{dx^2} + \frac{4\pi^2}{\lambda^2} \psi = 0$$

If the wave length λ is constant, this equation is easily solved; and, as can be verified by differentiation, its solution can be written as

$$\psi = A \cos \left(\frac{2\pi x}{\lambda} + \delta \right)$$

The two constants of integration, A and δ, here define the maximum amplitude and the phase, respectively, of the wave; and λ is indeed seen to be the wave length. For three-dimensional waves with wave lengths that are functions of the coordinates, no such simple and general solutions are possible, but the differential equation 3 is always valid.[4]

The treatment up to this point has been far from general since it gives no hint how systems consisting of two or more particles can be treated, and since it has led to a final equation (1 or 5) in which one essential dynamical quantity, the time, is completely absent. Furthermore, it is incomplete also in that it has assigned no physical significance to the amplitude ψ. For the removal of these several deficiencies, the theoretical physicists have made the three special assumptions which will be stated in the three paragraphs following the one in fine print, below.

Although the assumptions which have just been referred to were initially proposed on the basis of certain presumed analogies with both classical mechanics and optics,[5] their only real justification lies in the fact that they lead to a great many predictions which are confirmed by experiment, and to no as yet recognized predictions which are definitely contrary to experiment. In this respect, they resemble many other basic and extremely general assumptions of science, such as Hamilton's principle in classical mechanics or the second law of thermodynamics, which also cannot be rigorously derived from the results of any small number of experiments. Since, however, it would carry us too far afield even to summarize the extensive evidence that has been accumulated in support of the wave-mechanical postulates stated below, we shall here merely refer the interested reader to the many textbooks on quantum mechanics that are now available.[1, 5]

[5] For a summary of the historical development of wave mechanics, see, for example, E. C. Kemble, *The Fundamental Principles of Quantum Mechanics*, McGraw-Hill Book Co., New York, 1937, Chapter I.

For a system consisting of altogether n particles, equation 1 (or 5) is generalized to

$$-\frac{h^2}{8\pi^2} \sum_{j=1}^{n} \frac{1}{m_j} \left(\frac{\partial^2 \psi}{\partial x_j^2} + \frac{\partial^2 \psi}{\partial y_j^2} + \frac{\partial^2 \psi}{\partial z_j^2} \right) + V(x_1, y_1, \cdots, z_n)\psi = W\psi \quad (6)$$

where m_j is the mass of the jth particle and x_j, y_j, and z_j are its three Cartesian coordinates. This equation is frequently abbreviated to the more convenient form

$$\mathbf{H}\psi = W\psi \qquad (7)$$

in which the so-called *Hamiltonian operator* **H** is defined sufficiently well for our purposes by the statement that equations 6 and 7 are completely equivalent, so that $\mathbf{H}\psi$ is simply an alternative expression for the function that appears on the left side of equation 6. Since equations 6 and 7 do not involve the time, they are conventionally described as *time free*.

Since we shall hereafter have little need for the more general *time-dependent* Schrödinger equation, we shall here mention only that this equation has the form

$$\mathbf{H}\Psi = -\frac{h}{2\pi i} \frac{\partial \Psi}{\partial t} \qquad (8)$$

in which i is the imaginary unit, $\sqrt{-1}$. The Hamiltonian operator **H** again has the same meaning as before, but the amplitude function $\psi(x_1, y_1, \cdots, z_n)$ is now replaced by a different function $\Psi(x_1, y_1, \cdots, z_n, t)$, which involves not only the spatial coordinates but also the time t. The relation between ψ and Ψ will be described more fully in the following paragraph and also in Section 9·17.

The physical significance of the time-free amplitude function ψ is the following. Although ψ may be complex, in the sense that it involves the imaginary unit i, the product of ψ and its complex conjugate ψ^* is necessarily real and either positive or zero for every set of values which can be assigned to the coordinates x_1, y_1, $\cdots$, z_n (see the following paragraph in fine print). The expression $q\,dv$, defined by the identities

$$q\,dv \equiv \psi^*\psi\,dv \equiv \psi^*\psi\,dx_1\,dy_1\,dz_1\,dx_2 \cdots dz_n \qquad (9)$$

is then assumed to be proportional to the probability that a set of simultaneous measurements would find each particle j to lie in the region between x_j and $x_j + dx_j$, between y_j and $y_j + dy_j$, and between z_j and $z_j + dz_j$. If ψ is real, then q, which is equal to $\psi^*\psi$, becomes simply ψ^2. In the more general case in which the time-dependent wave equation 8 and amplitude function Ψ must be used, the probability must be expressed as

$$Q\,dv \equiv \Psi^*\Psi\,dv \equiv \Psi^*\Psi\,dx_1\,dy_1\,dz_1\,dx_2 \cdots dz_n \qquad (10)$$

Unlike q, Q is ordinarily a function of the time. (The foregoing discussion needs to be slightly modified when the functions ψ and Ψ involve the spins. Cf. Section 9·7.)

Any complex quantity P can be expressed in the form

$$P \equiv R + iS$$

where both R and S are real. The *complex conjugate* P^* differs from P only in the replacement of the imaginary unit i, wherever it occurs, by $-i$; hence

$$P^* \equiv R - iS$$

The product P^*P therefore becomes

$$P^*P = (R - iS)(R + iS) = R^2 + S^2$$

Since R and S are real, P^*P must also be real; it can be zero only if $R = S = 0$, and it can never be negative.

It follows from the above discussion that the integral of $q \, dv$ over all of space is proportional to the probability that each particle really is somewhere in space. This probability must be equal to unity since unit probability means complete certainty. Consequently, it is desirable for the integral in question also to be equal to unity, since then the expression $q \, dv$ is not merely proportional to, but actually equal to, the probability that the particles are in the region dv. Whenever this condition is satisfied, the function ψ is said to be *normalized*. Now, from the form of the time-free Schrödinger equation 6, one can show that, if ψ is a solution corresponding to some specified value of W, then $k\psi$, where k is any constant, is also a solution corresponding to the same value of W; for if, in equation 6, ψ is everywhere replaced by $k\psi$, the net result is merely to multiply each side of the equation by the constant factor k. Consequently, if we have a function ψ that is not initially normalized, we can always make it normalized by multiplying it with an appropriate constant, provided only that the integral of $q \, dv$ is finite. Although unnormalizable functions are sometimes encountered in quantum-mechanical discussions, we shall hereafter always assume that the functions with which we deal are normalizable, and usually that they are normalized.

9·3 Auxiliary Conditions. From the general theory of differential equations, it follows that, for every value of the constant energy W, the time-free Schrödinger equation 6 of Section 9·2 may, and usually does, have a large number of different solutions ψ. Ordinarily, however, this large number of solutions is greatly decreased by the application of certain auxiliary conditions which, for the reasons that are briefly explained in the paragraph following the one in fine print below, must be imposed if the functions ψ are to be assigned the physical significance stated above. These conditions are that a function ψ, in order to be acceptable, must not only satisfy the wave equation, but must also, together with all its partial first derivatives, be everywhere single valued, finite, and continuous. (See the following paragraph.) Moreover, at any rate in all the problems in which we shall be interested, ψ and its derivatives must vanish at infinity or, in other words, must be equal to zero when any one of the coordinates x_1, y_1, $\cdots$, z_n is infinite. Any solution of the wave equation which does not satisfy all these additional conditions may be considered to correspond to a state of the system which is not physically realizable, and which is therefore of neither theoretical nor experimental significance.

A function is said to be everywhere single valued if, for each choice of all the independent variables, it has a unique value. The function $\cos^{-1} x$, for example, does not satisfy this condition since, when $x = 0$, $\cos^{-1} x$ can have any one of the values $\pm \pi/2$, $\pm 3\pi/2$, $\pm 5\pi/2$, $\cdots$. A function is said to be everywhere finite if, for each choice of all the independent variables, it has a finite value. The functions x^2 and $1/(1 - x)$, for example, do not satisfy this condition since the first becomes infinite when $x = \infty$, whereas the second becomes infinite when $x = 1$. Finally, a function is said to be everywhere continuous if, for each choice of all the independent variables, an infinitesimal change in the value of any independent variable produces only an infinitesimal change in that of the function itself. The function $f(x)$, which is defined as equal to zero when x is less than zero but to one when x is equal to or greater than zero, for example, does not satisfy this condition since the value of $f(x)$ changes abruptly at $x = 0$. In the paragraph in fine print on page 552, attention is called to a further function which, although continuous, has a discontinuous first derivative. On the other hand, numerous examples of functions which *do* satisfy all these auxiliary conditions will be given in the following sections.

The reasons for these various auxiliary conditions can easily be seen. For example, if ψ is not single valued, then the expression $q \, dv$ is also not single valued. Hence the probability of finding the various particles in specified regions of space would be ambiguous. No theory permitting such a situation to arise would be tenable. If ψ does not vanish at infinity, the particles are certain to be found outside any sphere, no matter how large, which can be drawn about the origin of the coordinate system as center. This conclusion follows because the integral of $q \, dv$ over the infinite region outside such a sphere would then be infinitely greater than the integral over the finite region within the sphere. Hence, any function ψ which does not vanish at infinity could refer only to a system which is itself located at infinity. Similar arguments can be brought forth in support of the remaining auxiliary conditions, but these need not here be further discussed.

As was stated above, an important result of the auxiliary conditions which every function ψ must satisfy is that they greatly limit the number of acceptable solutions of the Schrödinger equation. Indeed, it is usually found that this equation has no satisfactory solutions at all unless the energy W has one or another definitely specified value. Any value of

W which does permit such a solution is known as an *eigenvalue* (or *proper value*, or *characteristic value*) of the equation and of the system. Any satisfactory function ψ corresponding to any eigenvalue is known as an *eigenfunction* or *wave function* (or *proper function* or *characteristic function*). If each of the r functions ψ_1, ψ_2, · · · ψ_r is an eigenfunction corresponding to the same eigenvalue, then, as can be shown by a direct substitution in the wave equation (see equation 6, Section 9·2), any *linear combination*

$$k_1\psi_1 + k_2\psi_2 + \cdots + k_r\psi_r \tag{1}$$

with constant coefficients k_1, k_2, · · · k_r is also an eigenfunction corresponding to the same eigenvalue. Consequently, in order to keep from counting any eigenfunction more than once, we shall consider for each eigenvalue only those eigenfunctions ψ_1, ψ_2, · · · ψ_r which are *independent* of each other or, in other words, only those eigenfunctions for which a linear combination of the type 1 can be identically equal to zero only if $k_1 = k_2 = \cdots k_r = 0$. (Cf. the following paragraph in fine print.) If altogether s independent eigenfunctions belong to any given eigenvalue, then these functions, and likewise the eigenvalue, are said to be s-fold *degenerate*.

The significance of an independent set of functions can be illustrated with a simple example which will be of interest in connection with the wave functions for the hydrogen atom in its different spectroscopic states (cf. Section 9·6). The functions $\sin \phi$ and $\cos \phi$ are independent because, in order that the linear combination $k_1 \sin \phi + k_2 \cos \phi$ be equal to zero for all values of ϕ, it is necessary that $k_1 = k_2 = 0$. On the other hand, the larger set $\sin \phi$, $\cos \phi$, and $e^{i\phi}$ is not independent since $i \sin \phi + \cos \phi - e^{i\phi} \equiv 0$. Consequently, $e^{i\phi}$ need not be considered if both $\sin \phi$ and $\cos \phi$ are taken into account.

9·4   The Particle in a Box.   The foregoing statements can be made more concrete by consideration of a specific example, which is chosen so that it is simple enough to be easily treated, but complex enough to bring out a number of the points which are essential to an understanding of wave mechanics.

The problem which will here be discussed is that of a single particle constrained to move in a box. For the sake of simplicity, we shall first consider a one-dimensional box that lies along the x axis and extends from the origin, at which $x = 0$, to the point $x = a$. Since the box is one dimensional, the y and z coordinates do not enter into the treatment. In order to ensure that the particle will remain within the box, we shall set the potential energy V equal to infinity at all points which do not satisfy the relation $0 \leq x \leq a$. Then, in the region *outside* the box, the wave equation (cf. equation 1, Section 9·2), can be written as

$$-\frac{h^2}{8\pi^2 m}\frac{d^2\psi}{dx^2} + \infty \cdot \psi = W\psi \qquad (x < 0 \text{ or } > a) \tag{1}$$

Since the only possible solution of this equation is

$$\psi = 0 \qquad (x < 0 \text{ or } > a) \tag{2}$$

the probability of finding the particle outside the box is zero, in accordance with the original postulate.

In the region within the box, no forces act on the particle. Hence the potential energy V is equal to a constant, which we can without loss of generality take as zero. The wave equation is therefore

$$-\frac{h^2}{8\pi^2 m}\frac{d^2\psi}{dx^2} = W\psi \qquad (0 \le x \le a) \tag{3}$$

The general solution of equation 3 is

$$\psi = R \sin \sqrt{\frac{8\pi^2 m W}{h^2}}\, x + S \cos \sqrt{\frac{8\pi^2 m W}{h^2}}\, x \qquad (0 \le x \le a) \tag{4}$$

where R and S are the two constants of integration; this statement can most easily be verified by direct substitution of 4 into 3. Since ψ must not vanish identically, at least one of the constants R and S must be different from zero. In order to evaluate these constants, we first note the auxiliary condition that ψ must be a continuous function of x not only in the region in which $0 \le x \le a$ but also throughout the whole range for which $-\infty \le x \le +\infty$. Now, since $\psi = 0$ for all values of x less than zero or greater than a (cf. equation 2), this condition is satisfied only if $\psi = 0$ when $x = 0$ and also when $x = a$. But, from equation 4, we see that $\psi(0) = S$, and hence that $S = 0$. Therefore, R must *not* be equal to zero. Consequently, from the equation

$$\psi(a) = R \sin \sqrt{\frac{8\pi^2 m W}{h^2}}\, a = 0 \tag{5}$$

we find successively that

$$\sin \sqrt{\frac{8\pi^2 m W}{h^2}}\, a = 0 \tag{6}$$

$$\sqrt{\frac{8\pi^2 m W}{h^2}}\, a = \sin^{-1} 0 = n\pi \tag{7}$$

and finally

$$W = \frac{n^2 h^2}{8 m a^2} \tag{8}$$

where n is any positive integer $1, 2, 3, \cdots$.

If n were equal to 0, ψ would vanish identically. If n were allowed to assume also the negative integral values, no additional independent solutions ψ would result, since the functions obtained in this way would be merely the negatives of those corresponding to the positive values of n.

Perhaps somewhat unexpectedly, the application of the second boundary condition therefore does not fix the value of the remaining constant of integration R, but instead fixes that of the energy value W. In order to evaluate R, we must make use of the requirement that ψ be normalized. Thus,

$$\int_{-\infty}^{+\infty} \psi^2(x) \, dx = R^2 \int_0^a \sin^2 \left[\frac{\pi n}{a} \right] x \, dx = \frac{R^2 a}{2} = 1 \qquad (9)$$

so that $$R = \sqrt{2/a} \qquad (10)$$

The solution of equation 3 is therefore

$$\psi = \sqrt{2/a} \sin \left[\frac{\pi n}{a} \right] x \qquad (0 \leq x \leq a) \qquad (11)$$

The function ψ of equations 2 and 11 does not really satisfy all the auxiliary conditions stated in Section 9·3; for, although ψ is itself continuous at all points, its first derivative $d\psi/dx$ is discontinuous at both $x = 0$ and $x = a$. This defect, however, does not completely invalidate the treatment since it can be eliminated by a slight modification in one of the original assumptions. The procedure, which need not here be described in detail, is to admit that the potential energy cannot actually be infinite in the region outside the box. If, then, V is assumed to have in this region some large but finite value V_0, the function ψ is found no longer to vanish identically when either $-\infty \leq x \leq 0$ or $a \leq x \leq +\infty$, but instead to have a small finite value which rapidly and asymptotically approaches zero as x becomes either less than zero or greater than a. There is thus a nonvanishing probability that an experiment would find the particle *outside* the box but, if only V_0 is made sufficiently large, this probability can be made as small as desired. Equations 2 and 11 describe the (actually unrealizable) limiting case in which V_0 is infinite, and in which this probability is zero.

Let us now turn to the more complex problem of a particle in a three-dimensional box, which has the shape of a rectangular parallelepiped. The origin of a system of Cartesian coordinates can be taken at one corner of the box, and the x, y, and z axes can be taken to lie along three of the edges, which have the respective lengths a, b, and c. The geometrical relationships which are here assumed are shown in Figure 9·1. As in the above one-dimensional problem, we shall again set the potential energy equal to infinity at all points outside of the box; in the same way as before, the wave function can then be shown to vanish except in the region for which $0 \leq x \leq a$, $0 \leq y \leq b$, and $0 \leq z \leq c$. Hence, since

$$\psi = 0 \qquad \left. \begin{cases} -\infty \leq x \leq 0 \text{ or } a \leq x \leq +\infty \\ -\infty \leq y \leq 0 \text{ or } b \leq y \leq +\infty \\ -\infty \leq z \leq 0 \text{ or } c \leq z \leq +\infty \end{cases} \right\} \qquad (12)$$

the probability that an experiment would find the particle outside the box is zero.

Within the box, the potential energy V can be set equal to zero. The wave equation is here therefore

$$-\frac{h^2}{8\pi^2 m}\left(\frac{\partial^2\psi}{\partial x^2}+\frac{\partial^2\psi}{\partial y^2}+\frac{\partial^2\psi}{\partial z^2}\right)=W\psi \qquad \begin{pmatrix}0\le x\le a\\ 0\le y\le b\\ 0\le z\le c\end{pmatrix} \qquad (13)$$

This partial differential equation, with the three independent variables x, y, and z, is rather hard to solve in its original form, but it can be greatly

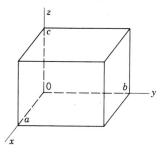

Fig. 9·1.   A box in the shape of a rectangular parallelepiped, with edges of length a, b, and c lying along the x, y, and z axes.

simplified by a *separation of the variables*. For this purpose, we make the assumption that

$$\psi = X(x)\,Y(y)Z(z) \qquad (14)$$

or, in other words, that ψ can be expressed as a product of a function $X(x)$ of x alone, a second function $Y(y)$ of y alone, and a third function $Z(z)$ of z alone. (For a discussion of the validity of this assumption, see page 555.) If we combine equations 13 and 14, and then divide by ψ, we obtain

$$-\frac{h^2}{8\pi^2 m}\left[\frac{1}{X}\frac{d^2X}{dx^2}+\frac{1}{Y}\frac{d^2Y}{dy^2}+\frac{1}{Z}\frac{d^2Z}{dz^2}\right]=W \qquad (15)$$

On the left side of this equation, we have a sum of three terms, each of which is a function of at most only a single independent variable, x, y, or z, respectively. The sum is, however, a constant which does not involve x, y, or z. The only way in which this equation can be valid is, therefore, for each term separately to be a constant, so that

$$-\frac{h^2}{8\pi^2 m X}\frac{d^2X}{dx^2}=W_x \qquad (16)$$

$$-\frac{h^2}{8\pi^2 m Y}\frac{d^2Y}{dy^2}=W_y \qquad (17)$$

and
$$-\frac{h^2}{8\pi^2 mZ}\frac{d^2Z}{dz^2} = W_z \tag{18}$$

with
$$W_x + W_y + W_z = W \tag{19}$$

Consequently, instead of the one original partial differential equation 13 with three independent variables, we now have three total differential equations, 16–18, with one independent variable each.

Equation 16 is readily seen to be identical with equation 3, except that the wave function is now called X instead of ψ, and the eigenvalue is now called W_x instead of W. From comparison with equations 11 and 8, therefore, we can immediately write down that

$$X = \sqrt{2/a}\,\sin\left[\frac{\pi n_x}{a}\right]x \qquad (0 \le x \le a) \tag{20}$$

and
$$W_x = \frac{n_x{}^2 h^2}{8ma^2} \tag{21}$$

where n_x is, as before, restricted to the positive integral values 1, 2, · · ·. Similarly,

$$Y = \sqrt{2/b}\,\sin\left[\frac{\pi n_y}{b}\right]y \qquad (0 \le y \le b) \tag{22}$$

$$W_y = \frac{n_y{}^2 h^2}{8mb^2} \tag{23}$$

$$Z = \sqrt{2/c}\,\sin\left[\frac{\pi n_z}{c}\right]z \qquad (0 \le z \le c) \tag{24}$$

$$W_z = \frac{n_z{}^2 h^2}{8mc^2} \tag{25}$$

with both n_y and n_z equal to 1, 2, · · ·. Hence

$$\begin{aligned}
\psi_{n_x n_y n_z} &= X(x)\,Y(y)\,Z(z) \\
&= \sqrt{8/abc}\,\sin\left[\frac{\pi n_x}{a}\right]x \sin\left[\frac{\pi n_y}{b}\right]y \sin\left[\frac{\pi n_z}{c}\right]z \qquad \begin{pmatrix} 0 \le x \le a \\ 0 \le y \le b \\ 0 \le z \le c \end{pmatrix} \\
&= 0 \quad \text{otherwise}
\end{aligned} \tag{26}$$

and
$$W_{n_x n_y n_z} = W_x + W_y + W_z = \frac{h^2}{8m}\left(\frac{n_x{}^2}{a^2} + \frac{n_y{}^2}{b^2} + \frac{n_z{}^2}{c^2}\right) \tag{27}$$

The energy given in equation 27 is purely kinetic since the potential energy inside the box (i.e., in the only region where the particle ever is) has been set equal to zero.

The question whether the set of functions $\psi_{n_x n_y n_z}$ given in equation 26 includes *all* the independent solutions of the wave equation must now be considered. The procedure by which we obtained this set of functions seems far from general since it is based on the apparently arbitrary assumption that the wave function is a product of three simpler functions, each of which depends on only a single coordinate. From the theory of Fourier series, however, one can show that the most general possible solution of the wave equation can be expressed as a linear combination of those functions $\psi_{n_x n_y n_z}$ which correspond to the same value of the total energy W. Since this question of completeness is not essential to the following discussion, we shall here pursue the problem no further.[6]

The foregoing discussion of a particle in a box has included several points that are generally valid throughout wave mechanics. In the first place, we should note that the *quantum numbers* n_x, n_y, and n_z, and their restriction to positive integral values, enter the treatment automatically and unavoidably. In the second place, since the lowest permissible value for each of these quantum numbers is 1, the lowest possible value for the (kinetic) energy of the particle is

$$W_{111} = \frac{h^2}{8m}\left[\frac{1}{a^2} + \frac{1}{b^2} + \frac{1}{c^2}\right] \tag{28}$$

where the three subscripts in the term W_{111} specify the respective values of the three quantum numbers n_x, n_y, and n_z (cf. equation 27). Consequently, as long as the particle is held in the box, it must have kinetic energy and hence must be in motion. The magnitude of this kinetic energy increases as either the mass of the particle or the size of the box decreases. If the system is a macroscopic one, so that m is of the order of, say, 1 g and a, b, and c are of the order of, say, 1 cm, then W_{111} has a negligibly small value of about 10^{-53} erg. On the other hand, if m, a, b, and c are of the much smaller orders of magnitude that are characteristic of atomic or molecular systems, then W_{111} becomes appreciable. For example, if $m = 9 \times 10^{-28}$ g (the mass of an electron), and if $a = b = c = 10^{-8}$ cm, then W_{111} is about 1.8×10^{-10} erg for a single particle. If this energy seems small, one should remember that it corresponds to about 1.1×10^{14} ergs, or 2600 kcal, for Avogadro's number of particles. The increase in the kinetic energy, which accompanies a decrease in the available volume, has many chemical effects. In particular, the repulsive forces which operate to prevent atoms from approaching each other too closely are in large part due to such increases in kinetic energy; hence these increases play an important role in the

---

[6] For additional details, see R. Courant and D. Hilbert, *Methoden der mathematischen Physik*, J. Springer, Berlin, 1924, pp. 58ff, or any book dealing with Fourier series.

determination of bond energies, bond lengths, and the like. In Section 9·5, we shall show how, in two specific instances, the above treatment of the particle in a box can lead to chemically interesting conclusions. (See also Section 9·28.)

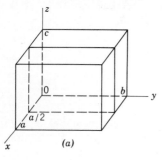

(a)

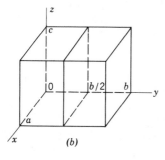

(b)

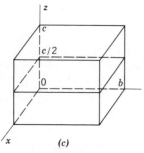

(c)

Fig. 9·2. Nodal planes bisecting the box for the wave functions (a) ψ_{211}, (b) ψ_{121}, and (c) ψ_{112}.

Further consideration of equations 26 and 27 brings out additional points of general interest. Thus, it is worthy of note that the eigenfunction ψ_{111}, corresponding to the lowest eigenvalue W_{111}, is positive at all points inside the box, and is zero only at the walls and outside the box. On the other hand, each of the next most stable eigenfunctions, ψ_{211}, ψ_{121}, and ψ_{112}, is equal to zero also at all points on a plane which bisects the box (see Figure 9·2). With ψ_{211}, this plane is the one $x = a/2$; with ψ_{121}, it is $y = b/2$; and with ψ_{112}, it is $z = c/2$. Such a plane is called a nodal surface or, more generally, a *node*. In general, and not only with the particle in a box, the energy increases with the number of nodes. In more complex systems, however, the nodes need not be planes since they may instead be curved surfaces and, if the eigenfunction refers to more than one particle, they must be "surfaces" in a space of more than three dimensions.

If the box is a cube, so that $a = b = c$, many of the eigenfunctions are degenerate. For example, W_{211} is then equal to both W_{121} and W_{112}, $W_{3,4,13} = W_{5,5,12}$, and so on. As in the problem of the particle in a box, degeneracy always becomes more common as the symmetry of the system increases.

Since the eigenfunctions $\psi_{n_x n_y n_z}$ are normalized, it follows that

$$\int \psi^*_{n_x n_y n_z} \psi_{n_x n_y n_z}\, dv = \int [\psi_{n_x n_y n_z}]^2 dx\, dy\, dz = 1 \qquad (29)$$

where, for simplicity, a single integral sign is employed to indicate integration with respect to each Cartesian coordinate between the limits $-\infty$ and $+\infty$. Since wave functions are frequently complex, the first integral on the left side of equation 29 is written in the most general form (cf. pages 547f), even though the particular functions which are here involved are real. A further property of the eigenfunctions is that any two *different* ones are mutually *orthogonal* or, in other words, that

$$\int \psi^*_{n_x n_y n_z} \psi_{n_x' n_y' n_z'} \, dv = \int \psi_{n_x n_y n_z} \psi_{n_x' n_y' n_z'} \, dv = 0 \tag{30}$$

unless $n_x = n_x'$, $n_y = n_y'$, and $n_z = n_z'$. (As before, the integral is written first in the more general form that must be used when the wave functions are complex.) Equation 30 is again merely one special example of a quite general rule. It can in fact be shown[1] from the general form of the Schrödinger equation that any two nondegenerate eigenfunctions of the same equation are necessarily orthogonal to each other, and that degenerate eigenfunctions can always be chosen so that they also are orthogonal. We shall therefore assume hereafter that any two different eigenfunctions are orthogonal. The normalization and orthogonality conditions can conveniently be expressed by the single equation

$$\int \psi_j^* \psi_k \, dv = \delta_{jk} \tag{31}$$

in which the subscripts j and k specify the complete set of pertinent quantum numbers, the integration is over all space, and the symbol δ_{jk} is defined as equal to 1 if $j = k$, and to 0 if $j \neq k$.

9·5 Some Applications of the Results Obtained for the Particle in a Box. Expression 27, Section 9·4, for the energy of a particle in a box, is valid for a particle of any weight and for a box of any size. In particular, it is valid for a particle as heavy as a molecule, and for a box as large as ordinary laboratory equipment. As an example, let us consider 1 mole of a perfect gas in a cubic box with $a = b = c$. Since, in a perfect gas, we can treat each molecule as if it were alone in the box, the energy of a single molecule is

$$W = \frac{h^2}{8ma^2} (n_x^2 + n_y^2 + n_z^2)$$

$$= \frac{h^2}{8mv^{2/3}} (n_x^2 + n_y^2 + n_z^2) \tag{1}$$

where $v = a^3$, the volume of the box. According to equation 1, the energy of each molecule is proportional to $v^{-\frac{2}{3}}$. Hence, the total energy E of the gas must also be proportional to $v^{-\frac{2}{3}}$, so that

$$E = Kv^{-\frac{2}{3}} \tag{2}$$

where the constant K is a complicated function of h, m, and the quantum numbers n_x, n_y, and n_z of all 6×10^{23} molecules. Now, if the volume v is changed so slowly that the molecules do not undergo transitions to states characterized by different values of the quantum numbers, then K remains constant, and we have

$$P = -\partial E/\partial v = (2/3)Kv^{-\frac{5}{3}} = (2/3)E/v \tag{3}$$

where P is the pressure on the walls of the box. Since the gas is perfect, it obeys the perfect-gas law, and so equation 3 can be rewritten as

$$E = (3/2)Pv = (3/2)RT \tag{4}$$

Thus, on a purely wave-mechanical basis, and without introducing any of the usual postulates of the kinetic theory of gases, we have derived one of the important equations of the kinetic theory.[7]

As a second example, which will bring out the origin of the repulsive forces between atoms, let us consider a greatly oversimplified model of the hydrogen molecule, H_2. Although the electrons and the protons are in constant motion, we shall assume that their average electrostatic interactions with each other are the same as if they were stationary and were located at the corners of a square, as in Figure 9·3. If the interprotonic distance is called r, then the interelectronic distance is also r, and the distance

FIG. 9·3.   A model of a hydrogen molecule, consisting of two protons, $+$, and two electrons, $-$, arranged at the corners of a square.

between each electron and each proton is $r/\sqrt{2}$. The total electrostatic potential energy V, as determined by Coulomb's law, is therefore

$$V = \frac{2e^2}{r} - \frac{4e^2}{r/\sqrt{2}} = \frac{-3.66e^2}{r} \tag{5}$$

Consequently, if there were no kinetic energy to be considered, the molecule would become more stable, without limit, as r decreases, and so it would collapse to a single point, with $r = 0$; and it would have a (purely potential) energy equal to $-\infty$. In order to estimate the kinetic energy, we shall consider that the electrons and protons are held within a cubic box, the size of which must decrease as r decreases. If, for definiteness, we set the side of the box equal to kr, where k is a constant that is presumably rather greater than 1 (see also below), we find from equation 27, Section 9·4, that the *minimum* kinetic energy of each electron is equal to $3h^2/8mk^2r^2$. Since that of each relatively very heavy proton is negligibly small, the total energy of the molecule, as a function of r, is therefore approximately

$$W = -3.66e^2/r + 2 \times 3h^2/8mk^2r^2 = -3.66e^2/r + 3h^2/4mk^2r^2 \tag{6}$$

(Cf. page 683.)   This expression, unlike the one of equation 5, does not decrease without limit as r decreases. Instead, it reaches a minimum value of $-4.47mk^2e^4/h^2$ at $r = h^2/2.44mk^2e^2$. If we now set this optimum value of r equal to the observed distance in the normal hydrogen molecule, 0.74 A, we find that the constant k has the entirely reasonable value of approximately 3.4. The calculated total energy of the molecule, i.e., $-4.47mk^2e^4/h^2$, then becomes equivalent to about -815 kcal per mole. Since the observed energy of 2 moles of isolated hydrogen atoms is -625 kcal, the calculated

[7] Cf. J. E. Mayer and M. G. Mayer, *Statistical Mechanics*, John Wiley & Sons, New York, 1940, p. 119.

bond energy is 190 kcal per mole, whereas the observed value is 103 kcal per mole. The present extremely crude treatment is therefore seen to lead to a result of the correct order of magnitude, and hence to be rather better than might perhaps have been expected. In view of the drastic approximations which have been made, however, the quantitative aspects of the treatment have little validity; the only significant conclusion that can be drawn from the calculation is instead the purely qualitative one that the kinetic energy of the electrons produces a repulsion between the nuclei, and so permits the existence of a stable molecule with finite energy.

9·6   The Hydrogen Atom.   A problem which is more obviously related to valence than is that of the particle in a box is presented by the hydrogen atom. Although this atom consists of two particles, the electron and the proton, we shall simplify the treatment by assuming that the relatively heavy proton is stationary, and hence that we need consider only the motion of the electron; the error which is thereby introduced can be shown[1] to be so small that, for our purposes, it is negligible. (In the more rigorous treatment, the only modification that is here significant is that the electronic mass m must be replaced by the *reduced mass* μ. Cf. page 24.) Now, in accordance with Coulomb's law, the potential energy is equal to $-e^2/r$, where e is the magnitude of the electronic (or protonic) charge, and r is the distance between the electron and the proton. Consequently, the Schrodinger equation can be written as

$$-\frac{h^2}{8\pi^2 m}\left(\frac{\partial^2\psi}{\partial x^2}+\frac{\partial^2\psi}{\partial y^2}+\frac{\partial^2\psi}{\partial z^2}\right)-\frac{Ze^2}{r}\psi$$

$$\equiv -\frac{h^2}{8\pi^2 m}\left(\frac{\partial^2\psi}{\partial x^2}+\frac{\partial^2\psi}{\partial y^2}+\frac{\partial^2\psi}{\partial z^2}\right)-\frac{Ze^2}{\sqrt{x^2+y^2+z^2}}\psi = W\psi \qquad (1)$$

where x, y, and z are the Cartesian coordinates of the electron with respect to the (stationary) proton as origin, m is the mass of the electron, and Z is the atomic number which, although equal to 1 and hence redundant, is here given explicitly for the sake of generality.

We shall make no attempt to describe the method that has been devised for the solution of equation 1.[1] Instead, we shall merely state the results as concisely as possible, and without proof. The eigenfunctions for the hydrogen atom depend upon three quantum numbers which are designated as the *principal*, the *azimuthal*, and the *magnetic* quantum numbers, and which are conventionally represented by the respective symbols n, l, and m_l. These constants are restricted to the integral values

$$\left.\begin{array}{l} n = 1, 2, 3, \cdots \\ l = 0, 1, 2, \cdots, n-1 \\ m_l = 0, \pm 1, \pm 2, \cdots, \pm l \end{array}\right\} \qquad (2)$$

The corresponding eigenvalues are

$$W_n = \frac{2\pi^2 m Z^2 e^4}{h^2 n^2}$$
(3)

Since the energy is therefore dependent on only the principal quantum number n, each level, except the first one, is degenerate. There are, in fact, n^2 degenerate eigenfunctions for each value of n.

It should, however, be noted that, with more complex atoms containing more than one electron, the degeneracy is decreased, since the energy W_{nl} of an individual electron is then dependent upon both of the quantum numbers n and l. In this more general case, each eigenvalue is only $(2l + 1)$-fold degenerate since, for each value of l, there are $2l + 1$ values of m_l. (Cf. also page 564.)

Before discussing the explicit forms of the various wave functions, we can profitably consider some aspects of the conventional nomenclature. In the first place, it may be mentioned that any one-electron wave function, which may or may not be an exact eigenfunction of some Schrödinger equation, but which must involve only the three coordinates required for the specification of the position of the single electron in space, is commonly called an *orbital*.[8] This terminology is convenient because it distinguishes such a function both from the more complex ones that refer to two or more different electrons, and also from the spin-orbit functions which are described in Section 9·7. Each solution of equation 1 is, accordingly, an orbital.

The unique orbital with $n = 1$ is said to constitute the K-shell of the atom; the four degenerate but independent orbitals with $n = 2$ are said to constitute the L-shell; and so on in alphabetical order. Any orbital with $l = 0$ is described as an s orbital, and any with $l = 1, 2, 3, 4, \cdots$ is described as a $p, d, f, g, \cdots$ orbital. For the complete specification of an orbital, all three quantum numbers must usually be stated. Thus, ψ_{432} is the eigenfunction with $n = 4$, $l = 3$, and $m_l = 2$. Frequently, however, a less complete specification, in which the value of m_l is not stated, is more convenient. When this procedure is adopted, the value of n is explicitly stated, and that of l is indicated by the appropriate letter $s, p, d, \cdots$. Thus, the $1s$ orbital ψ_{1s} is ψ_{100}; the three different $2p$ orbitals ψ_{2p} are $\psi_{21\bar{1}}$, ψ_{210}, and ψ_{211}; and so on. (Note that, with $\psi_{21\bar{1}}$, the minus sign in the subscript is placed *over* the number to which it refers.)

Since, in the following, we shall have no occasion to mention any orbitals for which the principal quantum number n is greater than 2, we can here restrict our attention to the five functions of the K- and L-shells.

[8] This convenient term is due to R. S. Mulliken, *Phys. Rev.* **41**, 49 (1932).

In view of the spherical symmetry of the hydrogen atom, the Cartesian coordinates x, y, and z are conveniently replaced by the *spherical polar coordinates* r, θ, and ϕ, which are defined by either one of the two equivalent sets of equations

$$\left.\begin{aligned} r &= \sqrt{x^2 + y^2 + z^2} \\ \theta &= \cos^{-1} z/\sqrt{x^2 + y^2 + z^2} \\ \phi &= \tan^{-1} y/x \end{aligned}\right\} \tag{4}$$

$$\left.\begin{aligned} x &= r \sin \theta \cos \phi \\ y &= r \sin \theta \sin \phi \\ z &= r \cos \theta \end{aligned}\right\} \tag{5}$$

In terms of these coordinates, the single orbital of the K-shell is

$$\psi_{1s} \equiv \psi_{100} = \sqrt{\frac{Z^3}{\pi a_0^3}} e^{(-Zr/a_0)} \tag{6}$$

and the four orbitals of the L-shell can be written as

$$\psi_{2s} \equiv \psi_{210} = F(r) \left(\frac{2a_0}{Z} - r \right) \tag{7}$$

$$\psi_{2p^-} \equiv \psi_{21\bar{1}} = \frac{1}{\sqrt{2}} F(r)\, r \sin \theta\, e^{-i\phi} = \frac{1}{\sqrt{2}} F(r)(x - iy) \tag{8}$$

$$\psi_{2pz} \equiv \psi_{210} = F(r)\, r \cos \theta = F(r)\, z \tag{9}$$

$$\psi_{2p^+} \equiv \psi_{211} = \frac{1}{\sqrt{2}} F(r)\, r \sin \theta\, e^{i\phi} = \frac{1}{\sqrt{2}} F(r)(x + iy) \tag{10}$$

where $\quad F(r) \equiv \sqrt{\frac{Z^5}{32\pi a_0^5}} e^{(-Zr/2a_0)} \tag{11}$

and a_0, the so-called *radius of the first Bohr orbit*, is

$$a_0 \equiv \frac{h^2}{4\pi^2 m e^2} \simeq 0.53 \text{ A} \tag{12}$$

Since the functions ψ_{2p^-} (or $\psi_{21\bar{1}}$) and ψ_{2p^+} (or ψ_{211}) involve the imaginary unit i, and since they are not equivalent to the remaining $2p$ function ψ_{2pz} (or ψ_{210}), they have been found rather inconvenient for use in discussions of molecular structure. Here and throughout this chapter, therefore, we shall follow the most common procedure of replacing these functions by their linear combinations

$$\psi_{2px} = \frac{1}{\sqrt{2}}\,(\psi_{2p^-} + \psi_{2p^+}) = F(r)r\sin\theta\cos\phi = F(r)x \qquad (13)$$

and $$\psi_{2py} = \frac{i}{\sqrt{2}}\,(\psi_{2p^-} - \psi_{2p^+}) = F(r)r\sin\theta\sin\phi = F(r)y \qquad (14)$$

These new orbitals not only are real, but also are equivalent to ψ_{2pz}; and since the original functions ψ_{2p^-} and ψ_{2p^+} are degenerate for poly-electronic atoms as well as for the monoelectronic hydrogen atom (cf. the

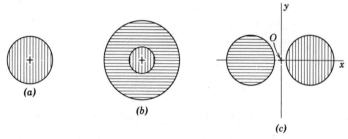

Fig. 9·4.   Schematic representation of (a) a 1s orbital, (b) a 2s orbital, and (c) a $2p_x$ orbital.

paragraph in fine print on page 560), the combinations ψ_{2px} and ψ_{2py} are still always solutions of the Schrödinger equation, even though they no longer correspond to unique values of the magnetic quantum number m_l.

It is to be noted that, in the K-shell, with $n = 1$, the azimuthal quantum number l can have only the value 0.   Consequently, only an s function can occur.   Similarly, in the L-shell, with $n = 2$, only s and p functions can occur.   Since we shall not consider the M-, N-, $\cdots$ shells, we shall therefore not encounter any $d, f, g, \cdots$ orbitals.

An important characteristic of an s orbital is that it is always a function of only the distance r between the electron and the nucleus.   Since it is therefore independent of the angular coordinates θ and ϕ, the corresponding charge distribution, defined by the expression $(\psi_{ns})^2$, is always spherically symmetrical.   In other words, the electron is exactly as likely to be found in any one direction from the nucleus as in any other.   The most stable s eigenfunction ψ_{1s} has no nodes, whereas the less stable one ψ_{2s} has one spherical node at the distance $r = 2a_0/Z$ from the nucleus. The forms of these two orbitals are shown schematically in Figures 9·4a and 9·4b, in which, as in Figure 2·3, Section 2·9, the $+$ signs represent the atomic nuclei and the closed curves represent surfaces surrounding the regions in which the electrons are most likely to be found. The vertical straight lines designate the regions in which the wave functions are positive, and the horizontal lines designate those in which the functions are negative. (The 2s orbital is equal to zero at all points on the nodal sphere which, in Figure 9·4b, is represented by the circle separating the area with horizontal lines from the one with vertical lines.)

Unlike an s function, a p function depends not only on the distance r but also on the angle θ, and usually on the further angle ϕ as well. Hence, the charge distribution is far from spherically symmetrical. The symmetries which the p functions do possess can be seen from Figure 9·4c, in which the orbital ψ_{2p_x} is schematically represented (see also Figure 2·7, Section 2·10). This orbital is positive at all points on one side of the yz-plane and negative at all points on the other side of that plane; it is equal to 0 at all points that lie in the yz-plane, which is therefore a nodal surface. An electron occupying (i.e., with a probability distribution described by) the orbital ψ_{2p_x} is more likely to be found on or near the x axis than in any other direction from the nucleus, but it can never be found in the yz plane. The probabilities of positive and negative values of x are equal. These various relations of ψ_{2p_x} to the x axis and to the yz plane are exactly repeated in the relations of ψ_{2p_y} to the y axis and to the xz plane, and again in those of ψ_{2p_z} to the z axis and to the xy plane. Since the three directions in space are completely equivalent to one another, the three 2p orbitals are likewise equivalent.

The orbital ψ_{2p_x}, as we have seen, projects equally in both directions along the x axis. Since, however, all directions in free space are equivalent, there arises the question how the orientation of this axis is to be determined. The answer is that, in the absence of any external field, there is no experimental way for deciding whether the electron is occupying the particular orbital ψ_{2p_x}, or is instead occupying one of the other two equivalent orbitals ψ_{2p_y} and ψ_{2p_z}. Consequently, the most precise statement which can then be made is that the wave function is some linear combination, $a_x\psi_{2p_x} + a_y\psi_{2p_y} + a_z\psi_{2p_z}$, with unspecified constant coefficients. Since we have no information regarding the values of a_x, a_y, and a_z, the atom is spherically symmetric in the sense that it has the same relation to each of the three coordinate axes; hence knowledge of the orientations of these axes is not necessary. On the other hand, in the presence of an external electric or magnetic field, there is one direction, namely, that of the field, which is physically distinguished from all others; this unique direction is then conventionally identified with that of the z axis, since, when spherical polar coordinates are employed, this axis is mathematically distinguished from the other two (cf. equations 4 and 5).

Any other system which consists of a single nucleus plus a single electron can be treated in exactly the same way as the hydrogen atom. For the ion He^+, for example, the wave equation again has the form of equation 1, but now the atomic number Z is equal to 2 instead of 1. Moreover, the K- and L-shell eigenfunctions are given by equations 6–10,

13, and 14, with Z again equal to 2. In a similar way, for the further ion Li++, the only necessary modification in the treatment is to set Z equal to 3; and so on for still heavier ions with one electron. The situation becomes, however, considerably more complicated with atoms or ions that have two or more electrons. The difficulty arises from the fact that, on account of the terms corresponding to the interelectronic repulsions in the potential energy V, the independent variables cannot be separated in the way that permitted the solution of the wave equation for the particle in a three-dimensional box (and also of that for the hydrogen atom). Before we can discuss the treatment of di- and polyelectronic systems, we must first gain an understanding of the Pauli exclusion principle (see Section 9·7). We can at this time, however, outline some of the fundamental concepts upon which this treatment is based. If the atom contains altogether k electrons, its wave function must be a function of all $3k$ coordinates x_1, y_1, z_1, x_2, $\cdots$, z_k. Nevertheless, as a rather crude approximation, we can think of each electron as moving alone in a potential field that is due to the nucleus and to the average charge distribution of the other $k - 1$ electrons. The (approximate) Schrödinger equation for an individual electron is therefore

$$-\frac{h^2}{8\pi^2 m}\left(\frac{\partial^2 \psi}{\partial x^2} + \frac{\partial^2 \psi}{\partial y^2} + \frac{\partial^2 \psi}{\partial z^2}\right) + V\psi = W\psi \qquad (15)$$

in which V represents the field just described. This equation differs from the one (equation 1) for the hydrogen atom only in the potential-energy term V. Although solution of equation 15 is impossible until the exact form of V is specified, several generally valid statements regarding the solutions can nevertheless be made. Thus, the quantum numbers n, l, and m_l again enter, just as with the hydrogen atom, and they are again restricted to the integral values listed in equations 2. The energy now, however, depends both on n and on l, and not solely on n as before. It is, however, still independent of m_l. (Cf. the paragraph in fine print on page 560.) In general, the energy increases with both n and l, and usually faster with n than with l. The most stable eigenfunction is therefore always ψ_{1s}, and the succeeding ones in order of decreasing stability are ψ_{2s}, ψ_{2p}, ψ_{3s}, $\cdots$. As is implied by the use of these symbols, the division of the orbitals into K-, L-, $\cdots$ shells is retained with the more complex atoms, as are also the distinctions among s, p, d, $\cdots$ orbitals. The s functions are again, as in the hydrogen atom, independent of the angles θ and ϕ, so that the corresponding charge distributions are again spherically symmetric. The various p orbitals also have the same symmetries as before since they differ from the hydrogen eigenfunctions of equations 8–10, 13, and 14 only in the form of the radial function $F(r)$; they can, accordingly, be schematically represented by the same Figure 9·4c that was drawn for the corresponding hydrogen functions.

A convenient, but incomplete, description of the state of any atom is given by its so-called *configuration* (or, more precisely, electronic configuration), which is merely a statement of the numbers of electrons assigned to each of the orbitals ψ_{1s}, ψ_{2s}, $\cdots$. The normal hydrogen atom, for example, has the configuration $1s$, and the normal helium atom has the configuration $1s^2$, where the superscript is not an exponent but a designation of the number of electrons. (The mathematical significance of the "assignment" of electrons to specified orbitals is more fully explained in Section 9·7.) Since the $1s$ orbital is the most stable of all, the normal lithium atom might be expected to have the configuration $1s^3$. However, the Pauli exclusion principle, which is discussed in Section 9·7, states that no more than two electrons can ever have the same set of quantum numbers n, l, and m_l. Consequently, the most stable configuration for the lithium atom is $1s^2\,2s$. Similarly, we can write $1s^2\,2s^2$ for beryllium, $1s^2\,2s^2\,2p$ for boron, and $1s^2\,2s^2\,2p^2$ for carbon. Since as many as six electrons can be assigned to the three independent $2p$ orbitals, we can continue further with $1s^2\,2s^2\,2p^3$ for nitrogen, $1s^2\,2s^2\,2p^4$ for oxygen, and so on throughout the periodic table.

9·7 Electron Spin and the Pauli Exclusion Principle.[1] In Section 1·4, we saw that an electron has a spin, so that it behaves like a small bar magnet with a north pole and a south pole. The magnetic moment μ of a magnet is defined as the product of the pole strength of the north pole and the distance between the north and south poles. For an electron, μ has been found to be equal to $eh\sqrt{3}/4\pi mc$, or to $\sqrt{3}\mu_B$, where c is the velocity of light and μ_B is the so-called *Bohr magneton* with the value 0.93×10^{-20} erg per gauss. In an external magnetic field, a force will act upon the electron in such a way as to line up the spin parallel to the field. The facts of both spectroscopy and chemistry, however, require us to assume that only two different orientations of the spin are physically realizable. In one of these, the magnetic moment is approximately parallel to the field; in the second, the moment is approximately *anti*-parallel to the field. The components of the magnetic moment in the direction of the field are, respectively, $+\mu_B$ and $-\mu_B$.

Like numerous other and more familiar physical quantities, such as force, velocity, electric dipole moment (cf. Chapter 5), etc., a magnetic moment has both a magnitude and a direction, and so must be considered a *vector*. The magnitude of the moment has the value μ which was defined in the preceding paragraph; the direction is that of a straight line drawn from the south to the north pole of the magnet. As is true of any vector, a magnetic moment can therefore be represented graphically by an arrow which has a length proportional to μ, and which is drawn in a direction parallel to that of the moment. Consequently, for an electron which is in a magnetic field along the

z axis, we can construct Figure 9·5, which depicts two congruent right circular cones, so placed that their axes lie on the z axis and their apexes meet at the origin O. If the electron has positive spin (see below), its magnetic moment is represented by an arrow such as OA; if it has negative spin, its moment is represented by an arrow such as OB. The length of each arrow is proportional to $\sqrt{3}\mu_B$, so that the projections OC and OD of the respective arrows OA and OB in the direction of the field (i.e., along the

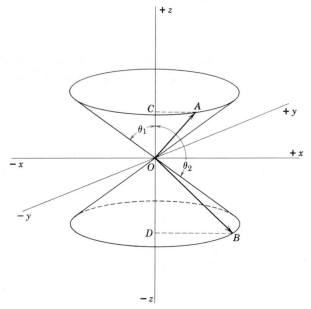

Fig. 9·5.   A graphical representation of the magnetic moment of an electron in a magnetic field along the z axis.

z axis) are proportional to the respective components $+\mu_B$ and $-\mu_B$ of the moment. The angles θ_1 and θ_2 are therefore determined by the relations $\mu_B = \sqrt{3}\mu_B \cos \theta_1$ and $-\mu_B = \sqrt{3}\mu_B \cos \theta_2$; hence, $\theta_1 = \cos^{-1}(1/\sqrt{3}) = 54°\ 44'$, and $\theta_2 = \cos^{-1}(-1/\sqrt{3}) = 125°\ 16'$. The magnetic moment need not, and in general does not, lie exactly in the direction OA, or OB, shown in the figure, since it may instead lie in any other direction along the surface of one or the other cone; the only restriction on the direction is that the angle between the moment and the z axis must have one of the values θ_1 and θ_2, defined above. Presumably, in the presence of the magnetic field, the moment *precesses* about the z axis, so that in the course of time the arrow makes a complete circuit round the cone on which it lies.

The foregoing picture of the electron spin is more definite and more precise than is strictly allowed by quantum mechanics; it is accordingly omitted in most modern presentations of the theory. It is, however, given here since it is not likely to cause serious misunderstanding, and since the average reader will doubtless be helped by having something fairly concrete to visualize. (The same remarks apply also to the later discussion of Figure 9·6, Section 9·10.)

For the inclusion of the electron spin in the wave-mechanical treatment, there has been developed a simple and convenient, but largely formal, procedure. The justification for this procedure, like that for wave mechanics itself, is that it leads to predictions which are verified by experiment. As before, however, we shall here again make no effort to summarize the empirical data, but shall instead refer the interested reader to the more detailed textbooks.[1]

The state of spin of an electron is assumed to be defined by a spin coordinate σ. Since this coordinate has no classical analog, we can assign to it no precise physical significance. We must, rather, think of it as a more or less undefined parameter which has meaning only with respect to the present largely formal treatment. Since, in the presence of a magnetic field, there are exactly two possible orientations of the spin, there must be exactly two corresponding eigenfunctions, each of which can be specified by a particular value of a quantum number m_s. By generally accepted convention, the field is taken to lie parallel to the z axis. When the component of spin is also parallel to this axis, the wave function is written as $\alpha(\sigma)$, the quantum number m_s is equal to $1/2$, and the spin is said to be positive; when the component is instead anti-parallel to the z axis, the wave function is written as $\beta(\sigma)$, the quantum number m_s is equal to $-1/2$, and the spin is said to be negative. The only properties of $\alpha(\sigma)$ and $\beta(\sigma)$ which we shall need to know are that they are normalized so that

$$\int \alpha^*(\sigma)\alpha(\sigma)\, d\sigma = \int \beta^*(\sigma)\beta(\sigma)\, d\sigma = 1 \qquad (1)$$

and are mutually orthogonal so that

$$\int \alpha^*(\sigma)\beta(\sigma)\, d\sigma = \int \beta^*(\sigma)\alpha(\sigma)\, d\sigma = 0 \qquad (2)$$

The complete wave function for a single electron must involve alto-gether four coordinates, i.e., the three spatial coordinates x, y, and z (or r, θ, and ϕ, or the like) plus the one spin coordinate σ. This wave function must be related to the probability that an experiment would find the electron not only in any specified region of space but also with any given component of spin along the z axis. Now, in the general theory of probability, it is shown that the probability of the simultaneous (or successive) occurrence of two independent events is the product of the individual probabilities. For example, if the probability of throwing a 3 with one die is $1/6$, then that of throwing two 3's with two dice is $1/6 \times 1/6$, or $1/36$. Consequently, we can reasonably assume that the *spin-orbit* wave function $\chi(x, y, z, \sigma)$ of an electron can be expressed as a product $\psi(x, y, z)\alpha(\sigma)$ or $\psi(x, y, z)\beta(\sigma)$ of two functions, of which one depends only on the spatial coordinates (i.e., is an orbital) whereas the other depends only on the spin coordinate.   This assumption can, in fact, be shown to be valid by a separation of the variables, as in the treatment of the particle in a three-dimensional box (cf. pages 553f).

Let us now turn to a more complicated system which contains two electrons.   For the sake of definiteness, we shall consider an excited helium atom, which has one electron in the $1s$ orbital with positive spin, and a second electron in the $2s$ orbital with again positive spin.   Extension of the argument based on the laws of probability (see the preceding paragraph) suggests that a reasonable approximation to the wave function for the atom could be written as

$$\Pi(x_1, y_1, z_1, \sigma_1, x_2, y_2, z_2, \sigma_2) = \psi_{1s}(x_1, y_1, z_1)\alpha(\sigma_1)\psi_{2s}(x_2, y_2, z_2)\alpha(\sigma_2) \quad (3)$$

or, more simply, as

$$\Pi(1, 2) = \psi_{1s}(1)\alpha(1)\psi_{2s}(2)\alpha(2) \quad (4)$$

where the numbers in parentheses represent all the pertinent coordinates of the specified electrons.   The function $\Pi(1, 2)$, as defined in equation 3 (or 4), is not unique.   Since the two electrons are indistinguishable, there is no theoretical or experimental way for deciding which electron is electron 1 with the coordinates x_1, y_1, z_1, and σ_1, and which is electron 2 with the coordinates x_2, y_2, z_2, and σ_2.   Consequently, the different function

$$\Pi(2, 1) = \psi_{1s}(2)\alpha(2)\psi_{2s}(1)\alpha(1) \quad (5)$$

is just as good as $\Pi(1, 2)$.   Since $\Pi(1, 2)$ and $\Pi(2, 1)$ are degenerate, any linear combination of them

$$\Omega(1, 2) = k_1\Pi(1, 2) + k_2\Pi(2, 1) \quad (6)$$

with constant coefficients k_1 and k_2 would also be as good as either simple product function alone (see page 550).   If the number of electrons is greater than 2, this complexity which arises from the identity of the electrons is still greater, and it rapidly increases with the number of electrons; if there are altogether r electrons, there are $r!$ different but equivalent product functions analogous to $\Pi(1, 2)$ and $\Pi(2, 1)$.

Fortunately, the situation is materially simplified by application of the so-called *Pauli exclusion principle*.   This principle is to be thought of as an additional postulate which cannot be derived from any more fundamental one, but which is abundantly supported by a wealth of experimental evidence.[1]   In its most general form, it states that no solution of the Schrödinger equation can correspond to an actually existing system unless it is *totally antisymmetric with respect to interchanges of the electrons*. The meaning of this rather impressive pronouncement can be made clear by a further consideration of the excited helium atom.   If, in the function

$\Pi(1, 2)$, all four coordinates of each electron are replaced by the corresponding coordinates of the other electron, the result is to transform $\Pi(1, 2)$ into the different function $\Pi(2, 1)$. Similarly, the same interchange of electronic coordinates changes $\Pi(2, 1)$ into $\Pi(1, 2)$. Neither of these two functions, therefore, satisfies the exclusion principle, since neither is antisymmetric or, in other words, since neither is simply multiplied by -1 when the electronic coordinates are interchanged. The only linear combination of $\Pi(1, 2)$ and $\Pi(2, 1)$ which does satisfy the exclusion principle is

$$\Omega(1, 2) = N[\Pi(1, 2) - \Pi(2, 1)] \tag{7}$$

where the normalization constant N is equal to $1/\sqrt{2}$ if the orbitals ψ_{1s} and ψ_{2s} are individually normalized and mutually orthogonal. That the function $\Omega(1, 2)$ of equation 7 is indeed properly antisymmetric follows because an interchange of the electronic coordinates transforms $\Omega(1, 2)$ into $N[\Pi(2, 1) - \Pi(1, 2)]$, which is clearly identical with $-\Omega(1, 2)$.

The antisymmetric function $\Omega(1, 2)$ of equation 7 can conveniently be written in the form of a determinant.[9] Thus,

$$\Omega(1, 2) = N \begin{vmatrix} \psi_{1s}(1)\alpha(1) & \psi_{2s}(1)\alpha(1) \\ \psi_{1s}(2)\alpha(2) & \psi_{2s}(2)\alpha(2) \end{vmatrix} \tag{8}$$

The complete equivalence of equations 7 and 8 is evident from the fact that expansion of each leads to the same expression

$$\Omega(1, 2) = N[\psi_{1s}(1)\alpha(1)\psi_{2s}(2)\alpha(2) - \psi_{1s}(2)\alpha(2)\psi_{2s}(1)\alpha(1)] \tag{9}$$

The antisymmetry of $\Omega(1, 2)$ is particularly easily shown from equation 8; since an interchange of the coordinates of the two electrons here corresponds to an interchange of the two rows of the determinant, it must therefore multiply the function by -1.

The antisymmetrizing of the wave function for a system with an arbitrary number of electrons can be most easily effected by a generalization of the second of the two above procedures. If there are altogether r electrons, of which one has been assigned to each of the spin-orbit functions $\chi_1, \chi_2, \cdots \chi_r$, then the function[9]

$$\Omega(1, 2, \cdots, r) = \frac{1}{\sqrt{r!}} \begin{vmatrix} \chi_1(1) & \chi_2(1) \cdots \chi_r(1) \\ \chi_1(2) & \chi_2(2) \cdots \chi_r(2) \\ \cdot & \cdot \qquad \cdot \\ \cdot & \cdot \qquad \cdot \\ \cdot & \cdot \qquad \cdot \\ \chi_1(r) & \chi_2(r) \cdots \chi_r(r) \end{vmatrix} \tag{10}$$

[9] J. C. Slater, *Phys. Rev.* **34**, 1293 (1929).

like the simpler one of equation 8, is antisymmetric since the interchange of the coordinates of any two electrons consists in the interchange of the two corresponding rows of the determinant. It can be shown that this function is the *only* antisymmetric combination which can be constructed from products of the given spin-orbit functions χ_1, χ_2, $\cdots$, χ_r. The constant factor $1/\sqrt{r!}$ normalizes the function $\Omega(1, 2, \cdots, r)$ if the individual spin-orbit functions χ_j are themselves normalized and mutually orthogonal.

If any two of the functions χ_1, χ_2, $\cdots$, χ_r are identical, the determinant of equation 10 has two identical columns and so is equal to zero. Since a wave function which vanishes for all values of the coordinates cannot describe a real system, we can therefore conclude that no two spin-orbit functions χ_j can ever be the same. It is possible for two electrons to occupy the same orbital ψ_j if they have opposite spins, but, since there are only the two spin functions α and β, it is never possible for more than two electrons to do so. This last statement expresses the Pauli exclusion principle in its simplest and possibly most familiar form. (Cf. page 565.)

9·8 The Variation Principle. The wave equation for any system which contains three or more particles (electrons and nuclei) is always so complicated that it cannot be solved rigorously by any method now known. Consequently, since every molecule must contain at least three particles, and since therefore no rigorous quantum-mechanical treatment of molecular structure is now possible, the theoretical study of valence must be based on approximate methods. Of the several such methods which have been developed, the one that has proved to be most generally useful consists in an application of the so-called *variation principle*. This principle, which can be derived from merely the form of the Schrödinger equation (however, see the paragraph below, in fine print), is of extremely general applicability. It states that, if W_1 is the lowest eigenvalue of the equation

$$\mathbf{H}\psi = W\psi \tag{1}$$

and if Φ is any arbitrary function which satisfies all the auxiliary conditions (including the Pauli exclusion principle) that are imposed upon eigenfunctions, then always

$$E \equiv \frac{\int \Phi^* \mathbf{H}\Phi \, d\tau}{\int \Phi^* \Phi \, d\tau} \geq W_1 \tag{2}$$

where $d\tau$, the volume element including spin, is defined as

$$d\tau \equiv dv \, d\sigma_1 \, d\sigma_2 \cdots d\sigma_r$$
$$\equiv dx_1 \, dy_1 \, dz_1 \, dx_2 \cdots dz_r \, d\sigma_1 \, d\sigma_2 \cdots d\sigma_r \tag{3}$$

The integrations, which are again for simplicity indicated by single integral signs, are here to be carried out over all of space and over all values of the spin coordinates σ_1, σ_2, $\cdot$ $\cdot$ $\cdot$, σ_r so that, if Φ is normalized, the denominator of the fraction in expression 2 is equal to 1. (The significance of the integrations over the spin coordinates will be explained, with specific examples, on page 574.) The equality sign at the right of relation 2 applies if Φ happens to be an eigenfunction ψ_1 of equation 1, corresponding to the eigenvalue W_1. Under any other conditions, however, the inequality sign must be taken.

It would be out of place here to attempt a rigorous justification of the variation principle.[10] A relatively simple derivation can, to be sure, be based on the assumption that the eigenfunctions ψ_j of the Schrödinger equation form a *complete set*[11] or, in other words, that any *variation function* Φ can always be expressed as a linear combination of all the ψ_j's. Since, however, this required completeness is no more obvious than is the variation principle itself, we shall instead adopt a different, and less conclusive, approach. Let us consider the problem of finding the lowest possible value that the quantity E, defined in the expression 2, can assume for any variation function Φ. By applying the procedures of the so-called *calculus of variations*,[12] we can now show that a necessary, but not a sufficient, condition which must be satisfied if the fraction E is to have a minimum value can be expressed in the form of a certain differential equation, known as *Euler's equation*. For the present problem, this equation is found to be

$$\mathbf{H}\Phi = E\Phi \tag{4}$$

and hence to be identical with the Schrödinger equation for the system of interest. It therefore follows that, if Φ is a function which gives E a minimum value, it must also be an eigenfunction of the Schrödinger equation. Consequently, we have some reason for supposing that, if Φ is *not* an eigenfunction, then E must be greater than the lowest eigenvalue W_1. The proof is, however, far from rigorous, and any attempts to achieve complete rigor encounter great mathematical difficulties.[10] Following the example of most physicists and chemists who have considered the problem, therefore, we shall here simply *assume* the validity of the variation principle as an additional postulate. The foregoing discussion should nevertheless be sufficient to show that this principle is not entirely arbitrary.

The ways in which the variation principle is used in the treatment of molecular structure will be more fully explained in the following sections. Here, we shall merely mention that, if the eigenfunction ψ_1 for any system in its ground state is approximated by a variation function Φ, then the

[10] Cf., however, E. C. Kemble, *The Fundamental Principles of Quantum Mechanics*, McGraw-Hill Book Co., New York, 1937, pp. 132ff.

[11] C. Eckart, *Phys. rev.* **36**, 878 (1930).

[12] See, for example, R. Courant and D. Hilbert, *Methoden der mathematischen Physik*, J. Springer, Berlin, 1931, Chapter 4; H. Margenau and G. M. Murphy, *The Mathematics of Physics and Chemistry*, D. Van Nostrand Co., New York, 1943, Chapter 6.

relations 2 show that E is necessarily greater than the desired eigenvalue W_1. Consequently, Φ must be improved by any change in it which lowers the calculated value of E, and the best possible Φ is the one that leads to the lowest possible E.

9·9 The Hydrogen Molecule. In order to show the application of the variation principle to a specific problem, we shall consider the hydrogen molecule, H_2. At the outset, and until further notice to the contrary, we shall imagine that the interprotonic distance has in some way been increased to such an extent that the interaction between the two atoms is very small. In other words, the hydrogen molecule in which we are now interested is not in its normal state, but is almost completely dissociated into its constituent atoms. Later, we shall discuss the modifications in the treatment which are required when the nuclei are allowed to assume their normal separation.

Let the $1s$ orbital centered about one of the two protons be designated as a, and let the corresponding orbital centered about the other proton be designated as b. Since the protons are assumed to be at a great distance from each other, the resulting system is most stable if one electron is in each of these two orbitals, a and b. We may therefore write the configuration as ab, in analogy with the terminology described on page 565 for monatomic systems. For the sake of definiteness, and in agreement with the experimental observation that the normal hydrogen molecule has zero resultant magnetic moment due to spin, we shall assume that the electron in orbital a has positive spin, whereas the one in orbital b has negative spin. The essential difference between the present system and the excited helium atom which was discussed on pages 568f is that the spin-orbit function $\psi_{1s}(1)\alpha(1)$ is now replaced by $a(1)\alpha(1)$, and the spin-orbit function $\psi_{2s}(2)\alpha(2)$ is now replaced by $b(2)\beta(2)$. Consequently, a reasonable first approximation to the wave function may here be expressed as

$$\Omega_1 = \frac{1}{\sqrt{2}} \begin{vmatrix} a(1)\alpha(1) & b(1)\beta(1) \\ a(2)\alpha(2) & b(2)\beta(2) \end{vmatrix}$$

$$= \frac{1}{\sqrt{2}} [a(1)\alpha(1)b(2)\beta(2) - b(1)\beta(1)a(2)\alpha(2)] \tag{1}$$

(cf. equations 8 and 9, Section 9·7). The factor $1/\sqrt{2}$ normalizes the function if the orbitals a and b are themselves normalized (and orthogonal). There is, however, no reason for supposing that the electron in orbital a must be the one which has the positive spin and that the electron in orbital b must be the one which has the negative spin, since the opposite arrangement is equally likely. Corresponding to this second possibility, we can write a second function

$$\Omega_2 = \frac{1}{\sqrt{2}} \begin{vmatrix} a(1)\beta(1) & b(1)\alpha(1) \\ a(2)\beta(2) & b(2)\alpha(2) \end{vmatrix}$$

$$= \frac{1}{\sqrt{2}} [a(1)\beta(1)b(2)\alpha(2) - b(1)\alpha(1)a(2)\beta(2)] \qquad (2)$$

which is different from, but entirely equivalent to, the first one Ω_1.

We now invoke the variation principle by setting up the variation function Φ as a linear combination

$$\Phi = k_1\Omega_1 + k_2\Omega_2 \qquad (3)$$

with constant coefficients k_1 and k_2. Now, from the variation principle, we know that the energy E defined in expression 2, Section 9·8, with Φ defined as in equation 3, can never be less than the energy W_1 of the ground state of the system, no matter what numerical values we may assign to the constants k_1 and k_2. Consequently, if we accept E as an approximation to W_1, we will get the best possible approximation by using those values of k_1 and k_2 which make E *as low as possible* (cf. the last paragraph of Section 9·8). Substitution of equation 3 into the definition of E (see page 570) gives us

$$E = \frac{k_1{}^2Q - 2k_1k_2J + k_2{}^2Q}{k_1{}^2 - 2k_1k_2S^2 + k_2{}^2} \qquad (4)$$

where the *coulomb integral*

$$Q = \int a(1)b(2)\mathbf{H}a(1)b(2)\, dv$$
$$= \int b(1)a(2)\mathbf{H}b(1)a(2)\, dv \qquad (5)$$

the *exchange integral*

$$J = \int a(1)b(2)\mathbf{H}b(1)a(2)\, dv$$
$$= \int b(1)a(2)\mathbf{H}a(1)b(2)\, dv \qquad (6)$$

and the *overlap integral*

$$S = \int a(1)b(1)\, dv = \int a(2)b(2)\, dv \qquad (7)$$

(See the following paragraph in fine print.) Since the orbitals a and b are real, the constants k_1 and k_2 can also be taken as real, and the asterisks which indicate complex conjugates need not be used. As long as the distance between the two protons is very great, the exchange integral J and the overlap integral S are very small and perhaps even negligible. Both are, however, written here explicitly since they will become important later in the discussion.

Further details regarding the derivation of equation 4 may help to make the treatment more concrete. If k_1, k_2, Ω_1, and Ω_2 are all assumed to be real, we have from equation 3:

$$\int \Phi \mathbf{H} \Phi \, d\tau = \int (k_1\Omega_1 + k_2\Omega_2)\mathbf{H}(k_1\Omega_1 + k_2\Omega_2) \, d\tau$$

$$= k_1{}^2\int\Omega_1\mathbf{H}\Omega_1 \, d\tau + k_1k_2\int\Omega_1\mathbf{H}\Omega_2 \, d\tau + k_1k_2\int\Omega_2\mathbf{H}\Omega_1 \, d\tau + k_2{}^2\int\Omega_2\mathbf{H}\Omega_2 \, d\tau$$

Moreover, from equation 1, we have also:

$$\int\Omega_1\mathbf{H}\Omega_1 \, d\tau = \tfrac{1}{2}\int a(1)\alpha(1)b(2)\beta(2)\mathbf{H}a(1)\alpha(1)b(2)\beta(2) \, d\tau$$

$$- \tfrac{1}{2}\int a(1)\alpha(1)b(2)\beta(2)\mathbf{H}b(1)\beta(1)a(2)\alpha(2) \, d\tau$$

$$- \tfrac{1}{2}\int b(1)\beta(1)a(2)\alpha(2)\mathbf{H}a(1)\alpha(1)b(2)\beta(2) \, d\tau$$

$$+ \tfrac{1}{2}\int b(1)\beta(1)a(2)\alpha(2)\mathbf{H}b(1)\beta(1)a(2)\alpha(2) \, d\tau$$

Since the Hamiltonian operator $\mathbf{H}$ does not involve the spin coordinates, the integrations over these coordinates can be performed at once with the aid of equations 1 and 2, Section 9·7. In this way, we find that

$$\int\Omega_1\mathbf{H}\Omega_1 \, d\tau = \tfrac{1}{2}\int a(1)b(2)\mathbf{H}a(1)b(2) \, dv - 0 - 0$$

$$+ \tfrac{1}{2}\int b(1)a(2)\mathbf{H}b(1)a(2) \, dv$$

$$= \tfrac{1}{2}Q + \tfrac{1}{2}Q = Q$$

Similarly, $\int\Omega_1\mathbf{H}\Omega_2 \, d\tau = \int\Omega_2\mathbf{H}\Omega_1 \, d\tau = -J$

$\int\Omega_2\mathbf{H}\Omega_2 \, d\tau = Q$

And finally, $\int\Phi^2 \, d\tau = k_1{}^2\int\Omega_1{}^2 \, d\tau + 2k_1k_2\int\Omega_1\Omega_2 \, d\tau + k_2{}^2\int\Omega_2{}^2 \, d\tau$

with $\int\Omega_1{}^2 \, d\tau = \int\Omega_2{}^2 \, d\tau = 1$

and $\int\Omega_1\Omega_2 \, d\tau = -S^2$

The above statements that the integrals J and S become vanishingly small when the interprotonic distance is very great can be justified in the following way. The integrand of S, for example, is the product ab of the two orbitals a and b; hence it can have an appreciable magnitude only when the electronic coordinates are such that the magnitudes of both a and b are simultaneously fairly large. The magnitude of a, however, cannot be large unless the electron is near the corresponding proton (cf. equation 6, Section 9·6); similarly, the magnitude of b cannot be large unless the electron is near the *other* proton. Consequently, the integrand must be small unless the electron is near both protons at the same time; this close approach is, however, impossible unless the protons themselves are close to each other. Thus we see that, if the interprotonic distance is large, the integrand is small for all values of the coordinates, and hence that the resulting integral S must also be small. The proof that the additional integral J is then likewise small proceeds similarly.

In order to determine the minimum value of E, we must differentiate equation 4 partially with respect to k_1 and also with respect to k_2, and we must set each of the partial derivatives $\partial E/\partial k_1$ and $\partial E/\partial k_2$ equal to zero. If equation 4 is rewritten in the equivalent form

$$k_1{}^2 E - 2k_1k_2 S^2 E + k_2{}^2 E = k_1{}^2 Q - 2k_1k_2 J + k_2{}^2 Q \qquad (4')$$

differentiation with respect to k_1 then shows that

$$2k_1E + k_1{}^2 \frac{\partial E}{\partial k_1} - 2k_2S^2E - 2k_1k_2S^2 \frac{\partial E}{\partial k_1} + k_2{}^2 \frac{\partial E}{\partial k_1} = 2k_1Q - 2k_2J$$

Consequently, since $\partial E/\partial k_1$ must now be set equal to zero,

$$2k_1E - 2k_2S^2E = 2k_1Q - 2k_2J$$

so that $$k_1(Q - E) - k_2(J - S^2E) = 0 \qquad (8)$$

Similarly, if we differentiate equation 4′ with respect to k_2 and then set $\partial E/\partial k_2$ equal to zero, we obtain a second condition

$$k_1(J - S^2E) - k_2(Q - E) = 0 \qquad (9)$$

From the first of the two equations 8 and 9, we obtain:

$$\frac{k_1}{k_2} = \frac{J - S^2E}{Q - E} \qquad (10)$$

and, from the second, we obtain instead:

$$\frac{k_1}{k_2} = \frac{Q - E}{J - S^2E} \qquad (11)$$

Consistency therefore requires either that $k_1 = k_2 = 0$ or else that

$$\frac{J - S^2E}{Q - E} = \frac{Q - E}{J - S^2E} \qquad (12)$$

Since the first of these two possibilities would lead to an identically vanishing, and hence unsatisfactory, wave function, we must accept equation 12 as correct. On solving this equation for E, we find that there are two roots

$$E_{\pm} = \frac{Q \pm J}{1 \pm S^2} \qquad (13)$$

Since, on numerical calculations,[1, 13] the lower value of E is found to result from the use of the plus signs in equation 13, rather than from that of the minus signs, we conclude that

$$E_+ = \frac{Q + J}{1 + S^2} \qquad (14)$$

is the best approximation which we can get to the energy W_1 of the system in its ground state. (If the interprotonic distance is so great that J and S are both negligibly small, then $E_+ = E_- = Q$.)

[13] W. Heitler and F. London, Z. Physik **44**, 455 (1927); Y. Sugiura, ibid. **45**, 484 (1927).

Before continuing further with our variational treatment of the hydrogen molecule, let us first reconsider, from a more general point of view, the derivation and significance of equation 12. In the preceding paragraph, this equation was obtained as the condition that the set of simultaneous equations 8 and 9 have a solution other than the trivial one that $k_1 = k_2 = 0$; it assumed the particular form 12 because equations 8 and 9 not only are *linear* in the unknown quantities k_1 and k_2, but also are *homogeneous* or, in other words, contain no constant terms (other than 0) which are independent of k_1 and k_2. With more complicated sets of simultaneous, linear, homogeneous equations with which the number of unknowns is greater than 2, the corresponding conditions for the existence of nontrivial solutions cannot so conveniently be derived by the straight-forward method employed above. Fortunately, however, the mathematicians have shown how these conditions can be expressed both quite generally and also rather simply.[14] The fundamental theorem, which need not be proved here, is the following: If there are altogether t equations

$$a_{s1}k_1 + a_{s2}k_2 + \cdots + a_{st}k_t = 0 \qquad (s = 1, 2, \cdots, t) \qquad (15)$$

for the t unknowns $k_1, k_2, \cdots, k_t$, and if the t^2 coefficients $a_{11}, a_{12}, \cdots, a_{tt}$ are not themselves functions of these unknowns, then a nontrivial solution (i.e., a solution other than $k_1 = k_2 = \cdots = k_t = 0$) exists if, and only if, the determinant of the a's is equal to zero, so that

$$
\begin{vmatrix}
a_{11} & a_{12} & \cdots & a_{1t} \\
a_{21} & a_{22} & \cdots & a_{2t} \\
\cdot & \cdot & & \cdot \\
\cdot & \cdot & & \cdot \\
\cdot & \cdot & & \cdot \\
a_{t1} & a_{t2} & \cdots & a_{tt}
\end{vmatrix} = 0 \qquad (16)
$$

With particular reference to the pair of equations 8 and 9, equation 16 becomes

$$
\begin{vmatrix}
(Q - E) & (J - S^2E) \\
(J - S^2E) & (Q - E)
\end{vmatrix} \equiv (Q - E)^2 - (J - S^2E)^2 = 0 \qquad (17)
$$

in which form it is seen to be equivalent to equation 12. When t is greater than 2, the necessity of the condition 16 is more difficult to demonstrate than it is when t is equal to 2; always, however, it arises for the same reasons that were more explicitly explained in our first derivation of equation 12.

[14] See, for example, R. Courant and D. Hilbert, *Methoden der mathematischen Physik*, J. Springer, Berlin, 1931, pp. 5ff.

Let us now return to the discussion of the hydrogen molecule. Our original purpose in obtaining the set of simultaneous equations 8 and 9 was to determine the optimum values of k_1 and k_2, and then with this information to determine the minimum value of E. It turned out, however, that we bypassed the first of these steps and obtained equation 13 somewhat more directly than might have been expected. If now we still wish to know the values of k_1 and k_2, we must backtrack somewhat and, in equation 8 (or 9), replace E by E_+ from equation 14. In this way, we find that

$$k_1/k_2 = -1$$

In order to obtain the absolute, and not merely the relative, values of k_1 and k_2, we must introduce the condition that Φ be normalized, or that

$$\int \Phi^2 \, dv = k_1^2 - 2k_1k_2S^2 + k_2^2 = k_1^2(2 + 2S^2) = 1$$

Consequently $\quad k_1 = -k_2 = 1/\sqrt{2 + 2S^2}$

so that the best variation function which can be expressed in the form 3 is

$$\Phi_+ = \frac{1}{\sqrt{2 + 2S^2}} [\Omega_1 - \Omega_2]$$

$$= \frac{1}{2\sqrt{1 + S^2}} [a(1)b(2) + b(1)a(2)][\alpha(1)\beta(2) - \beta(1)\alpha(2)] \quad (18)$$

If the two protons are at a great distance from each other, as we have so far assumed them to be, the function Φ_+ of equation 18 is essentially the rigorous solution ψ_1 of the wave equation, and the energy E_+ of equation 14 differs only slightly from the corresponding, rigorously correct eigenvalue E_1. It therefore seems not unreasonable to suppose that, even when the protons are at the distance (about 0.74 A) characteristic of the normal hydrogen molecule, the function Φ_+ and the energy E_+ can still be used as first approximations to ψ_1 and to W_1, respectively. A convenient measure of the closeness of this approximation is provided by the difference

$$\Delta W \equiv E_+ - W_1 \quad (19)$$

between the approximate calculated energy E_+ and the experimentally observed energy W_1. Since, in equation 14, E_+ is expressed in terms of the integrals Q, J, and S, which are themselves defined in the identities 5, 6, and 7, respectively, the problem is now reduced to one of evaluating these three integrals as functions of the interprotonic distance. Since this concluding step of the calculation is extremely tedious, since it is of only mathematical interest, and since it is adequately discussed in numerous other places,[1, 13] we shall here merely describe the results that have been obtained.   The error ΔW is found to be positive for all finite internuclear distances, as the variation principle requires it to be; and it is found to be equal to about 37 kcal per mole for the (calculated) equilibrium internuclear distance of 0.80 A.   Although the treatment is therefore far from exact, it is much more accurate than is the still cruder one outlined in Section 9·5 and, in any event, it is definitely not without value.   In particular, the calculation shows that a stable H_2 molecule is indeed formed; it predicts, with an error of only about 0.06 A, the most stable internuclear distance; and it accounts for about two-thirds of the total binding energy of the molecule.   No method of calculation which was known before the development of quantum mechanics was able to accomplish any one of these feats.

Up to this point, the treatment of the hydrogen molecule has been equivalent, in all essential details, to the superficially rather different one of Heitler and London,[13] and it has led both to the same final approximate wave function Φ_+ and to the same final value E_+ for the total energy.   Most, if not all, of the subsequent developments in the quantum-mechanical theory of valence may be considered extensions of this pioneering work of Heitler and London.

An essential feature of the above variational treatment of the hydrogen molecule was the use of a variation function which was a linear combination, with constant coefficients, of the antisymmetrized product functions Ω_1 and Ω_2 (cf. equation 3).   Now, if the protons about which the orbitals a and b are centered are designated by the respective symbols H_a and H_b, and if a dot and an asterisk are used to represent electrons with, respectively, positive and negative spin, then the functions Ω_1 and Ω_2 can be considered to describe the respective "structures" I and II (cf. "structures"

$$·H_a \quad H_b* \qquad\qquad *H_a \quad H_b·$$
$$\text{I} \qquad\qquad\qquad\qquad \text{II}$$

I and II of Section 2·6).   The approximate wave function Φ_+ is therefore, in a sense, intermediate between Ω_1 and Ω_2, and the charge distribution that corresponds to the intermediate wave function is itself intermediate between the distributions that are depicted by "structures" I and II. Whenever, as here, the variation principle is applied to an approximate wave function that is a linear combination of simpler functions, the system of interest is said to be a *resonance hybrid* of the conditions that are implied by those simpler functions.   The only way in which this present example of resonance is not entirely typical is that, ordinarily, resonance is presumed to involve structures, rather than "structures" (cf. the first paragraph of Section 3·1).

By further application of the variation principle, the function Φ_+ of equation 18 can be made to approach ψ_1 much more closely, even for small separations of the protons.   In the calculations which have just been described, the orbitals a and b were assumed to be exactly the $1s$ functions characteristic of isolated hydrogen atoms.   In other words, a and b were of the form given in equation 6, Section 9·6, with $Z = 1$. A fairly obvious way for improving the function Φ_+ is therefore to consider that Z is not a constant, but is instead a new variation parameter, in addition to k_1 and k_2 of equation 3.   For each internuclear distance, then, Z is assigned that value $Z_{optimum}$, which makes E_+ as low as possible. In this way, $Z_{optimum}$ has been found[15] to vary from 1, when the protons are at an infinite distance from each other, to 1.166, when the protons are at their equilibrium distance.   The error ΔE in the calculated energy of the normal molecule is thereby reduced from 37 to 22 kcal per mole. The calculated value of the most stable internuclear distance, 0.76 A, is now almost exactly correct; and about 80 per cent of the total binding energy is accounted for.

Still further elaborations of the foregoing treatment, which likewise are based on the variation principle, have led to still further improvements in the function Φ_+ and in the energy E_+.[16]   Since, however, these modifications have not provided a rigorous solution of the wave equation we shall here remark only that in general they merely involve more drastic changes in the form of the orbitals a and b.   The evaluation of the necessary integrals Q, J, and S is thereby made considerably more difficult, but the essential features of the treatment are not seriously affected. (See also Section 9·23.)

In 1933, James and Coolidge[17] published an almost completely rigorous treatment of the normal hydrogen molecule.   Although their calculation, like each of the ones briefly described above, consists in an application of the variation principle, the individual terms which appear in the linear combination replacing Φ of equation 3 are quite different from Ω_1 and Ω_2, and cannot readily be correlated with any definite "structures" or structures.   In particular, this more accurate treatment makes no use of orbitals which are analogous to a and b in being centered about single nuclei.   Since, however, the calculation has not yet been successfully extended to any molecule more complex than that of hydrogen, we shall here consider it no further.

9·10   Paired and Unpaired Electrons.   Before leaving this discussion of the hydrogen molecule, let us return to equation 13 of Section 9·9, and let us consider the significance of the hitherto disregarded energy

$$E_- = \frac{Q - J}{1 - S^2} \tag{1}$$

[15] S. C. Wang, *Phys. Rev.* **31**, 579 (1928).

[16] See, for example, N. Rosen, *Phys. Rev.* **38**, 2099 (1931); S. Weinbaum, *J. Chem. Phys.* **1**, 593 (1933); C. R. Mueller and H. Eyring, *ibid.* **19**, 1495 (1951).

[17] H. M. James and A. S. Coolidge, *J. Chem. Phys.* **1**, 825 (1933).

Although the variation principle, in the form originally stated in Section 9·8, tells us nothing about E_-, there is an extension of this principle which shows that, just as E_+ is an approximation to the energy W_1 of the molecule in its ground state, so also E_- is an approximation to the energy W_2 of the molecule in a certain one of its excited states.[18]   More particularly, just as E_+ is necessarily greater than W_1, so also E_- is necessarily greater than W_2.

In order to learn more regarding this excited state, let us see what we can find out about the corresponding wave function Φ_-.   Insertion of E_- for E in either one of equations 8 and 9, Section 9·9, leads to the result that

$$k_1/k_2 = 1 \tag{2}$$

whence $$\Phi_- = \frac{1}{2\sqrt{1-S^2}} [a(1)b(2) - b(1)a(2)][\alpha(1)\beta(2) + \beta(1)\alpha(2)] \tag{3}$$

Now, if on page 572 we had assumed that both electrons of the hydrogen molecule had positive spin, we would ultimately have obtained the (antisymmetrized) wave function

$$\Phi_-' = \frac{1}{\sqrt{2-2S^2}} [a(1)b(2) - b(1)a(2)]\alpha(1)\alpha(2) \tag{4}$$

Similarly, if we had assumed that both electrons had negative spin, we would have obtained the function

$$\Phi_-'' = \frac{1}{\sqrt{2-2S^2}} [a(1)b(2) - b(1)a(2)]\beta(1)\beta(2) \tag{5}$$

An important point now appears: the three functions Φ_-, Φ_-', and Φ_-'' are identical with respect to their dependence upon the spatial coordinates x_1, y_1, $\cdots$, z_2 so that, aside from a constant numerical factor which enters from the requirement that the functions be normalized, they differ only in their dependence on the spin coordinates σ_1 and σ_2.   Since the Hamiltonian operator $\mathbf{H}$ does not involve the spin coordinates, it therefore follows that

$$\frac{\int\Phi_-\mathbf{H}\Phi_-\,d\tau}{\int\Phi_-^2\,d\tau} = \frac{\int\Phi_-'\mathbf{H}\Phi_-'\,d\tau}{\int\Phi_-'^2\,d\tau} = \frac{\int\Phi_-''\mathbf{H}\Phi_-''\,d\tau}{\int\Phi_-''^2\,d\tau} = E_- \tag{6}$$

and hence that all three wave functions correspond to the same energy E_-.   (Cf. the first of the two paragraphs in fine print on page 574.)

[18] R. Courant and D. Hilbert, *Methoden der mathematischen Physik*, J. Springer, Berlin, 1931, pp. 20ff; J. K. L. MacDonald, *Phys. Rev.* **43**, 830 (1933).

When the molecule is in the state described by the function Φ_-, Φ_-', or Φ_-'', its component of magnetic moment along the positive direction of the z axis is equal, respectively, to 0, $2\mu_B$, or $-2\mu_B$. Such a triply degenerate level is commonly called a *triplet*, and it is said to have a *multiplicity* equal to 3. The physical picture of a triplet level, which is provided by a more extensive quantum-mechanical treatment,[1] is one in which the spins of the two electrons are oriented in approximately parallel directions, so that the resultant magnetic moment due to spin is $2\sqrt{2}\mu_B$

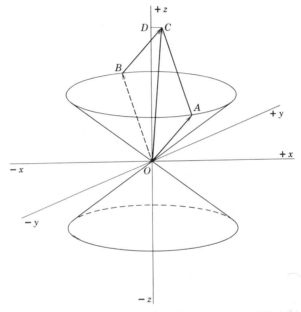

Fig. 9·6.   A graphical representation showing the vectorial addition
of the magnetic moments of two electrons.

(see also the following paragraph in fine print).   This resultant moment can now itself be oriented in any one of three different directions with respect to the z axis, so that its component along the z axis can have any one of the three values just stated.   The situation is therefore analogous to the simpler one, discussed earlier, in which the spin of a single electron, with total magnitude $\sqrt{3}\mu_B$, can be oriented in such a way that its component along the z axis is either μ_B or $-\mu_B$.

Since a magnetic moment is a vector, the resultant moment of two electrons cannot be obtained by ordinary arithmetical addition, but instead only by vectorial addition (cf. Section 5·1).   If the magnetic moments of two different electrons are represented by the arrows OA and OB of Figure 9·6, then the resultant (i.e. the vector sum) is represented, in both magnitude and direction, by the arrow OC; and its component along the z axis is given by the distance OD. In the construction of this figure, the position of the point C, which marks the head of the arrow OC, is determined with the aid of the auxiliary arrow BC, which has its tail at point B, and which is equal in length, and is parallel, to OA. When, in a more general problem, the number of electrons is greater than 2, the magnitude and direction of the resulting magnetic moment, and the component of this resultant along the z axis, can be determined, as was explained in Section 5·1, by a straightforward generalization of the method just described. (However, see also the second of the two paragraphs in fine print on pages 565f.)

The ground state of the hydrogen molecule forms an interesting contrast to the excited triplet level. Here, there is no degeneracy, and the molecule has zero component of magnetic moment along the z axis. Such a state is described as a *singlet*, and it is said to have the multiplicity 1. The physical picture which is provided by the complete quantum-mechanical treatment is now that the spins of the two electrons are in exactly opposite directions, so that their resultant is zero. There is, therefore, no possibility for this resultant moment to be oriented in different directions, and so the existence of only the one state is explained.

In the triplet level, in which the electron spins are commonly, but not quite correctly, described as *parallel*, the electrons themselves are said to be *unpaired*. In the singlet level, in which the electron spins are commonly, and now correctly, described as *antiparallel*, the electrons are said to be *paired*.

A slight elaboration of the foregoing discussion may help to make clearer the distinction between paired and unpaired electrons. As has just been said, two electrons which are paired with each other have exactly antiparallel spins. Consequently, if the component of one along the z axis is μ_B, that of the other must be $-\mu_B$, and vice versa. Hence, the component (again along the z axis) of the resultant moment for the two electrons must always be $\mu_B + (-\mu_B) = 0$. Since the z axis can be assumed to lie in *any* desired direction, we can conclude that the magnetic moment due to spin has a zero component in *all* directions and so must itself be equal to zero. On the other hand, if the two electrons are unpaired, their spins are neither exactly parallel nor exactly antiparallel. Consequently, if the component of one along the z axis is μ_B, that of the other may be either μ_B or $-\mu_B$; and similarly, if the component of the first is instead $-\mu_B$, that of the second may again be either μ_B or $-\mu_B$. Hence, the component (still along the z axis) of the resultant moment for the two electrons may have any one of three values: $2\mu_B$, if both spins are positive; or $-2\mu_B$, if both are negative; or 0, if one is positive and the other is negative. Since, in at least one of these possibilities (actually in two of them), the component of the total magnetic moment due to spin is different from zero, we can conclude that the total moment must itself be different from zero. Since the component cannot be greater than the magnitude of the moment, we can conclude further that this magnitude is at least as great as $2\mu_B$. On the basis of the present elementary and qualitative reasoning, however, we cannot show the justification for the statement, made above, that the magnitude of the moment is exactly $2\sqrt{2}\mu_B$.

In the general case, some of the electrons may be paired while the others are unpaired. Let us designate the total number of electrons as $r = 2p + u$, where $2p$ is the number of paired and u is the number of unpaired electrons. As in the simpler system which has just been considered, here also the spins of the two electrons which form any one of the p pairs must always be exactly antiparallel to each other, whereas the spins of the u unpaired electrons (although commonly described as parallel) are neither exactly parallel nor exactly antiparallel to one another. Of the $2p$ paired electrons, therefore, p must have positive, and the remaining p must have negative, spin. Consequently, the net contribution of these electrons to the resultant magnetic moment of the entire system is zero. Of the u unpaired electrons, on the other hand, $0, 1, 2, \cdots, u - 1$, or u may have positive spin, so that $u, u - 1, \cdots, 2, 1$, or 0, respectively, must have negative spin. The component of magnetic moment along the z axis then has the corresponding one of the $u + 1$ different values $u\mu_B$, $(u - 2)\mu_B, \cdots, -(u - 2)\mu_B, -u\mu_B$. Consequently, the resultant spin moment, which can be shown to have the magnitude $\sqrt{u(u + 2)}\mu_B$, can be oriented in any one of altogether $u + 1$ different directions with respect to the z axis. The multiplicity is therefore $u + 1$. The specific examples which were previously considered are easily seen to provide special cases of this more general treatment. With a single electron, p and u are necessarily equal, respectively, to 0 and 1; the multiplicity is $1 + 1$, or 2, and so the level is a doublet; and the total magnetic moment is $\sqrt{1(1 + 2)}\mu_B$, or $\sqrt{3}\mu_B$. Similarly, with two electrons, either $p = 1$ and $u = 0$, or else $p = 0$ and $u = 2$. In the former event, the level is a singlet with zero resultant spin; in the latter, it is a triplet with a total magnetic moment of $\sqrt{2(2 + 2)}\mu_B$, or $2\sqrt{2}\mu_B$.

Stable molecules usually contain even numbers of electrons all of which are paired. Consequently, we shall in the following be concerned largely with molecules in singlet states. The existence of the excited states with higher multiplicity is, however, of considerable importance since, as we shall see later, it must often be taken explicitly into account even in the treatment of normal singlet molecules.

9·11 Linear Variation Functions. The function Φ of equation 3, Section 9·9, is a rather simple member of a large and extremely important class of functions known as *linear variation functions*. In the remainder of this chapter, we shall encounter a number of additional, and often more complicated, examples of such functions. It is therefore desirable for us now, even at the expense of some repetition, to consider the convenient and general procedure which is available whenever the variation function has the form

$$\Phi = k_1\phi_1 + k_2\phi_2 + \cdot \cdot \cdot + k_p\phi_p \tag{1}$$

or, more concisely, $\quad \Phi = \sum_{j=1}^{p} k_j\phi_j \tag{2}$

with p equal to any positive integer.

In equation 1 (or 2), the k_j's are, as before, the variation parameters which are to be so chosen that the calculated energy is a minimum. Each function ϕ_j must involve all the coordinates (both spatial and spin) that are necessary for the description of the system, each must be properly antisymmetric, and each must satisfy all the other auxiliary conditions (cf. Section 9·3) that are imposed on eigenfunctions. Aside from these three limitations, however, the ϕ_j's may be of any forms that seem reasonable. One example of the way in which these functions are selected has already been given in the discussion of the hydrogen molecule (cf. equation 3, Section 9·9); additional examples will be given in the subsequent sections. For the sake of simplicity, we shall assume that, as with the hydrogen molecule, the constant coefficients k_j and the functions ϕ_j are all real. This assumption, although not necessarily valid in every wave-mechanical calculation, greatly reduces the labor of the treatment; and, for our purposes, it has the justification that it causes no loss of generality in any of the problems which we shall hereafter consider. (Cf. also the paragraph in fine print, below.) Since, therefore, k_j is always identical with k_j^*, and ϕ_j is identical with ϕ_j^*, the asterisks which denote the complex conjugates can be uniformly omitted.

The condition that the approximate energy

$$E = \frac{\int\Phi H\Phi \, d\tau}{\int\Phi^2 \, d\tau} = \frac{k_1^2\int\phi_1 H\phi_1 \, d\tau + k_1 k_2\int\phi_1 H\phi_2 \, d\tau + \cdot \cdot \cdot + k_p^2\int\phi_p H\phi_p \, d\tau}{k_1^2\int\phi_1^2 \, d\tau + k_1 k_2\int\phi_1\phi_2 \, d\tau + \cdot \cdot \cdot + k_p^2\int\phi_p^2 \, d\tau}$$

$$= \frac{\sum_{j}\sum_{j'}k_j k_{j'}\int\phi_j H\phi_{j'} \, d\tau}{\sum_{j}\sum_{j'}k_j k_{j'}\int\phi_j\phi_{j'} \, d\tau} \tag{3}$$

be a minimum requires that all the partial derivatives $\partial E/\partial k_j$ be equal to zero. The indicated differentiations lead ultimately to the p simultaneous, homogeneous, linear equations

$$\sum_{j'=1}^{p} k_{j'}[\int \phi_j \mathbf{H} \phi_{j'}\, d\tau - E\int \phi_j \phi_{j'}\, d\tau] = 0 \qquad (j = 1, 2, \cdots, p) \qquad (4)$$

for the k_j's (cf. pages 574ff). One solution of these equations is always the obvious but trivial one that

$$k_1 = k_2 = \cdots = k_p = 0 \qquad (5)$$

This solution, however, is inadmissible since it leads to a vanishing wave function Φ. In order that there may exist additional, nontrivial solutions, it is necessary and sufficient that the *secular equation*

$$\begin{vmatrix} H_{11} - ES_{11} & H_{12} - ES_{12} & \cdots & H_{1p} - ES_{1p} \\ H_{21} - ES_{21} & H_{22} - ES_{22} & \cdots & H_{2p} - ES_{2p} \\ \cdot & \cdot & & \cdot \\ \cdot & \cdot & & \cdot \\ \cdot & \cdot & & \cdot \\ H_{p1} - ES_{p1} & H_{p2} - ES_{p2} & \cdots & H_{pp} - ES_{pp} \end{vmatrix} = 0 \qquad (6)$$

be satisfied (cf. equations 16 and 17, Section 9·9). Here, the symbols $H_{jj'}$ and $S_{jj'}$ are the so-called *matrix elements* of the energy and of unity, respectively. They are defined by the identities

$$H_{jj'} \equiv \int \phi_j \mathbf{H} \phi_{j'}\, d\tau \qquad (7)$$

and $\qquad\qquad S_{jj'} \equiv \int \phi_j \mathbf{1} \phi_{j'}\, d\tau \equiv \int \phi_j \phi_{j'}\, d\tau \qquad (8)$

In the second of these identities, the operator **1**, which implies merely a multiplication by 1, is explicitly written in order to call attention to the parallelism between the two types of matrix element.

It is easily seen that always

$$S_{jj'} = S_{j'j} \qquad (9)$$

and it can, moreover, be proved[1, 19] that always

$$H_{jj'} = H_{j'j} \qquad (10)$$

The *secular determinant* on the left side of equation 6 is therefore necessarily symmetrical about the main diagonal proceeding from the top left to the bottom right; this property provides a useful check upon the correctness of the determinant.

[19] E. Wigner, *Gruppentheorie und ihre Anwendung auf die Quantenmechanik der Atomspektren*, Friedr. Vieweg & Sohn, Braunschweig, 1931, pp. 40f.

In a more general treatment in which the ϕ_j's and k_j's are permitted to be complex rather than real, the secular equation has the same form 6 as before, but the identities and equations 7–10 must be replaced by

$$H_{jj'} \equiv \int \phi_j^* \mathbf{H} \phi_{j'} \, d\tau \tag{7'}$$

$$S_{jj'} \equiv \int \phi_j^* \mathbf{1} \phi_{j'} \, d\tau \equiv \int \phi_j^* \phi_{j'} \, d\tau \tag{8'}$$

$$S_{jj'} = S_{j'j}^* \tag{9'}$$

$$H_{jj'} = H_{j'j}^* \tag{10'}$$

The secular determinant, which is then no longer strictly symmetrical, is instead described as *Hermitian*, or *self-adjoint*.

Expansion of the determinant in equation 6 leads to a polynomial in E. Since this polynomial is of degree p, the secular equation has p roots, some of which may possibly, but need not, be equal. Since the secular determinant is symmetrical (or self-adjoint; see the paragraph in fine print above), all these roots are necessarily real.[1, 19] The lowest root, E_1, is then an approximation to the energy W_1 of the system in its most stable state, and the remaining $p - 1$ roots, $E_2, E_3, \cdots, E_p$ are approximations to the energies of the system in $p - 1$ different excited states.[18] For the lowest root, E_1, the error ΔE_1 satisfies the relation

$$\Delta E_1 \equiv E_1 - W_1 \geq 0 \tag{11}$$

in which the equality sign at the right is to be taken if, and only if, the corresponding linear combination Φ_1 happens to be identical with the eigenfunction ψ_1 of the Schrödinger equation. Since this condition is not likely to be satisfied in any problem concerned with molecular structure, we can therefore consider that the inequality sign in relation 11 is always valid.

In order to find the values of the constant coefficients k_j, and hence the form of the approximate wave function Φ_r, associated with any approximate energy E_r, we must put the value of this E_r into equations 4. Solution of these equations then gives the $p - 1$ ratios $k_2/k_1, k_3/k_1, \cdots, k_p/k_1$. Finally, the actual values of the k_j's are determined by the condition that Φ be normalized, or that

$$\int \Phi^2 \, d\tau = k_1^2 \int \phi_1^2 \, d\tau + k_1 k_2 \int \phi_1 \phi_2 \, d\tau + \cdots + k_p^2 \int \phi_p^2 \, d\tau$$

$$= \sum_j \sum_{j'} k_j k_{j'} \int \phi_j \phi_{j'} \, d\tau = \sum_j \sum_{j'} k_j k_{j'} S_{jj'}$$

$$= 1 \tag{12}$$

It is important to observe that, if we start with a variation function Φ which is a linear combination of p independent simpler functions ϕ_j, then we end with approximate descriptions of exactly p independent states of the system, each of which is characterized by its own approximate wave function Φ_r and energy E_r. Since the (algebraically) lowest root E_1 of the secular equation is equal to the lowest value that the expression E of equation 3 can assume for any choice whatever of the constants k_j, it is evident that E_1 must be as low as, or lower than, even the lowest of the expressions H_{jj}/S_{jj}; for, if some particular H_{jj}/S_{jj}, say H_{ss}/S_{ss}, were lower than E_1, then a value of E lower than E_1 could be obtained by setting $k_j = 1$ for $j = s$ and 0 otherwise. As we shall see later, it is just this feature of the treatment which is responsible for the existence of resonance energy.

9·12   Valence-Bond Wave Functions.[20]   By a logical generalization of the treatment which was given in Section 9·9 for the hydrogen molecule, we can now set up an approximate wave function corresponding to any desired valence-bond structure of any molecule. In order to illustrate the procedure with a specific example, let us consider the molecule of furan, I. If we assume that all the atomic nuclei are stationary,[21] and

I

that they lie in the xy plane of a Cartesian coordinate system, then the several atomic orbitals can be divided into two classes. On the one hand, all the hydrogen, carbon, and oxygen $1s$ orbitals, and all the carbon and oxygen $2s$, $2p_x$, and $2p_y$ orbitals are even functions of z since they are unaltered when, in each, the coordinate z is replaced by $-z$; on the other hand, the five carbon and oxygen $2p_z$ orbitals are odd functions of z since they are multiplied by -1 when, in each, the same replacement of z by $-z$ is effected. (Cf. pages 561f, 564f.) Since the xy plane is a plane of symmetry for the molecule, this difference between the two classes of orbital has proved to be rather important and, for this reason, a special system of nomenclature has been generally adopted. The orbitals of the first group, which are left unchanged by reflection in the xy plane, are commonly called sigma, or σ, orbitals; those of the second group, which change their signs on reflection in that plane, are called pi,

[20] J. H. Van Vleck and A. Sherman, *Revs. Mod. Phys.* **7**, 167 (1935); H. Eyring, J. Walter, and G. E. Kimball, *Quantum Chemistry*, John Wiley & Sons, New York, 1944, Chapters XII and XIII; G. W. Wheland in A. Farkas, *Physical Chemistry of the Hydrocarbons*, Academic Press, New York, vol. I, 1950, Chapter 1.

[21] For the justification of this approximation, see M. Born and J. R. Oppenheimer, *Ann. Physik* **84**, 457 (1927).

or π, orbitals.   With such planar molecules, it is usually considered a satisfactory approximation to treat the sigma and pi orbitals as completely independent of each other.   Consequently, the extremely complex problem presented by the molecule of furan is broken up into two somewhat simpler ones.   Thus, we can first consider the interactions among the thirty electrons that are assigned to all the $1s$, $2s$, $2p_x$, and $2p_y$ orbitals;   and then we can consider the interactions among the six remaining electrons that are assigned to the five different $2p_z$ orbitals. We shall here discuss only the second, and simpler, of these two problems. (Cf. also Sections 9·19–9·21.)

For ease of reference, let us rewrite structure I in the more general form II, and let us designate the $2p_z$ orbitals on the atoms A, B, C, D, and E by the letters a, b, c, d, and e, respectively.   Since we are at present ignoring all the sigma orbitals and all the electrons that are associated with them, let us consider, instead of the complete structure II, only that part of it, III, which involves the pi orbitals a, b, c, d, and e.   Now, from

analogy with the approximate function Φ_+ (equation 18, Section 9·9) which was obtained for the hydrogen molecule, we might presume that the bond between the orbitals a and b in structure III (see the second of the two following paragraphs in fine print) can be represented by a function of the form

$$[a,b:1,2] \equiv N_{ab}[a(1)b(2) + b(1)a(2)][\alpha(1)\beta(2) - \beta(1)\alpha(2)] \qquad (1)$$

where N_{ab} is a normalization constant.   Similarly, we might presume that the bond between the orbitals d and e can be represented by the corresponding function

$$[d,e:3,4] \equiv N_{de}[d(3)e(4) + e(3)d(4)][\alpha(3)\beta(4) - \beta(3)\alpha(4)] \qquad (2)$$

And, finally, the unshared pair of electrons in the orbital c can be described by the function

$$[c,c:5,6] \equiv N_{cc}c(5)c(6)[\alpha(5)\beta(6) - \beta(5)\alpha(6)] \qquad (3)$$

Equation 3 is of the form to which equations 1 and 2 reduce when the two orbitals that are involved are made identical with each other.   The functions $[a,b:1,2]$, $[d,e:3,4]$, and $[c,c:5,6]$ are here defined in such a way that they involve the coordinates of differently numbered pairs of electrons; for, when these three expressions are combined into an approximate wave function for the complete six-electron system (see below), each electron will need to have its own number.

It is not quite correct to speak of a *bond* between any specified pair of *orbitals*, or to say that the orbitals are bonded with each other. The word "bond," in its strictest sense, refers to a relation between entire atoms, and not to one between mathematical functions that describe the charge distributions associated with individual electrons. What is really meant by the statement that two orbitals are bonded is that the corresponding atoms are bonded because the electrons that are assigned to these orbitals are paired with each other. Since, however, the present somewhat loose terminology is extremely convenient, and since it can hardly lead to any misunderstanding, it will be retained throughout the remainder of this chapter.

If the three pairs of electrons that are taken separately into account in equations 1, 2, and 3 were in fact entirely independent of each other, an appropriate wave function for the system of six electrons would then be the product

$$[ab, de, cc] = [a,b: 1,2][d,e: 3,4][c,c: 5,6] \tag{4}$$

as can be shown either from considerations of probability or by a (partial) separation of the variables (cf. pages 567f). The function $[ab, de, cc]$ is, however, unsatisfactory since it is not completely antisymmetric with respect to interchanges of the electrons (or, more precisely, with respect to interchanges of the *coordinates* of the electrons), and since it therefore violates the exclusion principle. For example, although both the factor $[a,b: 1,2]$ and also the product $[ab, de, cc]$ are multiplied by -1 when electron 1 is exchanged with electron 2, each is instead transformed into a different and entirely independent function when electron 1 is exchanged with any of the remaining electrons, 3, 4, 5, or 6. In order to construct a wave function that is properly antisymmetric, we must form the linear combination

$$\Phi_{ab, de, cc} = N \sum_{j=1}^{720} (-1)^j P_j[ab, de, cc] \tag{5}$$

where N is a normalization constant, and the summation over j includes all 6!, or 720, permutations P_j of the six electrons. These permutations are to be considered numbered in such a way that P_j is an even permutation whenever j is an even integer, and an odd permutation whenever j is an odd integer.

Since an understanding of equation 5 requires some familiarity with the theory of permutations, a brief further explanation is here desirable. If, for example, the permutation P_1 is specifically the single exchange of electrons 1 and 2, and if $f(1, 2, 3, 4, 5, 6)$ is any function of the coordinates of the electrons 1, 2, 3, 4, 5, and 6, then by the symbol $P_1 f(1, 2, 3, 4, 5, 6)$ we mean the function $f(2, 1, 3, 4, 5, 6)$, which differs from $f(1, 2, 3, 4, 5, 6)$ only in that each coordinate of electron 1 has been replaced by the corresponding coordinate of electron 2, and vice versa. Similarly, if the permutation P_2 is the double exchange of electrons 1 and 2, and of electrons 3 and 4, then by $P_2 f(1, 2, 3, 4, 5, 6)$ we mean $f(2, 1, 4, 3, 5, 6)$; and so on for all the rest of the 720 permutations.

The distinction between *even* and *odd* permutations is based on the fact that any permutation, no matter how complex it may be, can always be thought of as the result of an integral number t of single exchanges. If t is even, the permutation is said also to be even but, if t is odd, the permutation is then said to be odd. A given permutation can always be thus expressed in several different ways, with different values of t, but its evenness or oddness is invariant. For example, the permutation which changes the electrons 1, 2, 3, 4, 5, 6 into 3, 2, 1, 4, 5, 6 can be produced by either of the two series of exchanges: $1, 2, 3, 4, 5, 6 \rightarrow 2, 1, 3, 4, 5, 6 \rightarrow 3, 1, 2, 4, 5, 6 \rightarrow 3, 2, 1, 4, 5, 6$ or $1, 2, 3, 4, 5, 6 \rightarrow 1, 3, 2, 4, 5, 6 \rightarrow 4, 3, 2, 1, 5, 6 \rightarrow 4, 3, 1, 2, 5, 6 \rightarrow 3, 4, 1, 2, 5, 6 \rightarrow 3, 2, 1, 4, 5, 6$. The first route requires only three steps, whereas the second requires five, but 3 and 5 are both odd integers. The permutation under discussion is therefore odd. In the general case, in which the total number of electrons is equal to r, it can be shown that exactly half of the $r!$ permutations are always even and exactly half are always odd.

The proof that the function $\Phi_{ab, de, cc}$, which is defined in identity 5, is antisymmetric is not difficult. If P_k represents any single interchange of two electrons, then

$$P_k \Phi_{ab, de, cc} = N \sum_{j=1}^{720} (-1)^j P_k P_j [ab, de, cc] \qquad (6)$$

where the symbol $P_k P_j$ represents the permutation that results from the successive application first of P_j and then of P_k. This permutation, $P_k P_j$, will hereafter be called simply P_l. Now, since P_k is a single interchange, the integer l must be even when j is odd, and it must be odd when j is even. Consequently,

$$(-1)^j = -(-1)^l$$

Moreover, since the summation over j in equation 6 includes all 720 permutations, the letter j under the summation sign can be replaced by l. Consequently,

$$P_k \Phi_{ab, de, cc} = -N \sum_{l=1}^{720} (-1)^l P_l [ab, de, cc]$$

or, since it makes no difference what the index of summation is called,

$$P_k \Phi_{ab, de, cc} = -N \sum_{j=1}^{720} (-1)^j P_j [ab, de, cc]$$

$$= -\Phi_{ab, de, cc} \qquad (7)$$

Inasmuch as P_k is, by definition, *any* single interchange of two electrons, the function $\Phi_{ab, de, cc}$ is therefore completely antisymmetric. This present method for bringing a wave function into agreement with the exclusion principle is closely related to the superficially quite different one that was employed in Section 9·7; the function $\Omega(1, 2, \cdots, r)$ of equation 10, Section 9·7 can, in fact, be equally well expressed in the form

$$\Omega(1, 2, \cdots, r) = \frac{1}{\sqrt{r!}} \sum_{j=1}^{r!} (-1)^j P_j \chi_1(1) \chi_2(2) \cdots \chi_r(r) \tag{8}$$

where P_j is now one of the $r!$ permutations of the electrons $1, 2, \cdots, r$ among the spin-orbit functions $\chi_1, \chi_2, \cdots \chi_r$. The complete equivalence of these two representations of the function $\Omega(1, 2, \cdots r)$ follows merely from the definition of a determinant.

The function $\Phi_{ab, de, cc}$ of equation 5 was said to be "appropriate" for representing a hypothetical molecule in which the three pairs of electrons do not interact with one another. This function is therefore somewhat analogous to Φ_+, which was defined in equation 18, Section 9·9, and which is strictly correct only for a hydrogen molecule with an infinite interprotonic distance. Since, however, Φ_+ has been found to be moderately satisfactory even for the interprotonic distance that is observed in the normal hydrogen molecule, we have some justification for using the function $\Phi_{ab, de, cc}$ in the treatment of the real molecule of furan. We shall therefore make the explicit, and rather drastic, assumption that, although $\Phi_{ab, de, cc}$ can be no better than a rough first approximation to the correct eigenfunction for the pi electrons in furan, it is nevertheless good enough to be qualitatively useful.

Just as the function $\Phi_{ab, de, cc}$ can be considered a satisfactory approximation to the wave function for the structure III, so also the different function

$$\Phi_{aa, bc, de} = N \sum_{j=1}^{720} (-1)^j P_j [aa, bc, de] \tag{9}$$

can be considered to represent the different structure IV, which is the pi part of the complete structure V (or VI). In equation 9, the notation is the same as that employed in equation 5, so that

$$[aa, bc, de] \equiv [a,a:1,2][b,c:3,4][d,e:5,6] \tag{10}$$

where $[a,a:1,2] \equiv N_{aa} a(1) a(2) [\alpha(1)\beta(2) - \beta(1)\alpha(2)] \tag{11}$

$$[b,c:3,4] \equiv N_{bc}[b(3)c(4) + c(3)b(4)][\alpha(3)\beta(4) - \beta(3)\alpha(4)] \tag{12}$$

and $[d,e:5,6] \equiv N_{de}[d(5)e(6) + e(5)d(6)][\alpha(5)\beta(6) - \beta(5)\alpha(6)] \tag{13}$

(cf. equations 1–4). Similarly, the structure VII, with a formal bond between the orbitals b and d can be represented by the analogous function

$$\Phi_{ae, bd, cc} = N \sum_{j=1}^{720} (-1)^j P_j[ae, bd, cc] \tag{14}$$

in which the function $[ae, bd, cc]$ is defined in the same way as $[ab, de, cc]$ and $[aa, bc, de]$ (see equations 1–4, 10–13); and so on for any other valence-bond structure that may be of interest. Again, it should be emphasized that the most that can legitimately be hoped for in connection with the functions $\Phi_{ab, de, cc}$, $\Phi_{aa, bc, de}$, $\Phi_{ae, bd, cc}$, and the like is that they may be as satisfactory as Φ_+ of Section 9·9.

9·13   A More General Treatment of Valence-Bond Wave Functions.[1, 20, 22] When the functions $\Phi_{ab, de, cc}$, etc., are written in the ways outlined in

TABLE 9·1

THE POSSIBLE ASSIGNMENTS[a] OF SPIN QUANTUM NUMBERS TO THE
ELECTRONS IN A MOLECULE WITH CONFIGURATION abc^2de

Assignment Number	a	b	c	d	e	Component of Resultant Magnetic Moment along the z Axis[b]
1	+	+	+ −	+	+	4
2	+	+	+ −	+	−	2
3	+	+	+ −	−	+	2
4	+	−	+ −	+	+	2
5	−	+	+ −	+	+	2
6	+	−	+ −	+	−	0
7	+	+	+ −	−	+	0
8	+	+	+ −	−	−	0
9	−	+	+ −	−	+	0
10	−	+	+ −	+	−	0
11	−	−	+ −	+	+	0
12	−	−	+ −	−	+	−2
13	−	−	+ −	+	−	−2
14	−	+	+ −	−	−	−2
15	+	−	+ −	−	−	−2
16	−	−	+ −	−	−	−4

[a] In this table, a plus sign (+) or a minus sign (−) indicates the assignment of an electron with, respectively, positive or negative spin to the electron in the orbital stated at the top of the column.

[b] In Bohr magnetons, μ_B (cf. page 565).

[22] J. C. Slater, *Phys. Rev.* **38**, 1109 (1931); H. Eyring and G. E. Kimball, *J. Chem. Phys.* **1**, 239 (1933); L. Pauling, *ibid.* **1**, 280 (1933).

Section 9·12, their relations to the structures which they represent are made particularly clear. These same functions can, however, be expressed also in a different way, which is based on a more general and, for some purposes, more useful approach to the problem.

Let us again consider a molecule of furan, but let us now restrict our attention to those structures which are derived from the configuration abc^2de or, in other words, to those in which a single electron is assigned to each of the orbitals a, b, d, and e, and two electrons are assigned to the orbital c. With this limitation, we can discuss structures III and VII of Section 9·12, but not structure IV. Our first step will be to list all the possible ways in which the spin quantum numbers m_s can be assigned to the six electrons. Since the exclusion principle requires that the two electrons occupying orbital c have opposite spin, only the 2^4, or 16, different assignments shown in Table 9·1 can be made. In assignment 6, for example, orbital c has one electron with positive, and one with negative, spin; and each of the remaining orbitals a, b, d, and e has a single electron with, respectively, positive, negative, positive, and negative spin. Since the numbers of electrons with positive and negative spin are therefore equal, the component of the resultant magnetic moment along the z axis is zero. Corresponding to this assignment of quantum numbers, we can set up the antisymmetrized product function

$$\Omega_6 = \frac{1}{\sqrt{6!}}
\begin{vmatrix}
a(1)\alpha(1) & b(1)\beta(1) & c(1)\alpha(1) & c(1)\beta(1) & d(1)\alpha(1) & e(1)\beta(1) \\
a(2)\alpha(2) & b(2)\beta(2) & c(2)\alpha(2) & c(2)\beta(2) & d(2)\alpha(2) & e(2)\beta(2) \\
\cdot & \cdot & \cdot & & \cdot & \cdot \\
\cdot & \cdot & & \cdot & \cdot & \cdot \\
\cdot & \cdot & \cdot & \cdot & \cdot & \cdot \\
a(6)\alpha(6) & b(6)\beta(6) & c(6)\alpha(6) & c(6)\beta(6) & d(6)\alpha(6) & e(6)\beta(6)
\end{vmatrix}$$

$$= \frac{1}{\sqrt{6!}} \sum_{j=1}^{6!} (-1)^j P_j a(1)\alpha(1)b(2)\beta(2)c(3)\alpha(3)c(4)\beta(4)d(5)\alpha(5)e(6)\beta(6) \quad (1)$$

(cf. equations 10, Section 9·7, and 8, Section 9·12). Similarly, for each of the remaining assignments 1–5, 7–16, we can set up the corresponding antisymmetrized product functions $\Omega_1–\Omega_5$, $\Omega_7–\Omega_{16}$, respectively. Since these sixteen different functions Ω_l are the only ones that are possible for the assumed configuration abc^2de, we now take as our variation function the linear combination

$$\Phi = k_1\Omega_1 + k_2\Omega_2 + \cdots + k_{16}\Omega_{16} = \sum_{l=1}^{16} k_l\Omega_l \quad (2)$$

In this way, we come to a secular equation which is of the sixteenth degree in the energy E, and which therefore has sixteen distinct, but not necessarily different, real roots (cf. Section 9·11).

The solution of this secular equation is greatly simplified by the fact that, as is shown in the paragraph below in fine print, all the matrix elements $H_{ll'}$ and $S_{ll'}$ are identically equal to zero unless the functions Ω_l and $\Omega_{l'}$ correspond to exactly the same components of resultant magnetic moment along the z axis. The secular determinant can therefore be written schematically in the form

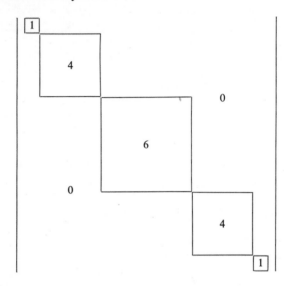

where the figures 1, 4, 6, 4, and 1 state the numbers of rows and of columns in the subdeterminants which lie wholly within the respective squares, and where all the matrix elements which lie outside these squares are equal to zero. As a result of the numerous zeros that are present, the original determinant, with sixteen rows and sixteen columns, automatically factors into a product of five simpler determinants, each of which consists of just those nonvanishing matrix elements within one of the five squares. Consequently, the original sixteenth-degree secular equation can be replaced by five simpler equations, which are, respectively, of the first, fourth, sixth, fourth, and first degrees, and which are obtained by setting each of these five smaller determinants separately equal to zero. For example, the equation corresponding to the square at the top left of the above figure is simply

$$|H_{11} - S_{11}E| = H_{11} - S_{11}E = 0 \qquad (3)$$

whereas the one corresponding to the central square is

$$\begin{vmatrix} H_{66} - S_{66}E & H_{67} - S_{67}E & \cdots & H_{6,11} - S_{6,11}E \\ H_{76} - S_{76}E & H_{77} - S_{77}E & \cdots & H_{7,11} - S_{7,11}E \\ \vdots & \vdots & & \vdots \\ & & & \\ H_{11,6} - S_{11,6}E & H_{11,7} - S_{11,7}E & \cdots & H_{11,11} - S_{11,11}E \end{vmatrix} = 0 \quad (4)$$

and so on.

The proof that $H_{ll'} = S_{ll'} = 0$ unless Ω_l and $\Omega_{l'}$ have the same component of resultant magnetic moment along the z axis proceeds as follows. Each matrix element $H_{ll'}$ is a linear combination of a great many integrals of the form

$$\int \chi_1(1)\chi_2(2) \cdots \chi_6(6) \mathbf{H}\chi'_1(1)\chi'_2(2) \cdots \chi'_6(6) dv \, d\sigma_1 \, d\sigma_2 \cdots d\sigma_6 \quad (5)$$

where each χ and each χ' is the product of some one of the orbitals a, b, c, d, or e by one of the spin functions α or β; and where χ_j and χ'_j are usually not identical. Since the Hamiltonian operator $\mathbf{H}$ does not in any way involve the six spin coordinates σ_j, the integration over these coordinates can be carried through at once (cf. the first of the two paragraphs in fine print on page 574). Since α and β are orthogonal to each other (equation 2, Section 9·7), the integral over σ_1 is zero unless χ_1 and χ'_1 involve the same spin function, either α or β; the integral over σ_2 is zero unless χ_2 and χ'_2 likewise involve the same spin function; and so on. Consequently, the integral 5 vanishes unless the spin associated with each one of the six electrons is the same, either positive or negative, at the left of the operator $\mathbf{H}$ as at the right of it. This required detailed matching of the spins is, however, impossible unless the total number of α's, and also of β's, is the same at the left as at the right. Consequently, each of the terms of which the matrix element $H_{ll'}$ is composed, and hence also $H_{ll'}$ itself, must vanish unless the functions Ω_l and $\Omega_{l'}$ correspond to the same numbers of positive and of negative spins or, in other words, to the same component of resultant magnetic moment along the z axis. The proof that the different integral $S_{ll'}$ is also zero unless this same condition is satisfied is carried out in exactly the same way and so should here require no further comment.

Solution of equation 3 shows that

$$E_q = H_{11}/S_{11}$$

is an approximation to the energy of the molecule in a particular one of the sixteen different states which can be represented by the variation function Φ of equation 2. The approximate wave function which is associated with this energy is simply

$$\Phi_q = N_q \Omega_1$$

where the normalization constant $N_q = 1$ if Ω_1 is already normalized, i.e., if $S_{11} = 1$. When the molecule is in the state that is represented by the function Φ_q, its component of magnetic moment along the z axis is equal to $4\mu_B$ (cf. Table 9·1). Since there is no other state with a component of greater magnitude, the state which we are now discussing must be one member of a quintet level with total magnetic moment of $\sqrt{4(4+2)}\mu_B$, or $2\sqrt{6}\mu_B$ (cf. Section 9·10). The four remaining members of this level then must have components of $2\mu_B$, 0, $-2\mu_B$, and $-4\mu_B$ along the z axis and so must be associated with the four remaining factors of the original sixteenth-degree secular equation. Since all five members of the quintet level have the same energy, it therefore follows that each of the four remaining factors must have E_q as one of its roots.

Let us now consider the fourth-degree factor that corresponds to a component of magnetic moment equal to $2\mu_B$. One of the four roots of this factor is equal to E_q, as we have just seen; the remaining three factors, which we may designate as E_{t1}, E_{t2}, and E_{t3}, must represent the approximate energies of three different triplet levels with total magnetic moment equal to $\sqrt{2(2+2)}\mu_B$, or $2\sqrt{2}\mu_B$. Since the two remaining members of each triplet level have components of magnetic moment along the z axis equal to zero and to $-2\mu_B$, the energies E_{t1}, E_{t2}, and E_{t3} must be roots also of both the sixth-degree factor (shown in equation 4) and the second fourth-degree factor of the secular equation. The approximate functions for the members of the quintet and triplet levels with components of magnetic moment equal to $2\mu_B$ are just four different linear combinations of the functions $\Omega_2 - \Omega_5$.

For reasons which should now be apparent, the six roots of the sixth-degree equation 4 must include E_q, E_{t1}, E_{t2}, and E_{t3}; and the two remaining roots, which we can designate as E_{s1} and E_{s2}, must be the approximate energies of two different singlet levels with zero magnetic moment due to spin. Since most stable molecules are found to be in singlet states, these last two roots, E_{s1} and E_{s2}, are the only ones in which we shall hereafter be interested. The respective functions Φ_{s1} and Φ_{s2}, to which they refer, are certain linear combinations of the six functions $\Omega_6 - \Omega_{11}$.

In principle, we could obtain the values of E_{s1} and E_{s2}, and also the forms of Φ_{s1} and Φ_{s2}, by first solving equation 4 for E; then in some way identifying the particular ones of the six roots which are equal to E_{s1} and E_{s2}; and finally determining the corresponding values of the coefficients in the expression

$$\Phi = \sum_{j=6}^{11} k_j \Omega_j \tag{6}$$

In practice, however, such a direct procedure would be extremely tedious. It is therefore fortunate that there exists also the following indirect, but much simpler, method[22] which is based on a further factorization of the secular equation 4.

The first step in this indirect method consists in replacing the six antisymmetrized product functions Ω_6–Ω_{11} by a certain set of six independent linear combinations of them

$$\Theta_j = \sum_{l=6}^{11} c_{jl}\Omega_l \qquad (j = 1, 2, \cdot \cdot \cdot, 6) \tag{7}$$

Since the Θ_j's are independent, any function Φ which can be expressed in the form 6 can be reexpressed in the alternative form

$$\Phi = \sum_{j=1}^{6} p_j\Theta_j \tag{8}$$

if only the values of the various constant coefficients k_j, c_{jl}, and p_j are properly related to one another. If we take as our variation function the Φ of equation 8, we are led to a secular equation which has the same form as equation 4, but in which the matrix elements H_{jl} and S_{jl} are now defined as

$$H_{jl} \equiv \int \Theta_j \mathbf{H} \Theta_l \, d\tau \tag{9}$$

and

$$S_{jl} \equiv \int \Theta_j \Theta_l \, d\tau \tag{10}$$

The advantage of this apparently more complicated procedure is that the constants c_{jl} of equation 7 can be chosen in such a way (see below) that the new secular equation assumes the form

$$\begin{vmatrix} \boxed{1} & & & \\ & \boxed{3} & \smash{\raisebox{1ex}{0}} & \\ & & & \\ \smash{\raisebox{-1ex}{0}} & & \boxed{2} \end{vmatrix} = 0 \tag{11}$$

and hence can be replaced by a set of three simpler equations of the first, third, and second degrees, respectively. Solution of the first-degree equation then gives the energy E_q of the quintet level; solution of the third-degree equation gives the energies E_{t1}, E_{t2}, and E_{t3} of the three triplet levels; and solution of the second-degree factor gives the energies E_{s1} and E_{s2} of the two singlet levels. Consequently, in order to obtain these last energy values, we need to expand only a determinant with two rows and two columns, and then to solve only a quadratic equation. The validity of these several statements is dependent upon the fact that the integrals H_{jl} and S_{jl}, as defined in identities 9 and 10, are equal to zero unless the functions Θ_j and Θ_l correspond not only to the same component of magnetic moment along the z axis but also to the same value of the total magnetic moment, i.e., to the same multiplicity. The complete proof is, however, too difficult to be given here.[22]

From what has just been said, it follows that, in order to effect the factorization which is schematically depicted in equation 11, we must know how to set up six linear combinations Θ_j in such a way that one of them corresponds to a member of a quintet level, with four unpaired electrons; three correspond to members of three different triplet levels, with two unpaired electrons; and two correspond to two different singlet levels, with no unpaired electrons. Since, however, we are not now interested in any states of higher multiplicity, we can here restrict our attention to only the singlet functions, which we shall call Θ_I and Θ_{II}, and which we shall relate to the respective structures I and II (cf. structures III and VII, Section 9·12).

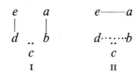

In structure I, the orbitals a and b are bonded to each other. (Cf. the paragraph in fine print at the top of page 589.) The two electrons occupying these orbitals are therefore paired with each other and hence must have opposite spins. Similarly, the two electrons occupying the orbitals d and e must also have opposite spins. Consequently, if the function Θ_I is to represent structure I, it must be a linear combination of only those functions Ω_6–Ω_{11} (see Table 9·1) in which opposite spins are assigned to the electrons in orbitals a and b, and also to those in orbitals d and e. Hence, we see that, of all the coefficients c_{jl} in equation 7, the only ones which are not equal to zero when $j = $ I are c_{I6}, c_{I7}, c_{I9} and $c_{I, 10}$. In order to determine the values of these four nonvanishing coefficients, we now apply the following rule,[22] the complete justification for which is again too difficult to be given here (however, see below). First, we set c_{I6} equal to a constant, which we shall designate as N_I, and which we shall later identify as a normalization constant. Now, the functions Ω_6, Ω_7, Ω_9, and Ω_{10} differ from one another only by the interchange of the spins associated with the two electrons of one or more pairs. For example, the spins of the electrons occupying the orbitals a and b are, respectively, positive and negative in the function Ω_6 but, respectively, negative and positive in the function Ω_9. Each of the functions Ω_6, Ω_7, Ω_9, and Ω_{10} can, accordingly, be characterized by the number of pairs for which the assignment of spins is the opposite of that in the standard function Ω_6. Thus, for Ω_6, Ω_7, Ω_9, and Ω_{10}, the numbers of such reversals are respectively, 0, 1, 2, and 1. The rule, referred to above, is then that c_{Il} is equal to $+N_I$ if Ω_l corresponds to either zero or any even number of reversals, but to $-N_I$ if Ω_l corresponds to an odd number of reversals. The function Θ_I is therefore

$$\Theta_I = N_I(\Omega_6 - \Omega_7 + \Omega_9 - \Omega_{10}) \tag{12}$$

Similarly, since the formal bond in structure II is treated in exactly the same way as are the effective bonds in structure I,

$$\Theta_{II} = N_{II}(\Omega_6 - \Omega_8 + \Omega_9 - \Omega_{11}) \tag{13}$$

If the atomic orbitals $a, b, \cdots, e$ are normalized and mutually orthogonal, the normalization constants N_I and N_{II} are equal to each other and to $1/2$.

In Section 9·12, we represented the structures I and II by the respective functions $\Phi_{ab, de, cc}$ and $\Phi_{ae, bd, cc}$, whereas here we have instead derived the functions Θ_I and Θ_{II}. As we have seen above, however, there are only two singlet levels for the configuration under discussion, and so there must be a relation between the two Φ's and the two Θ's. It is, in fact, not very difficult to show that $\Phi_{ab, de, cc}$ is identical with Θ_I, and that $\Phi_{ae, bd, cc}$ is identical with Θ_{II}. (The proof will, however, not be given here.) This identity of the Φ's and the Θ's supplies some of the steps which were missing in the arguments of both this and the preceding sections. Since the earlier functions were constructed in such a way that they are analogous to the approximate wave function for the normal hydrogen molecule in which both electrons are paired, the latter ones must similarly represent singlet states. Moreover, since $\Phi_{ab. de, cc}$ and $\Phi_{ae, bd, cc}$ were devised to represent molecules with the structures I and II, respectively, the statement that Θ_I and Θ_{II} correspond to these same structures is made to appear less arbitrary. And finally, since we have found that the configuration abc^2de permits only two singlet states, we see that we need not consider any additional structures besides I and II (see also below).

The method by which the functions Θ_I and Θ_{II} were obtained can be extended to more complex systems.[22] Since, however, we shall have no need for the completely general formulation of the theory, we shall here merely state, without proof, some of the important conclusions that can be reached. If, in any arbitrary molecule, there are altogether $2t$ orbitals that are singly occupied, then the number of independent singlet functions which are analogous to Θ_I and Θ_{II} is $(2t)!/[t!(t+1)!]$. There are, however, $(2t)!/[t!2^t]$ apparently different structures which can be drawn. Since the second of these numbers is always greater than the first (if $t > 1$), and since a function can be set up for any valence-bond structure, it is evident that these functions cannot be independent of each other. For example, with the configuration abc^2de, t is equal to 2, so that there are two independent functions, as we have seen, but altogether three structures. The third structure, which we have not as yet considered, is III

$$
\begin{array}{ccc}
e & & a \\
 & \ddots & \\
d & \cdots & b \\
 & c &
\end{array}
$$

III

and the corresponding approximate wave function is seen, by application of the same procedure that led to Θ_I and to Θ_{II}, to be

$$\Theta_{III} = N_{III}(\Omega_7 - \Omega_8 + \Omega_{10} - \Omega_{11}) \tag{14}$$

where N_{III} is again a normalization constant. From what has already been said, it is evident that Θ_{III} cannot be independent of Θ_I and Θ_{II}; and, indeed, a comparison of equations 12, 13, and 14 is sufficient to show that

$$\Theta_{III} = N_{III}(-\Theta_I/N_I + \Theta_{II}/N_{II}) \tag{15}$$

Since, in general, the number of structures exceeds the number of independent singlet states, we need to consider only those structures which are independent of each other. For the setting up of such a *complete* set of *canonical* structures, the following rule[23] has been found especially convenient. We first write down, in a circle which need have no relation at all to the shape of the actual molecule, the symbols for all the orbitals concerned; then we draw all possible structures in which each bond (whether effective or formal) lies wholly within the circle, and in which no bonds cross. Since, in structures I, II, and III, the orbitals are already arranged in the way specified, it is clear that the first two of these structures form the complete set for the configuration abc^2de, and hence that the third structure can be ignored. Our earlier conclusion that no other structures besides I and II need be considered is therefore confirmed.

We are now in position to consider more fully the reason why, in structures I, II, and III, the orbitals which were doubly occupied were considered not to be able to take part in any valence bonds. At first sight, this restriction upon the permissible structures seems somewhat arbitrary, since we might possibly suppose that, when the configuration is, say, abc^2de, the spin of one of the two electrons occupying orbital c could be kept always antiparallel to that of the electron occupying orbital b, whereas the spin of the remaining electron occupying orbital c could similarly be kept always antiparallel to that of the electron occupying

[23] G. Rumer, *Nachr. Ges. Wiss. Göttingen, Math.-physik. Klasse*, **1932**, 337.

orbital d. When the electrons are paired in this way, the resulting structure of the molecule should apparently be representable as IV.

$$e\text{——}a \qquad\qquad e\text{——}a$$

$$d\diagdown_{\;c}\diagup^{b} \qquad\qquad d \quad b$$
$$\diagdown c' \; c'\diagup$$

$$\text{IV} \qquad\qquad\qquad \text{V}$$

However, since the exclusion principle requires the two electrons in orbital c always to have opposite spins, the two in orbitals b and d must then also have opposite spins; and, since all electrons are considered to be paired, the two in orbitals a and e must likewise have opposite spins. Consequently, the structure of the molecule is not IV, but II.

The mathematical necessity for the foregoing conclusion can be shown by a rather straightforward method which will not be described here in detail, but only briefly outlined. If, in place of the single orbital c, there are two different orbitals c and c', then the configuration corresponding to abc^2de becomes $abcc'de$. Since each orbital is then singly occupied, an approximate wave function Θ_V, can be set up, by the general procedure mentioned above, for the representation of structure V. If, now, the orbital c' is again considered to be identical with c, the function Θ_V, aside from a constant numerical factor which would be of no significance after normalization, is found to reduce to Θ_{II}. Consequently, as was stated in the preceding paragraph, structure V does not become equivalent to structure IV when the orbitals c and c' are made identical, but it instead becomes equivalent to structure II.

9·14   Resonance.   When the wave function for any system is approximated by a linear combination of the form

$$\Phi = k_1\phi_1 + k_2\phi_2 + \cdots + k_p\phi_p = \sum_{j=1}^{p} k_j\phi_j \tag{1}$$

(cf. Section 9·11), and when each of the component functions ϕ_j can in some way be correlated with a definite structure, or "structure" (see the earlier discussion in Section 1·5), the system is described as a *resonance hybrid* of the specified structures, or "structures." For example, in Section 9·9, the hydrogen molecule was treated as a resonance hybrid of two "structures." In one of these "structures," the electron with positive spin was assigned to the orbital a, whereas the one with negative spin was assigned to the orbital b; in the second "structure," the two electrons were assigned to the two orbitals in the opposite way. Similarly, in the more general treatment outlined in Section 9·13, each approximate wave function Θ that was set up to represent a definite structure was expressed as a linear combination of antisymmetrized product functions Ω (cf. equations 12, 13, and 14, Section 9·13). Hence, here also, a molecule with any specified structure was regarded as a resonance hybrid of several independent "structures," which differed among themselves only with respect to the assignment of the spin quantum numbers m_s to the electrons in the individual orbitals. In most applications of the resonance concept, however, the functions ϕ_j represent structures (now *without* the quotation marks), and so they can be identified with the Θ's themselves.

In order to see how this latter and more important type of resonance arises, let us note that, in one important respect, our valence-bond treatment of the furan molecule has so far been incomplete. In Section 9·13, although we found that with the aid of the independent singlet functions Θ_I and Θ_{II} we could reduce the original secular equation to a quadratic, we did not consider the further problem of solving this final equation. Clearly, when the equation is solved, there must result two distinct, but not *necessarily* different roots, and each of these roots must be an approximation[18] to the energy of the molecule in a state which is approximately represented by a wave function of form 1, with $\phi_j = \Theta_j$ and $p = 2$. In the more general case, in which the number of singly occupied orbitals is greater than 4, so that the number of independent singlet functions is greater than 2, the treatment is completely analogous. Consequently, whenever the quantum-mechanical treatment of a molecule is carried through in the way that is outlined in Section 9·13, the molecule is automatically and unavoidably described as a resonance hybrid of all those independent structures for which the coefficients k_j in equation 1, with $\phi_j = \Theta_j$, do not happen to be equal to zero. In order to avoid resonance, therefore, we would need to have a molecule for which there is only one nonvanishing coefficient k_j. Since, however, with $2t$ singly occupied orbitals, there are $(2t)!/[t!(t + 1)!]$ independent singlet functions (see page 599), the final secular equation that must be solved will ordinarily be of degree $(2t)!/[t!(t + 1)!]$, and the molecule will be a hybrid of $(2t)!/[t!(t + 1)!]$ structures.

It is important to observe that resonance, as just defined, is not an inherent property of any molecule that is described as a resonance hybrid, but is instead a feature of the particular approximate method that the chemist or physicist has chosen to adopt for the convenient representation of the molecule. For this reason, the structures which are considered to be involved in the resonance are individually without any physical significance whatever. Only the hybrid corresponds to a real molecule. (Cf., however, Section 9·17.) The situation is therefore analogous to that encountered whenever, for example, an empirical function $F(x)$ is expressed as a Fourier series of the form

$$F(x) = a_0 + \sum_{j=1}^{\infty}(a_j \cos jx + b_j \sin jx) \qquad (2)$$

(See the paragraphs in fine print on pages 26 and 29.) The fact that such a series is used is not an inherent property of the empirical data that are in this way described, but is instead the result of a deliberate choice on the part of the experimenter (or observer), who wanted a convenient representation for his function $F(x)$. The individual terms, a_0, $a_j \cos jx$, and $b_j \sin jx$ are here also without physical significance, and, as before, only their sum, $F(x)$, corresponds to the result of an actual experiment (or observation).

Although any one term, say $a_2 \cos 2x$, in the Fourier series of equation 2 does not itself have any experimental meaning, we can nevertheless speak of its effect upon the empirical function $F(x)$. For, if this term were omitted from the summation, the resulting function $F'(x)$ would not in general be identical with $F(x)$. In fact, $F'(x)$ might differ so greatly from $F(x)$ that the superiority of the latter over the former, as a representation of the experimental data, is clearly apparent. In exactly the same sense, we can speak of the effects which individual structures have upon the properties of resonance hybrids. For example, in Section 5·4 we considered nitrobenzene to be a resonance hybrid not only of the four Kekulé structures I–IV but also of the three quinoid structures V–VII. Even though these several structures are merely intellectual constructions and so do not exist, the statement that the last three increase the dipole moment of the molecule has a physically significant meaning. This meaning is that the calculated value of the dipole moment is higher if the approximate wave function for the molecule is expressed as a linear combination Φ of all seven functions Θ_I–Θ_{VII} than it is if the wave function is instead expressed as a combination Φ' of only the four functions Θ_I–Θ_{IV}. Clearly, a completely analogous interpretation can, and

must, be understood also on every other occasion where a specified structure is said to have a certain effect upon an experimentally observable property of a resonance hybrid. (Cf. also pages 8f.)

9·15   Resonance Energy.   The calculated energy of a resonance hybrid in its ground, or lowest, state is equal to the (algebraically) lowest root, E_1, of the secular equation.   On the other hand, the calculated energy that is ascribed to the most stable contributing structure, M, is equal to H_{MM}/S_{MM}, the (algebraically) lowest of all the expressions H_{GG}/S_{GG} for all the contributing structures G.   The calculated *resonance energy*

$$RE_{calc} \equiv H_{MM}/S_{MM} - E_1 \qquad (1)$$

is therefore necessarily either positive or zero (cf. pages 586f).   We should, however, note that neither of the two terms on the right side of the identity 1 is exactly equal to the corresponding term in the different identity

$$RE_{emp} \equiv \text{(Estimated energy of most stable structure)}$$

$$- \text{(Observed energy of hybrid)} \quad (2)$$

which was used in Chapter 3 for the evaluation of the empirical resonance energies, RE_{emp}.   Presumably, if we knew how to set up a completely correct wave function for the representation of structure M, and if we had a completely accurate method for estimating the energy of that same structure, the first terms on the right sides of the identities 1 and 2 would be equal to each other.   Presumably also, if the wave function Φ which is finally obtained for the resonance hybrid were the rigorously correct solution of the Schrödinger equation, the second terms on the right sides of these identities would likewise be equal to each other.   Since, however, no one of these conditions is in fact satisfied, we cannot expect always to obtain perfect agreement between RE_{calc} and RE_{emp}.   We may, nevertheless, hope that the discrepancy between these two values of the resonance energy may be reasonably small; for, since essentially the same approximations are made in the calculation of H_{MM}/S_{MM} and of E_1, the errors which are present in the individual terms should, to a greater or less extent, cancel in their difference, RE_{calc}.   In Sections 9·19 and 9·20, we shall see that, in some cases at any rate, this hope is not entirely unjustified.

In concluding this section, let us re-emphasize that the resonance energy is not an intrinsic property of the molecule which is said to possess it, but that it has meaning only with respect to an approximate method of thinking about the molecule.   As was pointed out above, for example, RE_{calc} is merely the difference between the calculated energies obtained at two levels of approximation, and RE_{emp} is merely the difference between a predicted energy and the true energy.   The value of RE_{calc} must therefore depend upon the natures of the particular calculations involved, and that of RE_{emp} must vary with the method of prediction.   Although failure to recognize this limitation has in the past given rise to some confusion and misunderstanding, the concept of resonance energy, when properly defined and when applied with sufficient care, has been found so useful as to be almost essential in the interpretation of many chemical phenomena. (Cf., for example, Chapters 2 and 3.)

9·16 The Conditions for Resonance. In Section 1·4 we stated without proof a number of conditions which must be satisfied in order that resonance among a set of specified structures be possible. In this section, we shall discuss the derivation of these conditions.

For the sake of simplicity, let us first consider a molecule that is a resonance hybrid of only two structures. These structures might, for example, be the equivalent Kekulé structures I and II of benzene, or instead the nonequivalent structures III and IV of formic acid; we shall,

I   II   III   IV

however, designate them in general terms as A and B. Without loss of generality, we can assume that the corresponding functions Θ_A and Θ_B are normalized, so that $S_{AA} = S_{BB} = 1$; and that $H_{AA} \leq H_{BB}$. The variation function is

$$\Phi = k_A \Theta_A + k_B \Theta_B \tag{1}$$

so that the secular equation is

$$\begin{vmatrix} H_{AA} - E & H_{AB} - S_{AB}E \\ H_{BA} - S_{BA}E & H_{BB} - E \end{vmatrix} = 0 \tag{2}$$

Since $H_{AB} = H_{BA}$ and $S_{AB} = S_{BA}$ (cf. equations 9 and 10, Section 9·11), we find on expansion of the determinant that

$$(H_{AA} - E)(H_{BB} - E) = (H_{AB} - S_{AB}E)^2 \tag{3}$$

A necessary condition that the resonance energy be zero or, in other words, that E_1, the lower root of this equation, be equal to H_{AA}, is now that

$$H_{AB} - S_{AB}E_1 = 0 \tag{4}$$

This equation might be satisfied by accident, even if neither of the integrals H_{AB} and S_{AB} is itself equal to zero. Since, however, such an occurrence is improbable, we shall in the following discussion restrict our attention to the more important situation which arises when equation 4 is satisfied because

$$H_{AB} = S_{AB} = 0 \tag{5}$$

Under these circumstances, all the nondiagonal elements of the secular determinant vanish; the roots of the secular equation are $E_1 = H_{AA}$ and $E_2 = H_{BB}$; the corresponding approximate wave functions are, respectively, Θ_A and Θ_B; and, in short, there is no resonance.

Of the several conditions for resonance, which were stated in Section 1·4, the first three refer to three different types of situation in which the matrix elements H_{AB} and S_{AB} may both be vanishingly small. If the structures A and B differ widely in the average positions of either the atomic nuclei or the electrons, the corresponding functions Θ_A and Θ_B do not *overlap*. In other words, values cannot be assigned to all the coordinates x_1, y_1, $\cdots$, z_r of the nuclei and of the electrons in such a way that Θ_A and Θ_B are simultaneously different from zero. (However, see the paragraph below, in fine print.) Consequently, in each of the integrals H_{AB} and S_{AB}, the integrand is everywhere zero; hence, each of the integrals must itself be equal to zero (cf. page 574). It therefore follows that resonance is not possible. This conclusion provides the proof for the first and second conditions, referred to above. Moreover, as was mentioned on pages 597f, the matrix elements H_{AB} and S_{AB} are equal to zero also if the functions Θ_A and Θ_B correspond to different multiplicities. Consequently, there can be no resonance between structures with different numbers of unpaired electrons. This conclusion provides the proof for the third condition of Section 1·4.

In the two preceding paragraphs, the nondiagonal matrix elements H_{AB} and S_{AB} were considered to be exactly equal to zero. This extreme situation, however, is seldom encountered since the wave functions Θ_A and Θ_B extend to infinity and so must always overlap to some extent (cf. equations 6–11, Section 9·6), and since the requirement that the structures have the same number of unpaired electrons can be shown to be not absolutely binding. In a more accurate treatment of the problem, we should therefore say that, if the three specified conditions for resonance are not satisfied, the integrals H_{AB} and S_{AB} are extremely small in magnitude. Then the roots of the secular equation are extremely close to H_{AA} and H_{BB}, so that the resonance energy is negligible; and the corresponding wave functions differ only slightly from Θ_A and Θ_B, respectively. (See below.) Since the original statement of the theory was therefore essentially correct, the minor modifications which are required for complete rigor need not here be further discussed.

The fourth condition for resonance states that, when a substance is a hybrid of structures which differ greatly in stability, the resonance energy is small and only the most stable structure has an appreciable weight in the ground state. In order to treat this situation, let us again consider that only two structures, A and B, are involved; and let us again assume that Θ_A and Θ_B are normalized, and that the more stable structure is A. Then, since $H_{AA} \ll H_{BB}$, the quantity Δ, which is defined by the identity

$$H_{AA} \equiv H_{BB} - 2\Delta \qquad (6)$$

is not only large in magnitude but also positive in sign. Although the functions Θ_A and Θ_B are usually not orthogonal to each other, we shall nevertheless simplify the treatment by setting S_{AB} equal to zero. The error which is thereby introduced will not be great enough to invalidate the qualitative conclusions of the following discussion. With these definitions and approximations, equation 2, or 3, can be solved for E, with the result that the two roots, which are here designated as E_+ and E_-, are

$$E_{\pm} = \tfrac{1}{2}H_{AA} + \tfrac{1}{2}[H_{BB} \pm \sqrt{(H_{AA} - H_{BB})^2 + 4H_{AB}^2}]$$
$$= H_{AA} + \Delta \pm \sqrt{\Delta^2 + H_{AB}^2}$$
$$= H_{AA} + \Delta \pm \Delta\sqrt{1 + H_{AB}^2/\Delta^2}$$
$$= H_{AA} + \Delta \pm \Delta(1 + H_{AB}^2/2\Delta^2 - H_{AB}^4/8\Delta^4 + \cdots) \tag{7}$$

Hence, $E_+ = H_{BB} + H_{AB}^2/2\Delta - H_{AB}^4/8\Delta^3 + \cdots$ $\qquad\qquad$ (8)

and $\quad E_- = H_{AA} - H_{AB}^2/2\Delta + H_{AB}^4/8\Delta^3 + \cdots$ $\qquad\qquad$ (9)

Since Δ is large and positive, the lower of these two roots is E_- (equation 9), which is only slightly lower than H_{AA}; and the higher root is E_+ (equation 8), which is only slightly higher than H_{BB}. Consequently, the calculated resonance energy,

$$RE_{\text{calc}} = H_{AB}^2/2\Delta - H_{AB}^4/8\Delta^3 + \cdots \tag{10}$$

is indeed small, and it approaches zero as Δ approaches infinity. It should, however, be noted that, no matter how large Δ is, the resonance energy can still be appreciable if the magnitude of H_{AB} is sufficiently large.

The approximate wave function for the molecule when it is in its ground state and has the energy E_- is

$$\Phi_1 = \Phi_- = N_1[\Theta_A - (H_{AB}/2\Delta - H_{AB}^3/8\Delta^3 + \cdots)\Theta_B] \tag{11}$$

where N_1 is a normalization constant. Since the coefficient of Θ_B is relatively small, this function differs only slightly from Θ_A. Similarly, the different approximate wave function for the less stable state that results from the resonance is

$$\Phi_2 = \Phi_+ = N_2[(H_{AB}/2\Delta - H_{AB}^3/8\Delta^3 + \cdots)\Theta_A + \Theta_B] \tag{12}$$

and hence differs only slightly from Θ_B. With respect to each of these wave functions, however, the importance of the resonance is again determined by the magnitude of H_{AB} as well as by that of Δ. Indeed, we see that neither H_{AB} nor Δ is here significant on its own account, since only the ratio H_{AB}/Δ is involved.

If the molecule of interest is a resonance hybrid of more than two structures, the situation differs in no fundamental respect from the one just discussed. We shall here therefore say only that, in such a more complex example, the influence of the nondiagonal matrix elements H_{GF}, with the subscripts G and F designating *different* structures, can manifest itself in still a further way. If the structure Q, for example, is relatively unstable, but if the magnitudes of the various integrals H_{QG} are relatively large, then this structure may be so effectively "coupled" with the other ones that the coefficient k_Q of the corresponding function Θ_Q in the approximate wave function for the ground state may be larger than some of the other coefficients that refer to more stable structures. Hence, there can be exceptions to the generally valid rule that, the less stable a structure is, the smaller is its weight in the ground state of the molecule. In Section 9·20, we shall see some exceptions of this type (cf. also the paragraph in fine print on pages 23f).

9·17 The So-Called Resonance Frequency. In the preceding sections, the wave functions Φ for resonance hybrids have been expressed as linear combinations of simpler functions Θ_G, which have themselves referred to the individual valence-bond structures G. Since Φ, as thus defined, does not involve the time in any way, it clearly cannot describe any sort of transition from one structure to another. Consequently, if we wish to consider such transitions, we cannot start with the time-free Schrödinger equation

$$\mathbf{H}\psi = W\psi \tag{1}$$

but must instead employ the corresponding time-dependent equation

$$\mathbf{H}\Psi = -\frac{h}{2\pi i}\frac{\partial \Psi}{\partial t} \tag{2}$$

(Cf. Section 9·2.)

In order to solve equation 2, we first separate the variables by the method which we found to be successful in our treatment of the particle in a three-dimensional box (cf. Section 9·4). Thus, we set

$$\Psi(x, t) = \psi(x)T(t) \tag{3}$$

where x, in the parentheses, represents all the spatial and spin coordinates of all the particles, and $T(t)$ is a function of only the time t. When we put $\Psi(x, t)$ from equation 3 into equation 2, we find that

$$T(t)\mathbf{H}\psi = -\frac{h}{2\pi i}\,\psi\,\frac{dT(t)}{dt}$$

and hence that

$$\frac{1}{\psi}\mathbf{H}\psi = -\frac{h}{2\pi i}\frac{1}{T(t)}\frac{dT(t)}{dt} \tag{4}$$

Since each side of this last equation must be equal to a constant, we can replace 4 by the two simpler equations

$$\frac{1}{\psi}\mathbf{H}\psi = W \tag{5}$$

and

$$-\frac{h}{2\pi i T(t)}\frac{dT(t)}{dt} = W \tag{6}$$

Equation 5 is simply the time-free Schrödinger equation 1, to which we have hitherto restricted our attention. We can therefore consider that we already know how to obtain satisfactory approximate solutions for it.   The general solution of equation 6, on the other hand, is

$$T(t) = Ce^{-(2\pi i/h)Wt} \tag{7}$$

where C is a constant of integration.   Consequently, we find that the time-dependent wave function is

$$\Psi'(x, t) = N\psi(x)e^{-(2\pi i/h)Wt} \tag{8}$$

where the constant of integration C is now absorbed in the normalization constant N. Although the function $\Psi'(x, t)$ involves the time, the corresponding charge distribution, which is defined by the product $\Psi'^*\Psi'$ (see Section 9·2), is still independent of the time, since it is simply $\psi^*\psi$.   Consequently, we have as yet obtained no indication of a transition from any one structure to any other.

In order to pursue the problem further, let us consider a molecule which is a hybrid of two equivalent structures A and B.   (For specific examples, see below.)   By the methods which were described in the preceding sections, we can show that the approximate time-free wave functions for the two states that result from the resonance can be expressed as

$$\Phi_+ = N_+(\Theta_A + \Theta_B) \tag{9}$$

and

$$\Phi_- = N_-(\Theta_A - \Theta_B) \tag{10}$$

If the respective approximate energies are similarly designated as E_+ and E_-, the corresponding time-dependent wave functions are then seen from equations 3, 7, 9, and 10 to be

$$\Psi'_+ = \Phi_+e^{-(2\pi i/h)E_+t} = N_+(\Theta_A + \Theta_B)e^{-(2\pi i/h)E_+t} \tag{11}$$

and

$$\Psi'_- = \Phi_-e^{-(2\pi i/h)E_-t} = N_-(\Theta_A - \Theta_B)e^{-(2\pi i/h)E_-t} \tag{12}$$

Although the functions Ψ'_+ and Ψ'_- are not degenerate (cf. page 550), the linear combination

$$\Psi'_\pm = N_\pm \left[\frac{\Psi'_+}{N_+} + \frac{\Psi'_-}{N_-}\right] \tag{13}$$

is nevertheless a solution of the *time-dependent* equation 2.   This new function $\Psi'_\pm$ can now be expanded in the following steps

$$\Psi'_\pm = N_\pm[(\Theta_A + \Theta_B)e^{-(2\pi i/h)E_+t} + (\Theta_A - \Theta_B)e^{-(2\pi i/h)E_-t}]$$

$$= N_\pm[\Theta_A(e^{-(2\pi i/h)E_+t} + e^{-(2\pi i/h)E_-t}) + \Theta_B(e^{-(2\pi i/h)E_+t} - e^{-(2\pi i/h)E_-t})]$$

$$= N_\pm e^{-(\pi i/h)(E_+ + E_-)t}[\Theta_A(e^{-(\pi i/h)(E_+ - E_-)t} + e^{(\pi i/h)(E_+ - E_-)t})$$
$$+ \Theta_B(e^{-(\pi i/h)(E_+ - E_-)t} - e^{(\pi i/h)(E_+ - E_-)t})]$$

$$= 2N_\pm e^{-(\pi i/h)(E_+ + E_-)t}\left\{\Theta_A \cos\left[\frac{\pi(E_+ - E_-)t}{h}\right] - i\Theta_B \sin\left[\frac{\pi(E_+ - E_-)t}{h}\right]\right\} \tag{14}$$

At the time $t = 0$, the function $\Psi'_\pm$ therefore becomes equal to Θ_A, aside from a constant numerical factor required for normalization.   Similarly, at the time $t = h/(E_- - E_+)$, $\Psi'_\pm$ becomes equal to Θ_B times an analogous constant numerical factor; at the time $2h/(E_- - E_+)$, it becomes equal to Θ_A, again times a numerical factor; and so on.   Consequently, aside from these several factors, the function $\Psi'_\pm$ oscillates back and forth between Θ_A and Θ_B; hence, a molecule that is described by the wave function $\Psi_{\pm}$ must similarly oscillate back and forth between the structures A and B. The frequency of the oscillation, the so-called *resonance frequency*, is equal to

$$\nu_{res} = \frac{|E_- - E_+|}{h}$$

where $|E_- - E_+|$ is the absolute magnitude of the energy difference $E_- - E_+$.

In order to bring out the significance (or lack of significance) of the resonance frequency, let us first consider the two extreme cases in which $|E_- - E_+|$ is, respectively, very large and very small. An example of the former type is provided by benzene, with which the structures A and B can be identified with the two Kekulé structures. If we specify that the wave function Ψ_+, or Φ_+, and the energy E_+ refer to the ground state of this substance (cf. Section 9·19), then the function Ψ_-, or Φ_-, and the energy E_- refer instead to some one of the spectroscopically excited states. Since the observed ultraviolet absorption of benzene at a wave length of about 2550 A (see Table 6·2, Section 6·3) has been fairly definitely identified[24] as due to a transition from the state with wave function Ψ_+ to the state with wave function Ψ_-, we can calculate that $E_- - E_+$ must amount to approximately 110 kcal per mole. The resonance frequency is therefore approximately 1.2×10^{15} sec^{-1}. Such an enormous frequency is, however, experimentally quite meaningless since there is no conceivable way in which so rapid a transition between the two Kekulé structures could be observed. Moreover, the frequency is meaningless in still a further respect, since it does not refer to benzene in any state that is known to the chemist or physicist, but instead only to benzene in a purely imaginary state that is described by the wave function $\Psi_{\pm}$. Although this imaginary state can be mathematically defined, there is no known method by which it can be experimentally realized. If we were able in some way to force a sample of benzene into such a state, we would then no longer be able to specify the value of the internal energy with any reasonable precision; for, when the wave function is a linear combination of Ψ_+ and Ψ_-, a measurement of the energy of an individual molecule might lead, with equal probability, to either one of the corresponding values E_+ and E_-. Consequently, we can say only that the energy is equal to $(E_- + E_+)/2 \pm (E_- - E_+)/2$. With benzene, the uncertainty, $\pm(E_- - E_+)/2$, in the energy per molecule corresponds to one of approximately ± 55 kcal per mole. It is difficult to imagine a situation in which our knowledge would be so limited.

As an illustration of the opposite extreme, in which $|E_- - E_+|$ is very small, we can consider that the structures A and B correspond to a pair of enantiomorphs, say $(+)$- and $(-)$-lactic acid. Since these structures differ markedly in the relative positions of several atomic nuclei, resonance between them is, to a good first approximation, impossible. However, as was pointed out in the paragraph in fine print on page 606, the conditions for resonance are not absolutely rigorous, and so, even here, resonance is not absolutely excluded. Application of the now familiar method of calculation leads to a result which is *formally* identical with the one that was just obtained for benzene. The resonance again gives rise to two states, for which the wave functions are Ψ_+ and Ψ_-, or Φ_+ and Φ_- (cf. equations 9–12). Since H_{AB} is now extremely small, the respective energies E_+ and E_- are, however, only infinitesimally different either from each other or from H_{AA}/S_{AA}, which is equal to H_{BB}/S_{BB} (cf. equations 8 and 9, Section 9·16). The resonance energy is therefore negligibly small. If the linear combination $\Psi_{\pm}$ is now set up as before (cf. equations 13 and 14), the resonance frequency ν_{res} with which a corresponding molecule would oscillate between the structures A and B is essentially zero. A consideration of some numerical values

---

[24] See, for example, A. L. Sklar, *J. Chem. Phys.* 5, 669 (1937).

will here prove illuminating.   During the time that has elapsed since the optical activity of lactic acid was first recognized, there has been no report of a spontaneous inter-conversion of either enantiomorph into the other.   We can, therefore, feel quite safe in assuming that, for this substance, the period of the oscillation must be considerably greater than 100 years, so that ν_{res} must be considerably less than 10^{-2} year^{-1}.   The energy difference $|E_- - E_+|$ must then be considerably less than 2×10^{-36} erg per molecule, or 3×10^{-20} cal per mole.   This amount of energy is much too small to be observed by any method which is now known.   Consequently, the conclusion that the energy of a given molecule of, say, (+)-lactic acid is uncertain by $(|E_- - E_+|)/2$ is not necessarily inconsistent with any known fact of chemistry.   There is, however, one further point which must be established before we can be completely sure that no conflict exists between quantum mechanics and stereochemistry.   The quantity $|E_- - E_+|$ is in principle calculable without reference to the foregoing empirical data; hence, there arises the question whether the calculated value of this energy difference is indeed as small as has just been indicated.   Although no precise computation of this quantity seems to have been made either for lactic acid or for any other definitely specified optically active substance, Dennison and Uhlenbeck[25] have derived an approximate equation which applies to the general problem of the vibrations of a system with two equivalent positions of minimum potential energy, but which need not here be further described.   When this equation is used, and when any reasonable values are assumed for the several parameters which enter into the calculation, one finds that $|E_- - E_+|$ can hardly be greater than, and probably is much smaller than, about 10^{-100} cal per mole.   Clearly, therefore, the concept of resonance frequency is here entirely without experimental significance since an uncertainty of only about 10^{-100} cal per mole in the energy of a substance cannot be confirmed by any conceivable experiment, and since an interconversion of the enantiomorphs with the corresponding period of about 10^{82} years is obviously quite meaningless.   The situation is here rather analogous to a more familiar one which is encountered in statistical mechanics.   By the methods of this latter science, one can, for example, calculate the probability that a weight which is subject to no external forces will spontaneously leap into the air, or the probability that some water which is contained in an open vessel on a cake of ice at atmospheric pressure will commence to boil.   These calculated probabilities are found to be greater than zero, but so extremely small that, for all practical purposes, they may as well be considered equal to zero.   Similarly, the calculated probability that a molecule of an optically active substance will spontaneously go over into an enantiomorphic one is likewise greater than zero, but again negligibly small.

Intermediate cases, in which $|E_- - E_+|$ is neither very large nor very small, are also possible.   For the ammonia molecule, for example, we can again write two equivalent structures A and B.   If, for definiteness, we assume that the plane defined by the three hydrogen atoms is horizontal, then the nitrogen atom can be considered to lie above that plane in structure A, and below it in structure B.   Since we are now concerned with the motions of the atomic nuclei, and not explicitly with those of the electrons, we shall consider only the vibrational levels which are associated with some particular electronic state, say the most stable one (see Section 6·1).   The wave function Θ_A therefore describes a situation in which the nuclei are executing vibrations about the positions for which structure A has a minimum energy, and the function Θ_B describes a similar situation with respect to structure B.   As a result of the resonance between these two structures, each vibrational level of the molecule is split into two different levels which have nearly, but not exactly, the same energy.   As before, these two

[25] D. M. Dennison and G. E. Uhlenbeck, *Phys. Rev.* 41, 313 (1932).

energies can be called E_- and E_+. The quantity $|E_- - E_+|$ is now, however, of the order of a few calories per mole,[26] so that the resonance frequency is of the order of 10^{10}–10^{12} sec^{-1}. In a spectroscopic study, in which the energy is measured with great precision, an uncertainty of even a few calories per mole is inadmissible, and so the time-dependent wave functions must be expressed in the form of either Ψ_+ or Ψ_- (cf. equations 11 and 12). The resonance frequency therefore has no meaning. On the other hand, in a measurement of dipole moment, in which the energy is not precisely determined, an uncertainty of a few calories per mole can cause no trouble. Even though the resonance frequency is high, it is not high enough to prevent the orientation of the molecule in the electric field (provided that the field either is a static one or else is alternating with a frequency that is low in comparison with the resonance frequency). Consequently, here at last we have a situation where we can legitimately employ a wave function of the type $\Psi_\pm$, and where we can therefore assign a real significance to the frequency with which the molecule oscillates between the structures A and B. If the functions like Ψ_+ and Ψ_- were the only time-dependent ones possible, ammonia would have zero dipole moment, just like carbon dioxide (cf. page 217), since neither of these functions represents a molecule with a positive and a negative end. The more complex function $\Psi_\pm$, however, does represent such a molecule, except at those rare instants when the coefficients of Θ_A and Θ_B, which are functions of the time, are of equal magnitude.

If a substance is a hybrid of two structures which correspond to different energies, i.e., to different values of H_{GG}/S_{GG}, the treatment becomes more complicated. Under such circumstances, it is no longer possible to set up a time-dependent function, analogous to $\Psi_\pm$, which oscillates between Θ_A and Θ_B. The best that can then be done is to set up one which becomes identical with, say, Θ_A at certain instants, but which remains intermediate between Θ_A and Θ_B at all other times. The situation which thus arises is not, however, of sufficient interest to merit further discussion here. Finally, if the resonance involves more than two structures, the treatment again becomes both more complicated and less interesting. We shall accordingly not consider this further extension of the theory.

Many authors have strongly implied, and some have explicitly stated, that the concept of resonance frequency is an essential feature of the theory of resonance. From the foregoing discussion, however, it should now be apparent that this view is not correct. In fact, except under certain rare and special circumstances (of the sort involved in the "inversion" of ammonia, see above), the resonance frequency is clearly quite irrelevant and entirely without experimental meaning.

We are now in position to consider, in somewhat greater detail than would have hitherto been profitable, a further problem which is closely related to that of the resonance frequency. Throughout this book, we have maintained that the individual structures which contribute to the state of a resonance hybrid are merely intellectual constructions, and hence that they do not correspond to any actual molecules. The situation is, however, too complicated to be rigorously described by such a simple statement. In order to obtain a more adequate understanding of the problem, let us, as before, consider a hybrid of only two equivalent structures, A and B. If the energy difference $|E_- - E_+|$ is very large (e.g., if the substance is benzene), then the structures are indeed imaginary, and only the hybrid exists. On the other hand, if $|E_- - E_+|$ is very small (e.g., if the substance is lactic acid), then the *hybrid* is the fiction, and only the individual structures describe real molecules. Finally, if $|E_- - E_+|$ has an intermediate value (e.g., if the substance is ammonia), then the question of physical significance

---

[26] See, for example, M. F. Manning, *J. Chem. Phys.* **3**, 136 (1935).

cannot be answered except with reference to some fairly specific experiment. Clearly, therefore, the statement that the contributing structures are merely intellectual constructions is correct only if the substance of interest belongs to the first one of the three types that have just been considered. This restriction, however, is not a serious one since, in practice, $|E_- - E_+|$ is found to be very large in every instance in which the resonance concept is chemically useful. If the contributing structures differ *principally* in their electronic structures, and if they have essentially the same positions of all the atomic nuclei, the transition associated with the energy $|E_- - E_+|$ must be an electronic one. Hence, since electronic spectra are never found to extend very far into the infrared, the corresponding wave length λ can hardly be greater than, say, 30,000 A. From the relation

$$|E_- - E_+| = hc/\lambda = h\nu_{res}$$

it therefore follows that $|E_- - E_+|$ must be greater than about 9.5 kcal per mole, and that the resonance frequency ν_{res} must be greater than about 10^{14} sec^{-1}. Since we are now dealing with transitions between valence-bond structures of conventional type, and since such structures are chemically meaningless unless their energies are fairly precisely defined, the indicated uncertainty of approximately 5 kcal per mole (see page 610), or more, cannot be allowed. Consequently, neither the structures themselves nor the calculated frequency of transition between them can here be assigned any physical significance. Only with substances like ammonia or lactic acid, where the pertinent transitions are vibrational rather than electronic, can the values of $|E_- - E_+|$ and of ν_{res} be small enough so that the contributing structures acquire real meaning. Such substances, however, are not ordinarily treated as resonance hybrids, and they have not been so treated in this book (except in a few instances where, as in the present section, the most general aspects of the problem are explicitly considered).

The above discussion of the resonance frequency and of its physical significance may seem to be concerned only with certain fine points which are of no practical importance to anyone. As can easily be shown, however, much of the confusion and many of the misconceptions that are to be found in the current literature are directly attributable to the fact that these same "fine points" have not been sufficiently well understood by a sufficient number of the chemists who have written about resonance. One unfortunate result of this widespread lack of understanding is that the theory of resonance has itself come in for a considerable amount of unjustified criticism. Most of the attacks which, according to their authors, have been directed against this theory are found, on closer examination, to be directed instead against some common misinterpretation of it.

A single example will here be sufficient. Tatevskiĭ and Shakhparanov[27] have claimed that the theory of resonance is based upon a physically and ideologically inadmissible conclusion which, according to these same authors, has been drawn by "decadent bourgeois scientists" from a formal, but only superficial analogy between the "principle of superposition" and the variation principle. The first of these two principles is contained in the statement (cf. page 609) that, if each of the functions

$$\Psi_j(x, t) = \psi_j(x)e^{-(2\pi i/h)E_j t}$$

is a solution of the time-dependent Schrödinger equation, then any linear combination

$$\Phi(x, t) = \sum_j c_j \Psi_j(x, t) \tag{15}$$

[27] V. M. Tatevskiĭ and M. I. Shakhparanov, *Voprosy Filosofii* **3**, 176 (1949); the author is indebted to Dr. I. S. Bengelsdorf for an English translation of this paper.

with constant coefficients c_j is also a solution; the second, in the particular form in which it is used in the theory of resonance, says that the time-free wave function $\psi_1(x)$ of any molecule in its ground state can be approximated by a linear combination

$$\psi_1(x) \cong \sum_j a_j \Theta_j(x) \tag{16}$$

of previously selected functions $\Theta_j(x)$. (As before, the single letter x is here again used to represent all pertinent spatial and spin coordinates.) Tatevskiĭ and Shakh-paranov point out, quite correctly, that the obvious similarity in form between equations 15 and 16 corresponds to no analogous similarity in physical meaning, since the functions $\Psi_j(x, t)$ refer to actual states which real molecules could have, whereas the different functions $\Theta_j(x)$ do not refer to any such actual states. Consequently, the state of a molecule with the wave function $\Phi(x, t)$ can legitimately be described as a superposition of several real states; but that of a molecule with the wave function $\psi_1(x)$ cannot be similarly described. (As should be evident, we are here and below following Tatevskiĭ and Shakhparanov in considering only examples in which $|E_- - E_+|$, or, in more complex systems, the appropriate analogous energy difference, is very large.) These authors now go on, however, to say:[27]

"On the basis of the foregoing external resemblance (linearity) of equations 15 and 16 and by reason of the fact that equation 15 represents the principle of superposition of states in quantum mechanics, the theory of resonance asserts that in equation 16 the fundamental state of the system defined by the function $\psi_1(x)$ is also a superposition of certain states which, in accordance with this theory, are defined as the functions $\Theta_j(x)$.

"Consequently, according to the theory of resonance, the functions Θ_j define certain actually realizable states of the molecule, and equation 16 expresses the superposition of these states. Thus, according to this theory, the state of the molecule is a super-position, or 'resonance,' of a number of particular states which are described by the functions Θ_j. Hence, this theory draws the conclusion that, in chemical molecules, the 'phenomenon of resonance' occurs among the individual states. On this [fact] there is constructed the entire remaining course of argumentation, [and] all kinds of applications to the numerous concrete problems of organic, inorganic and physical chemistry are developed. . . .

"The invalidity of such an interpretation of the physical meaning of the functions $\Theta_j(x)$ follows from the fact that these functions which are employed in the linear version of the variation method do not define by any means any real states of the system being considered (molecule or ion) in the given physical conditions, whereas in equation 15 which expresses the principle of superposition of states the functions Ψ_j are functions defining these states of the system in which it may be found in given physical conditions.

"Hence it follows that, inasmuch as the functions Θ_j do not define any of the actually realizable states of the molecule, the fundamental state of the molecule is not a super-position of any of the states of this molecule which are defined by the functions Θ_j." [For the sake of consistency with the symbolism used in this chapter, the nomenclature used by Tatevskiĭ and Shakhparanov has in the foregoing quotation been slightly altered.]

If the theory of resonance did indeed have the character thus ascribed to it by Tatevskiĭ and Shakhparanov, it would, of course, be untenable, and the foregoing criticism of it would be largely valid. Actually, however, when this theory is correctly formulated, it is seen to be entirely independent of the formal resemblance between equations 15 and 16; and hence to be quite different from the erroneous and easily demolished version of it just described.   The only way in which equation 15 enters into the treatment is in connection with the above derivation of the resonance frequency; and, as we have emphasized in the preceding discussion, this frequency is both irrelevant and meaningless.   (It will be remembered that we are here considering that $|E_- - E_+|$ is large.)   The theory of resonance does not imply, as Tatevskiĭ and Shakhparanov claim it does, that the functions Θ_j describe real states of the molecule; it is instead a corollary of the obvious fact that, if the constant coefficients a_j are properly chosen, the linear combination ψ_1, equation 16, can be made a closer approximation to the correct wave function than is any one of its individual terms Θ_j.   Interestingly enough, Tatevskiĭ and Shakhparanov advance no serious criticism of the correctly interpreted theory; indeed, they explicitly say,[27] "The variation method of defining an approximate function and its particular linear version are not subject to any particular objections," and they add (in a footnote) only the minor, and quite correct, qualification that, "It should only be observed that this method gives an approximate function ψ_1; it is impossible to evaluate the accuracy of its determination in the general case."   It therefore appears that, like a number of other people in the United States as well as abroad, these authors have been misled by the carelessly worded expositions of the theory, which give an erroneous impression of its physical meaning, and which are unfortunately all too common.

9·18   The Mechanical Analogy.   The word "resonance," as it is used in this book, was introduced into quantum mechanics[28] in order to call attention to a formal mathematical analogy with the familiar resonance of classical mechanics.   Although this analogy is neither completely general nor quite exact, it is nevertheless a surprisingly close one when it is properly made, and it permits many of the properties of the quantum-mechanical system to be directly inferred from the corresponding ones of the classical system.   Often, however, it has been presented in a way that is highly misleading, if not actually wrong.   We shall here, therefore, attempt to clarify the relation which exists between the two types of resonance; and we shall attempt to show how a correct understanding of this relation can help to make more concrete the concepts that underlie the quantum-mechanical theory.

The analogy is to a set of coupled harmonic oscillators.   For definiteness, we shall consider that these oscillators are pendulums, each of which is constrained to move in a single plane, so that its position at any instant can be uniquely specified by the value of a single coordinate.   (See below.)   In order to ensure that the pendulums are indeed coupled with one another, we may imagine that they are all suspended from a common support, or that they are connected by weightless springs, or that they are caused to interact with one another in some still different way.   (The reader who does not wish to work through the following rather complicated and tedious mathematical development, and who is willing to accept on faith the conclusions to which it leads, may find it advantageous to skip from here to page 621.)

If the coordinate θ_j which defines the position of the jth pendulum is taken as the angle between this pendulum and the vertical, then the total kinetic energy T of the system can be expressed in the form

$$T = \frac{1}{2} \sum_{j=1}^{p} M_j \left(\frac{d\theta_j}{dt}\right)^2 \equiv \frac{1}{2} \sum_{j=1}^{p} \dot{\phi}_j^{\,2} \tag{1}$$

where p is the total number of pendulums;

$$\phi_j \equiv \sqrt{M_j}\,\theta_j \tag{2}$$

[28] W. Heisenberg, *Z. Physik* **38**, 411 (1926).

M_j is a constant which depends upon the mass and length of the jth pendulum, and also upon the way in which the mass is distributed; and $\dot{\phi}_j$ is equal to $d\phi_j/dt$. The total potential energy V, since it must be a continuous function of all the coordinates θ_j, and hence also of all the coordinates ϕ_j, can be expressed as a power series

$$V = a + \sum_{j=1}^{p} b_j \phi_j + \frac{1}{2} \sum_{j=1}^{p} \sum_{k=1}^{p} c_{jk} \phi_j \phi_k + \cdots \qquad (3)$$

in which a, b_j, c_{jk}, etc., are constants. Now, since the origin of the energy scale is arbitrary, we can conveniently set V equal to zero when all pendulums are vertical, i.e., when $\phi_1 = \phi_2 = \cdots = \phi_p = 0$. We then find that $a = 0$. Since the potential energy must be a minimum when all pendulums are vertical, it follows also that

$$\left. \frac{\partial V}{\partial \phi_j} \right|_{\phi_1 = \phi_2 = \cdots = \phi_p = 0} = b_j = 0 \qquad (j = 1, 2, \cdots, p) \qquad (4)$$

Finally, if we restrict ourselves to oscillations of small amplitude, so that the magnitude of each ϕ_j is always small, the first nonvanishing summation on the right side of equation 3 is much more important than the succeeding ones. Consequently, we can neglect these latter terms, and hence we can express the potential energy more simply as

$$V = \frac{1}{2} \sum_{j=1}^{p} \sum_{k=1}^{p} c_{jk} \phi_j \phi_k \qquad (5)$$

with $\qquad\qquad c_{jk} = c_{kj} \qquad\qquad (6)$

Indeed, if the cubic and still higher terms were not thus ignored, the motion would not be simple harmonic, and the subsequent treatment would be impossible.

The equations of motion in the Lagrangian form[29] are

$$\frac{d}{dt} \frac{\partial (T - V)}{\partial \dot{\phi}_j} - \frac{\partial (T - V)}{\partial \phi_j} = 0 \qquad (j = 1, 2, \cdots, p) \qquad (7)$$

Combination of the several equations and definitions 1, 5, and 7 now leads to the set of simultaneous differential equations

$$\frac{d^2 \phi_j}{dt^2} + \sum_{k=1}^{p} c_{jk} \phi_k = 0 \qquad (j = 1, 2, \cdots, p) \qquad (8)$$

In order to simplify these equations, we replace the coordinates ϕ_j by the p independent combinations q_m, which are defined by the equations

$$\phi_j = \sum_{m=1}^{p} r_{jm} q_m \qquad (9)$$

or $\qquad\qquad q_m = \sum_{j=1}^{p} s_{mj} \phi_j \qquad\qquad (10)$

[29] See, for example, H. Margenau and G. M. Murphy, *The Mathematics of Physics and Chemistry*, D. Van Nostrand Co., New York, 1943, Chapter 9; or any treatise on classical mechanics.

in which the coefficients r_{jm} and s_{mj} are constants. Since equations 9 and 10 must be mutually consistent, it follows that

$$\phi_j = \sum_{m=1}^{p} r_{jm} \sum_{k=1}^{p} s_{mk}\phi_k \tag{11}$$

and hence that

$$\sum_{m=1}^{p} r_{jm}s_{mk} = \delta_{jk} \begin{cases} \equiv 1 & \text{if } j = k \\ \equiv 0 & \text{if } j \neq k \end{cases} \tag{12}$$

Similarly,

$$q_m = \sum_{j=1}^{p} s_{mj} \sum_{n=1}^{p} r_{jn}q_n \tag{13}$$

so that

$$\sum_{j=1}^{p} s_{mj}r_{jn} = \delta_{mn} \tag{14}$$

With these modifications, the equations 8 now assume the forms

$$\sum_{m=1}^{p} r_{jm}\frac{d^2q_m}{dt^2} + \sum_{m=1}^{p}\sum_{k=1}^{p} c_{jk}r_{km}q_m = 0 \qquad (j = 1, 2, \cdots, p) \tag{15}$$

We next multiply each of the equations 15 by s_{nj} and sum over all j. In this way, we obtain

$$\sum_{j=1}^{p}\sum_{m=1}^{p} s_{nj}r_{jm}\frac{d^2q_m}{dt^2} + \sum_{j=1}^{p}\sum_{m=1}^{p}\sum_{k=1}^{p} s_{nj}c_{jk}r_{km}q_m = 0 \tag{16}$$

In view of equation 14, however, the double summation here reduces to a single term, and so we find that

$$\frac{d^2q_n}{dt^2} + \sum_{j=1}^{p}\sum_{m=1}^{p}\sum_{k=1}^{p} s_{nj}c_{jk}r_{km}q_m = 0 \qquad (n = 1, 2, \cdots, p) \tag{17}$$

The simplification which is permitted by this apparent complication of the equations results from the fact that the constants r_{jm} and s_{mj} of equations 9 and 10 can always be so chosen that the triple summation which remains in equation 17 likewise reduces to a single term. Thus, if we assume (see below) that

$$\sum_{j=1}^{p}\sum_{k=1}^{p} s_{nj}c_{jk}r_{km} = K_m\,\delta_{nm} \qquad (m, n = 1, 2, \cdots, p) \tag{18}$$

where K_m is a constant, the equations 17 become

$$\frac{d^2q_n}{dt^2} + \sum_{m=1}^{p} K_m\,\delta_{nm}q_m = \frac{d^2q_n}{dt^2} + K_nq_n = 0 \qquad (n = 1, 2, \cdots, p) \tag{19}$$

The general solutions of these last equations are

$$q_n = A_n \cos\left(\sqrt{K_n}\,t + \varepsilon_n\right) \qquad (n = 1, 2, \cdots, p) \tag{20}$$

where the constants of integration A_n and ε_n define, respectively, the amplitudes and the phases of the oscillations. The corresponding frequencies, ν_n, are then

$$\nu_n = \sqrt{K_n}/(2\pi) \tag{21}$$

so that

$$K_n = 4\pi^2\nu_n{}^2 \tag{22}$$

It remains to consider the conditions which must be imposed in order that the equations 18 be satisfied. If we multiply each of these equations by s_{mt} and then sum over all m, we find successively that

$$\sum_{m=1}^{p}\sum_{j=1}^{p}\sum_{k=1}^{p} s_{nj}c_{jk}r_{km}s_{mt} = \sum_{m=1}^{p} K_m\,\delta_{nm}s_{mt} \tag{23}$$

$$\sum_{j=1}^{p} s_{nj}c_{jt} = 4\pi^2\nu_n{}^2 s_{nt} = 4\pi^2\sum_{j=1}^{p}\nu_n{}^2 s_{nj}\delta_{jt} \tag{24}$$

$$\sum_{j=1}^{p} s_{nj}(c_{jt} - 4\pi^2\nu_n{}^2\delta_{jt}) = 0 \qquad (n,\ t = 1,\ 2,\ \cdots,\ p) \tag{25}$$

This set of simultaneous, homogeneous, linear equations for the constants s_{nj} has a nontrivial solution only if the determinant of the coefficients vanishes or, in other words, if

$$\begin{vmatrix} c_{11} - 4\pi^2\nu_n{}^2 & c_{12} & \cdots & c_{1p} \\ c_{21} & c_{22} - 4\pi^2\nu_n{}^2 & \cdots & c_{2p} \\ \vdots & \vdots & & \vdots \\ c_{p1} & c_{p2} & \cdots & c_{pp} - 4\pi^2\nu_n{}^2 \end{vmatrix} = 0 \tag{26}$$

(Cf. also pages 576, 585.) Solution of the secular equation 26 gives p independent, but not necessarily different, values of $\nu_n{}^2$, with $n = 1,\ 2,\ \cdots,\ p$. If all these values are positive, as we must assume them to be, there are therefore p independent positive frequencies ν_n (as well as the p corresponding negative ones which, since they add nothing new, will hereafter be ignored). It will be convenient to number the positive frequencies in order of increasing magnitude, so that

$$\nu_1 \leq \nu_2 \leq \cdots \leq \nu_p \tag{27}$$

It can then be shown that ν_1 is as small as, or smaller than, the smallest of the p quantities $\sqrt{c_{jj}}/(2\pi)$; and also that ν_p is as large as, or larger than, the largest of the same p quantities.

If some particular one of the above frequencies, say ν_m, is inserted in the equations 25, then these equations can be solved for the $p - 1$ independent ratios s_{m2}/s_{m1}, s_{m3}/s_{m1}, $\cdots$, s_{mp}/s_{m1}. Consequently, the corresponding so-called *normal coordinate* q_m is determined except for a constant numerical factor, the value of which is frequently so chosen that the *normalization* condition

$$\sum_{j=1}^{p} s_{mj}{}^2 = 1 \tag{28}$$

is satisfied. It can be shown that the different normal coordinates are mutually *orthogonal*, so that

$$\sum_{j=1}^{p} s_{mj}s_{nj} = 0 \tag{29}$$

if m is not equal to n. The normalization and orthogonality conditions can conveniently be expressed by the single equation

$$\sum_{j=1}^{p} s_{mj}s_{nj} = \delta_{mn} \qquad (m, n = 1, 2, \cdots, p) \tag{30}$$

Similarly, one can show that

$$\sum_{j=1}^{p} r_{mj}r_{nj} = \delta_{mn} \qquad (m, n = 1, 2, \cdots, p) \tag{31}$$

In order to see how an individual pendulum will oscillate, we must return to equation 9 which, with the aid of equations 2, 20, and 22, we are now able to rewrite in the form

$$\theta_j = (1/\sqrt{M_j})\phi_j = (1/\sqrt{M_j}) \sum_{m=1}^{p} r_{jm}q_m$$

$$= (1/\sqrt{M_j}) \sum_{m=1}^{p} r_{jm}A_m \cos(2\pi\nu_m t + \varepsilon_m) \qquad (j = 1, 2, \cdots, p) \tag{32}$$

The values of the constants r_{jm} are determined by the equations 12 or 14; or alternatively, except for a constant numerical factor, by the equations

$$\sum_{j=1}^{p} (c_{tj} - 4\pi^2\nu_m^2\,\delta_{tj})r_{jm} = 0 \qquad (t, m = 1, 2, \cdots, p) \tag{33}$$

which themselves result when the equations 18 are first multiplied by r_{tn} and then summed over all n. (Cf. the derivation of equations 25.) In the latter event, the absolute, rather than the relative, values of the coefficients r_{jm} can again be fixed by the normalization condition contained in equation 31.

In the equations 32, the constants A_m and ε_m, unlike r_{jm}, can be assigned any arbitrary values. In fact, these expressions define the most general solutions of the simultaneous differential equations 8. Clearly, therefore, the motion can be extremely complex. Let us now, however, consider a particularly simple situation in which all the coefficients A_m are equal to zero except for a single one, say A_l. Then equation 32 becomes

$$\theta_j = (r_{jl}A_l/\sqrt{M_j}) \cos(2\pi\nu_l t + \varepsilon_l) \qquad (j = 1, 2, \cdots, p) \tag{34}$$

so that each pendulum j is executing simple harmonic motion with amplitude $r_{jl}A_l/\sqrt{M_j}$, with the frequency ν_l, and with phase ε_l. It is to be noted that, on account of the presence of the coefficients $r_{jl}/\sqrt{M_j}$, the p different pendulums will in general have different amplitudes, although all of them must have the same frequency and phase. (However, see the following paragraph.) This type of motion is commonly described by the statement that only one of the *normal modes* of oscillation, the lth, is excited.

On the other hand, in the more general situation in which two or more normal modes are excited, i.e., in which two or more of the constants A_m are different from zero, the individual pendulums will ordinarily not have unique amplitudes, frequencies, or phases. The varying amplitudes of the oscillations then give rise to the well-known phenomenon of *beats*.

It was said above that, when only the lth normal mode is excited, all the pendulums have the same phase ε_l. This statement, however, requires some modification. More often than not, the constants r_{jl} will be found to be positive for certain values of j, but negative for other values of j. It thus appears that, if the constant A_l is positive, some of the pendulums must be assigned positive amplitudes $r_{jl}A_l/\sqrt{M_j}$, whereas others must be assigned negative amplitudes. Since, however, it seems illogical to speak of a negative amplitude, we shall hereafter modify equation 34 so that it becomes

$$\theta_j = (|r_{jl}|A_l/\sqrt{M_j}) \cos(2\pi\nu_l t + \varepsilon_l + \eta_{jl}\pi) \tag{35}$$

where $|r_{jl}|$ is the absolute magnitude of r_{jl}, and η_{jl} is defined as

$$\eta_{jl} \equiv 1 \quad \text{if } r_{jl} < 0$$
$$\equiv 0 \quad \text{if } r_{jl} > 0 \tag{36}$$

Although equations 34 and 35 are clearly equivalent, their interpretations are somewhat different. If A_l is positive, equation 34 says that all pendulums have the same phase, but that those for which r_{jl} is negative have negative amplitudes; on the other hand, equation 35 says that all pendulums have positive amplitudes, but that those for which r_{jl} is negative are exactly out of phase with those for which r_{jl} is positive. Similarly, we shall replace the more general equation 32 by

$$\theta_j = (1/\sqrt{M_j}) \sum_{m=1}^{p} |r_{jm}|A_m \cos(2\pi\nu_m t + \varepsilon_m + \eta_{jm}\pi) \quad (j = 1, 2, \cdots, p) \tag{37}$$

and we shall specify that each coefficient A_m is either positive or zero.

A simple example will serve to illustrate the general theory developed above. If there are only two pendulums, and if these are equivalent so that $M_1 = M_2$ and $c_{11} = c_{22}$, then the secular equation 26 has the form

$$\begin{vmatrix} c_{11} - 4\pi^2\nu^2 & c_{12} \\ c_{21} & c_{11} - 4\pi^2\nu^2 \end{vmatrix} = 0 \tag{38}$$

Since $c_{12} = c_{21}$, and since we may ordinarily assume that c_{12} is negative, we therefore find that

$$\nu_1 = [1/(2\pi)]\sqrt{c_{11} + c_{12}} \tag{39}$$

and

$$\nu_2 = [1/(2\pi)]\sqrt{c_{11} - c_{12}} \tag{40}$$

(Cf. the inequalities 27.) We therefore see that, as was stated on page 618, ν_1 is indeed smaller than $\sqrt{c_{11}}/(2\pi)$, whereas ν_2 is larger than $\sqrt{c_{11}}/(2\pi)$. The corresponding normal coordinates are

$$q_1 = (1/\sqrt{2})(\phi_1 + \phi_2) = \sqrt{M_1/2}(\theta_1 + \theta_2) \tag{41}$$

and

$$q_2 = (1/\sqrt{2})(\phi_1 - \phi_2) = \sqrt{M_1/2}(\theta_1 - \theta_2) \tag{42}$$

When only the coordinate q_1 is excited (i.e., when $A_2 = 0$),

$$\theta_1 = \theta_2 = (A_1/\sqrt{2M_1}) \cos(2\pi\nu_1 t + \varepsilon_1) \tag{43}$$

Both pendulums therefore oscillate with the same frequency ν_1 and with the same amplitude $A_1/\sqrt{2M_1}$; and the two are exactly in phase with each other. On the other hand, when only the coordinate q_2 is excited (i.e., when $A_1 = 0$),

$$\theta_1 = -\theta_2 = (A_2/\sqrt{2M_1}) \cos (2\pi\nu_2 t + \varepsilon_2) \tag{44}$$

Both pendulums therefore oscillate with the same frequency ν_2 and with the same amplitude $A_2/\sqrt{2M_1}$; but they are now exactly out of phase with each other. Finally, if both the coordinates q_1 and q_2 are excited with the same amplitude A and phase constant ε, then

$$\theta_1 = (A/\sqrt{2M_1}) \cos (2\pi\nu_1 t + \varepsilon) + (A/\sqrt{2M_1}) \cos (2\pi\nu_2 t + \varepsilon)$$
$$= A\sqrt{2/M_1} \cos [\pi(\nu_2 + \nu_1)t + \varepsilon] \cos [\pi(\nu_2 - \nu_1)t] \tag{45}$$

and
$$\theta_2 = (A/\sqrt{2M_1}) \cos (2\pi\nu_1 t + \varepsilon) - (A/\sqrt{2M_1}) \cos (2\pi\nu_2 t + \varepsilon)$$
$$= A\sqrt{2/M_1} \sin [\pi(\nu_2 + \nu_1)t + \varepsilon] \sin [\pi(\nu_2 - \nu_1)t] \tag{46}$$

Each pendulum is therefore characterized by two different frequencies, $(\nu_2 + \nu_1)/2$ and $(\nu_2 - \nu_1)/2$. If the second of these frequencies is small compared with the first, we may describe the complex motion of the pendulums in the following way. When $t = 0$, pendulum 1 is oscillating with frequency $(\nu_2 + \nu_1)/2$ and amplitude $A\sqrt{2/M_1}$, whereas pendulum 2 is at rest. As time passes, however, the amplitude of pendulum 1 decreases, whereas that of pendulum 2 increases. When $t = 1/[2(\nu_2 - \nu_1)]$, pendulum 1 is at rest, whereas pendulum 2 oscillates with frequency $(\nu_2 + \nu_1)/2$ and amplitude $A\sqrt{2/M_1}$. The direction of the change now reverses so that, when $t = 1/(\nu_2 - \nu_1)$, pendulum 1 is again oscillating with the maximum amplitude, and pendulum 2 is again at rest. The entire process then keeps repeating itself, so that the motion is transferred back and forth between the two pendulums with the frequency $\nu_2 - \nu_1$.

The reader should now be able to extend the above treatment to less simple problems in which the pendulums are not equivalent, or in which the number of pendulums is greater than two, or in which both these conditions are present at the same time. Let us here, however, consider the nature of the analogy that exists between, on the one hand, a mechanical system formed by altogether p pendulums and, on the other hand, a resonance hybrid of altogether p structures. This analogy arises from the fact that there is a close resemblance between the mathematical procedures used in the two types of problem. In many respects, the two treatments are *formally* identical, and they differ only in the physical significance of the several variables, parameters, etc., with which they deal. Thus, the functions Θ_j which represent the individual valence-bond structures in the quantum-mechanical system (cf. Sections 9·12 and 9·13) correspond to the coordinates ϕ_j which describe the displacements of the individual pendulums in the classical system. Similarly, the wave functions Φ_m which describe the resonance hybrid in its different stationary states correspond to the coordinates q_m which describe the pendulums in their different normal modes of oscillation. The matrix elements H_{jk} which appear in the secular equation for the resonance hybrid (cf. page 585) correspond to the force constants c_{jk} which appear in the analogous secular equation for the coupled pendulums (cf. page 618). And finally, the energy W of the molecule corresponds to $4\pi^2\nu^2$ when the two respective secular equations are compared with each other, but to $h\nu$ when the time dependence of the wave functions and of the coordinates is considered.

In several respects, the analogy between the classical and the quantum-mechanical treatments is not exact.   As has just been noted, the classical frequency v has no *unique* analog in the quantum-mechanical system.   Furthermore, although v occurs only in the diagonal elements of the secular equation 26, W is not similarly restricted unless the functions Θ_j that represent the individual structures are mutually orthogonal (cf. equation 6, Section 9.11); however, in most of the applications of the theory of resonance which have been considered in this book, the various functions have not satisfied this condition.   Still a third type of inexactness in the analogy is due to the fact that, when the coordinates of the pendulums are expressed as functions of the time t, then t appears in the arguments of *real* cosine functions whereas, when the wave functions are similarly expressed, then t appears instead in the exponents of *complex* exponential factors.   These several discrepancies are not, however, sufficient to prevent the analogy from being useful.   In particular, the last one of the three might have been anticipated since the coordinates of the pendulums are necessarily restricted to real values, and since the cosine functions are just the real parts of complex exponential functions.

For the sake of definiteness, let us now consider a number of specific applications of the analogy.[30]   Since we have already described in detail the general procedures by which both the classical and the quantum-mechanical calculations are made, we shall not here outline the frequently rather tedious steps that are required for the solution of the several individual problems.   Instead, we shall merely state the results to which these steps would ultimately lead.   In order that the analogy may be made as clear as possible, the classical and the quantum-mechanical systems are described in parallel columns.   In parts A, B, and C, below, we shall implicitly assume that the quantum-mechanical system is of the usual type represented by Figure 1·2, Section 1·4.   In part D, we shall discuss the further possibilities corresponding to Figures 1·1 and 1·3.

CLASSICAL SYSTEM	QUANTUM-MECHANICAL SYSTEM
A. For the present we shall consider that there are two pendulums of the same frequency.	A. For the present we shall consider that there are two structures of the same energy.
1. If the pendulums are not coupled, then all the constant coefficients c_{jk} and c_{kj} of equations 5 and 8 are equal to zero except when the two subscripts j and k are identical. Under such circumstances, there is no resonance; either pendulum can oscillate alone, the other remaining stationary. This situation is illustrated in Figures 9·7a and 9·7b, in which the displacements of the pendulums are plotted horizontally against the time vertically.	1. If the conditions 1, 2, and 3 of Section 1·4 are not satisfied (that is, if the structures differ markedly in nuclear or electronic configuration, or if they have different numbers of unpaired electrons), then all the matrix elements of the types H_{AB} and S_{AB} (cf. Section 9·16) are equal to zero except when the two subscripts A and B are identical. Under such circumstances, there is no resonance; the molecule can have either structure alone, with no contribution from the other.
2. If the pendulums are coupled, then the coefficients c_{jk} do not in general vanish when j and k are different; hence, resonance must take place. Under such	2. If conditions 1, 2, and 3 are satisfied, then the matrix elements of the types H_{AB} and S_{AB} do not in general vanish when A and B are different; hence, there

[30] The following discussion is an extension and elaboration of one given by C. K. Ingold, *Nature* **141**, 314 (1938).

CLASSICAL SYSTEM

QUANTUM-MECHANICAL SYSTEM

circumstances, neither pendulum can oscillate alone, but the two must oscillate simultaneously. The following situations can arise.

must be resonance. Under such circumstances, the molecule can have neither limiting structure alone, but must have one of intermediate type. The following situations can arise.

i. If one pendulum is started oscillating while the other is left stationary, it soon

i. If, by some method, it were possible to force the molecule into one of the

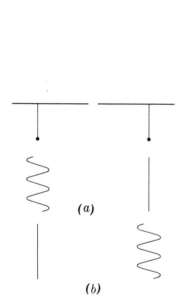

Fig. 9·7. Independent oscillations of two equivalent uncoupled pendulums.

Fig. 9·8. Different types of simultaneous oscillation of two equivalent coupled pendulums. In order that the curves may be more illuminating, the coupling has been made greater in parts *b* and *c* of this figure than in part *a*.

comes to rest while the other commences to oscillate, and then the process reverses as described on page 621. The interchange of motion from one pendulum to the other and back again continues indefinitely (aside from the damping due to friction). This situation is illustrated in Figure 9·8*a*. Such a state of motion, however, does not correspond to any one

limiting structures, it would rapidly go over into the other, and back again as described on pages 609f. (It need hardly be mentioned that this is a purely imaginary experiment, since there is no known method by which a molecule can be forced into a particular structure of the present type.) Such a state of the molecule, however, does not correspond to any of

CLASSICAL SYSTEM

of the normal modes of the system. This means that it has no definite and unique frequency. It is, accordingly, not analogous to any quantum-mechanical phenomenon of interest to us. (Nevertheless, the analogy to this type of motion has sometimes been made in qualitative discussions of resonance. Such comparison would be correct only if quantum-mechanical resonance were a form of tautomerism.)

ii. The analogy that is of interest is to the normal modes of oscillation that arise from the resonance of the two pendulums. There are two of these modes. In either one, the two pendulums oscillate with the same frequency and with the same constant amplitude; in one mode, the two pendulums are exactly in phase, and in the other they are exactly out of phase. These two types of motion are discussed on pages 620f, and they are illustrated in Figures 9·8b and 9·8c, respectively. Of these two modes of oscillation, the first has a lower, and the second has a higher frequency than the uncoupled pendulums. (In practice, these normal modes of oscillation are usually more difficult to produce experimentally than are the mathematically more complex motions of the type referred to above in paragraph A2i.) Under exceptional conditions, the frequency of one of the normal modes may be identical with that of one of the uncoupled pendulums. This same situation may occur also in the cases discussed below in paragraphs B and C.

QUANTUM-MECHANICAL SYSTEM

the stationary states. This means that it does not have any definite and unique energy. Since, as chemists, we are concerned only with molecules that are in states of definite energy, this state, although a conceivable one, is of no interest to us.

ii. The analogs of the normal modes of oscillation are the stationary states of the molecule, which result from the resonance between the two structures. There are two of these. In each, the molecule has a definite energy, and the two structures make equal, constant contributions. (Cf., for example, equations 9 and 10, Section 9·17.) There is also an analogy to the different phase relations of the two pendulums in their normal modes of oscillation; for, in equation 9, the functions Θ_A and Θ_B enter with the same sign, whereas, in equation 10, they enter with opposite signs. Of the two stationary states, one has a lower, and the other has a higher energy than either of the individual structures alone. The stationary state of lower energy is the normal (electronic) state, possessed by the molecule at ordinary temperatures; the stationary state of higher energy is an (electronically) excited one, transition to which gives rise to an absorption band in the visible or ultraviolet spectrum. Since we are usually interested only in molecules in their normal states, we shall consider that resonance always results in a lowering in energy. (In contrast with the classical system, the stationary states of the molecule are usually the only states that can be produced experimentally.) Under exceptional conditions, the energy of one of the stationary states may be identical with that of one of the contributing structures. This same situation may occur also in the cases discussed below in paragraphs B and C.

CLASSICAL SYSTEM

3. The type of motion described in paragraph A2i is a superposition, with equal amplitudes, of the two normal modes described in paragraph A2ii. When the oscillation is of this composite type, the frequency with which the motion changes from one pendulum to the other is equal to the difference between the frequencies of the two normal modes. (The alternate motion of the two pendulums is an illustration of the phenomenon of "beats." These beats are due to the "interference" of the two normal modes of oscillation that are excited simultaneously in the same set of pendulums, just as the more familiar acoustical beats are due to the interference of sound waves that are excited simultaneously in the same medium, namely, the air. The relation between the two systems is apparent when it is recalled that, in the acoustical case, the individual molecules in the air, like the bobs of the pendulums, are vibrating about more or less fixed positions of equilibrium.)

QUANTUM-MECHANICAL SYSTEM

3. The state of the molecule described in paragraph A2i is a superposition, with equal weights, of the two stationary states described in paragraph A2ii. (For further discussion of what precisely is meant by a superposition of two states, see Section 9·17.) When the molecule is in such a composite state, the frequency with which it changes from one structure to the other is equal to $1/h$ times the difference in energy between the two stationary states.

The usual statement that this frequency is equal to $1/h$ times the *resonance energy* (see Chapter 3) is correct only if all three of the following conditions are satisfied: (*a*) The two structures that contribute to the hybrid must be of equal energy. This condition is satisfied in benzene, for example, but not in butadiene. (*b*) The wave functions for the two structures must be mutually orthogonal. This condition, however, is practically never satisfied in any molecule. In particular, it is not satisfied in either benzene or butadiene. (*c*) The frequency must be defined as *one-half* the reciprocal of the time required for the molecule to return to its original structure. The factor of one-half arises from a consideration of the phases referred to in paragraph A2ii; since these phases are of no experimental significance in the present connection, however, the factor of one-half seems illogical and no corresponding factor has been introduced in the preceding discussion.

B. We shall now consider what modifications have to be made if the two pendulums are of different frequency.

1. If the pendulums are not coupled, then resonance does not occur, and either pendulum can oscillate alone, as before, with its own natural frequency. The independent motions are of the types illustrated in Figures 9·9*a* and 9·9*b*.

2. If the pendulums are coupled, then resonance occurs. There again result two normal modes of oscillation, of which one has a lower, and the other has a higher frequency than either of the uncoupled pendulums. In the normal mode

B. We shall now consider what modifications have to be made if the two structures are of different energy.

1. If conditions 1, 2, and 3 are not satisfied, then there is no resonance, and the molecule can have either limiting structure, as before, with its own normal energy.

2. If the conditions for resonance are satisfied, then there must be resonance, and the molecule must have an intermediate structure. There again result two stationary states of the molecule, of which one has a lower, and the other has

CLASSICAL SYSTEM

of lower frequency, the pendulum which itself has the lower frequency when uncoupled oscillates with a greater amplitude than the other; in the normal mode of higher frequency, the opposite is true. These two types of motion are illustrated in Figures 9·10a and 9·10b. In both cases, as the difference between the frequencies of the uncoupled pendulums

QUANTUM-MECHANICAL SYSTEM

a higher energy than either structure alone. As before, the state of lower energy is the normal one with which we shall be concerned, and the state of higher energy is an excited one of spectroscopic interest. In the stationary state of lower energy, the structure which itself has the lower energy when considered alone makes the larger contribution to the state of the

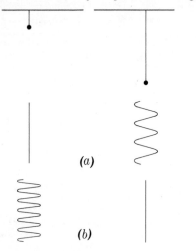

(a)

(b)

(a)

(b)

Fig. 9·9. Independent oscillations of two nonequivalent uncoupled pendulums.

Fig. 9·10. Different types of simultaneous oscillation of two nonequivalent coupled pendulums.

increases, the resonance becomes of less importance; that is to say, the motion becomes more nearly that of one pendulum alone, and the frequency becomes more nearly equal to that of the appropriate uncoupled pendulum.

molecule; in the stationary state of higher energy, the opposite is true. In both cases, as the difference in energy of the limiting structures increases, the resonance becomes of less importance. That is to say, the actual structure becomes more nearly identical with one of the limiting structures, and the energy becomes more nearly equal to that of the appropriate limiting structure.

C. Systems which consist of more than two coupled pendulums behave in an entirely similar manner. If there are altogether p pendulums, the resonance results in p normal modes of oscillation, of which at least one has a lower, and at least one has a higher frequency than

C. Molecules which are hybrids of more than two structures can be described in an entirely similar way. If there are altogether p structures, resonance among them results in p stationary states of the molecule, of which at least one has a lower, and at least one has a higher energy than

CLASSICAL SYSTEM

any of the uncoupled pendulums. In the mode of lowest frequency, all pendulums are ordinarily in motion (with constant amplitudes), but those which have the lowest frequencies when uncoupled oscillate with the greatest amplitudes. (Exceptions to this last generalization are possible here under conditions analogous to those considered in the last paragraph of Section 9·16.) It is not generally true, however, that pendulums which have identical frequencies when uncoupled must have exactly the same amplitudes when coupled (unless they are coupled in equivalent ways to all the remaining pendulums).

D. 1. To be strictly accurate, we would have to recognize that it is impossible for pendulums to be completely uncoupled, because, in the last analysis, they must have a common support, namely, the earth. In practice, however, the coupling can be made vanishingly small. In the particular case of two equivalent pendulums, the difference in frequency between the two normal modes can, therefore, also be made vanishingly small. As a result, in the composite motion of paragraph A2i, the length of time required for the motion to pass from one pendulum to the other and back again can be made very great, say a million years. Obviously, such a situation is of only mathematical interest and has no physical significance; it would be impossible to isolate the system so completely that the fortuitous disturbance of the motion by the environment would not completely obscure the effects of the resonance.

QUANTUM-MECHANICAL SYSTEM

any of the limiting structures alone. In the state of lowest energy, all the structures ordinarily contribute (and their contributions, if any, do not vary with the time), but those structures which have the lowest energies when considered separately have the largest weights in the most stable hybrid. (However, see the last paragraph of Section 9·16 and also pages 23f and 639.) It is not generally true, however, that structures which have identical energies when considered alone must make exactly the same contribution to the state of the molecule (unless they are equivalent in all respects).

D. 1. To be strictly accurate, we would have to recognize that it is impossible to prevent resonance completely, no matter how seriously the conditions 1, 2, and 3 are violated (except under certain special circumstances, which are too technical to be described here, but which would probably never arise in any actual molecule of interest to us). In practice, however, the effects of the resonance are often vanishingly small. In the particular case of resonance between two structures of the same energy, the difference in energy between the two stationary states can, therefore, also be made vanishingly small. As a result, in the composite state of paragraph A2i, the length of time required for the molecule to go from one structure to the other and back again can be made very great, say a million years. Obviously, such a situation is of only mathematical interest and has no physical significance; it would be impossible to isolate the molecule so completely that the fortuitous disturbance of its state by the environment would not completely obscure the effects of the resonance. In such an extreme case, it is not profitable to speak of resonance at all, but rather of isomerism or tautomerism between two forms that are possibly capable of isolation. (It should perhaps be mentioned here that the observed transitions between isomers or tautomerides, such as between the (+)- and (−)-forms of lactic acid or between the keto and enol

CLASSICAL SYSTEM

QUANTUM-MECHANICAL SYSTEM

forms of acetoacetic ester, are not due to the effect described above, but are rather the results of chemical reactions of familiar type.) The present situation is of the sort discussed more fully in Section 1.4 and illustrated in Figure 1.1 of that section. It is to be noted, however, that the point of view adopted here is quite independent of that employed in the concluding paragraph of part 1 of Section 1.4, in fine print. There, the discussion was of resonance between two structures, one unstrained and the other strained, with the same geometrical arrangement of the nuclei; here, it is of resonance between two structures, both unstrained, with widely different arrangements of the nuclei or electrons, or with different numbers of unpaired electrons.

2. It is possible also to have intermediate cases in which the coupling is very small, but not so extremely small as in the example considered in paragraph D1. The difference between the frequencies of the two normal modes of motion in a system composed of two equivalent pendulums can then be small but nevertheless observable. Two experimental possibilities require consideration.

2. It is possible also to have intermediate cases, in which the conditions 1, 2, and 3 are violated but not to so great an extent as in the example considered in paragraph D1. The difference between the energies of the two stationary states resulting from resonance between two structures of the same energy can then be small, but nevertheless observable. The situation under such circumstances would be that illustrated in Figure 1.3, Section 1.4. Two experimental possibilities require consideration.

i. If we are interested in determining which of the pendulums is oscillating, but are content to let the frequency of motion remain somewhat uncertain, we may find it advantageous to excite the composite motion of paragraph A2i. The frequency with which the oscillation changes from one pendulum to the other and back again is then significant.

i. If we are interested in determining which of the structures the molecule possesses but are content to let the energy remain somewhat uncertain (for example, if the molecule is ammonia and we are measuring its dipole moment) we may be interested in the composite state of paragraph A2i. The frequency with which the molecule goes from one structure to the other and back again is then significant.

ii. If we are interested in obtaining an extremely precise value of the frequency of motion, we will have to put the system into one of its normal modes of oscillation. The frequency with which the motion changes from one pendulum to the other then has no meaning at all.

ii. If we are interested in obtaining an extremely precise value of the energy of the molecule (for example, if we are examining the spectrum of ammonia) we will be interested only in the stationary states. The frequency with which the molecule changes from one structure to the other then has no meaning at all.

3. The type of resonance described in paragraph D1 is analogous to no situation of chemical interest, and that described

3. The type of resonance described in paragraph D1 is of no chemical interest at all, and that described in paragraph D2

CLASSICAL SYSTEM	QUANTUM-MECHANICAL SYSTEM
in paragraph D2 is analogous to very few.	is only seldom encountered. Consequently, we can ordinarily assume that, in any practical application of the resonance theory, the situation is of the kind discussed in parts A, B, and C of this section, in which the conditions 1, 2, and 3 of Section 1.4 are satisfied, and to which Figure 1.2 of Section 1.4 applies. (However, see Section 2.8.)

Before concluding this discussion of the mechanical analogy, let us now briefly consider the following often misunderstood aspect of the relation between a system of p coupled pendulums and a resonance hybrid of p structures. The pendulums can always, of course, be supposed actually to exist; on the other hand, the structures must usually be thought of as merely so many intellectual constructions. This important difference between the pendulums and the structures does not, however, correspond to any significant defect in the analogy; for, when the analogy is correctly applied, the analogs of the individual contributing structures are seen to be, not the respective pendulums, but rather the *independent motions* of those pendulums. The nonexistence of any real molecule with a particular one of the structures is therefore paralleled, in the system of coupled pendulums, by the nonexistence of any real state of motion in which only a particular one of the pendulums oscillates. Nevertheless, the true structure of the molecule can be conveniently described as a superposition of the several simpler, but imaginary, contributing structures, just as the true motion of the system of pendulums can be described as a superposition of the several simpler, but no less imaginary, independent motions of the individual pendulums.

9·19   The Valence-Bond Calculation of the Resonance Energy of Benzene.   In the foregoing discussion, we have developed a method by which we could, in principle, calculate the total energy, and hence also the resonance energy, of any molecule. If, however, we should attempt to apply this method to a specific example, we would find the mathematical difficulties to be extremely great. For this reason, all the calculations which have as yet been published for molecules more complex than that of hydrogen have involved further and still more drastic approximations. In this section, we shall consider only the earliest and crudest of the procedures which have been thus devised. The particular treatment which we shall briefly outline below is, in fact, so far from rigorous that we should probably describe it as an empirical one that is suggested by, rather than based on, quantum mechanics. (However, see pages 645ff.)

The molecule of benzene consists of twelve nuclei and forty-two electrons. Let us imagine that all the nuclei lie in the xy plane of a Cartesian coordinate system. The $1s$, $2s$, $2p_x$, and $2p_y$ orbitals of the six carbon atoms, and the $1s$ orbitals of the six hydrogen atoms, are then of the sigma type, which was defined on pages 587f; on the other hand, the $2p_z$ orbitals of the six carbon atoms are of the pi type, which was also defined there. As in our earlier discussion of furan, we shall here again assume that, on account of their difference in symmetry, the sigma orbitals and the sigma electrons can be treated separately from the pi orbitals and the pi electrons. Although this assumption may seem somewhat arbitrary, we shall later (cf. Section 9·24) find that, in the molecular-orbital treatment of any planar molecule, the corresponding assumption is both logical and necessary.

We shall consider that the electrons which occupy the $1s$ orbitals of the carbon atoms are taken into account by adjustment of the parameter Z which, in equations 7–11, Section 9·6, represents the atomic number; in other words, in the carbon L-shell orbitals, this parameter is taken to be not the true atomic number but a quantity which has been varied in such a way as to give the best possible resulting wave function for the molecule as a whole. We shall further consider that the electrons which occupy the carbon $2s$, $2p_x$, and $2p_y$ orbitals, and the ones which occupy the hydrogen $1s$ orbitals, are engaged in the formation of bonds or, more precisely, of sigma bonds. By such bonds, each carbon atom is *singly* linked to its adjacent hydrogen atom and to each of its two neighbors in the ring. In other words, the thirty-six sigma electrons give rise to that part of the complete structure which is represented by the symbol I, in which each bond is specifically a single bond. We shall take this framework, I, which refers to an ion with a charge of $+6$, as our starting

I

point for all subsequent calculations; hence, we need hereafter to consider only the way in which the true structure of benzene differs from I.

We have now accounted for thirty-six of the forty-two electrons, and we have employed all the sigma orbitals in the K- and L-shells. We have left, therefore, only six electrons and only the six different $2p_z$ orbitals on the carbon atoms. In accordance with the method described in Section 9·13, we now assign one of the remaining electrons to each of the remaining orbitals, and then we set up approximate wave functions to represent all the members of a complete set of independent structures. If the six pi orbitals are designated as a, b, · · ·, f, the five canonical structures, i.e., the ones without crossing bonds (see page 600), assume the forms II–VI, in which the sigma bonds are not explicitly represented. The first two of these diagrams correspond to the two equivalent Kekulé structures, whereas the last three correspond to the three equivalent Dewar structures.

$$
\begin{array}{ccccc}
e\!\!-\!\!f\quad a & e\quad f\!\!-\!\!a & e\!\!-\!\!f\quad a & e\quad f\quad a & e\quad f\!\!-\!\!a \\
|\quad | & |\quad | & \;\cdots\;\quad & |\quad : & \;\cdots\;\quad \\
d\!\!\diagdown_c\; b & d\quad _c\!\!-\!\!b & d\cdot\cdot\;\; _c\!\!-\!\!b & d\quad \dot{c}\quad b & d\!\!\diagdown_c\;\cdot\cdot b \\
\text{II} & \text{III} & \text{IV} & \text{V} & \text{VI}
\end{array}
$$

In the Dewar structures, IV–VI, the bonds linking diagonally opposite orbitals are twice as long as the others, and so they are *formal* bonds (see Section 1·4); they are, accordingly, written as dotted lines. The respective wave functions Θ_{IV}–Θ_{VI}, which represent these structures, are set up as if the diagonal bonds were exactly like the *effective* ones between adjacent orbitals. The difference between a formal bond and an effective one has no influence upon the treatment at this stage, although it will have to be taken into account later (see page 632).

The Claus structure VII and the Ladenburg structure VIII have crossing bonds and so, since they are therefore not independent of the Kekulé and Dewar structures, need not be considered. It can be shown that

$$\Theta_{VII}/N_{VII} = -\,\Theta_{II}/N_{II} - \Theta_{III}/N_{III} + \Theta_{IV}/N_{IV} + \Theta_{V}/N_{V} + \Theta_{VI}'/N_{VI}$$

and $$\Theta_{VIII}/N_{VIII} = \Theta_{II}/N_{II} + \Theta_{III}/N_{III} - \Theta_{IV}/N_{IV} - \Theta_{VI}/N_{VI}$$

$$
\begin{array}{ccc}
e\;\cdot\;f\;\;a & e\cdots f\cdots a & e\!\!\diagdown\! f\!\!\diagup\! a \\
d\cdot\cdot\;\vdots\;\cdot\cdot b & d\cdots\vdots\cdots b & d\!\!\diagup\!|\!\!\diagdown\! b \\
\dot{c} & \dot{c} & c \\
\text{VII} & \text{VIII} & \text{IX}
\end{array}
$$

The Armstrong-Baeyer structure IX, on the other hand, is essentially undefined, and so there is no way in which we can write a wave function to represent it. This structure also can therefore be ignored.

The next step in the calculation is to express the variation function in the form

$$\Phi = k_{II}\Theta_{II} + k_{III}\Theta_{III} + \cdots + k_{VI}\Theta_{VI} = \sum_{G=II}^{VI} k_G\Theta_G \qquad (1)$$

and then to set up the corresponding secular equation. Since each function Θ_G is itself a linear combination of a great many terms, each matrix element H_{GF} or S_{GF} must be a combination of an even greater number of terms. It can, however, be shown that, if the atomic orbitals $a, b, \cdots, f$ are orthogonal to one another, the only nonvanishing integrals which appear in the expressions for H_{GF} and S_{GF} are the *coulomb integral*

$$Q \equiv \int a(1)b(2)c(3)d(4)e(5)f(6)\mathbf{H}a(1)b(2)c(3)d(4)e(5)f(6)\,dv \qquad (2)$$

the several different *single-exchange integrals* of the energy, of which a typical example is

$$J_{bc} \equiv \int a(1)b(2)c(3)d(4)e(5)f(6)\mathbf{H}a(1)c(2)b(3)d(4)e(5)f(6) \, dv \qquad (3)$$

and the *normalization integral*

$$\int a^2(1)b^2(2)c^2(3)d^2(4)e^2(5)f^2(6) \, dv = 1 \qquad (4)$$

The coulomb and single-exchange integrals of the energy resemble each other in that the Hamiltonian operator $\mathbf{H}$ appears in the integrand of each. They differ, however, in the following respect. In Q, if the electronic coordinates 1, 2, $\cdots$, 6 are arranged in numerical order on both the left and the right sides of the operator $\mathbf{H}$, then the orbitals a, b, $\cdots$, f are arranged in alphabetical order on both sides of $\mathbf{H}$. In J_{bc}, on the other hand, if the electronic coordinates are arranged as before, the orbitals now come in alphabetical order only on the left, and not on the right, side of $\mathbf{H}$. More specifically, the order at the right differs from the alphabetical one by the single interchange of b and c. The remaining single exchange integrals, such as J_{ab}, J_{ac}, J_{cf}, etc., are defined in completely analogous ways.

Although the orbitals a, b, $\cdots$, f are not actually orthogonal to each other, we shall assume that we can ignore all integrals except the ones just discussed. This assumption is an extremely drastic one and no rigorous justification for it can be given. (However, see pages 645ff.) The integrals which we thus ignore are probably, to be sure, rather smaller in magnitude than the other ones which we retain. There are, however, an enormous number of the former integrals, and, even though some of them are positive and some are negative, we can have no assurance that their net effect is negligible. We shall, nevertheless, make the assumption in question because, without it, the calculation would become impracticably complicated, and because, with it, surprisingly satisfactory results can be obtained.

As a further approximation, we shall assume also that we can ignore even those single-exchange integrals which, like J_{ac}, J_{be}, etc., involve interchanges of nonadjacent orbitals. This assumption is much less questionable than the one described in the preceding paragraph, since these neglected exchange integrals are undoubtedly much smaller in magnitude, and not tremendously more numerous, than the ones which involve interchanges of adjacent orbitals. It is just here that the distinction is made between, on the one hand, the effective bonds which link adjacent atoms and, on the other hand, the formal bonds which are drawn between nonadjacent atoms.

Since we are considering resonance among altogether five structures, the secular determinant has five rows and five columns. With the approximations described above, each of the matrix elements H_{GF} is a linear combination of only the coulomb integral Q and the *adjacent* single-exchange integrals $J_{ab}, J_{bc}, \cdots, J_{fa}$. On account of the symmetry of the benzene molecule, it is evident that all six of these latter integrals must be equal; for simplicity, we shall represent their common value by the letter J. Furthermore, each of the remaining matrix elements S_{GF} is simply a numerical constant. Consequently, in order to evaluate any given element $H_{GF} - S_{GF}E$ of the secular determinant, we need only to determine the corresponding values of the coefficients of Q, J, and E. The following simple procedure,[31] the derivation of which is, however, too complicated to be given here, has been devised for the calculation of these coefficients. The first step is to construct the *superposition pattern* for the two structures G and F, that are involved in the term of interest, $H_{GF} - S_{GF}E$. This pattern consists merely of the two structures, drawn so that each lies on top of the other. For example, by the superposition of structure II upon itself, we obtain diagram X; by the superposition of structure II upon structure III, we obtain diagram XI; and by the superposition of structures IV and V, we obtain diagram XII. (In the last of these three diagrams, all bonds, and not merely the effective ones, are represented by full lines; this procedure is here adopted only in order that the diagrams may be more easily interpreted.) Each of these superposition patterns consists of a definite number p of polygons or, in Pauling's notation,[31] islands. Thus, in the diagrams X, XI, and XII, the

respective values of p are 3, 1, and 1. As is shown in these examples, a polygon may be a "digon," with only two sides, as in diagram X; or it may have sides which cross each other, as in diagram XII. In the latter event, any uncertainty regarding the exact number of polygons is removed by the requirement that there be an orbital (or, more precisely, the symbol that represents an orbital) at each corner of each polygon. For this reason, the point at the center of the ring in diagram XII is not, as it might appear to be, a corner of two different polygons; consequently, there is here only a single polygon.

In the term $H_{GF} - S_{GF}E$, Q and E appear only in the combination

[31] L. Pauling, *J. Chem. Phys.* **1**, 280 (1933). For a different method which provides the same values, see H. Eyring and G. E. Kimball, *ibid.* **1**, 239, 626 (1933).

$2^{p-t}(Q - E)$, where p has the value just defined, and t is equal to the total number of bonds, both effective and formal, in each of the structures G and F. The coefficient of the exchange integral J_{uv} between any two orbitals u and v is equal to $2^{p-t}r_{uv}$ where r_{uv} is equal to $-\frac{1}{2}$ if the orbitals u and v are in different polygons; to $+1$ if the orbitals u and v are in the same polygon and are separated by an odd number of bonds; and to -2 if the orbitals u and v are in the same polygon and are separated by an even number of bonds. For example, in the term $H_{\text{II II}} - S_{\text{II II}}E$, we see from diagram X that, since $p = t = 3$, the coefficient of $Q - E$ is equal to 2^{3-3}, or 1. Similarly, since the orbitals a and f are in different polygons in diagram X, we see also that the coefficient of J_{af} is equal to $2^{3-3}(-\frac{1}{2})$, or $-\frac{1}{2}$; and that the coefficient of J_{ab} is equal to $2^{3-3}(1)$, or 1. In each of the terms $H_{\text{II III}} - S_{\text{II III}}E$ and $H_{\text{IV V}} - S_{\text{IV V}}E$, the coefficient of $Q - E$ is equal to 2^{1-3}, or $\frac{1}{4}$; the coefficient of J_{ab} and of J_{af} is $2^{1-3}(1)$, or $\frac{1}{4}$; and the coefficient of J_{ac} (an integral which we are going to ignore) is equal to $2^{1-3}(-2)$, or $-\frac{1}{2}$. In this same way, but in greater detail, we find from the diagrams X, XI, and XII that

$$H_{\text{II II}} - S_{\text{II II}}E = Q - E + (J_{ab} + J_{cd} + J_{ef}) - \tfrac{1}{2}(J_{bc} + J_{de} + J_{fa})$$
$$= Q - E + \tfrac{3}{2}J$$

$$H_{\text{II III}} - S_{\text{II III}}E = \tfrac{1}{4}(Q - E) + \tfrac{1}{4}(J_{ab} + J_{bc} + J_{cd} + J_{de} + J_{ef} + J_{fa})$$
$$= \tfrac{1}{4}(Q - E) + \tfrac{3}{2}J$$

and $H_{\text{IV V}} - S_{\text{IV V}}E = \tfrac{1}{4}(Q - E) + \tfrac{1}{4}(J_{ab} + J_{bc} + J_{cd} + J_{de} + J_{ef} + J_{fa})$
$$= \tfrac{1}{4}(Q - E) + \tfrac{3}{2}J$$

Since the superposition of any structure G upon a different one F gives the same pattern as the superposition of the structure F upon the structure G, it is evident that, as was mentioned on page 585, $H_{GF} = H_{FG}$ and $S_{GF} = S_{FG}$.

The complete secular equation for benzene, when derived in the way illustrated above, can be written as

$$\begin{vmatrix} x + \tfrac{3}{2} & \tfrac{1}{4}x + \tfrac{3}{2} & \tfrac{1}{2}x + \tfrac{3}{2} & \tfrac{1}{2}x + \tfrac{3}{2} & \tfrac{1}{2}x + \tfrac{3}{2} \\ \tfrac{1}{4}x + \tfrac{3}{2} & x + \tfrac{3}{2} & \tfrac{1}{2}x + \tfrac{3}{2} & \tfrac{1}{2}x + \tfrac{3}{2} & \tfrac{1}{2}x + \tfrac{3}{2} \\ \tfrac{1}{2}x + \tfrac{3}{2} & \tfrac{1}{2}x + \tfrac{3}{2} & x & \tfrac{1}{4}x + \tfrac{3}{2} & \tfrac{1}{4}x + \tfrac{3}{2} \\ \tfrac{1}{2}x + \tfrac{3}{2} & \tfrac{1}{2}x + \tfrac{3}{2} & \tfrac{1}{4}x + \tfrac{3}{2} & x & \tfrac{1}{4}x + \tfrac{3}{2} \\ \tfrac{1}{2}x + \tfrac{3}{2} & \tfrac{1}{2}x + \tfrac{3}{2} & \tfrac{1}{4}x + \tfrac{3}{2} & \tfrac{1}{4}x + \tfrac{3}{2} & x \end{vmatrix} = 0 \qquad (5)$$

where $$x \equiv \frac{Q - E}{J} \qquad (6)$$

so that $$E = Q - xJ \qquad (7)$$

Solution of equation 5 by straightforward algebra would be extremely tedious since expansion of the determinant would lead to 5!, or 120, terms, each of which is itself the product of five factors. Fortunately, however, the high symmetry of the benzene molecule makes possible an extensive factorization of the determinant. The group-theoretical principles which are involved in this factorization need not here be discussed; we shall instead merely state the results without indicating their derivation.[32] Let us replace the functions Θ_{II}, Θ_{III}, $\cdots$, Θ_{VI} by their five independent linear combinations

$$
\begin{aligned}
\Lambda_1 &= \Theta_{II} + \Theta_{III} \\
\Lambda_2 &= \Theta_{IV} + \Theta_V + \Theta_{VI} \\
\Lambda_3 &= \Theta_{II} - \Theta_{III} \\
\Lambda_4 &= \Theta_{IV} - \Theta_V \\
\Lambda_5 &= 2\Theta_{III} - \Theta_{IV} - \Theta_V
\end{aligned}
$$

and let us express the variation function as

$$
\Phi = \sum_{j=1}^{5} k_j \Lambda_j
$$

The new secular equation then, as is immediately verified when the indicated substitutions are performed, assumes the form

$$
\begin{vmatrix}
\frac{5}{2}x + 6 & 3x + 9 & 0 & 0 & 0 \\
3x + 9 & \frac{9}{2}x + 9 & 0 & 0 & 0 \\
0 & 0 & \frac{3}{2}x & 0 & 0 \\
0 & 0 & 0 & \frac{3}{2}x - 3 & 0 \\
0 & 0 & 0 & 0 & \frac{3}{2}x - 3
\end{vmatrix} = 0 \qquad (8)
$$

so that it automatically factors into one quadratic factor

$$
\begin{vmatrix}
\frac{5}{2}x + 6 & 3x + 9 \\
3x + 9 & \frac{9}{2}x + 9
\end{vmatrix} = \frac{9}{4}(x^2 - 2x - 12) = 0 \qquad (9)
$$

and three linear factors

$$
\left| \tfrac{3}{2}x \right| = \tfrac{3}{2}x = 0
$$
$$
\left| \tfrac{3}{2}x - 3 \right| = \tfrac{3}{2}x - 3 = 0
$$
and
$$
\left| \tfrac{3}{2}x - 3 \right| = \tfrac{3}{2}x - 3 = 0
$$

[32] For additional details, see, for example, H. Eyring, J. Walter, and G. E. Kimball, *Quantum Chemistry*, John Wiley & Sons, New York, 1944, pp. 252ff.

The five roots, which can now be obtained without difficulty, are

$$x = -\sqrt{13} + 1, \sqrt{13} + 1, 0, 2, \text{ and } 2$$

Hence, $E = Q + 2.61J, Q - 4.61J, Q, Q - 2J, \text{ and } Q - 2J$

Since single-exchange integrals between nonorthogonal orbitals are usually found on numerical integration to be negative (however, see the following paragraph in fine print), the first of these roots is presumably the lowest one, corresponding to the ground state of the molecule.

An additional reason for assuming that J is negative is that, if J were positive, a more detailed calculation would find the ground state of the molecule to be not the above singlet level with energy $E = Q - 4.61J$ but instead a septet level with energy $E = Q - 6J$. In general, and not only with benzene, the calculation can never lead to a singlet ground state unless the single-exchange integrals are negative. This conclusion points up an awkward inconsistency in the present treatment since, if the orbitals $a, b, \cdot \cdot \cdot, f$ are orthogonal to each other, the single-exchange integrals can be shown to be necessarily positive.[33] Consequently, we must here admit that these orbitals are not actually orthogonal, even though on page 632 we essentially assumed that they are. As was mentioned earlier, therefore, the calculation does not have a firm quantum-mechanical basis but has only the empirical justification that it leads to satisfactory results. (However, see pages 645ff.)

The energy of the normal benzene molecule, to the present approximation, is equal to $Q + 2.61J$. On the other hand, if a molecule with the Kekulé structure II or III could exist, its energy would be equal to $H_{\text{II II}}/S_{\text{II II}}$ or $H_{\text{III III}}/S_{\text{III III}}$, and hence to $Q + 1.5J$ (see page 634). The calculated resonance energy is therefore

$$RE_{\text{calc}} = (Q + 1.5J) - (Q + 2.61J) = -1.11J$$

Since the observed resonance energy is about 36 kcal per mole (cf. Table 3·2, Section 3·2), we thus find that J must be equal to about -32 kcal per mole. Although this last value is of an entirely reasonable order of magnitude, it has not been confirmed by direct numerical calculation and, in fact, there is little reason for us to suppose that it can be so confirmed. For, in the above calculation, the value finally obtained for the integral J must automatically contain corrections for the many drastic approximations which have been introduced. These approximations include all the ones mentioned above, and, in addition, our failure to make any allowance for the differences between the carbon-carbon bond lengths in the (actually existing) resonance hybrid and in the (purely imaginary) Kekulé structures. Since we have thus ignored the compressional energy, the value of RE_{calc} that we have obtained applies strictly to the *vertical*

[33] Cf., for example, K. S. Pitzer, *Quantum Chemistry*, Prentice-Hall, New York, 1953, pp. 79 and 419.

resonance energy, and not to the *empirical* resonance energy with which we have just compared it (cf. Sections 3·7 and 3·8). Nevertheless, in spite of these difficulties and inconsistencies, we shall see in Section 9·20 that a considerable amount of evidence can be provided in support of the value here found for J.

The normalized approximate wave function for the benzene molecule in its ground state is found to be

$$\Phi = 0.37(\Theta_{II} + \Theta_{III}) + 0.16(\Theta_{IV} + \Theta_V + \Theta_{VI})$$

The coefficients of the Θ's that represent the Dewar structures IV–VI are therefore, as expected, rather smaller than are those of the ones that represent the Kekulé structures II and III. Hence, a fairly good wave function can still be obtained if the Dewar structures are ignored, so that Φ becomes (after normalization) simply

$$\Phi' = 0.63(\Theta_{II} + \Theta_{III})$$

The energy that corresponds to this more approximate wave function is $Q + 2.4J$ (cf. the element at the top left of the determinant in equation 9) and so, if the resonance were restricted to only the Kekulé structures, the resonance energy would be $0.9J$, or about 81 per cent of the total. Hence, we see that, in this respect as well, the Dewar structures have relatively little effect upon the properties of the substance. The common practice of ignoring these structures therefore receives considerable justification.[34]

9·20 Valence-Bond Calculations of the Resonance Energies of Other Aromatic Hydrocarbons. The method by which benzene was treated in Section 9·19 can be extended to the corresponding calculation for any other unsaturated or aromatic hydrocarbon that has a planar molecule. In every such further calculation, the framework that is formed by the sigma bonds between the sigma orbitals is again taken as the starting point so that, as with benzene, only the interactions of the pi electrons with one another remain to be considered. It is also again assumed that the only nonvanishing integrals which appear in the matrix elements H_{GF} and S_{GF} are the coulomb integral Q, the single-exchange integrals J_{uv} between adjacent orbitals u and v, and the normalization integral. The value of the coulomb integral Q doubtless varies from molecule to molecule but, since it always cancels in any calculation of resonance energy, we do not need to consider this variation. The several integrals J_{uv}, even though they are in general no longer required by the symmetry

---

[34] The foregoing treatment of benzene was first carried through, in a superficially quite different but nevertheless equivalent form, by E. Hückel, *Z. Physik* **70**, 204 (1931). It was subsequently put into the above, simpler form, by L. Pauling and G. W. Wheland, *J. Chem. Phys.* **1**, 362 (1933).

of the molecule to be equal to one another, are nevertheless assigned the common value of J within any given molecule. And finally, the same value of J is assumed to apply to all molecules.

Even with these great simplifications, the treatment of any molecule larger than that of benzene is likely to be extremely difficult, unless still additional approximations are made. With naphthalene, for example, there are ten pi electrons and hence $10!/5!6!$, or 42 independent singlet structures (cf. pages 599f). Consequently, the original secular determinant has forty-two rows and forty-two columns. Even when the secular equation is factored as completely as is permitted by the symmetry of the molecule, the simpler equations which are thus obtained are still of, respectively, the 16th, the 14th, the 6th, and the 6th degrees; and, unfortunately, the desired lowest root of the 42nd-degree equation appears only as a root of the particularly unmanageable 16th-degree factor. With the more complex molecules, anthracene and phenanthrene, the situation is much worse than it is with naphthalene since, for each of these substances, there are 429 independent structures; and the desired roots of the secular equations are to be found in factors which are of the 126th degree with anthracene, and of the 232nd degree with phenanthrene.

In spite of the complications just referred to, the secular equations for naphthalene,[35, 36, 37] anthracene,[37] and phenanthrene[37] have been set up in the approximate ways described above (however, see the paragraph below in fine print), and they have been rigorously solved. Their lowest roots are, respectively, $Q + 4.04J$, $Q + 5.45J$, and $Q + 5.52J$. Since the energies corresponding to the individual structures with the maximum numbers of double bonds are, respectively, $Q + 2.00J$, $Q + 2.50J$, and $Q + 2.50J$, the calculated resonance energies are, respectively, $-2.04J$, $-2.95J$, and $-3.02J$. If the empirical resonance energies are taken as 61, 84, and 92 kcal per mole, respectively (see Table 3·7, Section 3·3), the corresponding values of J are, respectively, -30, -28, and -31 kcal per mole. The agreement of these several values with one another and with that obtained with benzene (see Section 9·19) is much better than we would have had any right to expect. And, as is shown in Table 3·10, Section 3·8, the observed resonance energies for a considerable number of aromatic hydrocarbons can be fairly accurately predicted with the use of only a single value for J, -30 kcal per mole. This fact strongly suggests that, although the theoretical treatment is far from rigorous, the approximate constancy of J for the four hydrocarbons considered in this and the preceding sections is not purely accidental.

[35] J. Sherman, *J. Chem. Phys.* **2**, 488 (1934).
[36] C. Vroelant and R. Daudel, *Bull. soc. chim. France* **1949**, 36.
[37] M. B. Oakley and G. E. Kimball, *J. Chem. Phys.* **17**, 706 (1949).

Some features of the approximate wave functions found for naphthalene, anthracene, and phenanthrene are possibly unexpected, and for this reason deserve mention here. For naphthalene, the Erlenmeyer structure I and the two Erdmann structures II and III correspond to the same approximate energy, $Q + 2.00J$, and so we might expect the functions Θ_I, Θ_{II}, and Θ_{III} to have equal coefficients in the linear combination. (Here and below, for the sake of clarity, the carbon-carbon sigma bonds are explicitly represented in the structures that are drawn, although they are ignored in the approximate quantum-mechanical treatment.) Calculation shows, however, that the coefficients of Θ_{II} and Θ_{III}, although they are necessarily equal to each other because of the equivalence of the structures II and III, are only about 65 per cent as large as is that of

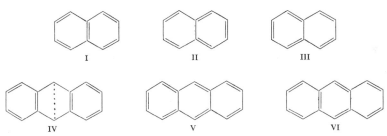

I   II   III

IV   V   VI

Θ_I.[35] Apparently, therefore, the nondiagonal elements of the secular determinant are such that an Erdmann structure is less effectively coupled with the forty-one remaining structures than is the Erlenmeyer structure (cf. page 608). In anthracene, the effect of the coupling is greater than it is in naphthalene, since the coefficient of the function Θ_{IV}, which represents structure IV with a formal bond, is actually larger than is that of the more stable function Θ_V, even though it is, as expected, smaller than is that of the likewise more stable function Θ_{VI}.[37]

In the above-mentioned calculations for anthracene and phenanthrene,[37] the procedure[38] which was adopted was somewhat different from, but completely equivalent to, the one described for benzene. In particular, the individual elements of the secular determinant that were set up were not of the form $H_{GF} - S_{GF}E$. However, the roots of the modified secular equations were identical with the ones which would have been obtained if the more usual procedure had instead been employed; and the corresponding approximate wave functions were likewise unaltered. Similarly, the calculations of Vroelant and Daudel[36] were based upon still a third superficially quite different, but actually equivalent, procedure.

Although rigorous solutions of the secular equations can thus be obtained for some rather complicated molecules, the labor that is required is very great. With still more complicated molecules, such as that of

[38] See G. W. Wheland, *J. Chem. Phys.* **3**, 230 (1935).

1,2-benzanthracene for which the original 4862nd-degree secular equation cannot be factored at all, rigorous solutions are quite impracticable. For this reason, several different types of approximate method have been devised. The tricks which have been used, either singly or in combination, for the simplification of the secular equations include: the neglect of all structures with formal bonds, or of all those with more than one formal bond; the use of the same coefficient for all the functions Θ_G which represent structures with the same number of formal bonds; the replacement of the correct values of the matrix elements H_{GF} and S_{GF} by estimated average values; and many others. In general, these different methods have been rather satisfactory.

One of the simplest of all these approximate methods, and apparently also one of the most accurate, does not require that any secular equation be set up at all. According to this method,[36] the derivation of which cannot be described here, the pi energy E of the molecule in its ground state is given approximately by the expression

$$E = Q - J\sum_j x_j \qquad (1)$$

where x_j is the negative root of the auxiliary equation

$$x_j^2 - n_j x_j - 1 = 0 \qquad (2)$$

and n_j is the number of unsaturated carbon atoms which, in the complete conjugated system, are adjacent to the two atoms that form the jth carbon-carbon bond. In equation 1, the summation over j includes all carbon-carbon bonds which are part of the conjugated system. (The approximate method based upon the use of these two equations is different from the rigorous one which was devised by the same authors,[36] and which was referred to in the above paragraph in fine print.) Solution of equation 2 shows that, when n_j is equal to 0, 1, 2, 3, or 4, x_j is equal to -1.0000, -0.6180, -0.4142, -0.3028, or -0.2363, respectively. The application of this particularly simple procedure can be illustrated with a few examples. In the molecule of benzene (or of toluene, or of any xylene, etc.), there are six bonds with $n_j = 2$ and hence with $x_j = -0.4142$; the approximate total energy is therefore $Q + 2.49J$, whereas rigorous solution of the secular equation gives an energy of $Q + 2.61J$. Similarly, in the molecule of naphthalene (or of any alkylnaphthalene), there are six bonds with $n_j = 2$ and $x_j = -0.4142$, four bonds with $n_j = 3$ and $x_j = -0.3028$, and one bond with $n_j = 4$ and $x_j = -0.2363$; the approximate total energy is therefore $Q + 3.93J$, whereas the rigorous solution[35, 36, 37] of the secular equation gives the energy of $Q + 4.04J$. Even for 1,2-benzanthracene, the calculation, which here leads to an approximate energy of $Q + 6.87J$, can be completed in a few minutes. Since for this hydrocarbon the energy of the most stable structure, i.e., of any structure without formal bonds, is seen by inspection to be $Q + 3.00J$, the calculated resonance energy is $-3.87J$, or about 116 kcal per mole. (Cf. also page 670 for a somewhat similar approximation that is based on the molecular-orbital treatment.)

Although the discussion has so far been limited to aromatic hydrocarbons, the same treatment can clearly be applied also to any other kind of unsaturated hydrocarbon which has, or can be assumed to have, a planar molecule. With simple conjugated olefins, however, the calculations are quantitatively less satisfactory than are the analogous ones for aromatic hydrocarbons. The reason for this difference is doubtless that, when the resonance energy is as small as it is in, say, 1,3-butadiene, the errors which are introduced by the several necessary approximations must become *relatively* very large. In particular, the neglect of the variations in the bond lengths, and the assumption that all the adjacent single-exchange integrals J_{uv} are equal, must under such circumstances be especially serious. Nevertheless, as is shown in Table 3·10, Section 3·8, fair agreement with the experimental resonance energies can still be obtained if the value of the integral J is now changed from -30 to -14 kcal per mole. It is, of course, not surprising that J must thus be assigned different values in the two classes of compound, for which the ratios of compressional energy to resonance energy must be quite different.

If the substance of interest has a nonplanar molecule, or if it is not a hydrocarbon, the various simplifications which were shown above to permit an approximate solution of the secular equation, are in general no longer possible. For such substances, therefore, no numerical calculations that are similar to the foregoing ones can be given. (Cf., however, Section 9·26.)

9·21 Some Extensions and Modifications of the Valence-Bond Treatment. In our discussion of the normal hydrogen molecule in Section 9·9, we assigned a single electron to each of the two hydrogen $1s$ orbitals, a and b. Thereby, we implicitly assumed that the molecule has the purely covalent structure I. The wave function

$$\Theta_{\mathrm{I}} = N_1[a(1)b(2) + b(1)a(2)][\alpha(1)\beta(2) - \beta(1)\alpha(2)] \tag{1}$$

which we finally derived for the representation of this structure (cf. equation 18, Section 9·9) was, however, only a rough first approximation to the correct solution of the Schrödinger equation. Consequently, we

H—H	: H⁻ H⁺	H⁺ H :⁻
I	II	III

can expect to obtain a somewhat better wave function if we consider the molecule to be a resonance hybrid of the covalent structure I and the two purely ionic structures II and III.   Thus, we set up the variation function

$$\Phi = k_I \Theta_I + k_{II} \Theta_{II} + k_{III} \Theta_{III}$$
$$= N[a(1)b(2) + b(1)a(2) + c_1 a(1)a(2) + c_2 b(1)b(2)][\alpha(1)\beta(2) - \beta(1)\alpha(2)]$$

(2)

and we determine the values of the constants c_1 and c_2 which minimize the calculated energy.   When this procedure is adopted, c_1 and c_2 are found to be exactly equal to each other, and approximately equal to $1/4$.[39]   In this way, the error in the calculated energy is reduced from 22 kcal per mole (cf. page 579) to about 17 kcal per mole.   As expected, therefore, the effects of the relatively unstable structures II and III upon the wave function and upon the energy are rather small, although not actually negligible.

Since the coefficients c_1 and c_2 are equal, the two ionic structures II and III make identical contributions to the state of the molecule.   Consequently, the effects of these structures upon the dipole moment of the resonance hybrid exactly cancel each other.   The calculated moment of the molecule is therefore still zero, just as it is when only structure I is taken into account.

With more complicated molecules, such as those of the aromatic hydrocarbons considered in Sections 9·19 and 9·20, the wave functions can doubtless be similarly improved by the inclusion of ionic structures in the resonance.   Benzene, for example, can be considered a hybrid of not only the Kekulé and Dewar structures, but also the twelve equivalent structures like IV, the six equivalent ones like V, and so on.   Here again,

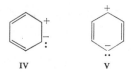

IV   V

the ionic structures should be relatively unstable, and so their effects upon the wave function and upon the properties of the molecule may be expected to be rather small.   The correctness of this expectation has not yet, however, been tested by an actual numerical calculation.

Ionic structures can be included in the resonance not only by the direct method just described but also by the following alternative procedure.[40]

[39] S. Weinbaum, *J. Chem. Phys.* **1**, 593 (1933).
[40] C. R. Mueller and H. Eyring, *J. Chem. Phys.* **19**, 1495 (1951).

For example, let us suppose that, in the hydrogen molecule, the orbitals a and b are polarized (i.e., distorted) by their mutual interactions in such a way that they are no longer spherically symmetric. Although there are a number of different ways in which this polarization might be mathematically represented, we shall here find it convenient to adopt the following procedure. Let us replace the original atomic orbitals a and b by the respective *semilocalized* orbitals

$$a' \equiv n(a + wb) \tag{3}$$

and
$$b' \equiv n(wa + b) \tag{4}$$

where n is a normalization constant and w is a small numerical factor. Now, if we set up a wave function Θ_I to represent a "purely covalent" bond between the orbitals a' and b', we obtain

$$\Theta_{I'} = N'[a'(1)b'(2) + b'(1)a'(2)][\alpha(1)\beta(2) - \beta(1)\alpha(2)]$$
$$= N'n^2\{(1 + w^2)[a(1)b(2) + b(1)a(2)] + 2w[a(1)a(2) + b(1)b(2)]\}$$
$$\cdot [\alpha(1)\beta(2) - \beta(1)\alpha(2)] \tag{5}$$

(Cf. equation 1.) This function, however, is identical with Φ of equation 2 if the variation parameters w, c_1, and c_2, and the normalization constants N, n, and N' are related by the equations

$$N = N'n^2(1 + w^2) \tag{6}$$

and
$$Nc_1 = Nc_2 = 2N'n^2w \tag{7}$$

Since, as was noted above, c_1 and c_2 are equal to each other, the conditions imposed by these equations can always be satisfied. Consequently, it follows that, even though we have not assigned two electrons to the same semilocalized orbital and hence have not *explicitly* introduced any ionic structures, we have nevertheless given the bond a partial ionic character by allowing the individual orbitals to be polarized. Hence, in order to include ionic as well as covalent structures in the resonance, we need only to change the definitions of the orbitals used, and we do not need to modify the formal procedure by which these orbitals are combined with each other in the "covalent" wave function for the molecule.

With a molecule that is more complicated than that of hydrogen, the ionic structures can again be implicitly included in the resonance if the individual orbitals are considered to be polarized, or semilocalized, in ways that are analogous to that illustrated in equations 3 and 4. This procedure is, however, less satisfactory here than it was in the simpler example since it ceases to be completely general when there are more than two orbitals. The number of parameters which can thus be introduced (cf. w, in the polarized orbitals a' and b') is in general so small that the coefficients of all the functions which represent the individual structures cannot be independently varied; this difficulty arises because the number of equations analogous to 6 and 7 becomes greater than the number of unknown quantities to be evaluated, so that a solution is possible only if there are relations among the unknowns. Even so, however, no better, but comparably simple, method for the inclusion of the ionic structures in the treatment of a complex molecule has as yet been discovered. We shall, therefore, find it convenient to imagine that, for example, the pi orbitals a, b, $\cdots$ which were used in Sections 9·19 and 9·20 are not centered about single atoms, but are instead spread over several adjacent atoms. The definitions of the integrals Q and J (cf. equations 2 and 3, Section 9·19) are then formally unchanged, although the symbols a, b, $\cdots$ which appear in the integrands must be reinterpreted; no further modification in the treatment is necessary. Clearly, in any numerical calculation which aspires to something like mathematical rigor, this method for dealing with the ionic structures offers no advantages over the previous, more direct one, since the two treatments require the evaluation of exactly the same integrals. On the other hand, in any calculation that is of the type described in Sections 9·19 and 9·20, where all the integrals that are not ignored or do not automatically cancel are estimated by comparison with empirical data, this alternative procedure is much the simpler of the two. Although, as was noted above, it does not introduce as many variation parameters as are required for complete generality, it does nevertheless introduce some such parameters, and so it should lead to some improvement in the resulting molecular wave function. Since even the best possible treatment would presumably find that the ionic structures have only small weights in the hybrid, and since therefore no really serious harm would be done if these structures were entirely ignored, the present rather crude treatment should be satisfactory.

One of the more serious disadvantages in the use of the semilocalized orbitals is that the errors arising from the nonorthogonality of the orbitals associated with different atoms (see page 636) are considerably increased. With the hydrogen molecule, for example, if the ratio of the coefficients of the purely ionic and of the purely covalent terms is set equal to $1/_4$,[39] then

$$\frac{2w}{1 + w^2} = \frac{1}{4}$$

(cf. equation 5), so that

$$w = 0.13$$

The (normalized) orbitals a' and b' thus become

$$a' = \frac{1}{\sqrt{1.0169 + 0.26S}} (a + 0.13b)$$

and

$$b' = \frac{1}{\sqrt{1.0169 + 0.26S}} (0.13a + b)$$

where

$$S = S_{ab} = \int ab \, dv$$

and

$$S_{aa} = S_{bb} = \int a^2 \, dv = \int b^2 \, dv = 1$$

Consequently,

$$S_{a'b'} = \frac{1}{1.0169 + 0.26S} \int (a + 0.13b)(0.13a + b) \, dv$$

$$= \frac{1}{1.0169 + 0.26S} (0.13 + S + 0.0169S + 0.13)$$

$$= \frac{0.26 + 1.0169S}{1.0169 + 0.26S}$$

If S_{ab}, which is identical with S, is equal to 0, $S_{a'b'}$ is therefore equal to 0.26; if S_{ab} is equal to 0.25, $S_{a'b'}$ is equal to 0.47; if S_{ab} is equal to 0.50, $S_{a'b'}$ is equal to 0.67. Always, $S_{a'b'}$ is considerably larger than S_{ab}, so that the neglect of the former integral is even less justified than is that of the latter. Moreover, since exactly similar difficulties are encountered also with all other, more complicated molecules, the general use of the semilocalized orbitals may be relatively unsatisfactory (however, see below).

By putting the valence-bond treatment upon a more frankly empirical basis, we can avoid some of the errors that arise from the above non-orthogonality of the atomic (or semilocalized) orbitals.[41] In order to bring out the essential features of the modified calculations, let us consider a valence-bond structure which we shall for the moment designate in general terms as A. (Specific examples illustrating the procedure will be given below.) Now, corresponding to this structure, we can set up an approximate wave function Θ_A in the way outlined in Sections 9·12 and

[41] G. W. Wheland, *J. Chem. Phys.* **23**, 79 (1955). For discussion of a quite different suggestion regarding these errors, see J. H. Van Vleck, *Phys. Rev.* **49**, 232 (1936).

9·13.   The energy associated with this structure, when calculated without the introduction of any *additional* approximations, can be expressed as

$$W_A = \frac{H_{AA}}{S_{AA}} = \frac{\int \Theta_A \mathbf{H} \Theta_A \, d\tau}{\int \Theta_A{}^2 \, d\tau}$$

$$= \frac{Q + \sum_{\substack{\text{bonding} \\ \text{in } A}} J_{rs} - \frac{1}{2} \sum_{\substack{\text{nonbond-} \\ \text{ing in } A}} J_{rs} + \begin{array}{c} \text{Higher exchange integrals} \\ \text{of the energy} \end{array}}{1 + \sum_{\substack{\text{bonding} \\ \text{in } A}} \Delta_{rs} - \frac{1}{2} \sum_{\substack{\text{nonbond-} \\ \text{ing in } A}} \Delta_{rs} + \begin{array}{c} \text{Higher exchange integrals} \\ \text{of unity} \end{array}} \tag{8}$$

where Q is the coulomb integral; J_{rs} is the single-exchange integral of the energy between the atomic (or semilocalized) orbitals r and s; Δ_{rs} is the corresponding single-exchange integral of unity, with the value $S_{rs}{}^2$ (see the following paragraph).   The first summation in both the numerator and the denominator of the fraction at the right of equation 8 is over all pairs of orbitals r and s which, in structure A are bonded to each other. The second summation is over all pairs of orbitals which, in structure A, are *not* bonded to each other.

The coulomb integral Q and the several single-exchange integrals of the energy J_{rs} were defined on pages 631f.   The single-exchange integrals of unity differ from the corresponding ones of the energy only in the absence of the Hamiltonian operator **H** from the integrands or, more precisely, in the replacement of this operator by the different one **1** (cf. page 585).   The "higher exchange integrals" of the energy and unity differ from the single-exchange integrals in being related to more complex permutations of the orbitals among the electrons.   (Since we shall not need to know the exact forms of these additional integrals, no more explicit definitions are here necessary.) In equation 8, and throughout the remainder of this section, the subscripts in such expressions as H_{AA}, J_{rs}, etc., refer to structures when they are capital letters, and to individual atomic or semilocalized orbitals when they are lower-case letters.

In the most approximate valence-bond treatment, equation 8 is simplified by the neglect of all higher exchange integrals of the energy and of all exchange integrals of unity.   This equation then becomes

$$W_A = Q - \frac{1}{2} \sum_{\substack{\text{nonbond-} \\ \text{ing in } A}} J_{rs} + \sum_{\substack{\text{bonding} \\ \text{in } A}} J_{rs}$$

$$= Q - \frac{1}{2} \sum_{\text{all}} J_{rs} + \frac{3}{2} \sum_{\substack{\text{bonding} \\ \text{in } A}} J_{rs} \tag{9}$$

Similarly, and with the same approximation, the energy associated with any different structure B is expressed as

$$W_B = Q - \tfrac{1}{2} \sum_{\substack{\text{nonbond-}\\\text{ing in } B}} J_{rs} + \sum_{\substack{\text{bonding}\\\text{in } B}} J_{rs}$$

$$= Q - \tfrac{1}{2} \sum_{\text{all}} J_{rs} + \tfrac{3}{2} \sum_{\substack{\text{bonding}\\\text{in } B}} J_{rs} \tag{10}$$

and so on for all further structures.

Although, for reasons which should now be clear, equations 9, 10, etc., cannot legitimately be expected to be even approximately correct, they are nevertheless of rather reasonable *form*. Indeed, the total energy associated with any given structure might be expected to be expressible as a sum of terms that belong to the two following types. In the first place, there are terms which depend upon the number and identities of the constituent atoms, and also upon their relative positions in space, but which are independent of the way in which these atoms are linked to one another by valence bonds. In the second place, there are terms that can be identified with the energies of the bonds that are present. When a molecule is a hybrid of several different structures $A, B, \cdot \cdot \cdot$, the terms of the first type have the same value for all the structures, whereas those of the second type vary from structure to structure. In equations 9, 10, and so on, Q and the summations of "all" exchange integrals clearly belong to the first group of terms; on the other hand, the final summations of "bonding" exchange integrals belong to the second group of terms.

Let us now, therefore, accept equations 9, 10, etc., as essentially correct, but with the understanding that Q and the several different quantities J_{rs} are purely empirical parameters that need have no close relation to the integrals with which they were originally identified. Since, however, the atomic (or semilocalized) orbitals associated with different atoms are, in general, not orthogonal to one another, we must no longer assume that the wave functions $\Theta_A, \Theta_B, \cdot \cdot \cdot$ are normalized (cf. the value of S_{AA} given in the denominator of equation 8). Consequently, if the energies of the structures $A, B, \cdot \cdot \cdot$ have the forms shown in equations 9, 10, $\cdot \cdot \cdot$, the diagonal matrix elements of the energy must be

$$H_{AA} = S_{AA} \left[Q - \tfrac{1}{2} \sum_{\text{all}} J_{rs} + \tfrac{3}{2} \sum_{\substack{\text{bonding}\\\text{in } A}} J_{rs} \right] \tag{11}$$

$$H_{BB} = S_{BB} \left[Q - \tfrac{1}{2} \sum_{\text{all}} J_{rs} + \tfrac{3}{2} \sum_{\substack{\text{bonding}\\\text{in } B}} J_{rs} \right] \tag{12}$$

and so on.

No such simple scheme can be used for the evaluation of the non-diagonal matrix elements of the type H_{AB}, with A not identical with B. In order to obtain these latter quantities, however, we can adopt a different procedure, which is most easily explained with reference to a specific example. Let us therefore consider the treatment of 1,3-butadiene, so that we can identify the structures A and B with VI and VII, respectively.

$$CH_2\!\!=\!\!CH\!-\!CH\!\!=\!\!CH_2 \qquad\qquad CH_2\!-\!CH\!\!=\!\!CH\!-\!CH_2$$

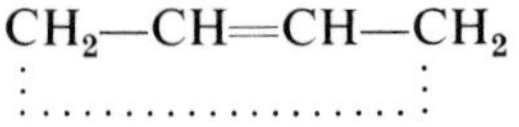

VI $\qquad\qquad\qquad\qquad\qquad\qquad$ VII

$$CH_2\!-\!CH\!-\!CH\!-\!CH_2$$

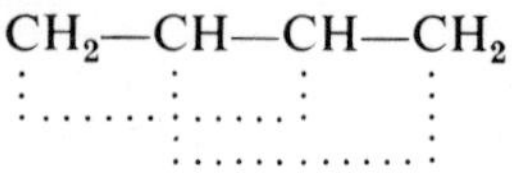

VIII

Moreover, for a reason which will immediately become apparent, we shall need also to define a further structure C, which we shall take as the noncanonical structure VIII, with crossing bonds. Now, by the same method that was used for the derivation of equation 15, Section 9·13, we can show that

$$\Theta_C = N_C(-\Theta_A/N_A + \Theta_B/N_B) \tag{13}$$

where N_A, N_B, and N_C enter the treatment as normalization constants. It is, however, more convenient to set these latter quantities equal to the values that they would have had if all the atomic orbitals were mutually orthogonal, and to allow for the fact that the functions Θ_A, Θ_B, and Θ_C are then not correctly normalized by admitting that the integrals S_{AA}, S_{BB}, and S_{CC} are not equal to 1. This procedure has, indeed, been implicitly adopted throughout the foregoing discussion, and it will be retained hereafter. The constants N_A, N_B, and N_C are then equal to each other and to $^1/_2$, so that equation 13 assumes the simpler form

$$\Theta_C = -\Theta_A + \Theta_B \tag{14}$$

(More generally, if a given structure R contains altogether t bonds, both effective and formal, the corresponding value of N_R is equal to $2^{-t/2}$.) From equation 14, we find that

$$H_{CC} = \int\Theta_C \mathbf{H}\Theta_C\, d\tau = \int(-\Theta_A + \Theta_B)\mathbf{H}(-\Theta_A + \Theta_B)\, d\tau$$

$$= H_{AA} - 2H_{AB} + H_{BB} \tag{15}$$

so that $\qquad H_{AB} = \tfrac{1}{2}(H_{AA} + H_{BB} - H_{CC}) \tag{16}$

Similarly, $\quad S_{AB} = \tfrac{1}{2}(S_{AA} + S_{BB} - S_{CC}) \tag{17}$

The secular equation is therefore

$$\begin{vmatrix} H_{AA} - S_{AA}E & H_{AB} - S_{AB}E \\ H_{AB} - S_{AB}E & H_{BB} - S_{BB}E \end{vmatrix}$$

$$= \begin{vmatrix} H_{AA} - S_{AA}E & \frac{1}{2}[(H_{AA} + H_{BB} - H_{CC}) - (S_{AA} + S_{BB} - S_{CC})E] \\ \frac{1}{2}[(H_{AA} + H_{BB} - H_{CC}) - (S_{AA} + S_{BB} - S_{CC})E] & H_{BB} - S_{BB}E \end{vmatrix}$$

$$= 0 \qquad (18)$$

Since H_{AA} and H_{BB} are given by equations 11 and 12, and since H_{CC} is given by a third, completely analogous equation

$$H_{CC} = S_{CC} \left[Q - \tfrac{1}{2} \sum_{\text{all}} J_{rs} + \tfrac{3}{2} \sum_{\substack{\text{bonding} \\ \text{in } C}} J_{rs} \right] \qquad (19)$$

all the terms in the secular equation can now, in principle, be obtained either from empirical data or from relatively simple calculations (see also below).

In order to proceed further, let us now divide the several atomic orbitals into two groups. The first of these groups consists of the orbitals which form the K-shells in the four carbon atoms, and also of those which are bonded to each other in exactly the same way in all three of the structures A, B, and C; the second group, on the other hand, consists of all the remaining orbitals, which are bonded to each other in different ways in the three stated structures. If the molecule is planar, the orbitals of the first group are the ones hitherto designated as sigma, whereas those of the second group are the ones hitherto designated as pi; even if the molecule is not planar, however, the distinction between the two classes of orbital still exists and so, for the sake of definiteness in terminology, we shall here retain the (possibly somewhat incorrect) expressions sigma and pi.

Let us now define a new parameter Q', which is equal to Q plus all those terms J_{rs} in equations 11, 12, and 19 that involve the interchange of a sigma orbital (in the sense just defined) with any other orbital. Of all the terms within the square brackets in these equations, therefore, the only ones that remain to be explicitly stated are then the ones involving interchanges of two different pi orbitals. For ease of reference, we can designate these pi orbitals, of which there is just one on each carbon atom, as a, b, c, and d in alphabetical order from left to right in the structures VI, VII, and VIII. Equations 11, 12, and 19 then become, respectively,

$$H_{AA} = S_{AA}[Q' - \tfrac{1}{2}J_{ac} - \tfrac{1}{2}J_{ad} - \tfrac{1}{2}J_{bc} - \tfrac{1}{2}J_{bd} + J_{ab} + J_{cd}] \qquad (20)$$

$$H_{BB} = S_{BB}[Q' - \tfrac{1}{2}J_{ab} - \tfrac{1}{2}J_{ac} - \tfrac{1}{2}J_{bd} - \tfrac{1}{2}J_{cd} + J_{ad} + J_{bc}] \qquad (21)$$

$$\text{and} \quad H_{CC} = S_{CC}[Q' - \tfrac{1}{2}J_{ab} - \tfrac{1}{2}J_{ad} - \tfrac{1}{2}J_{bc} - \tfrac{1}{2}J_{cd} + J_{ac} + J_{bd}] \qquad (22)$$

The quantity Q' has the same value in all three equations 20–22.

In order to simplify the calculation, let us assume that all carbon-carbon distances are equal, that

$$J_{ab} = J_{bc} = J_{cd} = J \qquad (23)$$

and that

$$J_{ac} = J_{ad} = J_{bd} = 0 \qquad (24)$$

(These assumptions are not necessary but, without them, the treatment would be more complicated.)   Then

$$H_{AA} = S_{AA}(Q' + \tfrac{3}{2}J) \qquad (25)$$

$$H_{BB} = S_{BB}Q' \qquad (26)$$

$$\text{and} \quad H_{CC} = S_{CC}(Q' - \tfrac{3}{2}J) \qquad (27)$$

$$\text{so that} \quad H_{AB} = \tfrac{1}{2}[S_{AA}(Q' + \tfrac{3}{2}J) + S_{BB}Q' - S_{CC}(Q' - \tfrac{3}{2}J)]$$

$$= S_{AB}Q' + (3J/4)(S_{AA} + S_{CC}) \qquad (28)$$

(See equations 16 and 17.)

In order to use these relations, we need values for the matrix elements S_{AA}, S_{BB}, etc.   First, let us consider the effect of adopting our earlier assumption that all exchange integrals of unity can be neglected, so that

$$S_{AA} = S_{BB} = S_{CC} = 1 \qquad (29)$$

Under these circumstances, combination of equations 18, 25, 26, 28, and 29 shows that the secular equation is

$$\begin{vmatrix} Q' + \tfrac{3}{2}J - E, & \tfrac{1}{2}Q' + \tfrac{3}{2}J - \tfrac{1}{2}E \\ \tfrac{1}{2}Q' + \tfrac{3}{2}J - \tfrac{1}{2}E, & Q' - E \end{vmatrix} = 0 \qquad (30)$$

with the roots

$$E = Q' + 1.73J, \qquad Q' - 1.73J$$

If the substance had the unique structure A, its energy would be

$$W_A = H_{AA} = Q' + 1.5J$$

so that the calculated resonance energy is

$$RE_{\text{calc}} = Q' + 1.5J - (Q' + 1.73J) = -0.23J \qquad (31)$$

Finally, the wave function for the hybrid in its ground state is found to be

$$\Phi = 0.82\Theta_A + 0.30\Theta_B \qquad (32)$$

These results are essentially identical with the ones which would have been obtained by the original procedure outlined in Sections 9·19 and 9·20. The only differences are, in fact, that we now have Q' where we formerly had Q, and that J is now frankly admitted to be a purely empirical parameter. The first of these differences, however, exists because the energy E that is here calculated is the total energy of the molecule, whereas the corresponding quantity in the original treatment was instead the energy associated with only the pi electrons; if, in Sections 9·19 and 9·20, we had been concerned with the total energies, we would there necessarily have introduced a quantity completely analogous to the present Q'. In any event, Q' cancels, just as Q does, in the calculated resonance energy RE_{calc}. The second of the two above differences is also not significant since it merely makes more explicit the unavoidably empirical character of either treatment.

We can now turn to a theoretically sounder procedure, in which we no longer assume orthogonality of the atomic orbitals. By direct integration,[42] S, which is equal to S_{ab}, S_{bc}, and S_{cd}, has been found to be approximately $1/4$ if a, b, c, and d are atomic, and not semilocalized, orbitals and if the distance between adjacent carbon nuclei is about 1.4 A. Consequently,

$$\Delta_{ab} = \Delta_{bc} = \Delta_{cd} = S^2 = \tfrac{1}{16}$$

and all other exchange integrals of unity are extremely small. If we therefore ignore all these remaining integrals, we find (cf. the denominator of the fraction in equation 8) that

$$S_{AA} = 1 + (3/2)(1/16) = 35/32 \qquad (33)$$

$$S_{BB} = 1 \qquad (34)$$

and $$S_{CC} = 1 - (3/2)(1/16) = 29/32 \qquad (35)$$

Unlike equation 29, these latter expressions for the matrix elements of unity are probably fairly accurate. By combining equations 18, 25, 26, 28, and 33–35 we finally obtain the secular equation

$$\begin{vmatrix} (35/32)Q'+(105/64)J-(35/32)E & (38/64)Q'+(192/128)J-(38/64)E \\ (38/64)Q'+(192/128)J-(38/64)E & Q'-E \end{vmatrix} = 0$$

with the roots $$E = Q' + 1.65J, \qquad Q' - 1.84J$$

[42] See, for example, R. S. Mulliken, *J. Chem. Phys.* 7, 20 (1939); R. S. Mulliken, C. A. Rieke, D. Orloff, and H. Orloff, *ibid.* 17, 1248 (1949).

Since the energy W_A associated with the single structure A is still equal to $Q' + 1.5J$, the calculated resonance energy now becomes

$$RE_{\text{calc}} = Q' + 1.5J - (Q' + 1.65J) = -0.15J \qquad (36)$$

The wave function for the hybrid in its ground state is found to be

$$\Phi = 0.80\Theta_A + 0.25\Theta_B \qquad (37)$$

Comparison of equations 31 and 36 suggests that, for 1,3-butadiene, the calculated resonance energy obtained in the present treatment is significantly smaller than is that obtained in the treatment of Sections 9·19 and 9·20 (i.e., with $S = 0$). Although this conclusion is supported also by some indirect evidence that is described below, it does not, however, strictly follow from anything said so far. Since J is an empirical parameter in both treatments, it need not have the same value in equations 31 and 36. A more significant feature of the calculations is therefore that the weight of the less stable structure B is smaller when S is set equal to $^1/_4$ (equation 37) than it is when S is set equal to 0 (equation 32).

If the orbitals a, b, c, and d are now considered to be semilocalized, so that ionic structures are included in the resonance, the integral S must be assigned a value that is even greater than $^1/_4$ (see page 645). However, when S is made too large, we are no longer justified in neglecting either the single-exchange integrals of unity between "nonadjacent" orbitals or the higher exchange integrals of unity. Consequently, the calculation becomes appreciably more difficult. In order to avoid these complexities, let us therefore assume that, even when S is as large as $^2/_5$, the matrix elements S_{AA}, S_{BB}, and S_{CC} can still be estimated in the way used in the preceding paragraphs. In this manner, we find that

$$S_{AA} = 1 + (3/2)(4/25) = 62/50$$
$$S_{BB} = 1$$
$$S_{CC} = 1 - (3/2)(4/25) = 38/50$$

(These values are, however, less trustworthy than are the analogous ones for the case in which $S = \frac{1}{4}$.) The energies obtained by solving the resulting secular equation are then

$$E = Q' + 1.56J, \qquad Q' - 2.08J$$

so that the calculated resonance energy is

$$RE_{\text{calc}} = Q' + 1.5J - (Q' + 1.56J) = -0.06J \qquad (38)$$

The corresponding wave function for the ground state is

$$\Phi = 0.79\Theta_A + 0.17\Theta_B \qquad (39)$$

The increase in the value of the integral S therefore further decreases both the magnitude of the coefficient of the parameter J in the calculated resonance energy (equation 38) and also the weight of the less stable structure B in the hybrid (equation 39).

The extension of the foregoing treatment to benzene turns out to be rather complicated. The reason for this relative difficulty is that, with six pi electrons, there are now not only the five canonical structures IX–XIII, without crossing bonds, but also altogether ten noncanonical structures belonging to the three types XIV–XVI, with crossing bonds (cf. pages 599f). The calculation cannot be simplified by ignoring any of these fifteen structures; for, even if we were willing to limit ourselves to a consideration of the resonance between only the two Kekulé structures IX and X, we would still need to evaluate the nondiagonal matrix elements

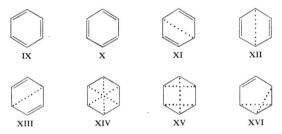

H_IX X and S_IX X, and each of these is a linear combination of the corre-sponding diagonal elements associated with all fifteen structures. We shall here, therefore, omit the details of the calculations, and we shall content ourselves with merely stating, in Table 9·2, the results obtained.

TABLE 9·2

CALCULATED RESONANCE ENERGIES AND CORRESPONDING WAVE
FUNCTIONS FOR BENZENE

	RE_{calc}	$k_K{}^a$	$k_D{}^a$
Kekulé Structures Only			
$S = 0$	$-0.90J$	0.63	0
$S = \frac{1}{4}$	$-0.78J$	0.59	0
$S = \frac{2}{5}$	$-0.65J$	0.54	0
All canonical structures			
$S = 0$	$-1.11J$	0.37	0.16
$S = \frac{1}{4}$	$-0.84J$	0.43	0.10
$S = \frac{2}{5}$	$-0.69J$	0.42	0.07

[a] The constants k_K and k_D are the coefficients of the functions which repre-sent, respectively, the Kekulé and Dewar structures in the normalized wave functions, $\Phi = k_K(\Theta_{IX} + \Theta_X) + k_D(\Theta_{XI} + \Theta_{XII} + \Theta_{XIII})$.

(When $S = 0$, the present treatment is completely equivalent to that of Section 9·19, and so leads to identical resonance energies and wave functions.)   It will be seen that, as the value of the overlap integral S is increased, all three of the following quantities decrease: the magnitude of the coefficient of J in the calculated resonance energy, the fraction of the total resonance energy that is due to the Dewar structures, and the relative weights of the Dewar structures in the ground-state wave function. The first of these variations implies that the magnitude of J must be increased as S is increased, so that the value of RE_{calc}, when expressed in kcal per mole, will remain constant.   The last two variations suggest, but are probably insufficient to establish, that in all calculations like those of Sections 9·19 and 9·20, in which S is assumed to be equal to zero, the importance of the unstable structures with formal bonds is considerably overestimated.   This conclusion then supports the inference (see page 652) that the calculated resonance energy of 1,3-butadiene is indeed small.

With molecules more complicated than that of benzene, the calculations rapidly become impracticable.   For naphthalene, for example, since there are ten pi electrons, we can write 42 canonical and 903 noncanonical structures (see pages 599f), and the nondiagonal matrix elements relating just the three (Erlenmeyer and Erdmann) structures without formal bonds would presumably involve all of the 945 diagonal elements.   The calculations for 1,3-butadiene and for benzene are sufficient, however, to show that the simpler treatments in the preceding sections are not necessarily invalidated by the assumption that the atomic orbitals are mutually orthogonal, or by the neglect of the ionic structures.   The frequent practice of ignoring the structures with formal bonds receives some justification; and doubt is cast on the correctness of the conclusion (see page 639) that the structure XVII has a larger weight in the normal anthracene molecule than does the more stable structure XVIII.

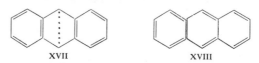

XVII   XVIII

9·22   Molecular Orbitals.   The approximate quantum-mechanical treatment of molecular structure can be carried out not only by the above valence-bond method but also by the so-called *molecular-orbital method* (cf. Sections 2·9 and 2·10).   These two alternative approaches to the problem start from superficially rather different basic assumptions but, as we shall see later, they are closely related.   So long as the treatments are restricted to the ground states of the molecules of interest, the two calculations *usually* lead to results of approximately equal accuracy, or inaccuracy (see, however, pages 147ff). The valence-bond method has the advantage that, since it makes explicit use of the conventional valence-bond structures, it has an obvious and direct relation to the classical structural theory with which all chemists are familiar. On the other hand, the molecular-orbital method has the great practical advantage that it involves much the simpler mathematics. As a result, the former treatment has been the more widely used in qualitative discussions like the ones, for example, in the preceding chapters of this book; whereas the latter has been found much the more generally applicable in numerical calculations. In fact, the molecular-orbital method is the only one that has so far been successfully used in detailed surveys of spectroscopically excited states (see also Section 9·28) or in *any* sort of numerical calculations for complex molecules which have net electric charges or which are not hydrocarbons.

The viewpoint that is adopted in the molecular-orbital treatment of a molecule is similar to the one that is adopted in the treatment of a single atom (cf. pages 564f). Thus, we first imagine that all the valence electrons are removed, so that only the atomic kernels remain; we then imagine that the electrons are allowed to return to the molecule one at a time. Each electron which returns will in general not occupy an atomic orbital that is centered about an individual kernel, but it will instead occupy a *molecular orbital* which extends over the entire molecule. For example, in the hydrogen molecule-ion, H_2^+, the single electron does not spend all its time near one of the two protons, but is instead free to wander over the entire ion. In Section 2·4, we made allowance for this wandering by treating the system as a resonance hybrid; here we achieve the same end by introducing the concept of a molecular orbital.

The first electron which returns to the molecule (see above) will occupy that particular orbital which is the most stable. The second electron can also go into this same orbital if its spin is exactly antiparallel to that of the first. On account of the exclusion principle, however, the third and fourth electrons must be assigned, with opposite spins, to the next most stable molecular orbital; and so on until all the electrons have been returned to the molecule.

In principle, the molecular orbitals ψ are obtained by solution of a one-electron Schrödinger equation

$$\mathbf{H}_{scf}\psi = -\frac{h^2}{8\pi^2 m}\left(\frac{\partial^2\psi}{\partial x^2} + \frac{\partial^2\psi}{\partial y^2} + \frac{\partial^2\psi}{\partial z^2}\right) + V_{scf}\psi = W\psi \qquad (1)$$

in which $\mathbf{H}_{scf}$ is the Hamiltonian operator for a single electron moving in the so-called *self-consistent field* (see below), and V_{scf} represents the potential energy that is due to the interaction of the electron in the orbital

ψ with the several nuclei and with the average charge distribution of all the other electrons. In order to solve equation 1, we must first know the exact form of the self-consistent-field potential $V_{\rm scf}$; but, in order to determine this potential, we must first know the exact forms of all the occupied orbitals. The calculation is therefore a difficult one in which, by a series of successive approximations, there is finally derived a potential energy $V_{\rm scf}$ such that, when the electrons are assigned to the orbitals ψ that are the solutions of the resulting equation 1, the corresponding average charge distribution gives rise to a potential identical with the one originally taken, $V_{\rm scf}$. Although this elaborate and tedious procedure has been carried through to completion for a number of single atoms, it is much too difficult to be practicable with a polyatomic molecule, with which the calculation cannot be simplified by the assumption that the field is spherically symmetric, i.e., by the assumption that $V_{\rm scf}$ is a function of only the distance r between the electron and the nucleus. For this reason, the approximate forms of the molecular orbitals have in practice been obtained by a much simpler, and quite different, method which, after a few further general remarks, will be described in Section 9·23.

If the individual molecular orbitals are designated as $\psi_1, \psi_2, \cdots, \psi_r$, and if the respective spin-orbit functions are designated as $\chi_1, \chi_2, \cdots, \chi_r$, the approximate wave function for the molecule is of the form $\Omega(1, 2, \cdots, r)$ shown in equation 10, Section 9·7, and again in equation 8, Section 9·12. The corresponding approximate energy of the molecule is then

$$E = \frac{\int \Omega^*(1, 2, \cdots, r) H\Omega(1, 2, \cdots, r)\, d\tau}{\int \Omega^*(1, 2, \cdots, r)\Omega(1, 2, \cdots, r)\, d\tau} \qquad (2)$$

where $\mathbf{H}$ is now not the self-consistent-field operator $\mathbf{H}_{\rm scf}$ which appears in the one-electron equation 1 but is instead the correct Hamiltonian operator for the r-electron system. In the simplest applications of molecular-orbital theory, however, and more particularly in all the applications which are described below in this and the succeeding sections, the following much less difficult procedure is used.   If we could solve equation 1, we would thereby obtain not only the eigenfunctions ψ, but also the corresponding eigenvalues W. Hence, since W is the energy of an electron in the orbital ψ, it seems reasonable to assume that the energy of the entire molecule is simply the sum of the eigenvalues which correspond to the occupied orbitals. Although this assumption is not strictly correct (see the following paragraph), we shall nevertheless adopt it in most of the subsequent discussion of the molecular-orbital method since, without it, the mathematical complexities would become too great for discussion here.

As was mentioned above, it is not correct to assume that the energy of a molecule is identical with the sum of the energies of the occupied orbitals; for, if electron j is in orbital ψ_j, and if electron k is in orbital ψ_k, the energy due to the electrostatic inter- action between electrons j and k is included in both W_j and W_k, and so it is counted twice in the sum of eigenvalues. Moreover, if the self-consistent-field potential V_{scf} is defined in such a way that it contains terms which correspond to the mutual repulsions between the atomic kernels, then, in the sum of eigenvalues, the resulting energy is counted as many times as there are electrons; on the other hand, if the potential V_{scf} is differently defined, so that it does not contain such terms, then the corresponding energy is not counted at all. In neither event, therefore, are the interactions between the kernels properly treated. However, if the several integrals which will later be found to enter the treatment are evaluated empirically (cf. the integral J in the valence- bond calculations described in Sections 9·19 and 9·20), and if our interest is restricted to energy *differences*, the errors which arise from these sources can be expected to be small.

9·23   The Molecular-Orbital Treatment of Hydrogen. Since the wave equation for the hydrogen molecule-ion, H_2^+, can be solved almost rigorously, the almost exactly correct forms of the molecular orbitals that correspond to the ground and excited states can therefore be obtained. This fact, however, is of little help to us in the treatment of the neutral hydrogen molecule, H_2, since, on account of the perturbations that arise from the interelectronic interactions, the molecular orbitals in the latter system are doubtless far from identical with those in the former. For this reason, we shall adopt a rather different approach.

In practically all applications of the molecular-orbital method to numerical calculations, the molecular orbitals ψ have been approximated by linear combinations of atomic orbitals ϕ.[43] If there are altogether r of the ϕ's,

$$\psi_1 = k_{11}\phi_1 + k_{12}\phi_2 + \cdots + k_{1r}\phi_r = \sum_{l=1}^{r} k_{1l}\phi_l$$

and similarly for the remaining molecular orbitals; or, in general,

$$\psi_j = k_{j1}\phi_1 + k_{j2}\phi_2 + \cdots + k_{jr}\phi_r = \sum_{l=1}^{r} k_{jl}\phi_l \qquad (j = 1, 2, \cdots, r) \quad (1)$$

When this procedure is followed, the method is frequently described as the LCAO MO method, i.e., the "linear-combination-of-atomic-orbitals molecular-orbital method."[44] The molecular orbitals are then approxi- mated as resonance hybrids of the r different atomic orbitals.

For the hydrogen molecule, the only atomic orbitals which we now need to consider are the $1s$ orbitals about the two protons. If, as in

[43] J. E. Lennard-Jones, *Trans. Faraday Soc.* **25**, 668 (1929).
[44] R. S. Mulliken, *J. Chem. Phys.* **3**, 375 (1935).

Section 9·9, we again designate these atomic orbitals by the letters a and b, we therefore write the approximate molecular orbitals in the form

$$\psi = k_a a + k_b b \tag{2}$$

Since the variation principle applies to the one-electron wave equation, as well as to the rigorously correct wave equation, we can consider the constant coefficients k_a and k_b to be variation parameters. Hence, if the orbitals a and b are normalized, application of the same procedure that led to equation 6, Section 9·11, leads here to the secular equation

$$\begin{vmatrix} \alpha - E & \gamma - SE \\ \gamma - SE & \alpha - E \end{vmatrix} = 0 \tag{3}$$

in which the *one-electron coulomb integral* α is defined as

$$\alpha \equiv \int a H_{\text{scf}} a \, dv = \int b H_{\text{scf}} b \, dv \tag{4}$$

the *resonance integral* γ is defined as

$$\gamma \equiv \int a H_{\text{scf}} b \, dv = \int b H_{\text{scf}} a \, dv \tag{5}$$

and the *overlap* integral S has the same value

$$S \equiv \int ab \, dv = \int ba \, dv \tag{6}$$

as heretofore.

Solution of equation 3 gives the two roots

$$E_\pm = \frac{\alpha \pm \gamma}{1 \pm S} \tag{7}$$

The corresponding molecular orbitals are

$$\psi_\pm = \frac{1}{\sqrt{2 \pm 2S}} (a \pm b) \tag{8}$$

Since the integral γ is presumably negative, the lower root is E_+, and the more stable orbital is ψ_+. Since both electrons are therefore to be assigned, with opposite spins, to ψ_+, the approximate wave function for the molecule in its ground state is seen from equation 10, Section 9·7 to be

$$\Omega_{\text{mo}} = \frac{1}{\sqrt{2}} \begin{vmatrix} \psi_+(1)\alpha(1) & \psi_+(1)\beta(1) \\ \psi_+(2)\alpha(2) & \psi_+(2)\beta(2) \end{vmatrix}$$

$$= \frac{1}{(2 + 2S)\sqrt{2}} [a(1)b(2) + b(2)a(1) + a(1)a(2) + b(1)b(2)]$$

$$[\alpha(1)\beta(2) - \beta(1)\alpha(2)] \tag{9}$$

Comparison with equation 2, Section 9·21, now shows that Ω_{mo} is very similar to the function Φ, which was previously set up to represent resonance among the structures I–III, and that the two functions become identical if the constants c_1 and c_2 in Φ are set equal to 1.   Since, however,

$$\text{H—H} \qquad\qquad :\text{H}^-\ \ \text{H}^+ \qquad\qquad \text{H}^+\ \ \text{H}:^-$$
$$\text{I} \qquad\qquad\qquad\quad \text{II} \qquad\qquad\qquad\quad \text{III}$$

the best value of both c_1 and c_2 is approximately $^1/_4$,[39] the corresponding best function Φ is closer to the purely covalent extreme, in which $c_1 = c_2 = 0$, than it is to the particular resonance hybrid Ω_{mo}.   We may therefore anticipate that the molecular-orbital wave function, when inserted in equation 2, Section 9·22, will give an approximate energy which is poorer than the one similarly obtained in Section 9·9 from the simpler function that represents the purely covalent structure I.   This expectation is indeed correct, for, when the atomic number is treated as a variation parameter, the errors in the energies calculated from the molecular-orbital function and from the purely covalent valence-bond function are, respectively, about 29 and about 22 kcal per mole.[45]   The difference is, however, not very great.

With molecules more complex than that of hydrogen, the relation between the valence-bond and the molecular-orbital wave functions is essentially the same as that found here.   In general, any molecule which is treated by the molecular-orbital method is necessarily considered to be a resonance hybrid of both covalent and ionic structures; the relative weights of the unstable ionic structures are invariably larger than one would ordinarily expect them to be;[46] and these weights cannot be reduced by the device of assuming that the atomic orbitals are themselves polarized or, in other words, by replacing the atomic orbitals by semi-localized orbitals (cf. Section 9·21).   Whether the calculated contributions of the ionic structures are so large that the molecular wave functions are always poorer than the corresponding ones obtained by the valence-bond method has not, however, been tested by any numerical calculations in addition to the one for hydrogen.

Within the framework of the molecular-orbital method, the procedure by which the contributions of the ionic structures can be varied is based on the concept of *configuration interaction* (cf. page 62).   The approximate wave function Ω_{mo} of equation 9 was derived from the configuration in

[45] S. Weinbaum, quoted by L. Pauling and E. B. Wilson, Jr., *Introduction to Quantum Mechanics*, McGraw-Hill Book Co., New York, 1935, pp. 347, 349.   See also C. A. Coulson, *Proc. Cambridge Phil. Soc.* **34**, 204 (1938).

[46] For some examples (cyclobutadiene and benzene), see G. W. Wheland, *Proc. Roy. Soc.* (*London*) *A* **164**, 397 (1938).

which both electrons are assigned to the more stable orbital ψ_+. If we had instead assumed the alternative configuration in which both electrons are assigned to the less stable orbital ψ_-, we would have obtained the molecular wave function

$$\Omega_{mo}' = \frac{1}{\sqrt{2}} \begin{vmatrix} \psi_-(1)\alpha(1) & \psi_-(1)\beta(1) \\ \psi_-(2)\alpha(2) & \psi_-(2)\beta(2) \end{vmatrix}$$

$$= \frac{1}{(2-2S)\sqrt{2}} [-a(1)b(2) - b(1)a(2) + a(1)a(2) + b(1)b(2)]$$
$$\cdot [\alpha(1)\beta(2) - \beta(1)\alpha(2)]$$

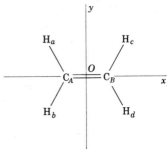

Fig. 9·11. The ethylene molecule in the xy plane. The z axis is to be considered perpendicular to the plane of the paper.

And finally, as can be verified by direct substitution, the wave function Φ of equation 2, Section 9·21, can be written in the form

$$\Phi = R\Omega_{mo} + S\Omega_{mo}'$$

where R and S are constants which are to be evaluated by the variation method. In this way, we see that the valence-bond method with a variable ionic character is mathematically equivalent to the molecular-orbital method with configuration interaction.

9·24 The Molecular-Orbital Treatment of Ethylene. The ethylene molecule contains twelve valence electrons, which must be distributed among the twelve orbitals in the valence shells of the several carbon and hydrogen atoms. If we assume that the molecular orbitals are linear combinations of these twelve atomic orbitals, we obtain a secular equation which is originally of the twelfth degree, but which, on account of the fairly high symmetry of the molecule, can be materially simplified by factorization.

Let us imagine that the molecule lies in the xy plane of a Cartesian coordinate system, so that the origin is at its center, and so that the carbon-carbon bond coincides with the x axis, as in Figure 9·11. Since the xy plane is a plane of symmetry for the molecule, the self-consistent-field Hamiltonian operator $\mathbf{H}_{\text{scf}}$ (cf. equation 1, Section 9·22) is even in z. In other words, this operator is unchanged, i.e., is multiplied by $+1$, if in it z is everywhere replaced by $-z$, so that $\mathbf{H}_{\text{scf}}$ is symmetric with respect to reflection in the xy plane. Consequently, each of the functions $\mathbf{H}_{\text{scf}}\phi$, where ϕ is one of the twelve atomic orbitals, has the same symmetry with respect to reflection in the xy plane as the corresponding orbital ϕ itself. In particular, if ϕ_σ is any sigma orbital (cf. pages 587f), $\mathbf{H}_{\text{scf}}\phi_\sigma$ is unchanged on reflection in the xy plane; on the other hand, if ϕ_π is any pi orbital, then $\mathbf{H}_{\text{scf}}\phi_\pi$ is multiplied by -1 on reflection in that plane. It therefore follows that $\mathbf{H}_{\text{scf}}\phi_\sigma$, like ϕ_σ itself, is an even function of z, and that $\mathbf{H}_{\text{scf}}\phi_\pi$, like ϕ_π itself, is an odd function of z. Now, let us consider an integral of the form

$$\gamma_{\sigma\pi} = \int \phi_\sigma \mathbf{H}_{\text{scf}} \phi_\pi \, dv$$

The integrand is here the product of a function, ϕ_σ, which is even in z, by a different function, $\mathbf{H}_{\text{scf}}\phi_\pi$, which is odd in z; hence it is itself an odd function of z. Consequently, the integral from $z = -\infty$ to $z = 0$ must be exactly equal to minus the integral from $z = 0$ to $z = +\infty$. The total integral from $-\infty$ to $+\infty$ is therefore zero. Hence

$$\gamma_{\sigma\pi} = \int \phi_\sigma \mathbf{H}_{\text{scf}} \phi_\pi \, dv = 0 \tag{1}$$

And, similarly, $$\gamma_{\pi\sigma} = \int \phi_\pi \mathbf{H}_{\text{scf}} \phi_\sigma \, dv = 0 \tag{2}$$

Moreover, the same kind of reasoning shows also that

$$S_{\sigma\pi} = S_{\pi\sigma} = \int \phi_\sigma \phi_\pi \, dv = 0 \tag{3}$$

An alternative derivation of equations 1–3 may help to make the argument clearer. Let $f(z)$ be any odd function of z, so that

$$f(-z) = -f(z)$$

for all values of z. Now, let us consider the integral

$$Z \equiv \int\limits_{z=-\infty}^{+\infty} f(z) \, dz$$

and let us define a new variable ζ by the identity

$$\zeta \equiv -z$$

Then $$Z = \int\limits_{\zeta=+\infty}^{-\infty} f(-\zeta) \, d(-\zeta) = \int\limits_{\zeta=+\infty}^{-\infty} f(\zeta) \, d\zeta = -\int\limits_{\zeta=-\infty}^{+\infty} f(\zeta) \, d\zeta$$

where the last equality at the right is valid because, when the limits of integration are interchanged, the integral is multiplied by -1. Since it makes no difference what the variable of integration in a definite integral is called, we have

$$Z = - \int_{\zeta=-\infty}^{+\infty} f(\zeta) \, d\zeta = - \int_{z=-\infty}^{+\infty} f(z) \, dz = -Z$$

Hence $Z = 0$ (4)

When $f(z)$ assumes the specific forms $\phi_\sigma H_{scf} \phi_\pi$, $\phi_\pi H_{scf} \phi_\sigma$, and $\phi_\sigma \phi_\pi$, equation 4 leads immediately to the respective equations 1, 2, and 3.

Equations 1, 2, and 3 are valid whether ϕ_σ and ϕ_π belong to the same or to different atoms, and whether ϕ_σ is an s, a $2p_x$, or a $2p_y$ orbital. Consequently, the original twelfth-degree secular equation automatically separates into two factors, which are of the second and the tenth degrees. The first of these factors involves only the two different pi orbitals, whereas the other involves only the ten different sigma orbitals. Thus we see that the separation of the sigma and the pi orbitals, which was more or less arbitrarily assumed in the valence-bond treatment (cf. pages 587f), is here a necessary consequence of the difference in symmetry. (However, see the last paragraph of this section in fine print.)

In our discussion up to this point, we have made use of the fact that the xy plane is a plane of symmetry for the molecule, but we have not as yet made use of the further fact that the xz and yz planes are also planes of symmetry, so that H_{scf} is even in y and in x, as well as in z. Now, although no one of the twelve atomic orbitals is, by itself, either symmetric or antisymmetric with respect to reflection in either of these additional planes of symmetry, linear combinations of them, which do have such properties, can easily be set up. If the $1s$ orbitals of the hydrogen atoms H_a, H_b, H_c, and H_d of Figure 9·11 are designated by the letters a, b, c, and d, respectively, the combination $a + b + c + d$ is symmetric with respect to reflection in each of the three planes of symmetry and hence is an even function of each of the coordinates x, y, and z. This conclusion follows because reflection in the xy plane leaves each of the orbitals a, b, c, and d unchanged; whereas reflection in the xz plane transforms a into b, b into a, c into d, and d into c; and reflection in the yz plane transforms a into c, b into d, c into a, and d into b. Consequently, reflection in any one of the planes transforms the sum $a + b + c + d$ into itself. Similarly, the different combination $a + b - c - d$ is an even function of y and z, but an odd function of x. If the $2s$ orbitals on the carbon atoms C_A and C_B of Figure 9·11 are designated as A_s and B_s, respectively, the combination $A_s + B_s$ is again an even function of all three coordinates x, y, and z; but the different combination $A_s - B_s$ is an even function of only y and z, and it is an odd function of x. A slightly more difficult problem is presented by the $2p_x$ orbitals on the carbon atoms C_A and C_B. If we designate these orbitals as A_x and B_x, respectively, then reflection in either the xy or the xz plane leaves both orbitals unchanged, whereas reflection in the yz plane transforms A_x into $-B_x$ and B_x into $-A_x$. Consequently, the sum $A_x + B_x$ is an even function of y and z, but an odd function of x; and the difference $A_x - B_x$ is an even function of all three coordinates. In this way, we can set up the twelve independent combinations θ_1–θ_{12}:

$$+++ \begin{cases} \theta_1 = a + b + c + d \\ \theta_2 = A_s + B_s \\ \theta_3 = A_x - B_x \end{cases}$$

$$-++ \begin{cases} \theta_4 = a + b - c - d \\ \theta_5 = A_s - B_s \\ \theta_6 = A_x + B_x \end{cases}$$

$$+-+ \begin{cases} \theta_7 = a - b + c - d \\ \theta_8 = A_y + B_y \end{cases} \tag{5}$$

$$--+ \begin{cases} \theta_9 = a - b - c + d \\ \theta_{10} = A_y - B_y \end{cases}$$

$$++- \{\theta_{11} = A_z + B_z$$

$$-+- \{\theta_{12} = A_z - B_z$$

where A_y and B_y are the $2p_y$ orbitals on the carbon atoms C_A and C_B, respectively; and A_z and B_z are the $2p_z$ orbitals on the carbon atoms C_A and C_B, respectively. In the symbols $+++$, $-++$, etc., at the left, the plus and minus signs signify that the corresponding functions are, respectively, even and odd in the coordinates x, y, and z; for example, θ_1 is even in all three coordinates, θ_9 is odd in x and y but even in z, and so on.

Since each of the three coordinate planes is a plane of symmetry for the ethylene molecule, the operator $\mathbf{H}_{scf}$, as was noted above, is unchanged by reflection in any of these planes. Consequently, the integrals

$$H_{jl} \equiv \int \theta_j \mathbf{H}_{scf} \theta_l \, dv$$

and
$$S_{jl} \equiv \int \theta_j \theta_l \, dv$$

must be equal to zero unless the functions θ_j and θ_i have exactly the same symmetry. Consequently, if we now write the variation function in the form

$$\Phi = \sum_{j=1}^{12} k_j \theta_j$$

we find that the resulting secular equation factors into two cubic, two quadratic, and two linear factors. One of the cubic factors, for example, arises from the three functions θ_1, θ_2, and θ_3 with the symmetry $++ +$; one of the linear factors arises from the single function θ_{11} with the symmetry $++-$; and so on.

The method by which the above combinations θ_1–θ_{12} were set up is quite simple. Each of the functions a, b, c, and d is even with respect to z, but neither even nor odd with respect to either x or y. Reflection in the xz plane transforms a into b (and vice versa), and it changes c into d (and vice versa). Consequently $a + b$ and $c + d$ are both even in y, whereas $a - b$ and $c - d$ are both odd in y. Although each of these four more complicated functions is still even in z, and although each has a definite symmetry (either even or odd) with respect to y, no one of them has a definite symmetry with respect to x. However, reflection in the yz plane changes $a + b$ into $c + d$ (and vice versa), and it changes $a - b$ into $c - d$ (and vice versa). Consequently, $(a + b) + (c + d)$ and $(a - b) + (c - d)$ are both even in x, whereas $(a + b) - (c + d)$ and $(a - b) - (c - d)$ are both odd in x. Since each of the four resulting functions is still even in z, and since each still has a definite symmetry with respect to y, we have obtained the desired set of linear combinations of the atomic orbitals a, b, c, and d. Indeed, the functions which we have thus derived are identical with θ_1, θ_7, θ_4, and θ_9, respectively.

Since we are at present interested only in the interaction between the two pi orbitals, we need to consider only the functions θ_{11} and θ_{12}, which correspond to the two linear factors of the secular equation. The approximate energies are

$$E_{11} = H_{11,11}/S_{11,11} = (\alpha + \gamma)/(1 + S) \tag{6}$$

and $\qquad E_{12} = H_{12,12}/S_{12,12} = (\alpha - \gamma)/(1 - S) \tag{7}$

where α, γ, and S are, respectively, the coulomb, resonance, and overlap integrals for the pi orbitals A_z and B_z (cf. equations 4, 5, and 6, Section 9·23). Since γ is presumably negative, like the corresponding integral for the hydrogen molecule, E_{11} is the lower of these two roots, and so θ_{11} (after normalization) is the more stable of the two molecular orbitals. When both pi electrons are assigned, with opposite spins, to this orbital, the resulting wave function for the molecule represents a resonance hybrid receiving large contributions from both the covalent structure I and the two ionic structures II and III (cf. pages 658f). Since the ionic structures are doubtless rather unstable, their weights in the ground state of the molecule are probably smaller than is here indicated, but can be decreased by configuration interaction (cf. pages 659f).

$$H_2C{=}CH_2 \qquad H_2\overset{..}{C}{}^-{-}C^+H_2 \qquad H_2C^+{-}\overset{..}{C}{}^-H_2$$
$$\text{I} \qquad\qquad\qquad \text{II} \qquad\qquad\qquad \text{III}$$

As was shown on pages 662ff, the approximate molecular-orbital approach leads to the conclusion that the pi orbitals can be treated quite independently of the sigma orbitals. This convenient simplification of the treatment is, however, not strictly valid since, in a more accurate calculation in which configuration interaction is taken into account, we can no longer say that, of all the valence electrons, a *certain definite number* occupy sigma molecular orbitals whereas the others occupy pi molecular orbitals. Thus, in ethylene, in addition to the several different configurations in which there are ten sigma and two pi electrons, there are numerous other ones in which all twelve electrons are assigned to sigma orbitals, or in which only eight electrons are assigned to sigma orbitals and the remaining four electrons are assigned to pi orbitals, and so on. Similarly, when the valence-bond approach is adopted, the assumption that the sigma and the pi orbitals are independent is again not completely valid since, in any but the simplest calculations, we would have to consider resonance with structures in which there are bonds between sigma and pi orbitals on adjacent atoms.[47] We shall here, however, ignore these several complications, and we shall continue to treat the sigma and pi electrons as independent of each other.

9·25   Molecular-Orbital Calculations of the Resonance Energies of Aromatic Hydrocarbons. The molecule of every purely aromatic hydrocarbon lies entirely in a single plane, which is necessarily therefore a plane of symmetry. Consequently, in the molecular-orbital treatment of such a molecule, just as in that of ethylene, each approximate molecular orbital can be expressed as a linear combination, either of only the sigma atomic orbitals, or else of only the pi atomic orbitals. Hence we shall again take as our starting point the framework that is formed by the sigma orbitals, so that only the pi orbitals remain to be considered. (Cf. also Section 9·19.)

In the treatment of benzene, we shall use the letters a, b, $\cdots$, f to represent the pi orbitals of the six carbon atoms. Since these orbitals are completely equivalent to one another, all the one-electron coulomb integrals like

$$\alpha_{aa} \equiv \int a\mathbf{H}_{\mathrm{scf}}a \, dv$$

are equal. Similarly, since the six carbon-carbon bonds may also be assumed to be equivalent, all the resonance integrals between adjacent orbitals in the ring, such as

$$\gamma_{ab} \equiv \int a\mathbf{H}_{\mathrm{scf}}b \, dv = \int b\mathbf{H}_{\mathrm{scf}}a \, dv$$

are equal, as are likewise all the corresponding overlap integrals such as

$$S_{ab} \equiv \int ab \, dv$$

[47] S. L. Altmann, *Proc. Roy. Soc.* (*London*) A **210**, 327, 343 (1952).

Consequently, these several integrals can be represented by the respective symbols α, γ, and S. If all integrals besides α, γ, and S are assumed to be equal to zero, the secular equation can be written as

$$
\begin{vmatrix}
x & 1 & 0 & 0 & 0 & 1 \\
1 & x & 1 & 0 & 0 & 0 \\
0 & 1 & x & 1 & 0 & 0 \\
0 & 0 & 1 & x & 1 & 0 \\
0 & 0 & 0 & 1 & x & 1 \\
1 & 0 & 0 & 0 & 1 & x
\end{vmatrix} = 0
\tag{1}
$$

where

$$
x = \frac{\alpha - E}{\gamma - SE}
\tag{2}
$$

so that

$$
E = \frac{\alpha - x\gamma}{1 - xS}
\tag{3}
$$

By taking advantage of all the planes of symmetry which the benzene molecule has, we can at best separate equation 1 into two quadratic and two linear factors. If the molecule is assumed to lie in the xy plane of a Cartesian coordinate system, with the center of the ring at the origin, and with the orbitals a and d lying on the y axis, as in Figure 9·12, the functions $a + d$ and $b + c + e + f$ are even in both x and y; the functions $a - d$ and $b - c - e + f$ are even in x but odd in y; the function $b + c - e - f$ is odd in x but even in y; and the function $b - c + e - f$ is odd in both x and y. (Cf. the paragraph in fine print on page 664.) If the secular equation is now set up with respect to these six functions, it assumes the form

$$
\begin{vmatrix}
2x & 4 & 0 & 0 & 0 & 0 \\
4 & 4x + 4 & 0 & 0 & 0 & 0 \\
0 & 0 & 2x & 4 & 0 & 0 \\
0 & 0 & 4 & 4x - 4 & 0 & 0 \\
0 & 0 & 0 & 0 & 4x + 4 & 0 \\
0 & 0 & 0 & 0 & 0 & 4x - 4
\end{vmatrix} = 0
$$

instead of 1. The six roots, which can now be found without great difficulty, are

$$
x = -2, -1, -1, 1, 1, \text{ and } 2
$$

so that

$$
E = \frac{\alpha + 2\gamma}{1 + 2S}, \frac{\alpha + \gamma}{1 + S}, \frac{\alpha + \gamma}{1 + S}, \frac{\alpha - \gamma}{1 - S}, \frac{\alpha - \gamma}{1 - S}, \text{ and } \frac{\alpha - 2\gamma}{1 - 2S}
$$

respectively (cf. equation 3).   Since γ is again presumably negative, the order in which the roots are here listed is that of increasing value.   The wave function for the molecule or, more precisely, that part of the wave function which refers only to the pi electrons, is obtained by assigning

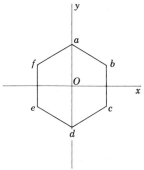

Fig. 9·12.   The benzene ring lying in the xy plane.

two electrons, with opposite spins, to each of the three most stable orbitals, which are

$$\psi_1 = \frac{1}{\sqrt{6 + 12S}} (a + b + c + d + e + f) \tag{4}$$

$$\psi_2 = \frac{1}{\sqrt{4 + 4S}} (b + c - e - f) \tag{5}$$

and $$\psi_3 = \frac{1}{\sqrt{12 + 12S}} (2a + b - c - 2d - e + f) \tag{6}$$

respectively.   This function describes a resonance hybrid of the Kekulé and Dewar structures, with large contributions also from their numerous ionic counterparts.[46]   The corresponding approximate energy is then

$$E_{\text{benzene}} = \frac{2(\alpha + 2\gamma)}{1 + 2S} + \frac{4(\alpha + \gamma)}{1 + S}$$

Since, to the same approximation (cf. equation 6, Section 9·24), the energy of the pi component of a carbon-carbon double bond is

$$E_{\text{ethylene}} = \frac{2(\alpha + \gamma)}{1 + S}$$

the calculated resonance energy of benzene becomes

$$RE_{\text{benzene}} = 3E_{\text{ethylene}} - E_{\text{benzene}}$$
$$= \frac{2(\alpha + \gamma)}{1 + S} - \frac{2(\alpha + 2\gamma)}{1 + 2S} \tag{7}$$

In our molecular-orbital treatment of benzene, we factored the original secular equation by taking advantage of only three planes of symmetry, the xy, the xz, and the yz planes. The molecule has, however, several additional planes of symmetry and also six twofold axes and one sixfold axis of rotation. Consequently, there is a possibility that the secular equation can be reduced to still smaller factors with the aid of these further symmetry elements. The remaining planes of symmetry and the several twofold axes can be shown to permit no factorization beyond what has already been achieved, but the sixfold axis enables equation 1 to be separated into six linear factors. Since the underlying principles of the method will not be needed below in either this or the succeeding sections, we shall here merely state the results which follow from a complete group-theoretical treatment.[48] The linear combinations of the atomic orbitals $a, b, \cdots, f$ which lead to the desired factorization are

$$\theta_j = \frac{1}{\sqrt{6 + 12S \cos (2\pi j/6)}} (a + e^{2\pi ij/6}b + e^{4\pi ij/6}c + e^{6\pi ij/6}d$$
$$+ e^{8\pi ij/6}e + e^{10\pi ij/6}f) \qquad (j = 1, 2, \cdots, 6) \qquad (8)$$

and the corresponding solutions of the equations are

$$x_j = -2 \cos (2\pi j/6) \qquad (j = 1, 2, \cdots, 6) \qquad (9)$$

The six roots are easily shown to be identical with those found earlier (page 666), but some of the molecular orbitals appear to be different. Although ψ_1 of equation 4 is clearly the same function as θ_6 of equation 8, the functions ψ_2 and ψ_3 of equations 5 and 6 cannot be obtained from equation 8. The discrepancy is, however, only apparent. The functions θ_1 and θ_5 are degenerate since, from equation 9, $x_1 = x_5 = -1$. Consequently, any linear combination of θ_1 and θ_5 will be as good as θ_1 or θ_5 itself, and it must correspond to the same value of x, namely, -1 (see page 550). The relation between the two treatments then follows from the identities

$$\psi_2 \equiv \frac{1}{i\sqrt{2}} [\theta_1 - \theta_5]$$

and

$$\psi_3 \equiv \frac{1}{\sqrt{2}} [\theta_1 + \theta_5]$$

Equation 7 is of a most inconvenient form since it shows that the resonance energy of benzene involves the three different integrals α, γ, and S. Even though S can be evaluated by direct integration,[42] the two remaining integrals α and γ cannot be thus obtained. The earliest and crudest of the methods which have been used for avoiding this difficulty consists in simply, but incorrectly (see below), assuming that S is negligibly small.[49] The resonance energy, which becomes equal to -2γ, has then lost its undesired dependence on the coulomb integral α. By equating

[48] For further details, see, for example, H. Margenau and G. M. Murphy, *The Mathematics of Physics and Chemistry*, D. Van Nostrand Co., New York, 1943, Chapter 15; H. Eyring, J. Walter, and G. E. Kimball, *Quantum Chemistry*, John Wiley & Sons, New York, 1944, Chapter X; or any book on group theory.

[49] E. Hückel, *Z. Physik* **70**, 204 (1931). See also G. W. Wheland, *J. Chem. Phys.* **2**, 474 (1934).

this calculated value with the empirical resonance energy (see Tables 3·2, Section 3·2, and 3·10, Section 3·8), we therefore find that γ is approximately equal to -18 kcal per mole.

A later, and theoretically better, method for eliminating the integral α from the calculated resonance[50] energy requires the introduction of a new parameter, which may be called β, and which is defined by the identity

$$\beta \equiv \gamma - S\alpha \qquad (10)$$

By combining this relation with equation 7, we find that

$$RE_{\text{benzene}} = \left(\frac{2}{1 + S} - \frac{4}{1 + 2S} \right) \beta$$

The resonance energy therefore becomes, as before, the product of a constant by a single parameter, β, and it is no longer an *explicit* function of α. If the overlap integral S is assumed to have the value $^1/_4$, which is close to that obtained by integration,[42] the resonance energy then becomes $-16\beta/15$, so that β must be approximately equal to -33 kcal per mole.

With aromatic molecules which are more complex than that of benzene, the above treatment can be carried through without essential change. With naphthalene, for example, the two planes of symmetry that are perpendicular to the plane of the molecule permit the original tenth-degree secular equation to be separated into two cubic and two quadratic factors. Although these latter equations cannot themselves be further factored, they are of such simple form that they can easily be solved by direct algebraic methods. In order to compare the resonance energy thus calculated for naphthalene with that obtained for benzene, we must however assume that all the coulomb, resonance, and overlap integrals here have the same values, α, γ, and S, respectively, as in benzene. If S is then set equal to zero, the calculated resonance energy of naphthalene is finally found to be -3.68γ, or about 66 kcal per mole; on the other hand, if S is instead set equal to $^1/_4$, the resonance energy is found to be -1.86β, or about 61 kcal per mole. The agreement of these two values with each other, with the one obtained by the valence-bond method (see Section 9·20), and with the empirical value (see Tables 3·7, Section 3·3, and 3·10, Section 3·8) is once more much better than we have any right to expect. Similar agreement has, however, been found with practically all other aromatic hydrocarbons for which the necessary calculations have been made, and for which the necessary empirical data are available. There is no obvious reason why such crude treatments should give such satisfactory results.

[50] R. S. Mulliken and C. A. Rieke, *J. Am. Chem. Soc.* **63**, 1770 (1941). See also G. W. Wheland, *ibid.* **63**, 2025 (1941).

An apparently quite empirical method for the molecular-orbital treatment of aromatic hydrocarbons has been given by Tatevskiĭ.[51]   In any such hydrocarbon, the carbon-carbon bonds which lie wholly within the conjugated system can be divided into three classes, since the number of saturated atoms that are joined to the two carbon atoms may be 2, 1, or 0.   Let us designate the numbers of bonds belonging to these three classes by the symbols A_2, A_1, and A_0 respectively.   Then, in benzene, $A_2 = 6$ and $A_1 = A_0 = 0$; in naphthalene, $A_2 = 6$, $A_1 = 4$, and $A_0 = 1$; and so on.   Now, if the overlap integral S is assumed to be equal to zero, the total pi energy of any aromatic hydrocarbon is found to be given, with only a small error, by the expression

$$E = N\alpha + (1.333A_2 + 1.145A_1 + 1.07A_0)\gamma \qquad (11)$$

where N is the number of atomic pi orbitals in the conjugated system.   With the use of this equation, the energy of benzene becomes $6\alpha + 6 \times 1.333\gamma = 6\alpha + 7.998\gamma$, whereas that of naphthalene becomes $10\alpha + (6 \times 1.333 + 4 \times 1.145 + 1.07)\gamma = 10\alpha + 13.65\gamma$; the values which are found by rigorous solution of the (approximate) secular equation are, respectively, $6\alpha + 8.000\gamma$ and $10\alpha + 13.68\gamma$.   Moreover, for a large number of other, more complex hydrocarbons, similar excellent agreement is obtained.[51]

Although Tatevskiĭ[51] did not consider how his treatment would have to be altered if the overlap integral S were not neglected, a simple modification of the basic equation 11 leads to quite satisfactory results.   If S is set equal to $^1/_4$ (see above), and if equation 11 is replaced by

$$E = N\alpha + (0.977A_2 + 0.820A_1 + 0.718A_0)\beta \qquad (12)$$

we find that E is equal to $6\alpha + 5.86\beta$ for benzene, and to $10\alpha + 9.86\beta$ for naphthalene; whereas the values found by solution of the corresponding secular equations, and with the use of equation 10, are $6\alpha + 5.87\beta$ and $10\alpha + 9.86\beta$, respectively.   As in the original treatment of Tatevskiĭ, excellent agreement is obtained also for all the other aromatic hydrocarbons for which the necessary calculations have been made.   (Cf. also pages 640f for a discussion of the similar valence-bond approximation of Vroelant and Daudel.[36])   Since equations 11 and 12 contain no terms in A_3, they cannot be applied, without further modification, to molecules, like that of styrene, in which there are *terminal* double bonds.

9·26   Molecular-Orbital Treatments of Substances Which Are Not Hydrocarbons.   A brief discussion of a single example will here be sufficient to show how the molecular-orbital method can be extended to the treatment of substances which contain heteroatoms.[52]

The molecule of pyridine, like that of benzene, is completely planar, and so the plane in which it lies is a plane of symmetry.   The separation of the sigma and the pi orbitals is therefore both possible and necessary here, as it is in benzene.   Hence, we again need to consider only the pi orbitals.   Now, since the one-electron coulomb integral for any atomic orbital is essentially a measure of the stability of an electron occupying

[51] V. M. Tatevskiĭ, *Zhur. Fiz. Khim.* **25**, 241 (1951) [*C. A.* **45**, 5988 (1951)].   The author is indebted to the National Research Council of Canada for an English translation of this paper, prepared by E. Rabkin.

[52] G. W. Wheland and L. Pauling, *J. Am. Chem. Soc.* **57**, 2086 (1935).   Cf. also G. W. Wheland, *ibid.* **64**, 900 (1942); E. Hückel, *Z. Physik* **72**, 310 (1931).

that orbital, let us assume that we can take into account the difference between the carbon atoms and the nitrogen atom by using different values for the corresponding coulomb integrals. Accordingly, we shall, as before, let the coulomb integral for the pi orbital on each carbon atom be equal to α; and we shall let the coulomb integral for the pi orbital on the nitrogen atom be equal to $\alpha + \delta\beta$, where δ is a dimensionless constant that can be considered an additional parameter in the treatment. We shall further assume that each resonance integral between adjacent atoms, whether carbon or nitrogen, is equal to γ; that each overlap integral between adjacent atoms, whether carbon or nitrogen, is equal to S, and that all other integrals are equal to zero. The secular equation can then be written as

$$\begin{vmatrix} x(1 - \delta S) + \delta & 1 & 0 & 0 & 0 & 1 \\ 1 & x & 1 & 0 & 0 & 0 \\ 0 & 1 & x & 1 & 0 & 0 \\ 0 & 0 & 1 & x & 1 & 0 \\ 0 & 0 & 0 & 1 & x & 1 \\ 1 & 0 & 0 & 0 & 1 & x \end{vmatrix} = 0 \qquad (1)$$

where x is defined as before (see equation 2, Section 9·25), and the term at the top left of the determinant assumes the form given here in consequence of the identity

$$\frac{\alpha + \delta\beta - E}{\gamma - SE} \equiv x(1 - \delta S) + \delta$$

Since the symmetry of the pyridine molecule is much less than that of the benzene molecule, the secular equation 1 cannot be extensively factored; the best that can be done is to obtain, with the aid of the plane of symmetry which is perpendicular to the ring and which passes through the nitrogen and the γ-carbon atoms, one fourth-degree and one quadratic factor. In order to solve these two resulting equations, we need to have a numerical value for δ; however, our only a priori knowledge of this parameter is that, since nitrogen atoms are more electronegative than carbon atoms, and since β is negative, it must be positive. Wheland and Pauling[52] at one time suggested that a reasonable value for δ might be approximately 2; more recently, Löwdin[53] has proposed the considerably lower value of approximately 0.6. As a result of more extensive studies, which cannot here be profitably described, it now appears unlikely that any unique value of δ can be completely satisfactory in all types of

[53] P.-O. Löwdin, *J. Chem. Phys.* **19**, 1323 (1951).

calculation for all types of molecule that contain nitrogen atoms. The present treatment should therefore be considered to have no more than qualitative validity; any quantitative conclusions to which it leads can be accepted only with the greatest reserve.

In attempts to refine the calculations for molecules with heteroatoms, the overlap integral S has been assigned values other than zero, the coulomb integrals α have been assumed to have different values for different carbon atoms, the values of both the resonance integral γ and the overlap integral S have been allowed to vary, and numerous other complications of similar type have been suggested. Although these modifications can individually be given a certain measure of theoretical justification, the net result of all of them has usually been to introduce a large number of additional parameters that must be evaluated by comparison with empirical data of one kind or another. In extreme cases, the number of parameters has sometimes exceeded the number of data to be fitted. Although such procedures as these are often *qualitatively* interesting and valuable, they clearly can have little, if any, greater *quantitative* validity than does the original, and simpler, treatment described above.

As a result of the relative simplicity of the mathematics that is required in any application of the molecular-orbital method, this method has been much more widely used than the more cumbersome and less flexible valence-bond method. Especially at the hands of Lennard-Jones, Coulson, and their students and co-workers,[54] the molecular-orbital approach has been extremely fruitful in the treatment of many quite different types of chemical and physical problem. We shall not here attempt, however, to summarize this extensive work since, in spite of its great importance, it cannot readily be described in terms of valence-bond structures or of resonance, and since it would therefore be somewhat out of place in this book which deals explicitly with the theory of resonance.

9·27 Hyperconjugation.[55] In Section 3·10, the concept of *hyperconjugation* was introduced from the valence-bond viewpoint. This

---

[54] Since the papers by these several authors have been extremely numerous, no attempt will here be made to list more than a few of the more recent and more significant ones. See, for example, J. Lennard-Jones and J. A. Pople, *Proc. Roy. Soc.* (*London*) *A* **210**, 190 (1951), and other papers referred to there; C. A. Coulson and H. C. Longuet-Higgins, *Proc. Roy. Soc.* (*London*) *A* **191**, 39 (1947), *A* **192**, 16 (1947), *A* **193**, 447, 456 (1948), *A* **195**, 188 (1948); H. C. Longuet-Higgins, *J. Chem. Phys.* **18**, 265, 275, 283 (1950); M. J. S. Dewar, *J. Am. Chem. Soc.* **74**, 3341, 3345, 3350, 3353, 3355, 3357 (1952).

[55] R. S. Mulliken, C. A. Rieke, and W. G. Brown, *J. Am. Chem. Soc.* **63**, 41 (1941). For discussions of hyperconjugation from a more qualitative and descriptive point of view, see also C. L. Deasy, *Chem. Revs.* **36**, 145 (1945); J. W. Baker, *Hyperconjugation*, Oxford University Press, Oxford, 1952; F. Becker, *Angew. Chem.* **65**, 97 (1953).

concept, however, enters more logically, and more inevitably, from the molecular-orbital viewpoint.

As a first example, let us consider cyclopentadiene, for which the conventional valence-bond structure is I. Since all five carbon atoms here

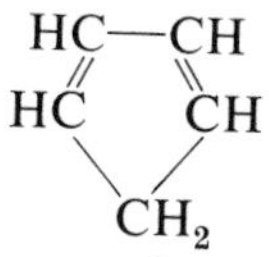

$$HC—CH$$
$$HC \quad CH$$
$$CH_2$$

I

lie in a single plane (or nearly in a single plane), which is a plane of symmetry for the entire molecule, we must again divide the atomic orbitals, and hence also the molecular orbitals, into the two classes, sigma and pi. As far as the carbon atoms and the four hydrogen atoms that are coplanar with them are concerned, the treatment is therefore exactly like that of an aromatic hydrocarbon. The orbitals of the two hydrogen atoms of the methylene group are, however, neither sigma nor pi, and so they require special consideration. In particular, they must be combined with each other in such a way that the resulting combinations are either symmetric (like sigma orbitals) or antisymmetric (like pi orbitals) with respect to reflection in the plane of symmetry. If we call these two atomic orbitals a and b, then $a + b$ is a diatomic sigma orbital which will combine with all its monatomic analogs; whereas $a - b$ is a diatomic pi orbital, which similarly will combine with all *its* monatomic analogs.

As in the treatment of an aromatic hydrocarbon, we now take as our starting point the framework that is formed by all the sigma bonds, and we consider only the interactions of the six pi electrons. The secular equation is, accordingly, of exactly the same form as is the one for fulvene II. The only difference between the calculations for cyclopentadiene and

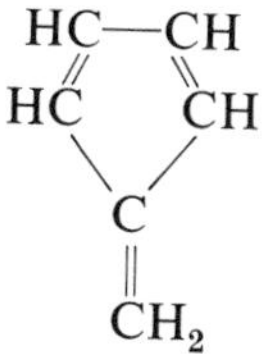

$$HC—CH$$
$$HC \quad CH$$
$$C$$
$$CH_2$$

II

for fulvene is therefore that, although the pi orbital which lies outside the ring is still a carbon $2p_z$ orbital in the latter molecule, it is instead the combination $a - b$ of hydrogen $1s$ orbitals in the former. Consequently, those coulomb, resonance, and overlap integrals which involve this orbital cannot legitimately be assumed to have the same values in cyclopentadiene that they have in either fulvene or an aromatic hydrocarbon.

Since, in cyclopentadiene there is no completely reliable way for estimating the values of these integrals (except for the overlap integral, which
would be available from direct integration), the treatment of this substance
loses much of its quantitative significance; it is still, however, of considerable interest in that it leads to the same wave function that we would
have obtained if, from the valence-bond viewpoint, we had represented
the substance as a hybrid not only of the usual structures I and III, but
also of several additional "hyperconjugating" structures like IV and V
(and all their respective analogs and ionic counterparts).

In a nonrigid molecule, in which there is free rotation about one or
more single bonds, the treatment becomes less certain. The procedure
which is usually adopted in such a case can be illustrated by a discussion
of propylene. Let us assume that the molecule of this substance is held
in the particular geometrical conformation shown in structure VI, in

which the heavy and broken lines represent, respectively, bonds to atoms
in front of and behind the plane of the paper. Since the molecule then
has a plane of symmetry, identical with the plane of the paper, all the
atomic orbitals except the ones of the two hydrogen atoms that do not lie
in this plane must be either sigma or pi; and these two noncoplanar
orbitals can, as before, be combined into diatomic sigma and pi orbitals.
Consequently, the treatment of propylene differs from that of 1,3-buta-
diene VII in the same way in which the treatment of cyclopentadiene
differs from that of fulvene. Propylene is therefore described as not
having the unique structure VI, but rather as being a resonance hybrid
of the structures VI, VIII, IX, and their respective ionic counterparts.

Although it is not immediately clear how the procedure should be modified when the molecule is no longer held in the most symmetrical conformation VI, the qualitative picture of propylene as a hybrid of structures VI, VIII, IX, etc., is probably still valid. The application of this same treatment to more complex systems proceeds in the same way and so should require no further comment.

9·28   The Free-Electron Model.[56] Still another kind of molecular-orbital method for the approximate quantum-mechanical treatment of molecular structure is based on the so-called *free-electron model.* This further method, which is often called the FE MO (free-electron molecular-orbital) method, and which has been found most valuable in its application to spectroscopic problems (cf. Chapter 6), can be illustrated first with reference to a linear conjugated polyene $C_{2k}H_{2k+2}$. As in each of the preceding valence-bond and molecular-orbital treatments, the nuclei of all the carbon and hydrogen atoms are again presumed to lie in a single plane, so that the various atomic orbitals are of either the sigma or the pi type. The framework that is formed by the sigma bonds is again taken as the starting point; hence, once more, only the pi electrons remain to be explicitly considered. The distinguishing feature of the treatment is now introduced in the assumption that these latter electrons behave as if they were in a one-dimensional box (see Section 9·4). Their potential energy is accordingly set equal to zero at all points inside this box, but to infinity at all points outside it (cf. pages 550ff); the length of the box is presumed to be at least approximately the same as that of the conjugated system.

In Section 9·4, we found that the energy of an electron in such a one-dimensional box is given by the expression

$$W_n = \frac{n^2 h^2}{8ma^2} \tag{1}$$

where m is the mass of the electron, a is the length of the box, and n is a quantum number which is restricted to the integral values 1, 2, 3, · · ·, ∞ (cf. equation 8, Section 9·4). Since there are altogether $2k$ pi electrons, each of the k most stable electronic levels (molecular orbitals) is doubly occupied in the ground state of the molecule. To the present approximation, therefore, the total energy of the pi electrons is then

$$E = 2 \left[\frac{h^2}{8ma^2} + \frac{4h^2}{8ma^2} + \cdots + \frac{k^2 h^2}{8ma^2} \right] = 2 \sum_{n=1}^{k} \frac{n^2 h^2}{8ma^2} \tag{2}$$

[56] N. S. Bayliss, *J. Chem. Phys.* **16**, 287 (1948); H. Kuhn, *ibid.* **16**, 840 (1948); *Helv. Chim. Acta* **31**, 1441 (1948); W. T. Simpson, *J. Chem. Phys.* **16**, 1124 (1948); J. R. Platt, *ibid.* **17**, 484 (1949).

Although no satisfactory method for the direct comparison of this calculated value with experimental data has as yet been found, a simple extension of the treatment permits a prediction of the wave lengths at which the substances will absorb ultraviolet (or visible) light. The first electronically excited state of any polyene is derived from the corresponding ground state by the promotion of one electron from the highest occupied level to the lowest unoccupied level, or, in other words, by a transition in which the quantum number of one electron changes from k to $k + 1$. The energy of excitation is therefore

$$\Delta W = W_{k+1} - W_k = \frac{(k+1)^2 h^2}{8ma^2} - \frac{k^2 h^2}{8ma^2}$$

$$= \frac{(2k+1)h^2}{8ma^2} \tag{3}$$

and the wave length of the first electronic absorption band is

$$\lambda = \frac{hc}{\Delta W} = \frac{8ma^2 c}{(2k+1)h} \tag{4}$$

where c is the velocity of light.

Equations 3 and 4 contain an additional approximation that is not brought out in the foregoing discussion. As was mentioned on pages 251ff, the excited electronic configuration, in which two levels, the kth and the $(k + 1)$st, are singly occupied, gives rise to two different spectroscopic levels, a singlet and a triplet, since electrons which occupy different orbitals may be either paired or unpaired, respectively, with each other (see Section 9·10). The excitation energy ΔW, defined in equation 3, therefore corresponds to an imaginary process in which the normal molecule is raised not to either of these states but to a point exactly midway between them. The true excitation energies are therefore, respectively, $\Delta W + \delta$ and $\Delta W - \delta$, where δ is a positive quantity of uncertain, but presumably rather small, magnitude. The ideal procedure is therefore to compare the calculated ΔW with the mean of the values measured for the appropriate pair of excited states. Unfortunately, however, it usually happens that, of the two theoretically possible absorption bands, only the one that is due to the transition from the ground state to the excited singlet state is intense enough to be observed; hence, in most instances, one essential datum is missing, and so no definite prediction is possible unless δ is arbitrarily, and incorrectly, set equal to zero. The error which is thus introduced is doubtless appreciable, but it is probably less serious than are the numerous other ones which are unavoidable in any treatment based on the crude free-electron model.

In order to check the accuracy of the wave lengths that can be calculated with the aid of equation 4, we need to have suitable values for the total lengths a of the respective conjugated systems. If the *average* length of the $2k - 1$ carbon-carbon bonds is assumed to be about 1.4 A, then the distance *along the zigzag chain* from either one of the terminal carbon atoms to the other is about $1.4(2k - 1)$ A. However, since the pi electrons are doubtless able to go a short distance beyond each of these terminal atoms, the lengths a might better be assigned slightly greater values (see also below). This uncertainty regarding the exact values of a is particularly unfortunate because the calculated wave length is proportional to a^2, so that any error in a is magnified in λ. For this reason, a convenient procedure is to compute the a's from the observed λ's, rather than vice versa. The extent of agreement between the distances which are thus obtained and the corresponding values of $1.4(2k - 1)$ A is shown in Table 9·3. In a qualitative sense, the treatment is seen to be

TABLE 9·3

CALCULATED LENGTHS OF CONJUGATED POLYENES

Substance	k^a	λ (Observed)[b] (angstroms)	a (Calculated)[b] (angstroms)	$1.4(2k - 1)$ A (angstroms)
Butadiene	2	2100	5.6	4.2
Hexatriene	3	2470	7.2	7.0
Octatetraene	4	2860	8.8	9.8
Vitamin A	5	3060	10.1	12.6
Carotene	11	4200	17.0	29.4

[a] The values of k which are here listed are the numbers of double bonds in the respective complete conjugated systems.
[b] N. S. Bayliss, *J. Chem. Phys.* **16**, 287 (1948). The observed values of λ have been measured in the gas phase or have been corrected to the gas phase.

much better than might have been expected in view of the drastic approximations that have been made. Indeed, the calculated distances not only are of the correct order of magnitude, but also change in the correct direction as the length of the conjugated system is increased. Quantitatively, however, the agreement is not very satisfactory since the calculated distances may differ from $1.4(2k - 1)$ A by a factor of nearly 2. Bayliss[56] considered it desirable to compare the calculated values of a not with $1.4(2k - 1)$ A but with the calculated maximum straight-line distances between the terminal carbon atoms; this modification, however, resulted in no significant improvement in the agreement. Kuhn,[56] on the other hand, suggested that the discrepancies are an unavoidable result of the alternation in the lengths of the carbon-carbon bonds, and hence that better agreement could not be expected with the conjugated polyenes.

In order to avoid this complication of alternating bond lengths, Kuhn[56] considered the group of cyanine dyes that are resonance hybrids of the two equivalent structures I and II, and also of numerous additional ones of which only III and IV need here be mentioned (see also pages 304ff).

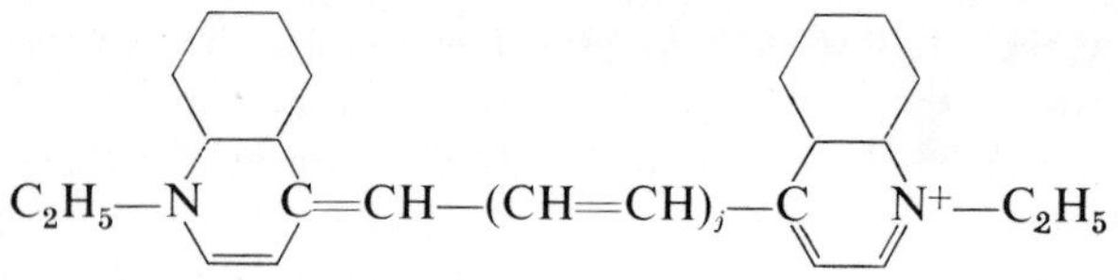

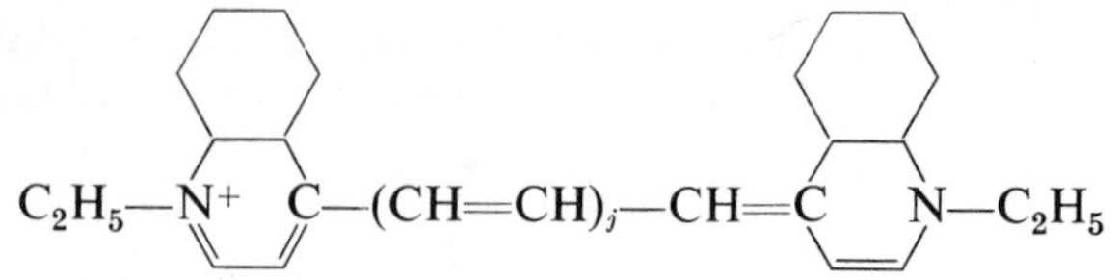

$$C_2H_5\!-\!N \qquad C\!=\!CH\!-\!(CH\!=\!CH)_j\!-\!C \qquad N^+\!-\!C_2H_5$$

$$C_2H_5\!-\!N^+ \qquad C\!-\!(CH\!=\!CH)_j\!-\!CH\!=\!C \qquad N\!-\!C_2H_5$$

II

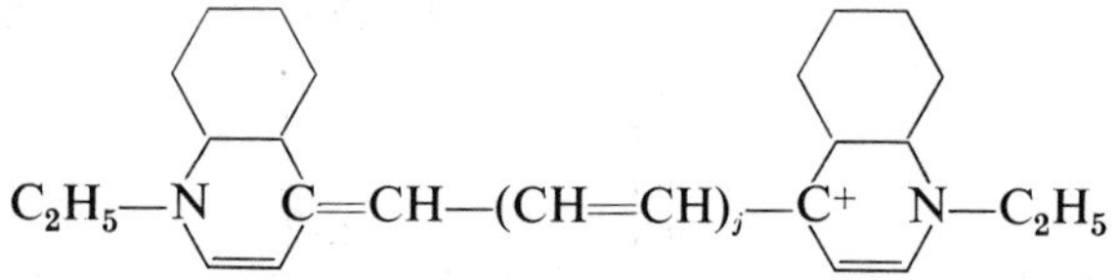

$$C_2H_5\!-\!N \qquad C\!=\!CH\!-\!(CH\!=\!CH)_j\!-\!C^+ \qquad N\!-\!C_2H_5$$

III

$$C_2H_5\!-\!N \qquad C^+\!-\!(CH\!=\!CH)_j\!-\!CH\!=\!C \qquad N\!-\!C_2H_5$$

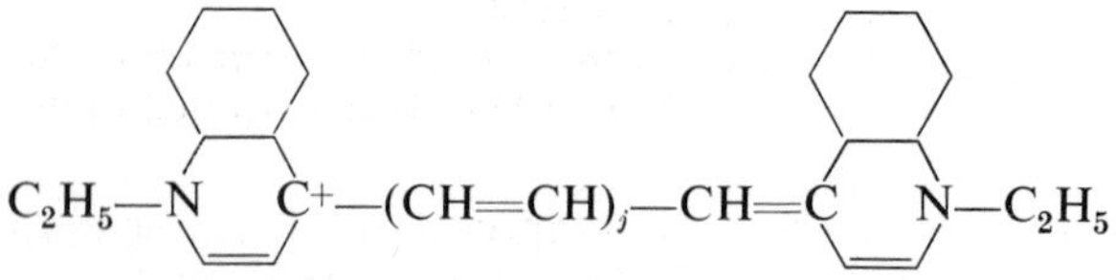

IV

Since, in the molecules of these substances, all the carbon-carbon bonds may be presumed to have the same length, the earlier source of error no longer exists. Two new kinds of difficulty, however, now enter: first, since nitrogen atoms are more electronegative than carbon atoms, the potential within the box should not be strictly constant; and, second, there is no convenient way for taking into account the two benzene rings which are parts of the complete conjugated systems (however, see pages 687ff). Kuhn avoided these complications in the simplest possible way, i.e., by ignoring them. In other words, he treated the dyes as if they were resonance hybrids not of the cationic structures I–IV, etc., but rather of the corresponding anionic structures V–VIII, etc. Since the total length of the conjugated system is then $(2j + 8)d$, where d is the distance between any pair of adjacent atoms, Kuhn assumed that the distance a has the slightly greater value of $(2j + 10)d$ (see page 677).

$$\overset{\displaystyle ..}{C}{}^-H_2 \quad CH{=}CH{-}(CH{=}CH)_j{-}CH \quad CH_2$$
$$\diagdown \quad \diagup \qquad\qquad\qquad\qquad \diagdown \quad \diagup$$
$$CH{=}CH \qquad\qquad\qquad\qquad CH{-}CH$$
$$V$$

$$CH_2 \quad CH{-}(CH{=}CH)_j{-}CH{=}CH \quad \overset{\displaystyle ..}{C}{}^-H_2$$
$$\diagdown \quad \diagup \qquad\qquad\qquad\qquad \diagdown \quad \diagup$$
$$CH{-}CH \qquad\qquad\qquad\qquad CH{=}CH$$
$$VI$$

$$\overset{\displaystyle ..}{C}{}^-H_2 \quad CH{=}CH{-}(CH{=}CH)_j{-}C^+H \quad \overset{\displaystyle ..}{C}{}^-H_2$$
$$\diagdown \quad \diagup \qquad\qquad\qquad\qquad \diagdown \quad \diagup$$
$$CH{=}CH \qquad\qquad\qquad\qquad CH{=}CH$$
$$VII$$

$$\overset{\displaystyle ..}{C}{}^-H_2 \quad C^+H{-}(CH{=}CH)_j{-}CH{=}CH \quad \overset{\displaystyle ..}{C}{}^-H_2$$
$$\diagdown \quad \diagup \qquad\qquad\qquad\qquad \diagdown \quad \diagup$$
$$CH{=}CH \qquad\qquad\qquad\qquad CH{=}CH$$
$$VIII$$

The total number of pi electrons in the ion is $2j + 10$, so that the calculated value of the first excitation energy becomes

$$\Delta W = W_{j+6} - W_{j+5} = \frac{(j + 6)^2 h^2}{8m(2j + 10)^2 d^2} - \frac{(j + 5)^2 h^2}{8m(2j + 10)^2 d^2}$$

$$= \frac{(2j + 11)h^2}{32m(j + 5)^2 d^2} \tag{5}$$

and the calculated wave lengths of the first absorption bands become

$$\lambda = \frac{hc}{\Delta W} = \frac{32(j + 5)^2 m d^2 c}{(2j + 11)h} \tag{6}$$

Although the theoretical significance of the present extreme simplifications is not immediately apparent, the results which are obtained with the use of the final equation 6, with d set equal to 1.39 A, are rather good (see Table 9·4).

Although the first of the two above complications seems to be unavoidable in any *simple* treatment,[57] the one that is caused by the presence

[57] However, see H. Kuhn, *Chimia* (*Switz.*) 4, 203 (1950), and also the discussion below, on pages 687ff.

TABLE 9·4

CALCULATED AND OBSERVED WAVE LENGTHS FOR THE ABSORPTIONS
BY CYANINE DYES

j^a	Wave Length	
	Calculated[b]	Observed[b]
	(angstroms)	(angstroms)
0	5790	5900
1	7060	7100
2	8340	8200
3	9590	9300

[a] For the significance of the letter j, see structures I–IV.
[b] H. Kuhn, *J. Chem. Phys.* **16**, 840 (1948); *Helv. Chim. Acta* **31**, 1441 (1948).

of the benzene rings has been eliminated by Simpson[56] in a study of three less complex cationic dyes which, although again resonance hybrids, can

$$(CH_3)_2N^+\!\!=\!\!CH\!-\!(CH\!=\!CH)_r\!-\!N(CH_3)_2 \qquad (r = 1, 2, 3)$$
$$\text{IX}$$

here be represented by the single typical structure IX. For these substances, the calculated first excitation energies and the calculated wave lengths of the first electronic absorption bands assume the respective forms

$$\Delta W = W_{r+3} - W_{r+2} = \frac{(r + 3)^2 h^2}{8ma^2} - \frac{(r + 2)^2 h^2}{8ma^2} = \frac{(2r + 5)h^2}{8ma^2} \qquad (7)$$

and

$$\lambda = \frac{hc}{\Delta W} = \frac{8ma^2 c}{(2r + 5)h} \qquad (8)$$

If the lengths a of the conjugated systems are assumed to be equal to $(2.48r + 5.04)$ A, where the major part of the additive term 5.04 is here necessary in order to allow for the lengths of the bonds outside the $-(CH\!=\!CH)_r-$ group, then the excellent agreement between observed and calculated wave lengths, shown in Table 9·5, is obtained.

TABLE 9·5

CALCULATED AND OBSERVED WAVE LENGTHS FOR THE ABSORPTIONS
BY SIMPLER ANALOGS OF THE CYANINE DYES

r^a	Wave Length	
	Calculated[b]	Observed[b]
	(angstroms)	(angstroms)
1	3090	3090
2	4090	4090
3	5090	5110

[a] For the significance of the letter r, see structure IX.
[b] W. T. Simpson, *J. Chem. Phys.* **16**, 1124 (1948).

A further type of molecule which can be treated with the aid of the free-electron model is represented by benzene. The box in which the pi electrons are assumed to move has here the shape of a closed circle. The eigenvalues for an electron in such a box can be shown to be

$$W_n = \frac{n^2 h^2}{8\pi^2 m R^2} \tag{9}$$

where R is the radius of the circle, and the quantum number n may have any one of the integral values $0, \pm 1, \pm 2, \cdots, \pm \infty$. (See also pages 692f.) Since there are altogether six pi electrons in the molecule, the first absorption band corresponds to a transition in which n changes from either $+1$ or -1 to either $+2$ or -2. The calculated excitation energy is then

$$\Delta W = \frac{4h^2}{8\pi^2 m R^2} - \frac{h^2}{8\pi^2 m R^2} = \frac{3h^2}{8\pi^2 m R^2} \tag{10}$$

so that the calculated wave length is

$$\lambda = \frac{hc}{\Delta W} = \frac{8\pi^2 m R^2 c}{3h} \tag{11}$$

The situation is rather more complicated here than with a conjugated polyene. Since there are four possible changes in the quantum number n (see above), the excited state to which the calculation refers is now an average of not just one singlet and one triplet, but of four different singlets and four different triplets (see also page 263). Simpson,[56] however, has estimated that a reasonable experimental value of λ is about 2050 A. From equation 11, it then follows that R must be about 1.37 A. This value is satisfactorily close to the observed distance, 1.39 A (see Table 4·3, Section 4·3), of each carbon atom from the center of the ring.

An interesting feature of the free-electron model, which here requires brief comment, is an apparent conflict with the so-called *virial theorem*. This theorem, which is rigorously valid both in classical mechanics and in quantum mechanics[58, 59] is most simply stated in the form of the equation

$$\overline{\text{Kinetic energy}} = -\tfrac{1}{2} \sum_i \overline{x_i X_i + y_i Y_i + z_i Z_i}$$

Here, x_i, y_i, and z_i are the three Cartesian coordinates of the ith particle (electron or nucleus); X_i, Y_i, and Z_i are the components of force which act on the ith particle in directions parallel, respectively, to the x, y, and z axes; the horizontal lines indicate that the *average values* of the specified quantities are to be taken; and the summation

[58] J. C. Slater, *J. Chem. Phys.* **1**, 687 (1933). See also J. O. Hirschfelder and J. F. Kincaid, *Phys. Rev.* **52**, 658 (1937).

[59] Cf., for example, K. S. Pitzer, *Quantum Chemistry*, Prentice-Hall, New York, pp. 139ff, 426ff.

is extended over all the particles in the system of interest. In the particular case in which the only forces that act between the individual particles are those arising from the electrostatic attractions and repulsions, the above equation can be shown[59] to become

$$\overline{\text{Kinetic energy}} = -\tfrac{1}{2} \overline{\text{Potential energy}}$$

so that

$$\overline{\text{Total energy}} = \overline{\text{Kinetic energy}} + \overline{\text{Potential energy}}$$

$$= -\overline{\text{Kinetic energy}}$$

Since, in any molecule, there are indeed no large forces except the coulombic ones, and since the kinetic energy is necessarily positive, two conclusions immediately follow. In the first place, the total energy must always be negative; and, in the second place, the average value of the kinetic energy must decrease as the system becomes less stable (i.e., as the total energy increases toward zero). Both these conclusions are exactly contrary to the results obtained from the free-electron model. The first of the two discrepancies is not extremely disturbing, since the treatment discussed above in this section would not have to be changed in any significant way if the potential in the box were assigned some sufficiently large, but still constant, negative value. The second discrepancy, however, is more serious. There is, in fact, no immediately obvious way for reconciling the free-electron conclusion that the total energy *in*creases as the kinetic energy increases, with the exactly opposite, but correct, inference from the virial theorem that the total energy *de*creases as the kinetic energy increases. (It should be noted that, since the summation in the first equation of this paragraph is over all the particles present in the system of interest, the "total energies" which are here referred to are the energies of the complete molecules and not those of any individual orbitals. As should be quite clear, however, this circumstance has no significant effect upon the problem that is now under discussion.)

The explanation of this conflict (which, incidentally, is not restricted to the free-electron model, but can be shown to be characteristic of *all* molecular-orbital treatments) is presumably the following. Let us consider an electronic transition in which a molecule is raised from its ground state to some excited state, and let us for the moment suppose that all the atomic nuclei are held fixed in their original positions. The free-electron treatment then requires that the kinetic energy be greater in the excited state than in the ground state. The virial theorem, on the other hand, no longer leads to any simple conclusion since we have assumed the existence of additional and non-coulombic forces, namely, the ones required to hold the atomic nuclei fixed. Now, let us suppose that these latter forces are relaxed so that the interatomic distances can change to the values characteristic of the electronically excited state. When this has been done, the molecule will have expanded somewhat, and so the kinetic energy, as well as the magnitude of the potential energy, will have decreased. It is not possible, with the use of only such qualitative arguments as these, to see whether the free-electron model can in this way be completely reconciled with the virial theorem; the following more detailed, but still far from rigorous treatment,[60] however, is sufficient to show that the free-electron model (and also, by inference, all other molecular-orbital treatments as well) can be made consistent with this theorem.

If the length of the one-dimensional box that is assumed in the free-electron calculation is designated as a, then the kinetic energy of the ith electron is, as we have seen, equal to $n_i^2 h^2/8ma^2$, where n_i is the relevant quantum number. More precisely, since

[60] W. Lichten, *J. Chem. Phys.* **22**, 1278 (1954).

the value of a may be expected to vary with the electronic state of the molecule, we may specify that, in the kth state, the length of the box is a_k, so that a more explicit expression for the kinetic energy of the ith electron is then $n_i^2 h^2 / 8 m a_k^2$. The kinetic energy, T_k, of all the particles contained in the molecule can therefore, to the present approximation, be written as A_k / a_k^2, where A_k is a positive constant that involves the quantum numbers and masses of all the particles concerned.

In order to proceed further, we need also an expression for the potential energy V_k as a function of the length of the box. Since this energy is determined solely by Coulomb's law, we shall now make the drastic, but not unreasonable, assumption that V_k is equal to $- B/a_k$, where B is a positive constant that has the same value for all electronic states of the molecule. Although this presumed form of the potential energy seems rather arbitrary, we shall see below that it can be given a certain amount of additional justification.

On the basis of the above assumptions, the total energy E_k of the molecule in the kth state is

$$E_k = T_k + V_k = A_k / a_k^2 - B/a_k$$

(Cf. equation 6, Section 9·5.) In order to find the value of a_k for which the energy E_k is a minimum, we differentiate this equation with respect to a_k and set the first derivative equal to zero. Thus we find that

$$\frac{dE_k}{da_k} = -2A_k/a_k^3 + B/a_k^2 = 0$$

so that
$$a_k = 2A_k/B$$

Hence,
$$T_k = A_k/a_k^2 = B^2/4A_k$$
$$V_k = -B/a_k = -B^2/2A_k$$

and
$$E_k = T_k + V_k = -B^2/4A_k$$

Similarly, for the lth electronic state, which we can without loss of generality take as less stable than the kth, we have:

$$E_l = T_l + V_l = A_l/a_l^2 - B/a_l$$

Hence, in the same way as before, we find that

$$a_l = 2A_l/B$$
$$T_l = B^2/4A_l$$
$$V_l = -B^2/2A_l$$

and
$$E_l = -B^2/4A_l$$

Since E_l is taken as (algebraically) greater than E_k, it follows that $-B^2/4A_l$ is greater than $-B^2/4A_k$, and hence that A_l is greater than A_k. Since $a_k = 2A_k/B$ and $a_l = 2A_l/B$, it follows also that a_l is greater than a_k. Consequently, as was inferred above, the molecule must expand when it undergoes a transition to a higher electronic state. And finally, in each of the states considered, the total energy is negative, and the relations among the kinetic, potential, and total energies are exactly those demanded by the virial theorem (see above). These several conclusions provide the most satisfactory support that can now be advanced for the belief that our assumed forms of the potential energies V_k and V_l are reasonable.

Although the results that have been obtained so far are gratifying, they are not extremely significant, since they may be considered to establish merely that a set of arbitrary assumptions leading to agreement with the virial theorem is not impossible. A more important problem, however, is the following: In the conventional applications of the free-electron model (described in the pages preceding the present group of paragraphs in fine print), the length of the box is assumed to have the same value a_k in the upper state as in the lower. On the basis of this (incorrect) assumption, the kinetic energy is found to increase during the excitation, whereas the potential energy is held constant. The excitation energy ΔE is therefore identified with $\Delta E'$, the calculated increase in kinetic energy (for a box with unchanging length a_k). In the actual molecule, however, the kinetic energy does not increase, but instead decreases, during the transition. In other words, although ΔE must be positive, the calculated $\Delta E'$ is positive only because of a fundamental error in the treatment, namely, the neglect of the expansion of the molecule; when this error is corrected, $\Delta E'$ is replaced by a quite different, and in fact negative, quantity. How then can we legitimately expect ΔE and $\Delta E'$ to be even approximately equal? Part of the answer to this question is doubtless that, so long as we are concerned with only the spectroscopically measured energies of electronic transitions, there is considerable theoretical justification for our assuming the length of the box to be constant. In accordance with the Franck-Condon principle (see page 258), the transition occurs so fast that the nuclei do not have time to reach their new positions; consequently, as far as the wave length of the absorption in the electronic spectrum is concerned, a_k and a_l are essentially equal.

The conflict with the virial theorem, however, presents a problem that is too fundamental to be explained away so simply. Before any theory of molecular structure can be completely acceptable, it must give not only the correct excitation energies for constant interatomic distances, but also the correct relations among the kinetic, potential, and total energies for the equilibrium configurations. In order to carry the discussion further,[60] let us now return to our earlier assumption regarding the dependence of the potential energy upon the length of the box. By employing the equations derived above, we find that

$$\Delta E \equiv E_l - E_k = -B^2/4A_l + B^2/4A_k = \frac{B^2}{4A_kA_l}(A_l - A_k)$$

and that
$$\Delta E' \equiv T_l \Big|_{a_l = a_k} - T_k \Big|_{a_k = a_k}$$

$$= A_l/a_k^2 - A_k/a_k^2 = (A_l - A_k)/a_k^2 = \frac{B^2(A_l - A_k)}{4A_k^2}$$

$$= \frac{B^2(A_l - A_k)}{4A_kA_l} \cdot \frac{A_l}{A_k} = \frac{A_l}{A_k}\Delta E = \left(1 + \frac{A_l - A_k}{A_k}\right)\Delta E$$

Or, since, in all the foregoing applications of the free-electron model, $(A_l - A_k)/A_k$ is doubtless small in comparison with unity,

$$\Delta E' \cong \Delta E$$

Consequently, to the extent that our basic assumptions are valid, the calculated true excitation energy ΔE is approximately equal to the (incorrectly) calculated quantity $\Delta E'$, so that the original simple treatment is justified. Although we cannot estimate the importance of the errors that have been caused by our use of rather unrealistic expressions for the potential and kinetic energies, we have, nevertheless, gained some insight into the way in which the free-electron model and the virial theorem can be reconciled. We shall now, therefore, return to the earlier treatment outlined at the beginning of this section, and we shall hereafter concern ourselves no further with the theoretical difficulties which have just been discussed.

As was pointed out on page 676, the treatments that are based on the free-electron model do not readily provide figures from which resonance energies can be calculated;[61] these treatments do, however, lead to definite and quite interesting conclusions regarding the average charge distributions that obtain when the molecules are in their ground states.[57] Let us, for example, compare in this respect octatetraene, X, and the cation IX, with $r = 2$ (see page 680).   Since each of the two molecules

$$CH_2=CH—CH=CH—CH=CH—CH=CH_2$$
X

contains eight pi electrons, the two corresponding treatments are identical except in the following ways: first, the total lengths a of the conjugated systems are not exactly equal; and second, there are eight atomic kernels in the neutral molecule, but only seven in the charged one.   Of these two differences, the latter is much the more important, and it is the only one with which we need here be concerned.

In view of the physical significance which wave functions are presumed to have (see Section 9·2), it follows that the average distribution of pi electronic charge in each molecule can be represented by the function

$$F(x) \equiv \psi_1{}^2 + \psi_2{}^2 + \psi_3{}^2 + \psi_4{}^2 = \sum_{n=1}^{4} \psi_n{}^2 \qquad (12)$$

where ψ_n is the *normalized* orbital for quantum number n.   Comparison with equations 2 and 11, Section 9·4, now shows that $F(x)$ can be written more explicitly as

$$\left. \begin{aligned} F(x) &= 0 & -\infty \leq x \leq 0 \\ &= \frac{4}{a} \sum_{n=1}^{4} \sin^2\left(\frac{\pi n x}{a}\right) & 0 \leq x \leq a \\ &= 0 & a \leq x \leq +\infty \end{aligned} \right\} \qquad (13)$$

where x is the distance, along the chain of atoms, from either end of the conjugated system.   This function is plotted in Figure 9·13, in which the squares and circles along the abscissa mark the approximate positions of the atomic kernels in, respectively, octatetraene and the ion IX ($r = 2$). In octatetraene, the net charges on the eight atoms are seen to be essentially equal, but the concentrations of the electrons in the regions between the kernels show considerable variation, with alternate high and low density of charge in the seven bonds.   The calculated charge distribution

[61] For a relatively unsuccessful attempt to calculate resonance energies, see C. W. Scherr, *J. Chem. Phys.* **21**, 1413, 1582 (1953).

is therefore close to what would have been expected for a molecule that is a resonance hybrid receiving a large contribution from only the conventional structure X, and smaller contributions from the several less stable structures like XI and XII.   On the other hand, in the ion IX, the

$$CH_2—CH=CH—CH—CH=CH—CH=CH_2$$

XI

$$CH_2—CH=CH—CH=CH—CH=CH—CH_2$$

XII

net charges on the seven atoms now alternate, but the concentrations of the electrons in the regions between the kernels are essentially equal.

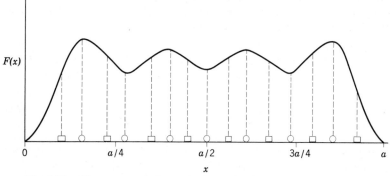

$F(x)$

0          $a/4$ $a/2$ $3a/4$ a

x

Fig. 9·13.   The average pi electronic charge density $F(x)$ as a function of the distance x from the end of the conjugated system in octatetraene (□) and in a simplified cyanine (○).

Indeed, the calculated charge distribution is here similar to that expected for an ion which is a resonance hybrid receiving large contributions from all five of the structures XIII–XVII.   In view of the particularly close

$$(CH_3)_2N^+=CH—CH=CH—CH=CH—N(CH_3)_2$$
XIII

$$(CH_3)_2N—CH=CH—CH=CH—CH=N^+(CH_3)_2$$
XIV

$$(CH_3)_2N—C^+H—CH=CH—CH=CH—N(CH_3)_2$$
XV

$$(CH_3)_2N—CH=CH—CH=CH—C^+H—N(CH_3)_2$$
XVI

$$(CH_3)_2N—CH=CH—C^+H—CH=CH—N(CH_3)_2$$
XVII

analogy between the present calculations and those based on the more conventional molecular-orbital (LCAO MO) treatment, the fact that this third approach can be shown also to lead to qualitatively the same charge distributions is only to be expected.   And finally, with benzene, all three methods are found similarly to agree in predicting that the six carbon atoms have the same net charge, and that the electrons are equally concentrated in the six carbon-carbon bonds.

Possibly the most interesting feature of the free-electron model is that the only empirical parameters which it requires are the distances a (or R) and the physical constants m, h, and c.   Of these several quantities, the only one which is not always precisely known is the first one, a (or R); and, even for this parameter, there is never a wide range of possible values. The present procedure therefore differs significantly from the earlier ones, in which the values of the respective parameters J, β, and γ could not be independently determined, but had always to be estimated by comparison with the very data which were the objects of the calculations.

The most serious limitation of the free-electron model, in the simple form described above, is that it is not strictly applicable to the treatment of molecules in which the conjugated systems are branched, as in the cyanine dyes that are hybrids of the structures I–IV, or in naphthalene, anthracene, etc.   For the treatment of these more complex molecules, there have been devised more elaborate procedures,[62] which, however, suffer from the disadvantage of being mathematically somewhat more tedious.   The remainder of this section will be devoted to a discussion of these treatments in essentially the form adopted in the comprehensive and systematic paper of Rüdenberg and Scherr.[62]

In order to extend the free-electron model to more complex types of unsaturated and aromatic hydrocarbon, we shall make the following simplifying assumptions: (1) the sigma electrons may, as usual, be ignored, so that only the pi electrons remain to be considered; (2) the distance between each pair of adjacent carbon atoms has the constant value D; and (3) each molecular orbital becomes equal to zero at a distance D beyond any terminal atom that may be present.   The significance of this last assumption can be made clearer with the aid of the diagram

$$|\text{---}C\text{---}C\text{---}C\text{---}C\text{---}|$$

which illustrates the situation that is considered to apply with 1,3-butadiene.   The C's here mark the positions of the four carbon nuclei, and the vertical lines mark the boundaries of the region in which the electrons

---

[62] H. Kuhn, *Helv. Chim. Acta* **32**, 2247 (1949); *Z. Elektrochem.* **55**, 220 (1951); K. Rüdenberg and R. G. Parr, *J. Chem. Phys.* **19**, 1268 (1951); K. Rüdenberg and C. W. Scherr, *ibid.* **21**, 1565 (1953); H. Kuhn, *ibid.* **22**, 2098 (1954).

can be found.   Each of the distances $|$—C, C—C, and C—$|$ is then equal to D, and no significance is to be attached to the lack of zigzags in the figure. (The treatment of Rüdenberg and Scherr is sufficiently general so that not all of these assumptions are necessary; they will here be adopted, however, since they materially simplify the following calculations.)

In addition to the three foregoing assumptions, we shall employ also the usual conditions that are always imposed on wave functions.   Each orbital must therefore be everywhere a continuous function of its co-ordinate, and so must its first derivative.

Let us begin by considering the region between a given pair of adjacent atoms r and s.   For definiteness, we can represent an orbital in this region as $\psi_{rs}(x_{rs})$, and we can specify that the coordinate x_{rs} is equal to zero at the nucleus of atom r, and to D at that of atom s.   The expressions $\psi_{rs}(0)$ and $\psi_{rs}(D)$ are therefore the values of the orbital at the first and second nuclei, respectively.   It is not required that either $\psi_{rs}(0)$ or $\psi_{rs}(D)$ be equal to 0.   Similarly, but somewhat inexactly, $d\psi_{rs}(0)/dx_{rs}$ and $d\psi_{rs}(D)/dx_{rs}$ are the values of the first derivative at the two points.

Since the potential energy is assumed to be zero, the orbital $\psi_{rs}(x_{rs})$, which is defined only in the region $0 \leq x_{rs} \leq D$, must have the form

$$\psi_{rs}(x_{rs}) = A_{rs} \cos (Kx_{rs} + \delta_{rs}) \tag{14}$$

where $$K \equiv \sqrt{\frac{8\pi^2 m W}{h^2}} \tag{15}$$

and A_{rs}, W, and δ_{rs} are, respectively, an amplitude constant, the energy of an electron occupying the orbital, and a phase constant.   (See Section 9·4.)   In each of the remaining regions between adjacent atoms, the wave function has a form similar to that shown in equation 14.   Thus,

$$\psi_{st}(x_{st}) = A_{st} \cos (Kx_{st} + \delta_{st}) \tag{16}$$

and so on.   For the sake of consistency in nomenclature, the coordinate x_{st} must now be defined so that it is equal to zero at the nucleus of atom s, and to D at that of atom t.   In general, the amplitudes A_{rs}, A_{st}, etc., and the phase constants δ_{rs}, δ_{st}, etc., are different for each pair of atoms; in any complete orbital that extends over the entire molecule, however, the energy W, and hence also the related constant K (cf. equation 15), must have the same value in all the various regions.

As a consequence of the way in which the functions ψ_{rs}, ψ_{st}, etc., and the coordinates x_{rs}, x_{st}, etc., are defined, the identities

$$\psi_{mn}(0) \equiv \psi_{nm}(D) \equiv \psi(m) \tag{17}$$

where $\psi(m)$ is the value of the orbital at the nucleus of atom m, are necessarily valid for any pair of adjacent atoms m and n.   Similarly,

$$\frac{d\psi_{mn}(0)}{dx_{mn}} \equiv -\frac{d\psi_{nm}(D)}{dx_{nm}} \tag{18}$$

From equations 14, 16, and their analogs, it follows that, within each region between adjacent atoms, both the orbital and its first derivative are continuous.   However, at the points at which the different regions touch, i.e., at the positions of the atomic nuclei, there will in general be discontinuities unless the values of the constants A_{rs}, A_{st}, etc., δ_{rs}, δ_{st}, etc., and W are properly chosen.   Since such discontinuities are not permitted (see above), we must now therefore consider how the correct values of these constants can be obtained.

There are three situations that must be separately considered, since (1) a given atom s may be adjacent to only a single other atom r; or (2) it may be adjacent to exactly two other atoms r and t; or (3) it may be adjacent to three other atoms r, t, and u.   Since the second of these possibilities is the most easily treated, we shall begin with it.   The condition that the wave function itself be continuous at the nucleus of atom s is then that

$$\psi_{sr}(0) = \psi_{st}(0) = \psi(s) \tag{19}$$

(cf. also the identities 17).   The condition that the first derivative also be continuous is that

$$\frac{d\psi_{rs}(D)}{dx_{rs}} \equiv -\frac{d\psi_{sr}(0)}{dx_{sr}} = \frac{d\psi_{st}(0)}{dx_{st}} \tag{20}$$

or that

$$\frac{d\psi_{sr}(0)}{dx_{sr}} + \frac{d\psi_{st}(0)}{dx_{st}} = 0 \tag{21}$$

In order to make use of equation 21, we need an additional relation, which we can derive in the following way.   From an equation analogous to 14 and 16, we have:

$$\psi(r) = \psi_{sr}(D) = A_{sr} \cos (KD + \delta_{sr})$$
$$= A_{sr}[\cos (KD) \cos \delta_{sr} - \sin (KD) \sin \delta_{sr}]$$
$$= \cos (KD)\psi_{sr}(0) + (1/K) \sin (KD) \frac{d\psi_{sr}(0)}{dx_{sr}}$$
$$= \cos (KD)\psi(s) + (1/K) \sin (KD) \frac{d\psi_{sr}(0)}{dx_{sr}} \tag{22}$$

Similarly $\psi(t) = A_{st} \cos (KD + \delta_{st})$
$$= \cos (KD)\psi(s) + (1/K) \sin (KD) \frac{d\psi_{st}(0)}{dx_{st}} \tag{23}$$

Now, by adding equations 22 and 23, and then making use of equation 21, we find that

$$\psi(r) + \psi(t) = 2\cos(KD)\psi(s) + (1/K)\sin(KD)\left[\frac{d\psi_{sr}(0)}{dx_{sr}} + \frac{d\psi_{st}(0)}{ds_{st}}\right]$$

$$= 2\cos(KD)\psi(s) \tag{24}$$

Hence it follows that

$$\psi(r) + x\psi(s) + \psi(t) = 0 \tag{25}$$

where

$$x = -2\cos(KD) = -2\cos\left(\sqrt{\frac{8\pi^2 m W}{h^2}}\, D\right) \tag{26}$$

For each atom s that has two, and only two, nearest neighbors, there will be an equation of the form 25.

When the atom s is adjacent to a single other atom r, the treatment is only slightly more difficult. Since the orbital is assumed to extend a distance D beyond the terminal atom s (see above), we can conveniently define a function $\psi_{st}(x_{st})$ which has the form shown in equation 16, but which now satisfies the relation

$$\psi_{st}(D) = \psi_{ts}(0) \equiv \psi(t) = 0 \tag{27}$$

Equation 25 therefore becomes

$$\psi(r) + x\psi(s) = 0 \tag{28}$$

and, since there is no atom t, there is no equation containing the term $x\psi(t)$. For each atom s that has only one nearest neighbor, however, there will be an equation of the form 28.

When the atom s is adjacent to three other atoms r, t, and u, the significance of the requirement that the first derivative be continuous at the nucleus of s is not immediately apparent. By a procedure which is too complicated to be given here, it can, however, be shown[62] that the correct generalization of equation 21 is the quite reasonable one

$$\frac{d\psi_{sr}(0)}{dx_{sr}} + \frac{d\psi_{st}(0)}{dx_{st}} + \frac{d\psi_{su}(0)}{dx_{su}} = 0 \tag{29}$$

Now, equations 22 and 23 can again be derived in the way already described, as can also the further, completely analogous one

$$\psi(u) = \psi_{su}(D) = \cos(KD)\,\psi(s) + (1/K)\sin(KD)\frac{d\psi_{su}(0)}{dx_{su}} \tag{30}$$

Addition of equations 22, 23, and 30 then gives

$$\psi(r) + \psi(t) + \psi(u)$$

$$= 3 \cos (KD)\psi(s) + (1/K) \sin (KD) \left[\frac{d\psi_{sr}(0)}{dx_{sr}} + \frac{d\psi_{st}(0)}{dx_{st}} + \frac{d\psi_{su}(0)}{dx_{su}} \right] \quad (31)$$

or, as a result of equation 29,

$$\psi(r) + \psi(t) + \psi(u) = 3 \cos (KD)\psi(s) \qquad (32)$$

or $$\qquad \psi(r) + \tfrac{3}{2}x\psi(s) + \psi(t) + \psi(u) = 0 \qquad (33)$$

For each atom s that has three nearest neighbors r, t, and u, there will be an equation of the form 33.

If the hydrocarbon molecule contains altogether N carbon atoms, the relations 25, 28, and 33 give us altogether N equations for the N unknown quantities, $\psi(r)$, $\psi(s)$, etc. Since each of these quantities is merely the value that the orbital of interest assumes at the position of the specified atomic nucleus, it is a numerical constant. Consequently, the set of N equations will have a nontrivial solution only if the determinant of the coefficients is equal to zero (cf. pages 576 and 585). As in the original molecular-orbital (LCAO MO) treatment, therefore, we are here also led to a secular equation, the roots of which determine the permissible energies W of the orbitals. For any given molecule, the secular equations that are based upon the two methods of calculation are superficially very similar. Indeed, the only difference between them is that, when the free-electron model is employed, each diagonal element of the determinant is equal to x, x, or $\tfrac{3}{2}x$ if the atom to which it refers is adjacent, respectively, to 1, 2, or 3 other unsaturated carbon atoms; but that, when the LCAO molecular-orbital approach is adopted, each diagonal element is instead equal to x regardless of the nature of the atom concerned. The resemblance between the two treatments is, however, only formal since the quantities which play analogous roles in the calculations have quite different physical significances. Although the parameter x is related to the orbital energy W by equation 26 in the free-electron treatment, it is related by the different equation

$$x = \frac{\alpha - W}{\gamma - SW} \qquad (34)$$

in the more usual molecular-orbital treatment (cf. equation 2, Section 9·25).

After the values of x have been found by solution of the secular equation, the ratios of the constants $\psi(r)$, $\psi(s)$, etc., can be obtained with the aid of the linear equations 25, 28, and 33; and from these ratios, together with the normalization condition, the complete orbitals can be determined.[62] Since, however, the procedure turns out to be rather tedious, and since the results to which it leads are not essential to our further discussion, we shall here consider it no further.

The relation between the foregoing development of the free-electron model and the earlier less general discussion can be most easily brought out by a consideration of a few simple examples. First let us treat a cyclic polyene C_nH_n of the type represented by benzene $(n = 6)$. Since each carbon atom has exactly two nearest neighbors, the secular equation is formally identical with the one derived in the molecular-orbital (LCAO MO) treatment:

$$
\begin{vmatrix}
x & 1 & 0 & \cdots & 0 & y \\
1 & x & 1 & \cdots & 0 & 0 \\
0 & 1 & x & \cdots & 0 & 0 \\
\cdot & \cdot & \cdot & \cdots & \cdot & \cdot \\
\cdot & \cdot & \cdot & \cdots & \cdot & \cdot \\
\cdot & \cdot & \cdot & \cdots & \cdot & \cdot \\
0 & 0 & 0 & \cdots & x & 1 \\
y & 0 & 0 & \cdots & 1 & x
\end{vmatrix} = 0 \tag{35}
$$

with $y = 1$ (cf. Section 9·25). The roots are

$$x = -2 \cos (2\pi j/n) \qquad (j = 1, 2, \cdots, n) \tag{36}$$

so that $KD \equiv \sqrt{\dfrac{8\pi^2 m W}{h^2}}\, D = \cos^{-1}\left[\cos (2\pi j/n)\right]$

$$= \frac{2\pi j}{n} + 2\pi k \qquad (k = 0, \pm1, \pm2, \cdots, \pm\infty) \tag{37}$$

(Cf. equation 26.) Hence

$$W = \left[\frac{2\pi(j + kn)}{n}\right]^2 \frac{h^2}{8\pi^2 m D^2} = \frac{(j + kn)^2 h^2}{2n^2 m D^2} \tag{38}$$

Now, nD is the circumference of the polygon formed by the n carbon atoms. If this polygon is distorted into a circle, with no change in the circumference, then the energy levels would be unaffected, and nD would become equal to $2\pi R$, where R is the radius of the circle. Equation 38 therefore becomes

$$W = \frac{h^2(j + kn)^2}{8\pi^2 m R^2} \tag{39}$$

Since the expression $j + kn$ can assume any of the values $0, \pm1, \pm2,$ $\cdots, \pm\infty$, equation 39 is completely equivalent to the one given in our earlier discussion of the same problem. (Cf. equation 9.) It is of interest that, although the secular equation 35 was of finite order n, and so had only n roots, an infinite number of energies W are obtained because the function $\cos^{-1}[\cos(2\pi j/n)]$ is not single valued. (Cf. equation 37.)

We now turn to a linear polyene $C_{2n}H_{2n+2}$ of the type represented by 1,3-butadiene ($n = 2$). Since each carbon atom has either one or two nearest neighbors, the secular equation is again identical with the one obtained in the molecular-orbital (LCAO MO) treatment, and it has the same form 35 as before, but now with y equal to 0. The roots can be shown to be[63]

$$x = -2 \cos \frac{\pi j}{2n + 1} \qquad (j = 1, 2, \cdots, n) \tag{40}$$

so that $KD \equiv \sqrt{\dfrac{8\pi^2 m W}{h^2}} \, D = \cos^{-1}\left[\cos \dfrac{\pi j}{2n + 1}\right]$

$$= \frac{\pi j}{2n + 1} + 2\pi k \qquad (k = 0, \pm 1, \pm 2, \cdots, \pm \infty) \tag{41}$$

Hence $\quad W = \left[\dfrac{\pi(j + 4kn + 2k)}{2n + 1}\right]^2 \dfrac{h^2}{8\pi^2 m D^2}$

$$= \frac{(j + 4kn + 2k)^2 h^2}{8m(2n + 1)^2 D^2} \tag{42}$$

Now, $(2n + 1)D$ is equal to the length a of the one-dimensional box in which the electrons are presumed to move, so that equation 42 becomes

$$W = \frac{(j + 4kn + 2k)^2 h^2}{8ma^2} \tag{43}$$

Since the quantity $j + 4kn + 2k$ can assume any of the values 1, 2, $\cdots$, ∞, equation 43 is identical with the one which we used in our earlier and more straightforward free-electron treatment of the system. (Cf. equation 1.) Again, although the secular equation 35 is of finite degree, an infinite number of different energies W are obtained.

The extension of the treatment to such other hydrocarbons as naphthalene, anthracene, etc., proceeds in a completely similar way. As was mentioned above, the secular equations differ from those obtained by the earlier molecular-orbital method only in that the diagonal elements are now equal to $\frac{3}{2}x$, instead of x, when they refer to atoms with three nearest

[63] Cf., for example, E. Hückel, Z. Physik 76, 628 (1932).

neighbors (and also in the significance of the parameter x). If the molecules have elements of symmetry, the equations can be factored in essentially the same way as before. No further comment, therefore, should here be necessary. The reader may again, however, be referred to the comprehensive paper by Rüdenberg and Scherr,[62] in which is demonstrated the essential identity of the results obtained from the free-electron and more conventional molecular-orbital (LCAO MO) methods.

Still another, much simpler, method for the treatment of relatively complex aromatic hydrocarbons has been devised by Platt.[64] This procedure is based on the assumption that the pi electrons can be imagined to move in a *two*-dimensional box with the approximate size and shape of the actual molecule. With benzene and with coronene, XVIII, the boxes are therefore circular and, with naphthalene and with anthracene,

XVIII   XIX

they are rectangular. Since the potential energy inside the box is again set equal to zero, no explicit account is taken of the framework formed by the sigma bonds. Nevertheless, the calculated charge distributions are qualitatively and semiquantitatively identical with those obtained by the methods described in the preceding sections. Even such relatively small effects as the greater densities of electronic charge in the bonds between the α carbon atoms and their adjacent β carbon atoms in naphthalene and in anthracene (cf. pages 192ff) are accurately reproduced. The most serious limitation of this method of treatment is that, with an unsymmetrical molecule like that of 1,2-benzanthracene, XIX, for example, the shape of the two-dimensional box would have to be so irregular that the solution of the wave equation would become impracticable. An example of intermediate complexity is represented by phenanthrene, for which fairly satisfactory results have been obtained with the use of a semicircular box.

[64] J. R. Platt, *J. Chem. Phys.* **22**, 1448 (1954).

Appendix

EXPLANATION FOR TABLE

Although many omissions must inevitably occur, the attempt has been made to have this list of organic compounds complete up to about July 1954. A few simple inorganic compounds are also included for purposes of comparison.

The various substances are listed in the order of their molecular formulas or, when the molecular weights are uncertain, in that of their empirical formulas. For most of the substances, the formulas and names are sufficient identification; for certain others, however, the structures must be indicated in greater detail in order that the identities of the bonds and angles referred to in the third and fourth columns may be unambiguous. For simplicity, only a single structure is given for each substance, even though resonance among several structures may be important; and frequently the multiplicities of certain bonds and the positions of tautomeric hydrogen atoms are not explicitly indicated. Since it would be inconvenient to use only a single system for the representation of the many different structures, several such systems have here been adopted. (1) Ordinarily, it is satisfactory to distinguish among the structurally nonequivalent atoms of a given element by the use of superscripts, as in C', C'', C^*, etc. (2) With more complicated structures, the bonds are represented by lower-case letters, as a, b, etc., and the angles are represented by the pair of letters that refer to the bonds concerned, so that, for example, the angle ab is the one between the bonds a and b. (3) With the most complicated structures, the values of the bond lengths and bond angles are written directly on the structures themselves.

All bond lengths are given in angstrom units, and all angles are given in degrees. The probable errors are as estimated by the original authors; those enclosed in braces are not strictly probable errors but are instead standard deviations. Assumed values are given in parentheses. Values separated by commas represent different values assigned by the original authors to different, but structurally equivalent, bonds or angles; especially with the data obtained from investigations of crystal structure, such divergences do not necessarily imply experimental errors, since each bond length or angle may be affected by the environment and, more particularly, by the presence of intra- or intermolecular hydrogen bonds. In the fourth column, values in square brackets give the distances, in angstroms, between the stated pairs of atoms which are bonded to a single common atom; from these distances and the pertinent bond lengths, the angles can be computed.

The experimental methods by which the bonds lengths and bond angles have been determined are indicated in the column with the heading "Exp. Method." The meanings of the symbols used in this column are: E, electron diffraction by the gaseous substance; S, spectroscopic method, including microwave; and X, x-ray diffraction by the crystalline substance (see Section 4·3).

695

Interatomic Distances and Bond Angles in Organic Molecules

Formula	Substance Name	Bond Lengths		Bond Angles		Exp. Method	Remarks	Reference*
C	Diamond	CC	1.5445 ± 0.00014	CCC	109° 28'	X		R, 1, 2
C	Graphite	CC	1.42	CCC	120°	X	3.41 A between planes.	R, 3, 4
CBrCl₃	Bromotrichloromethane	CBr CCl	2.01 1.76	[BrCl] [ClCl]	3.00 2.95	E		5
CBrF₃	Bromotrifluoromethane	CBr CF	1.91₁ ± 0.033 1.34₃ ± 0.021	FCF	109.5° ± 2°	E		6
		CBr CF	1.91 ± 0.02 1.33 ± 0.015	FCF	(108° ± 1°)	S		GST, 7, 8
CBrN	Cyanogen bromide	CBr CN	1.790 ± <0.01 1.158 ± <0.01	BrCN	180°	S		GST, 9, 10
		CBr CN	1.79 ± 0.02 1.13 ± 0.04	BrCN	180°	E		11
CBr₂Cl₂	Dibromodichloromethane	CBr CCl	1.93 1.75	[BrBr] [BrCl] [ClCl]	3.15 3.01 1.86	E		12
CBr₂O	Carbonyl bromide	CBr CO	2.05 ± 0.04 1.13 ± 0.02	BrCBr	110° ± 5°	E	Planar.	13
CBr₃F	Fluorotribromomethane	CBr CF	1.91 ± 0.04 1.44 ± 0.06	[BrBr] [BrF]	3.20 ± 0.03 2.70 ± 0.02	E		14
CBr₄	Carbon tetrabromide	CBr	1.94	BrCBr	109° 28'	E		15, 16
CCaO₃	Calcite	CO	1.313	OCO	120°	X	Planar anion.	17
CClF₃	Chlorotrifluoromethane	CCl CF	1.74₇ ± 0.040 1.32₃ ± 0.032	FCF	108.5° ± 3°	E		6
		CCl CF	1.740 ± 0.02 1.328 ± 0.008	FCF	(108° ± 1°)	S		GST, 7

* Citations in table begin on page 785.

Formula	Name	Bond distances (Å)	Angles	Method		Ref.
CCIN	Cyanogen chloride	CCl 1.629 ± <0.01; CN 1.163 ± <0.01	ClCN 180°	S		GST, 9, 10
		CCl 1.67 ± 0.02; CN 1.13 ± 0.03	ClCN 180°	E		11
CCl₂F₂	Dichlorodifluoromethane	CCl 1.74 ± 0.03; CF 1.35 ± 0.03	ClCCl 113° ± 2°; ClCF 110° ± 2°; FCF 109° ± 2°	E		18
CCl₂O	Phosgene	CCl 1.74 ± 0.02; CO 1.18 ± 0.03	ClCCl 112.5° ± 1.5°	E	Planar.	B, 13, 19, 20
		CCl 1.74 ± 0.02; CO 1.15 ± 0.02	ClCCl 111.0° ± 1.5°	X	Planar.	21
		CCl 1.746 ± 0.004; CO 1.166 ± 0.002	ClCCl 111.3° ± 0.1°	S	Planar.	22
CCl₂S	Thiophosgene	CCl 1.70 ± 0.02; CS 1.63	ClCCl 116°; ClCS 122°	E	Planar.	19
CCl₃F	Fluorotrichloromethane	CCl 1.76 ± 0.02; CF 1.40 ± 0.04	ClCCl 111.5° ± 1°; FCCl 107.5° ± 1°	E		18
CCl₄	Carbon tetrachloride	CCl 1.755 ± 0.005	ClCCl 109° 28'	E		16, 18
CCl₄S	"Perchlorthiophosgene"	CCl 1.76; CS 1.81; SCl 2.03	ClCS 109° ± 4°	E		23
CF₂O	Carbonyl fluoride	CF 1.32 ± 0.02; CO 1.17 ± 0.02	FCF 112.5° ± 6°	E		24
CF₃I	Iodotrifluoromethane	CF 1.32₈ ± 0.026; CI 2.12₂ ± 0.037	FCF 108.3° ± 2°	E		6
		CF (1.332); CI 2.14 ± 0.02	FCF (108° ± 1°)	S		GST, 7
CF₄	Carbon tetrafluoride	CF 1.33₇ ± 0.022	FCF (109° 28')	E		6, 18, 25

Formula	Substance Name	Bond Lengths	Bond Angles	Exp. Method	Remarks	Reference
CF_8S	Trifluoromethyl sulfurpentafluoride $CF_3—SF_5$	CF (1.35), CS 1.86, SF (1.57)	FCF (107° 30'), FSF (90°)	S	Chemical structure confirmed.	GST, 26
$CHBr_3$	Bromoform	CBr (1.91)	BrCBr 111° ± 2°	E		15
		CBr 1.930 ± 0.003, CH 1.07 ± 0.01	BrCBr 110° 48' ± 0° 16'	S		GST, 27
$CHClF_2$	Chlorodifluoromethane	CCl 1.73 ± 0.03, CF 1.36 ± 0.03	ClCF 110.5° ± 1°, FCF 110.5° ± 1°	E		18
$CHCl_2F$	Dichlorofluoromethane	CCl 1.73 ± 0.04, CF 1.41 ± 0.03	ClCCl 112° ± 2°, ClCF 109° ± 2°	E		18
$CHCl_3$	Chloroform	CCl 1.77 ± 0.02	ClCCl 112° ± 2°	E		18
		CH 1.073, CCl 1.767	ClCCl 110° 24'	S		GST, 28
CHF_3	Fluoroform	CH 1.098, CF 1.332	FCF 108° 48'	S		GST, 28
CHI_3	Iodoform	CI 2.12 ± 0.04	ICI 113.0°	E		16, 29
		CI 2.18 ± 0.02		X		30
$CHKO_3$	Potassium bicarbonate	CO 1.28, 1.32, 1.33	OCO 118.5°, 119.5°, 122°	X		31
CHN	Hydrogen cyanide	CH 1.0657, CN 1.1530	HCN 180°	S		GST, 32, 33
$CHNO$	Isocyanic acid	CN 1.19 ± 0.03, CO 1.19 ± 0.03	HNC 125°, NCO 180°	E		34
	HNCO	CN 1.207 ± 0.01, CO 1.171 ± 0.01, NH 0.987 ± 0.01	HNC 128° 5' ± 0° 30', NCO 180°	S		GST, 35

Formula	Name	Bond	Length	Angle	Value	Method	Notes	References
CHNS	Isothiocyanic acid	CN	1.2158	HNC	130° 15' ± 0° 15'	S	Some values for DNCS are slightly different.	GST, 36
	HNCS	CS	1.5609 ± 0.0020	NCS	180°			
		NH	1.013					
$CH NaO_2$	Sodium formate	CO	1.27	OCO	124°	X		37
$(CH_2)_n$	Polyethylene	CC	1.53	CCC	112°	X		R, 38
CH_2Br_2	Methylene bromide	CBr	1.91 ± 0.02	BrCBr	112° ± 2°	E		15, 39
CH_2ClF	Chlorofluoromethane	CCl	1.76 ± 0.02	ClCF	110° ± 2°	E		18
		CF	1.40 ± 0.03					
		CH	1.078 ± 0.005	HCH	(111° 56')	S		40
		CCl	1.759 ± 0.003	ClCF	110° 1' ± 2'			
		CF	1.378 ± 0.006					
CH_2Cl_2	Methylene chloride	CCl	1.77 ± 0.02	ClCCl	112° ± 2°	E		18, 39
		CH	1.068 ± 0.005	HCH	112° 0' ± 20'	S		GST, 41
		CCl	1.7724 ± 0.0005	ClCCl	111° 47' ± 1'			
CH_2F_2	Methylene fluoride	CH	(1.09)	HCH	(109.5°)	E		18, 42
		CF	$1.35_7 ± 0.01_7$	FCF	107.5° ± 1.5°			
		CH	1.092 ± 0.003	HCH	111° 52' ± 25'	S		GST, 43
		CF	1.358 ± 0.001	FCF	108° 17' ± 6'			
CH_2I_2	Methylene iodide	CI	2.12 ± 0.04	ICI	114.7°	E		16, 29, 39
CH_2N_2	Diazomethane	CN	1.34 ± 0.05	CNN	180°	E		B, 44
		NN	1.13 ± 0.04					
CH_2O	Formaldehyde	CH	1.09 ± 0.01	HCH	120° ± 1°	E, S	Planar.	45
		CO	1.21 ± 0.01					
		CH	1.060 ± 0.038	HCH	125° 48' ± 7° 0'	S	Planar.	GST, 46
		CO	1.230 ± 0.017					
CH_2O_2	Formic acid	C—O	1.36 ± 0.01	OCO	122.4° ± 1°	E	See also $C_2H_4O_4$.	47, 48
		C=O	1.23 ± 0.01					

699

Formula	Substance Name	Bond Lengths	Bond Angles	Exp. Method	Remarks	Reference
		C—O 1.26 ± 0.03 C=O 1.23 ± 0.03	OCO 123° ± 1°	X	Solid, at −50°C. Molecules arranged in infinite chains. O—H--O distance is 2.58 ± 0.03Å.	49
		CH 1.10 C—O 1.44 C=O 1.20 OH 0.96	HCO 120° OCO 120° COH 105°	S	Nonrigid planar molecule.	50
$(CH_3As)_n$	Arsenomethane	CAs 1.98 ± 0.04 AsAs 2.42 ± 0.02	AsAsAs 90° (mean value)	E, X	$3 \leq n \leq 5$.	51
CH_3BF_2	Methylboron difluoride	BF 1.30 ± 0.02 BC 1.60 ± 0.03	CBF 121°	E	Planar.	52
CH_3BO	Borine carbonyl H_3B—CO	BH 1.20 ± 0.03 CB 1.57 ± 0.03 CO 1.13 ± 0.03	BCO 180°	E	Chemical structure confirmed.	53
		BH 1.194 CB 1.540 CO 1.131	BCO 180° HBH 113° 52'	S		GST, 54
CH_3Br	Methyl bromide	CH (1.05) CBr 1.91 ± 0.06	HCH (109° 28') HCBr (109° 28')	E		15
		CH 1.100 ± 0.01 CBr 1.939	HCH 111° 0' ± 30'	S		GST, 55, 56, 57, 58
CH_3BrHg	Methyl mercury bromide	CHg 2.074 ± 0.015 HgBr 2.406 ± 0.005	CHgBr 180° HCH 109° 7'	S		GST, 59
CH_3Br_3Si	Methyltribromosilane	CH (1.09) SiBr 2.17 ± 0.02	HCSi (109° 28') BrSiBr 109° 28'	E		60
CH_3Br_3Sn	Methyltin tribromide	CSn 2.17 (approx.) SnBr 2.45 ± 0.02	BrSnBr 109.5° ± 2°	E		61

Formula	Name	Bond lengths (Å)	Angles	Method	Notes	Ref
CH₃Cl	Methyl chloride	CCl 1.77 ± 0.02	HCH 110° 13' ± 30'	E		18
		CCl 1.80₅		X	−125°C.	62
CH₃ClHg	Methyl mercury chloride	CH 1.101 ± 0.01 CCl 1.781 ± 0.005	CHgCl 180° HCH 109° 7'	S		*GST*, 55, 57, 58, 63
		CHg 2.061 ± 0.02 HgCl 2.282 ± 0.005 CH (1.092)		S		*GST*, 59
CH₃Cl₂N	N,N,Dichloromethylamine	CH (1.09) CN (1.47) NCl 1.74 ± 0.02	HCN (109.5°) CNCl 109° ± 2° ClNCl 108° ± 2°	E		61, 64
CH₃Cl₃Si	Methyl silicon trichloride	SiCl 2.01 ± 0.02	ClSiCl 109° ± 3°	E		65
		CH (1.093) CSi 1.876 SiCl 2.021	HCH (109° 28') ClSiCl (109° 22' ± 15')	S		66
CH₃Cl₃Sn	Methyltin trichloride	CSn 2.19 ± 0.05 SnCl 2.32 ± 0.03	ClSnCl 108° ± 4°	E		61
CH₃F	Methyl fluoride	CF 1.39		E		*B*, 18, 67
		CH 1.109 CF 1.385	HCH 110° 0'	S		*GST*, 68
CH₃I	Methyl iodide	CI 2.16 ± 0.05		E		39
		CH 1.100 ± 0.010 CI 2.140 ± 0.005	HCH 110° 58' ± 1°	S		*GST*, 55, 57, 69
CH₃I₃Sn	Methyltin triiodide	SnI 2.68 ± 0.02	ISnI 109.5° ± 2°	E		61
CH₃NO₂	Methyl nitrite	CO 1.44 ± 0.02 N—O 1.37 ± 0.02 N=O 1.22 ± 0.02		E		70
CH₃NO₂	Nitromethane	CN 1.46 ± 0.02 NO 1.21 ± 0.02	ONO 127° ± 3°	E	Planar.	19, 70

701

Formula	Substance Name	Bond Lengths	Bond Angles	Exp. Method	Remarks	Reference
CH_3NO_3	Methyl nitrate $CH_3—O—NO_2'$	CO 1.43 ± 0.05 NO 1.36 ± 0.05 NO' 1.26 ± 0.05	CON 105° ± 5° O'NO' 125° 16'	E		70, 71
CH_3N_3	Methyl azide $CH_3—NN'N''$	CN 1.47 ± 0.02 NN' 1.24 ± 0.02 N'N'' 1.10 ± 0.02	CNN' 120° ± 5° NN'N'' 180°	E		71
CH_4	Methane	CH 1.093	HCH 109° 28'	S		72
CH_4N_2O	Urea	CO 1.262 ± 0.011 CN 1.335 ± 0.009	NCN 118.0° ± 0.9° NCO 121.0° ± 0.45°	X	Planar. *See also* $CH_6N_2O_3$.	R, 73, 74
		CO 1.28 ± 0.02 CN 1.33 ± 0.02	[NN 2.30]	X	In complexes with hydrocarbons.	75
CH_4N_2S	Thiourea	CN 1.35 CS 1.64	[NN 2.18]	X	Planar.	R, 76
CH_4O	Methanol	CO 1.44 ± 0.01		E		20, 77
		CO 1.42 CH 1.1 OH 0.96	COH 104° 40'	X	−106° ± 8°C.	78
		CO 1.434 CH (1.093) OH 0.937	HCH 109° 30' COH 105° 56'	S		GST, 79
CH_4S	Methyl mercaptan	CS 1.82 ± 0.01		E		20
		CH 1.1045 ± 0.0020 SH 1.3298 ± 0.0040 CS 1.8170 ± 0.0002	HCH 110° 10' ± 0° 5' CSH 100° 20' ± 0° 10'	S		GST, 80
CH_5BF_3N	Methylamine-boron trifluoride	BN 1.57 BF 1.39 CN 1.50	FBF 110.5° FBN 108.5° BNC 114°	X		81

Formula	Compound	Bond	Distance (Å)	Angle	Method	Temp.	Ref.
CH₅N	Methylamine	CN	1.47 ± 0.01		E		20
		CN	1.48 ± 0.01₄		X	−150°C.	82
		CN	1.48		S		83
CH₅NO	O-Methylhydroxylamine	CO	1.44 ± 0.02	CON 111° ± 3°	E		19
		NO	1.37 ± 0.02				
CH₆BrN₃O₃	Guanidinium bromate	CN	1.34 ± 0.04	NCN (120°)	X		84
CH₆ClN	Methylammonium chloride	CN	1.465 ± 0.010		X		85
CH₆N₂O₃	Urea-hydrogen peroxide (NH₂)₂CO.H₂O₂′	CN	1.34 ± 0.03		X		86
		CO	1.24 ± 0.03				
		O′O′	1.46 ± 0.03				
CH₆Si	Methylsilane	CSi	1.857 ± 0.007	CSiH 107° ± 2°	E		87
		CH	1.09 ± 0.02	SiCH 109.5° ± 2°			
		SiH	1.48 ± 0.02				
CH₆Sn	Methylstannane	CH	(1.090)	All (109° 28′)	S		GST, 88
		CSn	2.143 ± 0.002				
		SnH	1.700 ± 0.015				
CIN	Cyanogen iodide	CI	1.995	ICN 180°	S		GST, 9, 10
		CN	1.159				
CI₄	Carbon tetraiodide	CI	2.15 ± 0.02	ICI 109° 28′	E		89
CNNaO	Sodium cyanate	CN	1.21		X		90
		CO	1.13				
CN₄O₈	Tetranitromethane	CN	1.47 ± 0.02	NCN 109° 28′	E		91
		NO	1.22 ± 0.02	ONO 127°			
CO	Carbon monoxide	CO	1.128227		S		GST, 92
COS	Carbon oxysulfide	CO	1.16 ± 0.03	OCS 180°	E		B, 13, 44, 93
		CS	1.56 ± 0.04				
		CO	1.161 ± <0.01	OCS 180°	S		GST, 9, 94
		CS	1.561 ± <0.01				

703

Formula	Substance Name	Bond Lengths	Bond Angles	Exp. Method	Remarks	Reference
COSe	Carbon oxyselenide	CO 1.1588 ± 0.0001 CSe 1.7090 ± 0.0001	OCSe 180°	S		GST, 95
CO_2	Carbon dioxide	CO 1.15	OCO 180°	E		B, 16, 96, 97
		CO 1.1615	OCO 180°	S		98
CSTe	Carbon telluride sulfide	CS 1.557 CTe 1.904	SCTe 180°	S		GST, 99
CS_2	Carbon disulfide	CS 1.56	SCS 180°	E		B, 16, 93, 96, 97
		CS 1.55	SCS 180°	S		100
$C_2Ag_2O_4$	Silver oxalate	CC 1.53 CO 1.15, 1.24	OCO 117° 31′ CCO 113° 50′, 102° 20′	X	Nonplanar anion.	101
C_2Br_2	Dibromoacetylene	CBr 1.80 ± 0.03 CC 1.20 ± 0.03	CCBr 180°	E		B, 102
C_2Br_4	Tetrabromoethylene	CBr 1.91 ± 0.05		E		B, 102
C_2Cl_2	Dichloroacetylene	CC 1.195 CCl 1.64	CCCl 180°	E		16, 103
$C_2Cl_2F_4$	1,2-Dichloro-1,2,2-tetrafluoroethane	CC (1.45) CCl 1.74 CF 1.33	CCF 108° ClCF 110° 30′ FCF 108°	E	Nearly equimolecular mixture of trans and gauche forms.	104
$C_2Cl_2I_2$	*trans* Dichlorodiiodoethylene	CC 1.34 CI 2.05	CCCl 123° 41′ CCI 123° 41′	E	Mp. 70°C.	105
$C_2Cl_2O_2$	Oxalyl chloride	CC 1.50 ± 0.03 CCl 1.72 ± 0.03 CO (1.20)	CCO 123° ± 2° ClCO 123° ± 2°	E		106
C_2Cl_4	Tetrachloroethylene	CC 1.30 ± 0.03 CCl 1.72 ± 0.01	CCCl 113.5° ± 1.5°	E	At least approximately planar.	19, 107, 108

Formula	Name	Bond lengths (Å)	Angles	Method	Notes	References
C_2Cl_6	Hexachloroethane	CC 1.54 ± 0.07 CCl 1.77 ± 0.02	ClCCl $108°\,45' \pm 1°\,30'$	E		16, 109, 110, 111
		CC 1.54 CCl $1.76, 1.77$	All $110° \pm 1.5°$	X	Orthorhombic.	112
C_2F_3N	Trifluoroacetonitrile	CC 1.464 ± 0.02 CF 1.335 ± 0.008 CN (1.158)	FCF $(108° \pm 1°)$	S		GST, 7
C_2F_4	Tetrafluoroethylene	CC 1.313 ± 0.035 CF 1.313 ± 0.010	FCF $114° \pm 2°$	E	Approximately planar.	24, 113
C_2F_6	Hexafluoroethane	CC 1.51 ± 0.06 CF 1.330 ± 0.015	FCF $108° \pm 1.5°$	E		114, 115, 116
C_2F_6S	Perfluoromethyl sulfide	CF $1.32_8 \pm 0.011$ CS $1.82_8 \pm 0.015$	CSC $105.6° \pm 3°$ FCF $(108.5°)$	E		117
$C_2F_6S_2$	Perfluoromethyl disulfide $CF_3\!-\!S\!-\!S\!-\!CF_3$	CF $1.33_4 \pm 0.013$ CS $1.82_9 \pm 0.017$ SS $2.05_3 \pm 0.019$	CSS $105.4° \pm 3°$ FCF $(108.5°)$	E	Probably nonplanar and trans.	117
$C_2F_6S_3$	Perfluoromethyl trisulfide $CF_3\!-\!S\!-\!S\!-\!S\!-\!CF_3$	CF $1.34_0 \pm 0.011$ CS $1.84_8 \pm 0.015$ SS $2.06_5 \pm 0.016$	CSS $(103.5°)$ FCF $(108.5°)$ SSS $103.8° \pm 3°$	E	Assumed nonplanar and trans.	117
C_2F_6Se	Perfluoromethyl selenide	CF $1.35_6 \pm 0.015$ CSe $1.95_8 \pm 0.022$	CSeC $104.4° \pm 5°$ FCF $(108.5°)$	E		117
$C_2F_6Se_2$	Perfluoromethyl diselenide $CF_3\!-\!Se\!-\!Se\!-\!CF_3$	CF $1.33_6 \pm 0.012$ CSe $1.93_4 \pm 0.018$ SeSe $2.33_5 \pm 0.032$	CSeSe $(103.5°)$ FCF $(108.5°)$	E	Assumed nonplanar.	117
$C_2FeN_2O_4$	Iron nitrosocarbonyl	CO 1.15 ± 0.03 CFe 1.84 ± 0.02 NO 1.12 ± 0.03 NFe 1.77 ± 0.02	FeCO $180°$ FeNO $180°$	E	Tetrahedral Fe.	118
C_2HBr	Bromoacetylene	CC 1.20 ± 0.04 CH (1.06) CBr 1.80 ± 0.03	CCH $(180°)$ CCBr $(180°)$	E		119

Formula	Substance Name	Bond Lengths		Bond Angles		Exp. Method	Remarks	Reference
C_2HBr_3	Tribromoethylene	CC	1.32 ± 0.08	[BrBr	3.67 ± 0.08]	E		120
		CBr	2.05 ± 0.08					
C_2HCl	Chloroacetylene	CC	1.21 ± 0.04			E		119
		CCl	1.68 ± 0.04					
		CH	1.052 ± 0.001	CCH	180°	S		*GST*, 121, 122
		CC	1.211 ± 0.001	CCCl	180°			
		CCl	1.632 ± 0.001					
C_2HCl_3	Trichloroethylene	CC	1.36 ± 0.04	CCCl	121.5° ± 1°,	E		19, 108
		CCl	1.72 ± 0.02		124° ± 2°			
C_2HCl_3O	Chloral	CC	1.52 ± 0.02	[ClCl	2.95 ± 0.03]	E		123
		CCl	1.76 ± 0.02					
		CO	1.15 ± 0.02					
$C_2HF_3O_2$	Trifluoroacetic acid	CF	1.36 ± 0.05	FCF	110° ± 4°	E	*See also* $C_4H_2F_6O_4$.	47
$C_2HK_2NO_4$	Dipotassium nitroacetate	CC	1.38 ± {0.02}	CCH	114° ± {1°}	X	Planar (including the H atom).	124
		CH	0.91 ± {0.02}	CCO *ab*	119° ± {1°}			
		CO *b*	1.27 ± {0.02}	*ac*	124° ± {1°}			
		c	1.33 ± {0.02}	CCN	128° ± {1°}			
		CN	1.39 ± {0.02}	NCH	118° ± {1°}			
		NO *e*	1.26 ± {0.02}	CNO *de*	114° ± {1°}			
		f	1.28 ± {0.02}	*df*	125° ± {1°}			
				OCO	117° ± {1°}			
				ONO	121° ± {1°}			

$$(K^+)_2 \left[\underset{O_c}{\overset{O_b}{<}} C \overset{H}{\underset{a}{-}} C \overset{d}{-} N \underset{f\ O}{\overset{e\ O}{<}} \right]^{--}$$

Formula	Substance Name	Bond Lengths		Bond Angles		Exp. Method	Remarks	Reference
C_2H_2	Acetylene	CC	1.205 ± 0.008	CCH	180°	E		125
		CH	1.06 ± 0.05					
		CC	1.20	CCH	180°	X	−117°C.	126
		CH	1.05					
		CC	1.201_0	CCH	180°	S		127
		CH	1.063_7					

Formula	Name	Bond distances (Å)	Angles	Method	Notes	References
$C_2H_2AsCl_3$	*cis* β-Chlorovinyldichloroarsene	CC 1.36 CCl 1.69 AsCl 2.17 CAs 1.90	CCCl 120°–125° AsCC 120°–125° ClAsCl ~100° CAsCl ~100°	E	Lewisite. B.p. 150.2°C.	128
$C_2H_2AsCl_3$	*trans* β-Chlorovinyldichloroarsene	CC 1.36 CCl 1.69 AsCl 2.17 CAs 1.90	CCCl 120°–125° AsCC 120°–125° ClAsCl ~100° CAsCl ~100°	E	Lewisite. B.p. 190°C.	128
$C_2H_2BaO_4$	Barium formate	CO 1.24–1.26	OCO 126°–128°	X		129
$C_2H_2Br_2$	*cis* 1,2-Dibromoethylene	CC 1.32 ± 0.08 CBr 2.05 ± 0.08		E		120
$C_2H_2Br_2$	*trans* 1,2-Dibromoethylene	CBr 1.86 ± 0.04	CCBr 121° ± 3°	E		102, 120, 130
$C_2H_2Br_4$	1,1,2,2-Tetrabromoethane	CC 1.54 CBr 1.94		E		16, 109
$C_2H_2CaO_4$	Calcium formate	CO 1.24, 1.25 ± 0.03	OCO 124°, 125° ± 4°	X		131
$C_2H_2Cl_2$	1,1-Dichloroethylene	CC (1.38) CCl 1.69 ± 0.02	CCCl 122° ± 1°	E		19, 132
$C_2H_2Cl_2$	*cis* 1,2-Dichloroethylene	CC (1.38) CCl 1.67 ± 0.03	CCCl 123.5° ± 1°	E		19, 132, 133
$C_2H_2Cl_2$	*trans* 1,2-Dichloroethylene	CC (1.38) CCl 1.69 ± 0.02	CCCl 122.5° ± 1°	E		19, 102, 132, 133
$C_2H_2Cl_2O_2$	Chloromethyl chloroformate Cl—CH₂—O—CO—Cl'	CCl 1.74 ± 0.02 CCl' 1.74 ± 0.02 C—O 1.40 ± 0.04 C=O 1.20 ± 0.03	ClCO 109.5° ± 3° Cl'C—O 112° ± 4° OCO 126° ± 4° COC 110° ± 4°	E	Cl *trans* to C of carboxyl group.	134
$C_2H_2Cl_4$	1,1,2,2-Tetrachloroethane	CC 1.54 CCl 1.76		E		16, 109

Formula	Substance Name	Bond Lengths	Bond Angles	Exp. Method	Remarks	Reference
$C_2H_2F_2$	1,1-Difluoroethylene	CC 1.311 ± 0.035 CH 1.07 ± 0.02 CF 1.321 ± 0.015	FCF 110° ± 3° HCH 117° ± 7°	E		113
		CC 1.31 CH 1.07 CF 1.32	HCH 110° FCF 110°	S		*GST*
$C_2H_2I_2$	*cis* 1,2-Diiodoethylene	CI 2.03 ± 0.04	CCI 125° ± 2°	E	M.p. −13.9°C.	105, 130
$C_2H_2I_2$	*trans* 1,2-Diiodoethylene	CI 2.03 ± 0.04	CCI 122° ± 2°	E	M.p. 70°C.	105, 130
$C_2H_2K_2O_5$	Potassium oxalate monohydrate				*See* $C_2K_2O_4$.	
C_2H_2O	Ketene	CC 1.30 ± 0.02 CH (1.07 ± 0.02) CO 1.16 ± 0.02	HCH (117.5°) CCO 180°	E		24, 135
		CC 1.329 ± 0.015 CH 1.071 ± 0.003 CO 1.150 ± 0.015	HCH 123.3° ± 1.5° CCO 180°	S		*GST*, 24, 136
$C_2H_2O_2$	Glyoxal	CH (1.09) CC 1.47 ± 0.02 CO 1.20 ± 0.01	CCO 123° ± 2°	E	Planar and *s-trans*.	137
$C_2H_2O_4$	α-Oxalic acid	CC 1.560 ± {0.0103} C—O 1.289 ± {0.0063} C=O 1.194 ± {0.0067}	CC—O 109° 3′ ± {33′} CC=O 122° 40′ ± {36′} OCO 128° 9′ ± {31′}	X	Planar and centrosymmetric.	138, 139
$C_2H_2O_4$	β-Oxalic acid	CC 1.59 C—O 1.30 C=O 1.20	OCO 134°	X	Planar.	138
$C_2H_2O_4$	Oxalic acid	CC 1.529 ± {0.020} C—O 1.285 ± {0.012} C=O 1.187 ± {0.022}	CC—O 112° 34′ ± {1° 13′} CC=O 121° 38′ ± {1° 4′} OCO 125° 48′ ± {49′}	X	As dihydrate. Planar.	140

Formula	Name	Bond distances	Angles	Method	Notes	Ref.
C₂H₂O₄Pb	Lead formate	CO 1.24–1.26	OCO 126°–128°	X		129
C₂H₂O₄Sr	Strontium formate	CO 1.25, 1.26 ± 0.03	OCO 126°, 127° ± 4°	X		141
C₂H₃BF₃N	Methyl cyanide-boron trifluoride	BF 1.33 BN 1.635 CC 1.44 ± 0.02 CN 1.13 ± 0.02	FBF 114° FBN 103°	X		81, 142
C₂H₃Br	Vinyl bromide	CBr 1.86 ± 0.04	CCBr 121° ± 3°	E		130
C₂H₃BrO	Acetyl bromide	CC (1.50) CH (1.09) CBr 2.00 ± 0.04 CO 1.17	CCBr 105° ± 5° BrCO 125° ± 5°	E	Planarity assumed.	120, 143
C₂H₃Cl	Vinyl chloride	CC (1.38) CCl 1.69 ± 0.02	CCCl 122° ± 2°	E		19
C₂H₃ClF₂	1-Chloro-1,1-difluoroethane	CF 1.37 ± 0.03 CCl 1.77 ± 0.03	CCF 111° ± 5° CCCl 111° ± 5° ClCF 108° ± 5° FCF 108° ± 5°	E		144
C₂H₃ClO	Acetyl chloride	CC (1.50) CH (1.09) CCl 1.82 ± 0.02 CO 1.17 ± 0.04	ClCO 122.5° ± 2.5° CCCl 105° ± 5°	E	Planarity assumed.	13, 143
C₂H₃ClO₂	Methyl chloroformate C'H₃—O—CO—Cl	CH (1.09) CCl 1.75 ± 0.02 C'—O 1.47 ± 0.04 C—O 1.36 ± 0.04 C=O 1.19 ± 0.02	HCH (109.5°) ClC—O 112° ± 3° COC' 111° ± 4° OCO 126° ± 4°	E	Approximately planar and cis.	145
C₂H₃Cl₂F	1,1-Dichloro-1-fluoroethane	CCl 1.78 ± 0.03 CF 1.40 ± 0.03	CCCl 111° ± 3° CCF 109.5° ± 3 ClCCl 109.5° ± 3°	E		144
C₂H₃Cl₃	1,1,1-Trichloroethane	CC (1.54 ± 0.04) CCl 1.77₅ ± 0.02	CCCl 110° ± 1.5° ClCCl 109° ± 1.5°	E		146, 147
		CC 1.55 CH (1.093) CCl (1.767)	HCH (109° 28') ClCCl (110° 24')	S		*GST*, 28

Formula	Substance Name	Bond Lengths	Bond Angles	Exp. Method	Remarks	Reference
$C_2H_3Cl_3$	1,1,2-Trichloroethane	CC 1.54 CCl 1.76		E		16, 109
$C_2H_3Cl_3O_2$	Chloral hydrate	CO 1.47, 1.48		X	Staggered conformation.	148
C_2H_3FO	Acetyl fluoride	CH (1.09) CC 1.50 ± 0.03 CF 1.37 ± 0.02 CO 1.16 ± 0.02	HCH (109° 28') CCF 110° FCO 125°	E	Planarity assumed.	143
$C_2H_3F_3$	1,1,1-Trifluoroethane	CC 1.45 ± 0.04 CF 1.33 ± 0.03	FCF 108.5°	E		114
		CC 1.53 ± 0.04 CF 1.36 ± 0.02	FCF 107° ± 3° CCF 112° ± 2°	E		144
		CC (1.54) CH (1.093) CF (1.33)	HCH (109° 28') FCF (109°)	S		GST
C_2H_3I	Vinyl iodide	CC (1.34) CI 2.03 ± 0.04	CCI 122° ± 2°	E		130
C_2H_3IO	Acetyl iodide	CC (1.50) CI 2.21 ± 0.04 CO (1.18)	CCI 110° ± 5° ICO 125° ± 5°	E	Planarity assumed.	143
C_2H_3N	Methyl cyanide	CC 1.49 ± 0.03 CN 1.16 ± 0.03	CCN 180°	E		149, 150
		CC 1.460 CH 1.092 CN 1.158	CCN 180° HCH 109° 8'	S		GST, 151
C_2H_3N	Methyl isocyanide $CH_3—NC'$	CN 1.44 ± 0.02 C'N 1.18 ± 0.02	CNC' 180°	E		149, 152
		CN 1.427 C'N 1.167 CH 1.094	CNC' 180° HCH 109° 46'	S		GST, 151

Formula	Name / Structure	Bond distances	Angles	Method	Notes	Ref.
C₂H₃NO	Methyl isocyanate CH₃—NC′O	CH (1.09) CN (1.47) C′N 1.19 ± 0.03 C′O 1.18 ± 0.03	CNC′ 125° ± 5° NC′O 180°	E		34
C₂H₃NS	Methyl isothiocyanate	CH (1.09) C—N (1.47) C=N (1.22) CS (1.56)	HCN (109°) CNC (142°) NCS (180°)	S		GST, 153
C₂H₃NS	Methyl thiocyanate CH₃—S—C′N	CH (1.09) CS (1.81) C′S (1.61) C′N (1.21)	HCS (109°) CSC′ (142°) SC′N (180°)	S		GST, 153
C₂H₄	Ethylene	CC 1.34 ± 0.02 CH 1.06 ± 0.03	HCH 110° ± 5°	E		154
		CC 1.353 ± 0.01 CH 1.071	HCH 119° 55′ ± 30′	S		155, 156
C₂H₄BrCl	1-Bromo-2-chloroethane	CC (1.54) CH (1.09) CBr 1.90 ± 0.02 CCl 1.75 ± 0.02		E		157
C₂H₄Br₂	Ethylene bromide	CC 1.54 CH (1.09) CBr 1.94		E		16, 109, 157
C₂H₄Cl₂	Ethylene chloride	CC 1.54 CCl 1.76		E		16, 109, 158
		CC 1.49 ± 0.03 CH 1.12 ± 0.04 CCl 1.78 ± 0.01	CCCl 110° 23′ ± 3°	E	Predominantly *trans*.	159
		CC 1.49 ± 0.04 CCl 1.80 ± 0.02	CCCl 105.5° ± 0.5°	X	−140°C. *trans* Conformation.	160
C₂H₄N₂O₂	Oxamide	CC 1.49 CN 1.31 CO 1.25		X	Centrosymmetry assumed.	161

Formula	Name	Bond Lengths	Bond Angles	Exp. Method	Remarks	Reference
$C_2H_4N_4$	Dicyandiamide NC—N′=C′(N″H₂)₂	CN 1.22 ± 0.02 CN′ 1.28 ± 0.02 C′N″ 1.36 ± 0.02 C′N″ 1.34, 1.37 ± 0.02	NCN′ 180° CN′C′ 120° N′C′N″ 116°, 120° N″C′N″ 124°	X	Nearly planar.	162
C_2H_4O	Acetaldehyde	CC 1.50 ± 0.02 CO 1.22 ± 0.02	CCO 121° ± 2°	E		163
C_2H_4O	Ethylene oxide	CC 1.46 ± 0.03 CO (1.44) CH (1.08)	HCH (116° 41′)	E		132, 164, 165
		CC 1.472 CH 1.082 CO 1.436	HCH 116° 41′ H₂CC 159° 25′ COC 61° 24′	S		*GST*, 166, 167
C_2H_4OS	Thioacetic acid	CC 1.54 ± 0.06 CH (1.09) CO 1.24 ± 0.04 CS 1.78 ± 0.02 SH (1.34)	CCO 125° ± 5° CCS 110° ± 5° OCS (125°)	E		168
$C_2H_4O_2$	Acetic acid	CC 1.54 ± 0.04 C—O 1.43 ± 0.03 C=O 1.24 ± 0.03	OCO 122°–138° CC=O 113°–128°	E	*See also* C₄H₈O₄.	47
$C_2H_4O_2$	Methyl formate C′H₃—O—CO—H	C—O 1.37 ± 0.04 C=O 1.22 ± 0.03 C′O 1.47 ± 0.04	OCO 123° ± 4° COC′ 112° ± 4°	E	Approximately *cis*.	145
$C_2H_4O_4$	Formic acid (dimeric)	C—O 1.36 ± 0.04 C=O 1.25 ± 0.03	OCO 121° ± 2°	E	O—H - - O distance is 2.73 ± 0.05 A. *See also* pages 54f.	47
C_2H_4S	Ethylene sulfide	CC 1.492 CH 1.078 CS 1.819	HCH 116° 0′ H₂CC 151° 43′ CSC 65° 48′	S		*GST*, 167

712

Formula	Name	Bond	Length	Angle	Value	Method	Notes	Ref.
C_2H_5Br	Ethyl bromide	CC CH CBr	(1.54) (1.09) 1.91 ± 0.02	CCBr All others	109° ± 2° (109° 28')	E		146, 169
C_2H_5Cl	Ethyl chloride	CC CCl	1.54 ± 0.02 1.77 ± 0.01	CCCl	110° ± 2°	E		20, 146, 169
C_2H_5ClO	Ethylene chlorohydrin	CC CCl CO	1.54 1.76 1.43			E		170
C_2H_5I	Ethyl iodide	CI	2.16 ± 0.05			E		39, 169
$C_2H_5KO_4S$	Potassium ethylsulfate $K^+[C_2H_5{-}O'{-}SO_3]^-$	CC CO' SO SO'	1.51 1.44 1.44, 1.45, 1.49 1.60	OSO OSO'	110°, 112°, 116° 101°, 106°, 109°	X		171
C_2H_5N	Ethylenimine	CC CN CH NH	1.480 1.488 (1.082) (1.00)	CNH HCH H_2CC	112° (116° 41') (159° 25')	S		172
C_2H_5NO	Acetamide	CC CH CN CO NH	1.53 ± 0.03 (1.09) 1.36 ± 0.02 1.21 ± 0.02 (1.02)	CCH CCO CNH NCO	(109° 28') 122° ± 4° (107°) 125° ± 3°	E	C, N, and O atoms assumed coplanar.	173
		CC CN CO	1.51 ± 0.05 1.38 ± 0.05 1.28 ± 0.05	CCO CCN NCO	129° ± 5° 109° ± 5° 122° ± 5°	X	Planar.	174
$C_2H_5NO_2$	Glycine	CC CN CO	1.52 ± 0.02 1.39 ± 0.02 1.25, 1.27 ± 0.02	CCN CCO OCO	112° ± 3° 119° ± 3° 122° ± 3°	X	Nearly planar.	175
C_2H_6	Ethane	CC CH	1.536 ± 0.016 1.114 ± 0.027	CCH	110.5° ± 3.5°	E		154, 176
		CC CH	1.533 1.110	CCH	110.4°	E, S		176
		CC CH	1.543 1.102	CCH HCH	109° 37' 109° 19'	S		177

Formula	Substance Name	Bond Lengths	Bond Angles	Exp. Method	Remarks	Reference
C_2H_6AsBr	Dimethylarsenic bromide	AsBr 2.34 ± 0.04	CAsBr $96° \pm 3°$	E		61
C_2H_6AsCl	Dimethylarsenic chloride	AsCl 2.18 ± 0.04	CAsCl $98° \pm 3°$	E		61
C_2H_6AsI	Dimethylarsenic iodide	AsI 2.52 ± 0.03 CAs (1.98)	CAsI $98° \pm 4°$	E		61
C_2H_6BF	Dimethylboron fluoride	BC 1.55 ± 0.02 BF 1.29 ± 0.02	CBF $121.5°$	E	Planar.	52
$C_2H_6BF_3O$	Methyl ether-boron trifluoride	CO 1.45 ± 0.03 BF 1.43 ± 0.03 BO 1.50 ± 0.06	All $109° 28'$	E		178
$(C_2H_6Be)_n$	Beryllium dimethyl $\left[\begin{array}{c} CH_3 \\ Be \\ CH_3 \end{array} \begin{array}{c} CH_3 \\ Be \\ CH_3 \end{array}\right]_{n/2}$	BeC 1.93 ± 0.02	BeCBe $66°$ CBeC $114° \pm 1°$	X	Approximately tetrahedral Be.	179
$C_2H_6Br_2Si$	Dimethyldibromosilane	SiBr 2.21 ± 0.03 SiC 1.92 ± 0.06	BrSiBr $109° 28'$	E		60
$C_2H_6Br_2Sn$	Dimethyltin dibromide	CSn ~ 2.17 SnBr 2.48 ± 0.02	BrSnBr $109° \pm 3°$	E		61
C_2H_6ClN	Dimethylchloroamine	CN 1.47 ± 0.02 ClN 1.77 ± 0.02	CNC (108°) CNCl $107° \pm 2°$ HCN (109.5°)	E		61, 64
$C_2H_6Cl_2Si$	Dimethyldichlorosilane	CSi 1.83 ± 0.06 SiCl 1.99 ± 0.03	ClSiCl $109.5° \pm 3°$ CSiC (109.5°)	E		65
		CH (1.093) CSi 1.87 SiCl 2.03	All (109° 28')	S		66
$C_2H_6Cl_2Sn$	Dimethyltin dichloride	SnCl 2.34 ± 0.03	ClSnCl $110° \pm 5°$	E		61

Formula	Name	Bond lengths	Angles	Method	Notes	Ref
C_2H_6Hg	Dimethylmercury	CHg 2.23 ± 0.04	CHgC (180°)	E		180
$C_2H_6I_2Sn$	Dimethyltin diiodide	SnI 2.69 ± 0.03	ISnI 109.5° ± 3°	E		61
$C_2H_6N_2$	Azomethane	CN 1.47 ± 0.06 NN 1.24 ± 0.05	CNN 110° ± 10°	E		44
$C_2H_6N_2O$	Dimethylnitroamine	CN 1.48 NN 1.30 NO 1.30	CNN 123° NNO 120°	E	Planar.	170
		CN 1.46 ± 0.05 NN 1.26 ± 0.05 NO 1.25 ± 0.05		X	Planar.	181
$C_2H_6N_2O_4$	*sym* Bisnitroaminoethane	CC 1.52 NN 1.41 NN 1.33 NO 1.21	CCN 111° 26' CNN 123° 9' NNO 117° 18', 118° 9' ONO 125° 21'	X	Centrosymmetric. Planar C—NH—NO₂ groups.	182
C_2H_6O	Ethanol	CC 1.55 ± 0.02 CO 1.43 ± 0.02	CCO 110° ± 3°	E		20, 77
C_2H_6O	Methyl ether	CO 1.43 ± 0.03	COC 111° ± 3°	E	*See also* $C_2H_6BF_3O$.	20, 183, 184, 185
C_2H_6OS	Methyl sulfoxide	CS 1.84 ± 0.02 SO 1.47 ± 0.04 CH 1.08	CSC 100° CSO 106° ± 6°	E	Pyramidal S.	186, 187
$C_2H_6O_2$	Ethylene glycol	CC 1.52 ± 0.02 CO 1.43 ± 0.02 CH 1.08 OH (0.97)	CCO	E	Angle between planes is 74°.	170, 188
$C_2H_6O_2S$	Methyl sulfone	CS 1.90 ± 0.03 SO 1.44 ± 0.03	CSO 105° ± 3° CSC 115° ± 15° OSO 125° ± 15°	E		189
		CS 1.80 ± 0.02 SO 1.43 ± 0.02		E		187

Formula	Substance Name	Bond Lengths	Bond Angles	Exp. Method	Remarks	Reference
$C_2H_6O_4S_4$	Dimethanesulfonyl disulfide $CH_3-SO_2-S'-S'-SO_2-CH_3$	CS 1.77 ± 0.05 SO 1.44, 1.45, 1.51, 1.52 ± 0.05 SS′ 2.10 ± 0.03 S′S′ 2.06 ± 0.03	CSS′ 98°, 105° ± 3° CSO 101°, 104°, 117°, 126° ± 3° OSS′ 96°, 99°, 106°, 110° ± 3° SS′S′ 102°, 106° ± 3° OSO 120°, 125° ± 3°	X		190
$C_2H_6O_6$	Oxalic acid dihydrate				*See* $C_2H_2O_4$.	
C_2H_6S	Ethyl mercaptan	CC 1.54 ± 0.02 CS 1.81 ± 0.01	CCS 113° ± 2°	E		20
C_2H_6S	Methyl sulfide	CS 1.82 ± 0.01	CSC <180°	E		20, 191
$C_2H_6S_2$	Methyl disulfide	CS 1.78 ± 0.03 SS 2.04 ± 0.03	CSS 107° ± 3°	E		192
$C_2H_6S_3$	Methyl trisulfide	CH (1.09) CS 1.78 ± 0.04 SS 2.04 ± 0.02	HCS (112°) CSS 104° ± 5° SSS 104° ± 5°	E	Chair configuration.	193
C_2H_7N	Dimethylamine	CH 1.08 ± 0.03 CN 1.47 ± 0.02	CNC 111° ± 3°	E		20, 194
C_2H_7N	Ethylamine	CC 1.54 ± 0.02 CN 1.47 ± 0.02	CCN 110° ± 3°	E		20
$C_2H_8N_2$	N,N-Dimethylhydrazine	CH (1.09) CN 1.47 ± 0.03 NH (1.04) NN 1.45 ± 0.03	CNC 110° ± 4° CNN 110° ± 4°	E		195
$C_2H_8N_2$	N,N-Dimethylhydrazine	CH (1.09) CN 1.47 ± 0.03 NH (1.04) NN 1.45 ± 0.03	CNN 110° ± 14°	E		195

Formula	Name	Bond distances	Angles	Method	Notes	Ref.
$C_2H_8N_2O_4$	Ammonium oxalate	CC 1.56 ± 0.05; CO $1.23,\ 1.25 \pm 0.05$	OCO $125° \pm 3°$	X	As monohydrate. Angle of 28° between OCO planes.	196
C_2H_8Si	Dimethylsilane	CH 1.09 ± 0.02; CSi 1.860 ± 0.004; SiH 1.48 ± 0.02	CSiC $110° \pm 3°$; SiCH $109.5° \pm 2°$	E		197
$C_2H_{10}N_2O_5$	Ammonium oxalate monohydrate				*See* $C_2H_8N_2O_4$.	
$C_2H_{11}B_2N$	N,N-Dimethylaminodiborane	BN $1.55_4 \pm 0.02_6$; CN $1.48_3 \pm 0.02_9$; BB 1.92 ± 0.11; BH (1.25); CH (1.09)	CNB $116.2° \pm 1.0°$; CNC $111.5° \pm 2.5°$; BNB $76.4° \pm 5.5°$; HCH (109.5°); HBH (120°)	E	BH_2 groups assumed to be coplanar.	198
C_2I_2	Diiodoacetylene	CC 1.18; CI 2.03 ± 0.05	CCI 180°	E		B, 102
C_2I_4	Tetraiodoethylene	CI 2.10 ± 0.05	ICI 115°	X	Planar.	199
$C_2K_2O_4$	Potassium oxalate	CC 1.60; CO 1.14, 1.30	OCO 125°	X	As monohydrate. Planar anion.	138
C_2N_2	Cyanogen	CC 1.37 ± 0.02; CN 1.16 ± 0.02	CCN 180°	E		132, 150, 200
$C_2N_2S_2Se$	Selenium dithiocyanate $Se(—SCN)_2$	CN 1.13; CS 1.69; SSe 2.21	CSSe 104°; SSeS 101°	X		201
$C_2N_2Se_3$	Selenium diselenocyanate $Se(—SeCN)_2$	CN 1.05; CSe 1.83; SeSe 2.33 ± 0.02	CSeSe 95°; NCSe 164°; SeSeSe $101° \pm 2°$	X	Nonplanar.	202
C_3AsF_9	Perfluorotrimethylarsine	CF $1.33_6 \pm 0.012$; CAs $2.05_3 \pm 0.019$	CAsC $100.1° \pm 3.5°$; FCF (108.5°)	E	CF_3 groups assumed to be in least hindered positions.	203

Formula	Substance Name	Bond Lengths	Bond Angles	Exp. Method	Remarks	Reference
C_3CoNO_4	Cobalt nitrosocarbonyl	CO 1.14 ± 0.04 CCo 1.83 ± 0.02 NO 1.10 ± 0.04 NCo 1.76 ± 0.02	CoCO $180°$ CoNO $180°$	E	Tetrahedral Co.	118
C_3F_6	Hexafluoropropene	CF 1.31–1.35 C—C ~1.52 C=C ~1.32	CCC $126°$ FCF $\sim109.5°$ CCF $114°$	E	No F atom in plane of C atoms.	204
C_3F_9P	Perfluorotrimethylphosphine	CF $1.34_2 \pm 0.013$ CP $1.93_7 \pm 0.017$	FCF $(108.5°)$ CPC $99.6° \pm 2.5°$	E	CF₃ groups assumed to be in least hindered positions.	203
C_3F_9Sb	Perfluorotrimethylstibine	CF $1.34_6 \pm 0.009$ CSb $2.20_2 \pm 0.016$	FCF $(108.5°)$ CSbC $100.0° \pm 3.5°$	E	CF₃ groups assumed to be in least hindered positions.	203
C_3HF_3	3,3,3-Trifluoro-1-propyne	CH 1.056 ± 0.005 C≡C 1.201 ± 0.002 C—C 1.464 ± 0.02 CF 1.335 ± 0.01	FCF $107.5° \pm 1°$ CCC $180°$ CCH $180°$	E, S		GST, 205, 206
C_3HN	Cyanoacetylene	CH 1.057 ± 0.001 C≡C 1.203 C—C 1.382 CN 1.157	CCC $180°$ CCH $180°$ CCN $180°$	S		GST, 122
C_3H_3Br	1-Bromo-1-propyne	CH (1.092 ± 0.01) C—C 1.46 ± 0.02 C≡C (1.207 ± 0.004) CBr 1.793 ± 0.005	HCH $(109° 8' \pm 1°)$ CCC $180°$ CCBr $180°$	S		GST, 207
C_3H_3Br	3-Bromo-1-propyne	C—C 1.47 ± 0.02 C≡C (1.20) CBr 1.95 ± 0.02	CCBr $112° \pm 2°$ CCC $180°$	E		208
C_3H_3Cl	3-Chloro-1-propyne	C—C 1.48 ± 0.02 C≡C (1.20) CCl 1.82 ± 0.02	CCCl $111° \pm 2°$ CCC $180°$	E		208

Formula	Name	Bond lengths	Angles		Type	Ref
$C_3H_3GdO_6$	Gadolinium formate	CO 1.27, 1.33	OCO 121°		X	209
C_3H_3I	1-Iodo-1-propyne	CH (1.092 ± 0.01) C—C (1.459) C≡C (1.207 ± 0.004) CI 1.99_1	HCH (109° 8' ± 1°) CCC 180° CCI 180°		S	GST, 207
C_3H_3I	3-Iodo-1-propyne	C—C (1.47) C≡C (1.20) CI 2.13 ± 0.03	CCI 111° ± 3°		E	208
$C_3H_3N_3O_3$	Cyanuric acid	CN 1.34_5, 1.35_5, 1.36_5 CO 1.21, 1.21_5	CNC 125° NCN 114.5°, 116° NCO 122°	Planar.	X	210
C_3H_4	Allene	CH (1.06) CC 1.34 ± 0.02	CCC 180° HCH ~109° 28'		E	154
C_3H_4		CH 1.087 CC 1.30	HCH 116° CCC 180°		S	155, 211
C_3H_4	Cyclopropene	C—C 1.52_5 ± 0.02 C=C 1.28_6 ± 0.04 CH 1.08_7 ± 0.04	HCH (118°) C—CH (118°) C=CH 152° ± 12° C—C—C 49.9°		E	212
C_3H_4	Methylacetylene CH_3—C≡CH'	CH (1.09) CH' (1.06) C—C 1.46 ± 0.02 C≡C 1.21 ± 0.03	CCH (109° 28') CCC (180°) CCH' (180°)		E	150
C_3H_4		CH 1.097 CH' 1.056 C—C 1.460 C≡C 1.207	CCH 108° 14' CCC 180° CCH' 180°		S	GST, 213, 214
$C_3H_4Cl_2$	1,1-Dichlorocyclopropane	CH (1.09) CC 1.52 ± 0.02 CCl 1.76 ± 0.02	CCC (60°) ClCCl 112° ± 4°		E	215
C_3H_4O	Acrolein	C—C 1.46 ± 0.03 C=C 1.36 ± 0.02 CO 1.21 ± 0.02	CCC 120° ± 3° CCO 120° ± 3°		E	216

719

Formula	Substance Name	Bond Lengths	Bond Angles	Exp. Method	Remarks	Reference
$C_3H_4O_2$	β-Propiolactone	CC 1.54 C—O 1.44 C=O 1.21-1.24	CCC 89° OCO 133°	E	Planar ring.	217
$C_3H_4O_3$	Ethylene carbonate 	CC 1.52 C'—O 1.33 C—O 1.40 C'=O 1.15	CCO 102° COC 109° O—C'—O 111° O—C'=O 124.5°	X	Nonplanar ring.	218
C_3H_5Cl	Chlorocyclopropane	CH (1.09) CC 1.52 ± 0.02 CCl 1.76 ± 0.02		E		215
C_3H_6	Cyclopropane	CC 1.54 CH 1.08	CCH 116.4° ± 2° HCH 118.2° ± 2°	E		16, 154, 219
$C_3H_6Br_2$	Propylene bromide	CBr 1.92 ± 0.02	CCBr 110° ± 1°	E	Br atoms are *trans*.	220
$C_3H_6Cl_2$	Propylene chloride	CC 1.56 CCl 1.79 ± 0.035	CCCl 108° ± 4°	E		221
$C_3H_6Cl_2$	2,2-Dichloropropane	CC 1.54 ± 0.04 CCl 1.77_6 ± 0.02	CCCl 109° ± 3° ClCCl 109.5° ± 2°	E		147
$C_3H_6N_2S$	Ethylenethiourea 	C'C' 1.536 C'N 1.471 CN 1.322 CS 1.708 CH 0.90 NH 0.99	C'C'N 102.4° C'NC 112.6° NCN 110.2° NCS 124.8° HCH 126.5°	X		222
$C_3H_6N_6$	Melamine $C_3N_3(N'H_2)_3$	CN 1.33, 1.34, 1.35 ± 0.02 CN' 1.35, 1.36 ± 0.02	NCN 123°, 124°, 125° CNC 116°, 117° NCN' 117°, 118°, 119°, 120°	X	At least approximately planar.	223

720

Formula	Name	Bond distances	Bond angles	Method	Remarks	Ref.
C_3H_6O	Acetone	CC 1.55 ± 0.02 CO 1.22 ± 0.03	CCO 119.6° ± 3°	E		186, 224
C_3H_6O	Trimethylene oxide	CC 1.54 ± 0.03 CO 1.46 ± 0.03	CCO 88.5° ± 3° COC 94.5° ± 3°	E		225
$C_3H_6O_2$	Methyl acetate (CH₃—C'(=O)—O—C"H₃)	C'=O 1.22 ± 0.03 CC' 1.52 ± 0.04 C'—O 1.36 ± 0.04 C"O 1.46 ± 0.04 CH (1.09)	C'OC" 113° ± 3° OC'O 124° ± 4° CC'—O 116° ± 3° HCH (109.5°)	E	Configuration approximately that shown. Average angle of 25° between CC'O and C'OC" planes.	145
$C_3H_6O_2$	1,3-Dioxolane	CC 1.54 ± 0.05 CO 1.42 ± 0.03	All ~109.5°	E		225
$C_3H_6O_3$	α-Trioxymethylene (trioxane)	CH (1.09) CO 1.40 ± 0.02	COC 112° ± 3° OCO 112° ± 3°	E	Predominantly in chair form.	225, 226
$C_3H_6S_3$	Trithioformaldehyde	CH (1.10) CS 1.81	CSC 114.5°* SCS 106.5°*	E	Chair form.	16
		CS 1.81 ± 0.06	All 109° 28′	X	Chair form.	227
C_3H_7Br	Isopropyl bromide	CC (1.54) CBr 1.91 ± 0.03	CCC 109° 28′ ± 3° CCBr 109° 28′ ± 3°	E		146
C_3H_7Cl	Isopropyl chloride	CC (1.54) CCl 1.75 ± 0.02	CCC 110° ± 3° CCCl 109° ± 3°	E		146
C_3H_7NO	Acetoxime	CC 1.49, 1.55 CN 1.29 NO 1.36	CCC 117° CCN 113°, 131° CNO 111°	X		228
C_3H_7NO	N-Methylacetamide (CH₃ NH—C(=O)—C'H₃)	C'N 1.44 ± 0.04	CNC' 117° ± 5°	E	Conformation probably that shown. Rest of structure assumed to be same as in acetamide. *See* page 713.	173

* These bond angles are as given in the original paper. Since, however, the SS distance is stated to be 3.05 A, it appears probable that the angles are here interchanged.

Formula	Substance Name	Bond Lengths	Bond Angles	Exp. Method	Remarks	Reference
C_3H_7NO	DL-Alanine $C''H_3-C'H-CO_2^-$ $\quad\quad\;\; \|$ $\quad\quad N^+H_3$	CC' 1.54 ± 0.01 C'C'' 1.51 ± 0.01 C'N 1.50 ± 0.01 CO 1.21, 1.27 ± 0.01	C''C'N 110° C'C'N 108° C'C'C'' 111° C'CO 113°, 121° OCO 125°	X		229
$C_3H_7NO_3$	DL-Serine $HO-CH_2-C'H-C''O_2^-$ $\quad\quad\quad\quad\;\; \|$ $\quad\quad\quad\quad N^+H_3$	CC' 1.51 C'C'' 1.53 C'N 1.49 CO 1.42 C''O 1.26, 1.27	CC'C'' 110° C'CO 112° CC'N 111° C''C'N 110° C'C''O 117° OC''O 125°	X	Staggered conformation about CC' and C'N bonds.	230
C_3H_8	Propane	CH (1.09) CC 1.54 ± 0.02	CCC 111.5° ± 3°	E		154
$C_3H_8N_2$	Pyrazolidine	CC 1.51 CN (1.47) NN (1.47)	CCC 107° CCN 107.5° CNN 109°	E	Assumed planar.	225
$C_3H_8O_2$	Methylal	CO 1.42 ± 0.02 CH 1.09 ± 0.04	COC, OCO (average) 112° ± 3°	E		188, 231
$C_3H_8O_3$	Glycerol	CC 1.54 CH 1.08 CO 1.43		E	Angle of 71° between CCO planes. Two H bonds assumed.	170
C_3H_9As	Trimethylarsine	CAs 1.98 ± 0.02	CAsC 96° ± 5°	E		232
C_3H_9B	Trimethylboron	CB 1.56 ± 0.02	CBC 120° ± 3°	E	Planar.	233
$C_3H_9BF_3N$	Trimethylamine-boron trifluoride	BN 1.585 BF 1.39 CN 1.50	FBF 107° NBF 112° CNC 114° CNB 105°	X		234
$C_3H_9BO_3$	Methyl borate	CO 1.43 ± 0.03 BO 1.38 ± 0.02	BOC 113° ± 3° OBO 120°	E	Planar BO_3.	235

Formula	Name	Bond distances	Angles	Method	Shape	Ref.
$C_3H_9B_3O_3$	Trimethyltriborine trioxane $(CH_3{-}B{-}O{-})_3$	CB 1.57 ± 0.03 BO 1.39 ± 0.02 CH (1.09)	OBO $128° \pm 4°$ BOB $112° \pm 4°$ HCH $(109.5°)$	E	Planar.	235
C_3H_9BrSi	Trimethylbromosilane	SiBr 2.21 ± 0.03 CSi 1.86 ± 0.05	CSiBr $105° \pm 4°$	E		60
C_3H_9BrSn	Trimethyltin bromide	CSn 2.17 ± 0.05 SnBr 2.49 ± 0.03	BrSnBr $\sim 109.5°$	E		61
$C_3H_9Br_2Sb$	Trimethylstibine dibromide	SbBr 2.63 CBr 2.13		X	Trigonal bipyramid.	236
C_3H_9ClSi	Trimethylchlorosilane	SiCl 2.09 ± 0.03 CSi 1.89 ± 0.03	CSiC $113° \pm 2°$	E		237
C_3H_9ClSn	Trimethyltin chloride	SnCl 2.37 ± 0.03 CSn 2.19 ± 0.03	ClSnCl $108° \pm 4°$	E		61
$C_3H_9Cl_2Sb$	Trimethylstibine dichloride	SbCl 2.49	[CCl 3.28]	X	Trigonal bipyramid.	236
C_3H_9ISn	Trimethyltin iodide	SnI 2.72 ± 0.03 SnC ~ 2.17	CSnI $\sim 109.5°$	E		61
$C_3H_9I_2Sb$	Trimethylstibine diiodide	SbI 2.88	[CI 3.58]	X	Trigonal bipyramid.	236
C_3H_9In	Trimethylindium	CIn 2.16 ± 0.04		E		238
C_3H_9N	Trimethylamine	CN 1.47 ± 0.01		E		20, 191
C_3H_9NO	Trimethylamine oxide	CN 1.49 ± 0.02 NO 1.44 ± 0.04	CNO $104° \pm 5°$ CNC $114° \pm 5°$	E		187, 189
C_3H_9P	Trimethylphosphine	CP 1.87 ± 0.02	CPC $100° \pm 4°$	E		232
$C_3H_{10}Si$	Trimethylsilane	CSi 1.873 ± 0.006 CH 1.09 ± 0.02 SiH $1.48° \pm 0.02$	CSiC $110° \pm 2°$ SiCH $109° \pm 2°$	E		197
$C_3H_{12}BN$	Borine trimethylamine $H_3B{-}N(CH_3)_3$	CN 1.53 ± 0.06 BN 1.62 ± 0.15		E		53

723

Formula	Substance Name	Bond Lengths	Bond Angles	Exp. Method	Remarks	Reference
C_3N_{12}	Cyanuric triazide $C_3N_3(-N'N''N^*)_3$	CN 1.31, 1.38 ± 1-2% CN' 1.38 ± 4% N'N" 1.26 ± 1-2% N"N* 1.11 ± 1-2%	N'N"N* 180° CNC 113° NCN 127° NCN' 113°, 120° CN'N" 114°	X	Planar.	239
C_3O_2	Carbon suboxide	CC 1.28 ± 0.03 CO 1.19 ± 0.03	CCC 180° CCO 180°	E		44, 240, 241, 242
C_4Cl_8	Octachlorocyclobutane	CC 1.59 CCl 1.74	CCC 88° ClCCl 109.4°	X	Puckered ring. All values are averages.	243
C_4F_6	Hexafluoro-2-butyne	CF 1.340 ± 0.020 C—C 1.465 ± 0.055 C≡C 1.22 ± 0.09	FCF 107.5° ± 1.0° CCC 180°	E		244
C_4F_8	Octafluorocyclobutane	CC 1.60 ± 0.04 CF 1.33 ± 0.02	FCF 109.5° ± 3° CCC ~89°	E	Puckered ring.	245
C_4HCoO_4	Cobalt carbonyl hydride $Co(CO)_3C'OH$	CCo 1.83 ± 0.02 C'Co 1.75 ± 0.08 CO 1.16 ± 0.05 C'O 1.16 ± 0.05		E	Tetrahedral Co.	246
C_4H_2	Biacetylene	C—C 1.36 ± 0.03 C≡C 1.19 ± 0.03	CCC 180°	E		150
		C—C 1.37₅ ± 0.01 C≡C (1.21) CH (1.060)	CCC 180° CCH 180°	S		214
$C_4H_2F_6O_4$	Trifluoroacetic acid (dimeric)	CC 1.47 ± 0.03 CF 1.36 ± 0.03 CO 1.30 ± 0.03 (average)	FCF 109° ± 2° OCO 130° ± 3°	E		47

724

Formula	Name	Bond lengths (Å)	Angles	Method	Notes	Ref
$C_4H_2FeO_4$	Iron carbonyl hydride $Fe(CO)_2(C'OH)_2$	CFe 1.84 ± 0.03 C'Fe 1.79 ± 0.04 CO 1.15 ± 0.05 C'O 1.15 ± 0.05		E	Tetrahedral Fe.	246
$C_4H_2O_4$	Acetylene dicarboxylic acid	C—C 1.43 ± 0.04 C≡C 1.19 ± 0.02 CO 1.26, 1.27 ± 0.04	CCC 180° CCO 117°, 120° OCO 123°	X	Planar. As dihydrate.	247
$C_4H_3Cl_2N_3$	2-Amino-4,6-dichloropyrimidine	CC' 1.36 CN 1.325 C"N 1.32 C"N' 1.30 CCl 1.78	CC'C 113° C'CCl 117° C'CN 125.5° ClCN 117.5' CNC" 114° NC"N 128° NC"N' 116°	X	Almost planar.	248
$C_4H_3Cl_2N_3$	4-Amino-2,6-dichloropyrimidine	CC a 1.347 b 1.400 CN c 1.332 d 1.314 e 1.304 f 1.331 g 1.339 CCl h 1.757 i 1.770	CCC ab 115.4° CCN bc 119.5° af 127.4° bg 123.2° NCN gc 117.9° de 132.3° CNC cd 115° ef 110.2° CCCl ah 118.5° di 113.5° NCCl ie 114.1° fh 114.0°	X	Almost planar.	249
$C_4H_4CrKO_{10}$	trans Potassium dioxalatodiaquochromate	CC 1.39 CO 1.30, 1.32 CO' 1.19, 1.28 CrO 1.92, 1.93 CrO" 2.02	CCO 116°, 117° CCO' 117°, 118° OCrO 83° CrOC 111°, 112°	X	As trihydrate. Octahedral Cr.	250

Formula	Substance Name	Bond Lengths	Bond Angles	Exp. Method	Remarks	Reference
C₄H₄KNaO₆	Sodium potassium (+)-tartrate K⁺O₂C—C'HOH—C'HOH—CO₂⁻Na⁺	CC' 1.58 C'C' 1.53 CO 1.19, 1.28, 1.29 C'O 1.40	CC'C' 113°, 114° CC'O 111°, 117° C'CO 111°, 114°, 118°, 123° C'C'O 108°, 122° OCO 124°, 125°	X	As tetrahydrate. Rochelle salt.	251
C₄H₄KNaO₆	Sodium potassium DL-tartrate K⁺O₂C—C'HOH—C'HOH—CO₂⁻Na⁺	CC' 1.52, 1.58 C'C' 1.53 CO 1.15, 1.22, 1.32, 1.38 C'O 1.40, 1.51	CC'C' 110°, 118° CC'O 112°, 115° C'CO 114°, 115°, 117° C'C'O 106°, 113° OCO 128°, 129°	X	As tetrahydrate.	252
C₄H₄N₂	Pyrazine	CC (1.39) CN 1.35 ± 0.02 CH (1.09)	CCN ~120° CNC ~120°	E	Planar.	253
C₄H₄N₂O₂	Uracil	as shown	as shown	X	Standard deviations 0.008–0.014 A and 0.6°–0.8°.	254
C₄H₄O	Furan	C—C 1.46 ± 0.03 C=C (1.35) CO 1.40 ± 0.03	COC 107° ± 3° CCO 109° ± 3° CCC 107° ± 2°	E		253, 255
C₄H₄O₂	Dioxadiene	CC 1.35 ± 0.03 CO 1.41 ± 0.03	COC 116° ± 4°	E	Assumed planar.	255
C₄H₄O₂	Ketene dimer	CC' 1.35 ± 0.06 C'C'' 1.48 ± 0.06 C''C* 1.46 ± 0.06 C'O 1.39 ± 0.06 C*O 1.40 ± 0.06 C*O' 1.24 ± 0.06	CC'C'' 136° ± 2° C'C'C* 83° ± 2° C'C'O 130° ± 2° C''C*O' 145° ± 2° C'C'O 94° ± 2° C'OC' 89° ± 2° OC*C' 121° ± 2°	X	Planar.	256

Uracil structure (bond lengths and angles as shown):

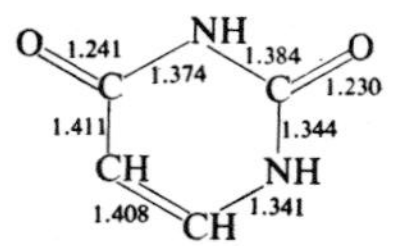

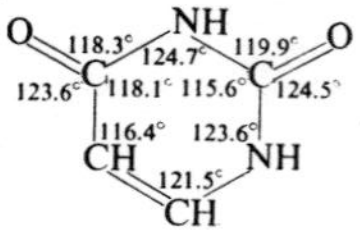

O=C (1.230), NH, NH, CH, CH, O (1.241); bond lengths 1.384, 1.344, 1.341, 1.374, 1.411, 1.408; angles 119.9°, 124.5°, 124.7°, 118.1°, 115.6°, 123.6°, 116.4°, 123.6°, 121.5°, 118.5°.

Ketene dimer structures:

O'
‖
C—C''H
O—C'
H₃C

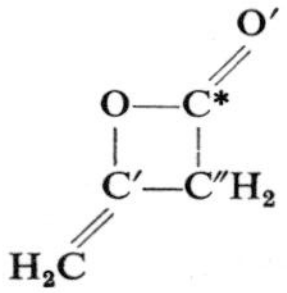

or

O'
‖
C—C''H₂
O—C'
H₂C

726

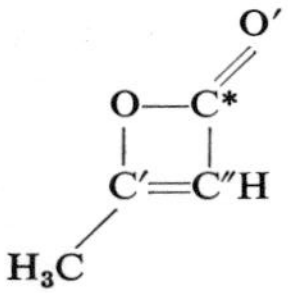

Formula	Name	Bond lengths	Angles	Method	Notes	Ref.
$C_4H_4O_4$	Maleic acid	C—C 1.44, 1.46$_5$ ± 0.02 C=C 1.43 ± 0.02 C—O 1.27, 1.27$_5$ ± 0.02 C=O 1.20, 1.21 ± 0.02	CCC 124.7°, 126.7° CC—O 114.8°, 124.1° CC=O 111.3°, 118.4° OCO 119.2°, 125.5°	X	Exceptionally short intramolecular O—H - - O bond (2.46 A).	257
C_4H_4S	Thiophene	C—C (1.44) C=C (1.35) CS 1.74 ± 0.03	CCC 113° ± 3° CCS 112° ± 3° CSC 91° ± 4°	E		253
$C_4H_5BrN_4$	5-Bromo-4,6-diaminopyrimidine Br—$(C_4N_2H)(N'H_2)_2$	CN 1.33, 1.36 CN' 1.32, 1.40 CC 1.36, 1.37 CBr 1.89	CCC 119.5° CCN 122°, 122.5° CCN' 123°, 124.5° NCN 129.5° NCN' 113°, 115° CNC 112°, 114° CCBr 119.5°, 121°	X	Assumed planar.	249
C_4H_5N	Pyrrole	C—C (1.44) C=C (1.35) CN 1.42 ± 0.02	CCC 108° ± 2° CCN 110° ± 3° CNC 105° ± 4°	E		253
C_4H_6	1,3-Butadiene	CH 1.06 C—C 1.47 C=C 1.37	CCC 122° C=CH 125°	E		170, 253
C_4H_6	Dimethylacetylene	C—C 1.47 ± 0.02 C≡C (1.20)	CCC 180°	E		150
$C_4H_6CuO_4$	Cupric acetate	CC 1.52 CO 1.29-1.36	OCO 108°, 116°	X	As monohydrate.	258
$C_4H_6N_2O_2$	Diketopiperazine $(OC—NH—C'H_2)_2$	CC' 1.47 ± 0.03 CN 1.33 ± 0.03 C'N 1.41 ± 0.03 CO 1.25 ± 0.03	All 120° ± 3°	X	Nearly planar.	259
$C_4H_6Br_4$	1,2,3,4-Tetrabromobutane	CC 1.54 CBr 1.94		E		170
$C_4H_6CoO_4$	Cobalt acetate	CC 1.56 CO 1.29, 1.31	OCO 121° 39'	X	As tetrahydrate.	260

Formula	Substance Name	Bond Lengths	Bond Angles	Exp. Method	Remarks	Reference
C₄H₆NiO₄	Nickel acetate	CC 1.56 CO 1.29, 1.31	OCO 121° 39'	X	As tetrahydrate.	260
C₄H₆O	Crotonaldehyde CH₃—C'H=C"H—C*HO	CC' (1.52) C'C" (1.36) C"C* (1.46) C*O (1.21)	CCC 120° ± 3° CCO 120° ± 3° HCH (109.5°)	E		216
C₄H₆O	2,5-Dihydrofuran	C—C 1.54 ± 0.03 C=C (1.34) CO 1.43 ± 0.03	COC 110° ± 3°	E		255
C₄H₆O	Vinyl ether	CC 1.34 ± 0.03 CO 1.40 ± 0.03	CCO 121.5° ± 2° COC 112° ± 2°	E		106, 261
C₄H₆O₂	Biacetyl CH₃—C'O—C'O—CH₃	CC' 1.54 ± 0.02 C'C' 1.47 ± 0.02 C'O 1.20 ± 0.02 CH (1.09)	C'C'O 123° ± 2° CC'O 122.5° ± 1°	E	Assumed to be planar. Probably s-trans	137
C₄H₆O₄	Methyl oxalate C'H₃—O—CO'—CO'—O—C'H₃	CC' 1.53 ± 0.08 CO 1.31 ± 0.05 CO' 1.19 ± 0.05 C'O 1.46 ± 0.05	CCO' 125° ± 3° CCO 110° ± 3° OCO' 125° ± 3° COC' 118° ± 3°	X	Planar and s-trans.	262
C₄H₆O₄	β-Succinic acid HO₂C—C'H₂—C'H₂—CO₂H	CC' 1.51 ± 0.02 C'C' 1.50 ± 0.02 C—O 1.30 ± 0.02 C=O 1.25 ± 0.02	CC'C' 112° C'C—O 114° C'C=O 124° OCO 122°	X	C atoms coplanar. Centrosymmetric.	R, 263
C₄H₆O₄Zn	Zinc acetate	CC 1.48 CO 1.30, 1.38	OCO 111°	X	As dihydrate.	264
C₄H₆O₆	Acetylene dicarboxylic acid dihydrate				See C₄H₂O₄.	
C₄H₆O₆	(+)-Tartaric acid HO₂C—C'HOH—C'HOH—CO₂H	CC' 1.49, 1.53 ± 0.05 C'C' 1.47 ± 0.05 C—O 1.20, 1.21 ± 0.05 C=O 1.17, 1.21 ± 0.05 C'O 1.48, 1.49 ± 0.05	CC'C' 102°, 107° ± 5° C'C=O 112°, 128° ± 5° C'C—O 108°, 125° ± 5° C'C'O 104°, 107° ± 5° C'C'O 111°, 113° ± 5° OCO 123°, 124° ± 5°	X		265

729

Formula	Name	Bond lengths	Bond angles	E/X	Notes	Ref.
$C_4H_6O_6$	DL-Tartaric acid HO_2C—$C'HOH$—$C'HOH$—CO_2H	CC' 1.44, 1.52 C'C' 1.53 C—O 1.28, 1.33 C—O 1.20, 1.22 C'O 1.36, 1.49	CC'C' 110° C'C=O 120°, 123° C'C—O 113°, 116° CC'O 110°, 112° C'C'O 108°, 110° OCO 120°, 124°	X	As monohydrate.	266
C_4H_7Cl	1-Chloro-2-methyl-1-propene	C—C (1.54) C=C (1.34) CCl 1.72 ± 0.02	CCC 111° ± 3° CCCl 123° ± 2°	E	Assumed planar.	146
$C_4H_7NO_3$	N-Acetylglycine CH_3—$C'O$—NH—$C''H_2$—$C*O_2H$	CC' 1.50 C'C* 1.51 C'N 1.32 C''N 1.45 C'O 1.24 C*—O 1.31 C*=O 1.19	CC'N 118° C*C''N 110° CC'O 121° C'C*=O 124° C''C*—O 112° NC'O 121° C'NC'' 120° OC*O 124°	X	Nearly planar.	267
C_4H_8	cis 2-Butene	C—C 1.54 ± 0.03 C=C 1.38 ± 0.03		E	B.p. 3.0°C.	268
C_4H_8	trans 2-Butene	C—C 1.56 ± 0.04 C=C 1.40 ± 0.04		E	B.p. ·0.3°C.	268
C_4H_8	Cyclobutane	CC 1.56_8 ± 0.02 CH 1.09_8 ± 0.04	HCH 114° ± 8°	E	Puckered ring.	269
C_4H_8	Isobutylene	CH (1.09) C—C 1.54 ± 0.02 C=C (1.34)	C—C—C (111.5°)	E		154
$C_4H_8Br_2$	2,3-Dibromobutane	CC (1.54) CBr (1.91)	CCC (110.5°) CCBr 109.5° ± 2°	E	Both meso and racemic forms; trans conformation.	270
$C_4H_8Cl_2$	2,3-Dichlorobutane	CC (1.55) CCl (1.77)		E	trans Conformation.	225
$C_4H_8Cl_2N_2$	N,N'-Dichloropiperazine	CC 1.54 CN 1.47 NCl 1.70		E		271

Formula	Substance Name	Bond Lengths	Bond Angles	Exp. Method	Remarks	Reference
$C_4H_8CuO_5$	Cupric acetate monohydrate				See $C_4H_6CuO_4$.	
$C_4H_8I_2S_3$	2,2'-Diiododiethyl trisulfide	CC 1.55 CI 2.09 CS 1.86 SS 2.05	CCI 109° CCS 114° CSS 98° SSS 113°	X	SCCI groups are planar and *trans*.	272
$C_4H_8N_2O_2$	Dimethylglyoxime $C'H_3-C(=NOH)-C(=NOH)-C'H_3$	CC 1.44 ± 0.05 CC' 1.53 ± 0.05 CN 1.27 ± 0.05 NO 1.38 ± 0.05	CCC 120.4° ± 2° C'CN 124.6° ± 2° CCN 115.1° ± 2° CNO 113.9° ± 2°	X	Planar and *s-trans*. Molecules are linked by H bonds in infinite chains.	273
$C_4H_8N_2O_2$	Succinamide	CC 1.54 CN 1.40 CO 1.22	CCC 110° CCO 123° CCN 114° NCO 123°	X		274
C_4H_8O	*cis* 2-Butene oxide	CC 1.54 ± 0.03 CO 1.43 ± 0.03		E	B.p. 59.3–59.9°C (746 mm).	268, 275
C_4H_8O	*trans* 2-Butene oxide	CC 1.54 ± 0.03 CO 1.43 ± 0.03		E	B.p. 52.9–53.7°C (746 mm).	268, 275
C_4H_8O	Tetrahydrofuran	CC 1.54 ± 0.02 CO 1.43 ± 0.03	COC 111° ± 2°	E		255
$C_4H_8O_2$	1,4-Dioxane	CC 1.51 ± 0.04 CO 1.44 ± 0.03	CCO 109.5° ± 5° COC 112° ± 5°	E	Chair form.	16, 184, 225, 226
$C_4H_8O_4$	Acetic acid (dimeric)	CC 1.54 ± 0.04 C—O 1.36 ± 0.04 C=O 1.25 ± 0.03	OCO 130° ± 3°	E	O—H – – O distance is 2.76 ± 0.06 A.	47
$C_4H_8O_7$	DL-Tartaric acid monohydrate				See $C_4H_6O_6$ (DL-Tartaric acid).	
$C_4H_8Se_2$	1,4-Diselenane	CC 1.50 ± 0.05 CSe 2.01 ± 0.03	CCSe 110.8°, 111.4° ± 1.0° CSeC 98.6° ± 2°	X	Chair form.	276

Formula	Name / Structure	Distances (Å)	Angles	Method	Ref.	Notes
C_4H_9Br	*tert*-Butyl bromide	CC (1.54) CBr 1.92 ± 0.03	CCC 111.5° ± 2°	E	277	
		CC (1.54) CH (1.093) CBr 1.94	CCC (109° 28') HCH (109° 28')	S	*GST*, 278	
C_4H_9Cl	*tert*-Butyl chloride	CC 1.54 ± 0.01 CCl 1.80 ± 0.01 CH 1.10 ± 0.02	CCCl 107° ± 1°	E	147, 277, 279	
		CC (1.54) CH (1.093) CCl 1.78	CCC (109° 28') HCH (109° 28')	S	*GST*, 278	
C_4H_9F	*tert*-Butyl fluoride	CF 1.38 ± 0.02	CCF 108° ± 1.5°	E	279, 280	
		CC (1.54) CH (1.093) CF 1.37 ± 0.01	CCF 108° ± 1.5° CCH 111.5° CCC 111° ± 1.5°	S	281	
C_4H_9I	*tert*-Butyl iodide	CC (1.54) CH (1.093) CI 2.14	CCC (109° 28') HCH (109° 28')	S	*GST*, 278	
$C_4H_9NO_2$	α-Aminoisobutyric acid $(CH_3)_2C'-C''O_2^-$ $\quad\quad\vert$ $\quad N^+H_3$	CC' 1.53, 1.54 C'C'' 1.52 C'N 1.49 C''O 1.20, 1.26	CC'C 112.2° CC'C* 108.7°, 114° C'C''N 104.9°, 107.5° C''C''N 108.8° CCO 117.7°, 117.9° OCO 125.3°	X	282	
$C_4H_9NO_3$	L-Threonine $CH_3-C'HOH-C''H-C*O_2^-$ $\quad\quad\quad\quad\quad\quad\vert$ $\quad\quad\quad\quad\quad N^+H_3$	CC' 1.50 ± 0.02 C'C'' 1.54 ± 0.02 C''C* 1.52 ± 0.02 C''N 1.49 ± 0.02 C'O 1.42 ± 0.02 C*O 1.24, 1.25 ± 0.02	CC'C'' 113° ± 1° C'C''C* 113° ± 1° C'C''N 108° ± 1° C*C''N 110° ± 1° C'C''O 110° ± 1° C''C*O 104° ± 1° C''C*O 116°, 117° ± 1° OC*O 127° ± 1°	X	283	Threo configuration confirmed.

Formula	Substance Name	Bond Lengths	Bond Angles	Exp. Method	Remarks	Reference
$C_4H_9N_3O_2$	Creatine 	CC 1.51 CN a 1.35 b 1.32 c 1.32 d 1.49 e 1.46 CO 1.25	CCN 113° ± 4° CNC cd 121° ± 4° ce 119° ± 4° de 117° ± 4° NCN ab 118° ± 4° ac 121° ± 4° bc 121° ± 4° CCO 118°, 121° ± 4° OCO 123° ± 4°	X	As monohydrate. Zwitterionic structure confirmed. Guanidine group planar.	284
C_4H_{10}	Butane	CC 1.51 ± 0.05		E		132
C_4H_{10}	Isobutane	CC 1.54 ± 0.02	CCC 111.5° ± 2°	E	See $C_4H_4CrKO_{10}$.	154, 277, 285
$C_4H_{10}CrKO_{13}$	trans Potassium dioxalatodiaquochromate trihydrate					
$C_4H_{10}N_4NiO_5Sr$	Strontium nickelcyanide pentahydrate				See C_4H_4NiSr.	
$C_4H_{10}O$	Ethyl ether	CC 1.50 ± 0.02 CO 1.43 ± 0.02	CCO 110° ± 3° COC 108° ± 3°	E		B, 20
$C_4H_{10}S$	Ethyl sulfide	CC 1.55 ± 0.02 CS 1.81 ± 0.01	CCS 112° ± 2°	E		20
$C_4H_{10}O_6Zn$	Zinc acetate dihydrate				See $C_4H_6O_4$ Zn.	
$C_4H_{11}ClSi$	Silico-neopentyl chloride $(CH_3)_3Si—CH_2Cl$	CSi 1.88 ± 0.04 CCl 1.73 ± 0.03 CH (1.09)	All 109.5° ± 2°	E		286
$C_4H_{11}N_3O_3$	Creatine monohydrate				See $C_4H_9N_3O_2$.	
$C_4H_{12}Al_2Br_2$	Dimethylaluminum bromide (dimeric) 	CAl 1.90–2.05 AlBr 2.42 ± 0.03	CAlC 115°–130° BrAlBr 90° ± 3°	E	"Ethane-like" structure less satisfactory.	287

732

Formula	Name	Bond	Length	Angle	Angle value	Method	Notes	Ref
$C_4H_{12}Al_2Cl_2$	Dimethylaluminum chloride (dimeric)	CAl AlCl	1.85–2.00 2.31 ± 0.03	CAlC ClAlCl	120°–135° 89° ± 4°	E	Structure analogous to that of bromide.	287
$C_4H_{12}Ge$	Tetramethylgermanium	CGe	1.98 ± 0.03			E	Tetrahedral Ge.	191
$C_4H_{12}KNaO_{10}$	Sodium potassium(+)-tartrate tetrahydrate						*See* $C_4H_4KNaO_6$.	
$C_4H_{12}KNaO_{10}$	Sodium potassium DL-tartrate tetrahydrate						*See* $C_4H_4KNaO_6$.	
$C_4H_{12}O_2Si$	Diethylsilanediol $(C_2H_5)_2Si(OH)_2$	CSi SiO	1.90 ± 0.03 1.63 ± 0.02	CSiC OSiO	111° 110°	X		288
$C_4H_{12}O_4Si$	Methyl orthosilicate	CO SiO	1.42 ± 0.04 1.64 ± 0.03	COSi	113° ± 2°	E		289
$C_4H_{12}Pb$	Tetramethyllead	CPb	2.29 ± 0.05			E	Tetrahedral Pb.	191
$C_4H_{12}Si$	Tetramethylsilane	CH CSi	1.10 ± 0.05 1.888 ± 0.02	SiCH	110° ± 3°	E	Tetrahedral Si.	191, 290
$C_4H_{12}Sn$	Tetramethyltin	CSn	2.18 ± 0.03			E	Tetrahedral Sn.	191
$C_4H_{14}CoO_8$	Cobalt acetate tetrahydrate						*See* $C_4H_6CoO_4$.	
$C_4H_{14}NiO_8$	Nickel acetate tetrahydrate						*See* $C_4H_6NiO_4$.	
$C_4H_{16}Cl_3CoN_4$	*trans* Dichlorodiethylenediamine cobalt chloride	CN CC CoCl CoN	1.47, 1.48 1.55 2.33 1.98, 2.00	CCN CNCo	108°, 110° 104°, 106°	X	Octahedral Co. As hydrochloride dihydrate.	291

Formula	Name	Bond	Length	Angle	Angle value	Method	Notes	Ref
$C_4H_{21}Cl_4CoN_4O_2$	*trans* Dichlorodiethylenediamine cobalt chloride hydrochloride dihydrate						*See* $C_4H_{16}Cl_3CoN_4$.	

733

Formula	Substance Name	Bond Lengths	Bond Angles	Exp. Method	Remarks	Reference
C_4N_2	Dicyanoacetylene	C—C 1.37 C≡C 1.19 CN 1.14	CCC 180° CCN 180°	X		292
C_4N_4NiSr	Strontium nickelcyanide	CN 1.18 CNi 1.86		X	As pentahydrate.	293
C_4NiO_4	Nickel carbonyl	CNi 1.82 ± 0.03 CO 1.15 ± 0.02	NiCO 180°	E	Tetrahedral Ni.	294
		CNi 1.84 ± 0.03	NiCO 180°	X	Tetrahedral Ni. NiO distance is 2.99 ± 0.03 A. −55°C.	295
C_5F_{10}	Decafluorocyclopentane	CC (1.54) CF 1.38		E	Ring probably puckered.	296
C_5FeO_5	Iron pentacarbonyl	CFe 1.84 ± 0.03 CO 1.15 ± 0.04	FeCO (180°)	E	Trigonal bipyramid.	246
C_5H_4	1,3-Pentadiyne 	CC a 1.460 b 1.207 c 1.377 d 1.207 CH e 1.06		S		297
$C_5H_4O_3$	Furoic acid 	CC a 1.47 ± 0.05 b 1.30 ± 0.05 c 1.46 ± 0.05 d 1.35 ± 0.05 CO e 1.30 ± 0.05 f 1.31 ± 0.05 g 1.26 ± 0.05 h 1.16 ± 0.05	CCC ab 127° bc 105° cd 103° CCO bf 113° de 112° ag 119° COC ef 101° OCO gh 124°	X	Planar.	298

734

Formula	Name / Structure	Bond lengths (Å)	Angles	Method	Notes	Ref.
C_5H_5N	Pyridine	CC (1.39) CH (1.09) CN 1.37 ± 0.03	All ~120°	E		253
		CC 1.39 CH 1.08 CN 1.35–1.36	CNC 114°–117°	S		299
C_5H_5NO	2-Pyridone	CC a 1.371 ± {0.010} b 1.421 ± {0.010} c 1.334 ± {0.010} d 1.444 ± {0.010} CN e 1.401 ± {0.010} f 1.335 ± {0.010} CO g 1.236 ± {0.010}	CCC ab 116.0° bc 122.2° cd 122.3° de 112.7° CCN af 121.8° CNC ef 125.1° CCO dg 126.0° NCO eg 121.3°	X	Pyridone structure confirmed.	300
C_5H_5NS	2-Thiopyridone	CC a 1.37 ± 0.065 b 1.52 ± 0.065 c 1.29 ± 0.065 d 1.44 ± 0.065 CN e 1.39 ± 0.065 f 1.33 ± 0.065 CS g 1.68 ± 0.065	CCC ab 111° bc 123° cd 123° CCN de 115° ef 127° CNC af 127° CCS dg 127° NCS eg 119°	X		301
$C_5H_5N_3O_2$	6-Amido-3-pyridazone	CC a 1.46 ± {0.014} b 1.40 ± {0.014} c 1.34 ± {0.014} d 1.44 ± {0.014} CN e 1.33 ± {0.014} f 1.32 ± {0.014} g 1.38 ± {0.014} h 1.25 ± {0.014} CO i 1.24 ± {0.014} NN j 1.36 ± {0.014}	CCC ab 121° bc 122° cd 119° CCN af 118° bf 120° ae 118° dg 114° ah 119° CCO di 126° NCO eh 123° CNN gi 120° fj 118° gj 126°	X	Planar, except for N and O atoms of amido group.	302

Formula	Substance Name	Bond Lengths	Bond Angles	Exp. Method	Remarks	Reference
C_5H_6	Cyclopentadiene $C'H=C''H-C''H=C'H$ with CH_2 bridge	CH (1.09) CC' (1.53) C'C'' (1.35) C''C'' 1.46 ± 0.04	C'CC' 101° ± 4° CC'C'' 109° ± 3° C'C''C'' 110° ± 2°	E		253
C_5H_6	1-Pentene-3-yne $C'H_3-C\equiv C-CH=CH_2$	C'C (1.47) C≡C (1.20) C—C (1.42) C=C (1.35)	C—C≡C (180°) C—C=C (125°)	E	Assumed planar. Pirylene.	303
$C_5H_6ClN_3$	2-Amino-4-methyl-6-chloropyrimidine	CC a 1.34 ± 0.02 b 1.38 ± 0.02 c 1.69 ± 0.02 CCl 1.76 ± 0.02 CN d 1.32 ± 0.02 e 1.33 ± 0.02 f 1.32 ± 0.02 g 1.33 ± 0.02 h 1.30 ± 0.02	CCC bc 117° CCN bg 125.5° cg 117.5° CNC fg 114° NCN ef 128° eh 116° fh 116°	X	Almost completely planar.	248
$C_5H_6ClN_5$	Adenine hydrochloride	CC a 1.37 b 1.40 CN c 1.30 d 1.38 e 1.37 f 1.30 g 1.36 h 1.36 i 1.33 j 1.35 k 1.37	CCC ab 118° CCN bc 126.5° bd 114° ag 128° ah 107° ak 111° NCN cd 119.5° ef 124.5° ij 115° CNC de 123° fg 112.5° hi 105° jk 102°	X	Planar.	304

$C_5H_6ClN_5O$	Guanine hydrochloride		CC a 1.34
			    b 1.40
			CN c 1.41
			    d 1.32
			    e 1.33
			    f 1.35
			    g 1.34
			    h 1.32
			    i 1.33
			    j 1.41
			CO k 1.20
				CCC ab 124°
				CCN bc 108°
				      aj 108°
				      af 124°
				      ag 107°
				      bj 128°
				CNC cd 126°
				      ef 113°
				      gh 111°
				      ij 106°
				NCN de 124°
				      fg 109°
				      hi 108°
				CCO bk 136°
				NCO ck 116°
					X	305

C_5H_8	1-Methylcyclobutene		C—C All 1.54 ± 0.03 C=C 1.34 ± 0.03	CCC ab 93° 40' ± 3° bc 125° ± 4°	E	306
C_5H_8	Methylenecyclobutane		C—C All 1.55 ± 0.02 C=C 1.34 ± 0.03	CCC ab 92.5° ± 2°	E	306, 307

C_5H_8	Spiropentane		CC a 1.51 ± 0.04
			    b 1.48 ± 0.03
			    c 1.48 ± 0.03
			CH (1.08)
				CCC bc 61.5° ± 2°
				HCH 120° ± 8°
					E	308

Formula	Substance Name	Exp. Method	Bond Lengths	Bond Angles	Remarks	Reference
$C_5H_8Br_4$	Pentaerythritol bromide	E	CC 1.54 CBr 1.94		These results have been questioned. See ref. 310	309
$C_4H_8I_4$	Pentaerythritol iodide	E	CC 1.54 CI 2.10			311
$C_5H_8N_4O_{12}$	Pentaerythritol tetranitrate $C'(CH_2\!-\!O\!-\!NO'_2)_4$	X	CC' 1.50 ± 0.02 CO 1.37 ± 0.02 NO 1.36 ± 0.02 NO' 1.27, 1.28 ± 0.02	CC'C 112.5° ± 4° C'CO 108° ± 4° CON 116° ± 4° ONO' 116° ± 4° O'NO' 123° ± 4°		
$C_5H_8O_2S$	β-Isoprene sulfone	X	CC a 1.47$_4$ ± {0.023} b 1.37$_6$ ± {0.023} c 1.47$_1$ ± {0.023} d 1.52$_3$ ± {0.023} CS e 1.75$_9$ ± {0.017} f 1.74$_4$ ± {0.017} SO 1.43$_6$	CCC ab 117.0° bc 114.2° bd 124.5° cd 121.0° CCS ae 104.2° cf 106.3° CSC 98.3°	Plane of ring is a plane of symmetry.	312
$C_5H_8O_4$	β-Glutaric acid $HO_2C\!-\!C'H_2\!-\!C''H_2\!-\!C'H_2\!-\!CO_2H$	X	CC' 1.53 ± 0.03 C'C" 1.53 ± 0.02 C—O 1.30 ± 0.03 C=O 1.23 ± 0.03	CC'C" 115° C'C"C' 109° C'C—O 115° C'C=O 123° OCO 122°		313
$C_5H_9NO_3$	Hydroxy-L-proline	X	CC a 1.52 ± 0.03 b 1.53 ± 0.03 c 1.50 ± 0.03 d 1.52 ± 0.03 CN e 1.48 ± 0.03 f 1.50 ± 0.03 CO g 1.25, 1.27 ± 0.03 h 1.46 ± 0.03	CCC ab 113° ± 1° bc 108° ± 1° cd 104° ± 1° CCN bf 105° ± 1° af 111° ± 1° de 105° ± 1° CNC ef 109° ± 1° CCO ch 106° ± 1° dh 109° ± 1° ag 115°, 119° ± 1° OCO gg 126° ± 1°		314

738

Formula	Compound / Structure	Bond lengths (Å)	Angles	Method	Notes	Ref.
$C_5H_9NO_4S_2$	N-Methyl-2,2-dimethylsulfonylvinylidene-amine $(C'H_3-SO_2-)_2C=C=N-CH_3$	CC 1.342 ± {0.0083} C—N 1.426 ± {0.0087} C≡N 1.154 ± {0.0076} CS 1.726 ± {0.0067} C'S 1.770 ± {0.0087} SO 1.433 ± {0.0056, 0.0062}	CCN 180° CNC 180° CSC 106° 50' ± {0.4°} SCS 122° 36' ± {0.4°} OSO 118° 25' ± {0.4°}	X		315
C_5H_{10}	Cyclopentane	CC 1.54 CH 1.09	HCH ~109.5°	E	Ring nearly, if not quite, planar.	16, 154, 316
C_5H_{10}	Methylcyclobutane $C_4H_7-C'H_3$	CC 1.56 ± 0.03 CC' 1.54 ± 0.06 CH (1.09) C'H (1.09)	CCC' ~118° HCH (116°)	E		245
$C_5H_{10}ClNO_4$	DL-Glutamic acid hydrochloride	CC a 1.51 ± 0.03 b 1.55 ± 0.03 c 1.51 ± 0.03 d 1.54 ± 0.03 CO e 1.31 ± 0.03 f 1.21 ± 0.03 g 1.20 ± 0.03 h 1.32 ± 0.03 CN i 1.52 ± 0.03	CCC ab 109° ± 3° bc 115° ± 3° cd 109° ± 3° CCO ae 114° ± 3° af 123° ± 3° dg 124° ± 3° dh 112° ± 3° CCN ai 111° ± 3° bi 110° ± 3° OCO ef 124° ± 3° gh 125° ± 3°	X		317
$C_5H_{10}N_2O_3$	L-Glutamine	CC a 1.54 b 1.47 c 1.50 d 1.52 CN e 1.28 f 1.51 CO g 1.27 h 1.22, 1.27	CCC ab 115° bc 113° cd 114° CCN ae 118° cf 110° df 111° CCO ag 118° dh 116° NCO eg 123° OCO hh 128°	X		318

Formula	Substance Name	Bond Lengths	Bond Angles	Exp. Method	Remarks	Reference
$C_5H_{10}N_2O_3S$	Cysteylglycine $HS\overset{i}{-}CH_2\overset{a}{-}CH\overset{b}{-}C\overset{d}{-}NH\overset{e}{-}CH_2\overset{c}{-}CO_2^{-}$ $\underset{N^+H_3}{\overset{f}{\vert}}\ \underset{O}{\overset{g}{\Vert}}$	CC a 1.51 ± 0.05 b 1.54 ± 0.05 c 1.59 ± 0.05 CN d 1.32 ± 0.05 e 1.33 ± 0.05 f 1.42 ± 0.05 CO g 1.21 ± 0.05 h 1.23, 1.28 ± 0.05 CS i 1.64 ± 0.05	CCC ab 111° ± 3° CCN bd 126° ± 3° ce 126° ± 3° af 108° ± 3° bf 110° ± 3° CCO bg 109° ± 3° ch 113°, 121° ± 3° CNC de 139° ± 3° CCS ai 125° ± 3° OCO hh 126° ± 3°	X		319
$C_5H_{11}Cl$	Neopentyl chloride $(CH_3)_3C'\!-\!C''H_2Cl$	CC' 1.54 ± 0.03 C'C'' 1.58 ± 0.04 C''Cl 1.74 ± 0.03 CH (1.09)	CC'C 108° ± 2° CC'C'' 111° ± 2° C'C''Cl 111° ± 2° HCH (109.5°)	E		286
$C_5H_{11}NO_2S$	DL-α-Methionine $CH_3\overset{d}{-}S\overset{e}{-}CH_2\overset{a}{-}CH_2\overset{b}{-}CH\overset{c}{-}CO_2^{-}$ $\underset{N^+H_3}{\overset{f}{\vert}}$	CC a 1.51 b 1.55 c 1.47 CN f 1.52 CO 1.21, 1.28 CS d 1.77 e 1.79	CCC ab 111° bc 111° CCN bf 110° cf 112° CCO 119°, 120° CCS 111° CSC 100° OCO 121°	X		320
$C_5H_{11}NO_2S$	DL-β-Methionine $CH_3\overset{d}{-}S\overset{e}{-}CH_2\overset{a}{-}CH_2\overset{b}{-}CH\overset{c}{-}CO_2^{-}$ $\underset{N^+H_3}{\overset{f}{\vert}}$	CC a 1.54 b 1.58 c 1.52 CN f 1.50 CO 1.21, 1.27 CS d 1.78 e 1.80	CCC ab 113° bc 108° CCN bf 109° cf 110° CCO 118°, 120° CCS 109° CSC 100° OCO 122°	X		320
C_5H_{12}	Neopentane	CC 1.54 ± 0.02 CH (1.09)	CCC (109.5°)	E		154
C_5H_{12}	Pentane	CC 1.53 ± 0.05		E		97, 132

Formula	Name	Bond lengths	Bond angles	Method	Notes	Ref.
$C_5H_{12}O_4$	Pentaerythritol	CC 1.50 ± 0.03, CO 1.46 ± 0.03	CCC 108.5°, 111.5° ± 1°, CCO 111.5° ± 1°	X		321
$C_5H_{12}S_4$	Methyl orthothiocarbonate $C'(SCH_3)_4$	CS 1.8 ± 0.1, C'S 1.81 ± 0.02	[SS 2.95, 2.96]	X		322
$C_6Br_4O_2$	Bromanil	C—C 1.54, C=C 1.36, CBr 1.89, CO 1.14	C—C—C 114°, C=CBr 124°	E		323, 324
C_6Br_6	Hexabromobenzene	CC 1.40, CBr 1.87		E	Br atoms not in plane of ring.	325, 326
$C_6Cl_4O_2$	Chloranil	C—C 1.54, C=C 1.36, CCl 1.72, CO 1.14	C—C—C 110°, C=CCl 123°	E		323, 324
C_6Cl_6	Hexachlorobenzene	CC (1.40), CCl 1.72		E	Cl atoms not in plane of ring.	325, 326, 327
C_6CrO_6	Chromium hexacarbonyl	CCr 1.92 ± 0.04, CO 1.16 ± 0.05	CrCO 180°	E	Octahedral Cr.	328
C_6F_{12}	Dodecafluorocyclohexane	CC (1.54), CF 1.38	All ~109.5°	E		296
$C_6H_2Br_4$	1,2,3,5-Tetrabromobenzene	CC 1.40, CBr 1.88		E	Br atoms not in plane of ring.	326
$C_6H_2Br_4O_2$	Tetrabromohydroquinone	CBr 1.87	CCBr 122.5°	E		323
$C_6H_2Cl_4$	1,2,4,5-Tetrachlorobenzene	CC (1.40), CCl 1.72 ± 0.04		E		327
$C_6H_2Cl_4O_2$	Tetrachlorohydroquinone	CCl 1.70	CCCl 122°	E		323

Formula	Substance Name	Bond Lengths	Bond Angles	Exp. Method	Remarks	Reference
$C_6H_2IN_3O_6$	Picryl iodide	CC 1.39 CI 2.10 CN 1.45 CN' 1.35	CCC 120° ONO 127° ON'O 120°	X	N'O₂ in plane of ring. NO₂ at 80° to plane.	329
$C_6H_3Br_3$	1,3,5-Tribromobenzene	CC 1.39 ± 0.03 CBr 1.84 ± 0.02	CCBr 119° ± 2°	E		325, 330
$C_6H_3Cl_3$	1,3,5-Trichlorobenzene	CC (1.41) CCl 1.69 ± 0.03		E		327
$C_6H_3I_3$	1,3,5-Triiodobenzene	CC (1.41) CI 2.05 ± 0.03		E		325
$C_6H_3N_3O_6$	1,3,5-Trinitrobenzene	CC 1.4 CN 1.4 NO 1.2₃	ONO 120°	X	In addition compound with p-iodoaniline. Planar.	331
C_6H_4BrF	p-Bromofluorobenzene	CC (1.40) CH (1.04) CBr 1.87 ± 0.02 CF 1.30 ± 0.03		E		332
$C_6H_4Br_2$	o-Dibromobenzene	CC 1.405 CBr 1.89		E	Br atoms not in plane of ring.	326
$C_6H_4Br_2$	p-Dibromobenzene	CC 1.40 CBr 1.88		E	Planar.	325, 326
$C_6H_4Br_2$		CC (1.41) CBr 1.84 ± 0.02		X		333

Formula	Name	Bond distances	Bond angles	Method	Remarks	Reference
C_6H_4ClF	o-Chlorofluorobenzene	CC (1.40) CH (1.04) CCl 1.69 ± 0.02 CF 1.30 ± 0.03	CCCl 121° ± 1° CCF 121° ± 1°	E		332
C_6H_4ClF	p-Chlorofluorobenzene	CC (1.40) CH (1.04) CCl 1.68 ± 0.02 CF 1.30 ± 0.03		E		332
$C_6H_4ClIO_2$	p-Chloroiodoxybenzene	CC 1.41 CCl 1.80 CI 1.93 IO 1.60, 1.65 ± 0.05	CCC 120° CCl 109°, 129° OIO 103°	X	Plane containing IO_2 group nearly perpendicular to that of ring.	334
$C_6H_4Cl_2$	m-Dichlorobenzene	CC (1.40) CCl 1.69 ± 0.03		E		327
$C_6H_4Cl_2$	o-Dichlorobenzene	CC 1.405 CCl 1.735		E	Cl atoms not in plane of ring.	326, 327
$C_6H_4Cl_2$	p-Dichlorobenzene	CC (1.40) CCl 1.69 ± 0.03		E		327
		CC 1.40 CCl 1.64	All 120°	X	Planar.	335
$C_6H_4F_2$	o-Difluorobenzene	CF 1.35 ± 0.03		E		336
$C_6H_4I_2$	m-Diiodobenzene	CC (1.42) CI 2.00 ± 0.10		E, X		B, 337
$C_6H_4I_2$	o-Diiodobenzene	CC (1.42) CI 2.00 ± 0.10		E, X	CI bonds bent away from each other by about 10°.	B, 337
$C_6H_4I_2$	p-Diiodobenzene	CC (1.42) CI 2.02 ± 0.03		E, X		B, 325, 337

743

Formula	Substance Name	Bond Lengths	Bond Angles	Exp. Method	Remarks	Reference
$C_6H_4N_2O$	Benzofurazan	CC 1.43 ± 0.07 CN 1.35 ± 0.07 NO 1.20 ± 0.07	CCC $120°$ CCN $101°$ CNO $113°$ NON $112°$	X	Assumed planar.	338
$C_6H_4N_2O_4$	m-Dinitrobenzene	CC 1.41 CN 1.54 NO (1.20)	CCC $120°$ ONO $130°$	X	CN bonds make $15°$ angle with plane of ring.	339
	p-Dinitrobenzene	CC 1.33–1.42 ± 0.04 CN 1.39, $1.46* \pm 0.04$ NO 1.19 ± 0.04	ONO $120°*$, $128°$	X	Planar. Values designated by asterisks are relatively unreliable.	340
$C_6H_4N_2O_4$		CC 1.38 ± 0.03 CN 1.48 ± 0.03 NO 1.21 ± 0.03	CNO $118° \ 3'$, $117° \ 29' \pm 3°$ ONO $124° \ 28' \pm 3°$	X	NO_2 planes at $9° \ 25'$ to that of ring.	341
$C_6H_4N_2S$	Piazthiole (2,1,3-Benzothiadiazole)	CC $a \ 1.41 \pm 0.03$ $b \ 1.46 \pm 0.03$ $c \ 1.29 \pm 0.03$ $d \ 1.46 \pm 0.03$ CN 1.34 ± 0.03 NS 1.60 ± 0.03	CCC $ab \ 119°$ $bc \ 120°$ $cd \ 121°$ CCN $114°$ CNS $105°$ NSN $102°$	X	Assumed planar.	338, 342
$C_6H_4N_2Se$	Piaselenol (2,1,3-Benzoselenadiazole)	CC $a \ 1.46 \pm 0.04$ $b \ 1.42 \pm 0.04$ $c \ 1.30 \pm 0.04$ $d \ 1.42 \pm 0.04$ CN 1.30 ± 0.04 CSe 1.83 ± 0.04	CCC $ab \ 119°$ $bc \ 118°$ $cd \ 123°$ CCN $118°$ CNSe $104°$ NSeN $95°$	X	Assumed planar.	338, 343

Formula	Name	Bond lengths (Å)	Bond angles	Method	Notes	Ref.
$C_6H_4O_2$	p-Benzoquinone	CH (1.08) C—C 1.49 ± 0.04 C=C 1.32 ± 0.04 CO 1.23 ± 0.04	C—C—C 116 ± 3°	E	Assumed planar and symmetrical.	344
		C—C 1.50 C=C 1.32 CO 1.14	C—C—C 109° C—C=C 125°	X	Planar.	345
$C_6H_4S_2$	Thiophthene	CC a 1.36 ± {0.018} b 1.41 ± {0.018} c 1.36 ± {0.018} CS d 1.72 ± {0.018} e 1.74 ± {0.018}	CCC ab 111.7° bc 114.3° CCS ad 116.5° ce 110.2° ef 135.5° CSC de 91.2°	X	Centrosymmetric.	346
C_6H_5Br	Bromobenzene	CC 1.39 ± 0.02 CBr 1.86 ± 0.02		E		347
C_6H_5Cl	Chlorobenzene	CC 1.39 ± 0.02 CCl 1.69 ± 0.03		E		327
$C_6H_5Cl_2I$	Benzene iododichloride	CC (1.40) CI 2.00 ± 0.05 CII 2.45 ± 0.015	CCC (120°) ClICl 86° ClIICl 180°	X	ICl_2 plane approximately perpendicular to ring.	348
$C_6H_5Cl_5$	2,3,4,5,6-Pentachlorocyclohexene	CC a 1.22 b 1.48 c 1.48 d 1.49 e 1.51 f 1.46 CCl g 1.81 h 1.85 i 1.78 j 1.82 k 1.84	CCC ab 130° bc 107° cd 106° de 108° ef 113° af 118° CCCl ag 117° bg 113° bh 110° ch 106° ci 111° di 108° dj 112° ej 106° ek 110° fk 107°	X		349

745

Formula	Substance Name	Bond Lengths	Bond Angles	Exp. Method	Remarks	Reference
C_6H_5F	Fluorobenzene	CC 1.39 ± 0.02 CF 1.30 ± 0.03		E		16, 336, 347
		CC 1.4043 CH (1.05) CF 1.29₄	CCC (120°) CCH (120°) CCF (120°)	S		350
$C_6H_5NO_2$	Nicotinic acid	CC a 1.379 ± 0.012 b 1.388 ± 0.015 c 1.378 ± 0.012 d 1.385 ± 0.012 e 1.482 ± 0.012 f 1.343 ± 0.015 CN g 1.336 ± 0.012 C—O 1.338 ± 0.015 C=O 1.184 ± 0.015	CCC ab 117.8° ± 1.1° bc 119.1° ± 1.1° cd 119.2° ± 1.1° ae 124.0° ± 1.1° be 118.2° ± 1.1° CCN df 122.4° ± 1.1° ag 124.0° ± 1.1° CNC fg 117.5° ± 1.1° C—O 114.1° ± 1.1° C=O 124.0° ± 1.1° OCO 121.9° ± 1.1°	X		351
C_6H_6	Benzene	CC 1.39 ± 0.02 CH 1.08 ± 0.04	CCC 120°	E		253, 352, 353, 354
		CC 1.378 ± {0.0033} (mean)	CCC 120° (mean)	X	At −3°C. Planar.	355
C_6H_6	Dimethylbiacetylene $CH_3-C'\equiv C''-C''-C'\equiv C'-CH_3$	CC' 1.47 ± 0.02 C'C'' 1.20 ± 0.02 C''C'' 1.38 ± 0.03	CC'C'' 180° C'C''C'' 180°	E		150
		CC' 1.466 C'C'' 1.199 C''C'' 1.375	CC'C'' 180° C'C''C'' 180°	X		356
$C_6H_6Br_6$	β-Benzene hexabromide	CC (1.54) CBr 1.94	CCC (109° 28′)	X	All Br atoms equatorial.	R, 357
$C_6H_6Cl_3Sb$	trans, trans, trans-tris(2-chlorovinyl)-di-chlorostibine $(CHCl{=}CH{-})_3SbCl_2$	CC 1.31 CCl 1.70 CSb 2.15 SbCl 2.45	CCCl 120° CCSb 120° Cl₂SbC 84°	X		358

746

Formula	Name	Structure / Bond lengths (Å)	Angles	E	Remarks	Ref.
C₆H₆Cl₆	β-Benzenehexachloride	CC 1.54 CCl 1.76	CCC (109° 28')	X	All Cl atoms equatorial.	R, 357
C₆H₆Cl₆	γ-Benzenehexachloride	CC (1.54) CCl 1.81	CCC 105°–123° CCCl 103°–116°	X	Gammexane. Configuration a, a, a, e, e, e. Detailed structure given in original paper.	360
C₆H₆IN	p-Iodoaniline	CC 1.4 CN 1.4₃ CI 2.1		X	In addition compound with 1,3,5-trinitrobenzene. Planar.	331
C₆H₆N₂O	Nicotinamide	as shown	as shown	X	Planar ring, but amido group is not coplanar with ring. Standard deviation 0.012 Å.	361
C₆H₆N₂O₂	p-Nitroaniline O₂N—C₆H₄—N'H₂	CC 1.31–1.39 ± 0.04 CN 1.39 ± 0.04 CN' 1.36 ± 0.04 NO 1.26 ± 0.04	CNO 117°, 120° ± 3° ONO 123° ± 3°	X	NO₂ group in plane of ring.	362
C₆N₉Na₃O₃	Trisodium tricyanomelamine trihydrate				See C₆N₉Na₃.	
C₆H₆O₂	Hydroquinone	CC 1.39 ± 0.03 CO 1.36 ± 0.03		X	In addition compound with SO₂. SO₂ is rotating.	363

Nicotinamide structural diagram values: O=C 1.22; C–NH₂ 1.34; ring C–C(=O) 1.52; ring bond lengths 1.40, 1.41, 1.39, 1.35, 1.37; ring angles 118°, 117°, 125°, 120°, 123°, 117° (at NH₂), 119°, 121°, 118°, 123°, 118°, with N in ring.

747

Formula	Substance Name	Bond Lengths	Bond Angles	Exp. Method	Remarks	Reference
$C_6H_6O_2$	α-Resorcinol OH, OH (b, a)	CC 1.39 ± 0.01 CO 1.36	CCC 120° CCO ab 121.5°	X		364
$C_6H_6O_2$	β-Resorcinol OH, OH (b, a; d, c)	CC 1.39 CO b 1.37 d 1.36	CCC 120° CCO ab 117.6° cd 123.0°	X	CO bond d not co-planar with ring.	365
$C_6H_6O_3$	Phloroglucinol	CC 1.40 ± 0.01 CO 1.36 ± 0.01		E	Planar. Triphenolic structure.	16, 366
C_6H_7NO	p-Aminophenol OH (a,b,c,d,e,f) NH₂	CC a 1.36 b 1.39 c 1.39 d 1.40 e 1.37 f 1.37 CN 1.39 CO 1.47	All 120° ± 1°	X	Planar.	367
$C_6H_8Br_4$	1,2,4,5-Tetrabromocyclohexane	CC 1.54 CBr 1.93	All 109° 28′	E, X	M.p. 185°C.	368
C_6H_8ClN	Aniline hydrochloride	CC 1.395 ± 0.005 CN 1.35		X		369
$C_6H_8Cl_4$	1,2,4,5-Tetrachlorocyclohexane	CC (1.54) CCl 1.79 (mean)		E, X	M.p. 174°C. Configuration 1a, 2a, 4e, 5e.	370

748

Formula	Name / Structure	Bond lengths (Å)		Bond angles		Method	Notes	Ref.
$C_6H_8N_2O$	4,6-Dimethyl-2-hydroxypyrimidine	CC	a 1.37 ± 0.04 b 1.39 ± 0.04 c 1.52 ± 0.04 d 1.56 ± 0.04	CCC	ab 118.5° ac 122° bd 122°	X	Planar.	371
		CN	e 1.38 ± 0.04 f 1.35 ± 0.04 g 1.34 ± 0.04 h 1.39 ± 0.04	CCN	ae 117° ce 121° bh 122° dh 116°			
		CO	i 1.25 ± 0.04	CNC	ef 124° gh 119°			
				NCN	fg 120°			
				NCO	fi 117° gi 123°			
$C_6H_{10}Br_2$	1,3-Dibromocyclohexane	CBr	1.93	CCC	(109° 28')	E	M.p. 45°C. Br atoms *cis* and equatorial.	372
$C_6H_{10}Br_2$	1,4-Dibromocyclohexane	CBr	1.93	CCC	(109° 28')	E	M.p. 111°C. Br atoms *trans* and equatorial.	372
$C_6H_{10}Cl_2$	1,4-Dichlorocyclohexane	CCl	1.76	CCC	(109° 28')	E	M.p. 101°C. Configuration as for 1,4-$C_6H_{10}Br_2$.	372
$C_6H_{10}I_2$	1,3-Diiodocyclohexane	CI	2.12	CCC	(109° 28')	E	M.p. 67.5°C. Configuration as for 1,3-$C_6H_{10}Br_2$.	372
$C_6H_{10}I_2$	1,4-Diiodocyclohexane	CI	2.12	CCC	(109° 28')	E	M.p. 142°C. Configuration as for 1,4-$C_6H_{10}Br_2$.	372
$C_6H_{10}O$	Cyclohexene oxide	CC CC' C'C' CO	1.54 1.54 1.54 1.42	CCC' CC'C' C'C'C' C'CO	118.5° 116.0° 109.5° 115°	E		373
$C_6H_{10}O_4$	Adipic acid $HO_2C-C'H_2-C'H_2-C'H_2-C'H_2-CO_2H$	CC' C'C" C"C" C—O C=O	1.52 ± 0.03 1.49 ± 0.02 1.54 ± 0.02 1.29 ± 0.04 1.23 ± 0.04	CC"C" C"C"C' C'C—O C'C=O OCO	115° 112° 114° 120° 126°	X	Centrosymmetric.	374

Formula	Substance Name	Bond Lengths	Bond Angles	Exp. Method	Remarks	Reference
$C_6H_{10}O_4$	Bi-1,3-dioxacyclopentyl	CC 1.534 ± 0.03 C'C' 1.523 ± 0.03 CO 1.402, 1.414 ± 0.03 C'O 1.413, 1.416 ± 0.03	CCO 102°, 104° C'C'O 106°, 111° COC' 109°, 111° OC'O 105°	X	Nonplanar rings. Chemical structure established.	375
$C_6H_{11}Cl$	Cyclohexyl chloride	CC 1.54 CCl 1.76		E		16, 376
$C_6H_{11}KO_2$	Potassium caproate	CC 1.53 ± {0.04}	CCC 106° ± {2.5°}	X	Mean values.	377
$C_6H_{11}N_3O_4$	Glycyl-L-asparagine	CC a 1.50 ± {0.014} b 1.56 ± {0.014} c 1.54 ± {0.014} d 1.51 ± {0.014} CN e 1.46 ± {0.014} f 1.32 ± {0.014} g 1.46 ± {0.014} h 1.39 ± {0.014} CO i 1.23 ± {0.014} j 1.26 ± {0.014} k 1.20 ± {0.014} l 1.22 ± {0.014}	CCC bc 112° ± {0.75°} cd 111° ± {0.75°} CCN ae 111° ± {0.75°} af 116° ± {0.75°} bg 109° ± {0.75°} cg 111° ± {0.75°} dh 115° ± {0.75°} CCO ai 120° ± {0.75°} bj 116° ± {0.75°} bk 120° ± {0.75°} dl 125° ± {0.75°} CNC fg 123° ± {0.75°} NCO hl 120° ± {0.75°} fi 124° ± {0.75°}	X		378
$C_6H_{11}NaO_7$	Sodium gluconate	CC a 1.55 ± 0.04 b 1.54 ± 0.04 c 1.57 ± 0.04 d 1.55 ± 0.04 e 1.53 ± 0.04 CO f 1.23, 1.28 ± 0.04 g 1.44 ± 0.04 h 1.40 ± 0.04 i 1.48 ± 0.04 j 1.43 ± 0.04 k 1.43 ± 0.04	CCC ab 108.5° bc 114° cd 105.5° de 103° CCO af 116°, 121° Others 101°–119.5° OCO ff 122.5°	X	Stereochemical configuration confirmed. Ca, K, and Rb salts also studied. Remaining CCO angles listed in original paper.	379

Formula	Name	Bond lengths (Å)	Bond angles	Method	Notes	Ref.
C_6H_{12}	Cyclohexane	CC 1.540 ± 0.015 CH (1.09)	CCC 109° 28'	E	Chair form.	16, 97, 133, 154, 380
C_6H_{12}	Tetramethylethylene	C—C 1.54 ± 0.02 C=C (1.34) CH (1.09)	C—C—C 111.5 ± 2° CCH (109° 28')	E		154
$C_6H_{12}N_4$	Hexamethylene tetramine	CH (1.09) CN 1.48 ± 0.01	CNC 109.5° ± 1° NCN 109.5° ± 1° HCH (109° 28')	E		381
		CN 1.45 ± 0.01	CNC 107° NCN 113.5°	X		73, 382
$C_6H_{12}O_2$	cis Cyclohexane-1,2-diol	CC (1.54) CO 1.43	CCO 112.5°	E	Chair form.	383
$C_6H_{12}O_2$	trans Cyclohexane-1,2-diol	CC (1.54) CO 1.43	CCO 112.5°	E	Chair form.	383
$C_6H_{12}O_3$	Paraldehyde	CC 1.54 ± 0.02 CO 1.43 ± 0.02	All (109° 28')	E	Puckered ring.	164, 231, 384
$C_6H_{12}O_6$	α-D-Glucose 	CC a 1.54 ± 0.03, b 1.56 ± 0.03, c 1.53 ± 0.03, d 1.54 ± 0.03, e 1.53 ± 0.03 CO f 1.32 ± 0.03, g 1.41 ± 0.03, h 1.44 ± 0.03, i 1.40 ± 0.03, j 1.40 ± 0.03, k 1.42 ± 0.03, l 1.32 ± 0.03	CCC ab 104°, bc 110°, cd 108°, de 112° CCO af 115°, ag 109°, bg 109°, bh 102°, ch 108°, ci 110.5°, di 112°, dj 109.5°, el 113°, ak 110°, ej 110° COC kj 111° OCO fk 112°	X	Stereochemical configuration confirmed. Chair conformation.	385
$C_6H_{12}S$	Cyclohexyl mercaptan	CS (1.87)		E		16

Formula	Substance Name	Bond Lengths	Bond Angles	Exp. Method	Remarks	Reference
$C_6H_{12}S_3$	α-Trithioacetaldehyde	CC (1.54) CH (1.10) CS 1.81	CSC 106.5° SCS 114.5°	E	M.p. 101°C. Configuration a, e, e.	16, 386
$C_6H_{12}S_3$	β-Trithioacetaldehyde	CC (1.54) CH (1.10) CS 1.81	CSC 106.5° SCS 114.5°	E	M.p. 125°–126°C. Configuration e, e, e.	16, 386
$C_6H_{13}NO_2$	α-DL-Norleucine $CH_3 \overset{e}{-} CH_2 \overset{d}{-} CH_2 \overset{c}{-} CH_2 \overset{b}{-} CH \overset{a}{-} CO_2^-$ $\overset{f}{\vert}$ N^+H_3	CC a 1.49 ± 0.04 b 1.58 ± 0.04 c 1.51 ± 0.04 d 1.57 ± 0.04 e 1.48 ± 0.04 f 1.50 ± 0.04 CN 1.48 CO 1.20, 1.26 ± 0.04	CCC ab 112° ± 5° bc 114° ± 5° cd 110° ± 5° de 120° ± 5° af 109° CCN bf 110° CCO 118°, 120° OCO 122°	X	Existence of a β form with the same distances and angles is indicated.	387
C_6H_{14}	Hexane	CC 1.54 ± 0.05		E		97, 132
$C_6H_{14}BrNO_5$	α-Chitosamine hydrobromide 	CC a 1.55 b 1.56 c 1.58 d 1.48 CO e 1.37 f 1.50		X	Configuration like that of glucose, not like that of mannose. N^+H_3 group cis to OH on "reducing" carbon atom. Chair form.	388
$C_6H_{15}N$	Triethylamine	CC 1.54 ± 0.02 CN 1.47 ± 0.02	CCN 113° ± 3° CNC 113° ± 3°	E		20
$C_6H_{15}N_3$	1,3,5-Triaminocyclohexane	CC 1.54 CN 1.47	All 109° 28′	X	As dihydrate. Configuration e, e, e.	389

Formula	Name / Structure	Bond lengths (Å)	Bond angles	Method	Remarks	Ref.
$C_6H_{16}N_2$	Hexamethylenediamine $H_2N \overset{f}{-} CH_2 \overset{a}{-} CH_2 \overset{b}{-} CH_2 \overset{c}{-} CH_2 \overset{d}{-} CH_2 \overset{e}{-} CH_2 \overset{g}{-} NH_2$	CC a 1.50 ± 0.03 b 1.55 ± 0.03 c 1.50 ± 0.03 d 1.55 ± 0.03 e 1.50 ± 0.03 CN f 1.51 ± 0.03 g 1.51 ± 0.03	CCC ab 115° ± 4° bc 116° ± 4° cd 116° ± 4° de 115° ± 4° CCN af 115° ± 4° eg 115° ± 4°	X	Planar.	390
$C_6H_{18}Al_2$	Trimethylaluminum (dimeric)	CAl 2.01 ± 0.04 AlAl 2.20 ± 0.15	CAlAl 100° ± 5°	E	The "ethane-like" structure here assumed is probably incorrect.	287, 391
	$CH_3{>}Al{<}^{C'H_3}_{C'H_3}{>}Al{<}^{CH_3}_{CH_3}$	CAl 1.99, 2.00 C'Al 2.23, 2.24	AlC'Al 70° CAlC 124° C'AlC' 110°	X	CAlC and C'AlC' planes mutually perpendicular.	392
$C_6H_{18}Cl_2N_2$	Hexamethylenediamine dihydrochloride $H_3N^+ \overset{a}{-} CH_2 \overset{b}{-} CH_2 \overset{c}{-} CH_2 \overset{b}{-} CH_2 \overset{a}{-} CH_2 - CH_2 - N^+H_3$ $Cl^- \quad\quad Cl^-$	CC a 1.50, 1.49 ± 0.04 b 1.53, 1.55 ± 0.04 c 1.50 ± 0.04 CN 1.52	CCC ab 110°, 110.5° bc 112.5°, 113.5° CCN 107.5°, 115.5°	X	Centrosymmetric. Nearly planar.	393
$C_6H_{18}OSi_2$	Hexamethyldisiloxane $(CH_3)_3Si{-}O{-}Si(CH_3)_3$	CSi 1.88 ± 0.03 SiO 1.63 ± 0.03	CSiC 111° ± 4° SiOSi 130° ± 10°	E		289
$C_6H_{18}O_3Si_3$	Dimethylcyclosiloxane (trimeric) $[(CH_3)_2Si{-}O{-}]_3$	CSi 1.88 ± 0.04 SiO 1.66 ± 0.04	CSiC 112° ± 6° OSiO 115° ± 5° SiOSi 125° ± 5°	E	Planar ring.	394
$C_6H_{18}Pb_2$	Dileadhexamethyl $(CH_3)_3Pb{-}Pb(CH_3)_3$	CPb 2.25 ± 0.06 PbPb 2.88 ± 0.03		E		395
$C_6H_{18}Si_2$	Hexamethyldisilane $(CH_3)_3Si{-}Si(CH_3)_3$	CSi 1.90 ± 0.02 SiSi 2.34 ± 0.10	CSiSi 109° ± 4°	E		287
$C_6H_{19}N_3O_2$	1,3,5-Triminocyclohexane dihydrate				*See* $C_6H_{15}N_3$.	

753

Formula	Substance Name	Bond Lengths	Bond Angles	Exp. Method	Remarks	Reference
$C_6H_{21}N_3O_3$	Acetaldehyde ammonia (trimeric)	CC (1.54) CN (1.47)	All (109° 28')	X	Configuration $e, e, e.$	396
$C_6H_{21}N_3Si_3$	Hexamethylcyclotrisilazane $[(CH_3)_2Si—NH—]_3$	CH (1.09) CSi 1.87 ± 0.05 SiN 1.78 ± 0.03	CSiC (110°) HCH (109° 28') NSiN 111° ± 5° SiNSi 117° ± 4°	E	Puckered ring.	397
$C_6I_4O_2$	Iodoanil	C—C 1.54 C=C 1.36 CI 2.06	C—C—C 122° C=C—I 125°	E		323, 324
C_6MoO_6	Molybdenum hexacarbonyl	CO 1.15 ± 0.05 CMo 2.08 ± 0.04	MoCO 180°	E	Octahedral Mo.	327
$C_6N_9Na_3$	Trisodium tricyanomelamine $(Na^+)_3[C_3N_3(N'{=}C'{=}N'')_3]^{\equiv}$	CN 1.34, 1.35 CN' 1.40 C'N' 1.32 C'N'' 1.21	N'C'N'' 180°	X	As trihydrate.	398
C_6O_6W	Tungsten hexacarbonyl	CO 1.13 ± 0.05 CW 2.06 ± 0.04	WCO 180°	E	Octahedral W.	327
$C_7H_2Cl_3N$	2,4,6-Trichlorobenzonitrile	CC a 1.47 b 1.39 c 1.41 d 1.38 CCl e 1.70 f 1.71 CN 1.16		X	Planar.	399
C_7H_6ClNO	syn p-Chlorobenzaldoxime $p\text{-}Cl—C_6H_4—C'H{=}NOH$	CC 1.35–1.38 CC' 1.45 CCl 1.78 C'N 1.31 NO 1.36	CC'N 125° C'NO 112.5°	X	Stereochemical configuration confirmed.	400

Formula	Name / Structure	Bond lengths (Å)	Bond angles	Method	Notes	Ref.
$C_7H_6O_2$	Tropolone	CC 1.39 CH 1.10 C—O 1.34 C=O 1.26		E	Regular plane heptagon.	401
$C_7H_6O_3$	Salicylic acid o-HO—C_6H_4—$C'O_2H$	CC 1.37–1.41 CC' 1.458 CO 1.361 C'—O 1.333 C'=O 1.241	CCC 118.6°–120.9° CCC' 120.3°, 121.1° CCO 118.3°, 122.1° CC'—O 117.0° C'=O 122.7° OC'O 120.2°	X	Planar.	402
$C_7H_7ClO_2$	Tropolone hydrochloride	CC a 1.42 b 1.43 c 1.41 d 1.39 e 1.34 f 1.41 g 1.37 CO h 1.40 i 1.42	CCC ab 124° bc 130° cd 129.5° de 127° ef 132° fg 120° ag 130.5° CCO ai 118° ah 106°	X	Approximately planar ring.	403
C_7H_{10}	Nortricyclene	CH, C'H, C"H (1.09) CC' 1.54 ± 0.02 C'C' 1.50 ± 0.02 C'C" 1.54 ± 0.02	CC"C' 96.5° ± 2° HC"H (109° 28')	E		404
$C_7H_{11}ClHgO$	cis 1-Chloromercuri-2-methoxycyclohexane	CC 1.52 ± 0.07 (mean) CHg 2.15 HgCl 2.50	CCC 109° ± 7° (mean) CHgCl 180°	X	Chair configuration.	405
$C_7H_{11}ClHgO$	trans 1-Chloromercuri-2-methoxycyclohexane	CC 1.56 ± 0.1 (mean) CHg 2.34 HgCl 2.53	CCC 113° ± 10° (mean) CHgCl 178°	X	Chair configuration.	405
$C_7H_{12}O_4$	pimelic acid HO_2C—${}^{a}CH_2$—${}^{b}CH_2$—${}^{c}CH_2$—${}^{c}CH_2$—${}^{b}CH_2$—${}^{a}CO_2H$	CC a 1.44 ± 0.05 b 1.49 ± 0.05 c 1.50 ± 0.05 C—O 1.38 ± 0.05 C=O 1.28 ± 0.05	[OO 2.35 ± 0.05]	X		406

755

Formula	Substance Name	Bond Lengths	Bond Angles	Exp. Method	Remarks	Reference
C_7H_{14}	1,1,2,2-Tetramethylcyclopropane $C_3H_2(C'H_3)_4$	CC, CC' 1.52 ± 0.03 (mean)	C'CC' 114° ± 6°	E		407
C_8H_5NO	Isatin	CC $\quad$ a 1.37 b 1.36 c 1.37 d 1.39 e 1.37 f 1.36 g 1.47 h 1.49 CN $\quad$ i 1.35 j 1.38 CO $\quad$ k 1.19 l 1.21	CCC $\quad$ ab 121° bc 118° cd 120° de 121° ef 118° af 122° ag 106° bg 133° gh 105° CCN $\quad$ hi 105° aj 111° fj 128° CCO $\quad$ gk 129° hk 125° hl 127° il 127° CNC $\quad$ ij 112°	X	Lactam form. Planar.	408
C_8H_6	Dimethyltriacetylene $CH_3 \overset{a}{-} C\equiv C \overset{b}{-} C \overset{c}{-} C \equiv C \overset{d}{-} C \overset{c}{-} C \equiv C \overset{b}{-} C \overset{a}{-} CH_3$	CH $\sim$1.0 CC $\quad$ a 1.466 ± 0.018 b 1.199 ± 0.017 c 1.375 ± 0.016 d 1.199 ± 0.022	CCC $\quad$ ab 180° bc 180° cd 180° CCH $\quad$ 105°	X		409
C_8H_8	Cycloöctatetraene	C—C $\quad$ 1.50 + q ± 0.01 C=C $\quad$ 1.35 − q ± 0.01 CH $\quad$ 1.12 ± 0.03	CCC $\quad$ 124° ± 1.5°	E	0 < q < 0.03 configuration. $\quad$ Tub	354, 410
		C—C $\quad$ 1.54 C=C $\quad$ 1.34	CCC $\quad$ 125°	X	Tub configuration.	411
$C_8H_8Br_2$	4,5-Dibromo-o-xylene $Br_2C_6H_2(C'H_3)_2$	CC $\quad$ 1.40 ± 0.02 CC' $\quad$ (1.54) CBr $\quad$ 1.88 ± 0.02	CCBr $\quad$ 122° ± 2°	E		330

Formula	Compound	Bond lengths (Å)	Angles		Remarks	Ref.
C₈H₉N₃Ni	Nickel cyanide-ammonia-benzene complex Ni(CN)₂·NH₃·C₆H₆	CC 1.38, 1.41 CN 1.22 ± 0.04 CNi' 1.76 ± 0.03 NiN 2.15 ± 0.03 NiN' 2.06	CNNi 180° NCNi'C 180° CNi'C *ab* 90°, *ac* 180° NNiN *de* 90°, *df* 180° N'NiN' 180° NNiN' 90°	X	The crystal consists of parallel Ni(CN)₂ planes, with the square form shown. The NH₃ molecules are between the planes. The C₆H₆ molecules are merely trapped in the resulting cavities, and are not bonded to anything else. Similar complexes are formed with thiophene, pyrrole, furan, pyridine, and aniline in place of benzene.	412
C₈H₁₀	*p*-Xylene *p*-C₆H₄(C'H₃)₂	CC 1.40 ± 0.01 CC' 1.50 ± 0.01		E		413
C₈H₁₀O₂	Hydroquinone dimethyl ether	CC *a* 1.36 ± 0.02 *b* 1.37 ± 0.02 *c* 1.44 ± 0.02 *d* 1.35 ± 0.02 CO *e* 1.36 ± 0.02	CCC *ab* 121° ± 2° *ac* 120° ± 2° *bc* 118.5° ± 2° CCO *ae* 119° ± 2° COC *de* 121° ± 2°	X	Almost planar. Centrosymmetric.	414
C₈H₁₂N₂	Tetramethylpyrazine C₄N₂(C'H₃)₄	CC 1.44 ± 0.03 CC' 1.50 ± 0.03 CN 1.31 ± 0.03	All 120° ± 2°	X	Planar.	415
C₈H₁₂O₂	Dimethylketene dimer [(C'H₃)₂C—C''O]₂	CC' 1.54 ± 0.05 CC'' 1.56 ± 0.05 C''O 1.22 ± 0.04	CC''C 93° ± 6° C'CC' 111° ± 6°	E	Chemical structure confirmed.	416
C₈H₁₃Br	1-Bromobicyclo[2,2,2]octane	CC 1.545 ± 0.004	CCBr 109° 50' ± 0° 10'	S		417
C₈H₁₃Cl	1-Chlorobicyclo[2,2,2]octane	CC 1.545 ± 0.004	CCCl 109° 50' ± 0° 10'	S		417

Formula	Substance Name	Bond Lengths	Bond Angles	Exp. Method	Remarks	Reference
$C_8H_{14}N_4NiO_4$	Nickel dimethylglyoxime	CC a 1.53 / b 1.46, 1.51 CN 1.20, 1.25 NO 1.37, 1.38 NNi 1.87, 1.90	CCC 121°, 124° CCN ac 109°, 113°; bc 126°, 127° CNNi 117°, 121° CNO 121° NiNO 118°, 122° NNiN 80°	X	Planar. The length of the O—H-—O bond is only 2.44 A.	418
$C_8H_{16}CuHgN_8S_4$	Mercury tetrathiocyanatocopper diethyl-enediamine $[Hg(SCN)_4]^=[Cu(N'H_2—CH_2—CH_2—CH_2—N'H_2)_2]^{++}$	CN 1.34 CS 1.57 HgS 2.55 CC 1.53 CN' 1.41 CuN' 2.07	CSHg 102° 5' NCS 163° 12' SHgS 109° 16' N'CuN' ~80°	X	Nonplanar 5-membered rings. Tetrahedral Hg. N' atoms nearly at corners of a square with Cu at center.	419
$C_8H_{16}Hg_2O_2$	"Mercury diethylene oxide"	CC 1.49 CO 1.37, 1.42 CHg 2.14	CCO 90°, 102° COC 96° CHgC 176° CCHg 93°, 103°	X		420
$C_8H_{16}O_4$	Metaldehyde $(CH_3—CH—O—)_4$	CC 1.54 ± 0.03 CO 1.43 ± 0.03	All 109.5° ± 3°	X	Puckered ring.	421
C_8H_{18}	Hexamethylethane $C_2'(CH_3)_6$	CC' 1.54 ± 0.02 C'C' 1.58 ± 0.03 CH (1.09)	All 111° ± 2°	E		307
$C_8H_{24}O_6Si_5$	Octamethylspiro-5,5-pentasiloxane	SiO 1.61 ± 0.03 Si'O 1.64 ± 0.03 SiC 1.88 ± 0.03 SiO' 1.67 ± 0.03	OSi'O 105° ± 4° OSiO' 108° ± 4° CSiC 106° ± 4° SiOSi' 134° ± 4° SiO'Si 129° ± 4°	X	Planar rings.	422

Formula	Name / Structure	Bond lengths (Å)	Bond angles	Method	Remarks	Ref.
$C_8H_{28}N_4Si_4$	Octamethylcyclotetrasilazane $[(CH_3)_2Si{-}NH{-}]_4$	CSi (1.87) CH (1.09) SiN (1.78)	CSiC (110°) NSiN (111°) SiNSi 123° ± 4° HCH (109° 28')	X	Puckered ring.	397
$C_9H_8Br_2$	5,6-Dibromohydrindene $Br_2C_6H_2(C'H_2)_3$	CC 1.42 ± 0.02 CC' (1.54) C'C' (1.54) CBr 1.84 ± 0.02	CCBr 122° ± 2°	E		330
$C_9H_{11}NO$	p-Isopropylideneaminophenol $p{-}HO{-}C_6H_4{-}N{=}C'(C''H_3)_2$	CC 1.39, 1.40 ± {0.04} C'C'' 1.47, 1.51 ± {0.04} CN 1.42 ± {0.04} C'N 1.33 ± {0.04} CO 1.38 ± {0.04}	CCC 118°–124° C''C''C'' 119.5° C''C=N 115°, 129° C'=NC 120°	X		423
C_9H_{12}	Mesitylene $C_6H_3(C'H_3)_3$	CC (1.39) CC' 1.54 ± 0.01		E		154, 413
$C_9H_{13}N_3O_5$	Cytidine	CC a 1.32 b 1.37 c 1.44 d 1.51 e 1.52 f 1.53 CN g 1.35 h 1.35 i 1.36 j 1.47 k 1.39 l 1.31 CO m 1.42 n 1.42 o 1.40 p 1.50 q 1.35	All in pyrimidine part 120° ± 5° All in ribose part 109° ± 5°	X	Cytosine-3-β-ribofuranoside stricture confirmed. Planar pyrimidine ring. All bond angles are given in the original paper.	424

Formula	Substance Name		Bond Lengths	Bond Angles	Exp. Method	Remarks	Reference
$C_{10}H_6Cl_2$	1,5-Dichloronaphthalene		CC a 1.32 ± 0.03 b 1.46 ± 0.03 c 1.32 ± 0.03 d 1.37 ± 0.03 e 1.30 ± 0.03 CCl 1.76 ± 0.03		X		425, 426
$C_{10}H_6N_2O_4$	1,5-Dinitronaphthalene		CC 1.41 CN 1.35 NO 1.10, 1.19 CH 1.10	CCC 120° CCN ab 125° bc 115° CNO 121°, 122° ONO 117°	X	Planar.	427
$C_{10}H_8$	Naphthalene		CC 1.397 (mean)		E	Planar.	428
			CC a 1.393 ± 0.010 b 1.425 ± 0.010 c 1.365 ± 0.010 d 1.404 ± 0.010		X	Planar.	R, 429, 430, 431
$C_{10}H_8Cl_4$	Naphthalene tetrachloride		CC 1.39–1.41 C'C' 1.55, 1.56 C'Cl 1.80, 1.81	CCC 120° C'C'C' 117° CCC' ac 127° bc 113° CC'C', C'C'Cl C'C'Cl, C'C'Cl 105°–113°	X	More detailed structure given in original paper.	432

760

Formula	Name / Structure	Bond lengths	Angles	Method	Notes	Ref
$C_{10}H_9BrN_4O_2S$	2-Metanilamido-5-bromopyrimidine	CBr 1.90 ± 0.04 CN 1.42 ± 0.06 SN 1.75 ± 0.04 SO 1.50 ± 0.04 CS 1.80 ± 0.04	CNS 113° ± 3° CSN 100° ± 3° OSO 132° ± 5°	X	Rings assumed to be regular plane hexagons, about 1.39 Å on the side.	433
$C_{10}H_{10}Br_2$	6,7-Dibromo-1,2,3,4-tetrahydronaphthalene $Br_2C_6H_2(C'H_2)_4$	CC 1.42 ± 0.02 CC' (1.54) C'C' (1.54) CH, C'H (1.09) CBr 1.86 ± 0.02	CCBr 122° ± 2°	E		330
$C_{10}H_{10}Fe$	Ferrocene	CC 1.41 CFe 2.0		X	"Sandwich" structure. Iron atom lies between two planar cyclopentadienyl rings. Pentagonal antiprism.	434
$C_{10}H_{14}$	Durene $C_6H_2(C'H_3)_4$	CC 1.39 (mean) CC' 1.47–1.54		X	Planar.	R, 435
$C_{10}H_{15}BrO$	α-Bromocamphor				*See* $C_{11}H_{15}NO$.	
$C_{10}H_{15}ClO$	α-Chlorocamphor				*See* $C_{11}H_{15}NO$.	
$C_{10}H_{16}$	Adamantane	CH (1.09) CC 1.54 ± 0.01	HCH (109.5°) CCC 109.5° ± 1.5°	E		436
$C_{10}H_{16}$		CH (1.08) CC 1.54 ± 0.02		X		437

761

Formula	Substance Name		Bond Lengths	Bond Angles	Exp. Method	Remarks	Reference
$C_{10}H_{16}ClNO$	Ephedrine hydrochloride		CC a 1.43 ± 0.022 b 1.35 ± 0.022 c 1.36 ± 0.022 d 1.45 ± 0.022 e 1.36 ± 0.022 f 1.37 ± 0.022 g 1.56 ± 0.022 h 1.48 ± 0.022 i 1.56 ± 0.022 CN j 1.50 ± 0.022 k 1.39 ± 0.022 CO l 1.40 ± 0.022	CCC af 121° ± 2° ab 118° ± 2° bc 121° ± 2° cd 122° ± 2° de 116° ± 2° ef 123° ± 2° eg 116° ± 2° fg 121° ± 2° gh 112° ± 2° hi 114° ± 2° CCN hj 116° ± 2° ij 107° ± 2° CCO gl 115° ± 2° hl 109° ± 2° CNC jk 119° ± 2°	X	Stereochemical configuration confirmed.	438
$C_{10}H_{16}CuN_2O_4$	Copper proline		CC a 1.50 b 1.52 c 1.50 d 1.52 CN e 1.53 f 1.52 CO 1.24 CuO 2.03 CuN 1.99	CCC ab 112° bc 97° cd 109° CCN de 96° bf 108° af 108° CNC ef 108° CCO 118°, 120° NCuO 82° OCO 122°	X	As dihydrate.	439

C₁₀H₁₈N₄O₆S₂   N,N′-Diglycyl-L-cystine

CC	a 1.52
	b 1.55
	g 1.55
CN	d 1.48
	e 1.35
	h 1.46
CO	c 1.21, 1.24
	f 1.21
CS	1.86
SS	2.04

CCC	117°
CCN	ad 118°
	bd 109°
	eg 113°
	gh 109°
CCO	bc 115°, 118°
	fg 121°
CCS	105°
CNC	122°
CSS	103°
NCO	125°
OCO	127°

X   As dihydrate. Average probable errors are ±0.02 Å and ±1°. More detailed structure is given in original papers.   440

C₁₀H₁₈O₄   Sebacic acid

CC	a 1.51 ± 0.03
	b 1.48 ± 0.02
	c 1.53 ± 0.02
	d 1.50 ± 0.02
	e 1.54 ± 0.02
C—O	1.27 ± 0.04
C=O	1.24 ± 0.04

CCC	ab 118°
	bc 114°
	cd 115°
	de 114°
CC—O	116°
C=O	120°
OCO	124°

X   Eight central C atoms coplanar.   441

C₁₀H₂₀ClN   Geranylamine hydrochloride

CC	b 1.53 ± 0.04
	c 1.32 ± 0.04
	d 1.53 ± 0.04
	e 1.54 ± 0.04
	f 1.45 ± 0.04
	g 1.52 ± 0.04
	h 1.32 ± 0.04
	i 1.55 ± 0.04
	j 1.53 ± 0.04
CN	a 1.48 ± 0.04

CCC	bc 126° ± 4°
	cd 124° ± 4°
	ce 119° ± 4°
	de 117° ± 4°
	ef 112° ± 4°
	fg 112° ± 4°
	gh 129° ± 4°
	hi 123° ± 4°
	hj 121° ± 4°
	ij 116° ± 4°
CCN	ab 109° ± 4°

X   442

C₁₀H₂₀CuN₂O₆   Copper proline dihydrate

X   See C₁₀H₁₆CuN₂O₄.

C₁₀H₂₂N₄O₈S₂   N,N′-Diglycyl-L-cystine-dihydrate

See C₁₀H₁₈N₄O₆S₂.

Formula	Substance Name	Bond Lengths	Bond Angles	Exp. Method	Remarks	Reference
C₁₁H₁₄ClN₅	4,6-Diamino-1-p-chlorophenyl-1,2-dihydro-2,2-dimethyl-1,3,5-triazine 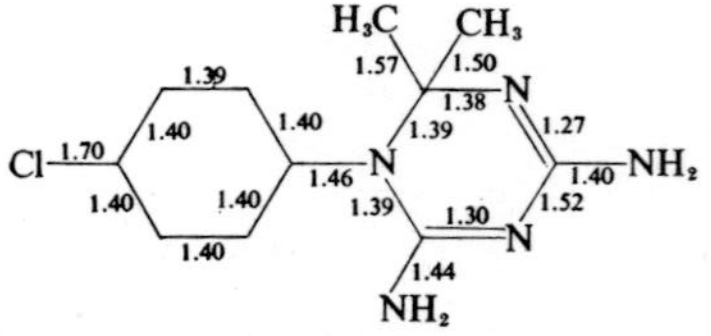	as shown		X	As hydrochloride. Slightly different values obtained for the hydrobromide. Chemical structure established. Bond lengths "not accurate."	443
C₁₁H₁₄BrClN₅	4,6-Diamino-1-p-chlorophenyl-1,2-dihydro-2,2-dimethyl-1,3,5-triazine hydrobromide				*See* C₁₁H₁₄ClN₅.	
C₁₁H₁₅ClN₂O₄	Glycyl-L-tyrosine hydrochloride	(see below)	(see below)	X		444

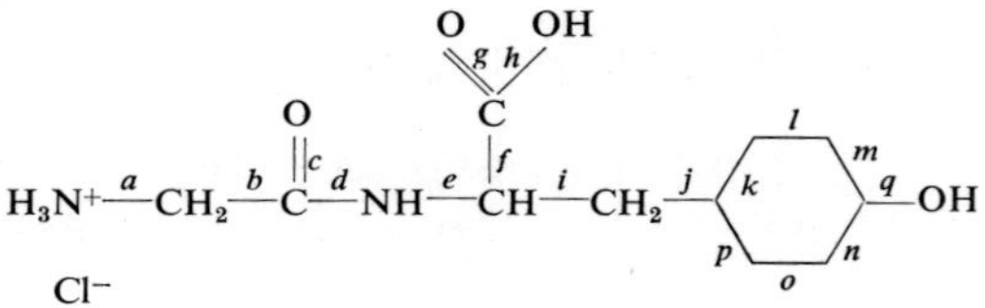

Bond Lengths (C₁₁H₁₅ClN₂O₄):

CC   b 1.53, f 1.51, i 1.54, j 1.54, k 1.41, l 1.46, m 1.35, n 1.40, o 1.43, p 1.37

CN   a 1.50, d 1.35, e 1.41

CO   g 1.21, h 1.26, q 1.38, c 1.16

Bond Angles (C₁₁H₁₅ClN₂O₄):

CCC   fi 109°, ij 113°, jk 118°, kl 118°, lm 119°, mn 123°, no 117°, op 122°, jp 122°, kp 120°

CCN   ab 112°, bd 111°, ef 111°, ei 106°

CCO   bc 117°, cd 132°, fg 123°, fh 115°, mq 119°

NCO   nq 118°

OCO   cd 132°

CNC   gh 121°, de 116°

(Bond lengths shown in structural diagram for C₁₁H₁₄ClN₅: H₃C–CH₃ 1.50, 1.57, 1.38, 1.39, 1.27, 1.40 NH₂, 1.52, 1.46, 1.30, 1.44 NH₂, Cl 1.70, ring 1.39, 1.40, 1.40, 1.40, 1.40)

Formula	Name / Structure	Bond lengths	Angles	Method	Notes	Ref
$C_{11}H_{15}Cl_2N_5$	4,6-Diamino-1-p-chlorophenyl-1,2-dihydro-2,2-dimethyl-1,3,5-triazine hydrochloride				See $C_{11}H_{14}ClN_5$.	
$C_{11}H_{15}NO$	α-Cyanocamphor	CC 1.41–1.65 CO 1.21 CN 1.16		X	Individual bond lengths listed in original paper. Similar, but much less complete, data given also for corresponding α-bromo and α-chloro compounds.	445
$C_{12}H_7IN_4O_6$	N-Picryl-p-iodoaniline $p\text{-I-C}_6H_4\text{—N'H}$	CC 1.40 CN 1.40 CN' 1.45 CI 2.1 NO 1.23	CN'C 138° CCN' ab 127° OO [2.20°]	X	Only the para NO_2 group is coplanar with ring. Three polymorphic forms with same lengths and angles.	446
$C_{12}H_8$	Biphenylene	CC a, c (mean) 1.41 ± 0.02 b 1.46 ± 0.05 CH (1.10)	CCC ac 121° ± 3°	E	Assumed planar and centrosymmetric. Chemical structure confirmed.	447
		CC a, c (1.40) b (1.46)	CCC aa, ac (120°) ab, bc (90°)	X	Assumed planar and centrosymmetric.	448
$C_{12}H_8Br_2$	3,3′-Dibromobiphenyl $BrC_6H_4\text{—}C'_6H_4Br$	CC, C'C' 1.40 CC' 1.49 CBr, C'Br 1.88		E	Angle of 54° between planes of rings.	170

765

Formula	Substance Name	Bond Lengths	Bond Angles	Exp. Method	Remarks	Reference
$C_{12}H_8Br_2N_2O_2$	p-Bromonitrosobenzene (dimeric) Br—C₆H₄—N—N—C₆H₄—Br (with O on each N)	NN ~1.31 NO ~1.35 CBr 1.88 ± 0.04 CN 1.40		X	Chemical structure confirmed. Centro-symmetric.	449
$C_{12}H_8Br_2O$	Bis (p-bromophenyl)ether	CC *a* 1.28 ± 0.08 CBr 1.83 ± 0.03 CO 1.28 ± 0.03	COC 123° ± 1°	X		450
$C_{12}H_8Br_2O_2S$	4,4′-Dibromodiphenylsulfone	CBr 1.89 ± 0.04 CS 1.84 ± 0.04 SO 1.54 ± 0.05	CSC 100° ± 0.5° OSO 131° ± 3°	X		451, 452
$C_{12}H_8Br_2S$	Bis (p-bromophenyl)sulfide	CC 1.41 CBr 1.88 ± 0.03 CS 1.75 ± 0.03	CSC 109.5° ± 0.5°	X		452, 453
$C_{12}H_8Br_2S_2$	Bis (p-bromophenyl)disulfide	CC 1.41 CBr 1.86 ± 0.04 CS 1.80 ± 0.04 SS 2.15	CSS 107° ± 0.5°	X		452
$C_{12}H_8I_2O$	Bis (p-iodophenyl)ether	CC (1.42) CI (2.00) CO (1.42)	COC 118° ± 3°	E		454
$C_{12}H_8N_2$	Phenazine	CC *a* 1.45 *b* 1.38 *c* 1.39 *d* 1.46 *e* 1.39 *f* 1.41 CN *g* 1.32 *h* 1.34	CCC *ab* 124° *bc* 120° *cd* 117° *fi* 115° *ef* 121° *ej* 122° CCN *cg* 118° *dg* 125° *eh* 119° CNC *gh* 116°	X		455

766

Formula	Name / Structure	Interatomic distances (Å)	Angles	Method	Remarks	Ref.
$C_{12}H_8N_2O_4$	p,p'-Dinitrobiphenyl $O_2N\!-\!C_6H_4\!-\!C_6H_4\!-\!NO_2$	CC, C'C' 1.40 CC' 1.48, 1.49 CN, C'N (1.53) NO 1.10	ONO 118°	X	In addition compound with p-hydroxybiphenyl. Rings coplanar. CN bonds at 5°–11° from plane of rings, one above and one below.	456
$C_{12}H_8Se_2$	Selanthrene	CC (1.41) CSe 1.96	CSeC 96°	X	Angle of 127° between planes of outer rings.	457
$C_{12}H_9IN_4O_6$	Trinitrobenzene-p-iodoaniline addition compound				See $C_6H_3N_3O_6$ and C_6H_6IN.	
$C_{12}H_{10}$	Acenaphthene C'H₂—C'H₂	C'C' 1.64 ± 0.04		X	Planar. Width of benzene ring 2.355 ± 0.01 A.	458
$C_{12}H_{10}$	Biphenyl $C_6H_5\!-\!C'_6H_5$	CC, C'C' 1.39 ± 0.02 CC' 1.52 ± 0.04		E	Angle of 45° between planes of rings.	170, 459
$C_{12}H_{10}$		CC, C'C' 1.42 CC' 1.48		X	Planar.	460
$C_{12}H_{10}Br_2Se$	Diphenylselenium dibromide	CSe 1.91 ± 0.03 SeBr 2.52 ± 0.01	CSeC 110° ± 10° BrSeBr 180° ± 3°	X		461
$C_{12}H_{10}Cl_2N_2$	2,2'-Dichlorobenzidine $H_2N\!-\!C_6H_3Cl\!-\!C'_6H_3Cl\!-\!NH_2$	CC, C'C' 1.29–1.46 ± 0.05 CC' 1.53 ± 0.02 CCl, C'Cl 1.72	CCC, C'C'C' 116°–125° CCC', CCC' 119° CCN, C'C'N 114°, 122°	X	36° out of s-cis configuration. CC distances are alternately long and short in rings. Detailed structure given in original paper.	462

767

Formula	Substance Name	Bond Lengths	Bond Angles	Exp. Method	Remarks	Reference
$C_{12}H_{10}Cl_2N_2$	3,3'-Dichlorobenzidine $H_2N—C_6H_3Cl—C'_6H_3Cl—NH_2$	CC, C'C' 1.40 CC' 1.50 CCl, C'Cl 1.73		E	Rings probably not coplanar.	170
$C_{12}H_{10}Cl_2Se$	Diphenylselenium dichloride	SeCl 2.30 ± 0.05	ClSeCl 180° ± 5°	X		463
$C_{12}H_{10}MgO_6S_2$	Magnesium benzenesulfonate	CC 1.32–1.47 CS 1.90 SO 1.42 (mean)		X	As hexahydrate.	464
$C_{12}H_{10}N_2$	anti Azobenzene	CC 1.39 CN 1.40 ± 0.03 NN 1.23 ± 0.05	CNN 123°	X	Planar. Two crystallographically different kinds of molecule; see also below.	465
		CC 1.39 CN 1.43 ± 0.03 NN 1.23 ± 0.05	CNN 120°	X	Phenyl groups in parallel planes 0.32 Å apart.	465
$C_{12}H_{10}N_2$	syn Azobenzene	CC 1.39 CN 1.46 ± 0.03 NN 1.23 ± 0.03	CCN 116° CNN 121°	X	Nonplanar.	466
$C_{12}H_{10}O$	p-Hydroxybiphenyl $C'_6H_5—C_6H_4—OH$	CC 1.40 C'C' 1.40 CC' 1.49 CO 1.34		X	In addition compound with p,p'-dinitrobiphenyl. Planar.	453
$C_{12}H_{10}O_4S_2Se$	Bisphenylsulfonyl selenide	CC $\quad a$ 1.37 $\quad\ b$ 1.39 $\quad\ c$ 1.39 $\quad\ d$ 1.38 $\quad\ e$ 1.38 $\quad\ f$ 1.42 CS 1.77 SO 1.40, 1.42 SSe 2.20 ± 0.03	CSSe 102° CSO 108° OSO 122° OSSe 109° SSeS 105° ± 2°	X	Unstated errors "may be considerably greater."	467

768

Formula	Name	Distances (Å)	Angles	Method	Notes	Ref.
$C_{12}H_{10}O_4S_3$	Bisphenylsulfonyl sulfide	CC 1.39 ± 0.04 (mean) CS 1.76 ± 0.02 SS 2.07 ± 0.02 SO 1.41 ± 0.04	CSO 107.5°, 115.9° ± 3° CSS 101.7° ± 1° OSO 117.2° ± 4° SSO 104.2°, 111.9° ± 3° SSS 106.5° ± 1°	X		468
$C_{12}H_{10}O_6S_2Zn$	Zinc benzene sulfonate	CC 1.32–1.47 CS 1.82 SO 1.39 (mean)		X	As hexahydrate.	464
$C_{12}H_{10}Se_2$	Diphenyl diselenide C_6H_5—Se—Se—C_6H_5	CC (1.39) CSe 1.93 ± 0.05 SeSe 2.29 ± 0.01	CCC (120°) CCSe (120°) CSeSe 107.5°, 104.6° ± 2°	X		469
$C_{12}H_{14}O_4$	Ethyl terephthalate	CC b 1.39 ± 0.05 c 1.38 ± 0.05 d 1.40 ± 0.05 g 1.48 ± 0.05 h 1.55 ± 0.05 C—O i 1.51 ± 0.05 j 1.32 ± 0.05 C=O k 1.28	CCC ab 123° ± 5° ef 119° ± 5° af 118° ± 5° fg 118° ± 5° ag 124° ± 5° CC—O gj 115° ± 5° hi 105° ± 5° CC=O gk 120° COC ij 117° OCO kj 125°	X	Planar except for CH_3 groups. Centrosymmetric.	470
$C_{12}H_{18}$	Hexamethylbenzene $C_6(C'H_3)_6$	CC (1.39) CC' 1.54 ± 0.01 CH (1.09)		E		154, 413
		CC 1.39 CC' 1.53		X		R, 471
$C_{12}H_{18}Be_4O_{13}$	Basic beryllium acetate	CC 1.54 ± 0.05 CO 1.29 ± 0.05 BeO 1.65 ± 0.05	OCO 124° ± 3°	X	Tetrahedral Be (slightly distorted).	472, 473
$C_{12}H_{18}Cl_2FeN_6$	Hexamethylisocyanidoferrous chloride $[Fe(CNC'H_3)_6]^{++}(Cl^-)_2$	CFe 1.85 CN 1.18 C'N 1.47	CNC' 173°	X	As trihydrate. Octahedral Fe.	474

Ethyl terephthalate structure (labelled): ring carbons a–f with substituent d—$CO_2C_2H_5$; side chain g, CH_2—h—O—i—CH_2—CH_3, with k=O.

Formula	Substance Name	Bond Lengths	Bond Angles	Exp. Method	Remarks	Reference
$C_{12}H_{18}O_{13}Zn$	Basic zinc acetate	CC 1.55 CO 1.24 ZnO 1.96, 1.98	OCO 125°	X	Tetrahedral Zn.	473
$C_{12}H_{22}MgO_{12}S_2$	Magnesium benzenesulfonate hexahydrate				See $C_{12}H_{10}MgO_6S_2$.	
$C_{12}H_{22}O_{11}$	Sucrose	CC a 1.44 ± 0.04 b 1.41 ± 0.04 c 1.43 ± 0.04 d 1.45 ± 0.04 e 1.53 ± 0.04 f 1.60 ± 0.04 g 1.60 ± 0.04 h 1.42 ± 0.04 i 1.51 ± 0.04 j 1.49 ± 0.04 CO k 1.38 ± 0.04 l 1.42 ± 0.04 m 1.43 ± 0.04 n 1.41 ± 0.04 o 1.43 ± 0.04 p 1.49 ± 0.04 q 1.48 ± 0.04 r 1.39 ± 0.04 s 1.48 ± 0.04 t 1.50 ± 0.04 u 1.41 ± 0.04 v 1.44 ± 0.04 w 1.43 ± 0.04 x 1.32 ± 0.04	Average in furanose ring 104°; in pyranose ring 108°.	X	As complex with composition $C_{12}H_{22}O_{11}$. NaBr.$2H_2O$. Both rings puckered. An α-glucoside and a β-fructoside. Chemical structure and stereochemical configuration confirmed.	475
$C_{12}H_{22}O_{12}S_2Zn$	Zinc benzenesulfonate hexahydrate				See $C_{12}H_{10}O_6S_2Zn$.	
$C_{12}H_{24}Cl_2FeN_6O_3$	Hexamethylisocyanidoferrous chloride trihydrate				See $C_{12}H_{18}Cl_2FeN_6$.	
$C_{12}H_{26}BrNaO_{13}$	Sucrose-sodium bromide dihydrate				See $C_{12}H_{22}O_{11}$.	

770

476

C₁₂H₂₆N₂O₄   Hexamethylenediammonium adipate

H_3N^+—CH_2—$\overset{a}{C}H_2$—$\overset{b}{C}H_2$—$\overset{c}{C}H_2$—$\overset{b}{C}H_2$—$\overset{a}{C}H_2$—CH_2—N^+H_3

^-O_2C—$\overset{d}{C}H_2$—$\overset{e}{C}H_2$—$\overset{f}{C}H_2$—$\overset{e}{C}H_2$—$\overset{d}{C}H_2$—CO_2^-

CC   a 1.55 ± 0.05
     b 1.54 ± 0.05
     c 1.54 ± 0.05
     d 1.50 ± 0.05
     e 1.54 ± 0.05
     f 1.52 ± 0.05
CN   1.50 ± 0.05
CO   1.24, 1.28 ± 0.05

CCC   ab 107° ± 5°
      bc 112° ± 5°
      de 109° ± 5°
      ef 112° ± 5°
CCN   110° ± 5°
CCO   120°, 122° ± 5°
OCO   118° ± 5°

X

477

C₁₃H₁₀   Fluorene

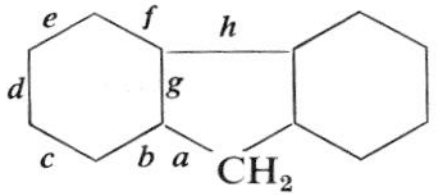

CC   a 1.468
     b 1.438
     c 1.381
     d 1.383
     e 1.406
     f 1.408
     g 1.410
     h 1.486

CCC   ag 109.6°
      bc 119.4°
      cd 121.0°
      de 122.2°
      ef 116.8°
      fg 122.0°
      bg 118.1°
      gh 104.6°

X

Planar molecule with plane of symmetry perpendicular to it.

478

C₁₃H₁₆IN₅O₃   2′,3′-Isopropylidene-3′,5′-cycloadenosine iodide

As shown   As shown   X

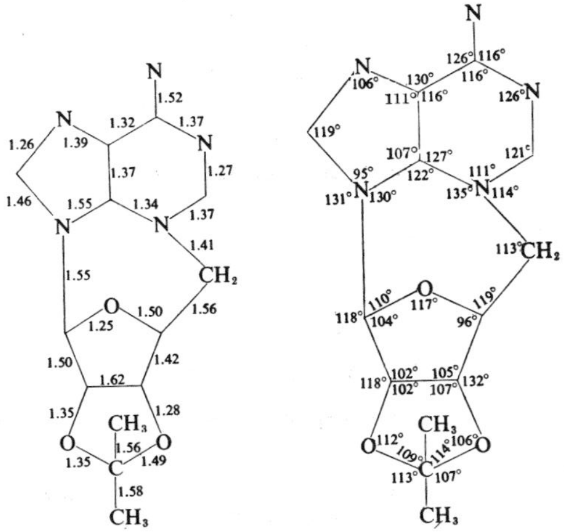

Formula	Substance Name	Bond Lengths	Bond Angles	Exp. Method	Remarks	Reference
$C_{13}H_{20}O_8$	Pentaerythritol tetraacetate $C(C'H_2—O—C'O'—C*H_3)_4$	CC' 1.52 ± 0.03 C'C* 1.52 ± 0.03 C'O 1.41 ± 0.03 C"O 1.41 ± 0.03 C"O' 1.33 ± 0.03	C'CC' 108.5° ± 3° CC'O 105° ± 3° C'OC" 111° ± 3° C*C"O 108.5° ± 3° C*C"O' 124.75° ± 3° OC"O' 124° ± 3°	X		479
$C_{14}H_8Cl_2$	1,5-Dichloroanthracene 	CC a 1.45 ± 0.03 b 1.37 ± 0.03 c 1.42 ± 0.03 d 1.34 ± 0.03 e 1.42 ± 0.03 f 1.30 ± 0.03 g 1.42 ± 0.03 h 1.41 ± 0.03 CCl 1.70 ± 0.03		X		425, 480
$C_{14}H_{10}$	Anthracene 	CC a 1.370 ± 0.010 b 1.423 ± 0.010 c 1.396 ± 0.010 d 1.436 ± 0.010 e 1.408 ± 0.010		X	Planar.	R, 430, 431, 481
$C_{14}H_{10}$	Diphenylacetylene (tolane) $C_6H_5—C'{\equiv}C'—C_6H_5$	CC (1.39) CC' 1.40 ± 0.02 C'C' 1.19 ± 0.02	CC'C' 180°	X	Planar.	482

772

Formula	Compound	Distances (Å)	Angles	X	Remarks	Ref.
$C_{14}H_{10}CuO_4$	Cupric tropolone	CC a 1.41, b 1.38, c 1.41, d 1.39, e 1.45, f 1.39, g 1.37 CO h 1.34, i 1.25 CuO j 1.83, k 1.98	CCC ab 131°, bc 126°, cd 133°, de 125°, ef 129°, fg 131°, ag 127° CCO ah 118°, bh 111°, ai 116°, gi 117° COCu hj 112° OCuO ik 111°, jk 84°	X	Planar or nearly planar. Centrosymmetric.	R, 483
$C_{14}H_{10}O_4$	Benzoyl peroxide $C_6H_5—C'O'—O—O—C'O'—C_6H_5$	CC 1.41 CC' 1.54 C'O 1.47 OO 1.45	C'OO 113° 15'	X		484
$C_{14}H_{11}KO_4$	Potassium acid benzoate $C_6H_5—C'O_2^-$	CC 1.36–1.40 ± 0.04 CC' 1.53 ± 0.04 C'O 1.22, 1.24	OC'O 122°	X	More detailed structure given in original paper.	485
$C_{14}H_{11}KO_6$	Potassium acid p-hydroxybenzoate $HO—C_6H_4—C'O'_2^-$	CC 1.31–1.39 CC' 1.50 CO 1.34 C'O' 1.20, 1.29		X	More detailed structure given in original paper. As monohydrate.	486
$C_{14}H_{12}$	trans Stilbene $C_6H_5—C'H=C'H—C_6H_5$	CC 1.39 CC' 1.44 ± 0.02 C'C' 1.33 ± 0.04	CC'C' 133°	X	Planar. Two crystallographically different kinds of molecules. See below.	487
$C_{14}H_{13}KO_7$	Potassium acid p-hydroxybenzoate monohydrate	CC 1.39 CC' 1.45 ± 0.02 C'C' 1.33 ± 0.04	CC'C' 128°	X	Apparently not planar. See also above.	487
					See $C_{14}H_{11}KO_6$.	

Formula	Substance Name	Bond Lengths	Bond Angles	Exp. Method	Remarks	Reference
$C_{14}H_{14}$	Bibenzyl	CC a 1.48 ± 0.01 b 1.50 ± 0.01 c 1.37 ± 0.01 d 1.39 ± 0.01 e 1.365 ± 0.01 f 1.365 ± 0.01 g 1.39 ± 0.01 h 1.36 ± 0.01	CCC ab 115° ± 1° bc 120° ± 1° cd 119.6° ± 1° de 120.7° ± 1° ef 119.4° ± 1° fg 119.9° ± 1° gh 120.9° ± 1° bh 120.5° ± 1° bc 119.1° ± 1°	X	Phenyl groups in parallel planes. Centrosymmetric.	488
$C_{14}H_{14}Br_2Se$	Di-p-tolylselenium dibromide $(C'H_3—C_6H_4—)_2SeBr_2$	CC 1.39 ± 0.05 CC' 1.54 ± 0.05 CSe 1.95 ± 0.03 SeBr 2.55 ± 0.02	CCC (120°) CCC' (120°) CSeC 108° ± 1° BrSeBr 177° ± 1°	X		489
$C_{14}H_{14}Cl_2Se$	Di-p-tolylselenium dichloride $(C'H_3—C_6H_4—)_2SeCl_2$	CC 1.39 ± 0.05 CC' 1.54 ± 0.05 CSe 1.93 ± 0.03 SeCl 2.38 ± 0.02	CCC (120°) CCC' (120°) CSeC 106.5° ± 1° ClSeCl 177.5° ± 1°	X		489
$C_{14}H_{14}NO_3$	Di-p-anisylnitroxide	CC a 1.38 ± 0.05 b 1.37 ± 0.05 c 1.39 ± 0.05 d 1.38 ± 0.05 e 1.35 ± 0.05 f 1.40 ± 0.05 g 1.44 ± 0.05 h 1.40 ± 0.05 CO 1.44 ± 0.05 CN 1.44 ± 0.05 NO 1.23 ± 0.05	COC 124° ± 5° CCO 120° ± 5° CCN 120° ± 5° CNC 124° ± 5°	X	Rings rotated 33° from the planar conformation.	490
$C_{14}H_{18}Cl_2N_2$	m-Tolidine dihydrochloride	CC a 1.55 Others 1.31–1.41 CC' 1.50, 1.53 CN 1.44, 1.45	All 108°–128°	X	Angle of 86° between planes of rings. More detailed structure given in original papers.	491

774

$C_{15}H_{26}N_2$	α-Isosparteine	As shown	X	As monohydrate.	492
$C_{15}H_{28}N_2O$	α-Isosparteine monohydrate	As shown		See $C_{15}H_{26}N_2$.	
$C_{16}H_{10}$	Diphenylbiacetylene C_6H_5—C≡C'—C''—C''≡C'—C_6H_5	CC 1.39 ± 0.03 CC' 1.44 ± 0.03 C'C'' 1.18 ± 0.03 C''C'' 1.39 ± 0.03	X	Planar.	493
		CC'C' 180° C'C'C'' 180°			
$C_{16}H_{10}$	Pyrene 	CC a 1.45 ± 0.04 b 1.39 ± 0.04 c 1.42 ± 0.04 d 1.39 ± 0.04 e 1.45 ± 0.04 f 1.39 ± 0.04	X	Planar.	R, 494, 495
$C_{16}H_{15}KO_4$	Potassium hydrogen phenylacetate C_6H_5—C'H_2—C''O_2^-	CC 1.36₅–1.44 ± 0.05 CC' 1.57 ± 0.05 C'C'' 1.52 ± 0.05 C''O 1.18₅, 1.24₅ ± 0.05 [OO 2.22]	X	More detailed structure given in original paper.	496

775

Formula	Substance Name	Bond Lengths	Bond Angles	Exp. Method	Remarks	Reference
$C_{16}H_{16}$	Bi-*m*-xylylene 	CC 1.369–1.404 CC′ 1.515, 1.554 C′C′ 1.559	CCC 116° 42′–122° 16′ CCC′ 118° 38′–123° 36′ CC′C′ 109° 49′, 110° 48′	X	Centrosymmetric. Benzene rings boat shaped. More detailed structure given in original paper.	497
$C_{16}H_{16}$	Bi-*p*-xylylene 	CC 1.39, 1.40 CC′ 1.54 C′C′ 1.55	CCC 118° 36′, 120° 14′ CCC′ 119° 55′ CC′C′ 114° 37′	X	Benzene rings boat shaped.	498
$C_{16}H_{17}KN_2O_4S$	Potassium benzylpenicillin 	As shown	As shown	X		499

776

Formula	Name / Structure	Bond lengths / angles		Code	Remarks	Ref.
$C_{18}H_{18}$	p,p'-Dimethylbibenzyl (CH_3—C'_6H_4—$C'H_2$—)$_2$	CC' 1.52 C'C' 1.36–1.39 C"C" 1.53 C'C" 1.51	CC'C', C'C'C', C'C'C" 120° ± 1° C'C"C" 116°	X	Accuracy "not very high."	500
$C_{18}H_{12}$	Chrysene	CC 1.41		X	Planar.	R, 501
$C_{18}H_{12}$	Triphenylene	CC a 1.47 ± 0.03 b 1.435 ± 0.03 c 1.39 ± 0.03 d 1.375 ± 0.03 e 1.385 ± 0.03		X		R, 502
$C_{18}H_{14}$	o-Terphenyl C_6H_5—C'_6H_4—C_6H_5	CC 1.39 ± 0.02 CC' 1.52 ± 0.04 C'C' 1.39 ± 0.02		E	Central ring perpendicular to other two.	459
$C_{18}H_{14}$	p-Terphenyl C_6H_5—C'_6H_4—C_6H_5	CC 1.42 CC' 1.48 C'C' 1.42		X	Planar.	503
$C_{18}H_{15}Bi$	Triphenylbismuth	CBi 2.30 ± 0.03		X		504
$C_{18}H_{18}O_8S$	Hydroquinone-sulfur dioxide				See $C_6H_6O_2$ (hydroquinone).	
$C_{18}H_{24}$	Octamethylnaphthalene	CC a 1.38 b 1.42 c 1.36 d 1.43 e 1.55 f 1.54		X	Nonplanar rings.	505

777

Formula	Substance Name	Bond Lengths	Bond Angles	Exp. Method	Remarks	Reference
$C_{20}H_{12}$	Perylene	CC a 1.38 ± 0.04 b 1.45 ± 0.04 c 1.38 ± 0.04 d 1.45 ± 0.04 e 1.45 ± 0.04 f 1.38 ± 0.04 g 1.50 ± 0.04		X	At least approximately planar.	R, 506
$C_{22}H_{12}$	1,12-Benzoperylene	CC a 1.38 ± 0.03 b 1.41 ± 0.03 c 1.41 ± 0.03 d 1.43 ± 0.03 e 1.42 ± 0.03 f 1.43 ± 0.03 g 1.42 ± 0.03 h 1.42 ± 0.03 i 1.43 ± 0.03 j 1.43 ± 0.03 k 1.38 ± 0.03 l 1.41 ± 0.03 m 1.40 ± 0.03 n 1.41 ± 0.03 o 1.40 ± 0.03		X		R, 495, 507
$C_{22}H_{14}$	Dibenz[ah]anthracene	CC a 1.39 ± 0.04 b 1.40 ± 0.04 c 1.40 ± 0.04 d 1.39 ± 0.04 e 1.41 ± 0.04 f 1.40 ± 0.04 g 1.45 ± 0.04 h 1.40 ± 0.04 i 1.38 ± 0.04 j 1.44 ± 0.04 k 1.44 ± 0.04 l 1.38 ± 0.04 m 1.40 ± 0.04		X		R, 495, 508

$C_{22}H_{20}$	1,10-Diphenyl-1,3,5,7,9-decapentaene 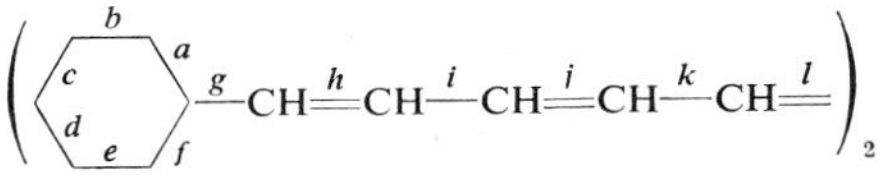	CC *a* 1.40 *b* 1.36 *c* 1.38 *d* 1.38 *e* 1.37 *f* 1.37 *g* 1.45 *h* 1.40 *i* 1.40 *j* 1.38 *k* 1.39 *l* 1.38	CCC *ab* 124° *bc* 120° *cd* 116° *de* 124° *ef* 121° *af* 115° *ag* 123° *gh* 127° *hi* 125° *ij* 124° *jk* 124° *kl* 123°	X	Monoclinic form. Standard deviations are 0.03–0.04 A and 2°–3°. All-*trans* configuration. Centrosymmetric. Almost, but not quite planar. Orthorhombic form similar, but with slightly different bond lengths and bond angles.	509
$C_{24}H_{12}$	Coronene 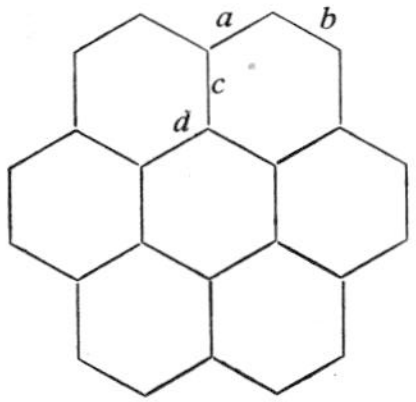	CC *a* 1.415 ± 0.02 *b* 1.385 ± 0.02 *c* 1.430 ± 0.02 *d* 1.430 ± 0.02		X	Bond lengths given are averages over chemically equivalent bonds.	*R*, 495, 510
$C_{24}H_{16}$	Tetraphenylene $C_6H_4\langle(C'_6H_4)_2\rangle C_6H_4$	CC, C′C′ 1.39 ± 0.02 CC′ 1.52 ± 0.04		E	Central 8-membered ring is puckered.	459
$C_{24}H_{18}$	*p*-Quaterphenyl $C_6H_5—C'_6H_4—C_6H_4—C'_6H_5$	CC, C′C′ 1.42 CC′ 1.48		X	Planar.	511
$C_{24}H_{18}$	1,3,5-Triphenylbenzene $C_6H_3(C'_6H_5)_3$	CC 1.37–1.39 CC′ 1.48–1.51 C′C′ 1.37–1.41	Average of all 120° ± 5°	X	Outer rings twisted +34°, −27°, and +24° about CC′ bonds out of plane of central ring.	512

Formula	Substance Name	Bond Lengths	Bond Angles	Exp. Method	Remarks	Reference
$C_{24}H_{18}N_2O_5$	p,p'-Dinitrobiphenyl-p-hydroxybiphenyl addition compound				See $C_{12}H_8N_2O_4$ and $C_{12}H_{10}O$.	
$C_{25}H_{20}AsI$	Tetraphenylarsonium iodide	CC 1.39 CAs 1.95		X	Tetrahedral As.	513
$C_{25}H_{20}$	Tetraphenylmethane $C'(C_6H_5)_4$	CC 1.39 CC' 1.47		X		514
$C_{26}H_{14}N_8Ni$	Unnamed analog of nickel phthalocyanine	CC 1.31–1.48 ± 0.05 CN 1.29–1.45 ± 0.05 NiN 1.98_5, 1.90	CNC $122°$, $124°$ NNiN $89.7°$, $90.3°$	X	Nonplanar. More detailed structure given in original paper.	515
$C_{26}H_{16}$	Dibiphenyleneethylene	CC a (1.48) others (1.40) CC' (1.48) C'C' (1.33)	CC'C $118°$	X	Approximately planar.	516

780

$C_{27}H_{45}I$	Cholesteryl iodide		C—C 1.47–1.60 (mean = 1.55) C=C 1.30 CI 2.08	C—C—C 91°–129° 30′ (mean = 108° 36′) C—C=C 124° 45′, 125° 33′	X	More detailed structure given in original paper. Accuracy "not great." Data support chemical structure and stereochemical configuration.	517
$C_{28}H_{12}N_2O_2$	Flavanthrone		As shown		X		518
$C_{28}H_{24}$	1,2,3,4-Tetraphenylcyclobutane $[-C'H-C_6H_5]_4$		CC 1.39 ± 0.02 CC' 1.50 ± 0.02 C'C' 1.555, 1.585 ± 0.02	CCC 120° ± 2° CC'C 115°, 119°, 122° ± 2° C'C'C' 89°, 91° ± 2°	X	Centrosymmetric.	519
$C_{30}H_{14}O$	Acebianthrone		As shown		X	All bond lengths ± 0.06 A. Centrosymmetric. Chemical structure confirmed.	520

781

Formula	Substance Name	Bond Lengths	Bond Angles	Exp. Method	Remarks	Reference
$C_{30}H_{16}$	Diphenylenenaphthacene	As shown	As shown	X	Angle of 8° between planes of naphthacene and benzene rings. Centrosymmetric.	521
$C_{30}H_{20}$	1,1,6,6-Tetraphenylhexapentaene $(C'_6H_5)_2C=C=C=C=C=C(C'_6H_5)_2$	CC 1.31 ± 0.03 CC' 1.51 ± 0.05 C'C' 1.37 ± 0.05	C'CC' $112° \pm 3°$	X	Rings tilted $32° \pm 5°$ out of plane. CC' bond not in plane of ring.	522

Formula	Name	Bond lengths (Å)	Angles		Remarks	Ref.
C₃₂H₁₄	Ovalene	CC a 1.404 b 1.441 c 1.345 d 1.433 e 1.403 f 1.428 g 1.426 h 1.435 i 1.416 j 1.461 k 1.442 l 1.383		X	Planar and centrosymmetric.	R, 523
C₃₂H₁₈N₈	Phthalocyanine	CC (1.39) CC' 1.47 C'N 1.34		X	Planar. Structures of Ni and Pt derivatives also given in original papers.	R, 524
H₂O	Water	HO 0.958₄	HOH 104° 27'	S		72, 98
H₂S	Hydrogen sulfide	HS 1.334	HSH 92° 16'	S		98, 525
H₃N	Ammonia	HN 1.014	HNH 106° 47'	S		GST, 72, 98
NNaO₃	Sodium nitrate	NO 1.210	ONO 120°	X	Planar anion.	17

Formula	Substance Name	Bond Lengths	Bond Angles	Exp. Method	Remarks	Reference
NO	Nitric oxide	NO 1.1510		s		526
N_2O	Nitrous oxide	NN 1.1257 $\pm$ 0.0020 NO 1.1863 $\pm$ 0.0020	NNO 180°	s		GST, 527
N_2O_5	Nitronium nitrate (solid dinitrogen pentoxide) NO_2^+ $N'O_3^-$	NO 1.15$_4$ $\pm$ 0.01 N'O 1.24$_3$ $\pm$ 0.01	ONO 180° ON'O 120°	X		528
O_2S	Sulfur dioxide	SO 1.43$_3$ $\pm$ 0.01	OSO 120° $\pm$ 5°	E		93, 96, 97, 185, 529
		SO 1.430 $\pm$ 0.015	OSO 119° $\pm$ 2°	X	−130°C.	530
		SO 1.432	OSO 119.53°	s		GST, 531

References

AS. P. W. Allen and L. E. Sutton, *Acta Cryst.* **3**, 46 (1950). This is a comprehensive review article, summarizing all the electron-diffraction work on both organic and inorganic compounds up to the time of publication.

B. L. O. Brockway, *Revs. Mod. Phys.* **8**, 231 (1936). This is a review article of the same type as *AS*, but much earlier and hence less complete.

GST. W. Gordy, W. V. Smith, and R. F. Trambarulo, *Microwave Spectroscopy*, John Wiley & Sons, New York, 1953, Table A.9. This compilation of data is also similar to *AS* but, since it is restricted to the results obtained by microwave spectroscopy, it is much less extensive.

R. J. M. Robertson, *Organic Crystals and Molecules*, Cornell University Press, Ithaca, New York, 1953. This book contains a summary of the author's comprehensive work on the crystal structures of organic compounds.

1. D. P. Riley, *Nature* **153**, 587 (1944).

2. K. Lonsdale, *Trans. Roy. Soc. (London) A* **240**, 219 (1947).

3. J. D. Bernal, *Proc. Roy. Soc. (London) A* **106**, 749 (1924).

4. O. Hassell and H. Mark, *Z. Physik* **25**, 317 (1924).

5. P. Capron and M. de Hemptinne, *Ann. soc. sci. Bruxelles* **56B**, 342 (1936) [*C. A.* **31**, 2509 (1937)].

6. H. J. M. Bowen, *Trans. Faraday Soc.* **50**, 444 (1954).

7. J. Sheridan and W. Gordy, *Phys. Rev.* **77**, 292 (1950); *J. Chem. Phys.* **20**, 591 (1952).

8. A. H. Sharbaugh, B. S. Pritchard, and T. C. Madison, *Phys. Rev.* **77**, 302 (1950).

9. C. H. Townes, A. N. Holden, and F. R. Merritt, *Phys. Rev.* **71**, 64 (1947); **74**, 1113 (1948).

10. A. G. Smith, H. Ring, W. V. Smith, and W. Gordy, *Phys. Rev.* **74**, 370 (1948).

11. J. Y. Beach and A. Turkevich, *J. Am. Chem. Soc.* **61**, 299 (1939).

12. P. Capron and S. L. T. Perlinghi, *Bull. soc. chim. Belg.* **45**, 730 (1936).

13. R. W. Dornte, *J. Am. Chem. Soc.* **55**, 4126 (1933).

14. J. Wouters and M. de Hemptinne, *Nature* **141**, 412 (1938).

15. H. A. Lévy and L. O. Brockway, *J. Am. Chem. Soc.* **59**, 1662 (1937).

16. O. Hassel and H. Viervoll, *Acta Chem. Scand.* **1**, 149 (1947).

17. N. Elliott, *J. Am. Chem. Soc.* **59**, 1380 (1937).

18. L. O. Brockway, *J. Phys. Chem.* **41**, 747 (1937). For more recent electron-diffraction studies of carbon tetrachloride, see A. V. Frost, P. A. Akishin, L. V. Gurvich, G. A. Kurkchi; and A. A. Konstantinov, *C. A.* **48**, 11912 (1954); M. Rouault and C. Saint-Arnaud, *ibid.* **48**, 13367 (1954).

19. L. O. Brockway, J. Y. Beach, and L. Pauling, *J. Am. Chem. Soc.* **57**, 2693 (1935).

20. V. Schomaker, quoted by *AS*.

21. B. Zaslow, M. Atoji, and W. N. Lipscomb, *Acta Cryst.* **5**, 833 (1952).

22. G. W. Robinson, *J. Chem. Phys.* **21**, 1741 (1953).

23. H. A. Skinner, Thesis, Oxford, 1941, quoted by *AS*.

24. T. T. Broun and R. L. Livingston, *J. Am. Chem. Soc.* **74**, 6084 (1952).

25. C. W. W. Hoffman and R. L. Livingston, *J. Chem. Phys.* **21**, 565 (1953).

26. P. Kisliuk and G. A. Silvey, *J. Chem. Phys.* **20**, 517 (1952).

27. Q. Williams, J. T. Cox, and W. Gordy, *J. Chem. Phys.* **20**, 1524 (1952).

28. S. N. Ghosh, R. Trambarulo, and W. Gordy, *J. Chem. Phys.* **20**, 605 (1952).

29. O. Bastiansen, *Tidsskr. Kjemi, Bergvesen Met.* **6**, No. 1 (1946) [*C. A.* **40**, 4574 (1946)].

30. A. I. Kitaĭgorodskiĭ, T. L. Khotsyanova, and Yu. T. Struchkov, *Doklady Akad. Nauk S. S. S. R.* **78**, 1161 (1951) [*C. A.* **46**, 4314 (1952)]. See also T. L. Khotsyanova, A. I. Kitaĭgorodskiĭ, and Yu. T. Struchkov, *Zhur. Fiz. Khim.* **27**, 647 (1953) [*C. A.* **48**, 2438 (1954)].

31. I. Nitta, Y. Tomiie, and C. H. Koo, *Acta Cryst.* **5**, 292 (1952).

32. H. Verleger, *Physik. Z.* **38**, 83 (1937); J. W. Simmons, W. E. Anderson, and W. Gordy, *Phys. Rev.* **77**, 77 (1950); A. H. Nethercot, Jr., J. A. Klein, and C. H. Townes, *ibid.* **86**, 798 (1952); A. E. Douglas and D. Sharma, *J. Chem. Phys.* **21**, 448 (1953).

33. W. Gordy, *Revs. Mod. Phys.* **20**, 668 (1948).

34. E. H. Eyster, R. H. Gillette, and L. O. Brockway, *J. Am. Chem. Soc.* **62**, 3236 (1940).

35. L. H. Jones, J. N. Shoolery, R. G. Shulman, and D. M. Yost, *J. Chem. Phys.* **18**, 990 (1950).

36. C. I. Beard and B. P. Dailey, *J. Chem. Phys.* **15**, 762 (1947); **18**, 1437 (1950); C. Reid, *ibid.* **18**, 1512 (1950); L. H. Jones and R. M. Badger, *ibid.* **18**, 1511 (1950); G. C. Dousmanis, T. M. Sanders, Jr., C. H. Townes, and H. J. Zeiger, *ibid.* **21**, 1416 (1953).

37. W. H. Zachariasen, *J. Am. Chem. Soc.* **62**, 1011 (1940).

38. C. W. Bunn, *Trans. Faraday Soc.* **35**, 482 (1939).

39. Y. Morino, M. Kimura, and M. Hasegawa, *J. Chem. Soc. Japan.* **67**, 115, 116 (1946) [*C. A.* **44**, 10413 (1950)].

40. N. Muller, *J. Am. Chem. Soc.* **75**, 860 (1953).

41. R. J. Myers and W. D. Gwinn, *J. Chem. Phys.* **20**, 1420 (1952).

42. V. C. Hamilton and K. Hedberg, *J. Am. Chem. Soc.* **74**, 5529 (1952).

43. H. R. Stewart and H. H. Nielsen, *Phys. Rev.* **75**, 640 (1949); D. R. Lide, Jr., *J. Am. Chem. Soc.* **74**, 3548 (1952).

44. H. Boersch, *Monatsh. Chem.* **65**, 311 (1935).

45. D. P. Stevenson, J. E. LuValle, and V. Schomaker, *J. Am. Chem. Soc.* **61**, 2508 (1939).

46. D. W. Davidson, B. P. Stoicheff, and H. J. Bernstein, *J. Chem. Phys.* **22**, 289 (1954).

47. J. Karle and L. O. Brockway, *J. Am. Chem. Soc.* **66**, 574 (1944).

48. V. Schomaker and J. M. O'Gorman, *J. Am. Chem. Soc.* **69**, 2638 (1947); I. L. Karle and J. Karle, *J. Chem. Phys.* **22**, 43 (1954).

49. F. Holtzberg, B. Post, and I. Fankuchen, *Acta Cryst.* **6**, 127 (1953).

50. G. Erlandsson, *Arkiv Fysik*, **6**, 491 (1953) [*C. A.* **47**, 9154 (1953)]. Cf. also R. Trambarulo and P. M. Moser, *J. Chem. Phys.* **22**, 1622 (1954); R. G. Lerner, J. P. Friend, and B. P. Dailey, *ibid.* **23**, 210 (1955).

51. J. Waser and V. Schomaker, *J. Am. Chem. Soc.* **67**, 2014 (1945).

52. S. H. Bauer and J. M. Hastings, *J. Am. Chem. Soc.* **64**, 2686 (1942).

53. S. H. Bauer, *J. Am. Chem. Soc.* **59**, 1804 (1937).

54. W. Gordy, H. Ring, and A. B. Burg, *Phys. Rev.* **78**, 512 (1950).

55. W. Gordy, J. W. Simmons, and A. G. Smith, *Phys. Rev.* **74**, 243 (1948).

56. J. W. Simmons and W. O. Swan, *Phys. Rev.* **80**, 289 (1950).

57. S. L. Miller, L. C. Aamodt, G. Dousmanis, C. H. Townes, and J. Kraitchman, *J. Chem. Phys.* **20**, 1112 (1952).

58. J. M. Mays and B. P. Dailey, *J. Chem. Phys.* **20**, 1695 (1952).
59. W. Gordy and J. Sheridan, *J. Chem. Phys.* **22**, 92 (1954).
60. K. Yamasaki, A. Kotera, M. Yokoi, and M. Iwasaki, *J. Chem. Phys.* **17**, 1355 (1949).
61. H. A. Skinner and L. E. Sutton, *Trans. Faraday Soc.* **40**, 164 (1944).
62. R. D. Burbank, *J. Am. Chem. Soc.* **75**, 1211 (1953).
63. G. Matlack, G. Glockler, D. R. Bianco, and A. Roberts, *J. Chem. Phys.* **18**, 332 (1950).
64. D. P. Stevenson and V. Schomaker, *J. Am. Chem. Soc.* **62**, 1913 (1940).
65. R. L. Livingston and L. O. Brockway, *J. Am. Chem. Soc.* **66**, 94 (1944).
66. R. C. Mockler, J. H. Bailey, and W. Gordy, *J. Chem. Phys.* **21**, 1710 (1953).
67. V. Schomaker and D. P. Stevenson, *J. Am. Chem. Soc.* **63**, 37 (1941).
68. O. R. Gilliam, H. D. Edwards, and W. Gordy, *Phys. Rev.* **75**, 1014 (1949).
69. W. Gordy, A. G. Smith, and J. W. Simmons, *Phys. Rev.* **71**, 917 (1947).
70. F. Rogowski, *Ber.* **75**, 244 (1942).
71. L. Pauling and L. O. Brockway, *J. Am. Chem. Soc.* **59**, 13 (1937).
72. D. M. Dennison, *Revs. Mod. Phys.* **12**, 175 (1940).
73. R. W. G. Wyckoff and R. B. Corey, *Z. Krist.* **89**, 462 (1934).
74. P. Vaughan and J. Donohue, *Acta Cryst.* **5**, 530 (1952).
75. A. E. Smith, *Acta Cryst.* **5**, 224 (1952).
76. R. W. G. Wyckoff and R. B. Corey, *Z. Krist.* **81**, 386 (1932).
77. M. Kimura, *J. Chem. Soc. Japan* Pure Chem. Sect. **71**, 18 (1950) [*C. A.* **45**, 4979 (1951)].
78. K. J. Tauer and W. N. Lipscomb, *Acta Cryst.* **5**, 606 (1952); B. Dreyfus-Alain and R. Viallard, *Compt. rend.* **234**, 536 (1952).
79. E. V. Ivash and D. M. Dennison, *J. Chem. Phys.* **21**, 1804 (1953).
80. T. M. Shaw and J. J. Windle, *J. Chem. Phys.* **19**, 1063 (1951); N. Solimene and B. P. Dailey, *ibid.* **23**, 124 (1955).
81. S. Geller and J. L. Hoard, *Acta Cryst.* **3**, 121 (1950); J. L. Hoard, S. Geller, and T. B. Owen, *ibid.* **4**, 405 (1951).
82. M. Atoji and W. N. Lipscomb, *Acta Cryst.* **6**, 770 (1953).
83. R. G. Owens and E. F. Barker, *J. Chem. Phys.* **8**, 229 (1940).
84. J. Drenth, W. Drenth, A. Vos, and E. H. Wiebenga, *Acta Cryst.* **6**, 424 (1953). See also W. Theilacker, *Z. Krist.* **90**, 51, 256 (1935).
85. E. W. Hughes and W. N. Lipscomb, *J. Am. Chem. Soc.* **68**, 1970 (1946).
86. C.-S. Lu, E. W. Hughes, and P. A. Giguère, *J. Am. Chem. Soc.* **63**, 1507 (1941).
87. A. C. Bond and L. O. Brockway, *J. Am. Chem. Soc.* **76**, 3312 (1954).
88. D. R. Lide, Jr., *J. Chem. Phys.* **19**, 1605 (1951).
89. C. Finbak and O. Hassel, *Z. physik. Chem. B* **36**, 301 (1937); M. W. Lister and L. E. Sutton, *Trans. Faraday Soc.* **37**, 393 (1941).
90. M. Bassière, *Mém. services chim. état.* (Paris) **30**, 30 (1943) [*C. A.* **41**, 4020 (1947)].
91. A. J. Stosick, *J. Am. Chem. Soc.* **61**, 1127 (1939).
92. L. Gerö, G. Herzberg, and R. Schmid, *Phys. Rev.* **52**, 467 (1937); G. Herzberg and K. N. Rao, *J. Chem. Phys.* **17**, 1099 (1949).
93. P. C. Cross and L. O. Brockway, *J. Chem. Phys.* **3**, 821 (1935).
94. T. W. Dakin, W. E. Good, and D. K. Coles, *Phys. Rev.* **71**, 640 (1947).
95. M. W. P. Strandberg, T. Wentink, and A. G. Hill, *Phys. Rev.* **75**, 827 (1949).
96. R. Wierl, *Physik. Z.* **31**, 1028 (1930).
97. R. Wierl, *Ann. Physik.* **8**, 521 (1931).

788   REFERENCES

98. G. Herzberg, *Infrared and Raman Spectra*, D. Van Nostrand Co., New York, 1945.

99. G. A. Silvey, W. A. Hardy, and C. H. Townes, *Phys. Rev.* **87**, 236 (1952); W. A. Hardy and G. Silvey, *ibid.* **95**, 385 (1954).

100. L. N. Liebermann, *Phys. Rev.* **60**, 496 (1941).

101. R. L. Griffith, *J. Chem. Phys.* **11**, 499 (1943).

102. H. de Laszlo, *Nature* **135**, 474 (1935).

103. O. Hassel and T. Taarland, *Tidsskr. Kjemi, Bergvesen Met.* **1**, 172 (1941) [*C. A.* **37**, 6538 (1943)].

104. M. Iwasaki, S. Nagase, and R. Kojima, *J. Chem. Phys.* **22**, 959 (1954).

105. O. Hassel and T. Taarland, *Tidsskr. Kjemi, Bergvesen* **20**, 152 (1940) [*C. A.* **35**, 4653 (1941)].

106. J. E. LuValle, quoted by *AS*.

107. I. L. Karle and J. Karle, *J. Chem. Phys.* **20**, 63 (1952).

108. W. N. Lipscomb, quoted by *AS*.

109. O. Hassel and H. Viervoll, *Arch. Math. Naturvidenskab B* **47**, No. 13 (1944) [*C. A.* **40**, 3392 (1946)].

110. Y. Morino and M. Iwasaki, *J. Chem. Phys.* **17**, 216 (1949).

111. D. A. Swick, I. L. Karle, and J. Karle, *J. Chem. Phys.* **22**, 1242 (1954).

112. Y. Sasada and M. Atoji, *J. Chem. Phys.* **21**, 145 (1953).

113. I. L. Karle and J. Karle, *J. Chem. Phys.* **18**, 963 (1950).

114. L. O. Brockway, J. H. Secrist, and F. Lucht, paper presented at Buffalo, N. Y. meeting of the American Chemical Society, 1942. See *AS*.

115. J. L. Brandt and R. L. Livingston, *J. Am. Chem. Soc.* **76**, 2096 (1954).

116. S. H. Bauer and J. Y. Beach, quoted by *AS*.

117. H. J. M. Bowen, *Trans. Faraday Soc.* **50**, 452 (1954).

118. L. O. Brockway and J. S. Anderson, *Trans. Faraday Soc.* **33**, 1233 (1937).

119. L. O. Brockway and I. E. Coop, *Trans. Faraday Soc.* **34**, 1429 (1938).

120. R. W. Dornte, *J. Chem. Phys.* **1**, 566 (1933).

121. A. A. Westenberg, J. H. Goldstein, and E. B. Wilson, Jr., *J. Chem. Phys.* **17**, 1319 (1949).

122. A. A. Westenberg and E. B. Wilson, Jr., *J. Am. Chem. Soc.* **72**, 199 (1950).

123. C. Degard, *Bull. soc. roy. sci. Liége*, **7**, 36 (1938) [*C. A.* **33**, 467 (1939)].

124. D. J. Sutor, F. J. Llewellyn, and H. S. Maslen, *Acta Cryst.* **7**, 145 (1954).

125. H. Yearian, quoted by *AS*.

126. I. T. Sugawara and E. Kanda, *Science Repts. Research Insts. Tôhoku Univ. Ser. A*, **4**, 607 (1952) [*C. A.* **47**, 10309 (1953)].

127. B. D. Saksena, *J. Chem. Phys.* **20**, 95 (1952).

128. J. Donohue, G. Humphrey, and V. Schomaker, *J. Am. Chem. Soc.* **69**, 1713 (1947).

129. T. Sugawara, M. Kakudo, Y. Saito, and I. Nitta, *X-Sen (X-Rays)* **6**, 85 (1951) [*C. A.* **45**, 8319 (1951)].

130. J. A. C. Hugill, I. E. Coop, and L. E. Sutton, *Trans. Faraday Soc.* **34**, 1518 (1938).

131. I. Nitta and K. Osaki, *X-Sen (X-Rays)* **5**, 37 (1948) [*C. A.* **44**, 5178 (1950)].

132. R. Wierl, *Ann. Physik* **13**, 453 (1932).

133. R. Wierl, *Physik. Z.* **31**, 366 (1930).

134. M. Kashima, *Bull. Chem. Soc. Japan* **25**, 79 (1952) [*C. A.* **47**, 1999 (1953)].

135. J. Y. Beach and D. P. Stevenson, *J. Chem. Phys.* **6**, 75 (1938).

136. B. Bak, E. S. Knudsen, E. Madsen, and J. Rastrup-Andersen, *Phys. Rev.* 7

190 (1950); H. R. Johnson and M. W. P. Strandberg, *J. Chem. Phys.* **20**, 687 (1952); W. F. Arendale and W. H. Fletcher, *ibid.* **21**, 1898 (1953).

137. J. E. LuValle and V. Schomaker, *J. Am. Chem. Soc.* **61**, 3520 (1939).

138. S. B. Hendricks, *Z. Krist.* **91**, 48 (1935). Further data for several alkali-metal oxalates are also given in this paper.

139. E. G. Cox, M. W. Dougill, and G. A. Jeffrey, *J. Chem. Soc.* **1952**, 4854.

140. J. M. Robertson and I. Woodward, *J. Chem. Soc.* **1936**, 1817; J. D. Dunitz and J. M. Robertson, *ibid.* **1947**, 142; F. R. Ahmed and D. W. J. Cruikshank, *Acta Cryst.* **6**, 385 (1953).

141. I. Nitta and Y. Saito, *X-Sen* (*X-Rays*) **5**, 89 (1949) [*C. A.* **44**, 6227 (1950)].

142. J. L. Hoard, T. B. Owen, A. Buzzell, and O. N. Salmon, *Acta Cryst.* **3**, 130 (1950); J. L. Hoard, S. Geller, and T. B. Owen, *ibid.* **4**, 405 (1951).

143. P. W. Allen and L. E. Sutton, *Trans. Faraday Soc.* **47**, 236 (1951). For more recent, and somewhat divergent data for acetyl chloride, see Y. Morino, K. Kuchitsu, M. Iwasaki, K. Arakawa, and A. Takahashi, *J. Chem. Soc. Japan*, Pure Chem Sect. **75**, 647 (1954) [*C. A.* **48**, 8644 (1954)].

144. R. A. Spurr and W. Shand, quoted by *AS*.

145. J. M. O'Gorman, W. Shand, Jr., and V. Schomaker, *J. Am. Chem. Soc.* **72**, 4222 (1950).

146. J. Y. Beach and D. P. Stevenson, *J. Am. Chem. Soc.* **61**, 2643 (1939).

147. J. W. Coutts and R. L. Livingston, *J. Am. Chem. Soc.* **75**, 1542 (1953).

148. S. Kondo and I. Nitta, *X-Sen* (*X-Rays*) **6**, 53 (1950) [*C. A.* **45**, 3237 (1951)].

149. L. O. Brockway, *J. Am. Chem. Soc.* **58**, 2516 (1936).

150. L. Pauling, H. D. Springall, and K. J. Palmer, *J. Am. Chem. Soc.* **61**, 927 (1939).

151. M. Kessler, H. Ring, R. Trambarulo, and W. Gordy, *Phys. Rev.* **79**, 54 (1950).

152. W. Gordy and L. Pauling, *J. Am. Chem. Soc.* **64**, 2952 (1942).

153. C. I. Beard and B. P. Dailey, *J. Am. Chem. Soc.* **71**, 929 (1949).

154. L. Pauling and L. O. Brockway, *J. Am. Chem. Soc.* **59**, 1223 (1937).

155. E. H. Eyster, *J. Chem. Phys.* **6**, 580 (1938).

156. W. S. Galloway and E. F. Barker, *J. Chem. Phys.* **10**, 88 (1942).

157. J. Y. Beach and A. Turkevich, *J. Am. Chem. Soc.* **61**, 303 (1939).

158. J. Y. Beach and K. J. Palmer, *J. Chem. Phys.* **6**, 639 (1938).

159. J. Ainsworth and J. Karle, *J. Chem. Phys.* **20**, 425 (1952).

160. T. B. Reed and W. N. Lipscomb, *Acta Cryst.* **6**, 45 (1953).

161. C. Romers, *Acta Cryst.* **6**, 429 (1953).

162. E. W. Hughes, *J. Am. Chem. Soc.* **62**, 1258 (1940).

163. D. P. Stevenson, H. D. Burnham, and V. Schomaker, *J. Am. Chem. Soc.* **61**, 2922 (1939).

164. P. G. Ackermann and J. E. Mayer, *J. Chem. Phys.* **4**, 377 (1936).

165. M. Igarashi, *Bull. Chem. Soc. Japan* **26**, 330 (1953).

166. G. L. Cunningham, A. W. Boyd, W. D. Gwinn, and W. I. Le Van, *J. Chem. Phys.* **17**, 211 (1949).

167. G. L. Cunningham, Jr., A. W. Boyd, R. J. Myers, W. D. Gwinn, and W. I. Le Van, *J. Chem. Phys.* **19**, 676 (1951).

168. W. Gordy, *J. Chem. Phys.* **14**, 560 (1946).

169. L. Brú, *Anales soc. españ. fíz. y quím.* **31**, 115 (1933) [*C. A.* **27**, 2072 (1933)].

170. O. Bastiansen, quoted by *AS*.

171. J. A. J. Jarvis, *Acta Cryst.* **6**, 327 (1953).

172. T. E. Turner, V. C. Fiora, W. M. Kendrick, and B. L. Hicks, *J. Chem. Phys.* **21**, 564 (1953).

173. M. Kimura and M. Aoki, *Bull. Chem. Soc. Japan*, **26**, 429 (1953).
174. F. Senti and D. Harker, *J. Am. Chem. Soc.* **62**, 2008 (1940).
175. G. Albrecht and R. B. Corey, *J. Am. Chem. Soc.* **61**, 1087 (1939).
176. K. Hedberg and V. Schomaker, *J. Am. Chem. Soc.* **73**, 1482 (1951).
177. G. E. Hansen and D. M. Dennison, *J. Chem. Phys.* **20**, 313 (1952).
178. S. H. Bauer, G. R. Finlay, and A. W. Laubengayer, *J. Am. Chem. Soc.* **65**, 889 (1943); **67**, 339 (1945); H. C. Brown and R. M. Adams, *ibid.* **65**, 2253 (1943).
179. R. E. Rundle and A. I. Snow, *J. Chem. Phys.* **18**, 1125 (1950); A. I. Snow and R. E. Rundle, *Acta Cryst.* **4**, 348 (1951).
180. A. H. Gregg, G. C. Hampson, G. I. Jenkins, P. L. F. Jones, and L. E. Sutton, *Trans. Faraday Soc.* **33**, 852 (1937).
181. W. Costain and E. G. Cox, *Nature* **160**, 826 (1947).
182. F. J. Llewellyn and F. E. Whitmore, *J. Chem. Soc.* **1948**, 1316.
183. L. Brú, *Anales soc. españ. fíz. y quím.* **30**, 486 (1932) [*C. A.* **27**, 1269 (1935)].
184. L. E. Sutton and L. O. Brockway, *J. Am. Chem. Soc.* **57**, 473 (1935).
185. L. Pauling and L. O. Brockway, *J. Am. Chem. Soc.* **57**, 2684 (1935).
186. O. Bastiansen and H. Viervoll, *Acta Chem. Scand.* **2**, 702 (1948).
187. R. E. Rundle, quoted by *AS*.
188. J. Donohue, quoted by *AS*.
189. M. W. Lister and L. E. Sutton, *Trans. Faraday Soc.* **35**, 495 (1939).
190. H. Sorum, *Acta Chem. Scand.* **7**, 1 (1953).
191. L. O. Brockway and H. O. Jenkins, *J. Am. Chem. Soc.* **58**, 2036 (1936).
192. D. P. Stevenson and J. Y. Beach, *J. Am. Chem. Soc.* **60**, 2872 (1938).
193. J. Donohue and V. Schomaker, *J. Chem. Phys.* **16**, 92 (1948).
194. S. H. Bauer, *J. Am. Chem. Soc.* **60**, 524 (1938).
195. W. H. Beamer, *J. Am. Chem. Soc.* **70**, 2979 (1948).
196. S. B. Hendricks and M. E. Jefferson, *J. Chem. Phys.* **4**, 102 (1936); G. A. Jeffrey and G. S. Parry, *J. Chem. Soc.* **1952**, 4864.
197. A. C. Bond and L. O. Brockway, *J. Am. Chem. Soc.* **76**, 3312 (1954).
198. K. Hedberg and A. J. Stosick, *J. Am. Chem. Soc.* **74**, 954 (1952).
199. T. L. Khotsyanova, A. I. Kitaïgorodskiï, and Yu. T. Struchkov, *Doklady Akad. Nauk. S. S. S. R.* **85**, 785 (1952) [*C. A.* **47**, 7854 (1953)].
200. L. O. Brockway, *Proc. Natl. Acad. Sci. U. S.* **19**, 868 (1933).
201. S. M. Ohlberg and P. A. Vaughan, *J. Am. Chem. Soc.* **76**, 2649 (1954).
202. O. Aksnes and O. Foss, *Acta Chem. Scand.* **8**, 702, 1787 (1954).
203. H. J. M. Bowen, *Trans. Faraday Soc.* **50**, 463 (1954).
204. F. A. M. Buck and R. L. Livingston, *J. Chem. Phys.* **18**, 570 (1950).
205. J. N. Shoolery, R. G. Shulman, W. F. Sheehan, Jr., V. Schomaker, and D. M. Yost, *J. Chem. Phys.* **19**, 1364 (1951).
206. W. E. Anderson, R. Trambarulo, J. Sheridan and W. Gordy, *Phys. Rev.* **82**, 58 (1951).
207. J. Sheridan and W. Gordy, *J. Chem. Phys.* **20**, 735 (1952).
208. L. Pauling, W. Gordy, and J. H. Saylor, *J. Am. Chem. Soc.* **64**, 1753 (1942).
209. A. Pabst, *J. Chem. Phys.* **11**, 145 (1943).
210. E. H. Wiebenga and N. F. Moerman, *Z. Krist.* **99**, 217 (1938); E. H. Wiebenga, *J. Am. Chem. Soc.* **74**, 6156 (1952).
211. J. Overend and H. W. Thompson, *J. Opt. Soc. Amer.* **43**, 1065 (1953).
212. J. D. Dunitz, H. G. Feldman, and V. Schomaker, *J. Chem. Phys.* **20**, 1708 (1952).
213. G. Herzberg, F. Patat, and H. Verleger, *J. Phys. Chem.* **41**, 123 (1937); R.

Trambarulo and W. Gordy, *J. Chem. Phys.* **18**, 1613 (1950); G. Herzberg, A. V. Jones, and L. C. Leitch, *ibid.* **19**, 136 (1951).

214. A. V. Jones, *J. Chem. Phys.* **20**, 860 (1952).

215. J. M. O'Gorman and V. Schomaker, *J. Am. Chem. Soc.* **68**, 1138 (1946).

216. H. Mackle and L. E. Sutton, *Trans. Faraday Soc.* **47**, 691 (1951).

217. J. Bregnan and S. H. Bauer, quoted by *AS*.

218. C. J. Brown, *Acta Cryst.* **7**, 92 (1954).

219. O. Bastiansen and O. Hassel, *Tidsskr. Kjemi, Bergvesen Met.* **6**, 71 (1946) [*C. A.* **40**, 6059 (1946)].

220. V. Schomaker and D. P. Stevenson, *J. Am. Chem. Soc.* **62**, 2423 (1940).

221. W. W. Wood and V. Schomaker, *J. Chem. Phys.* **20**, 555 (1952).

222. P. J. Wheatley, *Acta Cryst.* **6**, 369 (1953).

223. E. W. Hughes, *J. Am. Chem. Soc.* **63**, 1737 (1941).

224. J. Hengstenberg and L. Brú, *Anales soc. españ. fíz. y quím.* **30**, 341 (1932) [*C. A.* **26**, 4217 (1932)]; M. Kimura and Y. Kurita, *J. Chem. Soc. Japan*, **72**, 396 (1951) [*C. A.* **46**, 4474 (1952)]; P. W. Allen, H. J. M. Bowen, L. E. Sutton, and O. Bastiansen, *Trans. Faraday Soc.* **48**, 991 (1952).

225. W. Shand, quoted by *AS*.

226. M. Kimura and K. Aoki, *J. Chem. Soc. Japan.* **72**, 169 (1951) [*C. A.* **46**, 3341 (1952)].

227. N. F. Moerman and E. H. Wiebenga, *Z. Krist.* **97**, 323 (1937).

228. T. K. Bierlein and E. C. Lingafelter, *Acta Cryst.* **4**, 450 (1951).

229. H. A. Levy and R. B. Corey, *J. Am. Chem. Soc.* **63**, 2095 (1941); J. Donohue, *ibid.* **72**, 949 (1950).

230. D. P. Shoemaker, R. E. Barieau, J. Donohue, and C.-S. Lu, *Acta Cryst.* **6**, 241 (1953).

231. K. Aoki, *J. Chem. Soc. Japan* **74**, 110 (1952) [*C. A.* **47**, 5191 (1953)].

232. H. D. Springall and L. O. Brockway, *J. Am. Chem. Soc.* **60**, 996 (1938).

233. H. A. Lévy and L. O. Brockway, *J. Am. Chem. Soc.* **59**, 2085 (1937).

234. S. Geller and J. L. Hoard, *Acta Cryst.* **4**, 399 (1951).

235. S. H. Bauer and J. Y. Beach, *J. Am. Chem. Soc.* **63**, 1394 (1941).

236. A. F. Wells, *Z. Krist.* **99**, 367 (1938).

237. R. L. Livingston and L. O. Brockway, *J. Am. Chem. Soc.* **68**, 719 (1946).

238. L. Pauling and A. W. Laubengayer, *J. Am. Chem. Soc.* **63**, 480 (1941).

239. I. E. Knaggs, *Proc. Roy. Soc. (London) A* **150**, 576 (1935).

240. H. Boersch, *Naturwissenschaften* **22**, 172 (1934).

241. L. O. Brockway and L. Pauling, *Proc. Natl. Acad. Sci. U. S.* **19**, 860 (1933).

242. H. Mackle and L. E. Sutton, *Trans. Faraday Soc.* **47**, 937 (1951).

243. T. B. Owen and J. L. Hoard, *Acta Cryst.* **4**, 172 (1951).

244. W. F. Sheehan, Jr., and V. Schomaker, *J. Am. Chem. Soc.* **74**, 4468 (1952).

245. H. P. Lemaire and R. L. Livingston, *J. Am. Chem. Soc.* **74**, 5732 (1952).

246. R. V. G. Ewens and M. W. Lister, *Trans. Faraday Soc.* **35**, 681 (1939).

247. J. D. Dunitz and J. M. Robertson, *J. Chem. Soc.* **1947**, 148.

248. C. J. B. Clews and W. Cochran, *Acta Cryst.* **1**, 4 (1948).

249. C. J. B. Clews and W. Cochran, *Acta Cryst.* **2**, 46 (1949).

250. J. N. van Niekerk and F. R. L. Schoening, *Acta Cryst.* **4**, 35 (1951).

251. C. A. Beevers and W. Hughes, *Proc. Roy. Soc. (London) A* **177**, 251 (1941).

252. R. Sadanaga, *Acta. Cryst.* **3**, 416 (1950).

253. V. Schomaker and L. Pauling, *J. Am. Chem. Soc.* **61**, 1769 (1939).

254. G. S. Parry, *Acta Cryst.* **7**, 313 (1954).

255. J. Y. Beach, *J. Chem. Phys.* **9**, 54 (1941).

256. L. Katz and W. N. Lipscomb, *Acta Cryst.* **5**, 313 (1952).

257. M. Shahat, *Acta Cryst.* **5**, 763 (1952).

258. J. N. van Niekerk and F. R. L. Schoening, *Acta Cryst.* **6**, 227 (1953).

259. R. B. Corey, *J. Am. Chem. Soc.* **60**, 1598 (1938).

260. J. N. van Niekerk and F. R. L. Schoening, *Acta Cryst.* **6**, 609 (1953).

261. L. L. Barricelli and O. Bastiansen, *Acta Chem. Scand.* **3**, 201 (1949).

262. M. W. Dougill and G. A. Jeffrey, *Acta Cryst.* **6**, 831 (1953).

263. H. J. Verweel and C. H. MacGillavry, *Nature* **142**, 161 (1938); *Z. Krist.* **102**, 60 (1939); J. D. Morrison and J. M. Robertson, *J. Chem. Soc.* **1949**, 980.

264. J. N. van Niekerk, F. R. L. Schoening, and J. H. Talbot, *Acta Cryst.* **6**, 720 (1953).

265. F. Stern and C. A. Beevers, *Acta Cryst.* **3**, 341 (1950).

266. G. S. Parry, *Acta Cryst.* **4**, 131 (1951).

267. G. B. Carpenter and J. Donohue, *J. Am. Chem. Soc.* **72**, 2315 (1950).

268. L. O. Brockway and P. C. Cross, *J. Am. Chem. Soc.* **58**, 2407 (1936).

269. J. D. Dunitz and V. Schomaker, *J. Chem. Phys.* **20**, 1703 (1952).

270. D. P. Stevenson and V. Schomaker, *J. Am. Chem. Soc.* **61**, 3173 (1939).

271. P. Andersen and O. Hassel, *Acta Chem. Scand.* **3**, 1180 (1949).

272. I. M. Dawson and J. M. Robertson, *J. Chem. Soc.* **1948**, 1256; J. Donohue, *J. Am. Chem. Soc.* **72**, 2701 (1950).

273. L. L. Merritt, Jr., and E. Lanterman, *Acta Cryst.* **5**, 811 (1952).

274. R. A. Pasternak, *Acta Cryst.* **6**, 808 (1953).

275. L. O. Brockway and P. C. Cross, *J. Am. Chem. Soc.* **59**, 1147 (1937).

276. R. E. Marsh and J. D. McCullough, *J. Am. Chem. Soc.* **73**, 1106 (1951).

277. J. Y. Beach and D. P. Stevenson, *J. Am. Chem. Soc.* **60**, 475 (1938).

278. J. Q. Williams and W. Gordy, *J. Chem. Phys.* **18**, 994 (1950).

279. O. Bastiansen and L. Smedvik, *Acta Chem. Scand.* **7**, 652 (1953).

280. F. Andersen, J. R. Andersen, B. Bak, O. Bastiansen, E. Risberg, and L. Smedvik, *J. Chem. Phys.* **21**, 373 (1953).

281. F. A. Andersen, B. Bak, and J. Rastrup-Andersen, *Acta Chem. Scand.* **7**, 643 (1953).

282. S. Hirokawa, S. Kuribayashi, and I. Nitta, *Bull. Chem. Soc. Japan* **25**, 192 (1952).

283. D. P. Shoemaker, J. Donohue, V. Schomaker, and R. B. Corey, *J. Am. Chem. Soc.* **72**, 2328 (1950).

284. H. Mendel and D. C. Hodgkin, *Acta Cryst.* **7**, 443 (1954).

285. J. Y. Beach and J. Walter, *J. Chem. Phys.* **8**, 303 (1940).

286. J. M. Hastings and S. H. Bauer, *J. Chem. Phys.* **18**, 13 (1950).

287. L. O. Brockway and N. R. Davidson, *J. Am. Chem. Soc.* **63**, 3287 (1941).

288. M. Kakudo and T. Watase, *Technol. Repts. Osaka Univ.* **2**, 247 (1952) [*C. A.* **47**, 10309 (1953)]; *J. Chem. Phys.* **21**, 167 (1953).

289. K. Yamasaki, A. Kotera, M. Yokoi, and Y. Ueda, *J. Chem. Phys.* **18**, 1414 (1950).

290. W. F. Sheehan, Jr., and V. Schomaker, *J. Am. Chem. Soc.* **74**, 3956 (1952).

291. A. Nakahara, Y. Saito, and H. Kuroya, *Bull. Chem. Soc. Japan* **25**, 331 (1952).

292. R. B. Shannan and R. L. Collin, *Acta Cryst.* **6**, 350 (1953).

293. H. Lambot, *Bull. soc. roy. sci. Liége* **12**, 439 (1943) [*C. A.* **42**, 7125 (1948)].

294. L. O. Brockway and P. C. Cross, *J. Chem. Phys.* **3**, 828 (1935).

295. J. Ladell, B. Post, and I. Fankuchen, *Acta Cryst.* **5**, 795 (1952).

296. O. Bastiansen, O. Hassel, and L. K. Lund, *Acta Chem. Scand.* **3**, 297 (1949).

297. G. A. Heath, L. F. Thomas, and J. Sheridan, *Nature*, **172**, 771 (1953).

298. T. H. Goodwin and C. M. Thomson, *Acta Cryst.* **7**, 166 (1954).

299. B. B. De More, W. S. Wilcox, and J. H. Goldstein, *J. Chem. Phys.* **22**, 876 (1954); B. Bak, L. Hansen, and J. Rastrup-Andersen, *ibid.* **22**, 2013 (1954).

300. B. R. Penfold, *Acta Cryst.* **6**, 591 (1953).

301. B. R. Penfold, *Acta Cryst.* **6**, 707 (1953).

302. P. Cuckla and R. W. H. Smith, *Acta Cryst.* **7**, 199 (1954).

303. R. Spurr and V. Schomaker, *J. Am. Chem. Soc.* **64**, 2693 (1942).

304. J. M. Broomhead, *Acta Cryst.* **1**, 324 (1948); W. Cochran, *ibid.* **4**, 81 (1951).

305. J. M. Broomhead, *Acta Cryst.* **4**, 92 (1951).

306. W. Shand, Jr., V. Schomaker, and J. R. Fischer, *J. Am. Chem. Soc.* **66**, 636 (1944).

307. S. H. Bauer and J. Y. Beach, *J. Am. Chem. Soc.* **64**, 1142 (1942).

308. J. Donohue, G. L. Humphrey, and V. Schomaker, *J. Am. Chem. Soc.* **67**, 332 (1945).

309. H. de Laszlo, *Compt. rend.* **198**, 2235 (1934).

310. O. Hassel and L. C. Strömme, *Z. phys. Chem.* B **38**, 349 (1938).

311. A. D. Booth and F. J. Llewellyn, *J. Chem. Soc.* **1947**, 837.

312. E. G. Cox and G. A. Jeffrey, *Trans. Faraday Soc.* **38**, 241 (1942); G. A. Jeffrey, *Acta Cryst.* **4**, 58 (1951).

313. J. D. Morrison and J. M. Robertson, *J. Chem. Soc.* **1949**, 1001.

314. J. Zussman, *Acta Cryst.* **4**, 493 (1951); J. Donohue and K. N. Trueblood, *ibid.* **5**, 414, 419 (1952).

315. P. J. Wheatley, *Acta Cryst.* **7**, 68 (1954).

316. O. Hassel and H. Viervoll, *Tidsskr. Kjemi, Bergvesen Met.* **6**, No. 3, 31 (1946) [*C. A.* **40**, 4580 (1946)].

317. B. Dawson, *Acta Cryst.* **6**, 81 (1953).

318. W. Cochran and B. R. Penfold, *Acta Cryst.* **5**, 644 (1952).

319. H. B. Dyer, *Acta Cryst.* **4**, 42 (1951).

320. A. M. Mathieson, *Acta Cryst.* **5**, 332 (1952).

321. F. J. Llewellyn, E. G. Cox, and T. H. Goodwin, *J. Chem. Soc.* **1937**, 883.

322. W. G. Perdok and P. Terpstra, *Rec. trav. chim.* **62**, 687 (1943).

323. C. Finbak, O. Hassel, and O. R. Nilsen, *Arch. Math. Naturvidenskab* **44**, 105 (1941) [*C. A.* **37**, 2627 (1943)].

324. L. Barricelli and O. Bastiansen, quoted by *AS*.

325. H. de Laszlo, *Proc. Roy. Soc.* (*London*) A **146**, 690 (1934).

326. O. Bastiansen and O. Hassel, *Acta Chem. Scand.* **1**, 489 (1947).

327. L. O. Brockway and K. J. Palmer, *J. Am. Chem. Soc.* **59**, 2181 (1937).

328. L. O. Brockway, R. V. G. Ewens, and M. W. Lister, *Trans. Faraday Soc.* **34**, 1350 (1938).

329. G. Huse and H. M. Powell, *J. Chem. Soc.* **1940**, 1398.

330. A. Kossiakoff and H. D. Springall, *J. Am. Chem. Soc.* **63**, 2223 (1941).

331. H. M. Powell, G. Huse, and P. W. Cooke, *J. Chem. Soc.* **1943**, 153.

332. H. Oosaka and Y. Akimoto, *Bull. Chem. Soc. Japan* **26**, 433 (1953).

333. S. Bezzi and U. Croatto, *Gazz. chim. ital.* **72**, 318 (1942) [*C. A.* **38**, 3180 (1944)].

334. E. M. Archer, *Acta Cryst.* **1**, 64 (1948).

335. U. Croatto, S. Bezzi, and E. Bua, *Acta Cryst.* **5**, 825 (1952).

336. H. Oosaka, *Bull. Chem. Soc. Japan* **15**, 31 (1940).

337. S. B. Hendricks, L. R. Maxwell, V. L. Mosley, and M. E. Jefferson, *J. Chem. Phys.* **1**, 549 (1933).

338. V. Luzzati, *Acta Cryst.* **4**, 193 (1951).

339. E. M. Archer, *Proc. Roy. Soc. (London) A* **188**, 51 (1946).

340. N. W. Gregory and E. N. Lassettre, *J. Am. Chem. Soc.* **69**, 102 (1947).

341. R. W. James, G. King, and H. Horricks, *Proc. Roy. Soc. (London) A* **153**, 225 (1935); F. J. Llewellyn, *J. Chem. Soc.* **1947**, 884; S. C. Abrahams, *Acta Cryst.* **3**, 194 (1950).

342. V. Luzzati, *Compt. rend.* **227**, 210 (1948).

343. V. Luzzati, *Compt. rend.* **226**, 738 (1948).

344. S. M. Swingle, *J. Am. Chem. Soc.* **76**, 1409 (1954).

345. J. M. Robertson, *Proc. Roy. Soc. (London) A* **150**, 106 (1935).

346. E. G. Cos, R. J. J. H. Gillot, and G. A. Jeffrey, *Acta Cryst.* **2**, 356 (1949).

347. T. Yuzawa and M. Yamaha, *Bull. Chem. Soc. Japan* **26**, 414 (1953).

348. E. M. Archer and T. G. D. van Schalkwyck, *Acta Cryst.* **6**, 88 (1953).

349. R. A. Pasternak, *Acta Cryst.* **4**, 316 (1951).

350. G. Erlandsson, *Arkiv Fysik* **6**, 447 (1953) [*C. A.* **47**, 8517 (1953)]; *Arkiv Fysik* **7**, 189 (1953) [*C. A.* **48**, 4979 (1954)]; K. E. McCulloh and G. F. Pollnow, *J. Chem. Phys.* **22**, 1144 (1954).

351. W. B. Wright and G. S. D. King, *Acta Cryst.* **6**, 305 (1953).

352. C. Finbak and O. Hassel, *Arch. Math. Naturvidenskab* **45**, No. 3 (1941) [*C. A.* **36**, 6408 (1942)].

353. J. H. Archer, C. Finbak, and O. Hassel, *Tidsskr. Kjemi, Bergvesen Met.* **2**, 33 (1942) [*C. A.* **38**, 2532 (1944)].

354. I. L. Karle, *J. Chem. Phys.* **20**, 65 (1952).

355. E. G. Cox and J. A. S. Smith, *Nature* **173**, 75 (1954).

356. R. C. Himes and P. M. Harris, paper presented at the Chicago meeting of the American Chemical Society, September, 1953.

357. R. G. Dickinson and C. Bilicke, *J. Am. Chem. Soc.* **50**, 764 (1928).

358. Yu. T. Struchkov and T. L. Khotsyanova, *Doklady Akad. Nauk S. S. S. R.* **91**, 565 (1953) [*C. A.* **48**, 422 (1954)].

359. O. Hassel and T. Taarland, *Tidsskr. Kjemi, Bergvesen Met.* **2**, 6 (1942) [*C. A.* **37**, 6538 (1943)].

360. G. W. Van Vloten, C. A. Kruissink, B. Strijk, and J. M. Bijvoet, *Acta Cryst.* **3**, 139 (1950).

361. W. B. Wright and G. S. D. King, *Acta Cryst.* **7**, 283 (1954).

362. S. C. Abrahams and J. M. Robertson, *Acta Cryst.* **1**, 252 (1948).

363. D. E. Palin and H. M. Powell, *J. Chem. Soc.* **1947**, 208.

364. J. M. Robertson, *Proc. Roy. Soc. (London) A* **157**, 79 (1936).

365. J. M. Robertson and A. R. Ubbelohde, *Proc. Roy. Soc. (London) A* **167**, 122 (1938).

366. A. Sanengen, *Tidsskr. Kjemi, Bergvesen Met.* **3**, No. 7, 92 (1943) [*C. A.* **40**, 3104 (1946)].

367. C. J. Brown, *Acta Cryst.* **4**, 100 (1951).

368. E. Halmöy and O. Hassel, *J. Am. Chem. Soc.* **71**, 1601 (1939).

369. C. J. Brown, *Acta Cryst.* **2**, 228 (1949).

370. O. Hassel and E. W. Lund, *Acta Chem. Scand.* **3**, 203 (1949); *Acta Cryst.* **2**, 309 (1949).

371. G. J. Pitt, *Acta Cryst.* **1**, 168 (1948).

372. J. G. Gudmundsen and O. Hassel, *Z. physik. Chem. B* **40**, 326 (1938).

373. B. Ottar, *Acta Chem. Scand.* **1**, 283 (1947).

374. C. H. MacGillavry, *Rec. trav. chim.* **60**, 605 (1941); J. D. Morrison and J. M.

Robertson, *J. Chem. Soc.* **1949**, 987; S. Hirokawa, *Bull. Chem. Soc. Japan* **23**, 91 (1950).

375. S. Furberg and O. Hassel, *Acta Chem. Scand.* **4**, 1584 (1950).

376. O. Hassel and H. Viervoll, *Tidsskr. Kjemi, Bergvesen Met.* **3**, 35 (1943) [*C. A.* **39**, 2244 (1945)].

377. T. R. Lomer, *Acta Cryst.* **5**, 14 (1952).

378. R. A. Pasternak, L. Katz, and R. B. Corey, *Acta Cryst.* **7**, 225 (1954).

379. C. D. Littleton, *Acta Cryst.* **6**, 775 (1953).

380. O. Hassel and B. Ottar, *Arch. Math. Naturvidenskab* **45**, No. 10, 1 (1942) [*C. A.* **38**, 2532 (1944)].

381. G. C. Hampson and A. J. Stosick, *J. Am. Chem. Soc.* **60**, 1814 (1938); V. Schomaker and P. A. Shaffer, Jr., *ibid.* **69**, 1555 (1947).

382. P. A. Shaffer, Jr., *J. Am. Chem. Soc.* **69**, 1557 (1947).

383. B. Ottar, *Acta Chem. Scand.* **1**, 521 (1947).

384. D. C. Carpenter and L. O. Brockway, *J. Am. Chem. Soc.* **58**, 1270 (1936).

385. T. R. R. McDonald and C. A. Beevers, *Acta Cryst.* **5**, 654 (1952).

386. O. Hassel and S. Ore, *Tidsskr. Kjemi, Bergvesen Met.* **6**, 72 (1946) [*C. A.* **40**, 6906 (1946)].

387. A. M. Mathieson, *Acta Cryst.* **6**, 399 (1953).

388. E. G. Cox and G. A. Jeffrey, *Nature* **143**, 894 (1939). Cf. also the table on p. 265 of C. A. Beevers and W. Cochran, *Proc. Roy. Soc. (London) A* **190**, 257 (1947).

389. P. Andersen and O. Hassel, *Acta Chem. Scand.* **5**, 1349 (1951).

390. W. P. Binnie and J. M. Robertson, *Acta Cryst.* **3**, 424 (1950).

391. N. R. Davidson, J. A. C. Hugill, H. A. Skinner, and L. E. Sutton, *Trans. Faraday Soc.* **36**, 1212 (1940).

392. P. H. Lewis and R. E. Rundle, *J. Chem. Phys.* **21**, 986 (1953).

393. W. P. Binnie and J. M. Robertson, *Acta Cryst.* **2**, 180 (1949).

394. E. Weller and S. H. Bauer, quoted by *AS*. For a more recent crystal-structure study of this compound, see G. Peyronel, *C. A.* **48**, 10401 (1954).

395. H. A. Skinner and L. E. Sutton, *Trans. Faraday Soc.* **36**, 1209 (1940).

396. E. W. Lund, *Acta Chem. Scand.* **5**, 678 (1951).

397. M. Yokoi and K. Yamasaki, *J. Am. Chem. Soc.* **75**, 4139 (1953).

398. J. L. Hoard, *J. Am. Chem. Soc.* **60**, 1194 (1938).

399. G. A. Gol'der, G. S. Zhdanov, and M. M. Umanskiĭ, *Zhur. Fiz. Khim.* **26**, 1434 (1952) [*C. A.* **48**, 6192 (1954)].

400. B. Jersley, *Nature* **166**, 741 (1950).

401. M. Kimura and M. Kubo, *Bull. Chem. Soc. Japan* **26**, 250 (1953). See also E. Heilbronner and K. Hedberg, *J. Am. Chem. Soc.* **73**, 1386 (1951).

402. W. Cochran, *Acta Cryst.* **6**, 260 (1953).

403. Y. Sasada, K. Osaki, and I. Nitta, *Acta Cryst.* **7**, 113 (1954).

404. E. Heilbronner and V. Schomaker, *Helv. Chim. Acta* **35**, 1385 (1952).

405. A. G. Brook and G. F. Wright, *Acta Cryst.* **4**, 50 (1951).

406. C. H. MacGillavry, G. Hoogschagen, and F. L. J. Sixma, *Rec. trav. chim.* **67**, 869 (1948).

407. H. P. Lemaire and R. L. Livingston, *Acta Cryst.* **5**, 817 (1952).

408. G. H. Goldschmidt and F. J. Llewellyn, *Acta Cryst.* **3**, 294 (1950).

409. G. A. Jeffrey and J. S. Rollett, *Nature* **166**, 475 (1950); *Proc. Roy. Soc. (London) A* **213**, 86 (1952).

410. O. Bastiansen, O. Hassel, and A. Langseth, *Nature* **160**, 128 (1947); O. Bastiansen and O. Hassel, *Acta Chem. Scand.* **3**, 209 (1949).

411. H. S. Kaufman, I. Fankuchen, and H. Mark, *Nature* **161**, 165 (1948).

412. J. H. Rayner and H. M. Powell, *J. Chem. Soc.* **1952**, 319.

413. P. L. F. Jones, *Trans. Faraday Soc.* **31**, 1036 (1935).

414. T. H. Goodwin, M. Przybylska, and J. M. Robertson, *Acta Cryst.* **3**, 279 (1950).

415. D. T. Cromer, A. J. Ihde, and H. L. Ritter, *J. Am. Chem. Soc.* **73**, 5587 (1951).

416. W. N. Lipscomb and V. Schomaker, *J. Chem. Phys.* **14**, 475 (1946).

417. A. H. Nethercot, Jr., and A. Javan, *J. Chem. Phys.* **21**, 363 (1953).

418. L. E. Godycki, R. E. Rundle, R. C. Voter, and C. V. Banks, *J. Chem. Phys.* **19**, 1205 (1951); L. E. Godycki and R. E. Rundle, *Acta Cryst.* **6**, 487 (1953).

419. H. Scouloudi, *Acta Cryst.* **6**, 651 (1953).

420. D. Grdenić, *Acta Cryst.* **5**, 367 (1952).

421. L. Pauling and D. C. Carpenter, *J. Am. Chem. Soc.* **58**, 1274 (1936).

422. W. L. Roth and D. Harker, *Acta Cryst.* **1**, 34 (1948).

423. D. R. Holmes and H. M. Powell, *Acta Cryst.* **6**, 256 (1953).

424. S. Furberg, *Acta Cryst.* **3**, 325 (1950).

425. A. I. Kitaĭgorodskiĭ and S. S. Kabalkina, *Doklady Akad. Nauk S. S. S. R.* **71**, 899 (1950) [*C. A.* **44**, 6838 (1950)].

426. A. I. Kitaĭgorodskiĭ and S. S. Kabalkina, *Zhur. Fiz. Khim.* **25**, 71 (1951) [*C. A.* **45**, 4994 (1951)].

427. N. G. Sevast'yanov, G. S. Zhdanov, and M. M. Umanskiĭ, *Zhur. Fiz. Khim.* **22**, 1153 (1948) [*C. A.* **43**, 1236 (1949)].

428. O. Specchia and G. Papa, *Nuovo Cimento* **18**, 102 (1941) [*C. A.* **35**, 6851 (1941)].

429. J. M. Robertson, *Proc. Roy. Soc.* (*London*) *A* **142**, 674 (1933); S. C. Abrahams, J. M. Robertson, and J. G. White, *Acta Cryst.* **2**, 238 (1949).

430. J. M. Robertson, *J. chim. phys.* **47**, 47 (1950).

431. F. R. Ahmed and D. W. J. Cruikshank, *Acta Cryst.* **5**, 852 (1952).

432. M. A. Lasheen, *Acta Cryst.* **5**, 593 (1952).

433. J. Singer and I. Fankuchen, *Acta Cryst.* **5**, 99 (1952).

434. E. O. Fischer and W. Pfab, *Z. Naturforsch.* **7b**, 377 (1952); P. F. Eiland and R. Pepinsky, *J. Am. Chem. Soc.* **74**, 4971 (1952); J. D. Dunitz and L. E. Orgel, *Nature* **171**, 121 (1953).

435. J. M. Robertson, *Proc. Roy. Soc.* (*London*) *A* **141**, 594 (1933); *A* **142**, 659 (1933).

436. W. Nowacki and K. W. Hedberg, *J. Am. Chem. Soc.* **70**, 1497 (1948).

437. W. Nowacki, *Helv. Chim. Acta* **28**, 1233 (1945); G. Giacomello and G. Illuminati, *Ricerca sci.* **15**, 559 (1945) [*C. A.* **40**, 6929 (1946)].

438. D. C. P. Phillips, *Acta Cryst.* **7**, 159 (1954).

439. A. M. Mathieson and H. K. Welsh, *Acta Cryst.* **5**, 599 (1952).

440. H. L. Yakel, Jr. and E. W. Hughes, *J. Am. Chem. Soc.* **74**, 6302 (1952); *Acta Cryst.* **7**, 291 (1954).

441. J. D. Morrison and J. M. Robertson, *J. Chem. Soc.* **1949**, 993.

442. L. Bateman and G. A. Jeffrey, *Nature* **152**, 446 (1943); G. A. Jeffrey, *Proc. Roy. Soc.* (*London*) *A* **183**, 388 (1945).

443. M. Bailey, *Acta Cryst.* **7**, 366 (1954).

444. D. W. Smits and E. H. Wiebenga, *Acta Cryst.* **6**, 531 (1953).

445. E. H. Wiebenga and C. J. Krom, *Rec. trav. chim.* **65**, 663 (1946).

446. E. Grison, *Acta Cryst.* **2**, 410 (1949).

447. J. Waser and V. Schomaker, *J. Am. Chem. Soc.* **65**, 1451 (1943).

448. J. Waser and C.-S. Lu, *J. Am. Chem. Soc.* **66**, 2035 (1944).

449. C. Darwin and D. C. Hodgkin, *Nature* **166**, 827 (1950).

450. J. Toussaint, *Bull. soc. roy. sci. Liége*, **15**, 86 (1946) [*C. A.* **42**, 7128 (1948)].

451. J. Toussaint, *Bull. soc. roy. sci. Liége* **13**, 163 (1944) [*C. A.* **42**, 7128 (1948)].

452. J. Toussaint, *Bull. soc. chem. Belg.* **54**, 319 (1945).

453. J. Toussaint, *Bull. soc. roy. sci. Liége* **13**, 111 (1944) [*C. A.* **42**, 7128 (1948)].

454. L. R. Maxwell, S. B. Hendricks, and V. M. Mosley, *J. Chem. Phys.* **3**, 699 (1935).

455. F. H. Herbstein and G. M. J. Schmidt, *Nature* **169**, 323 (1952).

456. D. H. Saunders, *Proc. Roy. Soc. (London) A* **188**, 31 (1946).

457. R. G. Wood and G. Williams, *Nature* **150**, 321 (1942).

458. A. I. Kitaigorodskii, *Zhur. Fiz. Khim.* **23**, 1036 (1949) [*C. A.* **44**, 897 (1950)].

459. I. L. Karle and L. O. Brockway, *J. Am. Chem. Soc.* **66**, 1974 (1944).

460. J. Dhar, *Indian J. Phys.* **7**, 43 (1932) [*C. A.* **26**, 4517 (1932)]; *Proc. Natl. Inst. Sci. India* **15**, 11 (1949) [*C. A.* **43**, 4655 (1949)].

461. J. D. McCullough and G. Hamburger, *J. Am. Chem. Soc.* **63**, 803 (1941).

462. D. L. Smare, *Acta Cryst.* **1**, 150 (1948).

463. J. D. McCullough and G. Hamburger, *J. Am. Chem. Soc.* **64**, 508 (1942).

464. J. M. Broomhead and A. D. I. Nicol, *Nature* **160**, 795 (1947); *Acta Cryst.* **1**, 88 (1948).

465. J. J. de Lange, J. M. Robertson, and I. Woodward, *Proc. Roy. Soc. (London) A* **171**, 398 (1939).

466. G. C. Hampson and J. M. Robertson, *J. Chem. Soc.* **1941**, 409.

467. S. Furberg and P. Öyum, *Acta Chem. Scand.* **8**, 42 (1954).

468. A. M. Mathieson and J. M. Robertson, *J. Chem. Soc.* **1949**, 724.

469. R. E. Marsh, *Acta Cryst.* **5**, 458 (1952).

470. M. Bailey, *Acta Cryst.* **2**, 120 (1949).

471. L. O. Brockway and J. M. Robertson, *J. Chem. Soc.* **1939**, 1324.

472. L. Pauling and J. Sherman, *Proc. Natl. Acad. Sci. U.S.* **20**, 340 (1934).

473. H. Koyama and Y. Saito, *Bull. Chem. Soc. Japan* **27**, 112 (1954).

474. H. M. Powell and G. W. R. Bartindale, *J. Chem. Soc.* **1945**, 799.

475. C. A. Beevers and W. Cochran, *Proc. Roy. Soc. (London) A* **190**, 257 (1947).

476. S. Hirokawa, T. Ohashi, and I. Nitta, *Acta Cryst.* **7**, 87 (1954).

477. G. M. Brown and M. H. Bortner, *Acta Cryst.* **7**, 139 (1954); D. M. Burns and J. Iball, *Nature* **173**, 635 (1954); *Proc. Roy. Soc. (London) A* **227**, 200 (1955).

478. J. Zussman, *Acta Cryst.* **6**, 504 (1953).

479. T. H. Goodwin and R. Hardy, *Proc. Roy. Soc. (London) A* **164**, 369 (1938).

480. A. I. Kitaïgorodskiï and S. S. Kabalkina, *Zhur. Fiz. Khim.* **25**, 185 (1951) [*C. A.* **48**, 4281 (1954)].

481. J. M. Robertson, *Proc. Roy. Soc. (London) A* **140**, 79 (1933); A. M. Mathieson, J. M. Robertson, and V. C. Sinclair, *Acta Cryst.* **3**, 245 (1950); V. C. Sinclair, J. M. Robertson, and A. M. Mathieson, *ibid.* **3**, 251 (1950).

482. J. M. Robertson and I. Woodward, *Proc. Roy. Soc. (London) A* **164**, 436 (1938).

483. J. M. Robertson, *J. Chem. Soc.* **1951**, 1222.

484. V. Kasatochkin, S. Perlina, and K. Ablesova, *Compt. rend. acad. sci. U. R. S. S.* **47**, 36 (1945); *Doklady Akad. Nauk. S. S. S. R.* **47**, 37 (1945) [*C. A.* **40**, 4044 (1946)].

485. J. M. Skinner, G. M. D. Stewart, and J. C. Speakman, *J. Chem. Soc.* **1954**, 180.

486. J. M. Skinner and J. C. Speakman, *J. Chem. Soc.* **1951**, 185.

487. J. M. Robertson and I. Woodward, *Proc. Roy. Soc. (London) A* **162**, 568 (1937).

488. J. M. Robertson, *Proc. Roy. Soc. (London) A* **150**, 348 (1935); G. A. Jeffrey, *Nature* **156**, 82 (1945); *Proc. Roy. Soc. (London) A* **188**, 222 (1947); D. W. J. Cruikshank, *Acta Cryst.* **2**, 65 (1949).

489. J. D. McCullough and R. E. Marsh, *Acta Cryst.* **3**, 41 (1950).

490. A. W. Hanson, *Acta Cryst.* **6**, 32 (1953).

491. F. Fowweather and A. Hargreaves, *Acta Cryst.* **3**, 81 (1950); F. Fowweather, *ibid.* **5**, 820 (1952).

492. M. Przybylska and W. H. Barnes, *Acta Cryst.* **6**, 377 (1953).

493. E. H. Wiebenga, *Z. Krist.* **102**, 193 (1940).

494. J. M. Robertson and J. G. White, *J. Chem. Soc.* **1947**, 358.

495. J. M. Robertson, *J. chim. phys.* **47**, 41 (1950).

496. J. C. Speakman, *J. Chem. Soc.* **1949**, 3357.

497. C. J. Brown, *J. Chem. Soc.* **1953**, 3278.

498. C. J. Brown, *J. Chem. Soc.* **1953**, 3265.

499. G. J. Pitt, *Acta Cryst.* **5**, 770 (1952).

500. C. J. Brown, *Acta Cryst.* **7**, 97 (1954).

501. J. Iball, *Proc. Roy. Soc.* (*London*) *A* **146**, 140 (1934).

502. A. Klug, *Acta Cryst.* **3**, 165, 176 (1950).

503. L. W. Pickett, *Proc. Roy. Soc.* (*London*) *A* **142**, 333 (1933).

504. J. Wetzel, *Z. Krist.* **104**, 305 (1942).

505. D. M. Donaldson and J. M. Robertson, *J. Chem. Soc.* **1953**, 17.

506. D. M. Donaldson, J. M. Robertson, and J. G. White, *Proc. Roy. Soc.* (*London*) *A* **220**, 311 (1953).

507. J. G. White, *J. Chem. Soc.* **1948**, 1398.

508. J. Iball and J. M. Robertson, *Nature* **132**, 750 (1933); K. S. Krishnan and S. Bannerjee, *Z. Krist.* **91**, 170, 173 (1935); J. Iball, *Nature* **137**, 361 (1936); J. M. Robertson and J. G. White, *J. Chem. Soc.* **1947**, 1001.

509. W. Drenth and E. H. Wiebenga, *Rec. trav. chim.* **73**, 218 (1954).

510. J. M. Robertson and J. G. White, *Nature* **154**, 605 (1944); *J. Chem. Soc.* **1945**, 607.

511. L. W. Pickett, *J. Am. Chem. Soc.* **58**, 2299 (1936).

512. M. S. Farag, *Acta Cryst.* **7**, 117 (1954).

513. R. C. L. Mooney, *J. Am. Chem. Soc.* **62**, 2955 (1940).

514. H. T. Sumsion and D. McLachlan, Jr., *Acta Cryst.* **3**, 217 (1950).

515. J. C. Speakman, *Acta Cryst.* **6**, 784 (1953).

516. C. P. Fenimore, *Acta Cryst.* **1**, 295 (1948).

517. C. H. Carlisle and D. Crowfoot, *Proc. Roy. Soc.* (*London*) *A* **184**, 64 (1945).

518. H. P. Stadler, *Acta Cryst.* **6**, 540 (1953).

519. J. D. Dunitz, *Acta Cryst.* **2**, 1 (1949).

520. P. H. Friedlander, T. H. Goodwin, and J. M. Robertson, *Acta Cryst.* **7**, 127 (1954).

521. A. Bennett and A. W. Hanson, *Acta Cryst.* **6**, 736 (1953).

522. M. M. Woolfson, *Acta Cryst.* **6**, 838 (1953).

523. D. M. Donaldson and J. M. Robertson, *Nature* **164**, 1002 (1949); J. M. Robertson, *Proc. Roy. Soc.* (*London*) *A* **207**, 101 (1951); D. M. Donaldson and J. M. Robertson, *ibid. A* **220**, 157 (1953).

524. J. M. Robertson, *J. Chem. Soc.* **1935**, 615; **1936**, 1195; J. M. Robertson and I. Woodward, *ibid.* **1937**, 219; **1940**, 36.

525. P. C. Cross, *Phys. Rev.* **46**, 536 (1934).

526. R. H. Gillette and E. H. Eyster, *Phys. Rev.* **56**, 1113 (1939); C. A. Burrus and W. Gordy, *Phys. Rev.* **92**, 1437 (1953). See also N. L. Nichols, C. D. Hause, and R. H. Noble, *J. Chem. Phys.* **23**, 57 (1955).

527. D. K. Coles, E. S. Elyash, and J. G. Gorman, *Phys. Rev.* **72**, 973 (1947); D. K.

Coles and R. H. Hughes, *ibid.* **76**, 178 (1949); G. Herzberg and L. Herzberg, *J. Chem. Phys.* **18**, 1551 (1950); A. E. Douglas and C. K. Møller, *ibid.* **22**, 275 (1954).
528. E. Grison, K. Eriks, and J. L. de Vries, *Acta Cryst.* **3**, 290 (1950).
529. V. Schomaker and D. P. Stevenson, *J. Am. Chem. Soc.* **62**, 1270 (1940).
530. B. Post, R. S. Schwartz, and I. Fankuchen, *Acta Cryst.* **5**, 372 (1952).
531. M. H. Sirvetz, *J. Chem. Phys.* **19**, 938 (1951).

AUTHOR INDEX

SUBJECT INDEX

The following pages contain no references to the Appendix, which is arranged in such a way that it serves as its own formula index.

A (angstrom unit), 12

Abnormal additions, of hydrogen chloride, 437, 439, 446
to carbon-carbon double bonds, 430, 437, 439, 442ff

Absorption bands, 247
see also Spectra

Acetoacetic ester, 10, 343, 406f

Acetone, 51f, 93, 165, 167f

Acetonitrile, 93, 165, 167f, 213

Acetylacetone, 49, 343f, 405f

Acetylene, acid strength of, 350, 357
order of carbon-carbon bond in, 189, 191
spectrum of, 269f

Acetylenes, acid strengths of, 350, 357
spectra of conjugated, 270f

Acetylenic halides, bond lengths in, 173, 185f
bond orders in, 185f
dipole moments of, 220, 223

Acetyl halides, bond lengths in, 173, 177, 185f
bond orders in, 185ff

Acetyl peroxide, 447ff

Acid azides, Curtius rearrangement of, 522

Acids, additions to carbon-carbon double bonds, 430ff
Lewis's generalized definition of, 351, 425

Acid strengths, effects of electrostatic interactions and resonance on, 340ff
of anilinium ions, 355f, 373f, 502
of benzoic acids, 353, 502
of hydrocarbons, 136, 347ff, 357
quantum-mechanical calculations of, 348

Acrylic acid, 462f

Acrylonitrile, 149, 230

Activated complex, 416ff
for abnormal addition of hydrogen bromide to propylene, 444
for abnormal addition of hydrogen bromide to styrene, 443f
for abnormal addition of hydrogen bromide to vinyl chloride, 445
for addition of a proton to *tert*-butylethylene, 437
for addition of a proton to propylene, 434f
for addition of a proton to styrene, 432f
for addition of a proton to a 3,3,3-trihalopropene, 438f
for addition of bromine to 1,3-butadiene, 458f
for allylic rearrangement by an alternative (push-pull) mechanism, 535f
for aromatic substitutions, 480f
for Claisen rearrangements, 537f
for Diels-Alder reactions, 516ff
for free-radical additions to olefins, 443ff, 447f
for intramolecular allylic rearrangement, 543
for nitration of trimethylanilinium ion, 502
for 1,2-shifts, 524ff
for substitution in piperonal, 506f
representation as a resonance hybrid, 416, 418, 421f
vs. unstable intermediate, 524f, 528ff

Activation energy, 417f, 497
see also Activated complex

"Activation" in aromatic substitution, 487

Addition compounds, binding forces in, 70ff

817